EGON RONAY'S

Heineke )5

Pubs ⌣ Inns

**The best pubs, bar food and B&B
in Great Britain and Ireland**

**Egon Ronay's Guides
35 Tadema Road
London SW10 0PZ**

Consultant **Egon Ronay**
Editorial Director **Bernard Branco**
Managing Editor **Andrew Eliel**
Publishing Director **Angela Nicholson**
Sales & Marketing Director **Stephen Prendergast**

Chairman **Roy Ackerman**

**Leading Guides Ltd
Part of the Richbell Group of Companies**

987654321

Cover Design © **Elizabeth Ayer**

Cover Concept and Illustration
© **Chris Ackerman-Eveleigh**

ISBN 0333 61548 4

Typeset in Great Britain by Spottiswoode Ballantyne,
Colchester, Essex.
Printed and bound in Great Britain by BPCC Hazell Books Ltd
A member of The British Printing Company Ltd

**First published 1994 by Pan Macmillan
Publishers Ltd, Cavaye Place,
London SW10 9PG**

*All pub and inn inspections are
anonymous and carried out by Egon Ronay's
Guides' team of professional inspectors.
Inspectors may reveal their identities at pubs
in order to check all the rooms and other facilities.
The Guide is independent in its editorial selection
and does not accept advertising, payment or
hospitality from listed establishments,*

Contents

listing all gazetteer entries in county groupings with details of Stars [★], FOOD, B&B and A[tmosphere] categories, ZZzz (Sleep) and Family symbols, plus telephone numbers, all-day opening information and waterside locations

Foreword

In their search for excellence, pub goers can't go wrong using Egon Ronay's Pubs and Inns Guide. The British pub is an important part of this country's heritage and excellence must be encouraged for this wonderful institution to evolve.

Heineken are delighted to renew their partnership with Egon Ronay's Guide. Dedication to the highest quality of beer in the highest quality environment is a shared desire.

Heineken is renowned all over the world for the consistently high quality of its beer. Whether you drink Heineken in Buenos Aires or Bolton, that smooth, refreshing flavour is guaranteed.

Using Egon Ronay's Heineken Pubs and Inns Guide, you will discover many wonderful pubs around the country and raise a glass to a great heritage and refresh the parts that other beers cannot reach.

Miles Templeman,
Managing Director,
The Whitbread Beer Company

Refreshing the pubs o

There are dozens of lagers - but there is only one Heineken as far as millions of consumers at home and abroad are concerned.

Walk into a bar in virtually any country and you will see the familiar green bottle. The best-known beer brand world-wide, it is available in more than 150 countries with a staggering 25 million pints enjoyed every day.

Heineken is the number one exported beer brand in the world, and the leading lager across Europe.

This global stature is reflected in Great Britain, where more than a million pints are sold every single day. A growing number of pub-goers are now also enjoying the premium strength Heineken Export.

The secret of Heineken's success is its refreshing character, an essential part of the recipe created by Gerard Heineken 130 years ago. This inspired the "refreshes the parts" advertising - one of the most famous campaigns ever.

The brand also benefits from a multi-million pound programme of music and sports sponsorship. It includes high profile involvement with The Whitbread Round the World Yacht Race which is now underway. Sponsorship of such a prestigious, international event underlines Heineken's world-class appeal.

er beers cannot reach

Introduction

'Pub Grub', 'Hot Meals', 'All-day Bar Snacks' – you see the signs everywhere you turn. Unfortunately, the one with the most hollow ring to it is still 'Good Food'. By fair means or foul – the latter still a good description of the majority of pub grub served up in this country – landlords are falling over themselves to attract diners into their pubs.

These days, 'fair' means a menu of well-cooked dishes using fresh produce, 'foul' means a combination of freezer-based convenience ingredients and bottled sauces that are defrosted and blitzed in a microwave or deep-fryer, producing an often overlong printed, plasticated menu of indifferent, tasteless, boring dishes that are a disgrace. They equate to supermarket convenience food, but is that what we really want when we stop at a pub for a meal? Are we all so short of time in this hectic world that we can no longer afford the time or staff to peel fresh vegetables?

This all may seem like an old story (and we *have* been telling it for over 30 years now), but the standard of cooking in the pubs and inns that we *do* recommend in this Guide continues to improve. Most of the best, starred pubs are competing with local restaurants (charging prices to match) and, although many have separate dining rooms, it is the bar food that we continue to concentrate on – restaurants were separately considered for our *1995 Cellnet Hotels & Restaurants Guide.*

However, while so many pubs strive for restaurant status by converting bars into fancier dining rooms, we praise those landlords who have the courage of their convictions by refusing to follow the herd and, instead, serve one menu throughout their pubs. In many cases this results in the majority of people in the pub coming to eat and the 'pubby local' feel of the bars gradually disappearing. This does not concern us greatly as everybody seems still to know a friendly boozer where you can pop in for a noggin and a natter. The most atmospheric and famous of these pubs are included in this Guide with a recommendation for Atmosphere [**A**] only – see How to use this Guide on page 8.

B&B means Better and Better?

One of the fastest expanding areas in the hotel business is that of roadside lodges where you can get your head down overnight in a convenient location. Pub accommodation competes very effectively within this market, but many pubs and inns don't have the resources to market themselves as aggressively as the large national lodge chains. We hope that this Guide will provide the reader with an invaluable source of characterful accommodation in both convenient and out-of-the-way locations, whether you are a businessman looking to liven up a midweek stopover on your travels (when B&B often means bed and beer!) or a family aiming, say, for a weekend break away from home. Just like pub food, pub B&B standards in our recommended establishments are constantly improving and almost every one of the places that we recommend for B&B now offers en-suite facilities. It is sad (but typical of general pub food standards) that so many of these establishments still can't be recommended for food, not even dishes in the bar. Our advice is: enjoy the accommodation but don't be swayed by any half-board deals; stick to simple snacks unless you can stay at a pub recommended by us for both B&B *and* food.

Not up to our Standards

As well as making sure that our current recommendations continue to come up to scratch, we have visited hundreds of pubs over the past year that have *not* come up to our standards. It has been an almost Herculean task keeping up with the movements of landlords and sales of pubs as the country's economy has gradually improved. We take note of hundreds of readers' comments (both favourable and not so) that arrive in our offices and while we appreciate that most of our readers enjoy good food when they eat it and sleep happily when the accommodation is both clean and comfortable, we urge our readers to keep up the good work – it is in all our readers' interests to pick out the bad apples before they turn sour on us. Sadly, every year our inspectors come back with one oft-repeated story – that a particular, fiercely traditional pub in a glorious setting is simply "in the wrong hands" with little interest shown in non-locals and even less interest in serving good food.

Poor Service

We report on what we find as objectively as we can, but clearly it is hard to report on the vagaries of one vital part of innkeeping, namely that of service. More complaints about poor service in fancified pub 'restaurants' have arrived this year than ever before. All the hard work of a devoted, loyal kitchen team is so easily undone by lacklustre, uninformed ("I'll just find out. . .") and uninterested (and almost under-age) 'service' from unhelpful amateurs. For this reason alone, the vast majority of pubs in this country do not deserve to promote themselves as a 'restaurant' or even as a serious venue for enjoying proper food – the prices in so many pubs are creeping higher and higher but the service is more often than not very unprofessional. Nevertheless, we praise those well-meaning and polite servers around the country who persevere with common sense and grace. No points, though, for the chain-run, mass-market pubs where the staff hide behind a no-service-without-a-table number, pay-at-the-bar system; one look at the bought-in chiller cabinet display of frozen gateaux should indicate to our discerning readers that the greatest efforts made by the landlords in this type of establishment is in making it to the bank after closing time (hoping that the freezer lorry doesn't turn up while they're gone!)

A Fine Pint

Just a word on beer – one of this country's finest products. We list typical real ales served at the end of each entry and, with the availability of many beers through wholesalers, it is often the unnamed, regularly-changing guest beers that are the most interesting. Be brave, try a pint of Old Thugwumper, you may help keep a micro-brewery in business – they deserve all our support as a counter balance to the onward advance of the larger breweries.

Replies to our annual pub questionnaires have proved a good source of humour throughout the year. In reply to the question "Where have the previous landlords gone?", we received answers that ranged from "Spain or jail" to "round the bend"; however, our favourite answer came from the Eliot Arms in Tregadillet: "to the big pub in the sky".

Finally, a word *to* our sponsors (to turn a well-known expression on its head), without whom our research would have been considerably less extensive. Continued sponsorship from Heineken has meant that we have been able to reach parts that other pub guides just don't seem to reach. American Express card-holders will doubtless have noticed a warmer welcome in many more pubs and inns over the last year, and Britvic have been seen mixing it in all the best places! Many congratulations also to all our award winners and food star pubs – they're the real pick of the bunch!

How to use this Guide

Order of Entries

London appears first and is in alphabetical order by **establishment name**. Listings outside London are in alphabetical order by **location** within divisions of England, Scotland, Wales, Channel Islands (inc the Isle of Man), Northern Ireland and Republic of Ireland. See contents page and the index for specific page numbers.

Map References

Map references alongside each pub entry refer to the map section at the back of the Guide. Use this to select establishments in the area that you wish to visit.

Good Bar Food

We include establishments where our team of professional inspectors found good-quality **Bar Food**. Such pubs and inns are indicated by the symbol **FOOD** printed in the margin alongside the entry. In the interest of clarity, reference may also be made to the pub's restaurant and opening hours; however, our chief concern (and only recommendation in this Guide) is with **Bar Food**. Pub restaurants are considered separately in *Egon Ronay's Cellnet Hotels & Restaurants Guide 1995*; note that many pubs now offer one menu throughout both bar and dining rooms.

Typical dishes are usually listed with prices valid at the time of our research. Prices may, however, have risen a little since then. We indicate when bar food is served and also any times when food is not available. Times of restaurant meals may differ and are then listed separately. If there is an outdoor eating area we include this information in the statistics.

Pubs serving outstanding bar food are indicated by a ★ alongside their name (see additional list of **Starred Pubs** on page 10).

Good Accommodation

We also inspect **accommodation**, and those pubs and inns recommended for an overnight stay are indicated by the symbol **B&B** in the margin alongside the entry. We list the number of bedrooms, the price for an en-suite double bedroom (where available) and a full cooked breakfast for two, and whether children are welcome overnight.

If check-in is confined to certain hours we print the time; if it's advisable to arrange a time when booking, we print *check-in by arrangement*. General closures around Christmas are not mentioned as these are so variable; however, if there is a regular period during the year that a pub is traditionally closed then we list that information.

We have assigned a 'Sleep' symbol **Zzzz...** to those pubs and inns that we consider offer particularly comfortable and/or quiet accommodation.

Pubs with Atmosphere

Pubs recommended for being particularly atmospheric, pleasant or interesting places in which to enjoy a drink (rather than the bar food or accommodation) are indicated by the symbol **A** alongside their entry. Interestingly located pubs and those with particularly good real ales (micro breweries, for example) are also highlighted by the **A** symbol.

All the pubs that we feature in this Guide now have a positive recommendation for Food **FOOD**, Accommodation **B&B** or Atmosphere **A**.

Opening Hours

Opening hours are generally only listed when they are exceptional, ie open all day or regularly closed for a session or more.

Beer

We indicate whether an establishment is a free house, and list the names of a number of real ales that were being offered when we last contacted the pub. These are often likely to change and should not be taken as permanent offers.

Children Welcome

Entries indicate whether the pub has facilities suitable for families; those that offer a good combination of the facilities (perhaps children allowed in the bar to eat, or a special children's menu, a family room or indoor or outdoor play area) are assigned the 'Family' symbol ☺. See also listings in the County Round-Up at the back of the Guide. If there is no mention of family facilities at all then readers should assume that the pub does not welcome children.

Credit Cards

We list credit cards accepted and also note those which accept none.

Symbols

★	Outstanding **Bar Food**
Zzzz...	Particularly comfortable and/or quiet accommodation
⬚	Good selection of British cheeses
♈	Good selection of wines served by the glass
☺	Suitable for families

Starred Pubs 1995

London

EC1, Farringdon: **The Eagle**
NW1, Clerkenwell: **The Peasant**
NW1, Primrose Hill: **The Lansdowne**
SW6 Parsons Green: **The White Horse**

England

Berkshire, West Ilsley: **Harrow Inn**
Buckinghamshire, Long Crendon: **The Angel**
Buckinghamshire, Waddesdon: **Five Arrows Hotel**
Cambridgeshire, Keyston: **Pheasant Inn**
Cambridgeshire, Madingley: **Three Horseshoes**
Cambridgeshire, Wansford-in-England: **The Haycock**
Cheshire, Higher Burwardsley: **The Pheasant**
Cornwall, Gunwalloe: **Halzephron Inn**
Cumbria, Cartmel Fell: **Masons Arms**
Devon, Kingsteignton: **Old Rydon Inn**
Dorset, Corscombe: **Fox Inn**
Dorset, Trusham: **Cridford Inn**
Durham, Romaldkirk: **Rose and Crown**
Essex, Horndon-on-the-Hill: **Bell Inn**
Gloucestershire, Coln St Aldwyns: **The New Inn**
Gloucestershire, Great Rissington: **The Lamb**
Gloucestershire, Lower Oddington: **The Fox**
Hampshire, Winchester: **Wykeham Arms**
Hereford & Worcester, Brimfield: **The Roebuck**
Hereford & Worcester, Winforton: **Sun Inn**
Kent, Ightham Common: **Harrow Inn**
Kent, Ivy Hatch: **The Plough**
Kent, Newnham: **George Inn**
Northumberland, Warenford: **Warenford Lodge**
Oxfordshire, Bledington: **King's Head Inn**
Oxfordshire, Sutton Courtenay: **The Fish**
Somerset, Batcombe: **The Batcombe Inn**
Somerset, Beckington: **Woolpack Inn**
Somerset, Monksilver: **Notley Arms**
Suffolk, Southwold: **Crown**
Suffolk, Stoke-by-Nayland: **Angel Inn**
Surrey, Grayswood: **Wheatsheaf Inn**
West Sussex, Lower Beeding: **Jeremy's at The Crabtree**
West Sussex, Midhurst: **Angel Hotel**
Wiltshire, North Newnton: **Woodbridge Inn**
Wiltshire, Rowde: **George & Dragon**
North Yorkshire, Hetton: **Angel Inn**
North Yorkshire, Starbotton: **Fox & Hounds**
North Yorkshire, Wass: **Wombwell Arms**
West Yorkshire, Shelley: **Three Acres**

Scotland

Fife, Kirkcaldy: **Hoffmans**
Strathclyde, Kilberry: **Kilberry Inn**

Wales

Gwent, Clydach: **Drum & Monkey**
Powys, Llyswen: **Griffin Inn**

Channel Islands

Alderney, St Anne: **Georgian House**

Republic of Ireland

Carlow, Leighlinbridge: **Lord Bagenal**
Cork, Castletownshend: **Mary Ann's**
Cork, Cork: **Reidy's Wine Vaults**
Cork, Glandore: **Hayes Bar**

Donegal, Rossnowlagh: **Smugglers Creek Inn**
Galway, Kilcolgan: **Moran's**
Kildare, Moone: **Moone High Cross**
Tipperary, Killaloe: **Goosers**
Wexford, Carne: **Lobster Pot**
Wicklow, Roundwood: **Roundwood Inn**

Pubs with starred bar food

Pubs with starred bar food and accommodation

Kirkcaldy

Kilberry

Warenford

Romaldkirk

Starbotton

Cartmel Fell

Wass

Hetton

Shelley

Higher Burdwardsley

Roundwood

Moone

Leighlinbridge

Wansford-in-England

Southwold

Carne

Brimfield

Keyston

Madingley

Winforton

Llyswen

Lower Oddington

Bledington

Stoke-by-Nayland

Great Rissington

Waddesdon

Clydach

Coln St Aldwyns

Long Crendon

Sutton Courtenay

LONDON

Horndon-on-the-Hill

West Ilsley

Rowde

North Newnton

Ightham Common

Newnham

Beckington

Ivy Hatch

Monksilver

Batcombe

Winchester

Grayswood

Corscombe

Midhurst

Lower Beeding

Trusham

Kingsteignton

Gunwalloe

Alderney

St Anne

Guernsey

France

CHANNEL ISLANDS

Jersey

© Leading Guides Ltd.

Pub of the Year 1995

The Angel
Hetton, North Yorkshire

600 years of history, wooden tables on cobbles underneath an ivy-clad facade, welcoming open fires, good ale and fine, sustaining fare within an oak-beamed interior – surely everyone's idea of the perfect pub? The Angel is almost as great an attraction as the Yorkshire Dales that flank the pretty village in which it nestles. It is by no means a secret (you need to arrive very early to park and get the pick of the seats) but thankfully, however, a new kitchen was installed last year. Most people come here to eat in the bar/brasserie or restaurant but a country pub feel remains – from no-smoking snug to comfortable dining room – and there's still a good pint of Marston's Pedigree bitter to go with one's ploughman's, calf's liver with Parmesan polenta and hot beetroot and horseradish shavings or chargrilled steak. Chef/partners Denis Watkins and John Topham's menus have modern Mediterranean overtones, with dishes incorporating the likes of fresh pasta, basil, aïoli, crostini and pancetta. Seafood is supremely fresh and superbly handled, while popular favourites like sticky toffee pudding, crème brulée with strawberries and warm apple strudel please the sweet-toothed. To complete the picture there's a good selection of malt whiskies at the bar and a globe-trotting wine list (a dozen or more are served by the glass) that complements the fine cooking on offer.

Previous Winners

1994 The Lamb
Great Rissington, Gloucestershire
1993 Rose & Crown
Romaldkirk, Co Durham
1992 The Roebuck
Brimfield, Hereford & Worcester

Family Pub of the Year 1995

The Batcombe Inn
Batcombe, Somerset

Just one and a half years since taking over the former Three Horseshoes in the tucked-away village of Batcombe, Derek and Claire Blezard have transformed their pub into a truly wonderful haven for parents with children of all ages. Last year in our family guide we said that "if ever there was a pub worth a detour for families, this is it" and since last year both food and facilities have improved further, with a new star awarded for food this year, a new car park, patio and pond plus an enormous children's area now built in the rear garden under the shadow of the local church spire. Derek and Claire know exactly what it takes to create a successful family pub – from a changing area for babies, booty box filled with finger food for toddlers, and indoor children's room with National Geographic videos and games, to outdoor adventure play areas for the more active teenagers. With three children aged 3, 8 and 11 of their own, it's not really surprising that they understand what's needed. Inside, parents can tuck into Claire's tip-top food in either bar or the more relaxed, airy dining room; high-chairs, of course, are provided. From tree houses to treacle tart and slides to stuffed spuds, there's much to keep children amused. The Batcombe Inn sets standards that others may find hard to follow – other publicans will find no better example of how a family pub should be run.

Previous Winners

1994   Bridge Inn
Ratho, Lothian, Scotland
1993   Star Inn
Harome, North Yorkshire
1992   Double Locks
Alphington, Exeter, Devon

Bed & Breakfast Pub of the Year 1995

The Angel
Stoke-by-Nayland, Suffolk

Standing at the crossroads in the ancient Suffolk village of Stoke-by-Nayland, midway between Colchester and Ipswich (5 miles off A12), The Angel Inn has been nurtured to its current level of comfort over the last seven years by Richard Wright and Peter Smith. Dating back to 1536, the name of 'The Angel' is thought to have been chosen in order to preserve a veneer of ecclesisatical continuity following the dissolution of the monasteries, when the tradition of accommodating travellers fell to the landowning nobility. Thankfully, the inn has few noble airs and graces these days but upholds fine innkeeping traditions: good grog in the guise of Greene King, Nethergate and Adnams – all local Suffolk brews – and an interesting, sensibly-priced wine list; welcoming, beamed bars warmed by log fires; terrific provender (a new star for their food this year) from chef Mark Johnson and his kitchen brigade of eight; and, of course, particularly restful overnight accommodation. The six guest bedrooms feature hotel-style comforts and are reached via a gallery over the former brewhouse (now a dining room) with its high-vaulted ceiling; one room is in an annexe. Decor is stylishly co-ordinated and housekeeping spot on. The Angel is an ideal base for exploring Dedham Vale – the inspiration for landscape artist John Constable – and conveniently close to Harwich and Felixstowe ferry ports. Children are discouraged (no under-10s overnight or in the bar) – it's an adult retreat and all the better for it.

Previous Winners

1994   Chequers Inn
Froggatt Edge, Calver, Derbyshire
1993   Falcon Hotel
Castle Ashby, Northamptonshire
1992   Griffin Inn
Llyswen, Powys, Wales

British Cheese Pub of the Year 1995

The Nobody Inn
Doddiscombleigh, Devon

For a pub to offer a globe-trotting wine list of over 800 bins is most unusual, but for the same pub to offer a choice of 250 whiskies, tip-top bar food that includes superb local cheeses and comfortable accommodation as well is simply exceptional. Among the fine bar food you'll find a countryman's platter offering you a choice of local cheese, sweet pickle, apple, celery, a small salad and good brown bread, freshly-baked locally; alternatively, you could opt for a plate of six cheeses with Bath Oliver biscuits or bread. But what a superb selection of local cheeses! A constant ebb and flow of up to 40 seasonal cheeses is hunted down by Nick Borst-Smith for the Nobody Inn. Evocative names such as Denhay, Trehill, Ticklemore, St Rumon, Capricorn, Colespark, Langleigh Meadow and Vulscombe cover a range from hard Cheddar-styles made with full-fat cow's milk to creamy, hard, blue-veined or herb-enhanced goat's and ewe's-milk cheeses. Only West Country cheeses are supplied, with a concentration on Devon varieties. The cheese list itself is well worth taking time to study – it has helpful, tempting descriptions – and is clearly a constantly-changing labour of love. They'll even sell you just a half glass of sweet muscat wine to complement your selection. Cheese can also be ordered to take away.

Previous Winners

1994 Shepherds Inn
Melmerby, Cumbria
1993 Down Inn
Bridgnorth, Shropshire
1992 Royal Oak
Didsbury

AM OF MANCHESTER.

ht Bitter. Brewed at the Strangeways Brewery since 1778.

Newcomers of the Year 1995

Cridford Inn
Trusham, Devon

Dating back to 1081, The Cridford Inn is probably the oldest newcomer of them all! Renowned as Devon's oldest domestic dwelling, the newly whitewashed longhouse now features a magnificent thatched roof. Inside, there are huge beams, open fires and a warm welcome from experienced innkeepers David and Sally Hesmondhalgh. Their two-year renovation programme was finally completed last summer, bringing the inn up to a wonderful standard with four country-style, comfortable, en-suite bedrooms upstairs and careful, sympathetic refurbishment enhancing many of the original features in the bar and dining rooms – from huge beams to stone floors and even a mosaic datestone. Decor is tasteful throughout, David's bar food is unusually good and service is reliable. It's truly a breath of fresh air, standing head and shoulders over the muddle of mediocrity often found in other self-appointed 'welcoming inns'.

Halzephron Inn
Gunwalloe, nr Helston, Cornwall

In a glorious position on the cliffs of the Lizard peninsula, with spectacular views across Mount's Bay, the Halzephron Inn is a 500-year-old former smugglers' inn, now completely revitalised by Angela and Harry Davy Thomas, both of whom are Cornwall born and bred. They have brought decidedly good food and a friendly welcome back to what was only recently a run-down pub open just two nights a week. Not least of the pub's charms are the tasteful bar areas and the Captain's Table dining room, complete with head-cracking beams, exposed stone walls, shipping memorabilia and charming sea views. Upstairs are two delightful bedrooms that offer comfort and style along with en-suite facilities and rolling country views inland.

MONTANA WINES LIMITED
New Zealand's Leading Winemaker

———

Pub Wine List
of the Year.

"Adventurous", "imaginative",
"well-informed" and "discerning"
are just a few of the
adjectives to describe this selection
of wines from the New World.

There is no better way to embark
on a discovery of the pleasures of
New World Wines than
through the vibrant flavours of the
still and sparkling wines from
Montana, New Zealand's
leading winemaker.

Congratulations

Wine Pub of the Year 1995

The Castle
Battersea, London SW11

There are several pub wine lists around the country that are veritable tomes, compiled by real wine enthusiasts, but this year we have given our Wine Pub award to the latest opening in a group of London pubs run by Charles and Linda Gotto. The four pubs include *The Ship* and *The Alma* (both in Wandsworth) and *The Coopers Arms* (in Chelsea) and now this year's award winner: *The Castle* in Battersea. In all of the pubs there are often at least 20 wines available for purchase by both bottle *and* glass. To be able to choose just a glass from a selection that includes, say, a Californian cabernet/sauvignon, a buttery Australian chardonnay, a gooseberryish New Zealand sauvignon, a classic, oaky Spanish Rioja or lively rosé, and a sweetish Portuguese muscat as well as 10 or so good-value French offerings is most unusual, even more so in London. It's an enterprising attitude to wine drinking in pubs and particularly appropriate as the food's considerably above average (for London) as well. Our award goes to *The Castle* for promoting the group policy right from the re-opening of the pub following refurbishment and for subsequently attracting discerning, wine-drinking customers to what was previously considered by many to be a London backwater in pub terms.

Previous Winners

1993 **George & Dragon**
Rowde, Wiltshire
1992 **Griffin**
Fletching, East Sussex
1990 **Inn at Whitewell**
Whitewell, Lancashire

MONTANA WINES LIMITED
New Zealand's Leading Winemaker

Montana is New Zealand's leading wine producer and exporter to over 20 countries, internationally renowned for its consistent commitment to quality.

Over twenty years ago Montana planted Sauvignon Blanc grapes in Marlborough, a far-reaching decision that has put New Zealand firmly on today's world winemaking map.

New Zealand winemakers enjoy a naturally favourable climate and soil which produce intensely-flavoured grapes, bursting with fruity flavours and aromas.

Montana takes additional advantage of the country's micro-climates to grow a broad range of grapes and has wineries in each of New Zealand's principle winegrowing areas. Marlborough's Riverlands Winery at Blenheim on the South Island produces its famous Sauvignon Blanc, fine sparkling wines, Chardonnay and Cabernet Sauvignons. On the North Island the

historic McDonald Winery in the Hawkes Bay area, specialises in Chardonnay and Cabernet Sauvignon while Gisborne's state-of-the-art winery makes high-quality whites.

Combining traditional winemaking skills with modern technology Montana produces classic varietals such as the award-winning Marlborouh Sauvignon Blanc, rich peachy Chardonnay, full-bodied Cabernet Sauvignon and quality sparkling wines which include Lindauer and Deutz Marlborough Cuvée, marrying venerable Deutz champagne-making traditions with flavourful Marlborough grapes.

Discover the New World of New Zealand wine by sampling Montana's exciting premium wines.

Keeping a skilled eye on the development of Montana's exceptional sparkling wines.

MARTELL

Congratulations

Martell Cognac is delighted to salute the Pub Host of the Year.

Santé!

Cognac remains the fine golden spirit which French writer Victor Hugo called *"the Liquor of the Gods"*. Since **Martell** was founded in 1715, generous hosts such as Winston Churchill and the Tsar of Russia have offered **Martell** Cognac to their guests.

Celebrate in style and impress new generations of connoisseurs with rich golden **Martell**, the perfect symbol of true hospitality.

Pub Hosts of the Year 1995

Penhelig Arms Hotel
Aberdovey, Gwynedd, Wales

The Penhelig Arms is in a superb waterside setting overlooking the Dyfi estuary, and all but one of the bedrooms that are squeezed into its rather narrow site benefit from the lovely views. Proprietors Robert and Sally Hughes of this welcoming pub/inn/hotel (call it what you will) show attention to detail that ranges from careful interior design of the smaller bedrooms to a varied bar menu that draws a crowd from some distance – always a good sign. The food is flavoursome and not over-elaborate, carefully cooked and nicely presented, with professional yet unfussy service complementing the relaxed surroundings; the extensive wine list – clearly Robert's labour of love as he used to work in the wine trade – offers fair value and the house wines are carefully chosen. The accommodation has been recently refurbished and is kept in spruce condition by good housekeeping. In what is a seasonal part of Wales the Penhelig Arms is sufficiently well patronised to stay open all year round (except at Christmas when the Hugheses take a well-earned break); the staff turnover is low and one gets a distinct feeling of pride and satisfaction from the staff. Robert and Sally thoroughly deserve this award after five years' hard graft making it all such a success.

The Story Of

MARTELL

THE FOUNDING OF MARTELL

In 1715 a young man named Jean Martell arrived in the small town of Cognac in the Charente region of France and set up a business trading in *eaux-de-vie*.

Since that time, eight generations of the **Martell** family have perfected the art of producing exceptional quality cognacs, maintaining the company's prestigious name over the centuries.

THE ART OF VINICULTURE

Martell own around 500 hectares of fine vine-yards in the officially designated Cognac region, noted for its temperate climate and chalky soil. The accumulated knowledge of vine growing within **Martell** is much of the reason behind the company's high and consistent standards.

THE ART OF DISTILLATION

The delicate process of charentais distillation begins once the wine has fermented and the fires lit under the pot stills. The fine liquid called *brouillis* produced from the condensed vapours is then collected and heated a second time in small batches to create a spirit of the highest quality. The **Martell** distillers, drawing upon their excellent tasting skills and inherent knowledge of Cognac remove the slightly impure substances which are produced at the beginning and end of the distillation. Then patiently and carefully they draw the heart or *bonne chauffe* from this second distillation. The clear, fiery *eau-de-vie*, or water of life, produced by this process is then aged to become golden, mellow Cognac.

THE ART OF AGEING

The ageing process which transforms these *eaux-de-vie* into Cognac is a long one. Skilled coopers make the oak casks by hand, without using nails or glue. The spirit stored in these casks is transformed by oxidation through the pores in the wood, taking colour and flavours from the oak. The spirit lost through evaporation is known poetically as *"le part des anges"* or *"the angels' share"*. As it ages the spirit gradually develops its aromatic bouquet and characteristic golden colour.

THE ART OF BLENDING

Once the *eau-de-vie* has reached its peak it is blended with others from different regions and of varied vintages to create a smooth Cognac. The skill lies in recreating the distinctive nutty **Martell** taste each time. This vital task rests with the Head Taster, who draws on the skills of generations to create the unique **Martell** style.

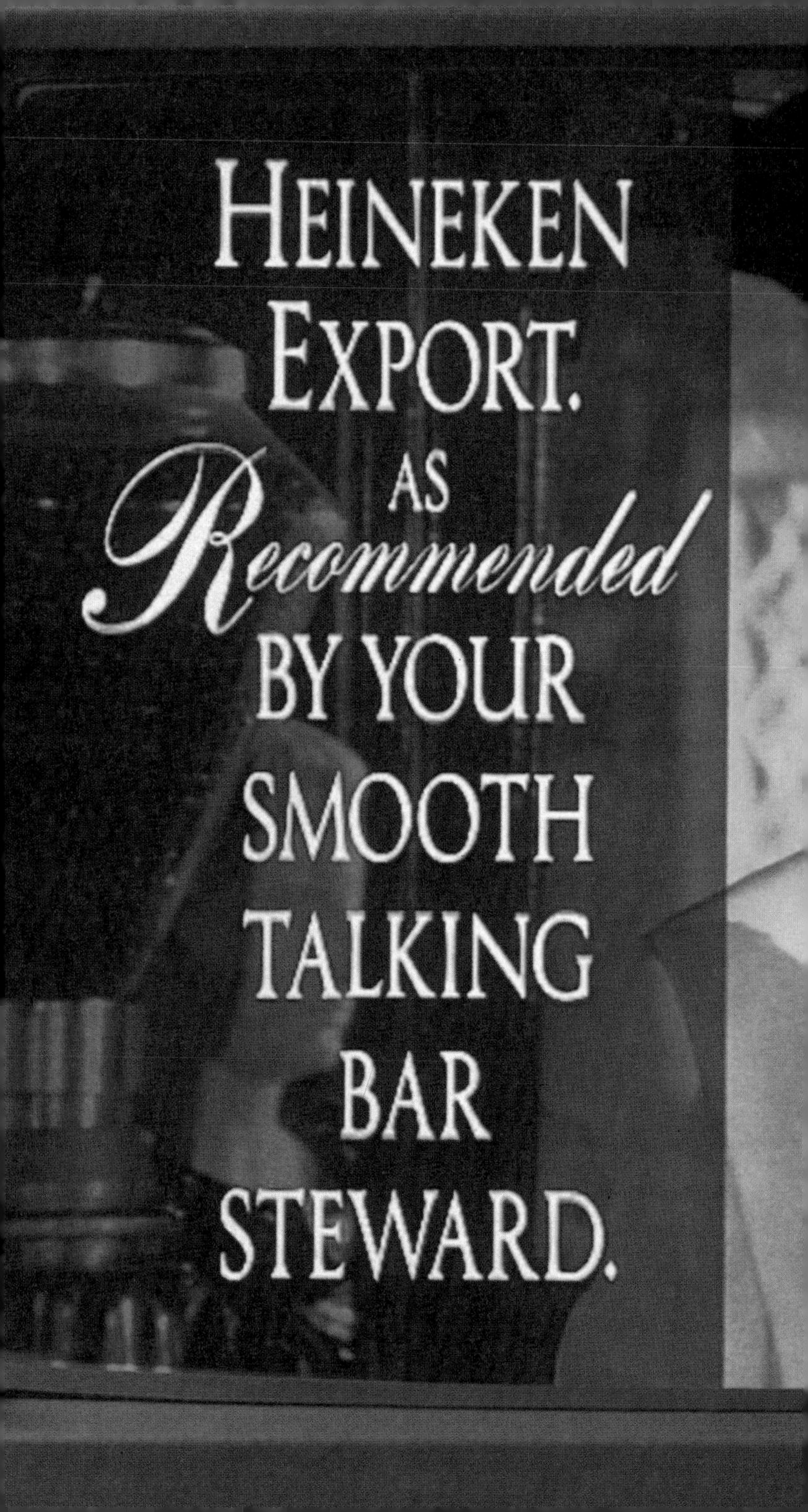
HEINEKEN
EXPORT.
AS
Recommended
BY YOUR
SMOOTH
TALKING
BAR
STEWARD.

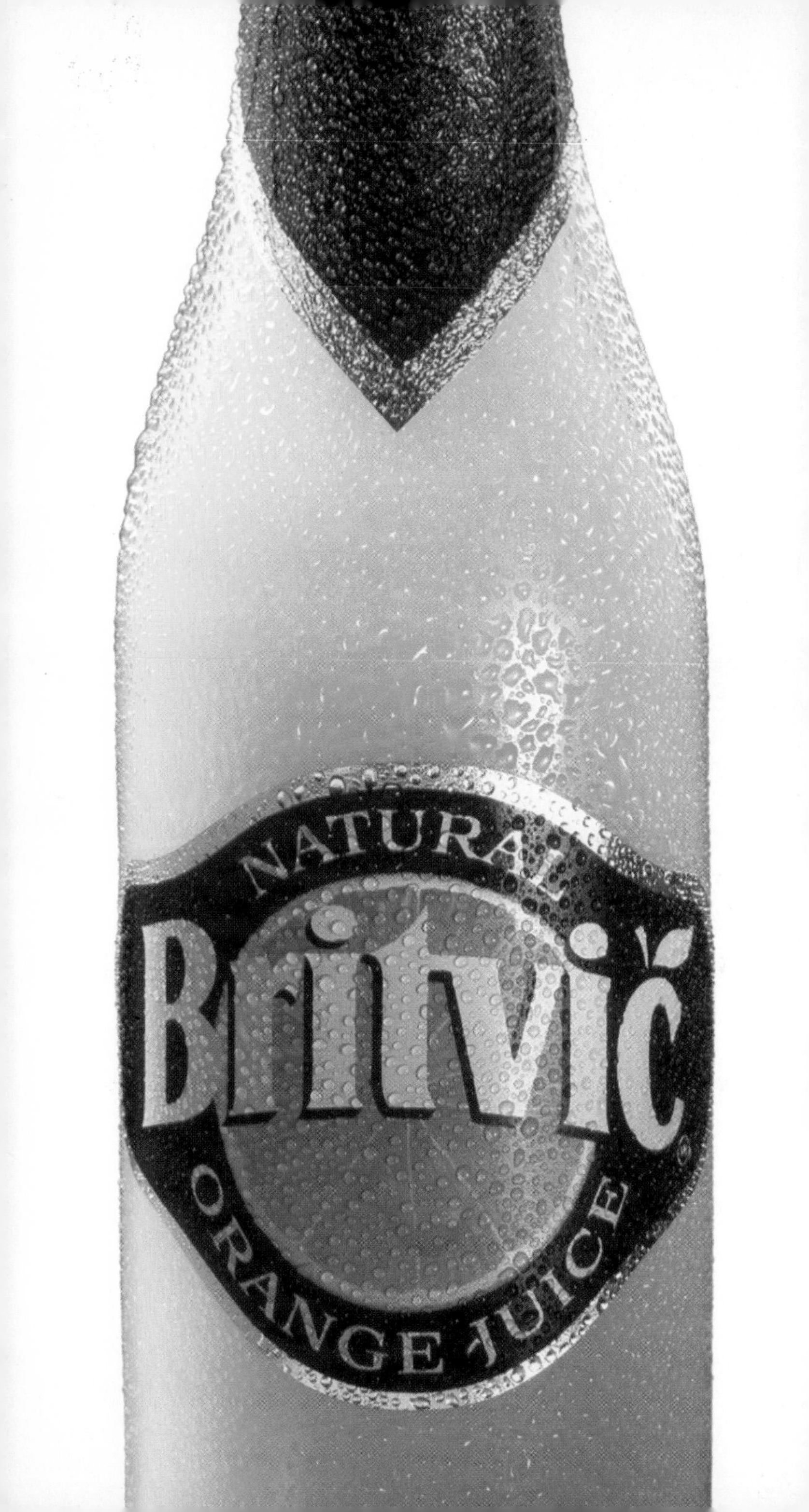
NATURAL
Britvic
ORANGE JUICE

THE BIGGER, NEW BOTTLE

With the new,
bigger Britvic bottles, you
now get better value with nearly
60% more juice. And it's even tastier.
So fill your glasses and sink a
few more ice cubes.
Cheers!

NOW LASTS THE ROUND

Go your

You've never seen a Ford like it; you've never driven a Ford like it.

The new Probe from Ford is the real thing – a genuine sports coupe. A coupe that has been designed to set your heart racing the way no souped-up, cut down saloon car ever could.

With the Probe you get the choice of two engines – a sporty, 16-valve, 2.0 litre

double-overhead camshaft four cylinder unit, or a silky-smooth, 2.5 litre, 24 valve, four cam V6.

The 5 speed close ratio gearbox is sweet and neat. The ride is right. The engine-sensitive power steering is precise at every speed.

The all disc braking system with ABS fitted as standard, is confidently

own Way.

reassuring.

Driver and passenger can relax in the supportive sports seats with the knowledge that airbags are standard for both.

And everything is protected by the electronic engine immobiliser.

The new Probe from Ford – to drive it is to want it.

To discover where you can slip behind the wheel call **0800 111 222** for the address of your nearest Ford Dealer.

The Probe. New from Ford.

Everything we do is driven by you.

Declan misunderstood the shout of 'fore', but like the Murphy's he wasn't bitter.

HAVE
YOU
GOT THE
BOTTLE
TO TRY THE
NEW
330ml
PEPSI AND
TANGO
RANGE FROM

BRITVIC
SOFT DRINKS
?

Turned out nice again

Everything turns out perfectly when you use
Homepride flour – because we've graded every grain
to give you the lightest, finest flour imaginable.
So, whether you use Homepride Plain or Self Raising
flour you can be sure that all your home baking will turn
out for the best.

GRADED GRAINS MAKE FINER FLOUR

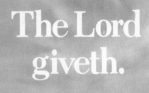

The Lord giveth.

It seems nothing in this world comes for nothing.

Least of all a pint of Stella Artois.

But in all fairness, you really shouldn't blame the poor publican.

He only charges the prices he does because of our brewers' extravagant habits.

Their insistence, for example, on using only the most fragrant of Czechoslovakian hops.

The Landlord taketh away.

Their determination to go all the way to France to secure a particular variety of maize.

And their unbending belief that only premium two-row malting barley will actually do.

Pernickety, perhaps. But how else should we make Stella Artois one of the finest lagers that money can buy?

As we sow, so shall ye reap.

STELLA ARTOIS

Reassuringly expensive.

From
God's own

EARTH

comes
the purity
of
crystal clear

WATER

taken
from source
in the
mythic Celtic
lands of

EIRE

BALLYGOWAN
IRISH SPRING
WATER

Michael had agreed to a life of celibacy, but like the Murphy's he wasn't bitter.

BIG
cove

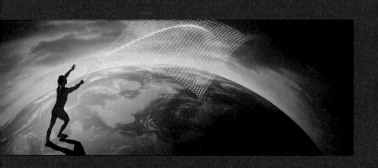

on
rage.

To make the most of your mobile
phone, you need Cellnet, the network
that offers truly national UK coverage
– and links to the world beyond.
After all, if you can't use your mobile
wherever life takes you – why have
one at all?

For further information call
0800 214000

Serving 98% of the UK population.

Cellnet is part of BT – the most advanced company in the telecommunications industry.

Since 1985, over £700 million has been spent in developing our original analogue (TACS) service, and by 1995, a further £300 million will have been invested in our digital service.

Today, Cellnet is one of the largest networks of its kind in the world, covering more than 98% of the UK population.

Monitoring the Cellnet network.

Cellnet's sophisticated mobile communications system is controlled from the Network Management Centre.

From here, Cellnet engineers keep a watchful eye over the entire network ensuring that potential problems are identified and rectified long before they can affect our service to customers.

**For further information call
0800 214000**

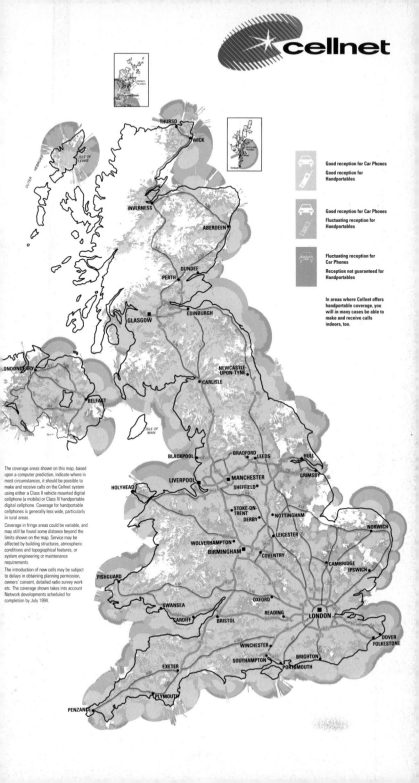

cellnet

Good reception for Car Phones

Good reception for Handportables

Good reception for Car Phones

Fluctuating reception for Handportables

Fluctuating reception for Car Phones

Reception not guaranteed for Handportables

In areas where Cellnet offers handportable coverage, you will in many cases be able to make and receive calls indoors, too.

The coverage areas shown on this map, based upon a computer prediction, indicate where in most circumstances, it should be possible to make and receive calls on the Cellnet system using either a Class II vehicle mounted digital cellphone (a mobile) or Class IV handportable digital cellphone. Coverage for handportable cellphones is generally less wide, particularly in rural areas.

Coverage in fringe areas could be variable, and may still be found some distance beyond the limits shown on the map. Service may be affected by building structures, atmospheric conditions and topographical features, or system engineering or maintenance requirements.

The introduction of new cells may be subject to delays in obtaining planning permission, owners' consent, detailed radio survey work etc. The coverage shown takes into account Network developments scheduled for completion by July 1994.

The American Express Card is now a regular at thousands of the U.K.'s favourite Pubs

In the best tradition of British hospitality, more and more pubs are serving food. And whether you're looking for a simple bar snack or sitting down to a full evening meal, the American Express Card covers it at thousands of the country's favourite pubs.

For more information call: 0273 675533

Always a good sign.

London

N1   The Albion

Tel 0171-607 7450

FOOD

10 Thornhill Road Islington N1

Map 16 C2

A Georgian pub which was once a coaching inn. In the middle
of a quiet residential part of Islington, the front is welcoming with
creeping ivy, tables and benches outside and an old-fashioned
illustrated sign of a coach. The front room has plenty of tables, settles
and chairs around a large wooden bar. The top part of the bar and the
walls are decorated with coaching and horse-related bric-a-brac. At the
back, there is a dark-panelled bar and a homely pinkish non-smoking
and non-dining lounge. The lovely paved garden (unusual for
London) has a weeping willow, a trellis covered with creepers
and plenty of tables and chairs. Food is served during meal hours
and, weather permitting in the summer, there is a barbecue as an
alternative menu. Excellent quality cooking covers a simple menu of
old favourites like vegetable soup (£1.60), steak and kidney pie with
creamed potatoes, lamb chops and mint sauce and battered fried fish
(from £4.25). *Bar Food & Restaurant Meals* 12-2.30, 7-9.30.
*Children allowed in bar to eat. Beer Webster's Yorkshire Bitter,
Theakston XB & Best. Garden. Access, Diners, Visa.*

SW18   The Alma

Tel 0181-870 2537

FOOD

499 Old York Road Wandsworth SW18

Map 17 B5

Conveniently located across from Wandsworth station and close to
Young's brewery, the Alma is distinctive with its bright green-tiled
facade and hanging flower baskets. In the dark wood atmosphere of
the airy central room, cast-iron tables and pinball and slot-machines
range around an island bar counter. At the back, the dining room
has yellow-painted walls, framed cartoons, illustrations and beautiful
pieces of antique kitchen and restaurant equipment. Daylight coming
through the ceiling gives a soft and comfortable feel. Stick to basic
dishes like Toulouse sausage and frites (£4.65), muffins d'Alma
(£4.65) or the bar menu offering the likes of pasta du jour
(£2.75/£4.25) and sandwiches. Other dishes might include monkfish
kebabs (£4.95), Stilton, walnut and smoked chicken salad (£3.95) and
fresh fish dishes on Fridays. Besides the Young's on handpump, you'll
find a superb selection of up to 24 international wines offered not only
by bottle but, rather unusually, also by glass; their turnover allows
such a good selection to be offered without any compromising of
quality. Espresso and regular coffee are also available. *Open 11-11, Sun
usual hours. Bar Food* 12-3 (exceot Sun), 7-10.45 (except Sat & Sun).
Restaurant Meals 12-2.45, 7-10.45 (not Sun eve). Children's portions.
Beer Young's. Access, Diners, Visa.

SE1   Anchor

Tel 0171-407 1577   Fax 0171-407 0741

A

34 Park Street Bankside SE1

Map 17 D4

Located south-east of Southwark Bridge, the original Anchor was
burnt down ten years after the Great Fire but the present Georgian
building is atmospheric with diverse split-level bars, intimate corners,
old beams, panelling and leather seating. The bankside terrace
overlooks the City. Good selection of draught beers. *Open 11.30-11
(Sun usual hours). Beer Courage, Ruddles, Adnams, Anchor Bitter, guest
beers. Riverview patio. Family room. Pub closed 25 & 26 Dec. Access,
Diners, Visa.*

SW3   The Australian

Tel 0171-589 3114

FOOD

29 Milner Street Chelsea SW3 2QD

Map 19 C5

A short walk from Harrods and Peter Jones is a haven for cricket fans with walls covered with pictures of famous British and Australian players; the name and theme of this Nicholson's pub celebrate a very early game played by the first Australian touring team in nearby Lennox Gardens. A few outside tables under the ivy-covered facade face south, taking in the sun. The bar snack menu is straightforward, ranging from ploughman's lunches to deep-fried cod or chili con carne, plus daily specials and freshly-cut sandwiches. *Bar Food 12-2.30, 6-9 (not Sat eve or all day Sun). Beer Wadworth 6X, Brakspear, Tetley, guest beer. Visa.*

W4   Bell & Crown

Tel 0181-994 4164

FOOD

Strand on the Green Chiswick W4 3PF

Map 17 A5

With a cane furniture-filled conservatory and two levels of tables and benches outside overlooking the river, this Thamesside pub is in a delightfully tranquil spot on the towpath. Long-term Fuller's tenants Mary and Gwynne Jones take pride in running their friendly waterside watering hole. Apart from the ever-popular (and sensibly priced) local brew, there's a small choice of home-made hot dishes. Salad plates made with either smoked mackerel, home-made paté, sardines or ham are carefully prepared and there are also ploughman's lunches. At lunchtime there's an extensive choice of sandwiches prepared while you wait with thick, crusty bread. *Bar Food 12-2.30, 6-10 (Sun from 7, Sat all day). Beer Fuller's. Patio, outdoor eating. No credit cards.*

EC4   Black Friar

Tel 0171-236 5650

A

174 Queen Victoria Street Blackfriars EC4

Map 17 D4

Built in 1875 on the site of the Black Friar monastery, the Black Friar also has a very distinctive art nouveau interior dating back to 1905. The decor is astonishing: marble arches, mirrors and extraordinary gold and coloured mosaics. Bas-relief bronze representations of monks in various stages of drunkenness adorn the outside walls; inside, they are represented going about their daily tasks and indulging their habits. It is difficult to tire of the busy decor, which constantly reveals unnoticed inscriptions or monk figures. The pub closes early and gets busy with a mix of tourists and City clientele. *Open 11.30-10 Mon-Wed (Thur & Fri to 11). Beer Tetley, Wadworth 6X, Brakspear, Adnams. Pub closed Sat & Sun all day. Access, Visa.*

W8   Britannia

Tel 0171-937 1864

A

1 Allen Street Kensington W8

Map 19 A4

Cheering and often surprisingly peaceful old pub just a few yards off Kensington High Street. At the front, public and saloon bars are divided by a partition, and share a horseshoe bar; wood panelling, settles and other seats, some in the bow windows. At the back, beyond the narrow saloon, a spacious room has its own bar and food servery. *Open 11-11, Sun 12-3, 7-10.30.* **Beer** *Young's. Family room/conservatory. No credit cards.*

SW1   Buckingham Arms

| Tel 0171-222 3386 | **FOOD** |
| 62 Petty France St James's SW1 | **Map 19 D4** |

The Buckingham Arms has an elegant feel to it with chintzy curtains and etched mirrors behind the long bar. Beyond the spacious bar area is the smaller dining room and food counter. The menu is simple: home-cooked ham (£3.50) with chips and salad, home-made lasagne (£3.50) and quiche (£3.50). Most dishes are prepared in the kitchen. One of the very few pubs in London where chips are deep-fried to order. Very busy at lunch time, it quietens down in the evening. *Open 11-11, Sat 11-3 & 5.30-11, Sun 12-3 & 7-10.30.* **Bar Food** *12-2.30, 6-9.30 (Sun 7-9).* **Beer** *Young's. No credit cards.*

SW11   The Castle

| Tel 0171-228 8181   Fax 0171-924 5887 | **FOOD** |
| 115 Battersea High Street SW11 3JR | **Map 17 B5** |

A new opening for Charles and Linda Gotto, who (as Young's tenants) also run *The Ship*, *The Alma* and *The Coopers Arms* – see entries). A little off the beaten track, tucked away in Battersea and overlooked by rather characterless blocks of flats, The Castle's simple frontage gives little clue to the well-run pub within. The turkey carpet is long gone and the interior has been transformed, using the successful combination of bare boards and rugs and an eclectic mix of furniture. Friendly bar staff serve well-kept Young's ales (including the sweetish Oatmeal Stout) and a long selection of wines served by the glass (up to 22 at any time) – winner of our Wine Pub of the Year award 1995. Three rooms are all served by one bar and include a little 24-seater bistro dining area (a bit gloomy in summer, but cosy in winter), an open-plan main bar room and a high-ceilinged conservatory to the rear, which opens on to a paved garden. A red leather chesterfield sofa claims the best position, right in front of the large open fire in the main bar area. Food is taken seriously and daily blackboard specials supplement the monthly-changing menu, heralding the day's fresh soup (minestrone £2.50), pasta (fusilli with creamy leeks and courgettes £2.75/£4.75) and fish dishes (pan-fried tiger prawns with garlic, lemon and parsley butter £5.50); fish cakes (served without vegetables) are always popular. On a recent visit lamb casserole included well-trimmed meat, baby carrots and sweetcorn in a tasty gravy (ask for a spoon!); deep-fried new potatoes were an unusual accompaniment. An over-chilled, gelatinous haddock and dill paté was the only dish that failed to live up to expectations in the last year. Thinly-sliced French stick is served in a basket with a couple of pats of butter in a separate saucer – hurrah! Carve-your-own roasts are offered at Sunday lunchtime, but they must be pre-ordered by Thursday midday. Fine British cheeses from Neal's Yard Dairy served with fruit (£3.50), ice cream cones (£1) or the likes of treacle tart with cream or custard to finish (£2.25). An espresso coffee machine is another little touch that distinguishes the Castle from so many of London's more mundane pubs. *Pub open 11-11, usual hours Sun.* **Bar Food** *12-3 (to 2.30 Sun), 7-10 (no food Sun eve).* **Beer** *Young's. Paved Garden, outdoor eating, summer weekend barbecue. Access, Visa.*

W8   The Churchill Arms

| Tel 0171-727 4242 | **FOOD** |

119 Kensington Church Street W8 4LN   Map 18 A3

Talk about atmosphere, charm and originality and the Churchill Arms qualifies for all of them. Its cheerful owner, Gerry O'Brien, is a collector *par excellence*; the walls of the attractive conservatory restaurant exhibit his impressive collection of 1600 butterflies and the ceiling of the bar is covered with chamber pots, brasses and copper ornaments. A typical menu mixes steak and kidney pie, moussaka and plaice and chips (all £3.75) with ever-popular Thai dishes such as beef in green curry paste and coconut milk (£4.25) or fried rice with chicken, spring onions and Thai spices (£3.95); both chef and staff are Thai. Sandwiches and ploughman's lunches (£2.95) are also offered. **Bar Food** *12-3, 6-9.30.* **Beer** *Fuller's. Access, Visa.*

WC1   Cittie of Yorke

| Tel 0171-242 7676 | **FOOD** |

22 High Holborn WC1   Map 16 C3

A fine piece of Victorian architecture with a long entrance under an ornate ceiling with plaster York roses. The front bar is cosy and comfortable with dark panelled walls and green velvet seats. The back room is the most impressive, with high ceilings, lamps suspended from the rafters, a coal-burning stove and intimate little booths across the very long bar. The gantry above is stacked with thousand-gallon wine vats. The Vaulted Bar downstairs is a long room with low, vaulted ceilings and a cellar atmosphere. Food is available on both floors. Daily specials might include pork and leek pie, nut cutlet provençale and lamb steak in red wine (£3.95 each). Sandwiches are made to order (from £1.95). The Vaulted Bar tends to be quieter and the queue at its food counter is usually shorter. *Open 11.30-11 (Sun usual hours).* **Bar Food** *12-2.30, 5.30-10. Pub closed Sun. Children allowed in bar to eat.* **Beer** *Sam Smith Old Brewery & Museum Ale. Access, Visa.*

W4   City Barge

| Tel 0181-994 2148 | **A** |

27 Strand on the Green Chiswick W4   Map 17 A5

Riverside pub dating back to the 15th century; charming original, intimate bar at river level, plus a modern extension and warm, bright conservatory upstairs. Live music Saturday nights. *Open 11.30-11 (Sun 12-3, 7-10.30).* **Beer** *Courage, Wadworth 6X, Theakston's Best & Old Peculier, John Smith's. Access, Visa.*

EC1   The Cock Tavern

| Tel 0171-248 2918 | **FOOD** |

East Poultry Avenue Central Markets EC1A 9LH   Map 16 D3

A large basement restaurant hidden away in a pub at the very heart of Smithfield market. Not a place known for its decor (which hasn't changed since the 60s), but certainly popular among food-hoovering meat traders, City folk and medics from Bart's. The animation and cheerful atmosphere start at 6.30am with a generous breakfast – choose from black pudding, kidneys, smoked haddock with poached egg, hash browns, bubble & squeak, eggs any way and so on … The choice is extensive: seven set breakfasts, omelettes, rolls or sandwiches, all at competitive prices (£1.60-5.25). The lunch menu concentrates on meat with 15 steak dishes including an 18oz T-bone steak with trimmings for £13.25. A fun place with gloomy decor enlivened by the banter of serious trenchermen! *Open 6.30am-11pm. **Bar Food** Breakfast, 5.30-10.30am. Lunch, 12-2.45. Dinner, parties only. Children allowed in restaurant and for lunch only. Free House. **Beer** Courage Best Bitter, John Smith's Yorkshire, Whitbread IPA, Young's. Pub closed at weekends & Bank Holidays. Access, Visa.*

SW3 Coopers Arms

Tel 0171-376 3120	**FOOD**
Flood Street Chelsea SW3 5TB	**Map 19 B5**

A small, lively Young's pub on two floors; the ground floor is a single room with a large, solid table on which newspapers are laid for perusal; the upstairs has been recently redecorated, and it's useful if you want to get away from the hustle and bustle downstairs. The blackboard menu offers a mix of traditional and more modern pub fare; most dishes are well executed and you can help yourself to bread and butter. Desserts might include crème caramel and trifle. Service can be slow when the pub is full, but it maintains a cheerful edge. Particularly good range of wines served by the glass. Under the same tenancy as *The Ship, The Alma* and *The Castle* (qv). *Open all day except Sunday from 3 to 6pm. **Bar Food** 12.30-3, 6.30-9.30. **Beer** Young's. Access, Visa.*

NW8 Crockers Folly

Tel 0171-286 6608	**FOOD**
24 Aberdeen Place Maida Vale NW8	**Map 18 B1**

Built in 1898, it was designed as a luxury hotel to accommodate passengers from Marylebone station which was eventually never built on the site. Recent refurbishment has retained the extravagant atmosphere of its original Victorian design. The entrance hosts a beautiful two-tone marble counter and a large fireplace. High, arched doors open on to two rooms: one mainly used by drinkers and game-lovers (bar billiards and fruit machines), the second for dining. In the large dining room a mix of armchairs, wall seats and tables complements the Victorian atmosphere of the room with its etched windows and high, baroque ceiling. A printed menu offers a large selection of tempting dishes prepared to order rather than kept on a hot plate: steak and stout pie (£4.95), breast of chicken in celery and Stilton sauce (£5.95), whole fresh trout stuffed with horseradsih paté (£6.25), chargrilled sirloin steak (£7.45) and even vegetarian ratatouille au gratin (£4.25). The traditional Sunday lunch offers a choice of two roasts (£5.95). Nursery-style desserts. Just off Edgware Road. *Open 11-11, Sun 12-3 & 7-9.30. **Bar Food** 12-2.30, 6.30-9.45 (hot), sandwiches served all day. Free House. **Beer** Wards Sheffield Best Bitter, Marston's Pedigree, Eldridge Pope Royal Oak, Wadworth 6X, guest beer. Access, Visa.*

W6 Dove

Tel 0181 748 5405	**FOOD**
19 Upper Mall Hammersmith W6	**Map 17 A4**

This riverside pub, which dates from the 17th century, has cleverly escaped the blitz of modernization, it also boasts the world's smallest public bar. There is, however, plenty of room elsewhere, including a river terrace for fine weather. Lunchtimes see well-cooked traditional dishes; shepherd's pie, stuffed baked potatoes (£2.95) and various ploughmans's – Cheddar, Brie, ham and paté (£3.50). On weekday evenings Thai food is on offer, individually cooked to a standard which rivals many of London's better-known Thai restaurants. A selection of mixed starters (£5.60), chicken satay (£4.10), stir fries of squid, beef or prawns (all £5.50 including carefully-cooked egg fried rice). Both red and green curries are usually available, a green of beef with bamboo shoots being particularly delicious. Good Fuller's beer, and friendly service. Not suitable for children under the age of 14. *Open 11-11 (Sun usual hours). Bar Food 12-3, 6-10 (except Sun). Beer Fuller's. Riverside patio/terrace, outdoor eating. No credit cards.*

EC1   The Eagle   ★

| Tel 0171-837 1353 | **FOOD** |

159 Farringdon Road EC1R 3AL   **Map 16 C3**

Sounds like a pub, feels like a pub, tastes sensational – but it's still a pub complete with sanded hardwood floor and magnolia walls! No bookings taken but persevere, share a table, order your food at the top of your voice and enjoy the robust Mediterranean dishes, cooked by David Eyre in an open-plan kitchen. Options are marked up on a blackboard, at least nine, often changing twice daily. There's always a cheese plate (Spanish Manchego with *dulce de membrillo*, or soft Italian with focaccia and rocket) and a simple dessert. One stalwart: the marinated rump-steak sandwich, *bifeana*, is a permanent fixture. Other recent hits have included prosciutto with grilled asparagus and shaved Parmesan, pappardelle with chicken livers and sage, *bacabada* (Lisbon-style salt cod and potatoes), *fabada* (Spanish butter beans with chorizo, pork, ham and black pudding), and a light lunch of aubergine purée with chopped coriander and Turkish olive bread. Great food, good prices, excellent range of wines by the glass. The first floor is an art gallery. *Bar Food 12.30-2.30, 6.30-10.30. Pub closed Sat & Sun, Bank Holidays, 2/3 weeks Christmas. No credit cards.*

N1   The Eagle Tavern

| Tel 0171-253 4715 | **A** |

2 Shepherdess Walk off City Road N1   **Map 16 D3**

"Up and down the City Road, in and out the Eagle, that's the way the money goes, pop goes the weasel". Probably better known through the song than the pub itself. Memories of the Royal Grecian theatre adorn the walls of the large comfortable bar, which has plenty of seating. The second bar has a simpler atmosphere with bare wooden floors and darkwood furniture. Background music and busy throughout the day. Live jazz Sunday. *Open 11.30-11 (Sat 5-11 only, Sun 12-3, 7-10.30). Closed lunch Sat. Beer Bass, Greene King, Fuller's London Pride, Wadworth 6X, up to seven guest beers. Paved garden. Access, Visa.*

NW3   Flask

| Tel 0171-435 4580 | **A** |

14 Flask Walk Hampstead NW3 1HE   **Map 16 B2**

Located in a pedestrian street off Hampstead High Street, the Flask is a favourite, friendly rendezvous for comedians, artists and drinkers alike. It has a proper public bar, separated from the saloon bar by the original Victorian panelling. The back room opens up on to a conservatory mainly used as a dining room but also as a set up for charity events and music hall nights which the landlords frequently organise. Good selection of wines by the glass. *Open 11-11 Sat, usual hours other days.* **Beer** *Young's. No credit cards.*

SE1   Founders Arms

Tel 0171-928 1899	**A**
52 Hopton Street Bankside SE1	**Map 17 D4**

Large modern building located alongside the river-bank near Blackfriars Bridge. The bar is airy and bright with large picture windows looking out over the city and St Paul's Cathedral. The front terrace is large enough to cater for crowds of drinkers on busy, sunny days. Wonderful location, panoramic views. *Open 11-11, Sun usual hours.* **Beer** *Young's. Riverside terrace. Access, Visa.*

EC1   Fox & Anchor

Tel 0171-253 4838 Fax 0171-250 0696	**FOOD**
115 Charterhouse Street EC1	**Map 16 D3**

The meat is undeniably fresh at this highly traditional old Smithfield pub, where the market men gather for generous plates of English breakfast (£6.50, 'veggie' £5.50), breakfast steaks (4.50 minute, £9.80 fillet) and smoked salmon with scrambled eggs (£5.50) or even a toasted black pudding sandwich (£1.75)! Grill menu and salads (ploughman's £5.75, home-made quiche £6.50) from noon. The steak and kidney pie (£7.25) is also recommended. Puddings of the Spotted Dick, apple tart and treacle sponge variety. *Pub open from 6am.* **Bar Food** *7-10.30 (breakfast), 12-2.15, 5.30-9.30.* **Beer** *Ind Coope Burton Ale, Tetley Bitter, guest beer. Access, Visa.*

SW19   Fox & Grapes

Tel 0181-946 5599	**A**
Camp Road Wimbledon SW19	**Map 17 B6**

Once a gin shop, converted with the next door stables into a pub in 1956, fronting Wimbledon Common. Lots of theme nights. Tapas bar. No children indoors. **Beer** *Courage Best & Directors, John Smith's, Magnet. Access, Visa.*

SW3   Front Page

Tel 0171-352 2908 Fax 0171-352 8162	**FOOD**
35 Old Church Street Chelsea SW3 5BS	**Map 19 B6**

In a quiet residential area of Chelsea, just off the hustle and bustle of Kings Road, stands the Front Page, on a prime corner site, its white-painted exterior decked with colourful hanging baskets and large, attractive gas lamps. Inside is spacious, extremely light and airy, thanks to high ceilings and large windows which let in plenty of natural daylight. Rich navy blue curtains are matched by painted ceiling borders, and whirling ceiling fans help keep the room fresh. Part-panelled, it's furnished in informal rustic style with solid stripped wood tables, round-back chairs and long benches on well-worn floorboards; walls have minimal covering, save some Victorian-style nudes. At either end of the bar, two large blackboards display the day's food choice, which is interesting and light in a bistro style: regular favourites include snacks like chicken and brandy paté (£3.70) or sautéed chicken livers and garlic butter (£3.20); as main courses, perhaps smoked salmon and scrambled eggs (£5.30), salmon fishcakes (£5.50) or Indonesian beef rendang and rice (£5.80). Those

traditionalists who crave a more solid English lunch are catered for
with dishes like sausage and mash (£4.25). The cooking here will
never win awards, but is reliable enough, and fresh produce is well
handled. Young, friendly and keen staff provide good service with
a smile. This is a pub worth knowing about, just moments from
the crush of the Kings Road and its array of noisier, busier, less
welcoming places. *Open 11-3, 5.30-11 (Sun 12-3, 7-10.30).* **Bar Food**
12-2.30, 7-10 (Sun to 9.30). **Beer** *Ruddles County, Webster's Yorkshire
Bitter, Boddingtons, Wadworth 6X. Access, Visa.*

SE1   George Inn

Tel 0171-407 2056   Fax 0171-403 6613   **A**

77 Borough High Street Southwark SE1 1NH   Map 17 D4

London's only surviving original coaching inn, dating back to when
London Bridge was the only way into the City. After almost 400
years of history it was rescued by the National Trust in the 1930s
and is now run by Whitbread. A large cobbled courtyard terrace
overlooks the beautiful black and white frontage with its galleried
section and hanging flower baskets. A series of bars is interlinked: the
wine bar contains a food counter, the George Bar has low ceilings,
dark beams, latticed windows and lantern lamps and the Old Bar has
a dark, quiet atmosphere and an open fireplace. A popular pub with
tourists and beer fans – a 'beer festival' with at least 12 real ales is held
on the 3rd Monday of each month. **Beer** *Boddingtons, Flowers, Fuller's
London Pride, Greene King IPA, Abbott, Castle Eden. Family room.
Access, Diners.*

E14   Grapes

Tel 0171-987 4396   **A**

76 Narrow Street Wapping E14   Map 17 D4

Over 300 years old, the Grapes probably hasn't changed much since
Dickens, a frequent visitor, used it as the model for the Six Jolly
Fellowship Porters in '*Our Mutual Friend*'. In this narrow riverside
pub, squeezed in between buildings that used to house ships' chandlers,
block and tackle makers, barge builders and the like, it's easy to
imagine Thames watermen drinking in the downstairs bar, with its
bare floorboards and boarded, nicotine-stained ceiling. Prime position
for watching the passing traffic is from the two tables on a (now
glassed-in) verandah overlooking the river, whose murky water laps at
the back wall of the building. **Beer** *Ind Coope Burton Ale, Tetley Bitter.*

SW1   The Grenadier

Tel 0171-235 3074   **FOOD**

18 Wilton Row Belgravia SW1 7NR   Map 19 C4

Not far from Hyde Park Corner, tucked away in the curve of cobbled
Wilton Row mews, the bright red and blue frontage of this intimate
Chef & Brewer pub can't be missed. The small dark bar and restaurant
were once used as a mess by the Duke of Wellington's Grenadiers. The
place is full of historical atmosphere with a few sabres, daggers and
bugles hanging from the ceiling. The dark panelled bar is small and
customers spread outside on to the quiet cul-de-sac. Two intimate
dining rooms (candle-lit at night) at the back are intimate with seats
for just 21; prices reflect the quality of the cooking and ingredients:
smoked Scottish salmon (£8.75), Stilton puffs (£5.25), beef
Wellington (£6.95). Traditional English food is presented at its best

with classics like fish 'n' chips served with mushy peas; there's usually a vegetarian dish. A set menu (£15.95) offers a traditional roast. Good snacks in the bar – from ploughman's lunches (£3.95) to sausage, beans and chips (£4.25) or scampi and chips (£5.25). Sunday lunchtime is the perfect time for a Bloody Mary – don't forget to buy one for the ghost! *Bar Food & Restaurant Meals 12-2.30, 6-10 (Sun from 7)*. *Beer John Smith's, Courage Best & Directors. Pub closed 24 Dec eve-26 Dec, 31 Dec eve & 1 Jan. Access, Visa.*

W1   The Guinea

Tel 0171-409 1728 (Rest 0171-499 1210) | **FOOD**

30 Bruton Place off Berkeley Square W1   Map 18 C3

Tucked away in a mews between Bruton Street and Berkeley Square, this Mayfair institution gained its reputation by serving charcoal-grilled Prime Scotch Highland steaks along with Rossmore oysters and Scottish smoked salmon in its rear restaurant. The bar menu offers a cheaper alternative to eating in the restaurant with classics like their superior steak and kidney pie, shepherd's pie or chili (at lunchtimes only). An interesting selection of hot ciabatta bread sandwiches is also out of the ordinary: try the Siciliano (£4.50) made with free-range chicken, smoked bacon, sun-dried tomatoes, mascarpone and chopped olives; or the Mirabeau (£4.50) with Aberdeen sirloin steak, lettuce, tarragon, anchovies, olives, tomatoes and mayonnaise; sandwiches are made to order (often at least a ten minute wait) and well worth the struggle through the Mayfair regulars who pack the small bar at lunchtime, when getting a seat is nigh on impossible. *Open 11-11 (Sat 12-3, 6.30-11)*. *Food from 12.30 and 6.30-10.30. Beer Young's. Pub closed Sun. Access, Diners, Visa.*

EC1   The Hope & Sir Loin

Tel 0171-253 8525 | **FOOD**

94 Cowcross Street Smithfield EC1M 6BH   Map 16 D3

Vast breakfasts start the day in the dining room above this traditional Smithfield pub. Gourmands can start the day with the whole works: egg, bacon, sausage, black pudding, kidneys, liver, baked beans, tomatoes, mushrooms and toast (£7.50). Less voracious appetites might settle for kippers or eggs-any-way. Grills and roasts are the lunchtime specialities, plus the likes of deep-fried scampi, veal in cream and mushrooms and steak & kidney pie. Open from 7-10am on Saturday, but not for food. Reservations essential. *Food 7.15am-9.30am, 12-2 (no food Sat or in evenings). Beer Courage, Webster's, Young's, Ruddles. Pub closed from 3.30pm Mon-Fri, from 10am Sat, all day Sun, Bank Holidays, 25 Dec-5 Jan. Access, Visa.*

SE1   Horniman's

Tel 0171-407 3611 | **FOOD**

Hay's Galleria Tooley Street London Bridge SE1 2HD   Map 17 D4

Right at the entrance of the newly developed Hay's Galleria on the south bank overlooking the Thames by London Bridge, Horniman's is a modern interpretation of Victorian style in the premises of the family's tea-packing company. The tribute to Frederick John Horniman's travels is discreetly paid through a painted mural on top of the bar. It's part pub, part café and the tables on the gallerias have views of the river and the City in the background. The restaurant offers good hot and cold dishes (turkey pie, liver and bacon, lamb chasseur casserole, broccoli and leek pie – all served with chips and vegetables £4.75) throughout the day; there's also a hot salt beef bar (platter with salad £4.75). A popular pub with both tourists and businessmen. Families are welcome in a special area in the Pantry restaurant and children are offered special portions at special prices. *Bar Food 11-5.30, evenings booking required. Restaurant Meals 12-3, evenings booking required. Children's portions. Beer Burton, Nicholson's Best, Wadworth 6X. Pub closed weekend evenings. Access, Visa.*

SW6   Imperial Arms

Tel 0171-736 9179   **FOOD**

577 Kings Road Chelsea SW6   **Map 19 A6**

At the back of the Imperial Arms, on Kings Road between World's End and Parsons Green, is a paved terrace where tables and chairs are set out in summer. It's very much an eating pub, specialising in crustacea, shellfish and the barbecue. Rossmore oysters are served just as they are (£6.75 for half a dozen rock, £10.75 for native) or cooked à la mornay, Rockefeller (on a bed of spinach with dash of Pernod and cheese sauce £7.75) or Kilpatrick, the last being an Aussie variant involving bacon strips and Worcester sauce (£7.75). Cromer crabs and Scottish lobster also appear in their season, as does some truly wild Irish smoked salmon (£9.75 platter, £5.75 sandwich). From the barbecue, overseen by larger-than-life landlord Cornelius O'Grady, come beefburgers (£6.75), gammon steak (£6.75), rump steak (£11.75) and wild boar sausages (£4.75). Daily curry (£4.75), seasonal stews and summer salads, with most dishes just over a fiver. Lighter snacks, too, like sandwiches and a good platter of cheeses (£4.75), but the oysters are really the thing to shell out on. Opening times may be affected when Chelsea football team play at home. *Open 10-11 Mon-Sat, regular hours Sun (from 10am for breakfast). Bar Food breakfast from 10, 12-3, 7.30-11. Beer Courage Best, Tanglefoot, Webster's Yorkshire. Patio, outdoor eating. Access, Visa.*

NW3   Jack Straw's Castle

Tel 0171-435 8885   **A**

North End Way Hampstead NW3 7ES   **Map 16 B2**

The Inn was built in 1721 on the site of what used to be the hay wagon from which Jack Straw addressed the peasants during the 1381 revolt. Damaged during the Second World War, it was rebuilt in the early sixties. The pub reopened last year after major refurbishment. It has a clean country pub look and an agreeable courtyard with an arts and craft fair at weekends. Being one of the highest points in London, the second-floor restaurant has beautiful panoramic views over Hampstead Heath. Occasional entertainment in the courtyard at weekends keeps families happy; children are welcome in the bar at any time. *Open 11-11.30. Beer Worthington Best, Bass, guest beer. Courtyard, outdoor eating area (restaurant only). Visa.*

W11   Ladbroke Arms

Tel 0171-727 6648   **A**

54 Ladbroke Road Notting Hill Gate W11 3NN   **Map 18 A3**

Opposite Notting Hill police station, on the corner of Ladbroke Road and the charming Willby Mews. The front terrace welcomes you with open arms: built a few steps above street level, it is well stocked with tables, benches and parasols. Inside is a traditional mixture of mahogany panelling, yellow velvet-covered banquettes, large etched mirrors, a semi-circular bar with pillars and a split-level area at the back. There's a very civilised atmosphere with smiling faces and classical music softly playing in the background. Parking can be difficult. *Pub open 12-10.* **Beer** *Courage Directors, Eldridge Pope Royal Oak, Ruddles Best, Webster's Yorkshire, Wadworth 6X. Outdoor eating. Family room. Access, Visa.*

WC1   Lamb

Tel 0171-405 0713

94 Lamb's Conduit Street off Theobalds Road WC1

FOOD

Map 16 C3

Atmospheric and friendly Victorian pub which retains some original features like a beautiful U-shaped counter with gantry and snob screens. On the walls hang photographs from the Holborn Empire, a Victorian music hall destroyed during the war. The pub gets very busy in the evenings with a jolly and friendly atmosphere. At lunchtime, home-cooked daily specials are worth a stop: beef stew in red wine (£3.95), chicken, ham and sweetcorn pie (£3.95), pork and Guinness pie and well-prepared salads. There is a small dining area and a few tables are set outside on the rear patio. On Sundays, the Carvery restaurant is open on the first floor. *Open 11-11, Sun 12-3 & 7-10.30.* **Bar Food** *12-2.30 (evening salads only until 9pm).* **Beer** *Young's. Access, Diners, Visa.*

WC2   Lamb & Flag

Tel 0171-237 4088

33 Rose Street (off Garrick Street) Covent Garden WC2

FOOD

Map 18 D3

A busy Georgian pub which retains its atmosphere from Dickens' time with low ceilings, dark-wood panelling and built-in benches on the ground floor. The two small, separate bars downstairs have limited seating areas and customers tend to spread out into the paved area in front of the pub or in the quieter dining room upstairs. The bar serves excellent ploughman's lunches (£2.50) made with French bread and Cheddar, Double Gloucester, Blue Shropshire or Stilton – all farmhouse cheeses. **Bar Food** *12-2.30, 6-9.30 (Sun 12-2 only).* **Beer** *Courage, Greene King IPA, Bass. Access, Visa.*

EC3   Lamb Tavern

Tel 0171-626 2454

10-12 Leadenhall Market EC3

FOOD

Map 17 D4

Right next to Richard Rodgers' ultra-modern Lloyds building is Leadenhall market, which is known for its Victorian cast iron and glass-covered cobbled lanes, as well as being home to the Lamb Tavern. A characterful place, with engraved glass windows, cast iron pillars, a tiled picture panel depicting Dick Whittington, and a spiral staircase leading up to a mezzanine floor. The pub was used as a location for the filming of *Brannigan* with John Wayne (as a photo of the 'Duke' together with landlady Linda Morris testifies) as well as a scene from the *Winds of War* with Robert Mitchum. Foodwise the thing to go for is the succulent hot roast beef sandwich (£4): the wing-rib is carved to order and served in lengths of real French bread. There are other things available: various sandwiches (from £1.40) in the tiled basement bar where the dart players congregate; some hot dishes of the day, like cottage pie (£4) and seafood mornay (£4) in the first floor bar, where there are also proper tables to sit at; but the beef is the best and by far the most popular choice. A delicious spin-off from all this beef-roasting is the dripping it generates, which can be had with a piece of French Bread – a real treat. About a dozen wines are listed on a blackboard with house wine and a Liebfraumilch available by the glass. *Pub closed Saturday and Sunday.* **Bar Food** *11-2.30.* **Beer** *Young's Bitter, Special. Access, Diners, Visa.*

NW1   The Lansdowne   ★

Tel 0171-483 0409

90 Gloucester Avenue Primrose Hill NW1

FOOD

Map 16 C3

A low-cost conversion job at this old Victorian Charrington pub has completely changed its character, giving it something of a café feel; it is still a pub though, with real ales. Opened up and reduced to bare boards there is a motley collection of tables and chairs (including some folding chairs stacked up against the wall), vases of fresh flowers and a few magazines piled up on an old chest. Amanda Pritchett can be seen at work in the small, spick and span kitchen where she cooks up the likes of coriander soup (£2.50), duck terrine and onion relish (£3), roasted cod and chips (£7), shell pasta with anchovy and chili (£6) and lamb chop with ratatouille and spinach (£7.50). The shortness of the menu – just five or six dishes written up on the blackboard daily – goes a long way to explain the excellence of the results. Not suitable for children under the age of 14. *Open 11-11 (Sun usual hours, Mon 6-11 only).* **Bar Food** *12-2.30 (except Mon, Sun from 1), 7-10.30 (Sun 7.3-9.30).* **Beer** *Bass, guest beer. Six outside tables. Pub closed Mon lunch. No credit cards.*

N1   Marquess Tavern

Tel 0171-354 2975

32 Canonbury Street off Essex Road Islington N1

FOOD

Map 16 D3

Imposing Young's pub at the corner of Canonbury Street and Arran Walk. Tables set outside look out on to the green scenery of the canal running just yards away. The bar inside is roomy and comfortable with elegant fireplaces and oil portraits. Food is served in the high-ceilinged dining room at the back (unfortunately not as bright as the rest of the rooms). Lamb chops provençale, boiled bacon and parsley sauce or lamb's liver and mash (all at £4.50) are examples of the typical daily specials that are prepared to order and come straight out of the kitchen. The selection of cold dishes is equally tempting: cheese- or paté-stuffed mushrooms, chips and salads (£4) and quiches are home-made. Daily roast (£5), pies (£4.50), vegetarian dishes and regular pub favourites complete the picture. *Open 11-11 (Sun 12-3, 7-10.30).* **Bar Food** *11-9.30 (no food Sun).* **Beer** *Young's. Patio. No credit cards.*

W2   Monkey Puzzle

Tel 0171-723 0143

30 Southwick Street off Sussex Gardens W2 1JQ

FOOD

Map 18 B2

Set on the ground floor of a modern building, the Monkey Puzzle benefits from a flowery outdoor terrace. The main attraction is the good selection of draught bitters, although there is also an extensive menu with fair cooking showing some attention to detail (coconut, mango chutney and salad served with lamb curry). Home-made, minestrone soup (£1.50), teriyaki beef (£6.95), seafood salad (£3.25), Cajun chicken (£7.30), Lancashire hot pot (£4.50). Tables are set for both lunch and dinner. Traditional Sunday lunch £5.50. *Open 11-11 (Sun 12-10.30).* **Bar Food & Restaurant Meals** *12-2.30, 6-9.30 (Sun all day). Children's portions. Free House.* **Beer** *Brakspear, Monkey Puzzle Bitter, Tetley, Wadworth 6X, Gales HSB. Terrace, outdoor eating, barbecues. Pub closed 25 Dec. Access, Visa.*

SW1   Morpeth Arms

Tel 0171-834 6442	**FOOD**
58 Millbank SW1P 4RW	Map 19 D5

Located at the corner of Ponsonby Place, it was purpose built for the Wardens of the old Millbank prison. Today, an escaped prisoner still haunts this Young's pub and an impressive collection of law books graces the walls. Home-made daily specials of cottage pie, lamb casserole (£3.95) and salads are available at the food counter for quick service. Scampi, deep-fried plaice (£3.95) and special home-made burgers (£3) are prepared to order. Large selection of wines by the glass. A perfect stop for Tate Gallery visitors. New landlords. *Open 11-11, Sun 12-3 & 7-10.30.* **Bar Food** *12-9.* **Beer** *Young's. Patio. Access, Visa.*

W1   Mulligans of Mayfair

Tel 0171-409 1370	**FOOD**
13-14 Cork Street W1X 1PF	Map 18 D3

In the basement of a busy pub and oyster bar, the restaurant is quieter, with a traditional feel assisted by half-panelled walls and portraits of notable Irishmen. Irish rock oysters are of course on the menu, along with traditional dishes like home-made white pudding with fried apple and grain mustard sauce, baked ham and colcannon or Irish stew. **Restaurant Meals** *12-2, 6.15-11. Closed L Sat, all Sun, Bank Holidays. Access, Diners, Visa.*

SW1   Nag's Head

Tel 0171-235 1135	**FOOD**
53 Kinnerton Street Belgravia SW1	Map 19 C4

Probably the smallest pub in London but certainly not the least interesting. The front was built in 1780, when horses running around on Grosvenor Estate provided the inspiration for the name. The low-ceilinged, panelled bar and dining room communicate through a narrow stairway. A 1930s' what-the-butler-saw machine and a fortune-telling machine taking old pennies are popular features, with takings going to Queen Charlotte's Hospital. Personal bric-a-brac and photographs give a homely and intimate feel. The home-made cooking brings steak and mushroom pie (£3.95), beef curry (£3.95) and real ale sausage ploughman's (£3.65) back to life. Vegetarians are offered the likes of tomato and onion quiche (£3.95) plus macaroni cheese (£2.95). No puddings in the summer; spotted dick and sponge puddings in the winter. A cover charge of £1 is made for meals served between 7 and 10pm. Kinnerton Street runs between Motcomb Street and Wilton Place (off Knightsbridge). *Open all day, usual hours Sun.* **Bar Food** *All day. Children's portions. Children allowed in bar to eat (minimum age 12 after 7pm). Free House.* **Beer** *Benskins, Young's, Adnams. No credit cards.*

W1   Newman Arms

Tel 0171-636 1127 | **FOOD**

23 Rathbone Street off Oxford Street W1P 1AG | **Map 18 D2**

Cosy, panelled bar set in a 260-year-old building on the site of an old ale house. The upstairs dining room has a pleasant homely feel with red velvet curtains and wall seats, blue and white chequered tablecloths and a gas fire in winter. Pies (£5.95), home-made with only the best ingredients, are a speciality. The selection includes steak and kidney, spicy shepherd's, fisherman's, vegetarian and chicken and broccoli, all baked to order. Rhubarb crumble, trifle and apple pie are some of the home-made desserts (£1.80) which change daily. *Food 12-3.30.* **Beer** *Bass, Fuller's London Pride. Access, Visa.*

EC4   Old Bell Tavern

Tel 0171-583 0070 | **A**

95 Fleet Street EC4Y 1DH | **Map 17 D4**

The tavern was built by Sir Christopher Wren during the construction of St Bride's church nearby and features darkwood half-panelled walls with ochre sponge paint and cast-iron gas fireplaces. The bar is cosy and characterful. Solid wooden bar stools are set along the rear window with a selection of daily papers and more seating is available near the entrance. Food is limited to sandwiches made to order and there's an interesting selection of beers. Nicholson's. *Open 11-11.* **Beer** *Wadworth 6X, Tetley, Marston's Pedigree, Nicholson's, Brakspear, guest beer. Pub closed ·Sat & Sun. Access, Visa.*

EC2   The Old Dr Butler's Head

Tel 0171-606 3504 | **FOOD**

Mason's Avenue Coleman Street Moorgate EC2V 5BT | **Map 16 D3**

Built in 1610, it was destroyed during the Great Fire and rebuilt in 1666. Today, under the direction of Whitbread, it retains its beamed and panelled 17th-century atmosphere. Extremely busy at lunchtime, they prepare one of the City's best sandwiches, made with thick delicious crusty bread, filled with carved turkey, ham, roast beef, sausages or cheese (£3). The same choice of meat and cheese is also available as a ploughman's (£3.95). The restaurant on the first floor has a full à la carte traditional menu offering roasts (£8.95), seafood casserole (£9.95) or calf's liver with bacon (£11.95). *Open 11-11.* **Beer** *Boddingtons, Flowers, Marston's Pedigree, Fuller's London Pride, Brakspear, two guest beers. Closed Sat, Sun & Bank Holdiays. Access, Diners, Visa.*

WC2   Opera Tavern

Tel 0171-836 7321 | **FOOD**

23 Catherine Street WC2 | **Map 17 C4**

Friendly Victorian pub right across from the Drury Lane Theatre Royal, completely refurbished last year. Original gas lamps remain above the bar and the walls are covered with theatre memorabilia. The small upstairs bar, cosily furnished with tables, chairs and a sofa, is used as the dining room. Daily specials, simple fare of perhaps meat and pasta bake or chicken and mushroom pie (£3.95) are home-made, generally well prepared and available throughout the day; additional dishes are prepared to order during meal hours (12-2.30, 5-7.30). Taylor Walker. *Open 12-11 (not Sunday).* **Bar Food** *12-8.* **Beer** *Tetley, Burton, Young's. Pub closed Sun. Access, Visa.*

SW1   Orange Brewery

Tel 0171-730 5984	**A**
37 Pimlico Road SW1	**Map 19 C5**

One of the few London pubs to brew their own beers: SW1 is a light
bitter, SW2 and Pimlico Porter are richer and caramelised. Victoria
lager, brewed according to the Bavarian purity laws, is a recent
addition. High ceilings, bare floors, tall stools around high tables and
sofas – the bar is comfortable (and popular in the evenings). The
Victorian gas wall lamps are still in working condition. A separate
darkwood panelled dining room has its own street entrance.
Beer SW1, SW2, Pimlico Light. Access, Visa.

EC1   The Peasant   ★

Tel 0171-336 7726	**FOOD**
240 St John Street EC1V 4PH	**Map 16 C3**

Built in 1890, the former George & Dragon – a substantial Victorian
gin palace – has been transformed by Craig Schorn and Michael
Kittos into a food-orientated establishment serving a very fine
selection of draught ales including strong Belgian cherry beer
(Liefmans Kriek), Bavarian wheat beer (Scherdel Weissbier) and Bière
du Desert, a French light (7%!) fruity beer. The original mosaic floor,
albeit with patched up sections, has been uncovered after years of lying
under concrete. The Pheasant now has a bright, lively ambience
during the day and pleasingly subdued lighting in the evenings.
Scrubbed wood tables and plain wooden seating add a spartan touch
which is reflected in Carla Tomasi's simple but superbly executed
peasant-style food. Based largely on new-wave Italian cooking the
brief menu changes weekly and might include the likes of mushroom,
sage and garlic soup (£3.50), baked sweet potatoes stuffed with
caciotta (a cheese) (£5) or hot smoked salmon with spicy potatoes
(£6). Starters come with delicious crusty, thickly-sliced rustic bread
and extra virgin olive oil. Main dishes come in extra-large china
bowls. Cianfotta (£8), a potato, celery and saffron stew with basil is
typical, as is poached lamb with ginger, lemon grass and Chinese
greens (£9) or squid in white wine, olive oil, parsley and capers
(£9.50). Good sweets such as lemon tart (£4), nut torte with coffee
cream (£4.50) or, more unusually, Flower Marie – English goat's
cheese served with a cold poached saffron pear with coriander and
semolina bread (£4). Menus and beers are seasonal, so you only find
cheese and, say, Theakston's heavier Old Peculier in winter. Best to
book; "10% service on all bills". *Bar Food 12.30-2.30 & 6.30-10.45.*
Beer constantly changing, but typically: Adnams Best, Charles Wells
Bombardier Best, Felinfoel Double Dragon. Closed Sat lunch, all Sun,
Bank Holidays, 10 days Christmas. Access, Visa.

SW3   Phene Arms

Tel 0171-352 3294 Fax 0171-352 7026	**FOOD**
9 Phene Street off Oakley Street Chelsea SW3 5NY	**Map 19 B6**

An unassuming neighbourhood pub tucked away in a quiet Chelsea
cul-de-sac with the added attraction of having a terrace and quite a
large garden for alfresco eating. There's a new French chef here, so the
menu (see blackboard for daily specials) has a distinct continental style,

right down to the sauces and generous use of garlic! The cheeseboard
(£3.95) also leans towards France, though the puds are definitely
British: orange and lemon cake, treacle nut tart, apple pie (£2.50) and
summer pudding (£3.25). Typical examples from the blackboard are
starters (priced from £3.95 to £5.95) such as grilled mussels with
garlic butter; pasta, tomato and mozarella salad; or a brochette of king
prawns. For a main course try the pork medallions with a Dijon sauce,
a rabbit casserole provencale, or a grilled tuna steak with sauce vierge
– these are priced from £5.95 to £7.50. Bar food snacks are plainer:
ordinary but decent sandwiches (not on Sunday) and 'things' with
chips/fries – the home-made beefburger is 100% pure beef.
Incidentally, a portion of baked beans will set you back ten bob!
Open 11-11 (Sun 12-10.30). **Bar Food** *12.30-2.30 (Sat to 3, Sun to 4),
7.30-10.30 (Sat and Sun to 10). Children allowed to eat in restaurant
only.* **Beer** *Ruddles County & Best, Webster's Yorkshire. Garden, outdoor
eating. Access, Diners, Visa.*

SE5   Phoenix & Firkin

Tel 0171-701 8282	**FOOD**
5 Windsor Walk Denmark Hill SE5 8BB	Map 17 D5

Denmark Hill station was destroyed by a fire in 1980; the Phoenix
& Firkin rose from its ashes thanks to Bruce's Brewery and public
support. Now under the ownership of Taylor Walker, but the house-
brewed beer (three permanent, three seasonal) is still the major
attraction. The interior structure of the station remains, with an
extremely high ceiling allowing enough room for a comfortable
mezzanine level. An enormous double-faced clock stands near the
door. The decor is of brick, green paint and bare wood and there is
live music Monday anmd Thursday nights. The large food counter
offers an appetising selection of varied salads, cold cuts, pies, samosas
and onion bhajis (£1); two daily hot dishes (mushroom and ham
quiche with three salads £3.30, chicken with rice, diced peppers and
lemon sauce, beef and ale £3.80) and a Sunday roast (£3.95). Large
baps with various fillings are served with salad (£2.10). *Open 11-11,
usual hours Sun.* **Bar Food** *all day from 12.* **Beers** *Own brews: Rail Ale,
Phoenix, Dogbolter, two guest beers. Family room. No credit cards.*

WC1   Princess Louise

Tel 0171-405 8816	**A**
208 High Holborn WC1V 7BW	Map 16 C3

A remarkable Victorian pub which has changed little this century and
still boasts original mirrors surrounded by decorated floral tiles and
ornate plasterwork. A minimum of eight traditional beers is gathered
from around the country and is the major attraction, along with the
impressive U-shaped bar that threads through the main room with its
bare floorboards. Nevertheless, food on offer comprises freshly-made
sandwiches (11am-10pm), all generously filled, that might include
roast beef (£2.75), salmon and cucumber (£2.25) or avocado and
bacon (£2.75). The more comfortable upstairs lounge bar, whose
bamboo plants and ceiling fans suggest a colonial feel, albeit with up-
to-date, not-so-background music. A Thai menu offers the likes of pre-
prepared (microwaved to order – somewhat of a let-down) red
chicken curry, a stir-fry of beef with oyster sauce, sweet and sour pork
or vegetarian paht thai noodles, which at £4.50 (including rice)
provides good value for simple, well cooked dishes. Prawn crackers

(£1). *Open 11-11 Mon-Fri, 11-3 & 6-11 Sat. Free house.* **Beer** *Sheffield Best Bitter, Thorne Best, Bass, Brakspear, Marston's, Theakston, Vaux. No credit cards.*

WC2   Salisbury

Tel 0171-836 5863

A

90 St Martins Lane WC2N 4AP

Map 18 D3

A Victorian pub whose bronze nymph lamps dividing the semi-circle benches are a classic design. Original etched-glass partitions still remain but some walls have been plastered with theatre ads. One of London's oldest theatre pubs, it is still a popular meeting place for the theatre world. Taylor Walker. *Open 11-11, Sun 12-3 & 7-10.30.* **Beer** *Tetley, Burton Ale, Theakston. Access, Diners, Visa.*

SW18   The Ship

Tel 0181-870 9667

FOOD

41 Jews Row Wandsworth SW18

Map 17 B5

Directions to find the Ship don't sound promising: drive past Wandsworth bus garage and you'll see the pub beside a ready-mix concrete plant. Once there, though, things immediately begin to look up. A delightful terrace, complete with rose-covered rustic trellis and gardens that mix flowers and vegetables, stretches all the way to the riverside and heaves with drinkers on fine days. The conservatory bar makes a pleasant, airy, most un-London-like venue, with its motley collection of old wooden tables, benches, chairs and pews; there's also a public bar, very much a locals' haunt. The setting is informal throughout and the food can be very good, although attempts at more involved restaurant-style dishes are not always successful. Light meals, snacks and full lunches and dinners are offered – from pre-wrapped sandwiches in freshly-baked French stick, through traditional British food like steak and kidney pudding and Lancashire hot pot to dim sum, bouillabaisse to bison burgers! Ploughman's lunches with pickled gherkins and onions are always popular, with a choice of five or so British cheeses. Daily specials are announced on a blackboard and might include the likes of Creole fish cakes (£6.50), a daily pasta dish or risotto with lemon calamari (£4.50), very mildly spiced Creole fish cakes (£6.50); puddings (£1.75) on a recent visit were a disaster: Puddings (£1.75): bread-and-butter pudding and apple charlotte were both served cold in the middle but in a searingly hot plate. Other dishes might include thick carrot and coriander soup, lemon sole fillets filled with crab mousse and a cognac sauce, tricolour pasta dish, bresaola with Parmesan shavings – all quite intelligently served with some flair, but often failing in the final execution. The Ship is a Young's pub, under a joint tenancy with the nearby *Alma*, *The Coopers Arms* in Chelsea and now also *The Castle* in Battersea (see entries). The beer is good and there's a superb selection of wines sold by the glass – sometimes up to 28 at any one time. Note that when weather permits, the barbecue (lamb and sun-dried tomato kebabs, tuna steaks, hamburgers, Thai prawns, veal cutlets in pesto) is very much the focal point of the pub, more or less replacing the indoor hot menu, apart from dishes that lend themselves to barbecuing. *Open 11-11, usual hours Sun.* **Bar Food** *12-3 (Sat from 12.30, Sun to 2.30), 7-10 (Sun 7.30-9.30).* **Beer** *Young's. Riverside garden, outdoor eating, summer barbecue. Access, Visa.*

N1   Slug & Lettuce

Tel 0171-226 3864

FOOD

Islington Green N1 2XH

Map 16 D3

An airy and bright pub at the corner of Islington Green. All the Slug
& Lettuces have different lay-outs but similar decor and green-painted
front. Here, the menu encompasses Cumberland sausages in mild
mustard sauce (£4.25), home-made salmon fishcakes (£5.75), deep-
fried Brie with cranberry sauce (£3.95) and a variety of pastas and
salads. Pies, patés and mousses are also home-made. Sunday lunch
£4.95/£9.50. Unfortunately, not all Slug & Lettuce pubs are up to
this standard. Tea, coffee and biscuits are available between 3 and 6.
Comedy club in the first-floor lounge every Sunday night from
8.30pm Sep-Apr. Grosvenor Inns. *Open 11.30-11 (Sun 12-3, 7-10.30).*
Bar Food 12-3, 6-9 (Mon-Fri), 12-4 (Sat), 12-2.30, 7-9 (Sun).
Beer Courage Directors, Ruddles Best, Webster's Yorkshire Bitter.
Access, Visa.

NW3   Spaniards Inn

Tel 0181-455 3276

A

Spaniards Road Hampstead NW3 7SS

Map 16 B2

Popular weekend pub with a warm, friendly atmosphere; it was once
the home of a Spanish ambassador. The downstairs bar overlooks the
garden and has lovely old settles, open fires and intimate corners,
while upstairs is quieter. The vast garden is split in two by a narrow
walkway covered with climbing ivy; one side has wooden tables and
benches, the other pretty garden furniture with umbrellas. Budgies
happily sing in the background aviary. Perfect stop for Hampstead
hikers. Children are welcome. Parking for 42 cars. *Beer Bass, Fuller's
London Pride, Hancock's Traditional, up to three guest beers. Garden.*
Access, Visa.

SW10   Sporting Page

Tel 0171-352 6465   Fax 0171-352 8162

FOOD

6 Camera Place Chelsea SW10 0BH

Map 19 B6

The former Red Lion was remodelled and renamed a couple of years
ago, and now has the atmosphere of a wine bar, with a predominantly
young clientele. There are dark blue walls above pale wood dado
panelling, with decorative tiled panels depicting famous sporting
events, the Boat Race among them, and sporting figures like W G
Grace, while the seating is largely made up of upholstered benches
around solid lightwood tables. Typical bar food dishes include hot
chicken salad (£4.95), croque monsieur (£2.80) and home-made
salmon fishcakes with hollandaise (£5.75). *Open 11-3, 5.30-11 (Sun
12-3, 7-10.30). Bar Food 12-2.30, 7-10 (to 9.30 Sun). Beer Wadworth
6X, Webster's, Boddingtons. Patio, outdoor eating. Closed 25 & 26 Dec.*
No credit cards.

EC1   Thomas Wethered

Tel 0171-278 9983

FOOD

33 Rosoman Street Farringdon EC1 0OH

Map 16 D3

A Whitbread pub, renovated with a country theme four years ago,
and the first pub in London to serve Wethered Bitter. The U shape is
laid out into different bars and lounges and comfortable Directors
Lounge at the back is used as a family room. The real ale bar offers

live jazz on Tuesday evenings and piano music on Sunday mornings. They serve delicious salt beef baps (£2.65) – except on Saturdays – with mustard and gherkins, and the salad counter is varied; hot dishes (steak and kidney pie, beef curry £3.95) are less successful. *Bar Food* 12-3 *(to 2.30 Sun), 6-9 Mon-Fri (No food Sat lunch or Sun eve).* *Beer* *Brakspear, Boddingtons, four guest beers. Family room. Pub closed Sun evening. Access, Visa.*

SW6   White Horse   ★

Tel 0171-736 2115 Fax 0171-610 6091	FOOD

1-3 Parson's Green Fulham SW6   Map 17 B5

A substantial part-red sandstone Victorian pub standing at the northern end of Parsons Green with a large triangular low redbrick walled patio at the front which in fine weather makes the most of the midday and afternoon sunshine. The interior can only be described as hugely spacious – emphasising the decidedly pubby character of the place. On the periphery of the U-shaped room, the bar occupying the centre of the U, is a selection of leather chesterfields and a few round tables with bentwood chairs. The food counter along one side of the bar has a series of booths each seating about six comfortably. Whether you're eating or just drinking, seating at peak times can be at a premium. This can rather detract from full and proper enjoyment of the food. A blackboard lists the foods on offer and includes snacky patés, terrines and crisp, fresh salads – perhaps grated carrot with poppy seeds, baby leaf spinach with toasted sesame seeds. The dressings too are wonderful – particularly a mustardy vinaigrette with balsamic vinegar. Hot dishes, about three at lunchtime, a few more for the evening session, make excellent use of the pub's other fine asset – its splendid selection of well-maintained beers. Dishes like beef marinated in Mackeson and casseroled with dumplings (£5.50); pan-fried lamb cutlets marinated in Highgate mild and Bass sausages with farmhouse bread and home-made chutney (£5.50) are typical. One or two puddings tend to be around when Sally Cruickshank is there to prepare them and are very much of the hot, sticky nursery variety (all £1.70). The ever-expanding wine list is extremely sensibly priced. 15 Trappist bottled beers. The White Horse under Sally's direction is an establishment other publicans, particularly in London, would do well to take account of and emulate. *Pub open 11.30-3 (Sat 11-4, Sun 11-3), 5-11 (Sun eve 7-10.30).* *Bar Food* 12-2.45, 5-10.30 *(Sat 11-2.45, 7-10.30, Sun 11-2.45, 7-10).* *Restaurant Meals* 1-4 winter Sun only *(£10 lunch menu).* *Beer* *Adnams, Bass, Highgate Mild, Harvey's Sussex Bitter, guest beer. Children allowed in bar to eat. Large paved terrace, outdoor eating. Closed 24-27 Dec. Access, Visa.*

W8   Windsor Castle

Tel 0171-727 8491	A

114 Campden Hill Road Kensington W8 7AR   Map 19 A4

A charming Georgian pub built in 1828 by two brewer brothers from Chiswick. The original panelling and built-in benches still remain and the three small bars have separate entrances. Originally, one could see Windsor Castle 20 miles away, the entrance on Campden Hill Road being at the same height as the top of St Paul's Cathedral. Traditional English cooking throughout the day; Sunday lunch roast beef. A shaded beer garden (one of London's busiest) at the rear is the main attraction in summer (and gets really packed), while a cosy country inn atmosphere prevails inside in winter. Both oysters

(£5 for six) and champagnes (£15.95) are sold at sensible prices. Not suitable for children inside. *Open 11-11 (Sun 12-4, 7-11)*. **Beer** *Bass, Charrington IPA, Young's, Adnams Extra, Wadworth 6X, three guest beers. Garden.*

EC4   Witness Box

Tel 0171-353 6427	**FOOD**
36 Tudor Street Temple EC4 YOBH	**Map 17 D4**

Between the Embankment and Fleet Street, tucked away in the long basement of a modern office building. The decor is a mixture of traditional wood features, modern brick walls and painted murals of the Thames bank. Framed newspaper clippings of famous criminal events hang on the walls; there is even a special award for the best crime story of the year. Plenty of seating accommodates the busy crowd of regulars. The home-made cooking is only available at lunchtime and vanishes quite fast. The range covers sandwiches, salads, steak and kidney pie (£4.25), lasagne (£3.95 with salad and home-made chips) and a few daily specials, possibly cheese, cauliflower and leek bake (£3.95), lamb curry (£4.25) or braised lamb's liver and bacon (£3.95). Good selection of desserts, but not home-made. A more extensive blackboard menu is available (lunchtime only) in Chambers Wine Bar/restaurant at street level. *Pub open all day.* **Bar Food & Restaurant Meals** *12-2.30 (no bar food eves).* **Beer** *Courage Best & Directors, John Smith's, Wadworth 6X. Pub closed weekends. Access, Diners, Visa.*

EC4   Ye Olde Cheshire Cheese

Tel 0171-353 6170 Fax 0171-353 0845	**FOOD**
Wine Office Court 145 Fleet Street EC4A 2BU	**Map 17 D4**

Advertised as re-built in 1667 after The Great Fire (a pub has stood here since 1538, but the current building was more recently refurbished in the latter part of the 20th century), the old bar and upper-floor dining rooms still retain their 17th-century Chop house atmosphere. New additions are more fashionably traditional. The Snug Bar, a new extension in the front part of the building (entrance off Cheshire Court), is reserved for games with bar billiards, darts and satellite television. What used to be the courtyard is now the Courtyard Bar, with its original pavement floor. The Cheshire Room is a high-ceilinged rustic room that hosts hot and cold food counters offering the likes of Lancashire hot pot, beef stew and dumplings, seafood pasta, barbecued chicekn and roast lamb. The Cellars Bar was recently extended and offers intimate corners and a pubby wine bar atmosphere; only sandwiches are available down here, with a speciality of hot Scotch roast beef carved from the joint. To complete the picture, three floors of dining rooms (The Chop Room seating 36, The Williams Room seating 35+25 in an annexe, The Johnson Room seating 32 and 25 in an annexe and top-floor Directors private room seating 16 – all available for private hire) offer a traditional à la carte menu. Sunday roast lunch (£4.95) is served in the bars only. No credit cards for bar meals. *Open 11.30-11, Sun 12-3.* **Bar Food** *12-2.30 (sandwiches weekdays, Sun lunch), 6-9 Mon-Thu only.* **Restaurant Meals** *12-2.30, 6-9.30 (closed Sun).* **Beer** *Samuel Smith Old Brewery & Museum Ale plus up to four guest beers. Pub closed Sun eve, 24-26 Dec, New Year's Eve & Day, Easter Bank Holiday period and all other Bank Holidays. Access, Diners, Visa.*

EC1   Ye Olde Mitre Tavern

Tel 0171-405 4751 | A

1 Ely Court Ely Place EC1 | Map 16 D3

Located behind St Ethelreda's church and converted from the Bishop's house, Ye Olde Mitre dates back to the 18th century and is run for Taylor Walker by Don Sullivan. Access is between numbers 8 and 9 Hatton Garden or though a small passage in Ely Place. The Tavern's two small bars get extremely busy at lunchtime, bringing some life into the narrow Ely Court. Popular for their salmon, ham and cheese, and cheese and onion toasted sandwiches. The Bishops Room holds up to 30 for functions. *Open 11-11 Mon-Fri only.* **Beer** *Burton, Friary Mieux, Tetley. Pub closed Sat, Sun & Bank Holidays. No credit cards.*

England

Abbots Leigh   George Inn

Tel 01275 372467	**FOOD**

Pill Road Abbots Leigh Bristol Avon BS8 3RP   Map 13 F1

There's a quaintly old-fashioned air to this flower-adorned old pub by
the busy A369, a two and a half mile climb from junction 19 of the
M5. The interior is hung with horse brasses and antique saddlery and
bar food is announced on a blackboard menu. Norman and Tracy
Grovden have recently taken over as landlords and Tracy takes charge
of the kitchen. Generous starters include deep-fried Camembert with
two Greek dips and pitta bread with onion relish (£3.75), green-
lipped mussels (£4.25) or pork satay with salad and French bread
(£3.75). Seafood features strongly in the main dishes – shark steaks,
creamy fish pie, fillets of lemon sole, salmon and broccoli gratin (all
£7.35-7.55), in addition to spinach and mushroom crepes (£6.95) or a
selection of pies (boozy beef, lamb and apricot £7.25). Puddings may
include lemon brulée, crumbles or banoffi pie (all £2.95). The large
garden seats 70. The George has recently been redecorated outside
and recarpeted inside. *Bar Food 12-2.30, 6.30-9.30 (Sun from 7).*
Beer Courage, fortnightly changing guest beer. Garden, outdoor eating.
Access, Visa.

Abbotsbury   Ilchester Arms

Tel 01305 871243	**B&B**

Market Street Abbotsbury Dorset   Map 13 F3

Abbotsbury is one of the prettiest villages in Dorset, its street lined
with mellow-stone cottages and with the added attractions of the
famous Swannery, the sub-tropical gardens, a medieval tithe barn and
the ancient St Catherine's Chapel, it is an extremely popular
destination. Also on the list of places to visit should be the Ilchester
Arms, a rambling 16th-century coaching inn that dominates the heart
of the village. Inside, a civilised and relaxed atmosphere prevails
within the several heavily beamed, part-panelled and comfortably
furnished rooms. Old tables, sofas in front of the inglenook, a wealth
of old pictures – over 1000 – copper, brass, encased fish and numerous
other old artefacts adorn the walls. The delightful en-suite bedrooms
make this welcoming inn a most agreeable base from which to
explore the area. All rooms are furnished to a high standard with dark
wood reproduction furniture and decorated with quality wallpaper
and matching fabrics – two rooms boasting canopied four-poster beds.
Spotlessly clean bathrooms are well equipped and other added
comforts include TV, telephone and tea-making facilities. Two of the
rooms are located in an adjacent converted stable block and all are
named after flowers found in the hotel garden. Summer outdoor
seating can be found on the sheltered patio, beyond the attractive and
airy conservatory and on the lawn which affords splendid views
towards St Catherine's Chapel on top of the neighbouring hill. Now a
part of Greenall's Premier House group. *Family room.* *Beer Flowers*
Original, John Smith's, Wadworth 6X. Garden. ***Accommodation***
10 bedrooms, all en suite, £50 (single £30). Children welcome overnight
(under-2s free, 2-6s £5, 6-10s half-price), cots available (£5).
Accommodation closed 24 & 25 Dec. Access, Visa.

Ainstable   The New Crown Inn

Tel 01768 896273	**B&B**
Nr Carlisle Cumbria CA4 9QQ	**Map 4 C3**

This recently reopened pub in a picturesque and remote village two miles above the Eden Valley has drawn instant praise from its early visitors. Totally reshaped and upgraded inside with not a hint of wasted space, the new bar, whose old flagstones and open hearth have been carefully restored, makes a fine setting for a fireside chat and the odd fishing story. Fittings and decor in the three bedrooms (one a single) have been kept just as simple with freestanding furniture, thick duvets and floral drapes. TVs and coffee-making facilities are all provided and each has its own neat, en-suite WC, bath and shower. Owned and run by Claire Gibbs, whose family run the *Duke's Head* in nearby Armathwaite (see entry), we're sure that this new venture will be crowned with success. Food here is looking promising also. *Free House.* **Beer** *Tetley Best, Ruddles Best, John Smith's Magnet. Garden, outdoor eating, patio. Family room.* **Accommodation** *3 bedrooms, all en suite, from £45 (single £25). Children welcome overnight, additional beds supplied. No credit cards.*

Albury Heath   King William IV

Tel 01483 202685	**A**
Little London Albury Heath nr Guildford Surrey GU5 9DB	**Map 15a E4**

A surprisingly old-fashioned pub in a popular walking area (children and dogs welcome); cottagey little rooms with flagstone floor, enormous inglenook fireplace in main bar (off which, up a few stairs, is a separate dining area), rustic furnishings and attractive odd bits of bric-a-brac. Loos are outside and equally old-fashioned, but the small front garden can be a delightful, dingly dell-style, away-from-it-all place for a quiet pint in good weather. Children welcome. *Open 11-3, 5.30-11, Sun 12-3, 7-10.30. Sunday hours on Bank Holidays. Free House.* **Beer** *Castle Eden, Courage Best, Boddingtons, Harveys, Hogs Back, regularly-changing guest beers. Small garden. Closed 25 Dec. No credit cards.*

Alciston   Rose Cottage

Tel 01323 870377	**A**
Alciston nr Polegate East Sussex BN27 6UW	**Map 11 B6**

Old-fashioned, wisteria-clad cottage pub nestling in the centre of a tiny hamlet on a dead-end lane near the base of the South Downs. Popular walkers retreat and a venue for locals seeking a peaceful drink, either in the small front garden or in one of the rambling cosy rooms inside. Each are furnished with a good mix of sturdy tables and old cushioned pews and adorned with collections of harnesses, traps, farming memorabilia, stuffed birds and fish in cases and other interesting bric-a-brac. Good relaxed atmosphere. Rear paddock with chickens, a goat and a pond. *Pub open 11.30-2.30, 6.30-11 (Sun 12-2, 7-10.30). Free House.* **Beer** *Harveys of Lewes, one guest beer. Garden, outdoor eating, tables in garden. Closed Christmas Day afternoon & Boxing Day.*

Alderminster   The Bell

Tel 01789 450414 Fax 01789 450998	FOOD

Alderminster nr Stratford-on-Avon Warwickshire CV37 8NX   Map 14 C1

Devoted to the enjoyment of some quite serious food, the Bell now
defines itself as a "Bistro and bar". It has, nonetheless, a more than
adequate public real ale bar and the Brewers, Keith and Vanessa,
produce meals of a qulity that is too good to ignore in a Guide
devoted to good Pub food. As a dining venue it falls somewhere
between the two, with food ordered from daily-changed blackboards
at the bar and delivered with a fair amount of bustle in the bistro.
Choice is extensive, from a courgette and coriander soup (£2.50),
Stilton and Guinness paté (£4.25) and apricot and cashew nut roast
(£6.50) to a mini-rack of lamb with Madeira sauce, "dauphinoise"
potatoes and fresh vegetables (£9.50). Much attention is given to the
demands of healthy eating with plainly grilled fish (whole sea bream
£8.50) and vegetarian options clearly marked. The kitchen's
dedication to all fresh ingredients plays its part, and there's hardly a
chip in sight. The luscious puddings, such as sticky toffee pudding or
the baked marbled chocolate cheesecake (both £2.95) may, however,
fail to restrict the damage at the end of the day. Special events, from
"Symphony Suppers" to a Hallowe'en Pie Party play a regular part in
the Bell's repertoire with complimentary year planners provided for
diners to plan their next visit well ahead. *Free House. **Bar Meals** 12-2,
(12-1.45 Sun), 7-9.45 (7-9 Sun). Children's portions. **Beers** Marston
Pedigree, Flowers Original, Hook Norton Best, guest beers. Garden. Family
room. Access, Visa.*

Aldworth   Bell Inn

Tel 01634 578272	A

Aldworth nr Reading Berkshire RG8 9SE   Map 14a C3

Especially popular with walkers on the Ridgeway Path, the Bell, of
14th-century origins, has been in the same family's hands for over 200
years. It has to be said that, externally, the pub's not particularly
prettified and the old inn sign is decrepit, but its a Grade I listed
building nonetheless and the interior has changed little either over the
centuries. Six real ales, excellent Arkells BBB for instance, are
dispensed from a glass-panelled hatch which serves instead of any bar
counter. Drinkers stand around in the hall or squeeze themselves into
one of the candle-lit brick alcoves which give the place so much
character. Food is restricted simply to hot, filled crusty rolls served up
in wicker baskets: varieties range from cooked meats (90p) to smoked
salmon with cream cheese or Cornish crab (£1.50). The pickled
onions are extra. Worth a look nearby is the Norman village church
famed for its massive stone effigies of the De La Beche family.
*Beer Morells Mild, Arkells BBB & Kingsdown, Badger Best, Hook Norton
Best. Garden, children allowed indoors. Pub closed all Mon (except Bank
Holidays). No credit cards.*

Alford   White Horse Hotel

Tel 01507 462218	FOOD
	B&B

29 West Street Alford Lincolnshire LN13 9DG   Map 7 F2

A traditional well-restored coaching inn dating from 1640 and located
near the centre of this small market town – look out for the carved
stone horse above the door. Beneath the thatched roof is a friendly and
comfortable bar with a low ceiling, upholstered wall seats, stools,

copper topped round tables and a coal-effect gas fire. Reliable bar food ranges from an extensive list of imaginatively filled sandwiches to a blackboard menu featuring standard favourites and more interesting dishes like chicken breast in whisky and ginger sauce (£5.95), garlic mussels (£2.95), broccoli and cream cheese soup (£1.50), pork fillet with demerara and Dijon mustard (£6.25) and halibut with prawns and mushrooms (£6.95). Puddings (£2) may include chocolate, brandy and banana mousse. Upstairs are nine average sized and attractively decorated bedrooms, all with pretty wallpapers and fabrics and simple free-standing furniture. All are neatly equipped with TVs, direct-dial telephones, clock-radios and beverage-making facilities. En-suite facilities are kept spick and span, some have baths, others good shower units. Residents lounge. *Free House.* **Bar Food** *12-2, 7-10. Children's portions available.* **Beer** *Batemans XB, Worthington Best Bitter, Bass.* **Accommodation** *9 bedrooms, 7 en suite, £40 (Single £30). Children and dogs welcome overnight. Access, Visa.*

Almondsbury   Bowl Inn

Tel 01454 612757 Fax 01454 619910	**B&B**
16 Church Road Lower Almondsbury nr Bristol Avon BS12 4DT	**Map 13 F1**

Just off the A38 and only two minutes' drive from the M5 (Junction 16), turn down Sunday's Hill to St Mary's Church in Lower Almondsbury; right next to it stands the Bowl, which in 1146 was a row of monks' cottages. Today's stone structure dates from the 16th century, though the just-completed bedroom conversions will wear well into the 21st! Uncovered wall niches, exposed roof timbers and original fireplaces all contribute to these rooms' unique charm, to which individual fabrics in bright colours and spotless fitted bathrooms have been added with flair and style. Beverage tray, colour TV, clock radio, trouser press and hairdryer comprise the comprehensive modern-day amenities. The single bar with its attendant two tiers of restaurant space is a buzzing, highly popular local venue with plenty of overspill to picnic tables by the roadside and an enclosed beer garden. **Beer** *Courage. Patio and beer garden.* **Accommodation** *8 rooms, all en suite, £80-£74 (single £50-£38). No dogs. Access, Diners, Visa.*

Alphington   Double Locks Hotel

Tel 01392 56947	**FOOD**
Alphington Exeter Devon EX2 6CT	**Map 13 D2**

The Double Locks isn't easy to find but it's well worth the effort. First find the Marsh Barton Trading Estate and drive through it to the council incinerator – don't worry, the pub is some way yet – until you reach the plank canal bridge, which is made for vehicles, although it may not appear to be. Once across, turn right, and a single-track road will bring you to the red-brick Georgian Double Locks in a splendid canalside location within sight of the Cathedral. Equally popular with business people and students, this is the perfect summer pub: there are swans on the canal next to the eponymous lock, a large garden shaded by huge pine trees, and a barbecue both lunchtime and evening in summer, weather permitting. There's even a small marquee in which to shelter from errant showers. Inside is very informal. Several rooms have black and white tiled floors, draw-leaf domestic dining-room tables and lots of posters advertising local events – not far removed from a student bar at University. Chess, draughts,

Monopoly, Scrabble and bar billiards are all keenly played. A huge blackboard displays the day's offerings, featuring almost as many options for vegetarians as for carnivores. Start with mushroom and coriander soup (£1.40), garlic mushrooms and Stilton on toast (£3.40) or a selection of garlic breads with Cheddar, Stilton or goat's cheese topping (£1.25-£2.65), followed perhaps by turkey and mushroom pie (£3.30), lasagne (£3.30), baked potatoes with a variety of toppings (ranging from £1.25-£3.80) plus either vegetarian or meat crepes (£3.85). Late breakfasts here mean a traditional fry-up, either meat or vegetarian, plus a pint of the beer of your choice at the all-in price of £4. There is no special children's menu but most things also come in smaller portions at smaller prices, and several rooms can be used by families, who are made genuinely welcome. *Bar Food 11-10.30 (Mon-Sat),12-2, 7-10 (Sun). Free House. Beer Adnams Broadside, Greene King Abbot Ale, Marston's Pedigree. Riverside garden, outdoor play area, outdoor eating, summer barbecue. Family room. No credit cards.*

Alresford   Globe on the Lake

Tel 01962 732294 Fax 01962 766008	**FOOD**
The Soke Alresford Hampshire SO24 9DB	Map 15 D3

A superbly sited pub, only recently rejuvenated by new tenants, located at the bottom of Broad Street and on the banks of a reed-fringed lake – Alfresford pond – complete with swans and dabbling ducks. The delightful waterside garden is a splendid summer spot for alfresco imbibing. Inside, the characterful main bar has been refurbished with new carpets, sturdy tables and chairs, and a deep, comfortable sofa in front of the open fire; local photographs and prints decorate the walls. The adjacent cosy restaurant has linen-clothed tables, candles and fresh flowers and includes a new restaurant extension providing seating which looks out over the lake. Home-cooked, value-for-money bar snacks are listed on the twice-daily-changing blackboard, which may include cauliflower cheese (£2.95), cottage pie and vegetables (£3.95), pork casseroled in cider (£5.95) and ling (cod) baked with a cheese and bacon crust (£5.50). Evening restaurant fare – also available in the bar – can be chosen from the weekly-changing board; examples include celery and walnut soup (£1.95), duck rillettes with gooseberry conserve or smoked salmon and prawn quiche (both £2:95) to start, followed by salmon poached on leeks with a watercress sauce (£5.95), pork loin in a cider and cream sauce (£5.75) and duck breast 'sweet and sour' (£6.95). Good, crisp vegetables. Raspberry mousse (£1.95) and peach and apple tart with kiwi sauce (£2.50) are typical puddings. Park over the bridge on Broad Street. *Bar Food & Restaurant Meals 12-2, 6.30-9.30 (Fri & Sat to 10, Sun 7-9). Beer Wadworth 6X, Marston's Pedigree, John Smith's. Garden, outdoor eating. Access, Visa.*

Alstonefield   George Inn

Tel 0133 527 205	**A**
The Green Alstonefield nr Ashborne Staffordshire DE6 2FX	Map 6 C3

The nearby Manifold Valley is a famous haunt for ramblers, and easy to get lost in. Drivers should follow the Deve valley road which connects Hulme End (B5054) with the A515. At the heart of this picturesque Derbyshire stone village, the Grandjean family warmly welcomes all comers, as long as muddy boots are left at the door. Service is from a tiny triangular stone-built bar; seating in three

rooms in front of cosy fires, at picnic tables in the rear stable yard
(with family camping available in the next field) or in front of the
pub by the village green. The George gets pretty hectic at peak times
and the crush can be quite convivial. Queue at the kitchen door to
place food orders, which are very much of the chicken-and-chips
genre. **Beer** *Burtonwood, James Forshaw. Patio, outdoor eating. Family
room. No credit cards.*

Alveston   Ferry Inn

Tel 01789 269883	FOOD

Ferry Lane Alveston nr Stratford-on-Avon Warwickshire CV37 7QX	Map 14 C1

Just off the B4086, past three miles from Stratford, those looking for a
sunny riverside spot may be a tad disappointed as there is only a
footpath from here to the banks of the Avon. Undeterred, diners drive
out in their legions to sample substantial daily offerings prominently
posted on the blackboard. Equally prominent in this open-plan
conversion of three tiny bar rooms is the notice beseeching fellow
diners not to obscure the view as they choose from chicken liver paté
(£3.50) or avocado, crab and prawn salad (£4.95) for starters or a
light snack, gravitating to braised home-made faggots (£4.95),
chicken and vegetable korma (£5.95) or sirloin steak with garlic
butter (£7.95). Orders for desserts, largely chocolatey, or fruity, and
fattening (all £2.45) are promptly solicited at the table. Service, too, is
friendly and efficient, led from the front by the ever-present Sarah and
David Russon. Space limitations also determine a restriction inside on
the under-5s (altogether) and other youngsters who can't be persuaded
to sit tight. There's a super front patio by the village green for
summer drinking. **Bar Food** *11.45-2, 6.30-9 (12-2 Sun).*
Beers *Theakston, Wadworth 6X, Youngers IPA, guest beers. Garden,
outdoor eating. Access, Visa.*

Amberley   Black Horse

Tel 01453 872556	A

Amberley Gloucestershire GL5 5AD	Map 14 B2

Teetering on the very edge of the escarpment just below
Minchinhampton Common, the pub's westerly aspect comes into its
own on glorious summer evenings. Behind the bar itself is a picture
window, and beyond it a prominent new conservatory from which to
soak in the panoramic views. Below are a tiered patio and garden,
though parents should be mindful of a steep drop from the bottom
wall to the meadow below. The upper garden has swings and picnic
tables, and there's a separate games room which opens on an occasional
basis. A wide and regularly changing range of real ales draws
afficionados from far and wide, and a real sense of community
underscores the fact that the pub is communally owned; as, it appears,
are several pub dogs, though customers are respectfully requested not
to feed them. *Free House.* **Beer** *Arkells 3B, Tetley & Archers Best, Burton
Ale, guest beers. Garden. Access, Visa.*

Amersham   King's Arms

Tel 01494 726333 Fax 01494 433480	A

30 High Street Old Amersham Amersham Buckinghamshire HP7 0DJ	Map 15a E3

The jetty gables of the ancient black and white timbered King's Arms
overlook the broad High Street of this attractive old market town.
Dating back to the 15th century it is one of the oldest pubs in England

and a mellow atmosphere fills the main bar which retains much of its original character. A wealth of beams, standing timbers, tiny alcoves, two huge inglenook fireplaces and an assortment of settles and old furniture make it a fascinating pub to visit. There is a flower-filled courtyard and a sheltered lawn with seating. Cream teas are served from 3-5pm. *Open 11am-11pm, usual hours Sun. Free House.* *Beer Greene King IPA, Benskins Bitter, Ind Coope Burton Ale. Garden. Access, Diners, Visa.*

Ampney Crucis   Crown of Crucis

Tel 01285 851806   Fax 01285 851735   **B&B**

Ampney Crucis Gloucestershire GL7 5RS   Map 14a A2

One of four Gloucestershire Ampneys, Crucis stands by the A417, 3 miles from Cirencester. Established over 400 years, the Crown has seen rapid growth in the last five with the building of a 25-bedroom extension, and refurbishment of the oak-beamed bar and two-tiered restaurant into a refined, upmarket inn. Furnishings and decor in the bedrooms are uniform, as are up-to-date amenities and neat, fully tiled bathrooms with over-bath showers. Fourteen ground-floor rooms are especially handy for both the elderly and youngest residents (baby listening available), while the clever courtyard lay-out affords most rooms a view over Ampney Brook, connected to the cricket ground opposite by a rustic wooden bridge. Good selection of wines by the glass. *Pub Open 11.45-10. Free House. Beer Theakston's XB, Ruddles County, Archers Village. Stream-side garden.* **Accommodation** *25 bedrooms, all en suite, £60. Children welcome overnight (£17.50 if sharing parents' room, £25 in interconnecting room). Additional beds & cots available. Access, Diners, Visa.*

Zzzz...

Ansty   The Ansty Arms

Tel 01203 611817   Fax 01203 603115   **B&B**

Brinklow Road Ansty Coventry West Midlands CV7 9JP   Map 7 D4

Pub with accommodation lodge, two-tier eating, large conservatory and children's "Jungle Bungle" play area on high ground overlooking (and within earshot of) both motorways – a good spot and highly accessible – once you know the way! Take B4065 to Ansty from M6 at Junction 2 where it connects with the M69, and then follow B4029 signs to Rolls Royce PLC. Premier House – Greenalls. *Bar Food 11-11.* **Accommodation** *28 rooms, all en suite. £39.50 (single £28.50-£39.50). Children welcome overnight (high-chairs, cots and an extra child's bed in parents' bedroom). Dogs welcome. Disabled access. Beer Tetley Best, Greenalls Strongarm. Garden, outdoor eating. Access, Visa.*

Appleby-in-Westmorland   Royal Oak Inn

Tel 017683 51463   Fax 017683 52300   **B&B**

Bongate Appleby-in-Westmorland Cumbria CA16 6UN   Map 5 D3

Parts of the original building here are documented as being over 750 years old, and as it was once a coaching inn on the Penrith to Scarborough route, the Royal Oak can boast an unbroken history as a hostelry back to the 17th century. Both the snug and the Taproom are pristine examples of the traditional English pub. Oak panelling and stone walls, smoky-black beams and open smoky fires make a perfect environment in which to enjoy a particularly well-kept pint of real ale of which at least half a dozen brands plus guests and the specially-brewed "Bongate Special Pale" are always on tap. Bedrooms are necessarily small but nonetheless homely with leaded windows and creaky floors. A heavily-beamed attic is used as the family bedroom, and two rear rooms have doors opening directly on to the garden. There are also two stylish dining rooms, one of them reserved for non-smokers, and a first-floor residents' lounge looking out over the Bongate towards Appleby Castle. *Beers Bongate Special Ale, Westmorland Bitter & Premium, Yates, Bass, Theakston Best, Youngers Scotch, guest beer. Garden. Family room. **Accommodation** 9 rooms, 7 en suite, from £58 (single £38). Children welcome overnight, cots supplied. Access, Diners, Visa.*

Armathwaite — Duke's Head Hotel

Tel 016974 72226	**B&B**
Armathwaite nr Carlisle Cumbria CA4 9PB	Map 4 C3

A long-standing favourite in the area, the Lynchs' pub stays firmly traditional, and retains an instant appeal for those with plenty of time to linger and reminisce. Its fishing connections are well documented in the Last Cast Lounge, from where it's only a few paces into a glorious garden with flower beds and beech trees disappearing down to the very banks of the river Eden below. The half-dozen bedrooms are traditionally furnished with TVs and beverage facilities throughout; most popular are the three with en-suite facilities, the remainder sharing two neatly-kept public bathrooms. *Beers Whitbread Castle Eden Bitter. Riverside garden. **Accommodation** 6 bedrooms, 3 en suite, from £40 (singles £25). Children welcome overnight (under-2½ years stay free), additional beds (charged according to age), cots supplied. No credit cards.*

Arnold — Burnt Stump

Tel 0115 963 1508	**A**
Burnt Stump Hill Arnold Nottingham Notts NG5 8PA	Map 7 D3

It is the location, in 30 acres of country park on the fringe of Sherwood Forest, which makes the evocatively-named Burnt Stump such a popular spot. Four miles out of Nottingham turn off the A60 Mansfield road a mile or so north of its junction with the A614. There's a wealth of open space for one or more of the family to exercise the dog, a cricket pitch below the terrace for others to watch Ravenshead cricket club at play, while children can act out their latest Robin Hood adventures in an extensive playground under the trees. Hereabouts in summertime there are bouncy castles and barbecues and a covered pop and crisps counter. Indoors, hungrier little outlaws have their own menu and non-alcoholic cocktail list, while at lunchtime the peckish in-laws are promised a "Hot Hoagie" in less than nine minutes. *Open 11-11 (Sun usual hours). Beer Mansfield Best, Riding Mild & Bitter. Garden, children's play area. Family room. Access, Visa.*

Asenby — Crab & Lobster

Tel 01845 577286	**FOOD**
Asenby nr Thirsk North Yorkshire YO7 3QL	Map 5 E4

A very different pub both in concept and performance whose popularity is truly burgeoning in the region. With an almost Bohemian interior of scatter rugs, jazz accompaniments (live every first Tuesday of the month), and liberally scattered junk in every nook and cranny, the Crab and Lobster almost countermands its own description as a pub. Yet, alongside a brasserie-type menu with a natural affinity towards fish, the bar leaves plenty of room by day for pub-goers happy with a pint of Theakston's and a toasted "BLT" sandwich (£3.95). Light lunches might include scallops with Gruyère (£5.95) and roast Piedmont peppers with anchovy, olives and Parmesan (£4.50) or, more substantially, chicken confit with coconut and Basmati rice (£8.50). By mid-evening, space is taken up with crudités and garlic sausage nibbles at the bar, where some congestion does occur in the wait for tables. Fish soup with aioli and croutons (£4.75) and paella (£8.95) head the list of fish specialities with sea bass with ratatouille and parmesan (£14.50) and salmon with crab crust and lobster sauce (£9.50) further indications of the kitchen's vast and varied output. Such has become the demand for space that a further extension, built to match the present thatched and listed building, is due for completion in early 1995. Restaurant tables can be reserved separately by those wanting a little more elbow room and willing to pay a little extra. ***Bar Food & Restaurant Meals*** *11.30-3 (Sun from 12), 7-10 (except Sun eve). Free House.* ***Beer*** *Theakston Best, Younger's Scotch and No3. Garden. Family room. Pub closed Sun eve. Access, Visa.*

Ashby St Ledgers	Olde Coach House Inn	**FOOD**
Tel 01788 890349 Fax 01788 891922		**B&B**
Ashby St Ledgers nr Rugby Warwickshire CV23 8UN		Map 15 D1

Despite its Warwickshire address, Ashby St Ledgers is just across the county border in Northants, 3 miles from the M1, J18; alternatively, take the single track road signed off the A361, 4 miles north of Daventry. At the centre of this once-feudal village (population now 70) is the McCabes' admirable pub where, from outside, you'd least expect to find one. Behind its ivy-covered facade is the cavernous, hollowed-out interior of a row of former cottages. Stone chimney breasts and cast-iron ranges still point to a certain antiquity. The printed menu is arguably too long, encompassing char-grills (sirloin £8.95), "Old Favourites" (chilli, curry and lasagne (£4.75), vegetarian options (burger £3.50) and a children's corner (from £1.50). Yet the blackboard adds an array of specials for the more adventurous: hot gunpowder chicken (£3.25), spicy cottage pie (£5.50), venison bourguignon (£7.25) and nut cutlets (£5.75). Rather more predictable desserts, on display in the chill cabinet, are the likes of moccha choux buns and lemon cream gateau (£2.75) with something of a factory feel. There are just half a dozen bedrooms, all en-suite, with TVs and tea trays; with pine bedsteads and floral drapes they have a countryfied appeal and offer abundant peace and quiet. Children are welcome (under-5s stay free), Phillipa, Brian and their family prove to be the most welcoming of hosts. *Free House.* ***Bar Meals*** *12-2, 6-9.30 (7-9 Sun). Garden, outdoor eating. Children's portions. High-chairs and cots available.* ***Accommodation*** *6 Bedrooms, all en suite £46 (Single £39). Children welcome overnight.* ***Beers*** *Flowers IPA & Original Wadworth 6X, Boddingtons, Everards Old Original, Beechwood Bitter, guest beers. Access, Visa.*

ZZZz...

Ashford-in-the-Water   **Ashford Hotel**

Tel 01629 812725   **B&B**

1 Church Street Ashford-in-the-Water nr Bakewell Derbyshire DE4 1QB   Map 6 C2

The former Devonshire Arms stands at the head of this picturesque
Derbyshire village, just off the A6 and a mere stone's throw from the
historic stone Sheepwash Bridge. Much original oak is retained in the
beamed bar where log fires burn in winter: residents have use of their
own cosy lounge, which opens on to a rear courtyard and enclosed
garden. Each of the seven bedrooms (two with four posters) have been
carefully remodelled in appropriately country style with floral
patterned wallpapers and bed linen: all are well-equipped with direct
dial phones, TVs, clock radios and trouser presses. Generally youthful
staff are friendly and eager to please. *Open 11-11 (Sun 12-10.30). Free
House.* **Beer** *Bass, Stones, Ashford. Garden, outdoor eating. Family room.*
Accommodation *7 bedrooms, all en suite, £70 (single £50). Children
welcome overnight (meals charged as taken), additional beds (£10) and cots
supplied. Access, Diners, Visa.*

Ashprington   **Durant Arms**

Tel 01803 732240   **FOOD**

Ashprington nr Totnes Devon TQ9 7UP   Map 13 D3

Off the tourist trail in a popular part of Devon and situated in the
heart of a sleepy village, this neat and tidy, cream-painted 18th-
century pub has developed a good local clientele, who favour the
honest home-cooked food that can be enjoyed here. A flagged entrance
hall leads into the main bar, with a sought-after bay window seat
overlooking the village street, and into the spick-and-span dining
room with neatly laid-out darkwood tables and chairs and a few
settles. Plates adorn a high shelf around the walls and fresh flowers are
an added touch on the tables. Lunchtime fare consists of hearty snacks
listed on a daily-changing board and may include sweet and sour pork
(£3.75), beef curry, rabbit pie (both £3.95) and the speciality 'big
brown pot' – steak, kidney, vegetables and potatoes cooked in ale and
topped with pastry. More imaginative dishes are featured on the
evening blackboard which could offer creamy garlic mushroom pot
(£2.50) or melon and raspberries for starters, followed by a choice of
twelve main courses, for example pork tenderloin with orange and
apple sauce (£7.75), poached salmon with dill and cucumber sauce
(£8.50) and monkfish in cream and garlic (£8.50). Well-cooked and
separately-plated vegetables accompany the main course. Good home-
made puddings range from chocolate mousse and rhubarb crumble to
Dutch apple tart. Only fresh local produce is used and only so many
portions of each dish are available, so arrive early – especially at
weekends – as the board may be wiped clean! *Free House.* **Bar Food**
12-2 & 6.30-9.30. **Beer** *Exmoor Ale, Palmers IPA, Bass. No credit cards.*

Ashprington   **Waterman's Arms**

                                                                  FOOD

Tel 01803 732214   **B&B**

Bow Bridge Ashprington nr Totnes Devon TQ9 7EG   Map 13 D3

Delightfully situated on the banks of the River Harbourne, at the top
of Bow Creek, the Waterman's is a favourite summer venue for
alfresco riverside imbibing with resident ducks and – if you are lucky
– kingfishers to keep you company. Bow Bridge is recorded in the
Domesday Book and the inn until recently was a smithy and prior to
that a brewery and a prison during the Napoleonic Wars. Acquired

two years ago by enthusiastic owners Phoebe and Trevor Illingworth, it has been transformed from the original small cottage into an efficiently-run and friendly inn with quality overnight accommodation. 'Tardis'-like inside, a series of neatly furnished rooms radiates away from the central servery, all filled with a mix of rustic furniture, old photographs, brass artefacts and other memorabilia. Home-cooked bar food caters for all tastes, from hearty snacks such as sandwiches, salads and platters to regular menu favourites including steak and kidney pie (£5.95), rack of Devon lamb (£7.95) and steaks (from £8.95), all accompanied by good fresh vegetables, or (if desired) decent chips and salad. Fresh authentic pasta dishes and a few Thai dishes represent the unusual and a daily-changing blackboard lists the fresh soup, for example courgette with oregano (£1.95), walnut and lentil bake (£5.95) and escalope of turkey 'annabella' (£6.95). A separate pudding board may include home-made banoffi pie, bread-and-butter pudding and crème brulée (£2.75). Ten beautifully fitted-out bedrooms have floral, cottagey fabrics and co-ordinating friezes around the walls, attractive dark-stained modern furniture and spotlessly-kept bathrooms with shower cubicles and efficient, thermostatically-controlled showers. Added comforts include telephone, cabinet-housed TV and tea-making facilities. The front rooms overlook the river and surrounding valley sides. Good breakfasts include a selection of fruits and a cooked menu choice that features smoked haddock and kippers. *Open 11-11 (Sun 12-3 & 7-10.30). Free House.* **Bar Food** *12-2.30 & 6.30-9.30 (Sun 7-9.30).* **Beer** *Dartmoor Best, Palmers IPA, Tetley Bitter. Garden, outdoor eating. Family Room.* **Accommodation** *10 bedrooms, all en suite, £53-£57 (single £28.50). Access, Visa.*

Ashwell   Bushell & Strike

Tel 01462 742394	**FOOD** °
Mill Street Ashwell Hertfordshire SG7 5LY	**Map 15a F1**

This unassuming, white-painted building stands opposite the large stone village church and its pretty garden, patio and uncluttered interior make a peaceful retreat from the madness of the A1(M), just four miles away through attractive countryside. Having developed a thriving food business over the past 25 years, the Lynch family have retired, but on early inspection the new landlord/chef Peter Clayton seems to be succeeding in maintaining the standards set by his predecessors. The ever-popular pine table laden with cold meats off the bone, fresh salmon, prawns (£4.95-£6.75) and at least ten large pots of freshly-replenished salads remain a feature, as do the Sunday lunchtime self-service (£9.95) hot and cold buffet in the restaurant area and the commendable selection of farmhouse cheeses that make up a delicious ploughman's (£3.50). The main menu is displayed on a large wall-mounted board and may include paté en croute (£3.25), herring roes (£3.50), decent, generously-filled pies – chicken and mushroom, steak and kidney, leek and ham (all £5.75) – plus chicken dhansak (£5.25), liver and bacon (£4.75) and rainbow trout (£4.75). Food is served in three interconnecting rooms, decorated in Victorian style and furnished with an assortment of rustic tables and chairs. It can get very busy. **Bar Food** *12-2.30, 7-9.30. Children's portions.* **Beer** *Charles Wells Eagle IPA & Bombardier Best, guest beers. Garden, patio, outdoor eating. Family room (buffet bar). Access, Visa.*

Askerswell   Spyway Inn

Tel 01308 85250	**A**

Askerswell nr Bridport Dorset DT2 9EP   Map 13 F2

Tucked down a winding country lane a mile off the busy A35
Dorchester to Bridport road, this gloriously situated pub is the perfect
spot in which to escape traffic tensions. Unwind in the traditional
Spyway Bar where scrubbed pine tables, old settles, longcase clock and
a timeless atmosphere pervades. A further bar and dining area are pine
furnished and display an impressive assortment of farming
memorabilia, brass artefacts and a collection of cups hanging from the
beams. The garden is a delightful summer retreat, complete with
shrubs, flowers, tiny stream and superb downland views. It is a
popular tourist area; be early in summer. Good selection of wines by
the glass. *Free House.* **Beer** *Ruddles County, Ushers Best, Wadworth 6X.
Garden. No credit cards.*

Askham   Punch Bowl Inn

Tel 01931 712443	**FOOD**

Askham nr Penrith Cumbria CA10 2PF   Map 4 C3

Four miles from junction 40 of the M6 this low, stone-built 18th-
century inn, opposite the longest village green in Cumbria, is at the
heart of the Earl of Lonsdale's Lowther Estate. Despite the cramped
and often crowded bar which serves the front lounge, it is deceptively
spacious beyond, with a family room, a second bar and a cosy dining
room to the rear. A vast menu which claims international status serves
throughout. Alongside the 'Punch Bowl Specials' (Bampton chicken
fritters £5.95; Dacre turkey bake £5.30) are French smokehouse quail
(£8.80), Chinese pork kebab (£5.90), tagliatelle eglofski (£6) and a
vegetarian Mexican bean pot (£6.80). With plenty to please and
amuse the youngsters, and the entire village green to play out on, the
Punch Bowl's a popular family venue. *Open all day Mon-Sat during
summer holiday season.* **Bar Food** *12-2 (Sun only), 7-9.* **Restaurant
Meals** *7-9 only. Children allowed in bar to eat before 9pm.*
Beer *Whitbread, Castle Eden, Timothy Taylor's Landlord, Old Speckled
Hen, guest beer. Patio, outdoor eating. Family room. Access, Visa.*

Askrigg   King's Arms Hotel

Tel 01969 650258 Fax 01969 650635	**FOOD**
	B&B

**Market Place Askrigg in Wensleydale nr Leyburn North Yorkshire
DL8 3HQ**   Map 5 D4

Liz and Ray Hopwood's characterful, friendly inn has an unbroken
history dating back to 1760 when outbuildings, where the Back
Parlour is now, housed John Pratt's racing stables. Turner is known to
have stayed here while recording on canvas the tranquil Dales scenery
of the early 1800s; today, the high-ceilinged main bar, complete with
saddle hooks, oak settles and hunting prints, is universally recognised
as *The Drover's Arms* as depicted on TV in James Herriot's *All
Creatures Great and Small.* The smaller, low-beamed front bar retains
a wig cupboard within its panelling; side snugs surround the green
marble fireplace. The back bar is simply furnished and home to shove
ha'penny and darts boards. Food outlets operate on two floors of this
fascinating maze of interlocked cottages. A large blackboard menu
complements the printed bar menu and evolves with the seasons.
Typical of the 20 or so offerings are moules marinière with samphire
(£2.95), chicken liver parfait (£2.75), smoked haddock and onion

rings (£5.50), toad in t'hole (£5.25), Dales' lamb with Madeira sauce (£7.50), whole 16oz plaice with lemon beurre noisette (£5.95), and home-made puddings like steamed chocolate pudding or bread-and-butter pudding (£2.50). Proper sandwiches and children's favourites are also offered. Upstairs, the elegant, panelled Clubroom Restaurant (30 seats, no children under 7, no smoking) serves à la carte (but fixed-price at £25) dinners and table d'hote lunch (£12.50, including Sunday, with a short choice that includes vegetarian dishes); the adjacent, 40-seater, no-smoking Silks Grill Room provides a balancing act between substantial Yorkshire breakfasts, simple steaks and fish, and sumptuous afternoon teas (£4.50). All of the eleven bedrooms retain original features that are in keeping with the inn's manor-house style, the many oak beams and uneven floors complemented by antique furniture, four-poster, half-tester and canopied brass beds, and colour co-ordinated fabrics of commensurate quality. A new private residents' entrance, reception lounge and off-street parking has raised the entire King's Arms to a yet higher degree of comfort, making it more of a "small hotel with a pub within".
Bar Food 12-2, 6.30-9 (7-8.30 Sun) Restaurant Meals 12-2, 7-9. Children's menu and portions (no children under 5 in the bar after 8pm). Free House. Beer Younger's No 3, Theakston Bitter, McEwan's 80/-, Dent Bitter, guest beer. Accommodation 11 bedrooms, all en suite, £70/£80 (£50/£55 single); 2 suites (£95, £70 single). Children welcome overnight (under-7s free if sharing parents' room, own room 70% rate), cot (£6) available. Courtyard, family room. Access, Visa.

Aston   The Flower Pot

Tel 01491 574721

FOOD
B&B

Ferry Lane Aston nr Henley-on-Thames Oxfordshire RG9 3DG   **Map 15a D3**

Situated off the A423 down a narrow lane in Aston. The 1890s' building is solid brick with plants attempting to climb the outside. Two small rooms provide a bar with banquette seating, rowing gear decorating the walls, and tables for 20 people. A large garden seats about 50. The pub is situated by a bridle path and, as it is 300 yards from the river towpath (where a sign advertises the pub's presence), walkers make up a large part of its trade. Food is simple but served in ample portions: home-made soup (£2), beef and Guinness pie (£4.50), fish and pasta bake (£4.25), date and apple crumble (£2). A traditional Sunday lunch is served in winter (£4.95). *Bar Food 12-2, 6.30-9 (not Sun eve). Children are allowed to eat in the bar. Free House. Beer Brakspear. Garden, outdoor eating. Accommodation 3 bedrooms, 2 en suite, £49 (single £33). Children welcome overnight (under-10s stay free in parents' room) additional beds and cots available. No dogs. Access, Visa.*

Zzzz...

Aston Clinton   The Oak

Tel 01296 630466

FOOD

119 Green End Street Aston Clinton Buckinghamshire HP22 5EU   **Map 15a E2**

The Oak is self styled as an 'ale house' catering for the middle age group – there is no draught lager (but a wide selection of bottled), cigarette machines (but they can be purchased from the bar), piped music or juke boxes. The building is part-thatched, painted black and white and there has been an ale house on this site since the 13th century. It has a stone floor, dark wood furniture and a large inglenook fireplace. There's a good choice of wines, plus special offers, and ale is available in 4-pint jugs. Most of the food is home-made including a selection of pies (£5.95), Oakmans' ham (£4.95), locally made sausages are a speciality (£4.95), half Aylesbury duck with citrus sauce (£9.95), Mighty Oak cook-up (£4.95). A traditional roast is served on Sundays (£5.95) and Wednesday night is curry night. If time is precious, you may telephone ahead to place your food order. *Bar Food* 12-2, 7-9.30 *(Sun & Mon to 9.15). Children are allowed in the bar to eat, children's menu.* **Beer** *Fuller's. Garden, outdoor eating. Access, Visa.*

Aswarby	**Tally Ho Inn**	**FOOD**
Tel 0152 95205		**B&B**
Aswarby nr Sleaford Lincolnshire NG34 8SA		**Map 7 E3**

Just south of Sleaford before the turning off the A15 to Aswarby stands this fine mellow stone estate inn, which dates back some 200 years. The pleasant bar boasts exposed stone and brickwork aplenty, country prints, old settles, leatherette wall benches, open log fire and additional woodburner for cold winter days. More especially a good atmosphere prevails for relaxing diners tucking into the reliable home-cooked fare that is listed on the quarterly changing bar menu. Satisfying choices may include Lincolnshire lamb casserole, oven baken chop (both £6), spicy Tally Ho chicken (£4.75), salmon, spinach and cheese pancakes (£5) and lighter bites such as bacon and mushrooms on toast (£3.50) and freshly filled baguettes with ham, beef or prawns (£3.50). Daily specials always feature a country soup and a hot dish – moussaka with mixed salad (£5.50). Accompanying vegetables are imaginative and well cooked. The trend extends into the attractive pine furnished rear restaurant where one can enjoy an interesting selection of dishes from the regularly changing menu. A typical meal could feature breast of woodpigeon with crispy bacon and apple salad tossed in hazelnut oil (£3.75), pan-fried duck breast with a plum sauce (£7.95) or medallions of pork with a grain mustard sauce (£6.75), with apricot and ginger upside down pudding (£3) to finish. Table d'hote Sunday lunch (2 courses £8.25, 3 courses £10.50). An adjacent stable block houses the six well kept bedrooms, all of which have spotless compact en-suite facilities (only one has a bath). Rooms are spacious, simply furnished, soothingly decorated and provide plenty of hanging and writing space. TVs and tea-makers are standard extras. *Free House.* **Bar Food** *12-2, 6.30-10 (12-2, 7-10 Sun).* **Beer** *Batemans XB, Bass, Adnams Southwold. Children's play area, garden.* **Accommodation** *6 bedrooms, all en suite, £42 (single £28). Children welcome overnight, cot accommodation. Access, Visa.*

Aust	**Boar's Head**	**A**
Tel 01454 52278		
Main Road Aust Avon BS12 3AX		**Map 13 F1**

A hidden, out-of-the-way spot, yet just a stone's throw from the M4 traffic thundering towards the Severn Bridge. The Aust lane is now a dead end. Standing by the church, the Boar's Head is a favoured local watering hole. Candles, lacy cloths and a succession of alcoves and inglenooks imbue an 18th-century feel to it all at night, and in winter a huge log fire flickers. To the rear there's a pretty stone-walled garden with a wishing well and beyond it a popular caravan site. **Beer** *Courage Best & Directors, Tetley, guest beer. Garden and patio. Children allowed indoors to eat (up to 9pm). Visa.*

Axbridge   Lamb Inn

Tel 01934 732253	**B&B**
The Square Axbridge Somerset TA6 2AP	Map 13 F1

Rambling, ancient town pub, romantically set opposite King John's hunting lodge, now an interesting museum. Open-plan bar area with bric-a-brac, beams and settles, as well as more modern intrusions. Overnight accommodation comprises a delightful large double room with older-style, free standing furniture, Laura Ashley fabrics and good sized bathroom, and two further more basic and homely bedrooms, including a spacious family room, which share a clean bathroom. Attractive rear patio. *Free House.* **Beer** *Butcombe, Bass, Wadworth 6X. Garden/patio, outdoor eating.* **Accommodation** *3 bedrooms, 2 en suite, £40 (single £22). Children welcome overnight, additional beds (£10) and cots (£5) available. Check-in by arrangement. Accommodation closed 24-26 Dec. Access, Visa.*

Axbridge   Oak House Hotel

Tel 01934 732444 Fax 01934 733112	**B&B**
The Square Axbridge Somerset B526 2AP	Map 13 F1

Less atmospheric than one would expect of an inn dating back to 1342 but it enjoys an enviable position overlooking the attractive village square, and is only a few yards from the parish church. New owners have created a bistro-style bar and are gradually upgrading the ten mostly en-suite bedrooms which vary greatly in standard and style of decor and furnishings, some being kitted out with comfortable modern co-ordinating fabrics and pine furniture, others are let down by old-fashioned bathrooms and a mish-mash of inexpensive furniture. TVs, telephones, tea-makers and radios are standard. **Beer** *Wadworth 6X, Boddington. Family room.* **Accommodation** *10 bedrooms, 9 en suite, £51 (single £38). Children welcome overnight, additional beds (£10) and cots (£5) available. Access, Visa.*

Axford   Red Lion Inn

Tel 01672 20271	**FOOD**
	B&B
Axford nr Marlborough Wiltshire SN8 2HA	Map 14a A4

In a small hamlet, three miles from Marlborough, this attractive 17th-century brick and flint inn offers clean and comfortable accommodation in a picturesque rural setting. Views across the lush Kennet Valley can be enjoyed from the modern, simply furnished dining room and bar and from the small grassy area with benches, adjacent to the car park. Local landscape paintings (many for sale) adorn the walls. A starter from the blackboard might be roulade of smoked salmon with smoked cheese and tarragon (£4.75) or chicken livers sautéed in Madeira (£3.75) and for main course, mixed pan-fried seafood (£10.50), lamb rack served in orange and rosemary (£10.50), or a more simple dish (chili con carne, lasagne or one of three vegetarian pastas – all £4.50) from the menu. Four compact and freshly decorated bedrooms are kept in very good order, each having TVs, beverage trays, hairdryers and newly fitted en-suite facilities with shower units. Two of the bedrooms are located in Pear Tree Cottage, reached by a path through the garden, where guests have use of a kitchen, sitting room and sunny patio with scenic views. 12 wines by the glass. No smoking in the restaurant. **Bar Food & Restaurant**

Meals 12-2.30, 6.30-10.30 (Sun 12-3, 7-10). *Children allowed in bar to eat, Children's menu. Free House.* **Beer** *Wadworth 6X, Hook Norton, Foxley Dog Booster. Garden, children's play area. Family room.* **Accommodation** *4 bedrooms, all en suite, £40 (single £25). Children welcome overnight (under-4s stay free in parents' room). Check-in by arrangement. No dogs. Access, Visa.*

Ayot St Lawrence   Brocket Arms

Tel 01438 820250 Fax 01438 820068	B&B

Ayot St Lawrence Hertfordshire AL6 9BT   Map 15a F2

Splendid medieval pub – an unspoilt 14th-century gem – set within an equally splendid village close to Shaw's Corner, where George Bernard Shaw lived for forty years (now National Trust owned). Classic unadulterated three-roomed interior with a wealth of oak beams, an inglenook fireplace, a rustic mix of furniture and tasteful piped classical music. Those wishing to experience the historic charm further can stay upstairs in one of the four characterful bedrooms built into the timbered eaves. Furnished in traditional style – one with a four-poster bed – the rooms are simple and homely, and reputedly haunted by a monk from the local abbey. All share two adequate bathrooms. Those guests craving more modern creature comforts can book one of the three newer bedrooms housed in a converted old stable block across the courtyard. These are neatly carpeted and comfortably furnished in modern pine (one also boasts a four-poster bed), and (unlike main building rooms) they have central heating. Two have rather compact shower rooms, the third a clean en-suite bathroom, and all are equipped with tea-makers and clock radios. Pleasant walled garden for peaceful alfresco drinking. Families welcome. *Pub open 11-11 Jul & Aug (ring to check), usual hours at other times. Free House.* **Beer** *Greene King Abbot & IPA, Wadworth 6X, Hook Norton Old Hooky, guest beer. Garden.* **Accommodation** *7 bedrooms, 3 en suite, from £40. Children welcome overnight, additional beds (£5) & cots supplied. No dogs. Access, Visa.*

☺

Zzzz...

Baginton   Old Mill Inn

Tel 01203 303588 Fax 01203 307070	B&B

Mill Hill Baginton nr Coventry West Midlands CV8 2BS   Map 6 C4

A handy place to stay, close to the A45, A46 and five miles from the M6, yet tucked away peacefully in pine-studded grounds running down to the river Sowe. Public areas still retain many features of the 19th-century working mill, and outside a riverside patio is linked by a bridge to the garden. A well-designed modern block houses the bedrooms which have views of the river and weeping willows, pine furniture and Laura Ashley designs. Ample car parking, Chef & Brewer. **Beer** *Webster's Yorkshire Bitter. Large garden, children's play area. Family room, children's menu.* **Accommodation** *20 bedrooms, all en suite, £62 (single £52). Children welcome overnight (under-12s stay free in parents' room), additional beds (£5) and cots available. No dogs. Access, Visa.*

Bainbridge   Rose & Crown Hotel

| Tel 01969 650225   Fax 01969 650735 | **B&B** |

Bainbridge Wensleydale North Yorkshire DL8 3EE   Map 5 D4

Originally a settlement at the heart of the Wensleydale forest,
Bainsbridge today is a village of mellow stone houses set around the   **Z**Zzz...
triangular green by which the old stocks still stand. At its head the
15th-century Rose & Crown still houses the Forest Horn, blown
nightly from Holy Rood to Shrovetide as a guide to travellers towards
its welcoming safety. Original beamed ceilings, open fires and antique
furnishings give the small flagstoned bar its great character. Though
the adjacent games room is rather more utilitarian and less appealing.
Bedrooms are cosy though not overly large. Three boast four poster
beds to complement their cottagey decor: all are equipped with TV,
radio and hair dryers. Only four, however, have full bathrooms en
suite, the remainder having WC and shower rooms only. Children
welcome overnight: cot available free of change; extra bed in parents'
room £10. *Free House. Open 11-3, 6-11 (Sun 12-3, 7-10.30).*
*Accommodation 12 bedrooms, all en suite £72 (Single £44). Children
welcome overnight (cot and extra bed if sharing). Garden, outdoor eatdoor.*
Beer John Smith's, Youngers Best. Access, Visa.

Baldwin's Gate   Slater's

| Tel 01782 680052   Fax 01782 680219 | **B&B** |

**Maerfield Gate Farm Baldwin's Gate nr Newcastle under Lyme
Staffordshire ST5 5ED**   Map 6 B3

Five miles from Junction 16 on the M6, this skilful conversion of   ☺
former outbuildings on a working farm (they still have a 100-head
milking herd) has created a stylish new accommodation pub with   **Z**Zzz...
super facilities for youngsters. In addition to the family room
(complete with nappy changing facility in an adjacent ladies' loo)
there's a safe, enclosed rear garden full of play equipment and a pair of
ducks and geese to talk to. The grown-ups may make time for a game
of bowls on the crown green lawn. Set around a cobbled courtyard
behind the pub proper, three self-contained cottagey suites contain just
about everything for short or long stays: en-suite bathrooms with
over-bath showers, fitted kitchenettes and breakfast area, plus extra
beds and cots at no extra charge. Breakfast in the dining room if
residents prefer: children's meals in pub or garden (all day on Sunday).
Bar meals and restaurant (book for Sunday) offer little out of the
ordinary. Music on Tuesday and Sunday evenings. *Pub open 10-11
(Sun 11-10.30). Free House. Beer Banks, Boddingtons, Marston's Pedigree.
Garden, children's play area. Family room. Accommodation 2 en suite
rooms (£49), 3 self-catering cottages (£57). Children welcome overnight
(free if sharing parents room), additional beds and cots available.
Access, Visa.*

Bamburgh   Lord Crewe Arms

| Tel 01668 214243   Fax 01668 213273 | **B&B** |

Front Street Bamburgh Northumberland NE69 7BL   Map 5 D1

An historical old inn, virtually in the shadow of Bamburgh Castle,
with a long tradition of North Country hospitality and a fiercely loyal
following. In new hands since early 1994, we found Malcolm Eden
and Sharen Holden feeling their way through the complexities of
redecoration and reorganisation. While much of the former is now
complete, the half-dozen bedrooms without en-suite facilities and some

dated room fittings in pine and formica are still unchanged. Of the remainder, five rooms contain shower/WCs only: all have TVs and beverage trays, but there are no room phones. No children under 5 overnight. Two bars (with Bass on draught) and a general air of camaraderie between new hosts, returning guests and long-standing locals nonetheless contribute to the pub's unique atmosphere. *Free House. Open 11-3, 6-11 (12-3, 7-10.30 Sun).* **Beer** *Bass. Access, Visa.*

Bamford   Yorkshire Bridge Inn

FOOD
B&B

Tel 01433 651361   Fax 01433 651812

Ashopton Road Bamford Derbyshire S30 2AB   Map 6 C2

In the heart of the Derbyshire Peak District this inn dates from 1826 and is named after an old packhorse bridge on the river Derwent. Views from the central bar take in the peak of Win Hill providing a beautiful setting in which to enjoy some good, reliable cooking. Bar food is split between a lunchtime and an evening menu. Daytime diners may choose from hot or cold sandwiches (from £1.95), ploughman's (£3.40), traditional hot dishes of the home-made steak and kidney pie (£4.59) variety, or from four vegetarian (cracked wheat and walnut casserole £4.95) or six salad (beef, ham, Cheddar £4.60-£5.60) dishes; fresh fish is available from the blackboard on market days. In the evening similar fare is supplemented by a charcoal grill offering 'giant' T-bone steak (£9.45) and honey-glazed rack of lamb (£7.25) to the hungry crowd of walkers and sightseers. Accommodation takes the form of an adjoining hotel recently built on the site of derelict barns belonging to the pub. It now houses ten en-suite bedrooms, all with satellite TV, radios, telephones, and beverage-making facilities, and for those wishing to escape the hurly-burly there is a peaceful lounge and a residents-only dining room. Non-smokers have the pleasure of the conservatory and children are well catered for both on the menu (fish fingers, sausages or burgers £1.95) and outside where there is a slide and climbing frame. **Bar Food** *12-2, 6-9 (Sat to 9.30, Sun from 7). Children's menu. Free house.* **Beer** *Stones, John Smith's, Bass. Garden, outdoor eating, children's play area. Family room.* **Accommodation** *10 bedrooms, all en suite, £48 (single £35). Children welcome overnight (under-3s stay free in parents' room, 3-12s £5). Additional beds and cots available. Access, Visa.*

Banbury   Ye Olde Reine Deer Inn

FOOD

Tel 01295 264031

47 Parsons Street Banbury Oxfordshire OX16 8NB   Map 14a B1

With its inn sign hanging out over the middle of the road, this town centre pub is the oldest building in Banbury (1570) where Oliver Cromwell once held court in a panelled back room – now used for functions. The tenancy has recently been taken over by John Milligan of the *Falkland Arms* at nearby Great Tew (qv) who has renovated the building and introduced a policy of 'over-21s only'. Food, served only at lunchtimes, is limited to a selection of filled jacket potatoes (from £2.50), ploughman's (from £3) and 'doorstep' sandwiches (from £1.60), plus a few dishes of the day such as salmon and broccoli quiche (£4.50), lentil and tomato soup (£1.60) and ham and eggs with mashed potatoes and peas (£4). Luxuriant hanging baskets of flowers decorate the front of the building and there is a small courtyard bar for summer drinking. Parking for about 18 cars to the rear. **Food** *11.30-2.* **Beers** *Hook Norton. Courtyard, outdoor eating. Pub closed all Sun, 25 Dec. No credit cards.*

Bantham   Sloop Inn

Tel 01548 560489	**B&B**
Bantham nr Kingsbridge Devon TQ7 3AJ	**Map 13 D3**

Set in an attractive coastal hamlet just 300 yards from the sea and one of the finest sandy beaches along this part of the coast, the 16th-century Sloop is a most peaceful inn in which to stay and explore the area. Associations with smuggling are deep for it was at one time owned by the notorious South Hams wrecker and smuggler John Whiddon. The atmospheric flagstoned interior has a strong nautical feel to it, with lots of sea-going memorabilia and the rear, plainly-furnished dining area is designed in the shape of a ship's cabin. In the main building there are five clean and neat en-suite bedrooms, generally of a good size, with modern furniture, clock/radio, TV and beverage-making kits. There are also self-catering flats available to the rear of the inn. *Free House.* **Beer** *Bass, Ushers Best Bitter, Courage Directors.* **Accommodation** *5 bedrooms, all en suite, £52. No credit cards.*

Bardwell   Six Bells

	FOOD
Tel 01359 250820	**B&B**
The Green Bardwell Suffolk IP31 1AQ	**Map 10 C2**

Approached via a track (once the original coaching highway) off the village green, this rather plain, cream-painted 16th-century inn is surrounded by open countryside, views of which can be appreciated from both the warm and comfortable beamed bars and the converted stable-block bedrooms. Reliable blackboard specials – lentil cottage pie, minted lamb salad (both £5.95), cauliflower soup (£2.25), game pie (£6.95), home-cooked gammon ham (£5.50) – enhance a printed bar menu offering fisherman's bake, steak and ale pie (both £4.95) and ploughman's (from £3.95). More elaborate restaurant fare (generally served in the simple country pine-furnished dining room) can also be ordered in the bar. Dishes include Oriental chicken (£8.95) and sole and salmon roulade with tomato and basil sauce (£10.95). Also available is a table d'hote menu (2 courses £9.95, 3 courses £12.50), good vegetarian meals and popular fondues (£11.95). Puddings (from £2.95) include luxury bread-and-butter pudding. Interesting list of wines from Adnams. Peaceful and homely overnight accommodation in eight en-suite bedrooms furnished with modern pine and co-ordinating bedcovers and fabrics. All have clean compact shower rooms, TVs, telephones and tea-makers and all are on the ground floor. Patio and large garden for fine days. *Free House.*
Accommodation *8 bedrooms, all en suite £50 (Single £35-40). Children and dogs welcome overnight (Children free under 2).* **Restaurant Meals** *12-1.30, 7-9.30 (12-1.45 Sat & Sun). Children allowed anywhere.* **Beer** *John Smith's Bitter, Ruddles Best, Adnams Southwold. Garden, outdoor eating, children's playing area. Access, Visa.*

Barley   Fox & Hounds

Tel 01763 848459	**FOOD**
High Street Barley nr Royston Hertfordshire SG8 8HU	**Map 15 F1**

Pleasingly traditional white-painted 15th-century village local, with rambling, low-ceilinged rooms, splendid open fires, plus a separate dining area and conservatory. A beer drinker's favourite – The Fox & Hounds have served 280 different real ales to date and eight handpumps are constantly in use. A small bar menu offers lunchtime snack meals such as filled jacket potatoes (from £1.20) or large granary baps (from £1.20), ploughman's (£3.15) and pork ribs (£3.95). The longer main menu operates throughout the pub at lunchtime and in the evenings (bar and restaurant): whole plaice (£5.95), whitebait (£3.25), various steaks (from £6.95), home-made curries (from £5.55) and pies (lamb and apricot (£5.55). Vegetarians are well catered for with their own menu of at least eleven choices. Children also have their own menu. Ice creams and sundaes are a speciality (9 varieties are on offer), as well as puddings such as strawberry pavlova, orange cheesecake and chocolate mousse (£1.70). Traditional pub games are very popular with indoor and outdoor skittles, bar-billiards, shove-ha'penny, darts and dominoes. *Bar Food & Restaurant 12.30-2, 6.30-9.30 (Sun 7-9.30). Children's menu. Free House. Beer Theakston's and home-brewed Nathaniel's Special & Flame Thrower. Garden, outdoor eating, children's play area, disabled facilities. No credit cards.*

Barming	The Bull	
Tel 01622 726468		**A**
5 Tonbridge Road Barming Maidstone Kent ME16 9HB		Map 11 C5

Neat exterior with pretty hanging baskets. Good choice of real ales. 15 tables set on the lawned garden. Bouncy castle for children. On the A26 Maidstone to Tonbridge road, 2½ miles from Maidstone; convenient for Junction 5 of the M20. Whitbread Wayside Inns. *Open 11-11 Mon-Sat, 12-10.30 Sun. Beer Harveys Sussex, Boddingtons, Fremlins, Wadworth 6X, Morland Old Speckled Hen, guest beer. Garden. Children's play area, children welcome inside to eat. Access, Visa.*

Barnard Gate	Boot Inn	
Tel 01865 881231 Fax 01865 881834		**FOOD**
Barnard Gate nr Witney Oxfordshire OX8 6AE		Map 14a B2

About 5 miles from Oxford, just off the Oxford-Cheltenham A40, the Boot Inn (formerly the Britannia) is run by George Dailey and his brother-in-law Steve Chick and has quickly established itself as one of the most popular pubs near Oxford. The secret of its success is happy, young staff offering good food at extremely competitive prices. The result is an extremely busy pub at almost all times, so you would be well advised to book a table, although the staff will do their utmost to fit you in providing you are prepared to wait. A well-built extension complements the bar with apricot walls covered with prints and stone-flagged floors and has enabled the Boot to offer a larger menu with special dishes of the day on a blackboard next to the large open log fire. A terrace complete with fountain offers more tables outside; it's illuminated at night, creating the festive feeling of being abroad. Recommended from the menu are the grilled king prawns (£3.95) or the home-made soup (£2.95), followed by a variety of pasta dishes (penne with pepper tomato and chili sauce £6.95) or a vegetarian dish such as chargrilled Mediterranean vegetables topped with melted goat's cheese (£6.95). Steaks are good, too, and there is a selection of puddings (sticky toffee pudding, banoffi pie or crème brulée – all £2.95). *Bar Food 12-2.30, 6.30-10. Free House. Beer Morland Old Speckled Hen, Hook Norton, Boddingtons, Wychwood. Patio, outdoor eating. Access, Visa.*

Barnoldby-le-Beck   Ship Inn

| Tel 01472 822308 | **A** |

Main Road Barnoldby-le-Beck Humberside DN37 OBG   Map 7 E2

17th-century village pub with a warming, real fire, separate restaurant
and an award-winning garden. The landlord, Mr Gillis, is an avid
supporter of Grimsby Town football team, who show an equal
support for his ales. Recent interior refurbishment has brought a
sparkle to the interior and a profusion of hanging baskets and tubs
brings a seasonal splash of colour to the exterior. Six miles from the
end of M180. Trent Taverns. *Beer Flowers, Theakston's Best, Younger's
No 3, Boddingtons. No credit cards.*

Barnsley   The Village Pub

| Tel 01285 740421 | **B&B** |

Barnsley Cirencester Gloucestershire GL7 5EF   Map 14 C2

Clearly once a row of roadside cottages next to the village school, the
Village Pub is commendable for retaining both its unusual name and a
cottage interior, quite in keeping with open fires, brass-hung beams
and antique settles. The single bar dispenses to carpeted lounges and
dining room on one side and to drinkers on the summer patio
through a quaint service window. So close is the main road that access
to the pub is now sensibly to the rear, as are the bedrooms (thus well
insulated from any traffic noise). Accommodation, as one might
expect, is modest yet comfortable, with TVs available for those who
tire of solitude. All but one have en-suite WC/shower rooms, the
remaining single enjoying the benefit of its own, consequentially
private, bathroom. On the B4425 Cirencester to Bibury road. *Bar
Food 12-2,7-9 (Fri & Sat -9.30). Children's portions available. Free
House. Beer Flowers IPA, Wadworth 6X. Garden, patio, outdoor eating.
Family room. Accommodation 5 Bedrooms, all en suite, £44 (single
£29). Children welcome overnight (small stay free). Additional beds (for up
to 5 years) available (£5). Check-in by arrangement. Pub and
accommodation closed 25 Dec. No dogs. Access, Visa.*

Barnston   Fox & Hounds

| Tel 0151 648 1323 | **FOOD** |

Barnston Road Barnston Merseyside L61 1BW   Map 6 A2

Lunchtime snacking pub by hazardous bends on the A551; Barnston
post office is 100 metres away. Alongside sandwiches and filled
potatoes, the likes of quiche and Coronation chicken are reliably fresh
(under £4). Cooking rises to chicken korma (£4.25) and grilled pork
chop (£4.50); vegetarian options of leek and mushroom crumble
(£3.90) and cheese and spinach pancakes, perhaps (£4.25). No food
Sunday lunch or any evening. *Open 11.30-11 Fri & Sat in summer,
otherwise usual hours. Bar Food 12-2. Free House. Beer Courage
Directors, Webster, Ruddles. Garden. Family room. No credit cards.*

Barrington   Royal Oak

| Tel 01223 870791 | **FOOD** |

31 West Green Barrington Cambridgeshire CB2 5R2   Map 15 F1

Dating from the 14th century, this striking half-timbered and thatched
pub stands close to one of the largest village greens in the country.
Colourful summer hanging baskets adorn its attractive facade which
overlooks the splendid bench- and brolly-filled lawn; an ideal spot for

fine weather imbibing. The rambling beamed and low-ceilinged interior is divided into traditionally furnished bars and filled with horsebrasses, gleaming upper pans, antlers and tack. To the rear is a neat conservatory restaurant extension. Featured strongly on the printed menu are home-prepared vegetarian dishes, with at least 14 imaginative main courses to choose from. Typical examples are vegetable and basil strudel with a lime glaze (£6.45), Barrington loaf with a redcurrant glaze (£6.25) and Pecan, mushroom and mango stroganoff (£6.25). Meat eaters are not left out, with traditional steak and kidney pie (£5.85), guinea fowl with a rosehip and peach glaze (£7.95) and rack of lamb (£6.20) making an appearance. Standard puddings. *Free House.* **Bar Food** *12-2, 6.30-10 (to 10.30 Fri/Sat, 7-10 Sun).* **Beers** *Greene King IPA, Abbot Ale, Adnams Southwold. Children allowed anywhere. Garden, outdoor eating area. Family room. Access, Visa.*

Bartlow   Three Hills

| Tel 01223 891259 | **FOOD** |
| Bartlow nr Linton Cambridgeshire CB1 6PW | Map 10 B3 |

The Dixons have created a welcoming atmosphere here, aided by fresh flowers, polished brasses and an inglenook fireplace. There's reliably good food on the twice-daily-changing blackboard menu which serves both bar and restaurant – avocado filled with fresh crab (£3.50), hot smoked peppered mackerel (£2.60), rack of English lamb (£9.45), supreme of Scotch salmon (£8.45), Tibetan loaf (bulgur wheat, spinach, mushrooms, red wine, walnuts served with Marsala sauce £8.35) and home-made puddings include banana split and cheesecake (both £2.40). A wide choice on the cheese board. Large garden. *Bar Food & Restaurant Meals 12-1.45, 7-9.30 (Sun to 9). Beer Greene King IPA & Abbot. Garden, outdoor eating area. Access, Visa.*

Bassenthwaite Lake   Pheasant Inn

| Tel 017687 76234   Fax 017687 76002 | **B&B** |
| Bassenthwaite Lake nr Cockermouth Cumbria CA13 9YE | Map 4 C3 |

There remains a Dickensian feel to the splendid bar whose counter unusually comes to little above waist height. Here the tobacco-brown panelled ceiling, walls hung with Victorian prints and the low oak settles are a snug winter retreat. In summer a splendid spot for afternoon tea is the flower garden whose array of lupin, honeysuckle and rhododendron seemingly meander off into oblivion. *Beers Theakston Best, Bass. Garden.* **Accommodation** *20 bedrooms, all en suite, from £64 (single £52). Children welcome overnight, additional beds (£12), cots supplied (charged). Access, Visa.*

Batcombe   The Batcombe Inn

| Tel 01749 850359   Fax 01749 850615 | **FOOD** |
| Batcombe nr Shepton Mallet Somerset BW4 6HE | Map 13 F1 |

Tucked away down a web of country lanes in the very rural Batcombe Vale, this old honey-coloured stone coaching inn enjoys a peaceful position away from the main village, next to the church. "It's not difficult to find. . . it's damned near impossible" they admit, but grid reference 36902 13906 (Lat 51- 39 06 N Long 03- 69 02 W) should get you to the front door! Having seen some uncertain times, the inn is now in the extremely capable hands of Derek and Claire Blezard, who created the highly successful *Royal Oak* at Over Stratton, near Yeovil and it is clearly evident that the same formula is being injected with enthusiasm here. The long and low-ceilinged main bar has exposed stripped beams and is warmly and tastefully decorated; terracotta sponged walls with ivy leaf stencilling are hung with several old paintings, creating a relaxed and homely atmosphere. A mix of individual chairs, deep window seats and darkwood furniture fronts a huge stone inglenook with log fire. Adjoining the bar is a newly refurbished dining area, in what used to be the old barn and toll-house. Bar food is reliably good with blackboards listing daily-changing specials such as home-made soups (£1.95), Somerset Brie pasty (£4.95), chicken piri piri (£8.50), plaice fillets and vegetarian dishes. The printed menu is better than most offering a range of hearty snacks, starters and main dishes, from smoked chicken and walnut salad (£3.95) and seafood crepes (£6.95) to Thai platter (chicken saté, Tiger prawns, spring rolls all in a chili dip £9.50). Accompanying salads are enormous and imaginative and main-dish vegetables are served separately and generously – meals here are not for the faint-hearted! A traditional 2-course Sunday lunch is available at £7.50. A big welcome is made to families: children not only have their own 'Kiddies Corner' menu but they also have their own fully-equipped room complete with mini-trampoline, doll's house, drawing board, books, toys and video recorder with National Geographic films – enough to pacify any child while relaxed parents enjoy their meal. Children's facilities extend to the rear garden play area for fine weather activity. A further car park extension, children's play areas and feature garden have recently been completed. Winner of our Family Pub of the Year Award 1995. ***Bar Food & Restaurant Meals*** *12-1.45, 7-9.45. Children allowed in bar to eat, children's menu. Free House.* **Beer** *Butcombe, Wadworth 6X, guest beer. Garden, patio, children's play area. Family room. Access, Visa.*

Bathampton George Inn

Tel 01225 425079	**FOOD**
Mill Lane Bathampton nr Bath Avon BA2 6TR	Map 13 F1

Hard by a stone-arched road bridge which crosses the Kennett and Avon canal (there's even a door into the pub from the tow-path), this is truly a picturesque spot. The Hall family have furnished it with hanging flower baskets every year for twenty years and the summer crowds regularly overflow on to the patio and into the garden. For their pains, though, diners must order their food on pre-printed pads at a single bar and then wait, often more than a little while. Woe betide them if they get their sums wrong or relocate from their chosen table! As ever, daily specials are probably the best bet: smoked chicken and broccoli pie (£5.50) or kidneys Turbigo (£5.60), with crunchy chocolate fudge, perhaps, to follow (sweets are £2.20). Children enjoy the creaky, spiral staircase which leads them to a beamed family room at eye level with the canal. Parents should beware, however, that the predictable burger and chips will set them back a handsome £3.50 per junior plateful. Summer barbecues with separate outside bar and food counters. **Beer** *Courage, Bass. Garden, patio and family room. No credit cards.*

Bathford   The Crown

Tel 01225 852297

2 Bathford Hill Bathford nr Bath Avon BA1 7SL

FOOD

Map 14 B2

Just off the A4, the Crown stands at the foot of Bathford Hill by a
wide road junction which was once the eastern terminus for a train
ride into nearby Bath. In its cavernous interior, which leads in turn to
a delightful summer patio, everything is made easy for the visitor.
Menus are available in French, German and Japanese. Those for the
children are jokey and user-friendly. There's ample family seating and
high-chairs in the no-smoking Garden Room and a magician appears
on Sunday lunchtimes. The menu promotes itself as 'not fast food' and
the selection is ambitious – some items may be suspended at peak
times. Go, though, for the daily specials: reliable crusty pies, perhaps of
duck and cherries or ham, leek and Stilton (both £5.95), cheese-
topped seafood pancakes (£6.95). Some exotic puddings with clotted
cream (terrine of summer fruits £2.95) and good local cheeses from
Longman's: Colston Bassett Stilton, Bath soft cheese and Somerset
Brie. *Bar Food 12-2, 6.30-9.30 (to 10 Fri, from 7 Sun). Beer Courage,
Ushers Best, Marston's Pedigree, Bass. Garden. Family Room and patio.
Pub closed Mon lunchtime (except Bank Hols). Access, Diners, Visa.*

Beaconsfield   Greyhound

Tel 01494 673823

Windsor End Beaconsfield Buckinghamshire HP9 2JN

FOOD

Map 15a E3

The 'Windsor End' is the peaceful end of Beaconsfield and the
unassuming Greyhound pub enjoys its relatively undisturbed position
on this tree-lined avenue, opposite the parish church. Its plain exterior
appearance belies the characterful interior which dates back to the
15th century, and comprises three traditional low beamed bars with
simple furnishings, open fires and a welcoming atmosphere. No music
or intrusive games. Small rear dining room with terracotta walls,
cloth and candle-topped tables, quality watercolours and a relaxing
ambience. Reliable home-cooked bar food is listed on an above
average printed menu – home-made burgers flavoured with garlic,
basil and tomato (from £3.95), seafood pie, steak and kidney pie (both
£4.75), freshly baked French bread sandwiches (from £2.75) – and
on twice-daily-changing blackboards, both available throughout the
pub. Interesting specials may include mushroom soup (£2.25) and
Greek salad (£2.95) as starters, followed by cod fillet in tomato sauce
topped with parmesan (£6.25) or perhaps pork, apple and cider pie
(£6.45). Provençal vegetarian lasagne (£4.95) and a choice of fresh
pasta dishes – tagliatelle topped with ham, peppers, tomato and garlic
(£4.95). Accompanying vegetables are crisp and plated separately.
Round off your meal with a fresh berry mousse or maybe steamed
apricot sponge (from £2.45). *Bar Food 12-2.15, 7-10. No bar food D
Sun. Free House. Beer Courage Best, Fuller's London Pride, Wadworth
6X. Garden, outdoor eating. Access, Visa.*

Beauworth   Milbury's

Tel 01962 771248

Beauworth Cheriton nr Alresford Hampshire SO24 0PB

A

Map 15 D3

Set on a hill just to the south of the village, the site of some bronze age
burial mounds or barrows, the pub's name is actually a corruption of
Mill-Barrow, the name of the last remaining mound just 150 yards
away. The South Down Way passes by the front door of this old tile-

hung pub. The main bar boasts old brickwork, a flagstone floor and rough hewn three-legged tables, but the most fascinating feature is an enormous treadmill, within which a poor donkey once walked to raise water from a 300-foot well. For the price of a donation to the Guide Dogs for the Blind, you are invited to drop an ice-cube down the well and count the nearly eight seconds it takes to splash in the water far below. Children are made positively welcome, with their own small section on the menu and swings out in a large garden carved from one corner of a field. There is also a new skittle alley which must be booked. *Free House.* **Beer** *Abbot, Directors, Tetley, Ansells, two local brews (King Alfred, Pendragon) and several guest beers. Garden, outdoor eating, children's play area. Family room. Access, Visa.*

Beckington	**Woolpack Inn** ★	**FOOD**
Tel 01373 831244 Fax 01373 831223		**B&B**

Beckington nr Bath Somerset BA3 6SP   Map 14 B3

Boarded up for fully two years prior to its reopening in late 1992, this splendidly restored former coaching inn has benefitted enormously from a new section of the A36 trunk road now bypassing Beckington. Subsequently its almost instant success has lain, perhaps in the vision of its new proprietors who have created here their own interpretation of what constitutes a fine old English inn. In an easy-going atmosphere which belies its real professionalism, diners are encouraged to consume simply what they'd like just how and where they'd like it, and there is plenty of choice in both instances. The bar boasts a revealed original fireplace, recreated window shuttering in lieu of curtains and re-laid traditional flagstone flooring. Behind it the garden room leads to a canopied courtyard and a high stone-walled, enclosed summer patio beyond. For non-smokers the separate lounge and dining room are now so popular that booking is virtually essential. Chef David Woolfall's menus are equally all-embracing with no obligation to order more than a warm tossed seafood salad with toasted sesame oil dressing (£5.95) or the daily hot dish such as grilled lamb's liver with creamed potato and onion gravy (£6.95). There's every temptation however, to splash out: to follow goat's cheese and sun-dried tomato crostini (£4.95) or smoked pigeon salad with red onion marmalade (£5.25), there's a predominance of fish among the daily specials (baked cod provençale with mozzarella, £7.95; red mullet with fennel compote, £10.50) or medallions of Somerset lamb with ratatouille (£11.95) and, for vegetarians, a courgette, almond and saffron strudel with tomato coulis (£9.95). Round off with chocolate and orange marquise (£4.95), ginger and apricot crème brulée (£3.95) or a plate of West Country cheeses (£4.50). Investment and attention to detail in the bedrooms have been no less unstinting with each room's individual design incorporating many original features supplemented by custom-built free-standing furniture and a comprehensive range of state-of-the-art amenities. The bathrooms are particularly well-appointed, with plenty of bright light, generous supplies of towels and toiletries and particularly powerful over-bath showers plumbed in to a new pressurised hot-water system. Planned additions for the coming year include two further bedrooms with direct access to the private rear garden, a new residents' lounge and a board room conference facility. Children welcome overnight (extra bed £5). Eight wines available by the glass. **Bar Food & Restaurant Meals** 12-2.30, 7-10. **Beer** *Eldridge Pope Hardy Country, Bass, Wadworth 6X, Morland Old Speckled Hen. Courtyard, outdoor eating.*

Family room. **Accommodation** *10 bedrooms, all en suite, £55 (single £50). Children welcome overnight, additional beds and cots available (£5). No credit cards.*

Beckley   Abingdon Arms

Tel 01865 351311	**FOOD**
High Street Beckley Oxfordshire OX3 9UU	**Map 14a C2**

There are inspiring views from the pretty garden of this beautifully positioned village pub. The interior is plainly furnished with cloth-covered wall seats in the lounge and a separate public bar. People come here for long-standing (22yrs) landlady Mary Greatbatch's excellent food that mirrors the seasons, with lots of delicious picnicky things in summer, cold poached salmon and smoked chicken (£7.20) amongst them, and warming bakes (£6.75), curries with Basmati rice (£5.50) and other hot dishes in winter (game pie with port sauce – £6.95). Puddings include home-made ice cream (flavours change every two weeks) and apple and almond tart (all £2.20). In winter, regular special evenings are organised (on Fridays) highlighting food from one particular country or region – booking is essential. Large, grassed garden with summer house, terrace and spacious seating. Only children over 14 inside. *Bar Food 12.15-1.45, 7.15-9.15 (except Sat & Sun). Restaurant Meals 7.15-9. Free House. Beer Adnams, Wadworth 6X, John Bull. Garden, outdoor eating. Family room. No credit cards.*

Bedford   Embankment Hotel

Tel 01234 261332 Fax 01234 325085	**B&B**
Embankment Bedford Bedfordshire MK40 3PD	**Map 15 E1**

Sitting on the embankment of the River Ouse, this small Tudor-style town-centre hotel provides comfortable accommodation that is popular with visiting businessmen. Twenty spacious upstairs bedrooms are furnished and decorated in uniform style with modern built-in furniture, good writing space and adequate en-suite shower rooms; TVs, tea-makers, radios and trouser presses are standard throughout. The rather tired facade and downstairs bars and lounges were due to be refurbished as we went to press. *Open 10am-11pm (except Sun).* **Accommodation** *20 bedrooms, all en suite, £59.95 (single £49.50); weekend £49.95/£29.95. Children welcome overnight (under-2s stay free in parents' room), additional beds (£5) and cots supplied. Access, Diners, Visa.*

Beenham Village   Six Bells

Tel 01734 713368	**FOOD**
	B&B
Beenham Village nr Reading Berkshire RG7 5NX	**Map 14a C4**

Dating back some 200 years, this pub is a mixture of old and new. The bar is old, dimly lit, with mahogany counter and all the characteristics of an old village pub. To the rear they have added an extension which has a large room suitable for parties and wedding receptions. All food is home-made: a large variety of omelettes (£2.80), garlic mushrooms (£4.50), soups (Stilton £2.50), stir-fried beef with black bean sauce (£5.50), lemon chicken (£5.50), poached fresh salmon (£5.50) with a treacle and walnut tart or lemon meringue pudding to finish (both £2). A two-course roast meal (£6.75) is served on Sundays. Upstairs, there are four letting rooms, with tea/coffee-making facilities, radios and televisions. The bathrooms are adequate, the beds comfortable and all the rooms have lovely views over the neighbouring farmland. *Bar Food 12-2.30, 6-10 (Sun 12-3, 7-10.30). Free House. Beer Flowers, Brakspears. Garden, outdoor eating. Accommodation 4 bedrooms, all en suite, £49 (single £36). Children welcome overnight (rate depends on age), additional beds available. Check-in by arrangement. Access, Visa.*

Beer   Anchor Inn

FOOD
B&B

Tel 01297 20386

Fore Street Beer nr Seaton Devon EX12 3ET

Map 13 E2

One of Britain's best-situated inns, the Anchor overlooks the stony beach whence the local crab boats set to sea in the early morning. Fish dominates the menu; dishes not only include local haddock (£7.95) and plaice (£6.50), but also in the evenings medallions of monkfish in Dijon mustard sauce (£10.95), baked whole red mullet with black olives, tomatoes and white wine (£11.95), fresh scallops with bacon and mushrooms (£8.95) and supreme of salmon topped with prawns (£10.25). They also cater well for meat-eaters and vegetarians in the spacious and comfortably furnished bars. Each of the eight bedrooms has a private bathroom (though not all are en suite); bright co-ordinated fabrics enliven them all, and some enjoy fine sea views. Entrance for residents is separate from the pub proper, there's a clubby TV lounge, while the clifftop garden opposite is a spectacular location for an early evening drink. No pets. *Bar open 11-11 Mon-Sat in summer, usual hours winter. Bar Food 12-2, 7-9.30. Free House. Beer Dartmoor Best, Wadworth 6X, Dartmoor Strong, Royal Oak. Garden, outdoor eating. Family room. Accommodation 8 bedrooms, 5 en suite, from £56. Children welcome overnight, additional beds & cots (price according to age) supplied. Access, Visa.*

Zzzz...

Beetham   Wheatsheaf

B&B

Tel 01539 562123

Beetham Kilnthorpe Cumbria LA7 7AL

Map 4 C4

Just off the A6, a mile or so North of the Lancashire border, Mrs Shaw's homely hostelry has been in the same ownership now for a quarter of a century. Unsurprisingly, her many returning guests are welcomed as members of the extended family. Behind a facade of black-and-white gables and leaded windows are three interlinked bars which are very much the focal point of village life, while for more retiring residents there's a comfortable TV lounge available upstairs. The bedrooms are neat and attractively decorated, if on the whole rather small. There are TVs and tea makers, and spotlessly kept carpeted private bathrooms. The popular front rooms have views over the village and church grounds down towards the river Bela. *Free House. Beers Thwaites Bitter, Theakston Best, Boddingtons. Accommodation 6 bedrooms, all en suite, from £40 (single £30). Children welcome overnight, cots supplied. No credit cards.*

Belford   Blue Bell Hotel

B&B

Tel 01668 213543   Fax 01668 215787

Market Place Belford Northumberland WE70 7WE

Map 5 D1

Creeper-clad, the Bell stands at the head of the village on a cobbled forecourt. In front are the old Market Place and stone cross, recently restored by English Heritage the Norman parish church stands on a hill behind. The pubbiest part is the Belford Tavern, licensed in old stables in the courtyard, where there's a games room and a children's

Zzzz...

menu, though there are no real ales at the bar. The hotel's stone-flagged foyer leads to a stylish cocktail bar boasting a collection of miniature hand bells, and a restful residents' lounge. Bedrooms are a mix, from those in the annex (with shower/WCs only) to superior and de luxe rooms with full bathrooms and lovely views of the Blue Bell's 2-acre "garden of 10,000 blooms". *Pub open 11-3, 6-11 (12-3, 7-10.30 Sun). Free House. **Accommodation** 17 bedrooms, all en suite, £84 (single £42). Children welcome overnight (under 12s stay free in parents' room) additional beds and cot available. Dogs welcome by arrangement. Access, Visa.*

Bellingdon   **Bull**

Tel 01494 758163

FOOD

Bellingdon Road Bellingdon Buckinghamshire HP5 2XU   **Map 15a E2**

Delightful little redbrick cottage on the north side of the village enjoying a peaceful rural aspect. The attractive, low-beamed bar boasts a large inglenook, various display cases and every table is neatly laid out with place mats, for the Bull is very much a dining pub. New landlords, however, are keen to attract a good local drinking trade, a sector of the market that was actively discouraged from the pub under the previous licensee. Bar food is still reliable with an interesting selection of dishes being listed on twice-daily-changing blackboard menus, although it can be pricey for a lunchtime outing as light snacks – sandwiches, ploughman's – are not readily available. Choices may range from home-made cauliflower and mushroom soup (£2.75) to fresh Norfolk samphire with vinaigrette for starters, followed by medallions of chargrilled venison in redcurrant and port (£9.95), grilled wild salmon with parsley and lemon mayonnaise (£10.95), pan-fried tuna steak with Cajun spices (£9.95), moussaka (£6.25), chicken tikka masala (£7.55) and stir-fried beef and noodles (£6.25). Some dishes are accompanied by chips and crunchy salads, others by good fresh vegetables. Vegetarian options may include mushroom and cashew nut fettuccine and a quiche with salad. Disappointing puddings seem to rely on bought-in items like Spotted Dick and death by chocolate (both £2.95). Visitors this year may find the planned, and much needed, conservatory extension in situ. *Pub open 11-11 (Sun 12-10.30). **Bar Food** 12-2.15, 7-9.30 (no food Sun eve). **Beer** Greene King IPA, Marston's Pedigree, Burton Ale, guest beer. Garden, outdoor eating, summer barbecue. Access, Diners, Visa.*

Benenden   **King William IV**

Tel 01580 240636

FOOD

The Street Benenden Kent TN17 5DJ   **Map 11 C6**

16th-century tile-hung village inn, up-market in style, reflecting its well-heeled location. Fresh flowers on plain wooden tables, a log fire in the huge inglenook, exposed beams and a relaxing lived-in air. By contrast, a splendidly traditional public bar with bare boards, TV, games machine and time-honoured pub games. Short daily-changing selection of good home-made dishes with fresh accompanying vegetables and little sign of chips – unless asked for. Choices may include smoked mackerel paté (£3.50), fresh poached salmon, beef in red wine (both £5.95), leek and ham mornay (£4.50) and lasagne and salad (£4.95). Peach melba torte and chocolate fudge cake (£1.95) may feature on the pudding board. *Pub open 11-3, 6-11 (Fri 5-11, Sat 11-11, Sun 12-3, 7-10.30). **Bar Food** 12-2.30, 7.30-9.30. No food Sun* *evening. Children allowed in the bar to eat, children's menu.* **Beer** *Shepherd Neame Master Brew, Spitfire Bitter, SN Best Bitter. Small side garden with benches. No credit cards.*

Bentley — The Star

Tel 01420 23184	**FOOD**
London Road Bentley nr Farnham Surrey GU10 5LW	**Map 15a D4**

Modestly comfortable roadside pub alongside the A31 offering a friendly welcome and blackboard menu of soundly cooked dishes. Run by Vic and Kathy Frith, it's Vic who does the cooking and his background in large hotel kitchens is evident in the attractive presentation of everything from sandwiches (made with good granary bread, the 'ham' version (from £2.95) filled triple-decker-style with thick slices of excellent gammon) and jacket potatoes (from £2.95) to the likes of braised pork and red cabbage (£5.25), salmon and prawn pasta bake (£5.25), and chicken legs in red wine and mushroom sauce (£4.95). A separate blackboard menu (prawn and mushroom thermidor, lamb cutlets dijonnaise £7.50) operates in a wheelback-chaired restaurant on Tue-Sat evenings. On Sunday lunchtimes a special menu operates throughout, with about half a dozen main dishes at £5.75; starters are £7.95 and puds £9.95. **Bar Food** *12-2.30, 7-9.30 (no food Sun eve).* **Restaurant Meals** *7-9.30 (not Mon or Sun).* **Beers** *Ushers Founders & Best, Courage Best. Patio. Access, Visa.*

Bentworth — The Sun Inn

Tel 01420 562338	**FOOD**
Sun Hill Bentworth Alton Hampshire GU34 5JT	**Map 15a D4**

Hidden down a tiny lane on the village edge, this pretty flower-bedecked and unspoilt rural pub dates from the 17th century when it was a pair of cottages. Little has changed inside over the years, where brick and board floors are laid with a rustic mix of old and new pine tables, benches and settles, original beams are hung with various horse brasses, walls are adorned with prints and plates and tasteful cosmetic touches – quality magazines, fresh and dried flowers – enhance the overall unblemished atmosphere. Two large inglenook fireplaces with open log fires warm the two main interlinking bars. To provide more seating space, a third adjoining room has recently been built in a similar style, maintaining the unique traditional character of the pub. As well as the Sun's charm, real ale and a good selection of home-cooked dishes (listed on a hand-written menu and a regularly changing blackboard menu) are prime reasons for stopping here. Reliable, uncomplicated dishes range from ploughman's and ham, egg and chips to seafood pasta (£4.95), steak and kidney pie (£6.50), sweet and sour chicken (£6.50), lamb casserole (£6.50) and speciality giant Yorkshire puddings filled with beef and gravy (£4.95). To finish, try the Bakewell tart or treacle tart (both at £2). Outside to the front and side, among the flower tubs and baskets, there are several wooden tables for alfresco sipping. **Bar Food** *12-2, 7-9.30 (Sun to 9), no food on Sunday Nov-Dec. Free House.* **Beer** *Wadworth 6X, Marston's Pedigree, Ruddles Best, Bass, Diggers Gold, Ringwood Best, several guest beers. Terrace, outdoor eating. Pub closed 25 Dec. No credit cards.*

Berwick   Cricketers

| Tel 01323 870469 | A° |

Berwick nr Polegate East Sussex BN26 6SP   **Map 11 B6**

Unspoilt, 500-year-old brick and flint creeper-clad cottage located just
off the A27 Lewes to Polegate road and a handy watering-hole for
walkers from the South Downs Way. Inside, three charming rooms
are delightfully unpretentious and traditional with half-panelled walls,
open fires and simply furnished with scrubbed tables and wall benches
on quarry-tiled floors. Popular locals pub with a good chatty
atmosphere and decent Harvey's ales tapped straight from the barrel in
a rear room. Surrounded by a magnificent cottage garden – foxgloves,
roses and flower-borders – it is an idyllic summer pub. No children
inside. *Pub open 11-2.30, 6-11 (Sun 12-3, 7-10.30).* **Beer** *Harveys
Sussex Bitter, Old Ale, Tom Paine (July). Garden, lawn, outdoor eating,
tables in garden. No credit cards.*

Bibury   Catherine Wheel

| Tel 01285 740250 | **FOOD** |
| | **B&B** |

Bibury Gloucestershire GL7 5ND   **Map 14a A2**

Carol Ann Palmer's 500-year-old, mellow stone pub, recently re-
roofed, carefully retains both the reputation and atmosphere of an
unpretentious, unspoilt local. Its summer attractions include the
colourful flower baskets, neatly tended lawns full of picnic tables and
the baby black rabbits constantly in residence. In winter there's a
chummy atmosphere at closely-set tables in front of warming wood-
burning stoves. Open all day every day, except Sundays, there's a
wealth of food on offer with sandwiches, filled baked potatoes and
children's choices by the dozen. Rather, though, look inside on the vast
chalk boards for the fresh daily-changing fare of two or three soups,
cabbage and Stilton, perhaps (£2.25), the likes of kidneys turbigo
(£5.25) or Mexican-style chicken breast (£6.75) and most likely fresh
grilled Bibury trout from the trout farm opposite – also well worth a
visit. Busy as the tiny kitchen usually is, the food is consistently
reliable and service is relaxed and friendly. New bedroom
accommodation was not completed at the time of our visit last
summer. A few steps across the car park the former outhouses have
been re-roofed in Cotswold stone and are set to house four double
bedrooms with en-suite bathrooms and comprehensively up-to-date
facilities; two are of family size with extra beds. *Pub open 11-11
(except Sun).* **Bar Food** *11-11 (Sun 12-3, 7-10.30). Free House.*
Beer *Archers Golden, Whitbread West Country Best, Tetley Best, guest
beers. Garden, outdoor eating. Family room.* **Accommodation** *4 bedrooms,
all en suite, from £45. Children welcome overnight, additional beds
supplied. Access, Visa.*

Bickley Moss   Cholmondeley Arms

| Tel 01829 720300 | **FOOD** |
| | **B&B** |

Bickley Moss nr Malpas Cheshire SY14 8BT   **Map 6 B3**

Virtually opposite Cholmondeley Castle and gardens on the A49 and
still part of the Viscount's estate is this redbrick former schoolhouse
replete with family heirlooms, educational memorabilia, bell tower
without and blackboards within. These last provide interesting reading
with hollandaise sauce accompanying salmon fishcakes (£6.95)
chicken piri piri (£7.95) and pasta carbonara (£6.50) alongside
traditional English steak and kidney or chicken and mushroom pie

(£6.50) and a "school lunch" of spicy sausage and onion in a baguette (£4). Finish with Caribbean hot fudged bananas or crepes laced with Grand Marnier (£3.25). Children's meals £3.60. Overnight accommodation is across the car park in what must have been the head teacher's house. Four self-contained bedrooms (three doubles and a family room) are bright and cottagey with en-suite WC and shower rooms. All have telephones, television and clock radios, tea trays and hairdryers. Children are welcome overnight, (£5 when sharing parent's room) with cots available. Then it's back to school in the morning to report in for a slap-up breakfast. *Free House*. **Food** *12-2.15 (Sun to 2), 7-10 (Sun to 9.30)*. **Beers** *Marston's Pedigree, Boddingtons, Flowers Original, weekly changing guest beer. Garden, outdoor eating. Family room*. **Accommodation** *4 bedrooms, all en suite, from £46 (single £34). Children welcome overnight (£5 when sharing parents' room), additional beds & cots available. Check-in by arrangement. Access, Visa.*

Biddenden — Three Chimneys

Tel 01580 291472	**FOOD**
Biddenden nr Ashford Kent TN27 8HA	Map 11 C5

The Three Chimneys has every natural advantage of being a classic country pub, its original, small roomed layout and old-fashioned furnishings intact. Old settles, low beams, nice decor, warming open fires, absence of music and electronic games – glorious. Then there's the range of more than decent bar food including carrot and orange soup (£2.40), kipper paté (£3.20), veal and Madeira casserole (£6.60) and chicken breast in red wine, bacon and mushroom sauce (£6.50). Basic bread and cheese – mature farmhouse cheddar or Stilton – comes with chunks of fresh granary bread and home-made chutney or pickled onions. Daily choice of four puddings – upside down marmalade pudding (£2.65), date and walnut pudding (£2.70). Good ales tapped direct from the barrel behind the bar and a heady farm cider from Biddenden. Family Garden Room and the shrub-filled garden is lovely for summer eating. Don't, incidentally, look for the three chimneys on the roof – the name comes from the pub's location at the meeting of three lanes, or Trois Chemins – 1 mile west of Biddenden on the A262 – as it was called by French prisoners of war kept near here in another century. No children under 14 inside. *Pub open 11-2.30, 6-11 (Sun 12-2.30, 7-10.30)*. **Bar Food** *12-2, 6.30-10 (Sun 7-10)*. **Restaurant Meals** *as the bar. Free House*. **Beer** *Fremlins, Adnams Best, Brakspear, Harvey's Best, Marston's Pedigree, Morland's Old Speckled Hen, Wadworth 6X, Harvey's Old Ale in winter. Lawned garden, outdoor eating area. Pub closed Christmas Day & Boxing Day. No credit cards.*

Birch Vale — Sycamore Inn

Tel 01663 742715 Fax 01663 747382	**B&B**
Sycamore Road Birch Vale Hayfield Derbyshire DE55 6FG	Map 6 C2

Surrounded by woods of sycamore and silver birch, this quietly located pub at the fringe of the village (turn off the A6015 at Station Road) is built precariously into the side of a steep hill. In ten acres of grounds, the paddock slopes steeply down to the River Sett (although you can't see it), while beyond the lower car park there are a barbecue terrace, dovecotes, mini-aviary and a children's Tarzan trail playground. There are bars at two levels, the lower with regular entertainment and a clubby atmosphere while that above is given over largely to eating in neatly partitioned dining areas which include non-smoking and family rooms. With one exception bedrooms look out across the valley; they're neatly appointed with whitewood furniture and patchwork quilts; all have full en-suite bathrooms, free satellite TV, radios, beverage trays and trouser presses. For those with other pressing business, the only telephone provided is on the upper landing. *Pub open 11-11 (usual hours Sun, except with food). Beer John Smith's, Marston's Pedigree, Courage Directors. Garden, family room.* **Accommodation** *7 bedrooms, all en suite, from £45 (single £29.50); family room £55. Children welcome overnight, additional beds and cots supplied. Access, Visa.*

Birchover   **Druid Inn**

Tel 01629 650302 | **FOOD**

Main Street Birchover Derbyshire DE4 2BL | Map 6 C2

Climb the long hill from the B5056 signposted Stanton Moor Stone Circle, and be sure not to miss a glimpse of Row Tor, high above the pub, where extraordinary fissures and passageways through the rock suggest very early occupation by man; hence the Druid's unusual name. The Druid is an egalitarian sort of place, frequented in about equal numbers by both county types and country walkers; Range Rovers and Transits rub car tyre tracks in the car park. From portal to chimney pot, it's entirely ivy-covered, with a terrace in front, and to one side, a partly no-smoking restaurant area on two floors, connected by a tiled umbilical passageway. There's no bar at which to stand, except when ordering food. The menu fills four blackboards, including a complete vegetarian selection (macaroni cheese with mushrooms and white wine sauce £4.70). A starter might be Szechuan-style spare ribs in garlic ginger soya sauce with salad (£3.90) or exotic prawn cocktail with brandy (£3.85) followed by a main course like trout topped with white wine sauce, prawns and mussels (£8.90) or honey-roast saddle of lamb with gooseberry and redcurrant sauce (£10.50), and perhaps finish with a Bakewell pudding (£2.30) for dessert, all partnered by an above average range of good value wines by glass or bottle. *Bar Food & Restaurant Meals 12-2, 7-9.30 (to 9 in winter). Free House. Beer Adnams, Mansfield, guest beer. Patio/terrace. Family room. Access, Diners, Visa.*

Birdlip   **The Air Balloon**

Tel 01452 862541 | **A**

Crickley Hill Birdlip Gloucester Gloucestershire GL4 6JY | Map 14 B2

A prominent 17th-century inn adjacent to the A417/A436 junction, equidistant from Gloucester and Cheltenham, amusingly named to commemorate the exploits of a local balloonist. He took off from the top of nearby Crickley Hill on a maiden flight in 1802 and promptly vanished into thin air (or so the story goes). Today's tale is of a busy Wayside Inn which packs in the families year-round. In winter are large log fires; on summer days hill-top gardens set out with play equipment and a bouncy castle. Sensibly, however, there are also picnic tables on the sheltered rear patio under a permanent awning. Food for the under-12s, both here and in a large family room, comes at down-to-earth prices, almost as cheap in fact as a pint of Boddingtons, to be enjoyed by their parents straight from the cask. Whitbread Wayside Inns. *Beer: Whitbread, Flowers Original, Boddingtons from cask, Guest Ale. Children welcome inside. Access, Visa.*

Bishop Wilton   Fleece Inn

Tel 01759 368251

B&B

Bishop Wilton Humberside YO4 1RU

Map 7 D1

Lovely village setting overlooking the green, the Norman church and
the Wolds beyond. A central bar divides lounge and public areas, with
a breakfast/dining room to the rear. Three bedrooms are in the
original building, and four en-suite rooms in a separate pantiled block
(former stables). Baby listening devices have been installed. Live
country and western music on Friday evenings. *Open 11-11 Sat,
regular hours other days. Free House.* **Beer** *John Smith's, Tetley.*
Accommodation *7 bedrooms, 4 en suite, £45 (single £30). Children
welcome overnight (under-5s stay free in parents' room, 5-12 £10),
additional bed and cot available. No dogs. No credit cards.*

Blackawton   Normandy Arms

Tel 0180421 316

B&B

Chapel Street Blackawton nr Dartmouth Devon TQ9 7BN

Map 13 D3

Homely, 15th-century village inn with a welcoming atmosphere.
Rustic pub furniture and various displays and memorabilia on the
Normandy Landings theme adorn the much-modernised bars.
Upstairs, comfortable accommodation is provided in four delightfully
cottagey bedrooms, all with modern pine furniture, matching fabrics
and spotlessly clean en-suite facilities. TVs and beverage-making
facilities are standard and hot-water bottles are thoughtfully provided
for cooler nights. Front rooms enjoy good rural views. **Beer** *Bass,
Blackawton Bitter, Gold, Ruddles Best Bitter. Garden, outdoor eating.*
Accommodation *4 bedrooms, all en suite, £44 (single £30). Access, Visa.*

Blackboys   Blackboys Inn

Tel 01825 890283

FOOD

Blackboys nr Uckfield East Sussex TN22 5LG

Map 11 B6

Recently reopened after a nine month closure following a serious fire,
this splendid black weatherboarded pub dates from 1389 and enjoys an
attractive position set back from the B2192 west of Heathfield,
overlooking an iris and lily-covered pond. Delightfully old-fashioned
interior with a series of inter-connecting rooms featuring various
pieces of antique furniture, interesting bric-a-brac and much sought
after alcove window seats with views over the pond. Separate
traditional public bar with bare boards, wooden furnishings, old juke
box and pub games. A reliable range of bar meals are listed on an
extensive blackboard menu above the bar and may include a large
bowl of home-made vegetable soup (£1.80), seafood gratinee and
mushrooms baked in port and Stilton sauce (both £2.85) for starters.
Main course choices range from Celanese fish curry (£4.50), steak and
kidney pie (£5) and seafood pancake to gigot of lamb in a rich
Catalan sauce with chick peas (£7.95), Cajun chicken (£6.95) and
calves liver sautéed in butter (£7.95). Good fresh accompanying
vegetables. For dessert try the bread-and-butter pudding, crème brulée
or treacle tart and custard (all £2.50). Ploughman's, filled jacket
potatoes and salads for those wanting a lighter bite. Good alfresco
seating beside the pond and the front green beneath the horse chestnut
trees. *Pub open 11-3, 6-11 (Sun 12-3, 7-10.30).* **Bar Food** *12-2.30,
6.30-10 (Sun 7-10).* ***Restaurant Meals*** *as the bar. Children allowed in*

Blacko   105

the bar to eat, children's portions. **Beers** Harveys Best Bitter, Armada Ale, Sussex Pale Ale, Old Ale in winter. Garden, lawn and paved terrace, tables in garden. Access, Visa.

Blackbrook   Plough

| Tel 01306 886603 | FOOD |

Blackbrook Road Blackbrook nr Dorking Surrey RH5 4DS   Map 15a F4

Popular, isolated rural inn located on a country lane south of Dorking, parallel with A24. Two spacious, comfortable and warmly welcoming bars with pleasant views through large windows and boasting a vast collection of over 500 ties and numerous old saws and farm tools. Fresh flowers top handsome copper-topped or old sewing machine tables. Well-stocked bar offering the full complement of King and Barnes ales, as well as 15 wines and seven vintage ports served by the glass. Choose one to accompany a reliable pub meal, especially a dish listed on the regularly-changing blackboard menu, such as home-made spinach and mushroom or, perhaps, watercress and potato soup (£2.45), chicken liver paté with cockles (£3.25), ginger and orange lamb (£5.25), chicken hotpot with herb dumplings (£5.95) and Bajan vegetable and nut curry (£4.95). Routine printed menu. Summer pudding, hot carrot pudding and Austrian chocolate cake (all £2.45) may feature on the pudding list. Sheltered rear garden with chalet-style children's play house. No children under 14 inside. **Beer** King & Barnes Sussex, Broadwood, Festive and Mild. Garden, children's play area. Pub closed 25, 26 & 31 Dec. No credit cards.

Blacko   Moorcock Inn

| Tel 01282 614186 | FOOD |

Gisburn Road Blacko nr Nelson Lancashire BB9 6NF   Map 6 B1

Standing on its own alongside the A682 north of Blacko, the whitewashed Moorcock Inn is situated in wonderful rolling countryside near Pendle Hill and the Forest of Bowland. Inside is unassuming and unpretentious. Two adjoining rooms have plain painted walls, simple prints, brass plates and a collection of china plates; stone fireplaces are topped with ornaments and brassware. All the tables are laid for dining, surrounded by upholstered bench seating and simple wooden chairs, a style continued in the large adjoining dining room. Large picture windows in both rooms offer lovely views over the surrounding landscape. Licensees Elizabeth and Peter Holt have built up an enviable reputation for good fresh food, and custom comes from far and wide. The printed menu is backed up by a daily changing specials board, where dishes could include a home-made game pie (£4.95), salmon fillet with seafood sauce (5.95) or medallions of fillet steak with red wine sauce (£6.95). Beside these, the menu covers tried and trusted pub favourites like ham shank with light mustard sauce (£5.95) and a good selection of vegetarian dishes. Home-made, old-fashioned puddings (all £2.15). Cooking is perfectly competent, without ever being spectacular; prices realistic, portions generous, service friendly and quick. Popular Sunday lunch (£4.95). The Moorcock's a useful resting place after a bracing morning on the moors, the Pendle Walk almost passes the door, and in sunny weather the garden is lovely. Open 12-10 Sun for food, regular hours other days. **Bar Food** 12-2, 7-10. Children allowed in bar to eat. Children's menu. **Beers** Thwaites. Garden. No credit cards.

Blakesley   Bartholomew Arms

| Tel 01327 860292 | **B&B** |

High Street Blakesley Northamptonshire NN12 8RE   Map 15 D1

Charming, welcoming 17th-century inn with a collection of model
ships and nautical artefacts in the public bar, plus guns and cricket
memorabilia in the lounge. Simple, well-kept bedrooms at very
reasonable prices. Pleasant garden with summer house. 86 malt
whiskies. *Free House. **Beer** Marston's Pedigree, Worthington. Garden.
Accommodation 4 bedrooms, 1 en suite, £40 (single £18). Children
welcome overnight (under-5s stay free in parents' room, 6-10s £5.50 inc
breakfast), additional beds and cots available. No credit cards.*

Blanchland   Lord Crewe Arms

FOOD

| Tel 01434 675251   Fax 01434 675 337 | **B&B** |

Blanchland nr Consett Durham DH8 9SP   Map 5 D2

Wild and remote, and some 3 miles below Derwent Water in a deep
valley. Blanchland Abbey can trace its origins back to 1165 – despite
dissolution in 1576 the layout of its surrounding village remains
unchanged to this day. At its heart is one of England's finest inns,
containing relics of the abbey lodge and kitchens and a cloister garden
which is now an ancient monument. Lord Crewe purchased the entire
estate in 1704 from one Tom Foster, a Jacobite adventurer, whose
sister Dorothy is claimed still to be in residence. A sense of history
pervades the building's remarkably modernised yet largely unchanged
interior, no more so than in the Crypt bar. The meals served here are
substantial: – bratwurst sausage with sauerkraut and warm potato
salad (£5.10), minced lamb kebab with Greek salad (£4.50) and wild
boar and pheasant pie with salad (£5.10) do not constitute the average
pub lunch. Evening options of baked salmon (£7.75), minute steak
(£8.20) or Brie and broccoli bake (£7.50) are rather more traditional.
Ploughman's (£4.35) and filled brown rolls (from £2.50) are
lunchtime alternatives, while Sunday lunch features a hot and cold
buffet (main course £4.50). A three-course Sunday lunch (£13.50)
is also served in the stylish first floor restaurant overlooking the
garden. Bedrooms, needless to say, are splendidly individual; suitably
traditional in the old house with stone mullion windows and restored
fireplaces and mantels, yet up-to-date with accessories from colour TVs
to bespoke toiletries and thoughtful extras from mend kits to
complimentary sherry. Altogether more contemporary are the style
and furnishings of rooms in the adjacent Angel Inn, which was once
a Wesleyan Temperance House, a mere newcomer dating from the
1750s. In private, and caring hands over the last five years, the Lord
Crewe Arms today relives its centuries of pre-eminence. *Free House.
Beer Vaux Samson. **Accommodation** 18 rooms, £70 (single £60).
Access, Diners, Visa.*

Zzzz...

☺

Blandford Forum   Crown Hotel

| Tel 01258 456626   Fax 01258 451084 | **B&B** |

Blandford Forum Dorset DT11 7AJ   Map 14 B4

This fine Georgian coaching house has a civilised old-fashioned air and
is busy in typical market-town style. Bars, lounges and reception area
are more hotelly than pubby in atmosphere, all being heavily wood-
panelled and furnished with comfortable deep leather chairs and
settees, especially in the traditional lounges. Rambling corridors lead to
32 well-maintained bedrooms. Uniformly decorated in pale green,

they all boast clean, fresh bathrooms, light modern furniture and are well equipped with satellite TV, telephones, radio alarms and beverage-making facilities. There is an attractive and secluded Victorian walled garden for residents' use and guests are welcome to fish – in season – on the banks of the River Stour, which flows through the hotel grounds. Badger Inns. *Beer Hall and Woodhouse, Badger Best, Tanglefoot, guest beers. Garden, outdoor eating. Accommodation 32 bedrooms, all en suite, £72 (4-poster £75, single £62). Children welcome overnight (under-2s stay free in parents' room). Additional beds (£15) and cots (£10) available. Check-in from noon. Accommodation closed 24-28 Dec. Access, Diners, Visa.*

Bledington	**Kings Head Inn** ★	**FOOD**
Tel & Fax 01608 658365		**B&B**
The Green Bledington nr Kingham Oxfordshire OX7 6HD		Map 14a A1

The quintessential Cotswold pub, this delightful 15th-century inn can almost claim dual citizenship standing as it does on the Gloucester border while its easterly wall is resident in Oxfordshire, and a more delightful spot would be hard to find as it faces the village green with its brook and border-patrolling ducks. There's no such crisis of identity inside, the low-ceilinged bar full of ancient settles and simple wooden furniture and the latterly added lounge and dining room proving equally agreeable settings for enjoyment of the Royces' imaginative and constantly varying pub food. Lunches, selected from the blackboard are on the lighter side and agreeably easy on the pocket. Summer dishes of mushroom caps with goat's cheese, spinach and pine nuts (£3.95) and bowls of pasta with smoked salmon and dill or Parma ham and Parmesan (£4.95) are supplemented in winter by jugged hare, local rabbit and venison. Year round the sausage, mash and onion gravy (£2.95) and steak and wine pie (£5.95) remain top sellers, while the unique "sandwich selection" includes roast beef, bacon and banana and perhaps even black pudding with mango (all £2.95). More substantial menus prove equally popular at night, there's plenty of variety without undue elaboration in the likes of terrine of jellied salmon and sole (£2.95) and chicken and noodle fritters with sweet and sour sauce (£3.25) as curtain raisers to some deftly sauced main courses – red mullet fillets with walnuts and lentils (£7.95), oven-roasted duck breast on a strawberry coulis (£9.95) and pork fillet with mushrooms, sherry and cream (£8.50) are typical of the choices. Sweets are all home-made, too, emanating from this prodigiously hard-working kitchen is a warm, bubblingly soft-topped crème brulée as good as you'll find in any pub in the land. There's an even wider choice of bedroom accommodation for 1995 as a new rear extension of six additional bedrooms has recently opened. Meticulous attention to detail by the many local craftsmen involved has assured them of a finish which can only ensure their instant popularity: the three ground floor rooms are an added bonus for less mobile guests. The older, cottagey bedrooms over the pub should not suffer by comparison though they may be less suitable for an early night, and the floorboards have become a little creaky. Their appointments nonetheless are top class with direct-dial phones, TVs, clock radios and an array of thoughtfully provided extras. Residents here enjoy the use of a quiet smokers' lounge (not in the bedrooms, please!) and a private patio. *Bar and Restaurant Meals 12-2, 7-9.30. Beer Hook Norton, 6X, Uley Old Spot, Adnams Broadside, guest beers. Garden, outdoor eating. Family rooms. Accommodation 12 bedrooms (all en suite) from £55. Children welcome overnight, additional beds (£5) & cots supplied. No dogs. Access, Visa.*

Bledlow   Lions of Bledlow

Tel 018444 3345	**A**
Church End Bledlow Buckinghamshire HP27 9PE	Map 15a D2

Tracks lead up into the Chiltern beechwoods from this unspoilt, low white-painted 16th-century former coaching inn, making it an ideal walking base. Summer visitors can imbibe in the attractive rear garden or on the edge of the village green, where benches enjoy a pleasant rural outlook. In winter, the charming, heavily-beamed and unadorned interior comes into its own. Ancient tiled floors, a huge inglenook with open fire, oak stalls with rustic tables, various brasses and copper pots and a chatty atmosphere characterise the four seating areas of this cosy, traditional country pub. *Open 11-3 & 6-11 (Sun 12-3 & 7-10.30). Free House. Beer Wadworth 6X, Young's, Ruddles Best, John Smith's, Gale's HSB. Garden. Access, Diners, Visa.*

Blewbury   Blewbury Inn

	FOOD
Tel 01235 850496	**B&B**
London Road Blewbury nr Didcot Oxfordshire OX11 9PD	Map 14a C3

Modest but appealing, white-painted roadside pub whose two rooms (one is the no-smoking restaurant) feature pine boarding to dado height and wheelback chairs. Recently taken over by a keen young couple: Martine looks after front-of-house and Paul, a professional chef, works away in the kitchen. A single menu serves both bar and restaurant with some four or five choices at each stage. It's priced à la carte to encourage snacking but with a maximum price of £21.95 if all three courses are taken. Well executed dishes such as red pepper mousse with basil sauce (£4.25), baked goat's cheese with hazelnut dressing (£4.95), braised lamb shank with tomato, olives and parsley sauce (£13.95), chargrilled baby aubergine with pesto-flavoured ratatouille (£9.95 – there's always a vegetarian option) and ragout of seafood with tagliatelle (£13.95) demonstrate Paul's modern style. Equally good puds might include a hot plum soufflé or freshly-baked chocolate pithiviers (both £4.50). The lunch menu is slightly simpler and cheaper but is in a similar vein (pigeon or smoked trout salad £4.50/£4.25, lemon sole with herb butter £9.95, herb omelette £4.95, trio of rabbit £10.25, redcurrant soup £3.50). Three simpler bedrooms (no phone, no remote-control for the TV and no dressing table/work space) are clean and well kept, each with its own en-suite shower room; a shared bathroom is also available for those who prefer a soak in the tub. *Bar Food & Restaurant Meals 12-2, 7-9.30 (no food Sun eve and all Mon). Free House. Beer Hook Norton, Arkell's 3B. Accommodation 3 rooms, all en suite, £50 (single £40). Check-in by arrangement. Access, Visa.*

Blickling   Buckinghamshire Arms Hotel

Tel 01263 732133	**B&B**
Blickling nr Aylsham Norfolk NR11 6NF	Map 10 C1

Splendid Grade 1 listed 17th-century inn which stands deferentially at the gates of the even more magnificent Blickling Hall. Once the estate builders, house and later the servants' quarters to the fine National Trust property, it is an excellent place to stay with two of the three bedrooms having dramatic evening views across to the flood-lit hall.

Zzzz...

☺

Attractively decorated, each room boasts original features, with "real"
four-posters and sturdy old stripped pine and dark oak furnishings
making this a most characterful and peaceful bed and breakfast stop.
One room has an en-suite shower room, the others share a clean,
good-sized bathroom with an old fashioned tub. Downstairs, the three
charming and well-furnished bars have open fires and are typically
National Trust in style of decor and taste. *Free House. Open 11-3, 6-11
(Sun 12-3).* **Accommodation** *3 bedrooms, one en suite £60 (single £45).
Check-in by arrangement. Children welcome overnight and anywhere.*
Beer *Adnams Southwold, Broadside, Woodefordes, Wherry & Baldric, guest
beer. Garden, outdoor eating. Access, Diners, Visa.*

Blockley	**Crown Inn & Hotel**	**FOOD**
Tel 01386 700245		**B&B**
High Street Blockley nr Moreton-in-Marsh Gloucestershire GL56 9EX		**Map 14a A1**

At the heart of this most picturesque of Cotswold villages the
Champion family's Crown is the jewel. Whilst retaining all the charm   Zzzz...
of a 16th-century coaching inn, it has been totally restored with
loving care and considerable style. At street level the inn is fronted by
a split-level bar decorated in muted tones and furnished with deep-
cushioned sofas and leather club chairs. Here at any time, and at
pavement tables in summertime, is a splendid spot to enjoy some
simply executed yet consistently tasty bar snacks, which are
supplemented daily by best-available produce from the fish markets.
Honey-baked ham or beef with horseradish come in 1½-round
sandwiches from £2.50; winter may see a steak, Guinness and
mushroom pie (£5.95) giving way in summer to Wye salmon salad
(£5.95) or a fan of avocado and Stilton (£4.95). In season are pristine
fresh oysters (£5.75 for 6), mackerel fillets with mustard vinaigrette
(£5.25) and baked trout with prawns and mushrooms (£6.25).
For a treat leave room for the fresh raspberry roulade (£2.95) and
flavourful cafetière coffee. Adjacent is the Crown's new brasserie
which extends the range of food choices, and away from the bar's
bustle, the relaxing residents' lounge opens on to a hidden rear garden.
Restoration of the Crown's bedrooms has also been immaculate, with
discreetly incorporated modern appointments such as en-suite bath or
shower rooms, TV, radio, hairdryer and beverage facilities. Exposed
timberwork and original beams, the mellow stone walls and cast-iron
bedroom fireplaces add to each room's individual appeal, while even
more spacious luxury is to be found in the splendid four-poster rooms
and suites. *Pub open 11-11 (except Sun) in summer, normal hours in
winter.* **Bar Food & Brasserie** *12-2, 7-10. Free House.* **Beer** *Hook
Norton, Donningtons, guest beers. Outdoor eating. Family room.*
Accommodation *21 bedrooms, all en suite, from £78 (single £53).
Children welcome overnight, additional beds (£7) & cots supplied. Access,
Diners, Visa.*

Boldre	**Red Lion**	
Tel 01590 673177		**A**
Boldre Lymington Hampshire SO41 8NE		**Map 14 C4**

Dating from around 1650 and mentioned as an alehouse in the
Domesday Book, this most attractive New Forest pub has been run by
the same family for the past 23 years. Outside an old cart is strewn
with flowers, and hanging baskets and troughs are a riot of colour in
summer. Inside, a rambling series of four black-beamed rooms have
their own country style, with real fires, a mix of old furnishings,

hunting prints, farm tools, man-traps, tapestries and unusual collections of old bottles and chamber pots. Delightful secluded rear flower garden. No children under 14 allowed inside. *Pub open 11-3, 6-11 (Sun 12-3,7-10.30). Beer Eldridge Pope. Garden. Pub Closed 25 & 26 Dec. Access, Visa.*

Bollington　　Church House Inn

Tel 01625 574014　　**FOOD**

Church Street Bollington Cheshire SK10 5PY　　Map 6 B2

This quiet corner of Cheshire's largest village is where the discerning drop in for carefully prepared lunchtime snacks and evening meals. The menu, if anything overlong, offers filled baked potatoes and sandwiches through to chicken à la creme (£7.25) and steak Diane (£8.95). There's an upper dining room for evening use and private parties; to the rear, an enclosed garden for summer drinking. Daily specials complete the picture: dressed crab (£3.25), vegetable moussaka (£4.95), pork casserole or lamb and chutney stew (£4.35); to follow, lemon mousse pie and raspberry pavlova (£1.95). Hand-pumped beers are well kept. *Bar Food 12-2. 6.30-9.30 (Sun 7-9). Children's menu. Free House. Beer Theakston Best & XB, Boddingtons, Thwaites, Jennings. Garden. Family Room. Access, Visa.*

Bolter End　　Peacock

Tel 01494 881417　　**FOOD**

Lane End Bolter End Buckinghamshire HP14 3LU　　Map 15a D3

Bolter End is a crossroads with a few houses and the pub is located opposite the Common. The only bar is divided into three sections and one menu applies throughout. Examples of menu dishes include chicken in fresh coriander (£5.95), stincotto (whole gammon hock cooked in herbs – £8.95), potato skins with feta cheese, sun-dried tomatoes and salad (£3.75) or Italian sausages with beans and hash browns (£4.25). Home-made puddings (from £2.30) are the traditional kind – fruit crumbles, jam roly-poly, honey oat and lemon tart or sticky toffee pudding. *Bar Food 12-2, 7-10 (except Sun). Beer Bass, Tetley, Ansells Mild. Garden, outdoor eating. Access, Diners, Visa.*

Bonchurch　　Bonchurch Inn

Tel 01983 852611　　**A**

The Shute Bonchurch Isle of Wight PO38 1NU　　Map 15 D4

Bonchurch's only pub has an invigorating Italian flavour and a good nautical atmosphere, too: the public bar is cut into the rocks of the Shute. *Beer Boddingtons, Flowers Original. Courtyard. Family room. No credit cards.*

Boot　　Burnmoor Inn

Tel 019467 23224　　**B&B**

Boot Eskdale Cumbria CA19 1TG　　Map 4 C3

An attractive pebble-dashed old inn in a tiny hamlet, only three minutes' walk from the Eskdale railway terminus. Across the Esk by an old stone bridge are the restored Corn Mill and bridleways to Eel Tarn and Wasdale Head. The Fosters have run a friendly house here for a decade or more with a popular Austrian slant to much of Heidi's cooking (Austrian flan £3.50, Wienerschnitzel £5.90). Residents enjoy the use of a neat, secluded dining and breakfast room – many come for the abundant peace and quiet. The bedrooms, six with WC & shower rooms en suite, the other two sharing a toilet and bathroom, look out down the dale, or back up the hills towards Scafell; unencumbered by TVs or telephones, they are neat and simply furnished. *Free House. Beer Jennings Bitter & Cumberland Ale. Garden, children's play area. Accommodation 8 bedrooms, 6 en suite, £52 (single £23). Check-in by arrangement. Children over 4 welcome overnight, additional beds (£1 per year of age) available. No dogs. Access, Visa.*

Bottlesford   Seven Stars

Tel 01672 851325 Fax 01672 851583	**FOOD**
Bottlesford nr Woodborough Pewsey Wiltshire SH9 6LU	**Map 14a A4**

Make for Woodborough from the A345 at Pewsey (past the hospital), or from the mini roundabout at North Newnton to find the Seven Stars lost (almost) down narrow lanes. The old thatched building fronted by creepers and climbing roses has a splendid rambling interior of beams and black oak panelling and a central brick bar with quarry tile flooring. There's plenty of room to enjoy some masterfully produced bar food from the ever-enthusiastic, sometimes inspired Philippe Cheminade. Moules marinière (£4.75), mousseline-sauced John Dory (£7.95) and the traditional cassoulet (£6.25) attest equally to his Gallic origins as to a broad range of skills, which also extend to five presentations of the more traditional liver, bacon and onions (£6.25), venison steak with garlic and mushrooms (£7.25) and seasonally available jugged hare (£8.45). Two self-contained rooms at either end of the building double up for evening dining à la carte where main courses extend to the likes of whole Dover soles and steak Diane. Thankfully, however, this is not to the detriment of its true identity as a pub, which also boasts splendid gardens and grounds. A nine-acre tranche of land borders a shallow stream which winds down to the River Kennet; some picnic tables have been installed here and by arrangement hampers can be organised. Meanwhile Fred and Max, the two pet rams, are not averse to giving rides to suitably small children. In this charming rural location, deep in the Vale of Pewsey with views across country to the White House, there's good news of the imminent addition of two en-suite bedrooms in the old brick barn for 1995. *Bar Food & Restaurant Meals 12-2.30, 6.30-9.30. Free House. Beer Badger Best, Wadworth 6X, guest beer. Garden, outdoor eating. Access, Visa.*

Boughton Aluph   Flying Horse Inn

Tel 01233 620914	**FOOD**
	B&B
Boughton Aluph nr Ashford Kent	**Map 11 C5**

15th-century vine and wisteria-clad inn occupying a charming spot overlooking the village green/cricket pitch, just off the A251 north of Ashford. Plenty of alfresco seating; ideal for lazy summer evenings watching the cricket. Single beamed front bar with open log fire and adorned with hopbines and a collection of old ties. Small neat rear dining rom. Promising, daily-changing blackboard specials outshine the list of standard pub snacks available. Choices may include paprika chicken, liver and bacon casserole, salmon steak with tarragon, Russian fish pie, steak and kidney pie and several fresh fish dishes, all accompanied by a selection of a least nine vegetables. Four neat and homely upstairs bedrooms have views across the green and surrounding countryside through unusual arched Gothic windows. Two have shower cubicles, all have washbasins and share two clean and spacious bathrooms. TVs and tea-makers are standard. *Open 11-11 Sat in summer (usual hours other days).* **Bar Food & Restaurant Meals** *12-2, 7-9.15. Children allowed in restaurant to eat.* **Beer** *Wadworth 6X, Courage Best, Shepherd Neame Master Brew, John Smith's. Garden, outdoor eating.* **Accommodation** *4 bedrooms, 2 en suite. Check-in by arrangement. Access, Visa.*

Bowden Hill   ·Rising Sun

Tel 01249 730363	**A**
32 Bowden Hill Lacock Wiltshire SN15 2PP	Map 14 B2

It's the location and the friendly, chatty atmosphere that draws people to this tiny honey-coloured stone pub, set high on the hill above historic Lacock. The single rustic bar and adjoining room have a mix of old chairs, pine settles and kitchen tables laid out on flagstoned floors. A few old prints adorn the walls and in winter a good log fire warms the bar. The pub is owned by the head brewer of Moles Brewery, so expect the full range of Moles ales as well as welcome guest beers, all kept in tip-top condition. On sunny, clear days space is at a premium on the two-level, flower-tub and bench-filled terrace, from where an unrivalled view of some 25 miles across the Avon Valley can be appreciated. On still summer evenings hot-air balloons can often be seen drifting across the sky. *Free House.* **Beer** *Moles Ales: Landlord's choice, Cask Bitter, IPA, Brew 97, guest beers. Garden, outdoor eating, children's play area. Pub closed 25 Dec. No credit cards.*

Bowland Bridge   Hare & Hounds

Tel 015395 68333	**B&B**
Bowland Bridge nr Grange-over-Sands Cumbria LA11 6NN	Map 4 C4

Truly rural, good-looking old inn owned by ex-international soccer player Peter Thompson. The bar successfully blends ancient and modern, with its rough stone walls, discreet farming bric-a-brac and simple wooden furniture; open fires spread warmth in winter weather. The dramatically high-ceilinged dining room is for residents only; the residents' lounge is rather more chintzy. Bedrooms are immaculately kept, beamy, floral, and on the small side. Delightful garden. *Pub open 11-11 (Sun to 10.30). Free House.* **Beer** *Tetley, Boddingtons. Garden, outdoor eating, children's play area.* **Accommodation** *16 bedrooms, 13 en suite, £46 (single £33). Children welcome overnight (under-2s stay free in parents' room, 5-12s £5, over-5s £10), additional beds and cots available. Access, Visa.*

Box   Bayly's

Tel 01225 743622	**FOOD**
	B&B
High Street Box nr Corsham Wiltshire SN14 9NA	Map 14 B2

Jan and George Gynn run this solid-looking Bath stone inn, standing four-square on the A4 Bath to Chippenham road, which was named after the pub's first landlord in the early 1600s, Jacob Bayly, whose last will and testament hangs to this day behind the bar. Most noteworthy of its many period features is a magnificent open stone fireplace, and among recent additions the circular pool table is quite a talking point. The greater part of the premises, however, is given over to eating, with speedy, informal service to its neatly laid tables. From a daily-changing blackboard, lunch dishes may well include Wiltshire ham with egg and chips (£2.95), chili con carne (£3.95) or a toasted club sandwich (£1.50). The comprehensive fixed menu offers a wider selection of Stilton & pork paté (£2.75), seafood platter (£3.95), liver and bacon (£4.95) or beef stew and dumplings (£4.75) with, to follow, the Vicar's Tart (almond and fruit flan – £2.25) and Wiltshire Whitepot (creamed bread-and-butter pudding £2.25). Jan's cooking is highly popular, and at peak times it is a busy, lively place. For peace and quiet, and for weary travellers, Bayly's offers three bedrooms, all with neat en-suite WCs and showers, colour TV and beverage trays. *Bar food & Restaurant Meals 12-1.45, 7-9. Free House.* *Beer Wadworth 6X, Bass, guest beers in summer. Garden.* *Accommodation 3 bedrooms, all en-suite, £45 (single £27.50). Children welcome overnight (0-3yrs free if sharing parents' room), additional beds & cots available. Small dogs only. No credit cards.*

Bradford-on-Avon   Bunch of Grapes

Tel 01225 863877	**FOOD**
14 Silver Street Bradford-on-Avon Wiltshire BA15 1JY	Map 14 B3

Appropriately, given its name, but somewhat incongruously for a town-centre pub, there is a grapevine clinging to the outside of the Bunch of Grapes. The pub was once a shop, and has a little bow window which now houses a copy of the blackboard menu and also, more often than not, the pub cat having a doze in the sunshine. Old enough that its true age is shrouded in mystery, an old indenture records that the Grapes changed hands in 1846 for £300. It's long and narrow with red hessian walls above dark brown dado panelling, and the decor is unpretentiously old rather than of the style known as olde worlde. It strives to keep the balance firmly on that of a pub that also serves food rather than becoming only a complete 'dining' pub, and stocks the selection of Smiles beers drawn up from the cellar by a genuine 1890s brass and porcelain beer engine. What's on the blackboard menu depends on the whim of the landlady, Lynne Cater. Stilton and cauliflower soup (£1.50), steak and kidney pie (£4.95), cheese and onion pie (£3.75) and, if your luck is in, a pie made from fruits from the garden – greengage and apple or gooseberry and elderflower. Smiles Brewery. *Bar Food 11.30-2, 6.30-8.45 (Sun to 7).* *Beer Smiles, guest beer. Access, Visa.*

Bradley Green   Malt Shovel Inn

Tel 01278 653432	**B&B**
Blackmoor Lane Bradley Green nr Cannington Somerset TA5 2NE	Map 13 E1

Located beside a tiny lane just outside Cannington, this rambling 300-year-old pub enjoys a peaceful rural position surrounded by open farmland. Traditional homely interior with settles and sturdy elm tables and chairs in the main bar and a cosy snug bar with quarry-tiled floor. Bedrooms are clean and comfortable – one being a spacious family room – with modern furnishings, TVs, tea-makers and views across open fields to the Quantock Hills; their proximity making this a natural base from which to explore. Non en-suite rooms share adequate bathroom and toilet facilities. Good, safe garden. *Beer Butcombe, John Smith's. Garden, outdoor eating. Family room.* *Accommodation 4 bedrooms, 1 en suite, £36 (single £19.50). Children welcome overnight (cot age stay free in parents' room, family room £42). Accommodation closed 24-26 Dec. No credit cards.*

Bramdean   **Fox Inn**

Tel 01962 771363	**FOOD**

Bramdean nr Alresford Hampshire SO24 0LP   Map 15 D3

Attractive 400-year-old white weatherboarded pub set back from the
main road (A272). Inside is extensively modernised, and very much
dining-orientated, but well-kept and comfortable. Good lunchtime bar
food is simple with such dishes as beef stroganoff (£7.95) and fresh
cod (£6.95). The evening menu is more restauranty with fillet steaks
accompanied by a choice of sauces (£10.95) and fresh fish from
Portsmouth (halibut fillet mornay £6.95); for dessert, home-made
puddings like pavlova, crème brulée and treacle tart are offered. Six
cheeses are available at any one time – Meldon (with beer & onions),
St Illtyd, Rutland, Cotswold, Cheddar, Stilton and Brie might make
up a typical platter. No children under 14 inside, but there's a large
garden at the rear and patio in front. *Bar Food & Restaurant Meals*
12-2, 7-9. Beer Marston's Pedigree & Bitter. Garden, outdoor eating,
children's play area. Access, Visa.

Branscombe   **Masons Arms**

Tel 0129780 300 Fax 0129780 500	**FOOD**
	B&B

Branscombe nr Seaton Devon EX12 3DJ   Map 13 E2

Picturesque Branscombe lies in a steep valley, deep in National Trust
land and only a ten minute walk away from the sea. Occupying most
of the village centre is this delightful 14th-century, creeper-clad inn
and its neighbouring terraces of cottages, which house most of the
comfortable bedrooms. Beyond the pretty front terrace is a most
charming bar with stone walls and floors, an assortment of old settles
and a huge inglenook with open fire, which not only warms the bar
but, throughout the winter, also cooks the spit-roasts offered on
Thursdays as well as the suckling pig suppers, served once a month.
Alternative and reliably cooked bar food from the regular menu
includes steak and kidney pudding (£5.75), duck and bacon pie
(£5.80) and fresh tagliatelle with a spinach, garlic, mushroom and
cheese sauce (£5.10), as well as decent ploughman's, choice of fresh
fish – sea bass (£6.10), lemon sole (£7.10) – and possibly crab and
lobster caught off the beach that morning. An interesting selection
of Devon cheeses is generally available. The attractive and tastefully
decorated restaurant has an old-world ambience and is a relaxing
room in which to enjoy a set dinner (3-course with lobster is £24,
with medallions of venison £19 and with baked wild salmon £20).
Exposed beams and the odd piece of antique furniture add to the
charm of attractive bedrooms in the inn and nearby old cottages.
All but three have en-suite facilities, while TVs, telephones and
clock/radios are standard throughout. Tea and coffee have to be
ordered and delivered to your room (at an extra charge); standards of
housekeeping in some of the rooms could be improved. No under-14s
in the bar. Conference facilities. *Bar Food 12-2, 7-9.30. Restaurant*
Meals 12-2 (Sun only), 7-9.30. Free House. Beer Bass, Wadworth 6X,
Dartmoor Best. Terrace, outdoor eating. Accommodation 20 bedrooms,
19 en suite, from £54 (single from £22). Children welcome overnight
(under-10s £10), additional beds & cots (£3.50) supplied. Access, Visa.

Brassington   **Ye Olde Gate**

Tel 01629 540448   **A**

Well Street Brassington Derbyshire DE4 4HJ   Map 6 C3

Revered by generations of pub-goers for its resolute resistance to change, two tiny rooms with a convivial atmosphere (accentuated by communal-sized tables) are hung everywhere with pewter tankards, copper pans and Toby jugs; big log fires in winter. They'll sell you a filled baguette (£3.15-£3.95), a 'hero' (£4.50) or 'submarine' (£5.95) to keep hunger at bay. No under-10s indoors. Ramshackle rear garden. *Beer Marston's. Garden, outdoor eating, barbecues. No credit cards. Closed Monday lunchtime (except Bank Holidays).*

Braunston   **Blue Ball Inn**

Tel 01572 722135   **FOOD**

6 Cedar Street Braunston Oakham Leicestershire LE15 8QS   Map 7 E4

The Blue Ball of its title represents previous obfuscation of the inn sign of the 'Globe' pub, which has stood in Braunston since the early 1600s. Reconversion to its former state, full of beams, inglenooks and crannies by the creative Celia and Colin Crawford is a masterpiece, and the food is nothing short of ambitious. Throughout the bars, menus of avocado Stilton (£3.50), spare ribs (£4.95) and vegetable cannelloni (£4.95) are supplemented by blackboards proclaiming warm goat's cheese salad (£3.50) and grilled sea bass on a bed of fennel (£9.50). A restaurant at the less frenetic end has a table d'hote menu at £13.95 for three courses – the food is very good, and the atmosphere of a quaint thatched village pub has been carefully retained. *Bar & Restaurant Food 12-2.30, 7-10 (Sun till 9.30). Free House. Beer Worthington, Bass, Marston Pedigree, guest beer. Access, Diners, Visa.*

Braunston   **The Old Plough**

Tel 01572 722714   Fax 01572 770382   **FOOD**

Church Street Braunston Leicestershire LE15 8QY   Map 7 E4

Well-regarded local innkeepers Amanda and Andrew Reid have brought a wealth of experience also to their tastefully modernised inn on the fringe of the village. Healthy eating options and vegetarian alternatives (mushroom and walnut cannelloni £6.95) are well interspersed throughout a menu encompassing 'famous Plough crusties' (large granary filled rolls from £1.95) through salads and steaks to chef Nick Quinn's specials. Chicken, leek and bacon pie (£6.50) or salmon and asparagus filo (£8.25) arrive with chef's potatoes of the day and crisp, fresh vegetables. Avoid, if you can, predictable fruit and ice cream concoctions for dessert in favour of the home-made crème brulée or chocolate rum truffle tarte. With light lunches on the terrace and candle-lit dining in the picturesque conservatory a sense of occasion is easily engendered; somewhat giving lie, perhaps, to the claim that two competing yet complementary pubs cannot co-exist in one small village. *Bar Food 12-2, 7-10 (Sun till 9.30). Children allowed in bar to eat for lunch only, children's menu. Free House. Beer Theakston XB & Old Peculier, guest beers. Garden, outdoor eating. Family Room. Access, Diners, Visa.*

Brearton   Malt Shovel

Tel 01423 862929	**FOOD**
Brearton nr Harrogate North Yorkshire HG3 3BX	Map 6 C1

A true family affair, this tiny yet unspoiled village pub where Marion
Parsons and her daughter Joanne continue into their second decade in
the kitchen while the cheerful and chatty young Landlord, son Leigh,
runs the bar single-handed dispensing interesting and well-kept North
Yorkshire ales including the novel "Fool's Gold". Short daily
blackboard menus display a healthy streak of invention in their
planning while the care and pride taken in preparation shine through
to the plate. Vegetarian dishes (mushroom stroganoff; nut roast with
tomato and mint sauce £4.50) appear especially prominent, their
accompanying salads generously filled out, perhaps, with pasta curls
and dotted with pine kernels. Generously parsleyed white sauce
accompanies both roast ham (£4.50) and smoked hake (£5.50);
haddock fillets are given a spicy Cajun coating (£5.50), the steak pie
cooked in red wine with plenty of mushrooms (£4.50). Good fresh
vegetables in generous quantities and all home-made puddings (toffee
and apple pie perhaps) with custard or cream, are further confirmation
(if any were needed) of a kitchen that cares. *Free House.* **Bar Food**
12-2, 7-9 (closed Sun eve & all Mon). **Beer** *North Yorkshire – Fool's
Gold, Theakston Best & Mild, Daleside Old Mill, Morland Old Speckled
Hen, guest beer. Garden, outdoor eating area. Family room. Pub closed
Mondays. No credit cards.*

Brendon   Stag Hunters Hotel

Tel 015987 222	**FOOD**
	B&B
Brendon nr Lynton Devon EX35 1PS	Map 13 D1

Nestling beside the East Lyn River deep in the Doone Valley, this
friendly family-run hotel makes a good base for guests wishing to
explore Exmoor. Adequate overnight accommodation in 12 neatly
kept en-suite rooms which are kitted-out with varying styles of
furniture plus TVs and tea-makers. Comfortable residents' lounge.
Homely, simply furnished bars offering a short menu of home-cooked
fare, such as steak and kidney pie (£5.75), cottage pie, trout pan-fried
with garlic and capers (both £5.50) and good snacks like ploughman's
and filled French sticks. Chicken in red wine with good vegetables or
home-made pork pie with salad may feature on the specials board.
Popular riverside garden. *Pub open 11-11 (except Sun) Mar-Nov (closed
for 2hrs winter afternoons).* **Bar Food** *11am-9.30pm (Sun 12-2, 7-9.30).
Free House.* **Beer** *Butcombe, Tetley, Staghunters (Burtons). Garden,
outdoor eating. Family room.* **Accommodation** *12 bedrooms, 11 en suite,
from £54 (single £30). Children welcome overnight (under-14s stay free
in parents' room). Access, Diners, Visa.*

Brereton Green   Bears Head Hotel

Tel 01477 535251 Fax 01477 535888	**FOOD**
	B&B
Brereton Green nr Sandbach Cheshire CW11 9RS	Map 6 B2

Fronted by the original half-timbered inn (which dates from 1615, if
not earlier), this celebrated roadhouse alongside the A50 has expanded
into a collection of buildings. Panels of wattle and daub, carefully
preserved and displayed in the bar, are evidence of the building's
longevity and, despite the many more recent extensions, its inglenook
fireplaces and oak beams hung with horse brasses still have lots of old-
fashioned charm. Today's pub, run by the Tarquini family for some

30 years, is divided into cosy alcoves by means of cleverly placed original timbers and panels, and is full of the fragrance of ubiquitous fresh flowers. Burtonwood Bitter and Bass are the bonuses for beer drinkers. Lunchtime and evening bar food is both stylish and substantial, ranging from open sandwiches (£3.95-£5.95) with salad to satisfying hot dishes like lamb chops in rosemary and garlic butter (£5.25) with seasonal vegetables, or grilled fillet of plaice Caprice (£5.25); daily specialities typically feature medallions of lamb in black bean sauce (£4.95), a roast (£5.95) or cold poached salmon with salad (£4.95). By night the restaurant evokes the stuff of dinner dates and anniversaries tinged with more than a hint of déjà-vu: spumantes and pink champagnes are popped in discreetly hidden corners, while dishes are prepared lovingly at your table. Mammoth desserts (£2.25 in bar/£3.25 in restaurant) arrive by trolley. And so to bed where practical considerations for the business traveller generally take precedence over romance, with formica-topped, dual-purpose dressing tables and work spaces, television, radio, dial-out phones and trouser presses. Choice of eight wines by the glass available. *Bar Food 12-2, 7-10.* *Restaurant Meals 12.30-2, 7.30-10 (except Sun eve). Children allowed in the bar to eat, children's menu. Free House.* *Beer Bass, Burtonwood Best, Courage Directors, guest beer. Patio/terrace, outdoor eating.* *Accommodation 24 bedrooms, all en suite, from £52.50 (luxury suite £65, single £35). No dogs. Access, Visa.*

Bretforton   Fleece Inn

| Tel 01386 831173 | A |

The Cross Bretforton nr Evesham Hereford & Worcester WR11 5JE   Map 14a A1

The stone, thatch and half-timbered Fleece has been owned by the National Trust since 1977, bequeathed by retiring landlady Lola Taplin on strict condition that the pub remained unaltered, and potato crisps weren't sold. It stands out today as a living, yet very lived-in, museum whose three interior rooms, the Brewhouse, the Dugout and the smoking-free Pewter Room (with unique pewter collection), are now preserved for posterity. Regular hand-pulled real ales such as Hook Norton and Brew XI are always supplemented by guests – including Uley's Fat Bastard, specially brewed for the Fleece. Every July the pub stages it's own beer festival. Children get a look in, except in the tiny bar, and are catered for superbly outside: there's a thatched heraldic barn, barbecue, extensive orchard garden and adventure playground. The wealth of hanging baskets and flower-filled stone tubs which adorn the central flagged and pebbled yard are an absolute picture in summer. *Free House.* *Beers Hook Norton Best, M&B Brew XI, guest beers. Garden, outdoor eating area. No credit cards.*

Bridgnorth   Down Inn

| Tel 0174 635624 | FOOD |

Ludlow Road Bridgnorth Shropshire WV16 6HA   Map 6 B4

There's always a friendly welcome at this 250-year-old pub, a couple of miles south of town on the B4364. Rough stone walls and baronial-style leather chairs add to the generally characterful atmosphere. Very much a family affair, with father-in-law behind the bar and Paul and Beverley Millington's own youngsters about the place, signalling that this is a genuinely child-friendly place (children's menu and portions plus high-chairs available). Paul Millington is the keen cook whose printed menu is almost doubled by the day's blackboard specials that major on his favourite fish and game: ploughman's (£2.95), baguettes (from £2.60), deep-fried potato skins (£2.90), beefsteak and kidney pie (£6.90), vegetable tikka masala (£7.85), marlin steak with herbed olive oil (£7.35), guinea fowl with winer and grapes (£7.85), spotted Dick and tiramisu (all puds £2.75) show the range. Over a dozen different English farmhouse cheeses on offer, too (£2.75 with biscuits and celery). *Bar Food 12-2 (Sun to 3), 6.30-9.30 (Sat to 10). Children allowed in bar to eat, children's menu. Free House. Beer Constantly changing – five at any one time, perhaps Bass, Marston's Pedigree, Morland Old Speckled Hen, Ruddles County, Young's. Patio, outdoor eating. Family room. Pub closed Sun evenings. Access, Visa.*

Bridgnorth   Falcon Hotel

Tel 01746 763134 Fax 01746 7655401	**B&B**
St John Street Lowton Bridgnorth Shropshire WV15 6AS	Map 6 B4

As its address suggests, the 16th-century Falcon, a former coaching inn, stands at the bottom of town only yards from the Severn river crossing: points east are the Midland Water Museum, the Stourbridge (A458) and Wolverhampton roads (A454). The main bar has been opened out and brightened up, with a single service counter, decent real ales, a large area devoted to food (including a salad bar) and a family area. Bedrooms have similarly been improved; all are now en suite and the TVs, telephones and beverage trays are standard. There's a large family bedroom, in several others there is room for an extra bed, and cots are available. *Free House. Beer Bass, guest ale. Family room. Accommodation 15 bedrooms (all en suite), £46 (single £39). Children welcome overnight (under-10s stay free in parents' room), additional beds and cots available. Access, Diners, Visa.*

Bridport   Bull Hotel

Tel 01308 22878	**B&B**
34 East Street Bridport Dorset DT6 3LF	Map 13 F2

This white-painted 16th-century coaching inn stands in the historic town centre. A traditional relaxing interior includes a convivial bar and a comfortably furnished reception area and lounge. Across the courtyard is a large function room and bar which attracts local bands and a good following at weekends. There are 22 bedrooms, 13 of which have full en-suite facilities. Rooms are light, clean and functional and decorated in soothing pastel shades and attractive fabrics. Modern cream-coloured units, TVs and beverage-making facilities are standard throughout. *Bar Food & Restaurant Meals 10.30-2.30, 7-9. Children's menu. Beer Bass, Flowers Original, IPA, Castle Eden Ale. Courtyard for outdoor eating. Snooker room. Accommodation 22 bedrooms, 13 en suite, £44 (single £36). Children welcome overnight. Additional beds (6-14yrs – £14) and cots available. Access, Diners, Visa.*

Bridport   George Hotel

	FOOD
Tel 01308 23187	**B&B**
4 South Street Bridport Dorset DT6 3NQ	Map 13 F2

The George has been spruced up in the past year, yet it still retains the delightful eccentric air that makes it so popular. A handsome Georgian building located opposite the Town Hall, it opens its doors at 8.30am for continental breakfast – excellent coffee and croissants – served in the relaxing and informal main bar and tiny dining room. Old-fashioned in style with Regency-style wallpaper, Victorian-style red

Zzz...

painted bar and oil paintings on the walls, it is filled with soothing classical music during the day and often louder jazz and opera in the evenings. Reliable bar food is produced from the kitchen – on view – at one end of the bar. The regular menu lists excellent snacks such as croque monsieur (from £3), curry and rice (£4.75), chicken breast in cream, mushroom and calvados sauce (£3.50), home-made paté (£2.25) and a variety of omelettes (from £3.75). Daily specials feature fish fresh from West Bay – lemon sole stuffed with crab in a cream and vermouth sauce (£3.95) – and might also include soft herring roe on toast (£2.75), home-made ham, chicken and mushroom pie (£3.25) and vegetarian stuffed pepper (£2.75). Vegetables, salads and potatoes are charged separately (£2.20). The full range of Palmers ales are dispensed on handpump and as the brewery is only just down the road, all are in tip-top condition. Four modest bedrooms share a bathroom and toilet. *Bar Food 12-2, 7-9.30 (No food L Sun, Bank Holidays, winter month evenings by arrangement). Children's portions available. Beer Bridport Bitter, Palmers IPA, Tally Ho. Family room. Accommodation 4 bedrooms, £37 (single £18.50). Children welcome overnight, cots available. Access, Visa.*

Brighton   The Greys

Tel 01273 680734	**FOOD**
105 Southover Street Brighton East Sussex BN2 2UA	**Map 11 B6**

Climb from the Old Steine towards Kemp Town to find this gem of a dining pub with just one bar and a few tables laid for lunchtime eating. Piped classical music, just one shared, handwritten menu and abounding enthusiasm set the tone. A short, daily-changing menu is provided by Belgian chef Jean-Paul Salpetier, and served with enthusiasm by the staff. Starters might include mushrooms with garlic and fresh herbs (£2.95), whitebait with chili, fennel and garlic oil (£3.50) or cassolette of snails and mushrooms with a pastis sauce (£3.50). Main courses are equally interesting: Mediterranean salad with king prawns and avocado (£5.95), Oriental-style sirloin steak with crispy noodles (£6.25) or perfectly cooked pigeon breasts with a cranberry and vodka sauce (£6.95). Good desserts (mainly from the deep freeze) such as iced soufflé with fresh cherries. Tuesday evening is Supper Club theme night, providing a table d'hote menu for £16.95 – each month a different area of the world is featured. Visitors are entertained with live jazz, blues or Latin music on Sunday lunchtimes and Monday evenings. No children under 14. *Open 11-11 Sat, regular hours other days. Bar Food 12-2.30 (not Sun), 7.30-9 (Tue & Wed only, bookings only on Tue). Beer Flowers Original, Fuller's London Pride, guest beer changes every 3-4 months. Patio/terrace, outdoor eating. No credit cards.*

Brightwell Baldwin   Lord Nelson

Tel 01491 612497	**FOOD**
Brightwell Baldwin nr Watlington Oxon OX9 5NP	**Map 14a C3**

Already a couple of hundred years old when it was named after Admiral Nelson – the pub's name was changed to Lord Nelson when England's most famous sailor was elevated to the peerage – some later additions to the original stone buildings include 18th-century gable ends and a quaint verandah at the front, where it faces the village church of a sleepy hamlet. Inside it is immediately clear that this is a 'dining' pub; half is set up as a restaurant and raffia place mats on the remaining tables are ready to receive the bar snacks. The wine list features around 50 bins including some interesting New World wines and Chateau Musar from Lebanon; some of the wines are offered on a 'dipstick' method, i.e. a full bottle is offered and customers may consume as much as they like (as long as it's at least half!). Peter Meal is the man behind the bar while partner Richard Britcliffe is in the kitchen preparing the food. The restaurant menu (also available in the bar) ranges from smoked salmon (£7.25), garlic mushrooms with bacon (£3.75) and steak and kidney pie (£7.50) to pear belle Hélène (£3.50) and guinea fowl with a creamy cider and onion sauce (£10.50). The more snacky bar menu might include Welsh rarebit (£5.25), pasta dishes and ploughman's lunch (£4.75). There's a patio with tables for summer eating and a pretty garden overhung by a large weeping willow. The pub reopened in 1974 after having been closed for nearly 70 years because the local squire disapproved of strong drink. Pub not suitable for children under 8. **Bar Food & Restaurant Meals** 12-2, 7-10 (except Sun eve). Free House. **Beer** Brakspear. Patio, outdoor eating. Pub closed Sun eve. Access, Diners, Visa.

Brimfield	**The Roebuck** ★	**FOOD**
Tel 01584 711230 Fax 01584 711654		**B&B**
Poppies Restaurant Brimfield nr Ludlow Shropshire SY8 4NE		Map 14 A1

There's no more individual a pub in these parts than the Roebuck, and no finer pub restaurant than this one, Poppies. Whether it's a pub with a restaurant, or a restaurant with rooms doesn't really matter because it remains the village local. Indeed, the public bar retains just that atmosphere, whereas the lounge bar, a characterful room with a 15th-century beamed ceiling and dark oak panels, could be the restaurant. It isn't – there's a separate dining room which has recently been refurbished from a bright and cheery room with parquet floor and cane-back chairs into a more chintzy style, in keeping with the rest of the building. You can now book tables in the lounge bar, where Carole Evans's food can also be enjoyed at a fraction of the restaurant price. Her command of composition and subtle blends of colour and flavour are frankly bewildering for one who is self-taught: fried chicken livers on a brioche (£5.50), old-fashioned steak and kidney pie (£7), spinach, pine kernel and cream cheese filo pastry pie with tomato and basil sauce (£6.25) and baked queen scallops stuffed with mushroom and garlic butter (£7) have all featured recently in the bar menu. Meanwhile, in the restaurant, diners can enjoy lobster ravioli with lemon grass (£9), fresh local asparagus served with a red and yellow pepper bavarois (£8), fillet of Hereford beef with walnuts and shallots (£18.50) or roast fillet of brill stuffed with mushrooms with a light leek and vermouth sauce (£18). The set lunch offers three courses for £18. There's a comprehensive list of hot and cold desserts to follow – try the fresh lemon tart (£5.50) – and some fourteen cheeses from a Hereford Hop to faraway Cashel Blue. The excellent wine list has a large selection of half bottles. And then, if you're wise enough to choose to stay, there are three lovely cottage bedrooms (two doubles with showers and a twin with full bathroom) to choose from. Here, you'll find home-made biscuits, cake, cafetière coffee and quality teas, an example of the care you're likely to receive. A wonderful country breakfast, including Herefordshire apple juice, honey from the garden and Carole's home-made sausages, will set you up for the day and set the seal on a memorable stay. **Bar Food & Restaurant Meals** (no food Sun & Mon) 12-2, 7-10.

Children allowed in bar to eat. Free House. **Beer** *Wood's, Hobson's'
Speckled Hen. Patio/terrace, outdoor eating.* **Accommodation** *3 bedrooms,
all en suite, £60. Children welcome overnight. Check-in by arrangement.
Pub and accommodation closed one week in Oct, fortnight in Feb.
Access, Visa.*

Brinkworth — **Three Crowns**

Tel 01666 510366

Brinkworth nr Chippenham Wiltshire SN15 5AF

FOOD

Map 14 C2

Set back from the road, close to the village church and green, this old
stone pub draws a discerning clientele from miles around, who seek
out the unusual and often adventurous dishes that are listed on the
comprehensive blackboard menu. Diners can sit in the main bar,
furnished with a variety of old and new pine and featuring two
remarkable tables created from huge 18th-century bellows, or they
can relax in the new light, airy and tastefully pine-furnished
conservatory extension, which overlooks the tree- and shrub-bordered
garden. Food is taken very seriously here, the selection of freshly
prepared dishes changing regularly, depending on the seasonal
availability of produce. Ambitious and elaborately described main
courses embrace a variety of meat and fish accompanied by inventive
sauces and at least six crisply-cooked vegetables – portions are
extremely generous and not for the faint-hearted. Results and
presentation are consistently good. On a recent visit venison
medallions came 'lightly sautéed with bacon, wild mushrooms and
served in a claret sauce, finished with redcurrants' (£11.75), duck was
'roasted and thinly sliced, served with fresh strawberries in a rich
redcurrant sauce' (£11.95) and halibut supreme was 'served in a
summer sauce of white wine and cream with a shredded lettuce,
tomato and cucumber garnish and a king prawn' (£12.45). Those
palates desiring plainer fare will not be disappointed: the menu may
include hearty pies, such as, steak and kidney, venison, veal and
mushroom (all £7.95), a range of steaks and salads plus a couple of
imaginative vegetarian dishes. Lighter 'big' bites are offered at
lunchtime, including filled giant potatoes (from £5), ploughman's
(from £4.95) and a selection of filled double-decker rolls (from
£1.50). Delicious home-made puddings may include Swiss chocolate
terrine, honey and yoghurt cheesecake, banana pancake (£2.95-£3.25)
and a range of ice creams (£2.95) made on the premises. To
accompany your meal there is a list of 32 competitively priced wines.
Bar Food *12-2, 6.30-9.30 (Sun 7-9.30). Children's menu and portions
available.* **Beer** *Flowers Original, Brakspear's Bitter, Bass, Boddingtons,
Wadworth 6X. Garden, outdoor eating. Access, Visa.*

Brisley — **Bell**

Tel 01362 668686

The Green Brisley Norfolk NR20 5DW

FOOD

Map 10 C1

Enjoying a magnificent, isolated position set back from B1145 and just
200 yards from the village centre, this attractive, 16th-century warm
brick-built pub overlooks the largest piece of common land in
Norfolk, some 200 acres. Small, refurbished bar area with old beams,
large brick fireplace and exposed brick walls, plus a separate, neatly
laid up dining room. Emphasis on the extensive blackboard menus,
especially the restaurant board, is on fresh fish (from £8.50) delivered
regularly from Lowestoft. Choose wisely from the bar food board and
printed list for a value-for-money, home-cooked meal. Chips are

evident, but there is the option for potatoes and generally well-cooked fresh vegetables. Dishes range from fresh asparagus (£3.95), freshly prepared mushroom soup (£1.85) and chicken liver paté (£2.95) to fresh salmon and hollandaise (£4.95), crab mornay (£4.75), lamb and vegetable lasagne (£4.05) and steak and kidney pie (£4.50). Puddings (£1.85) include apple pie and summer pudding. Sunny front patio and benches by the pond for fine weather alfresco eating. *Whitbread.* **Bar Food** *12-2.30 (to 3 Sat), 6-9.30.* **Beer** *Marston's Pedigree, Flowers IPA.* **Beer** *Garden, outdoor eating area.*

Bristol Highbury Vaults

Tel 0117 973 3203	**A**
164 St Michael's Hill Kingsdown Bristol Avon BS2 8DE	**Map 13 F1**

A serious contender for Bristol's busiest pub, close to the University and Infirmary, thus popular with students and nurses. The tiny front snug bar and rear bar as well as the walled patio at the back are all often crowded with young people who seem to enjoy the odd libation. No children indoors. *Open 12-11 Mon-Sat.* **Beer** *Smiles Exhibition, Best & Brewery, Brains, Stout (in winter), London Pride, guest beers. Patio, weekly barbecues closed 25 & 26 Dec. No credit cards.*

Broad Campden Bakers Arms

Tel 01386 840515	**FOOD**
Broad Campden nr Chipping Campden Gloucestershire GL55 6UR	**Map 14a A1**

Mid-way by road between Chipping Campden and Blockley, the pub stands at a convenient junction for walkers following the Heart of England Way. Real ales, real fires and "real food" are the promised order of the day. Of the first, seven are on tap at any one time, with up-coming guest ales ("at a pump near you") prominently displayed. Log fires burn when required at each end of the single bar; space can be limited here in poor weather. Real enough, the food is varied and invariably prepared to order with consequent delays: be sure to take a table number when ordering if sitting outside. Most ambitious are the daily specials: pancake cannelloni (£3.50) beef in beer casserole (£4.25) and chicken tikka masala (£4.50). Less adventurously, perhaps, herby tomato soup, chili con carne and apple pie will just leave change from £6. Good vegetarian choice. Family weekends (July), folk music nights, beer festivals and a hot air balloon meeting are annual events. **Bar Food** *12-2, 6-9.45 (Sun 7-8.45). Children allowed in bar to eat until 7.30pm. Free House. Children allowed in bar to eat.* **Beer** *Stanney, Old Speckled Hen, Donnington SBA, Theakston Best & XB, up to 5 guest beers. Garden, outdoor eating, children's play area. No credit cards.*

Broad Chalke Queens Head Inn

Tel 01722 780344	**B&B**
Broad Chalke nr Salisbury Wiltshire SP5 5EN	**Map 14 C3**

This homely stone-built village inn, located close to a meandering chalk stream in the Ebble valley, was once a bakehouse and stables before becoming an alehouse and outlasting the three other inns that once existed in the parish. The main Village bar has stone walls, a beamed ceiling and a large inglenook, but the place to sit on fine days is in the sheltered rear courtyard, amid the honeysuckle and roses. With doors leading off the courtyard is the modern brick-built accommodation, which houses four light and spacious bedrooms, all of which are in good order offering en-suite facilities, tea-making kits, remote-control TVs and direct-dial telephones. One non-smoking bar. *Open 12-11 (Sun to 10.30). Free House. **Beer** Badger Best, Wadworth 6X, Bass, Hook Norton. Courtyard. **Accommodation** 4 bedrooms, £45 (single £22.50). Children welcome overnight (£5), additional beds available. No dogs. Access, Visa.*

Broadhembury   Drewe Arms

Tel 01404 841267   **FOOD**

Broadhembury Devon EX14 0NF   Map 13 E2

Dating back to the 15th century, the small, thatched, Drewe Arms has a charmingly rustic feel with dado-boarded walls, a pile of old magazines next to the inglenook fireplace (with real log fire), various rural artifacts and a warm, convivial atmosphere created by Nigel and Kerstin Burge. The blackboard bar snack menu majors on open sandwiches – 'prawns in a crowd' (£4.25), Stilton and sirloin steak (£4.95), gravad lax with dill and mustard sauce (£4.25) plus good fresh seafood: hake with spicy tomato sauce (£5.15), red mullet with garlic (£8.25) and half a lobster (£10.25). There are also various ploughman's, soups of the day and puds like treacle tart and chocolate marquise (both at £2.50). Everything is freshly cooked and served in generous portions in unfussy style. *Bar Food 12-2, 7-10 (except Sun eve). Free House. **Beer** Otter Bitter, Ale, Head & Bride. Garden, outdoor eating. No credit cards.*

Brockhampton   Craven Arms

Tel 01242 820410   **FOOD**

Brockhampton Gloucestershire GL54 5XQ   Map 14a B1

A deservedly popular pub hidden down winding lanes deep in the rolling Gloucestershire countryside: Brockhampton is 2 miles north of the A436 Cheltenham to Gloucester road. Approached under a stone lych gate, the garden extends to an enclosed paddock with a children's play area which includes a small summer house containing games for soggier days. Revealed within the Craven Arms are stone-flagged floors and a warren of rooms given over primarily to eating. Real ales are well represented in the bar, where the less adventurous may order broccoli and walnut quiche (£5.95) and steak sandwiches with chips (£4.95). The daily blackboard menu, though, is the thing to go for, chicken in Stilton sauce (£7.50), poached salmon with lemon and thyme (£8.75) or Dundee lamb (£7.75) representing both quality and value. Puddings are the old favourites – sticky toffee, banoffi pie or chocolate fudge cake with chocolate rum sauce (all £2.75). Dining tables are predominantly pine, their evening adornment of fresh carnations and candles quite in keeping with the pub's relaxed environment: the girls who serve are friendly and informal too. *Bar Food & Restaurant Meals 12.30-2, 7-9.30. Free House. **Beer** Butcombe, Hook Norton, Wadworth 6X. Garden, outdoor eating, children's play area. Access, Visa.*

Brockton   Feathers

Tel & Fax 0174 636 202   **FOOD**

Brockton nr Much Wenlock Shropshire TF13 6JR   Map 6 B4

The historic Feathers stands at a crossroads on the B4378 Much Wenlock to Craven Arms road, signed left to Bridgnorth and right to Church Stretton. Deceptively small outside, it's half-timbered at one end and stone-clad to the rear, where the entrance leads via a picturesque patio through the conservatory. Inside, it divides into an intimate public bar where one corner table is formed by a huge bellows on legs, and three interconnecting rooms, on two levels, are devoted largely to eating. Martin and Andrea Hayward's food is commendable for both its quality and diversity. A two-page handwritten menu is supplemented by an extensive range of blackboard specials: fresh asparagus in season (£2.95), mussels (£4.25) and mushroom tortiglioni (£4.25). Of more substantial stuff are main courses, including rack of pork (£7.95) or salmon and crab meat in filo pastry (£8.95) and marinated duck breast in oyster and chili sauce (£9.25). Traditional puddings (£2.45) are guaranteed to fill up every remaining corner. Beer-drinkers will enjoy a good pint of hand-pulled Banks's bitter, house wine comes by the bottle, glass or goblet, there are half a dozen each of named reds and whites by the bottle, and coffee arrives in a cafetière. Andrea's kitchen hand-bell announces when each cooked-to-order dish is ready, ensuring prompt delivery to tables; salad and garnishes are generous and Martin arrives equally promptly with the two-pint jug of home-made dressing. *Bar Food 12-2 (except), 6.30-9.30 (Sun 7-9). Children allowed in bar to eat/children's menu. Free House. Beer Banks's Bitter, Camerons Strongarm. Patio. Pub closed Monday. No credit cards.*

Bromham   Greyhound Inn

Tel 01380 850241	**FOOD**
Bromham nr Chippenham Wiltshire SN15 2HA	**Map 14 B3**

Just three miles from Devizes Locks (longest set of locks in Europe), this lively Wadworth's pub is run with enthusiasm and verve. Parts of it go back 300 years – in the more recent bar extension, an old well still remains in the middle of the room. The menu is often ingenious, featuring fine Malaysian dishes, e.g. fiery pork. There are two dining-rooms seating 18 and 50 respectively but everyone eats everywhere in the Greyhound – beef in red wine (£6.40), chicken in cream and vinegar (£5.90) and steak and kidney pie (£5.10), with a summer fish menu featuring red snapper (£6.10), Dover sole (£11.50) and whole crab salad (£6), and on Sunday the roast lunch main course is £4.95. Tons of atmosphere, thanks largely to bric-a-brac festooned walls and ceilings in both bars – over 500 advertising jugs in one! Intriguingly-named puddings (£2.50): Mars Bar cheesecake, tiddly nickers and home-made ice creams such as banana and honey. Parents can get extra plates for informal children's portions. *Bar Food 12-2, 7-10.30 (Sun to 10). Children allowed in the bar to eat. Free House. Beer Wadworth IPA and 6X. Garden, outdoor eating, children's play area. No credit cards.*

Broom   Broom Tavern

Tel 01789 773656	**FOOD**
High Street Broom Warwickshire B50 5HL	**Map 14 C1**

Pretty, timbered village pub dating back to the 16th century with virginia creeper clinging to the outside and lots of black beams and brass within. The bar menu (mostly home-made although some puds and soups are not) offers plenty of choice from ploughman's (£3.75), sandwiches (from £2.50) and starters like duck paté (£3) and prawn cocktail (3.25) to main dishes such as chicken chasseur (£5), steak and kidney pie (£5.40), lasagne verde (£5.95) and steaks plus omelettes and salad platters. Children are catered for with a special menu, a

single high-chair and, on summer weekends and during school
holidays, a "bouncy castle" out in the garden. Whitbread. *Bar Food*
12-2 (Eves Mon-Fri 7-9.30, Sat 6.40-10, Sun 7-9). Childrens portions.
Restaurant Meals 12-2 (eves Mon-Fri 7-9, Sat 7-9.30). Closed Sunday
eve. Beer Bass, Boddingtons. Garden. Access, Visa.

Broom   Cock Inn

Tel 01767 314411   **FOOD**

23 High Street Broom Bedfordshire SG18 9NA   Map 15a F1

Stretching back from the only street of a village with no middle, no
shops and a postage stamp-sized post office in the postmistress's front
room, the Cock is a conversion of three interlinked Victorian cottages,
its three panelled sitting areas furnished with bench seats and varnished
table, and a games room complete with the locally popular chair-
skittles table. Look inside the two front rooms and find a novel
collection of metallised tobacco adverts and shelves of aged beer and
medicine bottles. The bar, central to everything here, has remained
unchanged for over a century, its cellar down four wooden steps,
where the Greene King IPA and Abbot ales are drawn direct from the
cask. There's a snacky day-time menu with the likes of crusty
sandwiches, jacket potatoes, ploughman's, lasagne and pies but the
evening may bring crispy coated Camembert with cranberry sauce
(£1.75), crab salad (£1.75), chicken stuffed with Stilton and served
with leek sauce (£7.95) or barbecue ribs (£6.95). Children are now
made equally welcome and offered smaller portions of almost
anything. *Bar Food 12-2, 7-9.30 (except Sun & Mon). Children's menu.*
Beer Greene King IPA, Abbot Ale. Garden, outdoor eating. Family room.
No credit cards.

Buckden   Buck Inn   FOOD

Tel 01756 760228   Fax 01756 760227   B&B

Buckden North Yorkshire BD23 5JA   Map 5 D4

Both the creeper-clad Georgian coaching inn and the village take their
names from the fact that this was once the meeting place for local stag
hunts; today it is tourists and walkers who are attracted to this fine
old inn. The small bar with flagstone floor and old stone fireplace is in
great contrast to the smart staff in wing collars and fancy bow ties
who offer swift, efficient service both in the extensive, carpeted bar-
meal areas with their tapestry banquette seating or wheelback chairs,
and in the pretty restaurant formed out of what was once the
courtyard where local sheep auctions were held. The menu offers
something for everybody from snacks like ploughman's (£4.40),
jacket potatoes (£3) and French stick sandwiches (from £2.95) to full
meals with such dishes as pan fried liver with chipolatas and bacon
(£5.50), lasagne al forno (£4.95), poached salmon (£6.95), steaks and
specials from the blackboard which could include beef and stout pie
with gravy (£5.50) and tortellini pasta with tomato and pesto sauce
(£5.50). There are also vegetarian and children's sections, and a long
list of home-made puddings at £1.95. Pretty bedrooms with matching
floral duvets and curtains are furnished in pine and all have TV,
direct-dial telephone and tea and coffee-making kit (although there
is also room service available throughout the day and evening).
Bathrooms, like the bedrooms, are smart and well-kept, mostly just
with showers but four have bathtubs. *Open 11-11 Mon-Sat. Bar Food*
& Restaurant Meals 12-2 (Sun all day), 6.30-9 (Sat to 9.30). Free
House. Beer Theakston's Old Peculier, Best & XB, guest beers. Patio,

outdoor eating. **Accommodation** *14 bedrooms, all en suite, £62 (single £31). Children welcome overnight (under-5s free, 5-10 ½ price, 11-14 two-thirds adult rate – if sharing parents' room), additional beds & cot (both £3) available. Access, Visa.*

Buckland Newton   Gaggle of Geese

Tel 01300 345249	A
Buckland Newton Dorset DT2 7BS	Map 13 F2

Formerly the *Royal Oak*, The Gaggle of Geese is so named since a previous landlord bred geese as a hobby; the building dates back to 1834 when it started life as the village shop. Twice-yearly goose charity auctions still take place here. Located on the B3143, about halfway between Dorchester and Sherborne, this tranquil village pub has a civilised and attractive main bar and pretty garden complete with pond. Children are allowed in the skittle alley and dining room. *Free House.* **Beer** *Hall and Woodhouse Badger Best, Bass, occasional guest beer. Garden, children's play area. Family room. No credit cards.*

Buckler's Hard   Master Builder's House Hotel

Tel 01590 616253 Fax 01590 616297	B&B
Buckler's Hard nr Beaulieu Hampshire SO42 7XB	Map 15 D4

Many famous ships were built for Nelson's fleet in Buckler's Hard. The grassy areas in front of this 18th-century hotel run right down to the banks of the Beaulieu River. Heavy beams and rustic furnishings make the Yachtsman's Bar popular with sailors and tourists alike, and residents have their own homely lounge with easy chairs, period furniture and a large inglenook fireplace. Creaky floorboards and old-world charm make the six bedrooms in the main house appealing; rooms in a purpose-built block are plainer but well equipped. The best rooms have four-posters. *Pub open 11-11 on Saturdays all year and Mon-Sat end-June to end-August.* **Beer** *Burton, John Bull, Tetley.* **Accommodation** *23 bedrooms (21 en suite), £85 (4-poster £100, single £55 with adjacent bathroom). Children welcome overnight (under 14s stay free in parents' room), additional beds and cots supplied. Garden. Access, Diners, Visa.*

Burcot   Chequers

Tel 01865 407771	FOOD
Abingdon Road Burcot Oxfordshire OX14 3DP	Map 14a C3

Originally a staging post for River Thames barges and their crews, until what is now the A415 was built outside. Charming, part 16th-century beamed and thatched building with unspoilt quarry-tiled bars, open fires and a choice of books for customers to read. A daily-changing blackboard menu is the same for the bar and dining room. Owner/chef Mary Weeks offers simple home-made fare (including bread) – tomato apple and celery (£1.95), chicken and tarragon and fish, cheese and broccoli pie (£5.45), chicken and fennel lasagne (£4.95) and (genuine old fashioned suet) steak and kidney pudding (£5.50) – followed by melting meringues filled with peaches and cream and home-made brown bread ice-cream (both £1.95). Sunday lunch is served on the first Sunday of every month (£4.95). Piano music on Friday and Saturday nights. *Bar Food & Restaurant Meals 12-2, 6.30-9 (closed Sun eve). Children allowed in bar to eat.* **Beer** *Ruddles County, Ushers Best, Webster's Yorkshire. Garden, outdoor eating. Access, Visa.*

Burford   The Angel

FOOD
B&B

Tel 01993 822438

Witney Street Burford Oxfordshire OX18 4SN

Map 14a A2

If the former Mason's Arms once fell from grace here, then today's
newly-named, and redecorated, Angel Inn has taken off in full flight.
Well worth seeking out just off the High Street, the Angel remains a
pub and foregoes intrusive juke box and amusements in favour of two
stylish cottage-style dining areas. The food is the better for it and
diners reap the benefit. Light meals and starters are interchangeable in
the lunch hour. Avocado stuffed with tuna and prawn mayonnaise or
chicken liver paté (£4.50); tagliatelle with cream and pesto (£4.95);
pan-fried calf's liver with sage and butter (£7.95), and at night time
there's no further compulsion to overspend. However, the daily fish
specials are immediately eye-catching, as in monkfish masala with
coconut and rice (£9.50). To finish are a very good summer pudding,
caramelised lemon tart and mocha chocolate demitasse with
cappuccino top, to name but three (all £2.95), and a fine cup of
cafetière coffee. Summer dining terrace and gardens to the rear. Those
in the know take full advantage of the three en-suite letting bedrooms
for a cosy, restful night's sleep. Good breakfasts and exceptionally
friendly service. *Bar Food* 12-2, 7-9. *Beer* Flowers IPA, Marston's
Pedigree, guest beer. Outdoor eating and garden. *Accommodation* 3 rooms,
all en suite, £45 (single £35). Children welcome overnight, extra bed
available. Check-in by arrangement. Access, Visa.

Burford   Inn For All Seasons

FOOD
B&B

Tel 01451 844324   Fax 01451 844375

The Barringtons Burford Oxfordshire OX18 4TN

Map 14a A2

Despite its Burford address, the inn's actually in Gloucestershire,
alongside the A40 by the Barringtons turn. A passageway runs from
the cellars to the old stone mines there, whence came the cutters for
their regular sustenance. The stone was sent as far afield as Oxford and
St Paul's Cathedral. From even further afield comes a regular clientele
to enjoy the comforts of a small hotel whose interior has been
meticulously restored to reflect 17th-century elegance. Leather wing
chairs grace a flagstone bar adorned with rugby, motoring and flying
memorabilia, much of the latter with local war-time connections. The
nine bedrooms are models of comfort with TVs, tea-makers, trouser
presses and hairdryers. All rooms have simple, neatly kept en-suite
bathrooms, and those in front are double-glazed against any intrusive
noise from the busy road. Residents enjoy extensive use of their own
lounge and the garden. The inn is now run by Matthew Sharp who
has taken over from his father, John. Matthew is an experienced chef
and owns *Circus* restaurant in Bath; his menus here might encompass
tomato and basil soup (£2.25), home-made taramasalata and hot toast
(£3.80), ploughman's lunches with granary bread (£3.95), lamb and
aubergine kebab with pilaf rice and a garlic and mint sauce (£7.50) or
10oz Scotch rump steak (£9.50). Only bread and ice cream are
bought in, all other fare is prepared on the premises; fresh fish and
meat is from good local butchers. The three acres of garden are
surrounded by cypress trees and a dry stone wall. *Bar Food* 11.30-2.30
(from 12 Sun), 6.30-9.30 (7-9 Sun). *Restaurant Meals* 7-9.30 (except
Sun). Free House. *Beer* Hall & Woodhouse Badger Best, Wadworth 6X,
Wychwood. Garden. *Accommodation* 10 bedrooms, all en suite, £70
(single £45). Children over 10 welcome. Additional beds available (25% of
tariff). No dogs. Access, Visa.

ZZzz...

Burford   Lamb Inn

FOOD
B&B

Tel 01993 823155

Sheep Street Burford Oxfordshire OX18 4LR   Map 14a A2

It's difficult to exaggerate the mellow charm of the 14th-century
Lamb Inn, tucked down a quiet side street in one of the Cotswolds'
most attractive towns. Public rooms range from a rustic bar at one
end of the building to a chintzy lounge at the other with in between a
combination of the two featuring rugs on the flagstone floor, a
collection of brass ornaments over the fireplace, a display of china
figurines on a window shelf, fresh flowers and antique furniture – all
polished and buffed to please the most exacting housekeeper. Redolent
of real log fires for most of the year, there is also a very pretty walled
garden to take advantage of the elusive English summer. Bar lunches,
served throughout the ground floor, run from various ploughman's
(all at £4.95), soup with granary bread (£2.50) and open prawn
sandwich (£4.50) to steak and kidney pie (£6.25), herb pancake with
salmon and prawns (£4.95) and sautéed chicken livers (£5.25). No
bar snacks in the evening, only restaurant meals (not recommended in
this Guide). What the 13 bedrooms lack in extras (there's only
unwrapped soap in the bathrooms for example), they make up for
with cottagey appeal – all having antique furniture, pretty floral
fabrics and many with old beams and timbers in evidence. Remote-
control TVs remind you it's the 20th century but there are no
telephones. *Bar Food 12-2. Free House. Beer Wadworth IPA & 6X, Old
Timer (in winter). Walled garden. Family room.* **Accommodation**
*13 bedrooms, all en suite, £80 (£35). Children welcome overnight,
additional beds (£15) and cots (£6) available. Dogs by arrangement.
Access, Visa.*

Burham   Golden Eagle

Tel 01634 668975

FOOD

80 Church Street Burham Kent ME1 3SD   Map 11 B5

Rather plain looking village local with a carpeted and simply
furnished open-plan bar, original beams adorned with mugs and jugs
and striking views across the Medway valley and the North Downs.
Worthy of a visit for its unusual bar food, the changing blackboard
menu consisting entirely of some 30-odd Malaysian dishes. Enjoyed on
a recent visit were a spicy nasi goreng (£4.75) and beef and black
peppers in black bean sauce (£6.20). Also available were Balinese
pork, coconut beef, duck in plum sauce and king prawns and peppers
in oyster sauce (all £6.50). *Pub open 11-2.30, 6.15-11 (Sun 12-3, 7-
10.30). Bar Food 12-2, 7-10. Free House. Beer Wadworth 6X, Marston
Pedigree, Flowers Original. Paved garden, outdoor eating. Pub closed
Christmas Day & Boxing Day. Access, Visa.*

Buriton   Five Bells

Tel 01730 263584

FOOD

Buriton High Street nr Petersfield Hampshire GU31 5RX   Map 15 D3

Dating back to the 16th century this well-refurbished brick and stone
free house nestles in an attractive village at the base of the South
Downs, a couple of minutes off the busy A3 (signposted heading
south). Popular with South Downs Way walkers – 400 yards away –
and a mixed local clientele, the pub offers a delightful rustic ambience
within the series of rambling bars. Warmed by four large open fires

and furnished with mainly sturdy pine on rug-strewn wood-block floors, it is a welcoming place in which to relax. The extensive menu – listed on beams and boards – is conveniently sectioned for ease of choice and the food is reliably good. The fish board may feature crab and sherry bake (£7.50), whole lemon sole and skate wing with black pepper and mustard sauce (both £8.50); the main-course board could offer rabbit and prunes in wine or Spanish pork casserole (both £6.50) or pigeon in ginger and wine (£7.50) in season. Other choices may include spicy lamb and aubergine (£5.50), mushroom and Brie flan (£4.75) and hearty snacks – filled jacket potatoes, French sticks and ploughman's to sustain hungry walkers. Interesting puddings (£2.25) such as apricot frangipane tart and gooseberry, honey and almond tart. Neat and cosy dining room offering 3-course menu (£16.50) and Sunday lunch (£12.50 – vegetarian £10.50). Good sheltered summer garden with vine-bearing trellis and fruit trees. Live monthly jazz and weekly Wednesday folk or country and western. *Free House.* **Bar Food & Restaurant** 12-2, 6.30-10 (12-2, 7-10 Sun). **Beer** *Ballards Best Bitter, Adnams Bitter, Ringwood Old Thumper, Friary Meux Best Bitter, Ind Coope Burton Ale, guest beer. Garden, outdoor eating. Access, Visa.*

Burnham Market   Hoste Arms

Tel 01328 738257   Fax 01328 730103

The Green Burnham Market Norfolk PE31 8HD

FOOD
B&B
Map 10 C1

Prior to Paul Whittome purchasing this handsome 17th-century inn, which occupies a prime position overlooking the green and parish church in this most picturesque village, it had suffered more than a century of brewery ownership and subsequent architectural abuse. Sound investment, enthusiasm and positive aspirations over the past five years have transformed the "Hoste" into one of the most popular inns along the Norfolk coast. As improvements continue, this most welcoming of establishments can only get better. Inside, two carefully renovated front bars feature darkwood panelling, open brick fireplaces with winter log fires, rustic wooden floors and cushioned bow window seats with delightful village views. Of note are the original paintings by wildlife artist Bruce Pearson illustrating a series of rural walks from the inn. Live traditional jazz and R&B are popular weekly events in the comfortably furnished piano bar. Above-average pub food draws on supplies of fresh local and seasonal produce from within a twenty mile radius – oysters from Burnham Norton, crabs and lobster from Wells – and everything is prepared on the premises. Varied printed menu choices range from six fresh oysters (£4.25) and goat's cheese and spinach parcel on a fresh tomato sauce (£3.25) to home-made crab cakes with a salsa sauce (£5.50), venison, smoked bacon and mushroom pie (£6.50), and Pad Thai – traditional Thai noodles served with pork, vegetables, peanuts and lemon (£6.75). Additional blackboard dishes may include spiced chick pea and spinach soup (£2), braised chicken with olives, egg plant and tomato (£5.95) or sautéed monkfish in a chervil cream sauce (£8.25). To finish, try the apple crumble, chocolate and hazelnut torte (both £2.50) or a good selection of cheeses (£3). Interesting vegetarian options – stir-fry mushrooms, tofu, coriander and fresh ginger (£5.50). Sunday roasts (£6.50). Restaurant cooking moves up a gear with an imaginative and value-for-money daily changing dinner menu (1-course £10.50, 2-course £13.25, 3-course £15.75). Global list of well-priced wines from Adnams with useful notes and tip-top ales

Zzzz...

drawn straight from the cask. Upstairs beyond the small gallery/lounge are fifteen charming bedrooms, two boasting four-posters. Individually decorated, some with free standing pine, others with antique pieces, all are being upgraded with designer colours, fabrics and fittings to match more recent rooms. Spotless en-suite facilities and TVs, radios, tea-makers, telephones and hairdryers for added comfort. First-rate breakfasts served in the conservatory, which is also the venue for afternoon teas, (free to residents incidentally). Ideally located for exploring the Norfolk coast and its many renowned bird reserves. *Free House.* **Accommodation** *15 bedrooms, all en suite £63-£82 (Single £47). Dogs and children welcome overnight (child free under 4).* **Bar Food & Restaurant** *12-2.15, 7-9.30. Children allowed anywhere.* **Beer** *Ruddles Country, Webster's Yorkshire Bitter, Woodforde's Wherry Bitter, Hook Norton Old Hooky, guest beers. Garden, outside area. Access, Visa.*

Burnham Thorpe — Lord Nelson

Tel 01328 738241   **A**

Walsingham Road Burnham Thorpe Norfolk   Map 10 C1

Unspoilt rural cottage located in a sleepy village close to Burnham Market and named after England's most famous seafarer, who was born in the nearby rectory. A narrow worn brick-floored corridor leads to two rooms; a timeless, old-fashioned bar on the left boasting some magnificent high-backed settles and a few sturdy tables and plain chairs on a re-tiled floor. Nelson memorabilia in the form of prints and paintings adorn the walls. There is no bar; excellent Greene King ales are drawn straight from the cask in the adjacent cellar room and brought to the table. Also available is a popular rum concoction called "Nelson's Blood", which is made to a secret recipe by the previous long-serving landlord who still resides near the pub. A further warmly decorated and simply furnished room is ideal for families. Good-sized garden with bowling green, bat & ball, football net, basketball net, swing and slide for active youngsters to let off steam. *Free House. Open 11-4, 5.30-11 (12-3, 7-10.30 Sun) Children are allowed in the bar to eat, children's portions.* **Beers** *Greene King IPA, Abbot Ale, Mild – straight from cask. Garden, children's play area and outdoor eating. No credit cards.*

Burnham-on-Crouch — Ye Olde White Harte Hotel

Tel & Fax 01621 782106   **B&B**

The Quay Burnham-on-Crouch Essex CM0 8AS   Map 11 C4

An old seaside inn where on sunny summer days you can take your drink to a lovely waterside terrace overlooking the busy yachting activity. Two characterful, wood-panelled bars have polished-oak furnishings, exposed beams, a good open fire and a nautical atmosphere; there's also a small, traditional residents' lounge. The best of the nineteen bedrooms (which vary in size and standard) are the eleven comfortable en-suite rooms with smart, modern decor, good fabrics and simple furniture. Some clean and tiled bathrooms have shower and bath. Original beams and brick fireplaces, and splendid estuary views are notable features. Eight rooms are self-styled as "basic". *Free House.* **Beer** *Adnams, Tolly Cobbold. Waterside Terrace. Family room.* **Accommodation** *19 bedrooms, 11 en suite, £46/£54 (single £30/£34). Children welcome overnight (if sharing parents' room: under-5s £6.50, 6-12 yrs £8, over-12s £10), additional beds and cots available. Access, Visa.*

Burpham   George & Dragon

Tel 01903 883131	**FOOD**
Burpham nr Arundel West Sussex BN18 9RR	Map 11 A6

Burpham is signposted off the A27 near Arundel. At the end of two
miles of a winding, climbing lane, one is rewarded with some fine
views of the Arun valley, with Arundel Castle in the distance, and the
pretty George & Dragon with its good food and real ales. Once the
haunt of smugglers, the mid-18th-century inn is now divided into two
very different halves; the bar with its exposed timbers, rustic tables
and country chairs, and the smart dining room with crisp white
napery and elegant Regency-style chairs. The printed bar food lunch
and supper menu covers the standard items – home-made soup
(£2.60), deep-fried mushrooms with garlic (£2.85), grilled sirloin
steak (£10.50), jacket potatoes (with cheese and bacon £3.60),
ploughman's (Stilton £3.50) and sandwiches – while a daily-changing
blackboard menu lists avocado crab (£4.90), vegetarian chili (£4.75),
Irish stew and rosemary dumplings (£5.65), fresh black bream
(£5.95) and chicken and leek crumble (£5.25). Another blackboard
lists a particularly good range of home-made puds (all at £2.70) from
white chocolate mousse and raspberry torte to bread-and-butter
pudding and passion fruit and mango cheesecake. The dinner menus in
the restaurant are £15.50 for 2 courses and £18.50 for 3. With the
100-year-old cricket club next door, it's a popular venue with
sportsmen. No music. No dogs. "Smoking not encouraged". *Bar Food
12-2, 7-9.45. Restaurant Meals 12-1.45 (Sun only), 7-9.30 (except
Sun). Children (but not babies) are allowed in the bar to eat. Beer Harveys,
Courage Best, Arundel, guest beers. Terrace, outdoor eating. Bar closed Sun
night mid Nov-Easter. Access, Visa.*

Bursledon   Jolly Sailor

Tel 01703 405557	**A**
Lands End Road Old Bursledon Hampshire SO31 8DN	Map 15 D4

Three miles from M27 Junction 8, the Jolly Sailor overlooks the busy
yachting marina activity on the River Hamble. Parking is restricted
outside the pub but there is free parking at Old Bursledon railway
station, which is a couple of minutes' walk up the lane; there are
then 40 steps down (and back up!) to the pub entrance. Built as a
shipbuilder's house in 1700 and later a vicarage, it became a pub
in the early 1900s. It has its own jetty and yachtsmen have used this
harbourside pub as a retreat ever since the days of Lord Nelson. More
recently, it was featured in BBC TV's *Howard's Way*. The large
terrace is a lovely spot to watch the nautical world go by and within
the unspoilt interior the nautical front bar also has good views from
sought-after bay window seats; the flagstoned back bar is old and
characterful. Splendid alfresco seating on the bench-filled front terrace
and along the jetty jutting out over the river. Try one of the fifteen
fruity country wines on offer from Gales of Havant. Small, lawned
garden area has a 100-year-old yew tree for shade. New landlord.
*Pub open all day Sat, usual hours other days. Beer Hall & Woodhouse
Badger Best and Tanglefoot, Gales HSB, Wadworth 6X, Gribble Ales'
Jolly Sailor & Reg's Tipple. Riverside garden. Access, Diners, Visa.*

Burton — Old House at Home

Tel 01454 218227
Burton nr Chippenham Wiltshire SN14 7LT

FOOD

Map 14 B2

Somewhat up-market for a village local, the Old House at Home produces considerably more than the home cooking its name suggests. Full-time chefs produce such daily fare as garlic steak (£11.50), Murphy's lamb (£8.20) alongside 'Sally's steak and mushroom pie' (£6.50) and oriental chicken (£9.55). Expect to pay rather more than standard pub prices as the extras can mount up a bit: granary bread is 50p. A soft-stone building with a warm and welcoming timbered interior and log fires in winter, its real ales include Smiles, Wadworth 6X and regular guest beers. Music, food and wine from various countries are featured on a Monday theme evening once a month. *Bar Food 12-2 (except Tue), 7-10 (Sun to 9.30). Children allowed in bar to eat at lunchtime only. Free House. Beer Smiles, Bass, Wadworth 6X, Old Timer (winter). Garden, outdoor eating, children's play area. Visa.*

Burton — Plume of Feathers

Tel 01454 218251
Burton nr Chippenham Wiltshire SN14 7LP

FOOD

B&B

Map 14 B2

Antipodean licensees bring a little Eastern magic to their mixed menus of 'Orientalities' such as sweet and sour (£6.45), daily curries (from £6.35 and graduated in strength from biryani to fiery) and Sunday 'Rijsttafel' buffet lunch which offers a large selection of Asian dishes (£12.50). Chicken and mushrooms on rosti (£7.45), liver and bacon casserole (£4.95) and steak, kidney and stout pie (£5.95) for the less adventurous: home-made sweets and ice cream specialities. Overnight accommodation in twin rooms with duvets and matching curtains with radio alarms and tea-makers: bathrooms are rather spartan. *Bar Food 12-2, 6.30-9.30 (Sun to 9). Children's menu. Free House. Beer Bass, Wadworth 6X, John Smith's. Garden, outdoor eating. Family room.* **Accommodation** *2 bedrooms, both en suite, £35 (single £29.50). No children overnight. Check-in by arrangement. Access, Visa.*

Bury St Edmunds — The Nutshell

Tel 01284 764867
The Traverse Bury St Edmunds Suffolk

A

Map 10 C2

Blink and you will miss this unique miniature pub tucked away between a newsagents and a building society on a pedestrianised zone just off the main market square. It claims to be the smallest pub in Britain, a title that is difficult to dispute as the single bar – measuring barely a hundred square feet – is positively crowded if eight people are inside drinking. Despite its size there are plenty of curios to interest the eye, notably collections of 'smallest' items, bank notes from around the world, military memorabilia and, unbelievably, a mummified cat and mouse hanging from the ceiling. Good, well-kept Greene King ales, a welcoming chatty atmosphere and the signing of the visitors book is obligatory. *Pub open 11-11 Mon-Sat. Beer Greene King IPA, Abbot Ale, Raments Bitter. Pub closed all Sun. No credit cards.*

Butterleigh   **Butterleigh Inn**

Tel 01884 855407   **A**

Tiverton-Cullompton Road Butterleigh Devon EX15 1PN   Map 13 E2

Unspoilt farming pub in glorious countryside, just three miles from
Junction 28 of the M5 motorway. The main bar is half lounge, half
public end with simple wooden furnishings; a tiny snug takes just four
intimate tables. Inglenook fireplace and old-fashioned pub games. No
children indoors but play area available in the garden. Black Hand
cider (made on a local farm) available in the summer. *Free House.*
Beer Cotleigh Tawny, Harrier and Old Buzzard, guest beer. Garden,
outdoor eating, children's play area. No credit cards.

Buttermere   **Bridge Hotel**

Tel & Fax 017687 70252   **B&B**

Buttermere Cumbria CA13 9UZ   Map 4 C3

Looking across the valley to Red Pike and High Stile between which
cascades Sourmilk Gill's waterfall, this is an idyllic spot, beloved of
generations of fell-walkers. There are distinctly contrasting sides to the
business, however. The Walker's bar is kept suitably rustic with rooms
for rucksacks and boots permitted. A major draw is the Scottish &
Newcastle beers, though the more independent-minded drinker will
hail the first Cumbrian outlet of Paul Theakston's Black Sheep brews.
A mere few paces distant, residents are treated to complimentary
afternoon tea in the hotel lounge, followed by a nightly table d'hote
(£17.50 for non-residents) which is included in a half-board rate.
Prices are shown accordingly. Most of the bedrooms get a share of the
majestic surrounding hills: the best of them have tiny wooden
balconies teetering above the fast-rushing stream which bisects the
property. Though general decor can be a little dark, all are enlivened
by bright tiled bathrooms. Meanwhile, atmospheric conditions are
blamed in the brochure for a total lack of room TVs and radio, which
in this satellite age may strike some of us as odd. Choice of twenty
malt whiskies from the bar. *Open 10.30-11, Sun 1-10.30. Free House.*
Beer Younger Best, Theakston Old Peculier, Black Sheep Best & Special
Bitter, two guest beers. Patio, High tea 3-5.30pm. **Accommodation**
22 bedrooms, 21 en suite, £104 (four-poster £114, single £52), six new
apartments in grounds available on weekly terms. Children welcome
overnight (under-4s stay free if sharing parents' room, 4-14s £17),
additional beds (£5 for under-4s) and cots available. Dogs by arrangement.
Access, Visa.

Bythorn   **White Hart**

Tel 01832 710226   **FOOD**

Bythorn nr Huntingdon Cambridgeshire PE18 0QM   Map 7 E4

17th-century coaching inn nestling in a peaceful village just off the
A14 Huntingdon to Kettering road. Rambling interior comprising
four relaxing and varied inter-connecting rooms featuring plenty of
exposed brick, beams and boards, quarry tiles and colourful rugs
topped with an interesting rustic assortment of furniture, including an
old Chesterfield. Huge open fireplaces with log fires for winter days
and tables strewn with books and magazines beckon those who intend
settling down for a relaxed stay. Food emphasis in this welcoming
establishment is rooted in the airy restaurant extension, although
recently a short blackboard bar menu has been introduced (except
Saturday evenings) listing good lighter bites – king prawns in batter

(£6.95), mussels in white wine and cream, spicy fish soup (both £5.95) and roast loin of pork with orange sauce (£6.95). However, those wishing to stay in front of the fire are welcome to choose from the more imaginative restaurant fare. Starters (£4.50) range from quail's eggs and smoked salmon with Madeira sauce to chicken and sweetbreads in a puff pastry case, followed by half-guinea fowl with fresh limes or calf's liver with crispy bacon and onion gravy (main courses £13.50). Puddings (£4) include toasted fruit sabayon and fresh strawberry Romanoff. Four-course Sunday lunch (£15). *Free House.* **Bar Food & Restaurant** *12-2, 6.30-10 (Sun 7-10, no Bar Food Sat eve).* **Beer** *Greene King IPA, Abbot Ale. Outdoor eating. Children allowed anywhere. Access, Visa.*

Byworth	**Black Horse**	

Tel 01798 42424	**FOOD**
Byworth nr Petworth West Sussex GU28 0HO	Map 11 A6

Built on the site of a 15th-century friary in a sleepy village setting – just off the A283 Petworth to Pulborough road – the unusual three-storey Georgian facade of this friendly pub hides an ancient rustic interior. Beams, bare-boarded floors, scrubbed tables and padded wall seats characterise the three attractive interconnecting rooms and extraordinary upstairs Elizabethan dining room. Bar food ranges from good standard pub snacks – grilled jacket potatoes (from £3.75), salads (from £4.95), steaks (from £10.75), cottage pie, £4.95) – to more imaginative daily changing blackboard specials, such as a well presented breast of chicken with a tarragon cream sauce (£6.95) accompanied by a dish of well cooked vegetables. Alternatives may include "real" French onion soup (£2.50), 16oz steak and kidney pudding (£7.95) and halibut with Szechuan sauce (£7.95). After all this, puddings are a bit of a disappointment. Splendid summer alfresco imbibing on an old cobbled patio or among the flower borders and shrubs in the fine terraced garden with peaceful wooded valley views. *Free House.* **Bar Food** *11.30-1.45, 6-9.45 (12-1.45, 7-9.45 Sun). Garden, outdoor eating. Children allowed anywhere, children's portions.* **Beer** *Young's Bitter, Wadworth 6X, Ballards Wassail, Hop Back Summer Lightning, guest beer. Access, Diners, Visa.*

Cadeby	**Cadeby Inn**	

Tel 01709 864009	**A**
Main Street Cadeby nr Doncaster South Yorkshire DN5 7SW	Map 7 D2

This atmospheric old inn was clearly once an elegant country farmhouse and stands today in a mature orchard garden full of flowering shrubs. There's plenty of space here for little ones to play safely, and the picnic tables are especially popular when there's a barbecue on. In poor weather, children are allowed in the snug only until 8pm. Original flagstones and fireplaces survive in the two bars whose counters are built in brick, while the walls are hung with horse collars, brasses and webbing. *Free House.* **Beer** *Tetley Best, Burton Ale, John Smith's Best & Magnet, Samuel Smith's Old Brewery. Garden, children's play area. Family room. Access, Visa.*

Cadnam   White Hart

Tel 01703 812277 Fax 01703 814632	**FOOD**

Cadnam nr Lyndhurst Hampshire SO40 2NP   Map 14 C4

Having run three successful New Forest pubs over the past decade the
Emberley family have joined forces to concentrate their efforts on this
attractive and smartly refurbished old coaching inn, located on the
edge of the Forest beside the A31, near the M27 (J1). A big welcome
awaits families either in the extensive sheltered garden, complete with
a paddock of animals, or in the spacious interior which boasts plenty
of exposed brick, open fires and a comfortable mix of old and new
furniture. The Emberleys' tried and tested bar food formula is again
proving very popular with a broad spectrum of dishes catering for all
tastes. Printed menu fare features the usual pub favourites –
ploughman's (£3.75), gammon steak and pineapple (£7.25), haddock
and chips (£4.50) – alongside more imaginative dishes like fillet of
lamb with cherry and almond sauce (£7.50). Blackboard specials
improve matters further with such choices as rabbit in port and
redcurrant (£6.50), beef in Stilton and celery (£6.25) and sauté of
venison in fruit sauce (£7.25). Accompanying vegetables are fresh and
well cooked. Set 3-course Sunday roast lunch (£12.50). Good selection
of real ales and at least eight wines available by the glass. *Bar Food
11-2, 6-9.30 (Sun 12-2, 7-9).* *Beer Flowers Original, Wadworth 6X.
Garden, outdoor eating. Pub closes at 10.30pm winter weekdays.
Access, Visa.*

Calver   Chequers Inn

Tel 01433 630231	**FOOD**
	B&B

Froggatt Edge Calver Derbyshire S30 1ZB   Map 6 C2

Originally four stone-built 18th century cottages, the Grade II listed
Chequers stands alongside the B6054, a mile or so above Calver on
the steep banks of Froggatt's Edge. Behind the pub, a landscaped beer
garden gives way to some ten acres of steep, wild woodland.
Following a recent chequered past, the newly renovated pub is again
in good hands, the bar menus having become instantly popular and
commendable. Successful experiments on a daily-changing blackboard
are soon incorporated into seasonal 'Innkeeper's Fare', cases in point
being the local rabbit and vegetable casserole (£4.55), and home-made
chicken and mushroom lasagne (£4.70). Hearty sandwiches are also
there for those not up to a full meal: hot roast beef (£3.40) and
seafood salad (£3.60). To follow, a whole traditional Bakewell
pudding (£3.95) is a challenge for two, sufficient even for four.
Bookings must be made for the adjoining non-smoking restaurant's
table d'hote dinner (£14.95) and 3-course Sunday lunch (£10.95).
Owing to demand, expansion is planned here, along with extensions
to an already hard-pressed kitchen. No such sense of crowding
bedevils the bedrooms, half a dozen of them, furnished with pine
bedsteads (one a four-poster) and pristine fabrics in muted tones. With
plenty of space for armchairs, satellite TV and cosy bathrooms (with
strong over-bath showers) these are truly comfortable rooms where
the promise of a restful night lives well up to expectations. *Free House.
Beer Wards Best & Thorne, Vaux Samson. Bar Food 12-2 (Sun to
2.30), 6-9.30 (Sun from 7). Restaurant Meals 12-2 (except Mon),
7-9.30. Garden, outdoor eating. Accommodation 6 bedrooms, all en suite,
£48 (single £38). Children welcome overnight (under-3s stay free in
parents' room) additional beds (£10) and cots available. Access, Visa.*

Cambridge   Eagle

Tel 01223 301286

A

Bene't Street Cambridge Cambridgeshire CB2 3QN

Map 15 F1

Splendidly atmospheric city-centre pub situated close to the Corn
Exchange and a stone's throw from King's College. Hidden behind the
plain Georgian stone facade are five rooms of great architectural
interest dating back to the 16th century. Sensitively restored in recent
years, each relaxing room has a distinct, individual charm, boasting
original features such as stripped pine panelling, mullioned windows,
fine brick fireplaces and two medieval paintings. Tastefully adorned
with sturdy wooden furnishing, William Morris fabrics and attractive
prints, it is the haunt of students, dons and businessmen alike. Of
particular interest is the red-painted ceiling in the Air Force Bar which
preserves the hundreds of signatures of British and American airmen
which were burnt on by candles and lighters during the Second
World War. Cobbled and galleried courtyard with summer seating.
Greene King. Open 11-11 (Sun 12-3, 7-10.30. **Beer** *Greene King IPA,
Abbot Ale, Rayments Bitter. Courtyard, outdoor eating. Access,
Diners, Visa.*

Cambridge   Free Press

Tel 01223 68337

FOOD

Prospect Row Cambridge Cambridgeshire CB1 1QU

Map 15 F1

Tiny, totally non-smoking and highly atmospheric rowing-mad pub
tucked away behind the police station, close to the city centre. Simply
furnished, unspoilt interior, the snug is also used as the dining area, and
rowing photographs are everywhere. It gets extremely busy; be early.
Simple, hearty home-cooking is of the sort to defrost a cold-numbed
oarsman – try the home-made soup (leek and potato or beef and
vegetable £1.75), followed by port and ginger casserole (£3.75),
pasta, tuna and broccoli bake (£3.75) or game pie (£4.50) and finish
with apricot or chocolate cake (£1.75). **Bar Food** *12-2, 6.30-8.30
(Sun 7-8.30).* **Beer** *Greene King IPA, Abbot. Garden, outdoor eating area.
Children welcome in bar area. No credit cards.*

Cambridge   Tram Depot

Tel 01223 324553

A

Dover Street Cambridge Cambridgeshire CB1 1DY

Map 15 F1

Located half a mile east of the city centre, just off East Road, this lively
and unusual pub occupies the brilliantly converted Cambridge Street
Tramway Company stables. Designed in classic alehouse style with
brick and flagstone floors topped with a rustic mix of old pine
furniture, it has a good city atmosphere. Further seating in an upstairs
gallery and out in the sheltered courtyard on warmer days. Piped
classical music plays at lunchtime; jazz and blues in the evening.
Beer *Everards Tiger Best & Old Original, Adnams Southwold, Ridleys
IPA, two guest beers. Courtyard, outdoor eating. Family room. No credit
cards.*

Canterbury   **Falstaff Inn**

Tel 01227 462138 Fax 01227 463525	**B&B**
8 St Dunstan's Street Canterbury Kent CT2 8AF	**Map 11 C5**

A centuries-old coaching inn by the outer walls of the city. Day
rooms get character from original beams, leaded windows and
polished oak tables. Bedrooms, all fully refurbished this year, are neat
and pretty and the majority use solid modern furniture that suits the
feel of the place perfectly; a room with a four-poster bed incurs a
small supplement. Children under 16 are accommodated free – with a
full traditional English breakfast – when sharing with an adult.
Within easy walking distance of the town centre, near the Westgate
Tower. Pubby bar. Country Club (Whitbread) Hotels. *Open 11-11,
Sunday usual hours.* **Beer** *Marston's Pedigree, Fremlins Bitter, Boddingtons.
Garden.* **Accommodation** *24 bedrooms, all en suite, £80. Children
welcome overnight (under-16s stay free in parents' room), additional beds
and cots available. Dogs by arrangement. Access, Diners, Visa.*

Carey   **Cottage of Content**

Tel 01432 840242 Fax 01432 840208	**B&B**
Carey nr Hereford Hereford & Worcester HR2 6NG	**Map 14 B1**

Follow prominent signs to Hoarwithy from the A49 or B4399 to find
the only river crossing on this hidden stretch of the Wye. Deep in the
valley, this aptly-named pub stands at the heart of a tiny village,
fronted by a patio and porch; across the lane is a small stream and
parking over a rickety wooden bridge. Within are flagstone floors and
timbered alcoves with hops hanging from the beams and a central
open staircase leading off the bar seemingly into the roof space. There
are just four, suitably cottagey, bedrooms with sloping floors under
their heavy roof timbers; three have en-suite bathrooms which are
carpeted and neat, yet tiny. Oak furniture is on the sturdy side, while
TVs and tea-makers appear almost incongruous in the setting. *Free
House.* **Beer** *Hook Norton Best & Old Hooky, Bass. Garden. Family room.*
Accommodation *4 rooms, 3 all en suite, £48 (£30 single). Children
welcome in rooms (cot age stay free in parents' room, otherwise full price).
Check-in by arrangement. Pub and accommodation closed 25 Dec.
Access, Visa.*

Zzzz...

Carlton in Coverdale   **The Foresters Arms**

	FOOD
Tel 01969 40272 Fax 01969 40272	**B&B**
Carlton in Coverdale nr Leyburn North Yorkshire DL8 2BB	**Map 5 D4**

Simon Thornalley and chef Barry Higginbothom are the new
licensees at this privately owned free house at the heart of Coverdale.
Look for signs off the A684 at West Witton. Internal refurbishment is
well in hand, and a fairly serious approach to food now prevails.
Indeed, the diversity of the blackboard menus suggests sufficient
ambition to test any kitchen, yet the quality of ingredients and results
are not seriously in doubt. From a simple soup and ham and eggs
through to creamed leeks with smoked bacon (£3.25) and strips of
beef fillet with a Dijon mustard sauce (£7.95), a broad range of tastes
can be pandered to: home-made burgers and minute steaks (both
£2.95) are the above-average fare for kids. Best available produce
from the fish markets is something of a speciality with whole roast sea
bass (£9.50) typical. Bread and butter or sticky toffee puddings
individually cooked to order (£2.25) represent some classily turned
out puddings. Freshly decorated and recarpeted, the three en-suite

bedrooms (with WC and showers rather than baths) have bright
cottagey decor and crisp white duvets. In addition to TVs, radios,
hairdryers and trouser presses, each room has its own plug for use of
communal pay phone. Ask for the rear twin for one of the finest
bedroom views in the Dales. *Free House.* **Bar Food** *12-2, 7-9.*
Restaurant Meals *Only available in evenings, closed Sun. Tues-Fri 7-9.
Sat 7-9.30.* **Accommodation** *3 bedrooms, £55 (Single £27.50). Dogs
welcome in one room only. Check-in by arrangement. Children welcome
overnight.* **Beer** *John Smith's, Theakston Best & XB. Outdoor eating area.
Access, Visa.*

Carterway Heads	Manor House Inn	FOOD
Tel 01207 55268		B&B
Carterway Heads Shotley Bridge Northumberland DH8 9LX		Map 5 D3

The former Bolbec Manor House, standing high on the A68 (close to
its junction with the B6278) was once part of an estate which traces its
history back to the Norman Conquest. Almost a millennium later the
Bolbec name has been revived in a dining room converted from 200-
year-old stables after renovations by the Pelley family which have
taken fully three years. Food choices, however, remain the same
throughout the pub's four rooms, massive chalk boards proclaiming
wide choices: for starters curried parsnip or Provençale fish soups
(£1.80 and £2.35), dill herrings with creme freche or grilled Craster
kippers (£3.55 and £4.60). Cumberland sausage with mash and
mustard sauce (£3.25) and Beef Casserole with peppers and thyme
(£5.95) are substantial main course. Additional choices in the Bolbec
Room might be Rib of Beef with Bearnaise and Turbot with leeks
and shallots (£8.75). There's a hand-picked selection of small grower's
wines on show here racked for inspection with Post-It notes. A final
stage of restoration was completed in 1994 with the opening of four
bedrooms fitted out in pine and equipped with TVs, beverage trays
and hair-dryers. Planning restrictions, however, have left them all
facing the main road, yet sharing two bathrooms, fully tiled and
comprehensively equipped, which arguably enjoy the best view of any
loos in the land. *Free House.* **Bar Food** *12-2.30, 7-9.30 (7-9 Sun).*
Beers *Hadrian Gladiator, Butterknowle Bitter always available, Edwin
Taylor's Stout, "Big Lamp" ESB, Regularly changing ales. Open 11-3,
6-11 (12-3, 7-10.30 Sun). Children allowed in bar area to eat before 8pm.*
Accommodation *4 bedrooms £35 (single £20). Children under 8 free,
over 8 £10 if sharing parents' room. Additional beds available. Check-in by
arrangement. Outdoor eating and garden. Access, Visa.*

Carthorpe	Fox & Hounds	
Tel 01845 567433		FOOD
Carthorpe nr Bedale North Yorkshire DL8 2LG		Map 5 E4

The B6285, some 10 miles North of Ripon off the A1, leads to this
sleepy Bedale village. If criticism there be of the former smithy which
now houses the village pub, it must be of a lack of innate pubbiness
which appears entirely due to Bernadette and Howard Fitzgerald's
success in catering to a well-heeled clientele with some thoughtfully
produced food. Served in both bar and restaurant of the L-shaped
interior is a single menu of reliably home-cooked dishes updated daily.
Strongly represented are the day's offerings from some careful
shopping at the fish markets; whole dressed crab and mixed seafood
hors d'oeuvre (both £4.95) as curtain-raisers to whole Dover sole
(£9.95), filleted lemon sole rolled around smoked salmon and prawns

($7.95) and poached salmon hollandaise ($7.95). Baby chicken cooked in Theakston's and rack of English lamb ($8.75) appease meat eaters and profiteroles with chocolate sauce or lemon cream pie to follow ($2.25) will assuage the heartiest appetites. It is a good bet that from their varied list more wines are sold than the single real ale, though never on a Monday when the pub closes entirely. Children are welcome to eat in the dining room. *Free House.* **Bar Food** *12-2, 7-10 (closed all day Mon).* **Beer** *John Smith's. No credit cards.*

Cartmel Fell   **Masons Arms**   ★

| Tel 015395 68486   Fax 0153 95 68780 | **FOOD** |
| Strawberry Bank Cartmel Fell Cumbria LA11 6NW | Map 4 C4 |

Signposted from the A5074, the justifiably famous, well-loved Masons Arms is a classic if ever there was one. The setting is glorious – perched on the hillside at Strawberry Bank with Lakeland views in all directions, and the interior is equally inspiring, a series of quaint, unspoilt little farmhouse rooms. In the main bar are polished old flagstones, a big open fire, sagging ceiling beams, simple country furniture and well-chosen pictures. Several cottagey anterooms offer old pews, odd bits of furniture, a sideboard, an old stove, and a curious little cupboard set into the wall. Tiny thickset windows frame pretty valley views; rough stone walls are freshly whitewashed. Aside from excellent bar food, there's the widest choice of drinks to be found anywhere – including their own three home brews (named after local resident Arthur Ransome's books), and, in edition II of their comprehensive bottled beer list, well over 200 interesting international names, including Kriek (brewed with cherries) and Weizenthaler (a tasty alcohol-free wheat beer). They make 'Knickerbocker Breaker' cider from their own apples (1500 gallons a year) as well as 'Damson Beer' – a cask fruit beer. The blackboard menu offers a pleasing variety of home-made dishes including half a dozen or so vegetarian choices. Simple country casseroles, like coachman's ($7.95) and damson and pork hotpots feature strongly on the list; pies are good too (farmhouse courgette and sage Derby pie $6.25). Also on offer are hazelnut and lentil paté ($3.95), French-style fish soup ($3.95), leek, butterbean and Stilton strudel ($6.25), nut roast layered with cranberries ($6.50), Flemish beef carbonnade with bacon braised in trappist beer ($7.95) or chicken and pepper lasagne ($6.50). Puddings, mostly of the good old-fashioned sort, are also not to be missed (peach melba crumble, toffee banoffi, Highland cream – all $2.50). Simple, well-cooked food tastes outstandingly fine in such splendid surroundings; be early for a seat on the terrace in summer. **Bar Food** *12-2, 6-8.45 (Sun from 7). Children allowed in bar to eat. Free House.* **Beer** *Home Brews: Amazon, Great Northern, Big Six; Thwaites, guest beers. Garden, outdoor eating. Family room. Access, Visa.*

Casterton   **Pheasant Inn**

| Tel 015242 71230 | **B&B** |
| Casterton nr Kirkby Lonsdale Cumbria LA6 2RX | Map 4 C4 |

Melvin and May Mackie run this well-maintained, white pebbledash building at the heart of the village, enjoying some fine rear views over open country to the hills beyond. At the front, next to the A683, a colourful paved patio is furnished with rustic tables and bench seating. The Garden Room, a small summery lounge full of parlour plants, leads to the main bar, which is sectioned around a central servery; burgundy banquette seating, polished wood tables with fresh flowers,

Zzz...

aerial photos of the pub and country pictures on the walls make for a pleasant, restful spot. While by no means luxurious, the bedrooms are both comfortable and well kept, with colour television, direct-dial phones, radios, beverage trays and neat, if rather small, bathrooms, all with showers recently added. There's one four-poster bed for the romantically inclined, and a twin-bedded ground-floor room suitable for the disabled; most bedrooms have lovely countryside views. Ever growing collection of malt whiskies. *Open 11-11 (Sun to 10.30). Free House. Beer Jennings, Burton, Tetley, guest beer. Garden, outdoor eating. Family room.* **Accommodation** *10 rooms, all en suite, £64, single £40. Children welcome overnight (rate depends on age), additional beds and cots available (£5). Dogs by arrangement. Pub and accommodation closed 1 week mid-Jan. Access, Visa.*

Castle Ashby   Falcon Hotel

Tel 01604 696200 Fax 01604 696673	**FOOD**
Castle Ashby Northamptonshire NN7 1LF	**B&B**
	Map 15 E1

Just six miles from Northampton and easily found off the A428 Bedford road, the Falcon strikes a happy balance between historic country inn and well-appointed modern cottage hotel. Its founding in 1594 is commemorated in the atmospheric cellar bar approached by way of an original flagstone stairway. Bar meals are served here on mahogany-topped beer barrel tables. Daily offerings might include carrot and coriander soup (£1.50), cold poached salmon (£6.50), steak and mushroom pie (£4.75) and vegetable chili (£5.00). Lunch and dinner are also served in the rear dining extension (the restaurant is also recommended) which overlooks a delightful garden; fresh from it come the courgette flowers, artichokes and garden herbs which feature on seasonal menus. Sunday lunch is traditional (£13.50). Whitewood furniture and gaily patterned fabrics imbue the main-house bedrooms with the country freshness their surroundings suggest; the bathrooms here are immaculately appointed. No less countrified, though rather plainer in decor, are the cottage bedrooms a stone's throw away at the heart of the village, just two minutes' walk away from the magnificent grounds and gardens of Castle Ashby House. Home-made jams and jellies are a memorable feature of the Falcon's hearty country breakfasts. *Bar Food 12.15-2, 7.15-9. Restaurant Meals 12-2, 7.30-9.30. Free House. Beer Adnams, Hook Norton Old Hookey, Websters. Garden, outdoor eating.* **Accommodation** *14 bedrooms, all en suite, from £75 (single £59.50). Children welcome overnight (under-14s stay free in parents' room), additional beds available. Access, Visa.*

Castle Cary   George Hotel

Tel 01963 350761 Fax 01963 350035	**B&B**
Market Place Castle Cary Somerset BA7 7AH	Map 13 F2

Stone from the original 13th-century castle was used to build this listed 15th-century coaching inn – one of the oldest pubs in the country. In part, it is even older – the elm beam over the inglenook fireplace in the front bar dates back a further 500 years and has been carbon dated to the 10th century. Each of the sixteen rooms is decorated in an individual, cottagey style using either pine or darkwood furniture. All rooms have TV, radio, telephone and tea or coffee-making facilities. *Free House. Beer Butcombe, Bass. Patio/terrace.*

Accommodation 16 bedrooms, all en suite, £65 (single £45). Children welcome overnight, additional beds (£12.50), cot available (£6). Access, Visa.

Castle Combe   Castle Inn

Tel 01249 783030 Fax 01249 782315	B&B
Castle Combe nr Chippenham Wiltshire SN14 7HN	Map 14 B2

At the centre of one of England's prettiest villages, right by the ancient monument stone cross, this famous hostelry can trace its own origins back to the 12th century. Following a period of closure, it has reopened under the Hatton Hotels' banner as arguably England's smartest inn. Attention to detail in exposing and retaining the intricate old stonework and centuries-old beams has been commendable, and nowhere is this better evidenced than in the new conservatory that opens on to a private, enclosed patio; as a location for breakfasts served in several international guises, it is perhaps unparalleled. Each of the bedrooms has been remodelled in indiviudal style to a very high standard. Two 'superior' rooms have en-suite whirlpool bathrooms and a third a Victorian-style slipper bath. Accessories which might elsewhere be thought of as luxuries are standard throughout, with remote-control TVs, radio-alarms with phones, trouser presses and hairdryers. Here, the truly cossetting extras are complimentary fruit and mineral waters, boiled sweets, towelling robes, rubber ducks and resident teddy bears. *Open 11-11, Sun 12-3, 7-10.30. Free House.* **Beer** Ruddles Best, Courage Directors. **Accommodation** 7 rooms, all en suite, £55 & £70 (single £45 & £60). No dogs. Access, Diners, Visa.

Zzzz...

Castle Combe   White Hart

Tel 01294 782295	A
Castle Combe nr Chippenham Wiltshire	Map 14 B2

Down and across the village square from the central stone cross stands the historic, white-painted White Hart. It's down another step into the main bar, all leaded lights, stone alcoves and flagstone floors, which echo times past, warmed by the thigh-high dog grate that can throw an uncomfortable height of heat in winter. Convivial at the best of times, it can also be a crush. Across the passage, a carpeted lounge and family room have rather more space and less frenetic activity. To the rear, a corrugated, covered porch which would be a conservatory houses the resident mynah bird who's literally a talking point with minors. "Out back" by the suntrap of a patio is the gentleman's outhouse which, though primitive by today's standards, is a positively new piece of the old White Hart's heritage. Parking is very limited in central Castle Combe; be warned that it's some 300 yards' walk down from the public car park. *Open 11-3, 5.30-11, Sun 12-3, 7-10.30.* **Beer** Wadworth IPA, 6X & Farmer's Glory, guest beer. Access, Visa.

Castleton   Castle Hotel

Tel 01433 620578 Fax 01433 621112	B&B
Castle Street Castleton Derbyshire S30 2WG	Map 6 C2

This pleasant old inn dating back in part to the 17th century features strongly for its accommodation. Comfortable bedrooms in the main house and stable-block annexe are all prettily decorated, with solid darkwood furnishings, including four-posters, and smartly tiled en-suite facilities (3 have whirlpool baths). Despite modernisation, the bars still offer plenty of old-world atmosphere – notably the Castle

Bar with its flagstoned floors and low beamed ceilings. Bass Taverns. *Open 11-11 (Sun usual hours). Beer Stones, Worthington, guest beer. Garden. Family room. Accommodation 9 bedrooms, all en suite, from £59 (single £39.50). Children welcome overnight (under-12s £12), additional beds and cots (no charge) available. Check-in by arrangement. Guide dogs only. Access, Diners, Visa.*

Castleton   Ye Olde Nags Head Hotel

FOOD
B&B

Tel 0143 3620248   Fax 01433 621604

Castleton Derbyshire S30 2WH

Map 6 C2

17th-century coaching house in a tiny village at the head of Hope Valley, under the hilltop site of Peveril Castle. Bar meals are served both lunchtime and evening with cream of watercress soup (£1.75), paté-filled mushrooms (£3.40) or plaice stuffed with prawns served in lobster sauce (£5.75) on offer; however, the emphasis is very much on the elegant two-tiered restaurant at night, where typical dishes could include poached sole rolled with asparagus and (£6.80), asparagus and ham pancake in mornay sauce (£6.25), smoked salmon and prawn croutons (£8.20), or steak Roquefort (£13.95), followed by chocolate and hazelnut meringue (£3.60) for dessert. There is also a table d'hote at £16.95. Bedrooms are also elegant, and furnished in a handsome period style, three with four-posters, all well-equipped. The most expensive offer spa baths; the cheapest shower and toilet only. A bright first-floor residents' lounge is done out in chintz and bamboo. *Bar Food 12-2.45, 6-10.45 (Sun 7-10). Restaurant Meals 12-2 (Sun to 2.30), 7-10 (Sat to 10.30, Sun to 9.30). Children allowed in bar to eat. Free House. Beer Bass, Boddingtons. Accommodation 8 bedrooms, 6 en suite, £66 (single from £42.50) Children welcome overnight, additional beds (£12), cot available. Dogs by arrangement. Access, Diners, Visa.*

Caterham   Royal Oak

FOOD

Tel 018833 43510

68 High Street Caterham on the Hill Surrey

Map 11 B5

Lots of royal photographs and WWII memorabilia (part of a Messerschmitt shot down during the Battle of Britain hangs over the bar) decorate this small high-street pub presided over with civility and good humour by Ron Coulston who gained numerous 'good pub' awards during his 28 years at the nearby *Wattendon Arms* at Kenley. Lunchtimes only there is a short blackboard menu of home-cooked fare – soups of the day (£1.60), ploughman's (£2.50) and sandwiches (from £1.30) plus about four main dishes like steak and kidney pie, chicken casserole (£4) and always ham and eggs (£4) that come with some splendid old-fashioned chips – hand-cut, crisp and golden. Leave room for a homely pud like apple or lemon meringue pie (all at £1.50). *Open 11-11, usual hours Sun. Bar Food 12-2.30 (not Sun). Beer Fuller's London Pride, Hancock's, Highgate Mild. Patio. No credit cards.*

Cauldon   Yew Tree Inn

A

Tel 01538 308348

Cauldon Waterhouses nr Stoke-on-Trent Staffordshire ST10 3EJ

Map 6 C3

Alan East has acquired his vast collection of antiques and bric-a-brac over the last 32 years as landlord of this old-fashioned, stone-built pub. Persian rugs overlay original quarry-tiled floors and there are cast-iron copper-topped tables, a working pianola and giant Victorian music boxes which still operate for just 2p. Sleepy and undiscovered it is not, but worth a visit, nevertheless; go in the evening and hear the landlord performing on the pianola. Between A52 and A523, eight miles west of Ashbourne, five miles from Alton Towers. Children allowed in the 'Polyphon Room'. *Open 10-2.30 (Sat to 3), 6-11, Sun 12-3, 7-10.30. Free House.* **Beer** *Bass, Burton Bridge, M&B Mild. Family room. No credit cards.*

Cawthorne   Spencer Arms

Tel 01226 790228   **A**

21 Church Street Cawthorne Barnsley South Yorkshire S75 4HL   **Map 6 C2**

Smart, well-run Whitbread pub with two bar rooms and a separate restaurant area. Uniformed staff try hard to lift this pub above the run-of-the-mill chain standards. Close to 17th-century Cannon Hall and County Park. 4 miles west of Barnsley on the A635 Barnsley to Denby Dale road, just off the M1. Whitbread Wayside Inn. *Open 11-11, Sun 12-10.30.* **Beer** *Boddingtons, Flowers, Castle Eden. Garden. Children's menu. Access, Visa.*

Cerne Abbas   New Inn

Tel 01300 341274   **FOOD**
                                                                            B&B
Cerne Abbas nr Dorchester Dorset DT2 7JF   **Map 13 F2**

'New' refers to 16th-century modernisation to an 11th-century structure – a red-brick arch and steep slate-stone roof – so no nasty architectural shocks here. It was originally used as a dormitory for the nearby Abbey, accommodating passing pilgrims, before becoming a coaching inn during the 16th century. Rooms are still available to passing travellers. Five modest bedrooms have sloping and creaking floors, attractive modern darkwood furniture, TVs and tea-making kits. All share two clean and well-equipped bathrooms and a further toilet, as the listed status of the building prevents any alterations to incorporate en-suite facilities. Downstairs, the comfortably furnished bar adorned with farming memorabilia is the scene of some good home cooking. A printed selection of dishes includes pheasant paté with armagnac (£3.75) or grilled goat's cheese, bacon and walnut salad (£4.45) to start, followed by spiced breast of chicken (£6.95), stir-fry of beef and vegetables (£7.90), grills (from £6.50) and skate with black pepper and capers (£9). All meals are served with a selection of crisp vegetables or a choice of freshly prepared salads from the cabinet. A short blackboard list of daily specials may include fresh mussels in a wine and cream sauce (£4.95), lasagne (£4.95) and cashew nut roast with peperonata (£4.95). Bread-and-butter pudding, chocolate and strawberry roulade or coffee and brandy syllabub completes the picture. There is an excellent selection of up to 14 wines by the glass, which are chosen from the wide-ranging list of 50 bottles. At the end of the courtyard is a large, peaceful walled garden with rose-beds and benches. The picturesque village is well worth a visit, as is the Bronze Age fertility symbol – the Cerne Abbas Giant – carved on the hillside above the village. New landlord. **Bar Food** *12-2, 7-9. Children's menu and portions available.* **Beer** *Eldridge Pope, Dorchester Bitter, Hardy Country, Royal Oak. Garden, outdoor eating, barbecue.* **Accommodation** *5 bedrooms, £30 (4-poster £36, single £25). Children welcome overnight. Additional beds available. Access, Visa.*

Cerne Abbas   Red Lion

Tel 01300 341441   **FOOD**

Cerne Abbas Long Street nr Dorchester Dorset DT2 7JF   Map 13 F2

Unassuming, ancient Grade II listed pub with an unusual Victorian
facade, thanks to a late 19th-century fire. The single carpeted bar is
simply furnished and boasts a splendid 16th-century fireplace,
crackling with logs in winter. Bar food ranges from a predictable
printed menu offering the usual favourites to a more interesting
blackboard selection of hearty home-cooked dishes, which are the
main emphasis of the kitchen. At least two choices of fish, fresh from
Poole, are featured as well as a further five enjoyable dishes such as
game pie in orange and port sauce (£5.85), chicken sauté sauce
(£6.10), pan haggerty and pork escalope, all served with a crisp
vegetable and a dish of new potatoes. There is always a freshly
prepared soup – mulligatawny, lemon and fennel or cucumber (£2).
Home-made desserts may include banana split and meringue nest
(both £2.50). In summer months the delightful, well-tended and
sheltered south-facing garden is a real oasis away from the busy village
street. The ladies' loo is a real 5-star luxury specimen. New landlord.
Bar Food 11.30-2.30, 6.30-11 (Sun 12-2.30, 7-10.30). Free House.
Beer Wadworth 6X & IPA, Bass, Ringwood Best Bitter. Garden, outdoor
eating area. No credit cards.

Chaddleworth   Ibex

Tel 01488 638311   **FOOD**

Chaddleworth nr Newbury Berkshire RG16 0ER   Map 14a B4

Landlord Colin Brown was once a professional jockey and rode Desert
Orchid to many of his early victories. His enthusiasm for the sport,
coupled with the pub's proximity to racing stables, ensures plenty of
horsey talk in the bar – not to mention a television for watching the
racing. Restaurant and bar offer the same menu of imaginative fare
(usually with a good choice of fish) such as eggy bread (£3.50), black
pudding (£3.50), Stilton and egg bake (£3.50), beef in Guinness
(£5.75), coronation chicken (£7.95), pigeon pie (£5.75), halibut in
mustard sauce (£11.95), plaice in parsley sauce (£7.25) and sturdy
home-made English puddings including treacle tart, banana cheesecake
and various fruit crumbles. Traditional Sunday roast is £7.25. Eight
to ten wines are available by the glass. *Bar Food & Restaurant Meals*
12-2, 7-9.30 (except Sun eve). Children's menu. Beer Morland Old
Speckled Hen & Original, Charles Wells Bombardier, guest beer. Garden,
outdoor eating. Family room. Pub closed Sun eve. Access, Visa.

Chadlington   Tite Inn

Tel 01608 676475   **FOOD**

Mill End Chadlington Oxfordshire OX7 3NY   Map 14a B1

This warm 16th-century Cotswold-stone pub is as pretty as a picture,
complete with cottage roses clambering up the walls. Inside, the
original rough stone walls remain, but otherwise it is almost too neat
and tidy, with its modern carpeted floor and wheelback chairs. A table
displaying newspapers and magazines is a nice touch, though, and
there is also a garden room which features bunches of grapes hanging
from a vine covering the roof. The origin of the unusual name is
uncertain but is thought to refer to the nearby springs which used to
feed a mill pond. Michael Willis behind the bar looks after the real
ales, which include the happily named Dr Thirsty's Draught from the

local Glenny brewery, while Susan looks after the kitchen. Hearty home-made soups (£1.95) and succulent gammon sandwiches made with superior wholemeal bread are amongst the offerings listed on the regularly changing blackboard menu, although bobotie (a sweet and spicy meat loaf from South Africa – £5.25) is, by popular demand, a permanent fixture, and there are always several vegetarian dishes available. At night, one end of the bar becomes a restaurant with dishes ranging from chicken breast in cider and honey sauce (£6.50) to duck sausages with Cumberland sauce (£5.95). A traditional roast is served on Sundays (£5.95). Popular puddings include fruit crumble (£2.25), hot sticky toffee pudding (£2.25) and chocolate and rum mousse (£2.25). The set menu is a little shorter in the evening. Children are made genuinely welcome and small portions are no problem. The huge garden with herbal and flower borders has tables laid out and children play on the lawn. *Bar Food (No food Monday) 12-2 (Sun to 1.30), 6.30-9 (Sun 7-8.30). Restaurant Meals 12-2 (Sun only), 7-9 (except Sun). Free House. Beer Badger Bitter, Wadworth Henry's IPA, plus two regularly changing guest beers. Garden, outdoor eating. Pub closed Mondays. No credit cards.*

Chale	**Clarendon Hotel & Wight Mouse Inn**	**FOOD**
Tel & Fax 01983 730431		**B&B**
Chale Isle of Wight PO38 2HA		Map 15 D4

This 17th-century coaching inn (on the B3399) is a perennial favourite, for food, atmosphere, bed and breakfast and the genuine welcome to children: the Wight Mouse Inn was our 1990 Family Pub of the Year. Parents with children are treated like first-class citizens both inside and out. There are decent home-made bar meals too, featuring delicious local fish and seafood including mushrooms in garlic butter (£2.70), local crab cocktail (£3.30) and breaded cod (£3.90), and an astonishing 365 whiskies. The dining room has a set five-course dinner menu for £17 which includes dishes such as chicken kebabs, carbonnade of beef, stuffed trout and chicken breast in cream sauce with grapes. Nice bedrooms in the Clarendon next door successfully blend period and modern comforts, excellent family facilities and pretty views of the sea. There are two family suites and the downstairs Clarendon suite has a waterbed. The rear garden overlooks Chalk Bay and the Needles. Apart from the playground and domestic animals (including this year's addition Arthur the Shetland pony), entertainment is provided in summer. *Open 11-midnight, Sun usual hours. Bar Food & Restaurant Meals 11.30-10 (Sun 12-2.30, 7-9.30). Children's menu. Free House. Beer Marston's Pedigree, Wadworth 6X, Boddingtons, Castle Eden, Morrells Strong County, Old Speckled Hen. Garden, outdoor eating, children's play area. 3 family rooms. Accommodation 13 bedrooms, 10 en suite, £65 (single £30). Children welcome overnight (under-2s stay free in parents' room, 3-5s £5, 6-12s half-price, 13-16s 66%), additional beds and cots available. Dogs £3. Access, Visa.*

Charing	**Royal Oak Inn**	
Tel 01233 712612		**B&B**
High Street Charing Kent TN27 0HU		Map 11 C5

Homely inn located in the centre of an attractive medieval village at the base of the North Downs, just off the A20. Good pubby bar with bare boards and simple pine furniture and an upstairs function area in the old malting room. Neat, simply furnished accommodation in nine en-suite bedrooms, the best rooms being located in the new rear extension. Good, clean bathrooms or compact shower rooms and TVs and tea-making facilities for added comfort. Handy overnight stop for the ferry ports or the Chunnel. *Pub open 11-11 (Sat 12-10.30). Free House. Beer Bass, Fuller's London Pride, Shepherd Neame, guest beer. Accommodation 5 bedrooms, all en-suite, from £40 (single £27.50). Children welcome overnight (under-5s stay free in parents' room). No dogs. Access.*

Charlbury   The Bell House

Tel 01608 810278 Fax 01608 811447	**B&B**
Church Street Charlbury Oxfordshire OX7 3PP	Map 14a B2

Historic Charlbury with its 7th-century St Mary's Church was royally chartered to hold cattle markets in 1256: the last one was held behind the Bell some 700 years later. With its own datestone of 1700, the mellow stone inn is full of character. The small flagstoned bar and sun-lounge makes guests feel much at home and in fair weather the patio looking down a long, sloping garden is a picturesque spot. Access to bedrooms is by steep staircases and narrow passageways yet the rooms themselves are spacious and neatly appointed with matching fabrics and up-to-date accessories which include hair-dryers, trouser presses and welcome clock-radios. The three smaller doubles have en-suite wc/showers only and one single is not en-suite, though its adjacent bathroom is private. Conference facilities in the converted stable block accommodate up to 55. Children welcome (under 16s stay free in parents' room) cot and extra beds provided. Free House. *Open 11-3, 6-11 (12-3, 7-10.30 Sun) Beer Hook Norton Best, Wadworth 6X. Accommodation 14 bedrooms, all en suite £75 (Single £50). Children welcome overnight and allowed anywhere inside. Family room. Access, Diners, Visa.*

Zzz...

Charlbury   The Bull at Charlbury

	FOOD
Tel 01608 810689	**B&B**
Sheep Street Charlbury Oxfordshire OX7 3RR	Map 14a B2

Of these once-derelict premises, lovingly restored by their own hand just two years ago, Peter and Lucy Wearing's own description of the Bull as a "Country Bistro and Bar with Rooms" is entirely appropriate. In addition to the now-thriving bistro (recommended in our *1995 Hotels and Restaurants Guide*) the new stone-flagged bar to the rear does a more-than-adequate line in hearty snacks. From club sandwiches of chicken and bacon or steak and mushroom (both £4.50) to the ever-popular chilli con carne (£4.95) and beef Stroganoff (£6.95) this is well-prepared, flavourful food. Try also the local Charlbury sausage with smoked bacon and mustard sauce (£5.50), washed down perhaps with a good pint. For a lighter snack or perhaps as a starter are the likes of warm winter salad or creamed garlic mushrooms (both £3.25): to follow try the lemon and sultana cheesecake (£2.75), vintage Stilton with black grapes or the fine home-made ice creams. Exposed beams and natural stone give the half dozen bedrooms their character. Matching fabrics, darkwood furniture and large comfortable beds are all of a high standard, while beverage trays and satellite TVs are provided for the less socially-inclined, who may also welcome the lack of room telephones. Check-in should be agreed with the landlords in advance, as there is not always someone at home in the afternoons: children are welcome by arrangement. *Bar Food 12-2, 7-9 Restaurant Meals 12-2 (Sun only), 7-9 (except Sun and*

*Mon). Free House. **Beers** Morland Original/Old Speckled Hen, Fuller's London Pride. **Accommodation** 6 bedrooms, all en suite £50 (single £45). 4 days Christmas. Access, Diners, Visa.*

Charlestown   Pier House Hotel

Tel 01726 67955 Fax 01726 69246	B&B
Charlestown St Austell Cornwall PL25 3NJ	Map 12 B3

Nearly all the rooms at this small, family-run 18th-century hotel have either far-reaching sea views or they overlook the attractive harbour in this charming and popular little port. Bedrooms vary in size and style; some feature attractive modern darkwood pieces of furniture, others are rather plain, but all are neat and clean with pretty floral fabrics, TVs, radio/alarms, telephone and tea-making facilities. Good shower/bathrooms. Public areas include a small pubby bar with red barrel seats and wall benches and a rear dining area, which is open during the day for snacks and cream teas. *Free House. **Beer** Bass, Boddingtons. **Accommodation** 12 bedrooms, all en suite, £57-£62 (single £30, family £78). Children welcome overnight. Access, Visa.*

Charlestown   Rashleigh Arms

Tel 01726 73635	B&B
Charlestown St Austell Cornwall PL25 3NJ	Map 12 B3

Under the same ownership as the Pier House Hotel on the quay, this much-extended and refurbished Georgian inn has an attractive flower-bedecked facade and a vast open-plan interior, furnished with blue velour padded wall bench seating and darkwood 'pub' furniture. The main interest of this inn is the five neat and comfortable first-floor bedrooms that are ideal for visiting St Austell businessmen and popular with holidaymakers not requiring the formalities and facilities of a hotel. All have modern pine furniture, floral duvets and curtains, bedside lamps and are light and airy with clean, compact shower rooms. *Free House. **Beer** Wadworth 6X, Ruddles County, Bass, Tetley Bitter, Boddingtons, guest beer. Garden, outdoor eating area. **Accommodation** 5 bedrooms, all en suite, £45 (single £22.50). Access, Visa.*

Charlton   Horse & Groom

	FOOD
Tel 01666 823904	B&B
Charlton nr Malmesbury Wiltshire SH16 9DL	Map 14 C2

The solidly elegant Cotswold stone house fronted by a tree-sheltered lawn stands in its own paddock well back from the B4040. Its history as a coaching inn dating back to the 16th century is well documented by the framed prints and drawings which hang in the rustic main bar which retains an evocative air of exposed stonework, woodblock flooring and assorted pine tables and chairs. The adjacent lounge and dining areas, undergoing a little revamping at the time of our last visit, are rather more intimately conducive to the enjoyment of some significantly improving bar food. Adventurous eaters are sorely tempted by starters of sweetcorn and celery soup (£2.50), sauté of mushrooms in ham and cheese sauce (£3.25) or perhaps a fine mange tout and prawn stir fry (£3.50); and no less by main courses of the likes of swordfish and monkfish skewers (£6.95), chicken breast in white wine and apricots (£7.95) and spicy tomato pasta bows with onions, peppers and cheese (£4.95). For a pub of apparently modest size and appointments, meanwhile, the three double bedrooms are a

Zzzz...

revelation: 32-channel satellite TV, hi-tech phones and complimentary fruit and mineral water are all provided. Gold-tapped, tiled bathrooms with towelling robes and his-and-hers toiletries provide all the trappings of luxury usually associated with much grander outfits. The task of co-ordinating operations, and fulfilling such high expectations, has fallen recently, following a change of ownership, on two of the country's youngest licensees, Nichola King and chef Philip Gilder who are approaching their new-found responsibilities with great relish and good humour. The physical improvements currently in hand promise to be matched in the fullness of time by their highly professional and personable performance. *Bar & Restaurant meals 12-2, 7-10 (Sun to 9.30). Free House. Beer Archers Village, Wadworth 6X, guest beer. Garden, outdoor eating. Family room. Accommodation 3 bedrooms, all en suite, from £69.50 (single £55). Children over 8 welcome overnight. No dogs. Access, Visa.*

Chatton   Percy Arms

Tel 01668 215244	**B&B**
Chatton nr Alnwick Northumberland WE66 5PS	Map 5 D1

"A romantic retreat, situated in a favourite neighbourhood, several miles of free fishing water in the Till. Half an hour's walk from Chillingham Castle, Park and wild cattle. Well-aired beds. Good stabling". Posted prominently at the bar, the words of John Fitzgerald, proprietor at the turn of the century, ring equally true today. Stabling – for residents – is as good as ever with beds as well-aired: one wonders what the former landlord would have made of en-suite WCs and showers, colour TVs and beverage trays, let alone the guests' private sauna. The sole village pub since 1874, today's black oak bar is many times bigger than that of yesteryear, with a childrens' and games room to the rear and a tiny garden in front. Children welcome overnight – one cot available free of charge. *Free House. Shut for 10 days at Christmas. Beer Theakston XB. Accommodation 7 bedrooms, 5 en suite, £40 (single £20). Children welcome overnight (under 2s free and under 10s £10 in parents' room), cots available. Garden. No credit cards.*

Chelsworth   Peacock Inn

	FOOD
Tel 01449 740758	**B&B**
The Street Chelsworth nr Hadleigh Suffolk QP7 7HU	Map 10 C3

This charming, well-restored 1470 cottage pub enjoys an enviable village centre location, close to the church and overlooking Chelsworth bridge and delightful parkland. Inside is oak timbered, inglenooked and immaculate with a good assortment of neatly arranged and polished darkwood furniture, brass, copper and tasteful prints throughout the three rambling rooms. Atmospheric appeal is enhanced by evening candlelight which tempts diners inside to peruse the above average, but little changing, menu listed on a blackboard. To start one will find local game paté (£3.50), grilled crab cake with a dill sauce (£3.25) and home-made soup, such as broccoli and Stilton (£1.95). Main course options feature an interesting range of sauced fish dishes, namely grilled halibut steak with tarragon and horseradish cream sauce (£5.95) and fillet of bream baked in a tomato and herb sauce (£6.45). Meat alternatives include leg of lamb steak with a mushroom and rosemary sauce (£6.95). All dishes are served with crisp vegetables. Vegetarian selection (from £4.25) and standard puddings (£2.50). Upstairs, five spotless cottagey bedrooms are furnished with old pine, including old-fashioned washstands, TVs and beverage-making facilities, but share a beamed bathroom and WC. The Old English Pub Company. *Bar Food 12-2.30, 6.30-9.30.* **Accommodation** *5 bedrooms, not en suite £45 (Single £25). Children welcome overnight and anywhere (free sharing with parents).* **Beers** *Ruddles Best, Adnams Southwold, Thwaites Bitter. Garden, outdoor eating area. Access, Visa.*

Chenies   **Red Lion**

Tel 01923 282722	**FOOD**
Chenies Rickmansworth Hertfordshire WD3 6ED	Map 15a E2

Just up the lane from Chenies Manor, an unassuming, white-painted pub with a plain, simply-furnished main bar and a charming small dining area housed in the original 17th-century cottage to the rear with a tiled floor, old inglenook and rustic furniture. A varied selection of home-cooked bar food includes French bread sticks, wholemeal baps and jacket potatoes with unusual fillings (from £2.95) and popular pies straight from the oven (Chenies lamb or venison and ale, both £5.95). A blackboard lists a few daily specials, including the vegetarian dish of the day. The pub is not suitable for children. **Bar Food** *12-2, 7-10 (to 9.30 Sun).* **Beer** *Benskins Bitter, Adnams Bitter, Wadworth 6X, Cotleigh Rebellion. Access.*

Cheriton   **Flower Pots**

Tel 01962 771318	**FOOD**
	B&B
Cheriton Alresford Hampshire SO24 0QQ	Map 15 D3

Originally built as a farmhouse in the 1840s by the head gardener of nearby Avington House, this unassuming and homely brick village pub has become a popular place in which to enjoy simple, honest bar food, good home-brewed ales and comfortable overnight accommodation since being released from Whitbread two years ago. Two traditional bars are delightfully music- and electronic game-free, the rustic public bar being furnished with pine tables and benches and the cosy saloon bar having a relaxing sofa among other chairs. Both have open winter fires and an added feature is a 27ft glass-topped well. A separate room has some easy chairs, numerous books and a television to keep children amused. A short value-for-money menu offers honest home-cooked snacks and features a range of jacket potatoes with decent fillings (from £2), generously-filled baps (from £1.50), chili (£3), beef stew (£3.50) and a couple of daily specials such as sweet and sour chicken with egg fried rice (£3.50), liver and bacon hotpot (£3.50) or chicken curry (£4.50). Puddings are not available. These quick, filling snacks can be washed down by a choice of four real ales of varying strengths, brewed on the premises in the newly constructed Cheriton Brewhouse. Also across the car park are five neat, pine-furnished bedrooms housed in a well-converted outbuilding. Downstairs rooms are compact, while the two attic rooms are light and airy with additional sofa beds; all have floral fabrics, TV, tea-makers, magazines and spotless, tiled shower rooms. *Free House.* **Beer** *Cheriton Brewhouse, Hopback Summer Lightning, Ballard's Best Bitter. Garden, outdoor eating area.* **Accommodation** *5 bedrooms, all en suite, £40 (single £22). No credit cards.*

Cheriton Bishop   Old Thatch Inn

FOOD
B&B

Tel 01647 24204

Cheriton Bishop nr Exeter Devon EX6 6HJ

Map 13 D2

Attractive, white-painted and thatched roadside inn, located on the old
A30 and a useful detour from the new dual carriageway for
comfortable overnight accommodation and above-average bar food. A
central fireplace is lit in winter and warms the rambling, carpeted and
plainly furnished main bar; the smaller side room – Travellers Nook
– is unusually decorated with Ordnance Survey maps. Bar food relies
on an extensive printed menu that features standard favourites
alongside a few more imaginative dishes that are well described;
results on the plate should not disappoint. Starters or snacks include
freshly prepared soups (tomato, onion and herb £1.35), salad niçoise
(£2.30) and sautéed kidneys (£2.65), while main course fare ranges
from steak and kidney pudding (£4.25), thatcher's pie (£4.75) and
sausage, mash and gravy (£2.95) to braised stuffed hearts (£4.40) and
beef olives (£5.75). One must ask about the daily paté, vegetarian
dish, curry and puddings. Regular sweets include baked spiced bread
pudding (£2.25) and thatch trifle (£2.50). Homely, good-value
accommodation is offered in two neat bedrooms with 'stag' furniture,
TVs, tea-making kits, radio/alarms and clean en-suite facilities. No
children under 14 on the premises. *Free House.* **Beer** *Wadworth 6X,
Cotleigh Tawny Bitter, Exmoor Ale.* **Accommodation** *2 bedrooms, both en
suite, £44 (single £32). Check-in by arrangement. Access, Visa.*

Chester   Ye Olde King's Head

B&B

Tel 01244 324855   Fax 01244 315693

48/50 Lower Bridge Street Chester Cheshire CH1 1RS

Map 6 A2

A striking black and white timber-framed building just a stone's
throw from the Roman walls and river, yet handy for high street
shopping. Residents find evening refuge from popular all-day bars in a
first-floor lounge bar and Hudson's restaurant. Second-floor bedrooms
house some remarkable features, the superb 16th-century roof trusses
fortunately reinforced with forged steel pins. Dark hardwood fittings
and co-ordinated fabrics stay in keeping, while comforts are plentiful
with dial-out phones, TVs, tea trays and trouser presses: en-suite
bathrooms are necessarily small, but are neatly appointed. Bar snacks
(lunchtime only, except Sun). *Premier House.* **Beer** *Greenalls Original,
Theakstons.* **Accommodation** *8 bedrooms, all en suite, £46.40 (single
£46.95). Children welcome overnight (£5, infants free), additional beds
and cots available. Access, Diners, Visa.*

Chicksgrove   Compasses Inn

FOOD
B&B

Tel & Fax 01722 714318

Chicksgrove Tisbury nr Salisbury Wiltshire SP3 6NB

Map 14 C3

A timeless air pervades this attractive 16th-century thatched inn, set on
a peaceful lane, deep in rolling Wiltshire countryside. An old cobbled
path leads to the entrance of the charmingly unspoilt bar, which has a
low-beamed ceiling, partly flagstoned floor and an assortment of
traditional furniture arranged in many secluded alcoves. Various
farming tools and tackle from bygone days adorn the bare walls and
a 100-year-old set of table skittles maintain the old-world atmosphere.
A small adjoining dining/children's room leads out to a sheltered rear
garden with rural views. Owners Bob and Ann Inglis have rescued the
inn from nearly two years of closure and neglect and are successfully

Zzz...

restoring its reputation of being a splendid inn. Ann Inglis is in
control of the cooking and takes pride in preparing the short selection
of dishes that make up the twice-daily-changing blackboard menus.
Fresh produce is used in creating her hearty and popular pies –
chicken, ham and mushroom, steak, wine and mushroom, fish (all
£7.50) – while other freshly prepared main choices may include port
fillet cooked in a parcel with thyme and garlic (£10.50), minty lamb,
apricot and cashew nut casserole and blanquette de veau (both £8.95);
all served with a selection of vegetables. Starters range from courgette
and Stilton soup (£2.50) to chicken liver and apple paté (£3.75). A
short set menu is to be introduced for Friday and Saturday evenings
featuring more imaginative fare. Ploughman's and sandwiches are
available lunchtimes for those wanting a lighter bite and on Sundays a
buffet-style lunch is prepared; using the barbecue when its sunny. A
stone covered stairway leads to the lawned front garden with benches
and brollies and to the inn's bedrooms. Three comfortable, neat and
spotlessly clean bedrooms (the largest tucked beneath the heavy
thatch) radiate off the private, well furnished sitting room, complete
with bookshelves, desk, chintzy three-piece suite, magazines and tea-
making facilities. Two of the bedrooms are ensuite with shower units,
the other having a private, but not ensuite, bathroom. Excellent hearty
breakfasts served in the bar (also available to pre-booked walkers)
feature home-made marmalade and jam plus locally-made sausages.
Note: the pub is closed Monday (except Bank Holidays), Tuesday and
Wednesday for food and drink, but remains open all week for bed and
breakfast. 5% surcharge for credit cards. *Bar Food 12-2.30, 7-10 (Sun
from 9). Free House. Beer Bass, Adnams, Wadworth 6X, guest beer.
Garden, outdoor eating, children's play area. Family room.*
*Accommodation 3 bedrooms, 2 en suite, £45 (single £30). Children
welcome overnight, additional beds and cots (both £10) available. Check-in
by arrangement. Access, Visa.*

Chiddingfold	**Crown Inn**	**FOOD**
Tel 01428 682255 Fax 01428 685736		**B&B**
The Green Petworth Road Chiddingfold Surrey GU8 4TX		**Map 11 A5**

Originally a guest house for pilgrims and Cistercian monks, the
creeper-clad, medieval timber-framed Crown (built around 1258) is
still offering hospitality to travellers. The soft furnishings in the main
bar area are a little tired but one's eye is taken by the massive old
beams and huge inglenook fireplace. A panelled restaurant, of slightly
later date, boasts an ornate plaster ceiling and examples of the stained
glass for which Chiddingfold was famous during the 13th and 17th
centuries. It's managed by a division of the Hall and Woodhouse
brewery and refreshment comes in the form of ales with names like
Tanglefoot and Badger. The inner man can feast on substantial fare
like soup of the day (£1.95), chili with rice (£4.95), steak and ale pie
(£5.95); sandwiches start at £2.50; or in the restaurant try avocado
en croute (£6.95) or stuffed trout (£10.75). Creaking stairs and
corridors lead to the bedrooms, some full of character with antique
furniture (three with four-poster beds), and others lighter and more
modern in style. All have remote-control TV, direct-dial phone,
beverage tray and trouser press. There is no family room but an
additional child's bed can be put up in a suite for no extra cost. Badger
Inns. *Open 11-11 (Sun usual hours). Bar Food & Restaurant Meals
12-2.30, 7-9.30 (no restaurant food Mon). Children allowed in bar to eat.
Beer Hall & Woodhouse Tanglefoot, Badger Best, Wadworth 6X, Charles*

Wells Eagle IPA. Terrace, outdoor eating. **Accommodation** *7 bedrooms, all en suite, from £57 (4-poster £78, suite £90, single £47). Children welcome overnight, additional beds and cots available. Check-in from 8am. Access, Diners, Visa.*

Chiddingstone   Castle Inn

Tel 01892 870247   Fax 01892 870808

A

Chiddingstone Edenbridge Kent TN8 7AH

Map 11 B5

Located at the end of a unique, unspoilt row of Tudor timbered houses opposite the parish church, this historic tile-hung building dates from 1420 and boasts leaded casement windows and projecting upper gables. Like the rest of the village street, the pub is owned by the National Trust and remains delightfully unchanged with two traditional, atmospheric bars. Classic public bar with chequered quarry-tiled floor, beams, an old brick fireplace and rustic wall benches. Extra comfort can be found in the beamed lounge bar and alfresco summer eating in the pretty rear garden and courtyard. *Open 10.30-11 Sat, usual hours other days. Free House.* **Beer** *Shepherd Neame Master Brew, Harveys Sussex Bitter, Larkins Sovereign. Garden. Access, Diners, Visa.*

Chilgrove   White Horse Inn

Tel 01243 59219   Fax 01243 59301

FOOD

Chilgrove nr Chichester West Sussex PO18 9HX

Map 15 D3

Wisteria-clad pub and restaurant (see our Hotel and Restaurant Guide) in a glorious Sussex Downs setting with not another building in sight. The bar is quite modest in appearance – red plastic banquettes and pink draylon chairs around simple wooden tables – and the only beer served comes from a small barrel sitting on the bar counter. The selection of wines is another matter though as landlord Barry Phillips (who celebrated 25 years here in 1994) has created one of the best cellars in the country and from which well over a dozen wines are available by the glass at any one time. Bar meals, the responsibility of chef-partner Neil Rusbridger, are displayed on cards pinned up on a cork noticeboard. Typically the selection might include a gratin of Selsey Crab (£6.95), gammon steak (£6.45), roast Aylesbury Duck (£6.95), coq au vin (£6.50) and steak au poivre (£10.95) along with ploughman's (£3.95), sandwiches (from £1.95) and salads. There are always a couple of vegetarian options and treacle tart (£3.25) and home made ices. In the evenings there is also a short, three-course supper menu at £12.50 including coffee. No children indoors but there's plenty of room outdoors in good weather. It is hoped there will be some bedroom accommodation available in an adjacent cottage from the end of 1994. *Free House.* **Bar Meals** *(no food Mon) 12-2, 6-10 (Closed Sun).* **Beer** *Ballard's. Outdoor eating on green opposite. Pub closed all Monday and Sunday evening. Access, Diners, Visa.*

Chilham   White Horse

Tel 01227 730355

A

The Square Chilham Kent CT4 8BY

Map 11 C5

Probably the most photographed pub in the county, this attractive white-painted and part-timbered pub nestles within, what is arguably, the prettiest village square in Kent. Sited next to the church and surrounded by medieval timbered houses, the White Horse dates from 1422 and offers weary tourists a welcome retreat within the three,

comfortably furnished inter-connecting rooms, which are warmed by
good winter log fires – one in a massive inglenook. An intriguing
history includes the discovery in 1956 of two skeletons, possibly
soldiers killed at the Battle of Chilham during the Wat Tyler
rebellion of 1380 and now buried in the churchyard next door.
Walled garden and front benches with village square views. No
children inside. Whitbread Wayside Inn. *Pub open 11-11 (Sun 12-3,7-
10.30).* ***Beer*** *Fremlins Bitter, Flowers Original, Fuller's London Pride,
Brakspear Bitter. Walled garden, outdoor eating area. Access, Visa.*

Chilham   Woolpack

Tel 01227 730208	**B&B**
The Street Chilham Kent CT4 8DL	Map 11 C5

Dating from 1420, this pretty salmon pink-painted inn lies within 100
yards of Chilham's charming square. Newish, enthusiastic managers
have rejuvenated this historic place after a long period in the
doldrums, by smartening up the exterior and refurbishing the old
world bar, the attractive dining room and the fourteen en-suite
bedrooms. Rooms vary in size and location, the sole main building
bedroom and one of the three wool store rooms boasting fine four-
poster beds. Good overnight accommodation for families, one of the
decent-sized family rooms having access to a sheltered garden with
seating. Appealing floral fabrics, modern dark mahogany furniture,
clean bath or shower rooms and TVs, tea-makers, telephones and
clock-radios for added comfort. *Pub open 11-3, 6-11 (Sun 12-3, 7-
10.30). Free House.* ***Beer*** *Shepherd Neame. Garden, courtyard, outdoor
eating area.* ***Accommodation*** *14 bedrooms, all en suite, from £45 (family
room with garden £55, four-poster £60, suite £70, single £35). Children
welcome overnight, first child under 14 free, 2nd child £15 plus food. Small
dogs only. Access, Visa.*

Chillington   Chillington Inn

Tel 01548 580244	**FOOD**
	B&B
Chillington nr Kingsbridge Devon TQ7 2JS	Map 13 D3

The front door of this white-painted 16th-century inn opens directly
on to the main road through the village, with no pavement in
between, so take care when leaving after a convivial evening. Inside,
the unpretentiously snug bar has some unusual carved oak wall
benches and tables, a warming open fire and two blackboards listing
the monthly-changing selection of bar food. The highlight of the
menu is the splendid range of nine home-made soups, for example
Stilton and broccoli, lettuce and herb, carrot, parsnip and coriander
and chicken and sweetcorn (£2.25), which are proving a lunchtime
favourite among customers. Other good-value and hearty home-
prepared snacks include chili with French bread (£3.95), beef curry
(£4.95), Devon chicken casserole (£4.50), various omelettes (from
£3.50) and baked fishcakes (£4.50). The traditional Sunday roasts are
very popular (from £5.95) in winter. For more substantial meals the
small attractive restaurant, boasting a fine stone fireplace, provides a
short hand-written menu listing more elaborate fare. Main course
emphasis is on West Country recipes such as chicken breast with cider,
leeks and cream (£8.95), herb-crusted rack of lamb with a
blackcurrant sauce (£10.95) and a rich venison casserole (£9.95).
Good puddings – bread-and-butter pudding and spiced apple pancakes
(£2.95) – come with thick clotted cream. Two charming bedrooms
have matching wallpaper and fabrics in a pretty trellis pattern with

bedhead drapes and ruffled blinds at the windows. Each room has a clean, good-sized bathroom across the corridor. This year there is also a new barn conversion family suite which will probably be made available at £250 per week but, like everything else about this friendly and relaxed pub, it's flexible. *Free House.* ***Bar & Restaurant Food*** *12-2 (Sat to 2.30)* & *7-10.* ***Beer*** *Bass, Palmers IPA, occasional guest beer. Small garden, outdoor eating.* ***Accommodation*** *2 bedrooms, £37 (single £21). Children welcome overnight (£10 for a zed-bed), family suite by arrangement. Access, Diners, Visa.*

Chipping Campden	**Eight Bells Inn**	**FOOD**
Tel 01386 840371		**B&B**
Church Street Chipping Campden Gloucestershire GL55 6JG		Map 14a A1

Originally built in the 14th century to house masons building the nearby church (and to store the bells), and over the years the pub is reputed to have played host to royalty, and quite possibly William Shakespeare as well. A tiny, low Cotswold stone frontage hung with flower baskets reveals through its cobbled entranceway a single, cosily intimate bar and an enclosed courtyard with abundant greenery. That the food merits serious attention is evidenced by the blackboard menu and the slick manner of its service. Green pea and mint soup (£2.50), warm bacon and avocado salad (£4.50), beefsteak and kidney pie (£5.75), mixed seafood en croute (£6.80), sirloin steaks peppered or plain (£9.25); to follow, apricot and ginger crumble (£2.50) or a Colston Bassett Stilton with biscuits: to accompany, good Tetley Bitter and numerous wines by the glass from a 30-bin list. Paul and Patrick Dare took over the Eight Bells a couple of years ago now and converted what was a derelict barn into five double bedrooms (two with WC/shower only), one with a third bed, another with a pair of extra bunks. TVs and tea trays are already installed, and further refining touches are gradually being added. ***Bar Food*** *12-2.30, 6-9.30 (Sun from 7). Children allowed in bar to eat before 8.30pm. Free House.* ***Beer*** *Tetley Bitter, Burton Ale, Wadworth 6X, Greene King Abbot. Garden, outdoor eating.* ***Accommodation*** *5 bedrooms, all en suite, £40. Children welcome overnight (under-2s stay free in parents' room, 2-10s £10). Check-in by arrangement. Additional bed available (£10). No dogs. No credit cards.*

Chipping Campden	**Noel Arms**	
Tel 01386 840317 Fax 01386 841136		**B&B**
High Street Chipping Campden Gloucestershire GL55 6AT		Map 14a A1

Centuries old traditions of hospitality live on at the inn where Charles II is said to have rested after his defeat at the battle of Worcester in 1651. In terms of atmosphere, however, the Noel Arms, right at the centre of this old wool-traders' town, has somehow lost a little of its former charm following its most recent extensions. The best and most authentic parts remain in the Dovers bar which opens direct on to the High Street through solid oaken doors. Lined in Cotswold stone and adorned with many genuine artefacts, the open double-sided fireplace and dog grate are of particular interest. From here, though, the pub opens out into the open-plan residents lounge and a newly-built (and rather unsympathetic) conservatory. Today's accommodation is a similar mixture of ancient and modern with the older bedrooms in the original building making up in character for what they lack in amenities, though by 17th-century standards the en-suite bathrooms, colour TV and dial-out phones are pretty civilized. Disabled guests

Zzzz...

will more greatly appreciate the newest bedrooms in the rear extension which have access direct from the car park. *Open 11-3 & 6-11 (Fri & Sat 11am-11pm, Sun 12-2.30 & 7-10.30).* **Beer** *Hook Norton Best, Bass, guest beer.* **Accommodation** *26 rooms, all en suite, from £92 (single £58). Children welcome overnight (under-10s stay free in parents' room), additonal beds & cots supplied. Access, Visa.*

Chipping Norton   Crown & Cushion

Tel 01608 642533 Fax 01608 642926	**B&B**
High Street Chipping Norton Oxfordshire OX7 5AD	Map 14a B1

The bar of this former coaching inn is full of character, with uneven flagstones, an inglenook and blackened beams. Bedrooms range from budget rooms in the annexe to suites with separate lounge, writing desk, sofa and traditional cast-iron bath. There are also some rooms with four-poster/half-tester beds. Public areas include a cosy lounge, beamed bar, numerous conference rooms and a leisure club with an indoor swimming pool, squash court, gym, solarium and snooker. *Free House.* **Beer** *McEwan's, Wadworth 6X, Hook Norton. Family room.* **Accommodation** *40 bedrooms, all en suite, from £50 (four-poster £85, single £43). Children welcome overnight (under-5s stay free in parents' room, 5-12s £5), additional beds and cots available. Dogs welcome by arrangement. Access, Diners, Visa.*

Chislehampton   Coach & Horses

Tel 01865 890255 Fax 01865 891995	**B&B**
Chislehampton nr Oxford Oxfordshire OX9 7UX	Map 14a C2

Though pretty much modernised over the years, the Coach & Horses still keeps some traces of its 16th-century beginnings. The bedrooms offer smartly kept, good practical accommodation with TVs and direct-dial phones. Showers are the norm, but a couple have bathtubs. The inn stands on the B480 south of Oxford. *Free House.* **Beer** *Hook Norton, Flowers, Boddingtons. Garden.* **Accommodation** *9 bedrooms, all en suite, £52 (single £37). Children welcome overnight (under-12s stay free in parents' room), additional beds & cots available. Access, Diners, Visa.*

Chorleywood   Sportsman Hotel

Tel 01923 285155 Fax 01923 285159	**B&B**
Station Approach Chorleywood Hertfordshire WD3 5NB	Map 15a E3

The Sportsman was built on a hillside across the road from the underground station and dates from the late 19th century. Popular with visiting businessmen, the 18 newly-refurbished bedrooms are a bit of a mix, but all are generally comfortable with modern darkwood furniture (some have modern pine) and brass light fittings; all are well equipped with TV, direct-dial telephones, radio-alarms, tea-making kits and trouser presses. En-suite bath/shower rooms are fully tiled. Light attractive decor extends to the public areas and the Garden Bar with its airy, plant-filled conservatory overlooks the spacious garden, terrace and children's play area. **Beer** *Bass.* **Accommodation** *18 bedrooms, all en suite, £52.50-£62.50 (£42.50-£52.50 single). Children welcome overnight, additional beds and cots supplied. Garden, large children's play area. Family room. Access, Diners, Visa.*

Church Enstone   Crown Inn

Tel 01608 677262	**B&B**

Mill Lane Church Enstone Oxfordshire OX7 4NN   Map 14a B1

Accommodation is a strong point at this 1760 Cotswold-stone inn
standing in a quiet village near the A34. Bedrooms – all kept in apple-
pie order – have pretty fabrics and furnishings, very comfortable beds,
private bathrooms, TVs and tea-makers. The bar has an inglenook fire
place and is usually full of lively chat, serving well-kept real ale and
decent wines. *Free House.* **Beer** *Boddingtons, Flowers Original, Marston's
Pedigree. Garden.* **Accommodation** *4 bedrooms, 3 en suite, £42 (single
£38). Children in own carrycot welcome overnight. No credit cards.*

Church Knowle   New Inn

Tel 01929 480357	**A**

Church Knowle nr Wareham Dorset BH20 5NQ   Map 14 C4

Overlooking the Purbeck Hills and located only 1½ miles from Corfe
Castle, this attractive 16th-century inn is a favourite refreshment spot
for both walkers and travellers enjoying an unspoilt corner of Dorset.
Half-thatched and half-stone slated with deep porches, it is a picture in
summer with carefully tended hanging baskets and tubs brimming
with flowers, brightening up its ancient stone facade. The homely and
welcoming interior includes an exposed stone-walled lounge with
open fire and a high-ceilinged main bar. Hatchway service is available
to those relaxing and admiring the splendid views from the delightful
sheltered rear garden. *Open 11-3, 6-11 (from 6.30 or 7 in winter), Sun
12-3, 7-10.30.* **Beer** *Flowers Original, Boddingtons, Castle Eden Ale.
Access, Visa.*

Clanfield   The Plough at Clanfield

Tel 0136781 222 Fax 0136781 596	**FOOD**
	B&B

Bourton Road Clanfield Oxfordshire OX18 2RB   Map 14a B2

The Plough is a 16th-century Cotswold stone manor house that's more
of an inn than a hotel, occupying a central position in pretty Clanfield
village. The lack of a residents' lounge restricts guests to either their
bedrooms – all of which are of a good size and comfortably equipped
(four have whirlpool baths) – or the hotel bar, which is no real
penalty as there's much original character in the form of old beams
and a stone fireplace. The cosy bedrooms come with baby teddy bears
to keep you company! In the 45-seat Tapestry Room restaurant
(recommended in our *1995 Hotels & Restaurants Guide*), chef Stephen
Fischer offers four different fixed-price menus ranging from the house
menu (£19.50 – with the likes of breast of chicken with forest
mushroom sauce and pan-fried fillet codling with herb crust) to the
seven course Gourmand (£33.95). Puddings are a speciality. The
lunch menus are £10.95 for two courses, and £14.50 for three.
Lighter lunches (snacks and sandwiches) are also available. Hatton
Hotels. **Bar Food** *12-2.* **Restaurant Meals** *12-2, 7-10 (Sun to 9.30).
Children allowed in bar (lunch only) & restaurant to eat. Free House.
Garden, outdoor eating.* **Accommodation** *6 bedrooms, £85. Children
welcome overnight (under-12s stay free in parents' room), additional beds
(£15) available. No dogs. Access, Diners, Visa.*

Clavering   Cricketers

Tel 01799 550442   Fax 01799 550882

Clavering nr Saffron Walden Essex CB11 4QT

FOOD

Map 10 B3

200 yards from the cricket green, this pub offers well-prepared home-made food on a menu that changes every 2-3 months. Start with prawn and smoked mackerel (£3.75) or walnut pastry tartlet (£4), with half a roast guinea fowl (£8.50), escalope of salmon (£8.75) or warm vegetable terrine (£7.95) to follow. The restaurant has seating for 70, the bar for 120 and 75 can eat outside. Dishes include chargrilled medallions of beef fillet with brandy and paprika sauce and supreme of chicken stuffed with mushrooms in puff pastry (£8). The restaurant offers a 3-course Sunday lunch with choice of 10 starters and main courses for £16.50. Suzanne, the resident pastry chef, cooks 12 desserts daily – treacle tart and lemon meringue pie (all £2.75). Wednesday night is 'Pudding Night' where the normal menu is supplemented with steak and kidney, Yorkshire and sweet steamed puds – all, of course, home-made. *Bar Food & Restaurant Meals 12-2, 7-10. Children's menu. Free House. Beer Flowers IPA, Wethered, Boddingtons. Terrace, outdoor eating. Family room. Access, Visa.*

Clearwell   Wyndham Arms

Tel 01594 833666   Fax 01594 836450

Clearwell nr Coleford Gloucestershire GL16 8JT

FOOD

B&B

Map 14 B2

Imperturbable hosts of the tranquil Wyndham John and Mary Stanford continue to enhance the comprehensive service here, including a newly completed private dining room seating 50 this year. Traditional real ales, 17 wines from seven different countries, and the famed malt whisky collection (with over 20 to choose from) are indicators of the public bar's civilised style, to which the menu is entirely apposite. A lunch still favoured by many is the 18-dish hors d'oeuvre trolley (£6.25), the daily special might be fresh salmon and caper fish cakes (£7.75), while open sandwiches of grilled bacon or chicken liver paté (both £4) are practically meals in themselves. Bar meals service, however, may be suspended when the restaurant is busy. Accommodation is divided between original bedrooms in the evocative 600-year-old main building and a stone extension where room sizes, decor and comforts are altogether more modern. There's plenty of space for young children (cots, high-chairs and baby-listening are all readily available), and the less mobile appreciate use of 6 ground floor bedrooms with easy ramps into the pub. Early evening turn-down and dawn shoe-cleaning patrol aren't found in every pub: along with a hearty breakfast, it's all part, here, of the Wyndham service. Secure car-parking. *Pub open 11-11 (Sun 12-3, 7-11). Bar Food & Restaurant Meals 12-2, 7-9.30. Children allowed in the bar to eat, children's menu. Free House. Beer Hook Norton, Bass. Garden, patio, outdoor eating. Accommodation 17 bedrooms, all en suite, £60 (single £35). Children welcome overnight. Additional beds and cots supplied free. Access, Diners, Visa.*

Cley-next-the-Sea   George and Dragon

Tel 01263 740652

High Street Cley-next-the-Sea nr Holt Norfolk NR25 7RN

B&B

Map 10 C1

Standing head and shoulders above its neighbouring whitewashed cottage, this striking brick inn was rebuilt in 1897 in Edwardian style and enjoys an enviable position close to Cley's fine windmill

overlooking an expanse of unspoilt salt marsh. For decades the inn has
been a popular base for visiting naturalists, walkers and holidaymakers,
and the good pubby bars have witnessed the forming of the Norfolk
Naturalists Trust in 1926 and today daily bird observations are
recorded in the "bird bible" – a large volume placed on a lectern –
in the main bar. Upstairs, most of the homely, simply furnished
bedrooms, including the four-poster room, have far-reaching salt
marsh views and six have clean, adequate en-suite facilities. TVs and
tea-makers are standard. The residents lounge is the internal hide,
complete with scrape-facing window and a pair of binoculars.
Housekeeping is of a good standard. Good-sized garden across the lane
with pétanque pitch. Being a well visited coastal village, families are
very welcome here and the provision of extra beds and cots in the
family or larger rooms. There is no charge for babies and nominal
charges for under and over 10s. Early evening meals can be provided
from 6pm and young diners have their own menu and use of a
high-chair. However, children must be carefully supervised in
the garden. *Free House. Open 11-2.30, 6.30-11 (12-3, 7-10.30 Sun).*
Accommodation *8 bedrooms, 6 en suite £50-65 (single £30). Check-in
by arrangement. Children welcome overnight (cots, high chair and extra bed
in parents' room available).* ***Beers*** *Greene King IPA, Abbot Ale, Tetley
Bitter, Rayments Bitter. No credit cards.*

Cliffe   The Black Bull   **FOOD**

Tel 01634 220893   Fax 01634 221382

186 Church Street Cliffe Kent ME3 7QP   **Map 11 B5**

Late-Victorian pub on a historic tavern site. The three bars offer a
constantly changing line-up of real ales provided by Hampshire
Brewery and at least eight wines by the glass. Eating may be in one of
these or in the non-smoking, 40-seat, 18th-century cellar restaurant
which is booked only once in an evening, so there's no hurry to leave,
especially as they have an extended licence to serve up to midnight.
The speciality is Far-Eastern – spring rolls (£3.95) and home-made
prawn crackers (£2.50) are two of the starters; sotong sambal (squid
with peppers and pineapple in spicy shrimp sauce £5.95) or hokkien
braised pork (£6) are options for main courses which can be ordered
with mee goreng (fried noodles with shrimps, meat and vegetables
£4.50) or egg fried rice (£3). There's also a set meal (two starters,
four main dishes, rice and dessert) for two (£18.50 each). The prices
are lower in the bar where the main dish price includes vegetables and
rice (chili chicken £6.25, sweet and sour £6.25) or beef stir fry
(£6.25). ***Bar Food*** *12-2, 7-10 (except Sun & Mon night).* ***Restaurant
Meals*** *7-10 (except Sun & Mon). Children allowed in bar to eat. Free
House.* ***Beer*** *Hampshire Brewery, Wadworth 6X, Courage Best, guest
beers. Access Visa.*

Clifton Hampden   Plough Inn   **FOOD**

	B&B

Tel 01865 407811   Fax 01865 407136

Clifton Hampden nr Abingdon Oxfordshire OX14 3EG   **Map 14a C3**

A 16th-century thatched and timber-framed gem of a building,
lovingly renovated over the past few years by Turkish-born landlord
Yuksel Bektas. It is now a delightful country pub that simply oozes
charm and character. The cosy main bar, adjoining room and separate,
less characterful, small dining room are pristinely kept and feature low
beams, deep red-painted walls, narrow wall benches; open fires at each
end of the main bar give a welcoming feel immediately on entering.

Mr Bektas – impeccably dressed, often in tail coat in the morning and dinner suit at night – and his wife Gulpembe (please make allowances for her English) have instilled their typical Turkish hospitality into the pub; characterful touches include Turkish coffee after dinner, pitta bread with toast at breakfast and a fox's head resplendent with fez in the bar. The pub has an open-all-day policy, and food is served as long as the doors are open; as we went to press we heard that a new chef had just been appointed – he is likely to continue the admirable "no fried or frozen foods" policy. One menu is served throughout, so one can either eat informally in the bar rooms (or garden) or more formally in the quieter, less pubby dining room up a few steps from the small bar. Up a few stairs, tucked beneath the thatch is a spacious bedroom, tastefully decorated with four-poster bed, deep pink walls, attractive floral rose fabrics and matching Oriental bedside lamps; a basket of fruit, remote-control TV, copper kettle, two easy chairs and a splendid private bathroom (down a few steps) with a good, solid tub all add up to unusually good comfort and value-for-money. Another spacious bedroom is up a few stairs at the other end of the building, also tucked under the thatch. A further bedroom, as stylish as the original, has been recently added in a separate, thatched building across the gravel yard. Enjoy a quiet pint in the garden (unless there's a wedding reception in a marquee) or take a stroll down the road to the baby river Thames. The Plough is one of a kind – no-smoking throughout, quality accommodation, good food and service, and Turkish hospitality (they'll even drive you home if you've had a few too many) – all in the heart of a pretty Oxfordshire village on the A415 Abingdon to Dorchester road. *Open 11am-11pm.* **Bar Food** *11am-11pm. Children's portions.* **Beer** *Webster's Yorkshire Bitter, Courage Best & Directors.* **Accommodation** *3 en-suite rooms, £45 (single £37.50). Children welcome overnight, extra mattress provided at no charge. Garden. No dogs. Access, Visa.*

Clifton	**Duke of Cumberland's Head**	**FOOD**
Tel 01869 338534		**B&B**
Clifton nr Deddington Oxfordshire OX5 4PE		**Map 14a C1**

The summer of '94 saw new owners at this comfortable thatched pub, on the B4031, with its old beams, inglenook fireplace and wheelback chairs. Not much else has changed though with Sam Harrison still in the kitchen producing a strictly French menu for the small restaurant and more varied blackboard menu for the bar. The latter can sometimes be hard to read as dishes are constantly being rubbed out to be replaced by others (a good sign) but a typical selection might include Stilton and onion soup (£1.95), garlic mushrooms (£2.50), salad niçoise (£3.25) sirloin steak (£8.25), kleftiko (£4.25), spaghetti bolognese (£3.95), chili con carne (£3.95), and grilled plaice (£5.25). Puds, like chocolate mousse, crème caramel and queen of puddings all come at £1.95 with cream (£2.25 with ice cream). Upstairs under the eves three simple bedrooms come with en-suite shower rooms with WC, old pine furniture, TV and tea and coffee kit but without telephones. Garden to the rear. *Free House.* **Bar & Restaurant Meals** *12-2, 7-9.30 (restaurant closed L Mon).* **Beers** *Hook Norton, Wadworth 6X. Garden, outdoor eating area.* **Accommodation** *3 bedrooms, all en suite, from £37.50 (single £25). Check-in by arrangement. Pub closed Sun eve.*

Cockfield **Three Horseshoes**

Tel 01284 828177	**FOOD**
Stones Hill Cockfield nr Lavenham Suffolk	Map 10 C3

This thatched, pink-washed 14th-century cottage pub – located south of the village on the A1141 – has been an alehouse since the 19th century. Diners can eat in the vaulted ceilinged and heavily beamed lounge or venture next door into the more rustic livelier locals public bar, which has sturdy tables and chairs on tiled floor. Tuck into the horseshoe-shaped roll made with bread specially baked in Lavenham and filled with Suffolk ham (£1.95), or choose one of the other hearty, home-cooked dishes on the short menu, such as beef in Abbot ale (£3.75), lamb casserole with pearl barley (£3.95). Two daily specials may include a "real" turkey pie (£3.93) served with fresh vegetables. The Three Horseshoes is home to a Pudding Lovers Club, for lovers of traditional, old-fashioned English puds – spotted dick, ginger sponge with rum sauce. Booking essential Thursday evenings. *Bar Food* 12-2, 6-9.30. *Garden with lovely views.* *Beer* Greene King IPA, Mild Abbot Ale. *Family room. No credit cards.*

Cockwood **Anchor Inn**

Tel 01626 890203	**FOOD**
Cockwood nr Dawlish Devon EX6 8RA	Map 13 E3

The small vine-covered verandah of this 400-year-old fisherman's cottage pub is a super spot in which to sit and watch the colourful fishing boats and wildlife in the tiny harbour across the lane and the Exe estuary beyond. Inside, although extended over the years, the rustic main bar remains unspoilt, with black panelling, low ceilings and lots of intimate little alcoves in the three snug areas, one of which has a welcoming coal fire. Local seafood, especially shellfish, is the main attraction here, especially the impressive range of sauces for mussels (£5.50 & £9.75) and oysters (from £5.25), which are delivered daily from local beds along the River Exe. Also worth investigating is the fresh fish board – red mullet in lemon butter, halibut in tarragon sauce – and the daily specials such as home-made soup (£2.30), seafood grill (£5.95) and honey-roast lamb (£6.95). The main printed menu offers a fairly routine choice of pub favourites. Parking can be difficult, especially on busy summer days. New landlords. *Pub open* 11-11 (*Sun from 12-2.30, to 10.30*). *Bar Food* 12-2.30 (*Sun to 2*), 6.30-10 (*Sun 7-9.30*). *Beer* Bass, Boddingtons, Royal Oak, Marston's Pedigree, Flowers. *Paved Garden, outdoor eating. Access, Visa.*

Cockwood **Ship Inn**

Tel 01626 8908373	**FOOD**
Cockwood nr Dawlish Devon EX6 8PA	Map 13 E3

Originally an old victualler's house, dating from 1640, this homely, cream-painted inn overlooks the old harbour inlet and reedbeds. Carefully modernised inside, it is a popular place in which to appreciate a bar food menu that favours the fishy. A blackboard lists the catch of the day, good local fish such as brill, haddock, cod, plaice, red mullet (£9.25) and salmon hollandaise (£9.30) among others. Printed menu fare also features good seafood, from green-lipped mussels cooked in cider and garlic (£3.95) to Cockwood bouillabaisse (£9.25), crab bake (£8.60) and Bert's Cockwood special (£9.25). A short bar snack menu offers sandwiches (from £2.95) and other light bites, while non fish-fanciers are limited to a range of steaks, cold meat salads and a vegetarian selection. Outdoor eating and drinking can be enjoyed from a high-level garden, which affords splendid open views across the Exe estuary to Exmouth. No children under 14 in the bar area. New landlords. *Bar Food 12-2 (Sun to 2.30), 6.30-10 (Sun 7-9.30). Family room. Beer Ushers Best & Founder's Ale, John Smith's. Garden, outdoor eating. Access, Visa.*

Colchester   Foresters Arms

Tel 01206 42646	FOOD
Castle Road Colchester Essex CO1 1UW	Map 10 C3

No-frills local situated near the castle and Roman wall. Built originally as two cottages and converted to a pub in the 1920s, it has two tiny, often bustling, interconnecting bars with simple furnishings, bar billiards, piped jazz music and, rather surprisingly, an above-average, daily-changing menu of home-cooked food. Beyond an extensive list of sandwiches with unusual fillings one might find pan-fried lamb's liver and onions, smoked haddock fish cakes with lemon sauce and a good salad (£4.25), aromatic crispy duck or chicken tikka, followed by sticky toffee pudding or vol-au-vent filled with fresh raspberries and cream. Front patio with benches. Sunday roast £3.95. Pretty basic (and rather studenty), but unusual for a bit of a back-street boozer! Whitbread. *Open 11.30-3, 5.30-11 (11-11 Fri & Sat), longer hours in school hols, Sun 12-3, 7-10.30. Bar Food 12-2.30, 7-9.30. No food Sun evening. Children allowed in bar to eat. Beer Flowers IPA, Boddingtons. No credit cards.*

Colchester   Rose and Crown

Tel 01206 866677 Fax 01206 866616	B&B
East Street Colchester Essex CO1 2TZ	Map 10 C3

Magnificent ancient black-and-white timbered inn that has stood on the corner of the old Ipswich and Harwich roads since the 15th-Century. Once an old posting house, it is now a well appointed inn having been carefully extended and refurbished over the past five years. A distinct 'pubby' bar attracts a busy local trade and is full of character with open fires, heavy beams and antique cushioned pews and settles. Old world charm extends upstairs into the main building bedrooms – two of which boast sturdy four-poster beds – with leaded windows, wall timbers and uneven floors. Newer extension bedrooms are uniform in size, decor and furnishings, all being very comfortable and well equipped with older-style darkwood furniture and quality co-ordinating fabrics. Clean fully-tiled bathrooms with overhead showers. Full complement of added comforts from remote-controlled TVs to trouser presses. Function room/conference facilities. *Open 11-11.30 (Sun usual hours). Free house. Beer Tetley Bitter. Accommodation 30 bedrooms, all en suite, £55-£99 (single £55). Children welcome overnight (under-5s stay free in parents' room, 5-12s ½-price), additional beds and cots available. No dogs. Access, Visa.*

Coleford   New Inn

Tel 01363 84242 Fax 01363 85044	FOOD
	B&B
Coleford Devon EX17 5BZ	Map 13 D2

Pretty, 13th-century thatched cottage inn set beside the River Cole in an equally attractive village, deep in the heart of unspoilt Devon countryside. 'Captain', the chatty resident parrot, welcomes folk into the characterful rambling interior, with the charming ancient bar blending successfully with dining room extension into the old barns: fitted red carpets, fresh white walls, heavy beams, simple wooden furniture and settles and a discreet variety of attractive brass and bric-a-brac. Bar food is reliable and home-cooked, relying on fresh local produce: Brixham fish, usually six Devon cheeses, eggs and cream from a nearby farm. The comprehensive blackboard menu has an international flavour, featuring Greek salad (£5.25), seafood provençale (£3.50) and a hearty lentil soup (£2.50) as a snack or starter, with main course options that include Mediterranean lamb (£7.15), Mexican pasta (£4.65), beef stifado (£7) and bobotie (£4.65). Local estate game appears regularly on the winter menu. Good puddings range from chocolate mousse to apple sultana puff. A decent list of 51 wines is supplied by Christopher Piper wines and several are served by the glass. Comfortable and peaceful overnight accommodation is guaranteed in the three spacious, light and airy en-suite bedrooms; newly refurbished, with quality floral fabrics and antique furniture plus TV and tea-making facilities as added comforts. Good breakfasts. There's a stream-side patio for quiet alfresco summer drinking. *Free House.* **Beer** *Otter Ale, Flowers IPA, Flowers Original, Wadworth 6X. Garden, outdoor eating area.* **Accommodation** *3 bedrooms, all en suite, £48 (single £30). Access, Visa.*

Colesbourne — The Colesbourne Inn

FOOD

B&B

Tel 01242 870376	Fax 01242 870397

Colesbourne nr Cheltenham Gloucestershire GL53 9NP

Map 14 C2

A traditional hostelry alongside the A417, where quietly efficient hotelkeeping from Eric and Mary Bird marks it out from the crowd. Meals in the equally traditional, stone-clad dining room are more the order of the day than any bar snacks, though sandwiches and filled baked potatoes (from £3.50) are readily available. Old English chicken pie (£6.50), mushroom in filo baskets and a nightly table d'hote (2-course £9.95, 3-course £11.95) feature alongside seasonal specials (eg supreme of guinea fowl with plum sauce £8.50). Bedrooms border the car park, well back from the road, in a neatly-planned extension: rear rooms enjoy the best views of rolling country. All have fully-equipped en-suite facilities with bath and shower, and efficient modern accessories, including trouser presses and hairdryers. A lively local atmosphere in the bar awaits those who enjoy some company prior to turning in. Lounge area for families. *Open 11-11, usual hours Sunday.* **Bar Food** *12-3, 6.30-10 (Sun 7-10).* **Restaurant Meals** *12-3, 7-9.30. Children allowed in bar to eat. Free House.* **Beer** *Wadworth 6X, Farmers Glory, Old Timer (in winter), guest beer. Garden, patio, outdoor eating.* **Accommodation** *9 bedrooms, all en suite, £50 (single £34). Children welcome overnight (under-12s stay free in parents' room), additional beds and cots available. Access, Diners, Visa.*

Collyweston — Cavalier Inn

B&B

Tel 0178 083288

Collyweston nr Stamford Lincolnshire DE9 3PQ

Map 7 E4

Previously the Slaters Arms, the pub here changed its name when the slate mine closed and the work force moved away. The inn itself is a terrace of small 19th-century cottages, yet a glass window let into the bar floor reveals a much earlier stone spiral stairway to a tiny cellar.

Four miles from Stamford on the A43. *Free House.* **Beer** *Ruddles Best Bitter & County, John Smith's. Garden. Family room.* **Accommodation** *6 bedrooms, all en suite, £32. Children welcome overnight. No dogs. Check-in by arrangement. Access, Diners, Visa.*

Coln St Aldwyns   New Inn   ★   FOOD B&B

Tel 01285 750651   Fax 01285 750657

Coln St Aldwyns nr Cirencester Gloucestershire GL7 5AN   Map 14a A2

Coln St Aldwyns is the kind of village where the milk might not arrive until midday, so sleepy in fact that the villagers here almost lost their local. Since Brian and Sandra Evans woke up to its opportunities in 1992, the New Inn has breathed new life and already demands to be measured against the country's best. Behind its picture postcard frontage of flower baskets and ivy, interior conversion has created a succession of little rooms as adaptable to the demands of diners as are the menus to satisfy them. The food on offer is less seasonally adjusted than daily devised, a true indicator of the markets. Lighter lunches may start with a pheasant and lentil terrine (£3.50) or cottage cheese salad with mixed fruit (£4.50), while fuller appetites are assuaged by braised ox-tail with red cabbage and roasted shallots (£5.25), 'beans on toast!' (a mixture of beans in a rich tomato and thyme sauce on toasted olive and herb bread – £3.95) or a simple steak and kidney pudding with stout (£5.25). Under the unworthy epithet of "Bar Meals", similar choices are available at night alongside an appetising Table d'hote (£15.50/£19.50) and an equally promising carte. Beer drinkers nonetheless can enjoy a filled baguette with their pint of Hook Norton. Configuration of the bedrooms, utilising virtually every angle of the roof space, is for each resident to discover and all to wonder at – here a romantic four-poster room, there the sunken bath in a former stair-well – and epitomise the delights in store for those who come to stay. *Open 11.30-2.30, 5.30-11 (Sat all day 11-11, Sun 12-3, 7-10.30).* **Bar Food** *12-2.15 (Fri & Sat to 2.30), 6.30-9.30 (Sat to 10, Sun from 7).* **Restaurant Meals** *12-2 (Sun only), 7-9.30. Free House.* **Beer** *Hook Norton Best, Wadworth 6X, Cotswold Best, changing guest beer. Terrace/garden, outdoor eating.* **Accommodation** *11 bedrooms, all en suite, £60 (single £45) inc. Continental breakfast. Increased weekend tariff. Children welcome overnight (under-4s stay free in parents' room), additional beds (4-12s £10, over-12s £15) and cots (£5) available. Dogs welcome by arrangement. Access, Visa.*

Colston Bassett   Martins Arms   FOOD

Tel 01949 81361

School Lane Colston Bassett Nottinghamshire NG12 3FD   Map 7 D3

Those who have enjoyed visiting the *Crown Inn* at Old Dalby (*qv*) will be instantly smitten by the abundant charm of landlords Lynne Bryan and Salvatore Inguantas' new venture the Martins Arms. Formerly the Squire's residence,' set among horse chestnuts in an estate garden, the pub exudes quiet country house charm, to which the bar itself seems almost an intrusion; though here, amongst others, you'll find some top-notch Bateman XB and impeccable wines from Lay & Wheeler. Recently-simplified menus apply in both the antique-furnished dining room complete with its own lounge, and the bar itself, which in turn opens on to the lawn. Salvatore's influence is paramount in a kitchen whose dedication is as marked as at the Crown, with equally consistent results. Light lunches and ladies' appetisers range from tomato bavarois with fennel salad (£5.95) to baked Camembert in filo pastry with cherry sauce (£6.50). Assuaging heartier appetites might be home-made gnocchi (£6.95), preceding fish hotpot pie (£8.95) or medallions of wild boar with bananas (£15.95). Freshly-made desserts and Colston Bassett Stilton of course to follow. Under-14s not permitted indoors. *Bar Food* 12-2, 6-10. *Restaurant Meals* 12-1.30, 6-9.30. *No food Sun eve. Free House. Beer Marston Best & Pedigree, Bateman XB & XXXB, guest beers. Garden. No credit cards.*

Combe Hay   Wheatsheaf

Tel 01225 833504	**FOOD**
Combe Hay nr Bath Avon BA2 7EG	Map 13 F1

Perched on a hillside looking across a small valley, the Wheatsheaf dates back to the 17th century and is as pretty as a picture, its black and white facade smothered in flowers and pierced with the entrances to dovecotes, built into the walls and still inhabited. Narrowing twisting lanes lead to this charming village, hidden away in a fold of hills to the south of Bath. Well-spaced rustic tables and benches in the large sloping garden make the best of the views, an ideal spot for summer eating and drinking. Inside there are rough stone walls, massive solid wooden tables, and also a huge blackboard menu: food is important here. Typical dishes from the bar menu are game terrine (£3.95), pan-fried chicken livers with mustard, white wine and cream sauce (£4.50) and home-made enchiladas (£4.95), whilst the specials board may feature pan-fried medallions of venison with a red wine, oyster and mushroom sauce or king prawns in garlic butter and whisky. Deep-fried mushrooms filled with Brie make a good starter, the hot filling spilling out to blend with the surrounding provençale sauce. Home-made puddings (£2.50-£2.75) include chocolate nut crunch, summer pudding and home-made cheesecakes. Real ales are drawn direct from the barrel. There is no background music as such, but a good deal emanates from the kitchen where, to judge by the singing, they are clearly happy in their work. Large selection of fruit wines. *Bar Food & Restaurant Meals* 12-2, 6.30-9 *(Sat to 9.30, Sun 7-9). Children allowed in bar to eat. Beer Courage Best, 6X, Hook Norton, 2 guest beers. Garden, outdoor eating. No credit cards.*

Compton   Coach and Horses

Tel 01705 631228	**FOOD**
The Square Compton nr Chichester West Sussex PO18 9NA	Map 15 D3

Located in the village square and beside the B2146 Chichester to Petersfield road, this white-painted 15th-century coaching inn caters for all desires within its homely Village Bar and separate beamed lounge and restaurant. Mellow pine characterises the lively locals' bar where one can enjoy a good hearty bar snack, such as chicken and mushroom pie (£5.65), grilled trout (£4.15), breast of chicken with mustard sauce (£7.95), Selsey crab (£5.95) as well as soup, ploughman's and sandwiches, all of which are listed on a blackboard menu. Those seeking a more convivial dining atmosphere could venture next door into the charming lounge and adjacent restaurant, both boasting open log fires. A further board features more imaginative and pricier fare to suit the surroundings, namely, baked sea bass (£15.75), steamed monkfish with sauce American (£10.75), grilled black bream (£8.75) and loin of lamb on creamed parsley

(£10.15), all served with fresh, crisp vegetables. Puddings include icky sticky toffee pudding (£2.95) and home-made brown bread ice cream (£3.15). Good range of six well-kept real ales and a short list of 15 good value wines to choose from. A small secluded garden lies beyond the skittle alley. *Free House.* **Bar Food** *12-1.30, 6-9.30 (7-9.30 Sun).* **Restaurant Meals** *12-1.30, 6-9.30 (Closed Mon, Sun eve. 6-9.30 Sat).* **Beer** *Palmers IPA, Fuller's ESB, Hop Back Summer Lightning, McEwans Export, King & Barnes Festive, Smiles Bitter, guest beer. Garden, outdoor eating. Children allowed anywhere. Access, Visa.*

Congresbury   White Hart

Tel 01934 833303	**FOOD**
Wrington Road Congresbury Avon BS19 5AR	Map 13 F1

Combined quaint village pub and dining venue hidden down a long lane off the A370 (follow the Wrington Road). A conventional line in snacks and salads is supplemented by some more promising home-cooked fare: steak and Guinness pie (£5.25), chicken curry (£5.25) through to haddock and broccoli gratin (£6.25), bobotie and poached salmon steak served with a choice of potatoes and vegetables or salad. An increasing attraction is Sunday lunch (main course £4.95), especially with families, who have use of a neat, fabric-lined conservatory looking across the large pub garden and away towards the Mendips; no children allowed in the bars. With plastic bottles of pop from the bar youngsters can amuse themselves in full view on the play equipment. There's also an aviary by the terrace. **Bar Food** *12-2, 6-9.30 (Sun 7-9).* **Beer** *Butcombe, H & W Badger & Tanglefoot. Garden. Patio and play area. Family room, children's menu. Access, Visa.*

Constantine   Trengilly Wartha Inn

Tel 01326 40332 Fax 01326 40332	**FOOD**
	B&B
Nancenoy Constantine nr Helston Cornwall TR11 5RP	Map 12 B4

One mile due south of Constantine down country lanes, the Inn sits in the beautiful wooded valley of Polpenwith Creek. The unpretentious main bar is happily unmodernised with games machines and pool table relegated to a separate room and another tapestry upholstered 'lounge' area where families are welcome; there's a small children's section on the menu too. For summer, there are tables on the vine-covered patio and in the garden beyond. A further alfresco area has recently been created around a newly constructed lake in the valley bottom. The main printed bar menu contains old favourites, from paté (£3) and filled jacket potatoes (from £2.50) to chili (£4) and salads (from £4.50). More interesting fare appears on the blackboard – Provence fish soup (£2.20), grilled goats cheese and olives (£3.20), courgette, feta filo pie and salad (£4.50), half a grilled lobster (£10), pork fillet with cider and apricots served on fine buttered noodles (£6) – followed by homely puddings (£2). Separate restaurant offering a good value 3-course dinner (£19). Good range of wines by the glass selected from a list of 160, four regularly-changing real ales and three strong scrumpy ciders. Six cosy bedrooms are light and pretty with good modern carpeted bathrooms and up-to-date conveniences such as remote-control TV and direct-dial telephones. Well maintained and comfortable accommodation. *Pub open 11-2.30 (Sat to 3), 6-11 (Sun 12-2.30, 7-10.30) – summer hours, ring to check winter hours.* **Bar Food** *12-2.15 (Sun to 2), 6.30-9.30 (Sun from 7.15). Family room, children allowed in bar to eat, children's menu, two high-chairs. Free House.* **Beer** *Tetley Bitter, Dartmoor BB, St Austell XXXX*

Mild, up to 4 guest beers from small, independent breweries. Garden, outdoor eating. **Accommodation** *6 bedrooms, 5 en suite, from £59 (single £42). Children welcome overnight, extra bed (£8) and cot (£2) provided in one larger room. Access, Diners, Visa.*

Cookham Dean   Inn on the Green

Tel 01628 482638

FOOD

The Green Cookham Dean Berkshire SL6 9NZ

Map 15a E3

Tucked away in one corner of the large village green, this interesting pub has four dining areas but only a small bar. Two small drinking rooms (with just seven tables) lead through to a Swiss chalet-style room (fondues from £9.95), off which the high-ceilinged Lamp Room restaurant and a small conservatory lead. The short bar menu is the best bet; the range might cover smoked mackerel mousse (£3.75), steak in a baguette with chips (£5.75), sausage and mash, bacon and three cheese salad (£4.25), warm goat's cheese salad (£3.75) and monkfish with capsicum, peppers and sherry (£10.35). Outside, there's a small patch of grass to the front (plus the enormous green a little further away), a large walled courtyard barbecue area (lit by wall lights and heated by tall gas burners, Apr-Oct) and an acre of paddock behind the car park. It's a wonderful summer pub for families with youngsters: the rear grassed area features a few picnic tables, a tree house, a chalet-style 'Nut House', double slide, climbing frame and rubber tyre swings; however, in winter the inside is too intimate for anything less than very well-behaved juniors. Casual food service, but generous portions – stick to the simpler dishes. Easy parking. *Bar Food 12-2, (Sun to 2.30), 6.30-10 (no food Sun eve). Children allowed in bar to eat for lunch only (and at all times in restaurant). Free House.* **Beer** *Brakspear, Boddingtons, guest beer. Garden, terrace, outdoor eating, children's play area. Pub closed 25, 26 Dec and 1 Jan pm. Access, Visa.*

Cookham Dean   Jolly Farmer

Tel 01628 482905

FOOD

Cookham Dean nr Marlow Berkshire

Map 15a E3

Homely and traditional village pub located opposite the parish church and close to the vast village green. Two simply furnished interconnecting bars with open fires, and a separate small and cosy dining room in which to enjoy wholesome, home-cooked pub food. Summer blackboard choices may range from Stilton and cider soup (£1.95) and warm goat's cheese on beef tomato salad (£4.25) to chicken and mushroom pie (£5.25), pork and vegetable curry and haddock and egg crumble at lunchtimes, with more imaginative evening options like pork medallions with a sherry and mustard sauce (£7.95). Apple pie and crème brulée (£2.75) are typical pudding options. In the winter a printed menu comes into operation with friendly staff taking orders. Good summer garden with children's play area. Well-behaved children only inside. *Open 11.30-3, 5.30-11 (Sat from 6), Sun 12-3, 7-10.30.* **Bar Food** *12-2.30 (Sun to 3), 7-10. No food Sun evening. Children allowed in bar to eat. Free house.* **Beer** *Courage Best, Wadworth 6X, guest beer. Garden, outdoor eating, children's play area. Access, Visa.*

Corbridge   **Angel Inn**

FOOD
B&B

`Tel 01434 632119`

Main Street Corbridge nr Hexham Northumberland NE45 5LA

Map 5 D2

Saxon Corbridge, just off both the A68 and A69 trunk routes, stands above the 17th-century stone bridge across the Tyne where the former Head inn was once the town's posting inn. Its latest guardian angel, Mandy McIntosh Reid, has certainly dusted the place with a little of her own magic. The Angel today is smartly carpeted throughout (except in the locals' Tap Room) and an up-market approach is reinforced by the food: here you will find reliable Northumbrian cooking of a style and value which has achieved instant local approval. Daily-changing menus encompass the likes of fennel and orange soup (£1.80), braised halibut with crabmeat (£6.75), stir-fried chicken with ginger (£5.25) and Cumberland sausage with onion gravy (£4.10). In the foyer lounge, nonetheless, space is found for morning coffees, a lunchtime sandwich and afternoon teas. The five recently completed bedrooms haven't been skimped over either. There are satellite TVs, roomy bathrooms with a certain feminine touch (cotton buds and bath foam) quality free-standing pine furniture and bold colour schemes. The tree twins (families welcome) are roomier than the doubles: views are either from the front down to the river or to the rear overlooking a pretty walled garden. *Free House.*
Beers Theakston Bitter XB, Younger's No 3, Newcastle Exhibition, guest beers. Open 11-3, 5-11 (12-3, 7-10.30 Sun). **Bar Food** 12-2.15, 6-9.15 (7-9.15pm Sun). **Accommodation** 5 rooms, all en suite, £54 (£39 single). Additional bed and cots available. Access, Diners, Visa.

Corfe Castle   **Fox**

`Tel 01929 480449`

A

West Street Corfe Castle Dorset BH20 5HD

Map 14 D4

Unspoilt 16th-century inn, with a very snug little front bar and slightly less enchanting larger lounge. Recent renovations uncovered a doorway which has been turned into an alcove. Its mature, pretty garden with views of the famous ruin make the Fox especially appealing in summer. Children under 14 are not allowed indoors. *Free House.* **Beer** Bishop's Tipple, Wadworth 6X, Abbot Ale, Burton, Wiltshire Traditional. Garden. No credit cards.

Cornworthy   **Hunters Lodge Inn**

`Tel 01803 732204`

FOOD

Cornworthy Totnes Devon TQ9 7ES

Map 13 D3

Unspoilt, simply-furnished country local with a low-ceilinged bar and a cosy dining room with an old stone fireplace and attractive blue table linen. Vast, little-changing blackboard menus hide some good home-cooked dishes among the deep-fried choices with chips and the bought-in puddings. Once identified and ordered they will not disappoint. The lunchtime-only board will offer good home-made soups – tomato and fresh basil (£1.80), cottage pie (£3.85), courgette and tomato bake (£4.50), fresh Brixham plaice (£5.50) and a splendid steak and kidney pie (£5.10) served with huge portions of four crisp vegetables and a bowl of potatoes. On the long menu (available in bar and restaurant) more elaborate dishes include lamb in redcurrant and red wine (£7.95), Greek-style lamb with rice and feta cheese salad (£7.95) and halibut in lime and wine with prawns and crab claws

(£10.95). Fish specialities are the special mixed grill (a mix of fish and meat £10.75), whole cracked crab and half a grilled lobster in herb butter (£7.25). A three-course Sunday lunch (£6.50) is a popular event and it is advisable to book in the evenings and at weekends. No children under 14 in the restaurant but very welcome in the bar with games and toys available. Cider lovers should sample the 'Pig's Squeal'. *Bar Food 12-2.30 & 7-10. Free House. Beer Blackawton 44, Ushers Best, guest beer. Garden, outdoor eating, children's play area. No credit cards.*

Corscombe   Fox Inn   ★

Tel 01935 891330	**FOOD**
Corscombe Dorset DT2 0NS	**Map 13 F2**

"Real Ale, Country Cooking. No Chips or Microwaves" it says on the postcard, showing Martyn Lee's pretty little thatched pub of stone and cob, built in 1620 and located down a web of narrow lanes deep in unspoilt Dorset countryside (the village is signposted off the A356 Crewkerne to Dorchester, then follow signs to the pub – it's not easy to find). All is equally appealing inside, and the small entrance lobby is decorated with a wild flower and ivy mural painted directly on to the walls. Beyond are two bars, one, with its hunting prints, old pine furniture and band of chatty locals, the other prettily furnished with blue gingham curtains, tablecloths, banquette seat covers – even the fabric covering the bar stools. A huge old stone fireplace boasts a real log fire in winter, while behind the bar a collection of plates, copper and pewter ware is displayed and real ale and farm cider is dispensed straight from the cask. All is overseen by an array of stuffed owls in glass cases. It's still very much a locals' pub, complete with local cricket team, but more and more discerning diners are beginning to find their way to this rural backwater for the imaginative choice of bar food on offer, particularly now that Will Longman (formerly at the *Three Horseshoes* in Powerstock) has taken over in the kitchen. Quality produce from good local suppliers, including fresh fish from Bridport and game in season from local estates help create the interesting daily-changing blackboard menu. Choices may include grilled goat's cheese salad (£3.25) and fine beans with Parma ham and garlic (£3.50) to start, followed by breast of guinea fowl with tarragon and cream (£8.50), fillet of turbot with cider sauce (£8.95) and whole John Dory baked with garlic and herbs (£7.95); good accompanying vegetables. Other dishes include beef casserole (£5.75), fish soup (£6) and Fox's Favourite chicken in a cream sauce (£5.75). Sunday roasts (£5.95). Puddings range from blackberry fool and caramelised apple tart (both £2.50) to an excellent cheeseboard featuring, among others, local Denhay Cheddar, Somerset goat's and Shropshire Blue. Alfresco eating across the lane by the brook or at the sturdy, long wooden table in the attractive rear courtyard – very Continental; it seats 16 and is ideal for parties. There is also a private room available for hire, seating up to 10. *Pub open all day Saturday. Bar Food 12-2, 7-9. Free House. Beer Smiles, Palmers BB, Fuller's London Pride, Exmoor. Garden, outdoor eating. Family room. No credit cards.*

Corsham   Methuen Arms

Tel 01249 714867 Fax 01249 712004	**B&B**
2 High Street Corsham Wiltshire SN13 0HB	**Map 14 B2**

Housed around the remains of a 14th-century nunnery, and converted into a brewery and coaching inn around 1608, there's abundant history here. Among notable features in public areas are the 100-foot

Long Bar containing its own skittle alley, and outstanding examples of stonemasonry through the ages to be found in the Winter's Court restaurant. Bedrooms in the main, Georgian, house overlooking a fairly constant stream of traffic, are on the utilitarian side (several with WC/shower rooms only). To the rear, and set around a courtyard facing the serene garden, the newer bedrooms have a touch more elegance, enhanced in the honeymoon suites by four-poster and half-tester beds. Banqueting/conferences for 120. No dogs. *Free House.* *Beer* Gibbs Mew Wiltshire Traditional & Salisbury Best, guest beer. *Accommodation* 25 bedrooms, all en suite £65 (single £47). Children welcome overnight, additional beds (£15) and cots (£8.50) available. Lounge for residents. Family room. Garden, skittle alley. Closed around Christmas (ring to confirm). Access, Visa.

Cotebrook   **Alvanley Arms**

Tel 01829 760200	**FOOD**
Forest Road Cotebrook nr Tarporley Cheshire CW6 9DS	**Map 6 B2**

Picturesque country gardens overlooking the pond, and a gentrified interior give lie to the noisy roadside position (on the A49) of the Whites' food-loving pub. Paper money from around the world decorates the public bar where diners from throughout the county foregather. For meals here and in the lounge best bets come from the blackboard: home-made vegetable soup (£1.75), monkfish with tomato and basil sauce (£7.95), pigeon breasts sautéed with mushrooms and port (£6.95). More conservative, though popular, pub fare from a long bar menu includes tuna and cheese paté (£2.95), hot pot (£4.10), steak and kidney (£4.65) and chicken tikka (£5.50). Similar fare, served with generous amount of fresh vegetables, is supplemented in the (evenings-only) restaurant by Dee salmon, Dover soles, steaks and grills which hover around the £10 mark. Popular home-made sweets run from bread-and-butter pudding (£2) to cream-enveloped chocolate éclairs (£2.25). Joe and Doreen pride themselves on their cooking of everything to order, and apologise in advance for waiting times: with some failings in production and service not entirely restricted to peak times, be prepared for it to be slow. A pair of small double rooms is available for overnight stays, each with a private bathroom. Infants in cots are made welcome, but there is scarcely room for an extra bed. *Bar Food* 12-2 (*Sun to 1.45*), 6-9.30 (*Sun 7-9*). *Restaurant Meals* 7-9. *Beer* Robinson's. Garden, children's play area. Family room. Access, Visa.

Cotherstone   **Fox and Hounds**

Tel 01833 650241	**FOOD**
	B&B
Cotherstone nr Barnard Castle Co Durham DL12 9PF	**Map 5 D3**

Not many yards from the river Tees and overlooking the village green, the Fox and Hounds has an unbroken history as a coaching inn dating back over 200 years. Today's resident hosts Patrick and Jenny Crawley continue this long tradition of hospitality with their unstinting hard work and enthusiasm and today's satisfied crowds of diners are no less enthusiastic about the results. There's a healthy leaning towards fresh fish on the daily-updated blackboards: crab and prawn cocktail (£4.65) and poached salmon with orange (£9.95); fresh Dover Soles and lobster salads or Thermidor (from £9.75) come at a fair price. Every day there's a pie or two (chicken to mushroom £6.95) with commendable herby shortcrust pastry and an array of fresh vegetables: wider choices encompass the ploughman's of local

Zzᴢᴢ...

Dales cheeses with home-made bread (£3.95) and the very popular
local duckling, roast perhaps with black cherry sauce (£10.95). Home-
made puddings, too, might be hot treacle sponge with custard or
chocolate cream crunch (£2.95). While Patrick earns the plaudits for
his food, Jenny oversees the entire house with relaxed assurance, taking
pride in good real ales, such as Hambleton and White Boar Bitter, and
a wine list of 50 bins with a dozen or more also available in half
bottles. Bedroom renovations meanwhile are all her own work and
each one of the three en-suite rooms (one with WC/shower only) is
sumptuously decorated and immaculately appointed. In two rooms the
original cast-iron fireplaces have been exposed and carefully restored.
A good night's sleep is virtually assured, with the bonus of a hearty
breakfast to look forward to. Accommodation rates quoted are on a
half-board basis. No children under 9. *Free House.* **Accommodation**
3 bedrooms, all en suite, £80 (single £52.50). Check-in by arrangement.
Children welcome overnight. **Bar Food** *12-1.45, 6.30-9 (Sun 7-9 Sun).*
Beer *John Smith's, Hambleton White Boar Bitter. Access, Visa.*

Cousley Wood   Old Vine

Tel 01892 782271	**FOOD**
Cousley Wood nr Wadhurst East Sussex TN5 6ER	**Map 11 B6**

Long a favourite, this 16th-century typical old-English dining pub has
inglenook fireplaces, beams, benches, farmhouse chairs, and climbing
roses. The blackboard bar menu (which may be ordered in the
restaurant) offers moules marinière (£3), peppered chicken in cream
(£4.75), steak and kidney pie (£4.25) and fresh plaice (£5.25), while
the 3-course restaurant menu in the evening is priced according to
choice of main dish (£10.50-13.50) – perhaps veal stroganoff or
grilled halibut supreme. All puddings are home-made: chocolate
cheesecake, sherry trifle and blackberry and apple pie (all £2) are
popular. Monday night is jazz music night. **Bar Food & Restaurant**
Meals *12-2 (except restaurant), 7-9.30 (music night menu only on Mon).*
Beer *Flowers Original, Fremlins, Harveys. Garden, outdoor eating.*
Access, Visa.

Coventry   William IV

Tel 01203 686394	**FOOD**
1059 Foleshill Road Coventry West Midlands CV6 6ER	**Map 6 C4**

There's a sign to Bedworth (B4113) from the M6, Junction 3, and the
pub is about equidistant from this point and the city centre in
Foleshill. What was arguably Britain's first authentically Indian pub
remains unusual today as the Himalayan Balti cooking much favoured
here – and more usually associated with the Muslim religion – is not
generally to be found on licensed premises. Perminder and Jatinder
Bains, however, being Sikhs of Kenyan origin espouse a broader
culinary church and the range of "Pele's" curries runs to one hundred
or more variations. Balti meat or chicken Rogan Josh (£4), both meat
and vegetarian thalis (£5.85 & £4.85) and the speciality chicken
saagwla (£3.70) are but the briefest indicators of this comprehensive
range. Eating here is quite an experience and shows up the
overwhelming majority of British pub curries for the sham that they
are. Bass Taverns. **Bar Food** *12-2.30, 6-10.30 (Fri/Sat 5-10.45). Now*
open on Sundays also for food (12-2.30, 7-10). Children allowed in the bar
to eat. **Beer** *M&B Mild. No credit cards.*

Coxwold	**Fauconberg Arms**	**FOOD**
Tel 01347 868214		**B&B**
Main Street Coxwold North Yorkshire YO6 4AD		**Map 5 E4**

This is a charmingly civilised, if invariably busy place, with handsome old furnishings and an open fire, located near Shandy Hall and Byland Abbey. Landlady Nicky Jaques produces adventurous and varied bar food: cream of celeriac and coconut soup (£1.95), smoked salmon and watercress mousse (£3.65), pan-fried lamb with apple, mint and rosemary gravy (£6.75). The restaurant's 3-course table d'hote menu for Sunday lunch is £10.45 (£5.25 children) and in the evenings one menu applies throughout the pub and offers choices such as hickory smoked chicken and melon with avocado dip (£3.25), envelopes of puff pastry with Stilton and celery paté and spiced peach mayonnaise (£3.25), boned half duckling with Bramley apple purée with walnut gravy (£10.75) or filo pastry pouches of salmon and halibut served with rhubarb and ginger sauce (£10.95). To accompany there are at least eight wines available by the glass. Bedrooms have long been popular here too, and still look like good value. The setting is delightful, in a peaceful, straggling village, and the church across the road is worth a look; Lawrence Sterne is buried there. An outdoor children's play area is planned for the near future. *Bar Food and Restaurant Meals 12-2, 7-9. Children allowed in bar to eat, children's menu. Free House. Beer Tetley, Theakston Best, John Smiths. Patio, outdoor eating. Accommodation 4 bedrooms, one with shower, £40 (single £24). Children welcome overnight, additional beds (£10) available. Access, Visa.*

Cranborne	**Fleur de Lys**	
Tel 01725 517282 Fax 01725 517631		**B&B**
5 Wimborne Street Cranborne Dorset BH21 5PP		**Map 14 C4**

Historical connections are many at this ivy-clad inn set in the heart of the village; Thomas Hardy visited when writing *Tess of the D'Urbervilles*, Rupert Brooke wrote a poem on the premises, and Hanging Judge Jeffreys also once stayed the night. The pub itself is modernised and pleasant, with period features remaining. Good-sized en-suite bedrooms are clean and comfortable, and decorated in country style with pretty floral fabrics and modern darkwood furniture. Equipped with central heating, TVs and tea-makers, they make an ideal base from which to explore this unspoilt part of Dorset, especially Cranborne Chase. *Beer Hall & Woodhouse Badger Best & Tanglefoot. Garden, outdoor eating. Accommodation 8 bedrooms, all en suite, from £42 (single £29). Children welcome overnight (under-5s free if sharing parents' room, 5-12s ½-price), additional beds & cot available. Access, Visa.*

Cranmore	**Strode Arms**	
Tel 01749880 450		**A**
Cranmore nr Shepton Mallett Somerset BA4 4QT		**Map 13 F1**

13th- and 14th-century coaching inn, formerly a farmhouse, opposite the village pond. Delightfully rustic within and full of memorabilia from the East Somerset Railway (otherwise known as the Strawberry Line) which is nearby. Particularly welcoming features are the provision of daily papers and a huge fireplace in the main lounge. Vintage cars meet outside on the first Tuesday of the month. Terrace overlooking the village pond and a beer garden to the rear. No children under 14 indoors; plenty of room outside in good weather. *Free House. Beer Flowers IPA, Marston's Pedigree, Wadworth 6X & guest beer. Garden. Pub closed Sun eves. Access, Visa.*

Craster   Jolly Fisherman

| Tel 01665 576461 | **A** |

Haven Hill Craster nr Alnwick Northumberland NE66 3TR   **Map 5 E1**

The village's only pub perches on a craggy hill above the quay, home of the local lifeboatmen and a summer haunt for visiting landlubbers. Its best aspects are from a raised lounge bar revealing massive seascapes through picture windows on two sides, and from a lower garden and patio, a little above high water, with pathways down by the harbour wall to the rocky shoreline. With boats in the harbour and the local fishery opposite, seafood sandwiches are their stock-in-trade; crab, prawn and salmon costing around £1.50. *Beer Castle Eden Bitter. Open 11-3, 6-11 (12-3, 7-10.30 Sun). Gardens. Family room. Quayside. No credit cards.*

Crawley   Fox & Hounds

| Tel & Fax 01962 772285 | **FOOD** |
| | **B&B** |

Crawley nr Winchester Hampshire SO21 2PR   **Map 15 D3**

A splendid redbrick pub built (like the rest of the picturesque village) at the turn of the century and converted to look much older than it is, with a fine overhanging timber facade and bow windows. The open-plan interior is comfortably furnished with a mix of padded benches and seats, arranged around a variety of tables, and lots of china plates decorate the walls of both bar and adjacent restaurant. The regularly-changing hand-written menu features good-value fresh fish – delivered twice a week from Poole and Cornwall – in dishes such as Spanish fish soup (£2.50), seafood pancakes (£9.25) and fresh whole lemon sole meunière (£9.25). Other popular speciality dishes include home-made pies – steak, venison and kidney (£5.95) – and a hearty spicy cheese and lentil loaf (£5.95). Crème caramel with fresh oranges and Grand Marnier or a chocolate shell filled with ice cream and fruits complete a meal. Upstairs are three pristinely-kept, en-suite bedrooms, all attractively decorated in pastel shades of peach and apricot with tasteful co-ordinating fabrics. Individual pieces of pine and antique furniture furnish the rooms and landing. Extra touches include well-equipped large bathrooms, good TVs, magazines and china crockery on each beverage tray. Bookings only in restaurant. *Bar Food 12-2, 7-9.30 (Sun to 9). Restaurant Meals 12-2, 7-9.30 (no food eve). Children's portions. Free House. Beer Wadworth 6X, Gales BB. Garden, patio, outdoor eating area. Accommodation 3 bedrooms, all en suite, £55. Children welcome overnight. Additional beds (£10) available. Dogs by arrangement. Access, Visa.*

Zzzz...

Cray   White Lion Inn

| Tel 01756 760262 | **A** |

Cray Buckden Skipton North Yorkshire BD23 5JB   **Map 5 D4**

Titular headquarters of the Wharfdale Head Gun Club, the Lion nestles in a deep valley on the road (B6160) between Wharfdale and Bishopsdale at the foot of Buckden Pike. For droves of fell walkers and families it's a sure shot in all weathers. Flagstoned within by a huge open range, the bar is a chummy place to dry off over a welcome pint of Moorhouses (leaving muddy boots outside, please!).

A sun-soaked front patio comes into its own in summer; parents can relax while across the road children in their dozens splash in and around the Beck, seemingly oblivious of the true purpose of its aged stepping stones. Children welcome indoors to eat. *Free House. Open 11-3, 5.30-11 (12-3, 7-10.30 Sun).* **Beer** *Tetley Best, Moorhouses Premier & Pendle Witches Brew. Family room. Outdoor eating area. Access, Visa.*

Crazies Hill   The Horns

Tel 01734 401416	FOOD
Crazies Hill Wargrave Berkshire RG10 8LY	Map 15a D3

Recently renovated (but not too much) by Brakspear's brewery, the Horns started life in Tudor times as a hunting lodge to which a barn (now part of the bar) was added some 200 years later. Very much the unspoilt country pub in style, it has no fruit machines and no piped music, just country furniture, traditional pub games – darts, shove ha'penny – and conversation. Not primarily a foody place but lunchtimes from Tuesday to Saturday there are various filled rolls (from £3), ploughman's (£3.80), a late breakfast (£4.25) and about half-a-dozen blackboard specials. Everything is home-made but not equally recommendable. Soup is a good bet, pasta dishes rather less so. On Friday and Saturday evenings a more brasserie-style menu is in operation (booking essential) and Monday nights feature live jazz. *Open all day Saturday and Sunday for barbecues in summer.* **Bar Food** *Noon-2 (not Sun or Mon).* **Beer** *Brakspear Mild, Bitter, Special, Old and OBJ. Garden, outdoor eating, disabled facilities. Pub closed 26 Dec and 1 Jan. No credit cards.*

Cresswell   Izaak Walton Inn

Tel 01782 392265	FOOD
Cresswell Stoke-on-Trent Staffordshire ST11 9RE	Map 6 B3

A good place to know in this area, despite being somewhat wedged between the busy A50 and the Stoke-Nottingham railway: turn off to the village from the old A522 at Draycott-in-the-Moors. Carpeted throughout with smartly varnished tables and chairs, yet very much a 'pub serving food', it is popular enough these days to render weekend booking virtually essential. Once tables are allocated, order at the bar from a lengthy, all-embracing menu supplemented by snacks and sandwiches at lunchtime (not Sunday) and chef's specials on a strategically placed blackboard: watercress and potato soup (£1.95); lamb and apricot curry (£5.95), or choose your own chicken supreme filling from blue cheese Stilton, crab meat or apples and cider sauce (all £6.50); and perhaps a gooey banana split (£2.25) to finish. No smoking in eating areas. *Pub open 12-11. Bar Food 12-2, 7-9.45 (Sat to 10). Free House.* **Beer** *Marston's Pedigree.* **Bar Food** *12-2 (except Fri-Sun), 7-9.45 (Fri & Sat to 10). Garden, outdoor eating. Family room. Pub closed 25 & 26 Dec. Access, Visa.*

Croscombe   Bull Terrier

Tel 01749 343658	B&B
Croscombe nr Wells Somerset BA5 3QJ	Map 13 F1

This lovely old pub was originally a priory where the abbots of Glastonbury used to live and was first licensed in 1612. Three bars: the Inglenook with red carpet, cushioned wall seats and original Jacobean beams, the Snug and the Common bar plus a family/dining room. The attractive, elevated walled garden which backs on to the church (floodlit at night) overlooks the surrounding countryside. Good real ales and a wide selection of carefully chosen wines which are also sold for 'off sales'. Simple overnight accommodation comprises three neat and homely upstairs bedrooms. Two sport compact en-suite facilities (one with tub, one with shower only) while the third shares with the landlord's family. All have TVs, radio-alarms and tea- and coffee-making facilities. No children or dogs overnight. *Free House.* **Beer** *small changing selection of real ales. Garden. Family room.* **Accommodation** *3 bedrooms, 2 en suite, £45 (single £25). No dogs. Pub closed all Monday Oct-Mar. Access, Visa.*

Cullompton   Manor House Hotel

| Tel 01884 32281   Fax 01884 38344 | **B&B** |
| 2/4 Fore Street Cullompton Devon EX15 1JL | Map 13 E2 |

Built as the town house for a rich wool merchant, this hotel-cum-inn dates in part to 1603, and fine old casement windows jut out from the freshly-painted black and white facade. Inside has an attractive mix of styles, the knotty pine bar Victorian in feel but with a distinct, pubby atmopshere. The appealing bedrooms are all individually decorated, with stylishly co-ordinated fabrics, nicely framed botanical prints, plenty of pieces of china and plates on the walls and good freestanding furniture in mahogany or an orangey pine finish. All the usual modern comforts: TV (with satellite), radio, telephone, tea/coffee-making facilities and a trouser press. Carpeted bathrooms have wooden toilet seats, good thermostatically-controlled showers over the baths, and nice touches like cotton wool, pot-pourri and decent toiletries. Most rooms are at the front of the building facing the main road (double-glazing helps to reduce the traffic noise) and one of the two quieter rooms to the rear has a pair of bunk beds for families. Recent new owners, Mr & Mrs Malcolm Powell, were intending to keep the same tariff, offering excellent value overnight accommodation. *Free House.* **Beer** *Boddingtons, Flowers. Patio/terrace. Family room.* **Accommodation** *10 bedrooms, all en suite, £50 (single £40). Children welcome overnight, additional beds, cots supplied. No dogs (guide dogs only). Access, Visa.*

Cumnor   The Bear & Ragged Staff

| Tel 01865 862329 | **A** |
| Appleton Road Cumnor nr Oxford Oxon OX2 9QH | Map 14a B2 |

To get to this large, ivy-clad coach house, which dates back to the 17th century, follow signs to Cumnor from the A420, follow the one-way system into village, bear left into the High Street and Appleton Road is on the left. The comfortable bar features flagstone floors, bare stone walls, beams, horse brasses, sofas, easy chairs, open fires and dried flowers. Very busy lunch trade. Separate restaurant area. Outside bar and barbecues in summer. Whitbread Wayside Inns. *Open 11-11 Mon-Sat, Sun 12-3 & 7.10.30.* **Beer** *Morrells Best & Varsity, guest beer. Garden. Children welcome inside. Access, Visa.*

Dalwood   Tuckers Arms

Tel 01404 881342	**FOOD**
	B&B
Dalwood nr Axminster Devon EX13 7EG	Map 13 E2

Picture-book-pretty, thatched pub in a delightful Axe Valley village, signposted off the A35 west of Axminster. Parts of the bar date back 700 years to when the building was a manor house; it later became an important coaching inn on the old London-Exeter road. The main low-ceilinged bar complete with inglenook, beams and rustic furnishings is the setting in which to sample some reliable bar food. Beyond the routine snack menu is a further menu listing popular dishes like 'Tuckers Tiddies' – a light puff pastry pillow filled with either mixed seafood or chicken in cider (both £8.95) – supreme of chicken with fresh tarragon (£8.25), rack of lamb (£9.55) and kidneys in red wine (£7.95). Extra blackboard dishes favour fresh fish salmon, local trout, freshwater pike and crab, as well as maybe cauliflower and Stilton soup (£1.75), rare roast beef and hash browns or maybe Cumberland sausage with redcurrant jelly and onion sauce. A rear extension houses the five clean and functional bedrooms with floral curtains and matching bed covers. All have TVs, tea-makers and well-fitted, fully tiled en-suite bathrooms with showers. In summer months the exterior is festooned with colourful flower tubs and baskets. *Pub open 12-3, 6.30-11 (7-10.30 Sun).* **Bar Food** *12-2, 7-10 (to 9.15 Sun). Free House.* **Beer** *Wadworth 6X, Boddingtons Bitter, Flowers Original. Garden. Outdoor eating.* **Accommodation** *5 bedrooms, all en suite, from £40 (single £25). Access, Visa.*

Damerham   Compasses Inn

Tel 017253 231	**B&B**
Damerham nr Fordingbridge Hampshire SP6 3HQ	Map 14 C3

Attractive 16th-century coaching inn located in the heart of the village next to the cricket green. Enthusiastic owners have smartly refurbished the carpeted open-plan lounge bar with new pine furniture, central woodburner, decent prints and pretty wallpaper. Separate spartan public bar with traditional games. Overnight accommodation in six bedrooms, of which the four individually decorated rooms are most acceptable. These are light and airy with small print wallpapers, co-ordinating fabrics, comfortable furnishings and good quality tiled shower rooms. TVs and tea-makers for added comfort. Good summer garden with children's play things. *Open 11-2.30, 6-11 (Sun 12-3, 7-10.30). Free House.* **Beer** *Wadworth 6X, Flowers Original, guest beer. Garden, outdoor eating, children's play area.* **Accommodation** *6 bedrooms, 4 en suite, £35 (single £19.50). Children welcome overnight (under-12s half-price). Access, Visa.*

☺

Zzz_{z...}

Danby   Duke of Wellington

Tel 01287 660351	**B&B**
Danby nr Whitby North Yorkshire YO21 2LY	Map 5 E3

Just two miles from the A171 and approached across a windswept moor, the ivy-clad stone pub stands at the head of Danby village; Esk Dale's activity centre is just a half-mile walk away. Despite its somewhat ramshackle exterior, there's a warm welcome within from the Hewat family who are well advanced into a programme of sprucing up. This is particularly apparent in the bedrooms with their pine furniture and appealing decor, colour TVs and tea-making equipment. All but one have their own en-suite facilities, the remaining room having an adjoining private bathroom. There's a cosy, private residents' lounge for these wishing to escape with a good book, while in the bars meanwhile an agreeable mixture of tourists, fell-walkers and locals soon strike up acquaintances over a pint or two of the Duke's well-kept real ales. Under-5s stay free in parents' room; cot available. *Free House.* **Accommodation** *5 bedrooms, 4 en suite £40* *(single £20).* **Beer** *John Smith's Magnet, Ruddles, Marston Pedigree, Cameron Strong Arm, guest beers. Garden, outdoor eating area. Access, Visa.*

Dartington	Cott Inn	**FOOD**
Tel 01803 863777 Fax 01803 866629		**B&B**
Dartington nr Totnes Devon TQ9 6HE		Map 13 D3

A delightful 14th-century thatched, stone and cob-built inn, continuously licensed since 1320, and severely damaged by fire in 1989, its 183ft long thatch – one of the longest in England – now fully restored. After a period of uncertainty, the Cott is firmly back on course due to the enthusiasm and energy of landlords David and Susan Grey, who bought the pub in May 1993. Both bar and tiny restaurant are neatly kept featuring lots of blackened beams, open fires, a mixture of antique and older pieces of furniture and plenty of gleaming brass bits and pieces. Lunch is an impressive hot and cold buffet affair offering home-made quiches, various meats, Dart salmon and an array of freshly prepared salads. Evening fare is more imaginative with blackboards in the bar listing such dishes as sauté of chicken with cream, tarragon and peppers (£6.50), carbonnade of beef (£6.25), seafood grill (gurnard, salmon, monkfish, mussels, king prawns), rack of lamb with bramble jelly, tournedos of beef with paté and red wine and tenderloin of pork stuffed with black olives in Madeira sauce (all £10-£12). Good accompanying vegetables. Puddings (£3.50). Roast Sunday lunch (£5.50). Overnight accommodation comprises six compact bedrooms tucked beneath the heavy thatch. All are neat and tidy with modern pine furnishings, pretty floral fabrics and compact bathrooms with overhead showers. TVs, tea-makers and telephones are standard throughout. **Bar Food & Restaurant meals** *12-2.15 (to 2.30 Sat & Sun), 6.30-9 (Sun from 7, restaurant from 7 every day). Garden, outdoor eating.* **Accommodation** *6 bedrooms, 5 en suite, from £50 (single £45). Children welcome overnight (not really suitable for under 5 years), additional beds (£10) supplied. Pub closed 25 Dec eve. Accommodation closed 25 Dec. Access, Visa.*

Zzzz...

Dartmouth	Cherub	**FOOD**
Tel 01803 832571		
13 Higher Street Dartmouth Devon TQ6 9BB		Map 13 D3

This magnificent example of a medieval timbered house (Dartmoor's oldest building, dating from 1380) was at one time a wealthy wool merchant's house. Famous for its overhanging beamed facade and the unusual first-floor windows, it takes its name from the type of boat built on the Dart for the wool export trade. Inside, the busy table-crammed tiny bar is full of atmosphere with original oak timbers and inglenook fireplace, plus a narrow, twisting staircase leading up into the small restaurant. Bar food includes beef and ale stew (£4.95), Cherub smokie (£3.75) and smoked chicken baked with cheese sauce, broccoli and ham (£5.95); all are served with salad or granary bread. Fresh fish dishes are featured on the little-changing blackboard menu – John Dory in Pernod and chive sauce (£11.95) and sole roulade with tarragon (£12.50) or for vegetarians, mushroom stroganoff (£9.95). These also appear on the more elaborate evening restaurant menu as does a selection of meat dishes, for example guinea fowl in a rosemary sauce (£11.50) and steaks (from £10.95), both served with six fresh vegetables. No children in the bar but children over four are allowed in the restaurant before 9pm. Choice of 50 malt whiskies. *Open 11-11 (Sun 12-10.30).* **Bar Food & Restaurant Meals** *12-2 & 7-9.30. Free House.* **Beer** *Wadworth 6X, Old Speckled Hen, Flowers Original, regularly changing guest beer. Access, Visa.*

Dartmouth   Royal Castle Hotel

Tel 01803 833033 Fax 01803 835445	B&B

11 The Quay Dartmouth Devon TQ6 9PS   Map 13 D3

Commanding the best site overlooking the small harbour and the Dart estuary beyond, this handsome, established inn/hotel is a most welcoming and comfortable place to stay. Originally four Tudor houses built on either side of a narrow lane, which now forms the lofty and attractive hallway, it boasts some oil paintings, antique furniture and the magnificent Bell Board, full of room-call bells, each one pitched at a different note. Of the two bars, the Harbour Bar is distinctly pubby and lively throughout the day, whereas the more refined and spacious Galleon Bar is a popular coffee stop and sports a weaponry display. All the 25 bedrooms are beautifully decorated, each in its own individual style with quality wallpapers and matching fabrics. Some rooms have four-posters, others antique brass beds and most are furnished with tasteful pieces of furniture. Several more expensive rooms enjoy river views and are light and airy with huge bathrooms, two with jacuzzi baths, some with showers only. Added touches include tissues, cotton wool balls and Woods of Windsor toiletries. TVs, telephones and tea-makers are standard throughout. If up early, linger over a good breakfast at one of the three sought-after window seats, overlooking the harbour and river. Twelve wines by the glass. *Open 10.30-11, Sun usual hours. Free House.* **Beer** *Boddingtons, Ruddles, Flowers IPA, Bass. Garden.* **Accommodation** *25 bedrooms, all en suite, £76 (single £48). Children welcome overnight (under-16s stay free in parents' room). Access, Visa.*

Dedham   Marlborough Head Hotel

Tel 01206 323250	FOOD
	B&B

Mill Lane Dedham Essex CO7 6DH   Map 10 C3

Dedham is a charming village surrounded by picturesque Constable country, and the Marlborough Head, which occupies that most traditional of sites directly opposite the church, has been dispensing hospitality for over 550 years. Woodcarving is a speciality here, outside on the black and white timbered upper storey of the building, inside above a massive old fireplace in the entrance lobby, as well as a particularly fine carved oak fireplace, original to the inn and now found in the family/coach party room. Several other rooms and bars, one featuring a heavily beamed ceiling, are furnished with good eating-height tables and the odd copper or brass ornament. Food orders are made at a leather-topped desk, quoting the number painted on a little stone on your table, from a long menu that runs the gamut from a simple jacket potato to the likes of paupiettes of haddock with prawn sauce (£5.50) and fresh breast of chicken with mushroom sauce (£5.85). Not to be missed is the Marlborough soup made with vegetables and a proper beef stock. Try to leave room for pudding, too, perhaps a hazelnut tart (£2.75) or a rhubarb crumble (£2.65). Spacious bedrooms, one double and two singles, are modestly but pleasantly furnished with a variety of pieces from the antiqueish and old pine to more modern bedside tables. Each has a few old timbers and sloping floors, and candlewick bedspreads add a homely touch.

Two have compact, lino-floored en-suite shower rooms with toilets, and the double a proper bathroom. *Open 10-11 Sat, regular hours other days. Bar Food 12-2.30 (Sun to 2.45), 6.45-9.30 (Sat to 10, Sun from 7). High teas and afternoon teas 3-6. Beer Worthingtons, Burton Bitter. Garden, patio, outdoor eating. Family room. Accommodation 3 bedrooms, all en suite, from £50 (single £32.50). Children welcome overnight (under-3s stay free in parents' room, 3-11s £10), additional beds and cots available. No dogs. Pub closed 25 Dec. Access, Visa.*

Dent   Sun Inn

Tel 0153 96 25208	A
Main Street Dent Cumbria LA10 5QL	Map 5 D4

Right on the cobbled main street and looking out over the parish church towards the Dale's surrounding hills, the Sun is picture postcard pretty outside and postage stamp size within, a shining example of a sadly-dying breed of village local. Dent beers, brewed nearby since 1990, prove a big draw here, and the setting of original timbers, winter log fires and a gravelled beer garden "out back" are all conducive to its enjoyment. Though the Sun has been well thought of recently for simply-served home cooking, we've refrained from further recommendation this year as the pub's cook moved on during the summer of 1994. Modest accommodation in three bedrooms sharing a bathroom. *Open 11-11 Sat, usual hours other days. Free House. Beer Theakston XB, Younger, Dent Brewery Bitter, Ramsbottom Strong Ale. Gravelled beer garden. Access, Visa.*

Derby   Abbey Inn

Tel 01332 558296	A
Darley Street Darley Abbey Derby Derbyshire DE22 1DX	Map 6 C3

Probably used for guest accommodation by the monks of the Abbey of St Mary of Darley in the 12th century, this medieval hall-house fell into gradual decay following the monasteries' dissolution in 1538. Fully 440 years elapsed before its restoration again saw the doors open for all to enjoy the Abbey's hospitality. High, exposed roof trusses and hammer beams are a feature of the upper bar whose leaded lights and church pew seating are quite in keeping. Approached by spiral stairs, the cavernous Under Croft Bar plays host to gregarious night-time activity, with jazz nights on Mondays and regular folk evenings. The toilets here, though, remain appropriately primitive. Home-made pies, the Friar's Favourite and Abbot's Feast are the staples on a short, simple menu operating at lunch only. *Bar Food 12-2.30 (except Sun). Children are allowed in the bar to eat (to 8pm). Beer Sam Smith's Old Brewery, Museum ale, guest beer. No credit cards.*

Derby   Ye Olde Dolphin Inn

Tel 01332 49115	A
6/7 Queen Street Derby Derbyshire DE5 1NR	Map 6 C3

The oldest pub in Derby, dating from the 16th century, in a conveniently central spot in the city centre. No juke box or machines and real open fire. There are four rooms: snug, bar, lounge and the Offilers Bar which is devoted to the former brewery of that name with memorabilia adorning the walls. Restaurant upstairs where children are welcome. *Beer M & B Highgate Mild, Bass, Stones, Worthington. Patio. Access, Visa.*

Devizes   **Bear Hotel**

FOOD
B&B

Tel 01380 722444   Fax 01380 722450

The Market Place Devizes Wiltshire SN10 1HS

Map 14 C3

This famous old town-centre coaching inn has been welcoming guests for over 400 years, including George III accompanied by Queen Charlotte and more recently Harold Macmillan when he was Prime Minister. It is still a comfortable place to visit and stay, for it retains that old-fashioned air within its beamed and panelled lounges and dining rooms. The main bar, furnished with winged wall settles and plush chairs around a large open fire, opens early, as it is a popular coffee stop for shoppers. Later, at lunchtime, it fills again with people seeking out the popular bar snacks, such as home-made soup (£1.80), giant Yorkshire pudding with Cheddar, sausage, turkey, Stilton or ham (£2.75-£3.25) and a range of ploughman's and freshly-cut sandwiches. A further selection of hot and cold dishes – which can also be eaten in the bar – is available in the traditional oak-panelled Lawrence Room restaurant at lunchtime. More imaginative and substantial meals, including table d'hote menus – lunch £10.50 (£10 for Sunday roast) and dinner £16 – and regularly changing à la carte menus – pan-fried pheasant (£12.95) and roast best end of lamb (£13.50) – are served in the Lawrence Room on weekend evenings and at both lunchtime and evening in the more elegant Master Lambton Restaurant. Rambling staircases and a labyrinth of sloping corridors lead to the comfortable and spacious en-suite bedrooms, all of which are equipped, furnished and maintained to a very high standard, as one would expect from a hotel of this standing. Several rooms have four-posters and residents have their own lounge with deep armchairs, sofas and open fires. *Hotel open 7.30 am-11.30pm.* ***Bar Food** 10-2.30, 7-9.30.* ***Restaurant Meals** 12.30-2 (Sun 12.15-2.30), 7-9.30 (Sat -10, not Sun eve). Children's menu and portions.* ***Beer** Wadworth 6X, IPA. Patio, outdoor eating. Family room.* ***Accommodation** 24 bedrooms, all en suite, £70 (single £45). Children welcome overnight (under-5s stay free in parents' room), additional beds (£15) available. Pub and accommodation closed 25 & 26 Dec. Access, Visa.*

Didsbury   **Royal Oak**

FOOD

Tel 0161-445 3152

729 Wilmslow Road Didsbury Greater Manchester M20 0RH

Map 6 B2

Quantity and quality of cheese draw people here, for the landlord has had a passion for it for 40 years. Landlord Arthur Gosling miraculously returned the Royal Oak to trading within ten weeks after a fire in April last year. At lunchtime the bar counter is piled high with a huge selection of English, French and Spanish cheeses. Enormous slices are served with wholemeal bread and bowls of onion and beetroot, or olives; alternatives may be a paté with cheese or salami (Milano & Napoli). Doggy bags are on hand for those who cannot do their portions justice. No children allowed. ***Bar Food** 12-2 (except Sat and Sun).* ***Beer** Marston's Pedigree & Best Bitter, Banks's Mild, Union Mild. Parking difficult. No credit cards.*

Diggle   **Diggle Hotel**

Tel 01457 872741	**B&B**
Station House Diggle Greater Manchester OL3 5JZ	Map 6 C2

If approaching from the north on the A670, you'll need to pass the
turn-off to the village of Diggle and use the turning circle as left turns
are prohibited. Once through the village, watch out for signs for the
Diggle Hotel (by the school). The hotel itself, a dark stone building by
the railway line, dates back to 1789, and is close to the (disused)
longest canal tunnel in Britain, some three and a quarter miles long.
The owners of the Diggle, Gerald and Barbara Mitchell and their
daughter Dawn White, gave up running a newsagents in Leeds to take
over this Free House some seven years ago. The interior of the
building is neat and unpretentious. The main room (and adjoining
small room where children can sit) is full of polished brass and
copperware, and the plain walls decorated with a number of country
pictures. One wall has a display of bank notes and coins, both past and
present – it's interesting to see how the notes have shrunk (in size and
value!) over the years. Over the bar itself there's a collection of photos
of the locals. Upstairs there are three neat, unfussy double bedrooms,
two of them quite compact, the largest with views towards the
village. Modern fitted furniture is used in all rooms, as are duvets with
pretty floral covers, and washbasins. The shared and carpeted
bathroom also has a separate shower unit. A homely residents' lounge
has fawn upholstered seating, books and games. The Mitchells are
friendly and charming hosts, and staff equally pleasant. *Pub open noon-
11 Sat, regular hours other days. Free House.* **Beer** *Timothy Taylor's,
Boddingtons. Garden. Family room.* **Accommodation** *3 bedrooms, sharing
bathroom, £35 (single £25). Children welcome overnight (free if sharing
parents' room), additional beds and cots available. No dogs. Access, Visa.*

Doddiscombleigh   **Nobody Inn**

	FOOD
Tel 01647 52394	**B&B**
Doddiscombleigh nr Exeter Devon EX6 7PS	Map 13 D3

Difficult to find, but this delightful old village inn is worth the
hazardous drive through narrow lanes off the A38 at Haldon
Racecourse, 3 miles west of Exeter. According to legend, a previous
owner closed and locked the door against the knocking of weary
travellers, pretending that there was nobody in, and it has remained
the 'Nobody Inn' ever since. Today one can be sure that somebody's
in, and of a warm welcome within its mellow bars. The mood is
enhanced by a wealth of old beams, ancient settles and a motley
collection of antique tables; horse brasses and copper pots and pans
decorate the inglenook fireplace, and a real fire burns in winter. The
varied and value-for-money bar menu includes a home-made coarse
duck liver paté with port and herbs (£3.10) and the special Nobody
soup (£1.95) made with chicken stock, vegetables and fruit. More
substantial dishes appear on the daily-changing blackboard, such as
duck and orange pie (£5.30), Arabian lamb, beef Provençal (both
£4.90) and for vegetarians stuffed aubergine and vegetable pasta (both
£3.50). But ensure you leave room for possibly the best collection of
Devonshire cheeses to be found anywhere. Six different cheeses can be
chosen from a selection of more than forty, including cow's, goat's and
ewe's milk cheeses, many of them unpasteurised, with wonderfully
evocative names like Langleigh, Meadow, Jacobstowe, Ticklemoor
and Toatley – winner of our 1995 Cheese Pub of the Year. Even

Zzz_{z...}

more impressive is the globe-trotting wine list, which features over 700 bins and is particularly strong in the Loire. Twenty wines are also offered by the glass at any time and there are no less than 250 whiskies from which to choose, as well as four real ales dispensed straight from the cask. Four of the modestly comfortably bedrooms are in the inn itself, two with en-suite shower and toilet, plus tea-makers and a drinks tray bearing full bottles of brandy, gin and sherry – charged up by consumption at bar prices. Soundproofing against the noise from the bar is very poor, so those seeking some peace and quiet should book one of the three larger en-suite rooms located in a small, early 17th-century manor house about 150 yards away, next to the church. These are comfortably and traditionally furnished and a ready-to-serve Continental breakfast is provided in the fridge. Alternatively, stroll up to the inn for a cooked breakfast. No children under 14. B&B for horses 150yds down the road! *Pub open 12-2.30 (to 3 Sun), 6-11 (to 10.30 Sun, from 7 in winter).* **Bar Food** *12-2, 7-10.* **Restaurant Meals** *7.30-9.30 (not Sun). Free House.* **Beer** *Bass, Branoc, Nobody's, guest beer. Garden, outdoor eating.* **Accommodation** *7 bedrooms, 6 en suite, from £53 (single £23). Children over 14 welcome overnight. Pub & accommodation closed 25 Dec eve. No dogs. Access, Visa.*

Donington-on-Bain   Black Horse

Tel 01507 343640	**B&B**
Main Road Donington-on-Bain Lincolnshire LN11 9TJ	Map 7 E2

Attractively set in a delightful Wolds village and on the Viking Way walk, this much extended and modernised inn is a popular destination locally and also with visitors seeking comfortable overnight accommodation. Inside, a rambling series of rooms radiate out from the original 18th-century core or snug back bar with its low ceiling (beware of the perilously low central beam) and brick fireplace with log fire. A central inner room is decorated with Viking murals, while numerous horsebrasses and farming implements adorn the simply furnished main area. Rather gloomy dining area and lively public bar and games room. Light and spacious bedrooms are housed in the adjacent "motel-style" block and feature modern pine furnishings, wicker chairs, pretty fabrics and extras like remote-controlled TV and tea-makers. Spotless, compact en-suite facilities with efficient showers. Wheelchair access. The Black Horse is also a favourite with families as children are made very welcome in the mural room and adjacent dining room, where they can order from their own menu and enjoy an early evening meal if staying overnight. Two highchairs and a changing shelf in the ladies toilet are handy extras. Summer days can be enjoyed in the safe rear garden where youngsters can let off steam on the swings, slide and climbing frame. *Free House.* **Beer** *Adnams Southwold, Courage Directors, Ruddles Best Bitter, John Smiths Bitter, Morland Speckled Hen, guest beers. Garden, children's play area. Family room.* **Accommodation** *8 bedrooms, all en suite, £40 (Single £25). Children welcome overnight (price varies depending on age). Visa.*

ZZzz...

☺

Dorchester-on-Thames   George Hotel

Tel 01865 340404 Fax 01865 341620	**B&B**
High Street Dorchester-on-Thames Oxfordshire OX10 7HH	Map 14a C3

With a history spanning more than 500 years, the George is one of the oldest inns in the land. Focal point of the public area is a fine beamed bar. Bedrooms in the main building have a solid, old-fashioned feel, some cosy and snug under oak beams, two with solid four-posters. Other rooms have less character but are still very adequate. *Pub open 11-11 Mon-Sat, regular hours Sun. Free House.* **Beer** *Brakspear, guest beer. Garden.* **Accommodation** *17 bedrooms, all en suite, £75 (single £62). Children welcome overnight, additional beds available at £10 charge. Accommodation closed 7 days Christmas. Access, Visa.*

Dorstone   Pandy Inn

Tel 01981 550273	**FOOD**
Dorstone Golden Valley Hereford & Worcester HR3 6AN	**Map 9 D5**

The Pandy (located off the B4348) is the oldest inn in Herefordshire. It was built in 1185 by Richard De Brito, a Norman knight, to house his workers while building Dorstone Church as atonement for his part in the murder of Thomas Becket. Vegetarians are well catered for with a variety of dishes to choose from including cheesy vegetable bake and spinach and mushroom lasagne (both £4.95). Fresh fish from Cornwall features on Fridays – plaice, scampi, king prawns (£8.25), sewin (£6.95). Among the 'Light Bites & Starters' on the menu are crispy whitebait and deep-fried Camembert (both £2.95). Follow with one of the 'House Specialities' – garlic chicken (£5.45), wild rabbit pie (£5.45) or the 'greedy gammon, with as many eggs as you can eat' (£6.35). Finally, choose one of the seven desserts on the 'Puddings & Treats' menu which includes locally-made sheep's milk ice cream in some unusual flavours. Lawned garden with swing for children. *Bar Food 12-2, 7-10. Children allowed in bar to eat. Free house.* **Beer** *Bass, Woods Parish Bitter, Hook Norton. Garden, outdoor eating. Pub closed Mon lunchtime and all day Tues Nov-Easter. No credit cards.*

Downham   Assheton Arms

Tel 01200 441227	**FOOD**
Downham nr Clitheroe Lancashire BB7 4BJ	**Map 6 B1**

The pub's unusual name commemorates the Assheton family, Earls of Clitheroe and landlords of the entire village since 1558. Standing at its head by the church and surrounded by picturesque stone cottages, the village local retains a cheerfully warm, traditional air. Single bar and sectioned rooms house an array of solid oak tables, wing-back settees and window seats. There's no mystery, either, attached to the food, ordered at a separate counter where the kitchen is in full view. Predictable starters run through ham and vegetable broth (£1.95), and Stilton paté (both £2.95). Grills of plaice (£5.95) or steaks (from £9.75) and treacle sponge and custard (£2.25) follow familiar lines. Herring pieces in dill (£3.25) and beef Madras (£4.95) extend the snack range on a specials board whose main courses have a generally fishy emphasis: poached salmon with prawn and cucumber sauce (£7.85) or a crab thermidor (£7.25) show the kitchen at its best. *Bar Food 12-2, 7-10. Children's menu.* **Beer** *Boddingtons, Castle Eden Best, Flowers Original. Patio, outdoor eating. Family room. Access, Visa.*

Drakeholes   Griff Inn

	FOOD
	B&B
Tel 01777 817206	
Drakeholes near Bawtry Nottinghamshire	**Map 7 D2**

Less a hamlet than a multiple road junction, where the A631 meets the B6045, Drakeholes marks a right-angle turn on the Chesterfield canal where it tunnels for 150 yards under the road system. Standing above

the basin, fronted by a large patio and canalside picnic tables, the Griff
(once known as the *White Swan*) is built in the same distinctive red
brick which characterises the estate village (both shopless and publess)
of nearby Wiseton Hall. The 18th-century inn's interior echoes the
grand style of an earlier age, with its marble-floored entrance foyer
and bar, and intimate oak-panelled cocktail lounge. Grand eating is
not, however, de rigueur, the extensive bar menu encompassing old-
fashioned pies like chicken and mushroom (from £4.75); sandwiches
start at £2. There is a carvery every day at lunchtime (£4.50) and
from 5.30-8pm (£3.95). The restaurant combines table d'hote and a
Sunday lunch with an ambitious à la carte, which is carefully cooked
and neatly presented. The Griff is certainly useful to know for a quiet
country stay in the Idle valley. Bedrooms are neatly appointed in
pastel shades and varnished pine, which create a cottagey effect
without frill or particular luxury. There are televisions but no phones.
En-suite bathrooms are spacious and airy with good, powerful showers
for early morning invigoration prior to a substantial country
breakfast. *Bar Food 11-2.15 (Sun 12-2.30, 7-9.30). Restaurant Meals
12-2 (Sun to 2.30), 7-10 (Sun to 9.30). Children allowed in bar to eat,
children's menu. Free House. Beer Tetley, Castle Eden, Boddingtons.
Garden, outdoor eating. Accommodation 3 bedrooms, all en suite, £50
(single £35). Children welcome overnight (£7.50 if sharing parents'
room), additional beds and cots available. Check-in by arrangement.
No dogs. Pub closed in winter all Mon and Sun eve. Access, Visa.*

Drayton	**Roebuck**	**FOOD**
Tel 01295 730542		**B&B**
Drayton nr Banbury Oxfordshire OX15 6EN		Map 14a B1

Standing next to the A422 about a mile from Banbury is an attractive
16th-century stone pub which has built up a strong local following for
its excellent food. The low-beamed bars with their rough, painted
walls and solid wooden tables provide a cosily atmospheric setting for
everything from the 'Roebuck Special' (£4.95 – fresh cold ham off the
bone), liver and smoked bacon casserole (£5.95), savoury crepes
(£4.85), smoked chicken and sweetcorn soup (£1.85) and Brie
wedges with salad (£3.15) to grilled lemon sole in butter (£10.95),
scampi provençale (£13.65), cracked wheat casserole (£4.95) or
tagliatelle in a cream sauce with vegetables (£8.95). There are two
neat, recently refurbished bedrooms with up-to-date furniture, one
with exposed beams and a sloping ceiling. They share a functional
shower room and are both equipped with remote-control TVs, tea-
makers and magazines. No dogs. *Bar Food 11.30-2 (Sun from 12),
7-9.45 (except Sun and Mon eves). Children allowed in the bar to eat. Free
House. Beer Hook Norton, Boddingtons, Ruddles County, Fuller's London
Pride, Marston's Pedigree. Patio. Accommodation 2 bedrooms with shared
bathroom, £33 (£23 single). Children welcome overnight. Accommodation
closed last 3 weeks in December. Access, Visa.*

Drewsteignton	**Drewe Arms**	
Tel 01647 21224		**A**
The Square Drewsteignton Devon		Map 13 D2

Mabel Mudge, or 'Auntie Mabel', landlady of this timeless gem of a
rural pub for over 75 years, finally retired last year at the grand old
age of 99! Elaine Chudley (who has been here for 20 years) has taken
over and vows to keep everything the same. The single bar, servery

and surroundings remain totally unmodernised, with lino floors, tan walls and ceilings and simple wooden benches and plain tables. A rear room in a lean-to off the servery area has a collection of old chairs. Excellent Flowers IPA and West Country Dry scrumpy are drawn straight from the cask and those in search of some food will be offered good cheese, bread and pickle or a ham sandwich. This old traditional Devon pub is a real rarity these days among the big brewery pubs and vast dining pubs – long may it survive! *Beer Flowers IPA. No credit cards.*

Driffield   Bell Hotel

Tel 01377 256661 Fax 01377 253228	**B&B**
Market Place Driffield Humberside YO25 7AP	**Map 7 E1**

Period charm and modern amenities combine in a coaching inn that's more than 250 years old, but now very much a hotel. Conference and function facilities are in the restored Old Town Hall, and further conversion houses a leisure complex. Day rooms include the 18th-century wood-panelled Oak Room, the flagstoned Old Corn Exchange buffet/bar and a residents' lounge. Bedrooms boast antique furniture and up-to-date comforts. No children under 12. *Free House. Beer Hambledon, Younger's Scotch No 3 & IPA. Garden, indoor swimming pool, spa bath, steam room, sauna, solarium, squash. **Accommodation** 14 bedrooms, all en suite, £75 (single £55). Children over 12 welcome overnight. No dogs. Access, Diners, Visa.*

Dronfield   The Old Sidings

Tel 01246 410023	**FOOD**
91 Chesterfield Road Dronfield Derbyshire S18 6XE	**Map 6 C2**

Tucked roadside by a bridge on the main Sheffield railway line, there's nothing particularly pretty about the Old Sidings, although extensive refurbishments have spruced up the interior with the installation of wood panelling and even more railway paraphernalia. Vast menus signal the galley's intentions, with plenty of goods on which to stoke up. Once aboard, the special Shunters menu (any two courses for £4.25 or three courses £5.50) and Buffet Car dining are just the ticket. Sunday lunch £6.95 (children £3.50). Eight wines by the glass. *Pub open 12-11 Mon-Sat, regular hours Sun. **Bar Food** 12-2.30 (Sun to 2), 6-8.30 (Sun from 7). **Restaurant Meals** 12-5 (Sun only), 6-9.30 (except Sun). Children allowed in the bar to eat. Free House. Beer Stones, Worthington, Marston's Pedigree, Highgate Dark, Hancocks HB. Patio. Access, Visa.*

Duddington   Royal Oak Hotel

Tel 01780 83267	**B&B**
Duddington nr Stamford Lincolnshire PE9 3QE	**Map 7 E4**

Popular, small family-run hotel set beside the A43 Stamford to Corby road at the end of this charming village. The bar is modern, but by no means without character, due in part to plush banquette seating, lots of greenery and well-lit prints of Victorian scenes. Comfortable overnight accommodation in six decent-sized rooms, attractively done out in pastel shades and floral wallpapers, have antique-style reproduction pieces, Victorian prints and good beds with brass bedsteads. TVs, phones and tea-makers are standard and the clean, carpeted shower rooms (one with bath) are fully tiled. Handy stopover point for weary travellers heading north or south. Food was

Zzz*z* ...

disappointing on our last inspection. *Free House.* **Beer** *Ruddles County, John Smith's, Webster's Yorkshire. Garden.* **Accommodation** *6 bedrooms, all en suite (5 with shower, 1 with bath), £40/£45 (single £28.50). Children welcome overnight, additional beds (£8). No dogs. Access, Visa.*

Dummer   The Queen

Tel 01256 397367

FOOD

Dummer nr Basingstoke Hampshire RG22 2AD

Map 14a C4

Handy for M3 travellers, this attractive whitewashed inn is set in an equally pretty and up-market village, 1 mile from Junction 7. The neat, low-ceilinged and softly-lit bar area is open-plan in style, with several brick and wall partitions creating cosy alcoves and a small, intimate dining area. A printed bar menu highlights some good favourites, ranging from pasta dishes, hearty burgers, steaks and omelettes to gigantic freshly-made sandwiches (from £2.75) served with salad and crisps. More imaginative fare features on the daily-changing blackboard: poached salmon with asparagus (£9.95), lamb cutlets in rosemary sauce (£10.95), a 10oz portion of cod in beer batter with chips (£7.95), or the ever-popular home-made steak and kidney pudding (£9.95) all served with a generous selection of vegetables. A good-value 4-course lunch (£10.95) is available on Sundays. The rear sun-trap terrace and lawn with benches is ideal for summer eating. Live music Sunday eves. *Bar Food 12-2.45, 6-10 (Sun 12-2.45, 7-9.30). Children allowed in the bar to eat, children's menu.* **Beer** *Courage Best, Directors, guest bitter every month. Garden, outdoor eating. Access, Diners, Visa.*

Dunbridge   Mill Arms Inn

Tel 01794 340401

FOOD

Dunbridge nr Romsey Hampshire SO51 0LF

Map 14 C3

The enthusiasm of owners Niall Morrow and Sean O'Brien has not waned since they took over at this village pub opposite the Mottisfont (Dunbridge) railway station two years ago. Dark blue banquettes and lots of greenery share the bar with fruit and quiz machines and there are tables outside in the garden when the weather is kind. A skittle alley to the rear (for pre-booked groups only) has a new pine bar and country-style decor with red gingham table cloths and curtains. A nicely varied blackboard bar menu ranges from sandwiches (from £2.75 including chips), steak and kidney pie (£5.95) and soup of the day to moules marinière (£4.95) and an individual Bailey's Irish Cream cheesecake that popular demand has made a permanent feature. One of the noticeable improvements this year is the new choice of 12-15 wines available by the glass as well as the bottle. The separate restaurant is included in our *1995 Hotels & Restaurants Guide.* **Bar Food & Restaurant Meals** *12-2.15 (Sun to 2.30), 7-10. Free House.* **Beer** *Courage Directors & Best, Wadworth 6X, King Alfred, Ringwood Fortyniner, Gales HSB. Garden, outdoor eating. Access, Diners, Visa.*

Duns Tew   White Horse Inn

FOOD

Tel 01869 40272

B&B

Duns Tew Oxfordshire OX6 4JS

Map 14a B1

Rugs laid out over old flagstones, a selection of the day's newspapers, inglenook fireplace, old beams and timbers – all the right ingredients for an English country pub, but this one also comes with air-conditioning (in bedrooms too) and its own private 18-hole golf course. Ask for the Golf package when booking. The blackboard bar menu is admirably simple with about ten savoury items – cottage pie, tagliatelle bolognese, grilled sardines, sausages and mash with onion gravy, smoked eel, chicken pie (all at £4) – and puds such as tiramisu, treacle sponge and apple crumble (all at £1.95). Bedrooms, 8 in a separate stable block, feature plain walls with 'old rose' patterned fabrics plus TV, direct dial phone and beverage kit but furniture is rather minimal with no dressing table/work space. Similarly the ensuite bathrooms have only very limited shelf space. A small terrace tucked away between a couple of pitched roofs makes an unusual spot for summer drinking. *Free House. Pub open 11-11 (except Sun).* **Bar Food** *12.30-2 (Sun to 2.30), 7.30-9.30.* **Beers** *Hook Norton, Wadworth 6X. Golf (18). Family suite.* **Accommodation** *12 rooms, all en suite, from £45 (single £29). Children welcome overnight. Access, Visa.*

Dunstan   Cottage Inn

Tel 01665 576658	**B&B**
Dunstan nr Alnwick Northumberland WE66 3SZ	**Map 5 D1**

Purchased as a row of derelict cottages by Lawrence & Shirley Jobling in 1975, reconstruction into quite a modest guest house preceeded their finally opening the Cottage Inn as a pub in 1988. Central to the entire conversion, and fully visible in the bar, is the three-foot thick orchard wall of Craster Tower, which stands on the fringe of the pub's 8-acre wooded garden. Newly completed in front, facing Dunstan's only street, are several self-contained apartments (now available for weekly lets) while to the rear the wing of ground-floor bedrooms faces a garden of pine and poplar, with dovecote and abundant wild-life. Fully equipped with baths and showers, all are equipped with TVs, room phones and coffee-making equipment, £57 (£35 single). In between are the clubby bar, games room and a wealth of memorabilia in the Harry Hotspur Room. Both children and wheelchair users are particularly well-catered for:- baby listening for the latter is all past of the service. Hearty breakfasts are served in the bright, flower-filled conservatory. *Free House.* **Beer** *Ruddles Best. Garden. Family room. Access, Visa.*

Dunwich   Ship Inn

	FOOD
Tel 01728 73219 Fax 01728 73675	**B&B**
St James Street Dunwich Suffolk IP17 3DT	**Map 10 D2**

Well-loved old smugglers' inn overlooking the salt marshes and sea in a peaceful coastal hamlet – 2½ miles off B1125 at Westleton – and popular with walkers and birdwatchers from the nearby RSPB Minsmere reserve. The delightful unspoilt public bar offers nautical bric-a-brac, a wood-burning stove in a huge brick fireplace, flagged floors and simple wooden furnishings. There's also a plain carpeted dining room and a conservatory room for families. The welcoming and enthusiastic owners – Stephen and Ann Marshlain – have been at the helm here for 10 years and offer good simple food; the restaurant menu applies throughout the pub in the evenings; bar meals at lunchtime only. Choose at lunchtime home-made soup (£1.30), chicken and mushroom pie (£4.90), prawn ploughman's (£4.50) from the galley and in the evenings maybe sardines marinaded in a citrus dressing (£3.95), the locally renowned Dunwich fish'n'chips (£5.95) or Ship's seafood pancake from the printed menu. Finish off with home-made desserts, such as boozy bread-and-butter pudding, apple crumble and apple and cider flan (all £2.75). Beyond the bars a fine Victorian staircase leads to simple cottagey bedrooms, light and clean with pretty fabrics, period features and splendid views from leaded pane windows. Summer imbibing on a sheltered paved terrace and in the very secure garden surrounded by a hedge. *Free House.* **Bar Food & Restaurant Meals** *12-2, 7.30-9.30. Family Room.* **Beer** *Adnams Broadside, Greene King, Abbot Ale, Southwold Bitter. Garden, outdoor eating.* **Accommodation** *5 bedrooms, 1 en suite, £52 (single £21). Children welcome overnight, additional beds (£10), cots supplied. Check-in by arrangement. Dogs welcome. No credit cards.*

Duxford — John Barleycorn

Tel 01223 832699 **FOOD**

Moorfield Road Duxford Cambridge CB2 4PP **Map 10 B3**

Tucked at the far end of the village, a mile from the A1301, this well-kept, 17th-century thatched pub is resplendent with hanging baskets, tubs and borders in high summer. Delightful, single low-beamed and softly-lit bar with a rustic mix of country furniture, large brick fireplace and neatly decorated with plates, horse harnesses and tasteful prints. A comfortable, relaxing and uncluttered bar and an ideal venue in which to enjoy a hearty home-cooked meal from a short list of dishes. Good favourites – ploughman's (from £3.50), salads (from £6.50), grills (from £7.90) served with mange tout or salad and new potatoes – plus substantial choices like ragout of lamb topped with parsley scones, beef, mushroom and ale pie (both £6.90) and smoked haddock with poached eggs (£6.50). Interesting open sandwiches – hot black pudding with gooseberries (£3.90). Puddings from £3. Summer alfresco eating on the rear patio with additional seating in the converted barn. No under 14s in the bar. **Bar Food** *12-2, 6.30-10 (Sun 7-10).* **Beer** *Greene King IPA, Abbot Ale. Garden, outdoor eating. No credit cards.*

Easington — The Mole & Chicken

Tel 01844 208387 **FOOD**

Easington Aylesbury Buckinghamshire HP18 9EY **Map 15a D2**

Between junction 7 of the M40 and Aylesbury; take the B4011 from Thame past Long Crendon (2 miles), following the Chilton road outside the village and turn left at the top of Carters Lane (opposite the Chandos Arms), then straight on for half a mile. Landlord Johnny Chick successfully runs this pretty pub, which boasts magnificent views of the Oxfordshire/Buckinghamshire countryside. Inside, the rag-washed walls are hung with hunting prints and candle lighting; a low, beamed ceiling and hand-painted floor in the Tuscany style are complemented by two roaring log fires. There's seating for 60 people at oak and pine tables, and half a ton of French oak on bricks forms the attractive bar. Good home-cooked food such as half shoulder of lamb with honey and provençale sauce (£9.95), Mexican tiger prawns stuffed with mozzarella and wrapped in bacon (£3.95) and roast crispy duck with orange (£10.50). A Sunday lunch (£8.95) is also served. *Free House.* **Bar Food** *11.30-2, 6.30-10 (Sun from 7). Children allowed in bar to eat.* **Beer** *Hook Norton, Fuller's London Pride. Garden, outdoor eating. Access, Visa.*

East Chaldon   Sailors Return

Tel 01305 853847

FOOD

East Chaldon Dorchester Dorset DT2 8DN   Map 14 B4

Two good reasons for tracking down this isolated and charming pub: to enjoy the glorious peaceful views across the village and beyond to the Purbeck Hills and to try the good range of home-cooked bar food on offer. Originally an 18th-century thatched cottage, it has been well extended at either end, providing a comfortable dining area and a larger bar area, complete with barn-type roof, old timbers, ropes, floats and lobster pots. Old flagstones maintain the character of the rustic core, which comprises two low-ceilinged interconnecting rooms, furnished with scrubbed pine tables. Also sited here is the large blackboard menu listing the wide range of good-value bar food. The home-cooked daily specials – fresh fish, pies and casseroles – are the best bet. These may include pork, celery and apricot casserole (£5.25), Lancashire hot-pot (£4.50), steak and Guinness pie (£4.75) and a freshly prepared soup. Fish choices such as black bream (£4.75), cod fillet (£3.25) and whole plaice (£4.95) are served with chips, although a selection of vegetables can be requested. Steaks ranging from 8oz to 24oz are very popular here. Alfresco diners are spoilt for choice with a front bench-filled terrace with uninterrupted views and a sheltered rear garden to choose from. *Bar Food & Restaurant Meals 12-2, 7-9 (Fri & Sat to 9.30). Vegetarian dishes. Children's menu available. Free House. Beer Wadworth 6X, Whitbread Strong Country, John Smith's Bitter, guest beers. Garden, terraced area, outdoor eating. No credit cards.*

East Dereham   Kings Head

Tel 01362 693842/693283   Fax 01362 693776

B&B

Norwich Road East Dereham Norfolk NR19 1AD   Map 10 C1

☺

A modest but immaculately kept 17th-century coaching inn near the town centre. A cosy red-carpeted bar, busy with locals, looks out past the patio to an attractive lawn (once the bowling green) with tables and chairs. Spotless bedrooms are gradually being upgraded by the new owners with tasteful darkwood furniture and pretty fabrics replacing the rather dated furnishings that grace some of the rooms. Five rooms are located in the light and airy converted stable block; the remainder lying beyond gloomily-lit corridors in the main building. All offer TV, clock-radio, direct-dial telephones and tea-making kits and twelve have neat en-suite facilities. Young families will find this inn a good base from which to explore the area. Two large rooms have an extra bed and further beds and cots are available at a small charge. Children are welcome in the bars and restaurant to eat; they have their own menu and can order an early supper from 5pm. Plans are afoot to convert the old bowling sheds in the safe garden into a play room with toys and a soft drinks bar. *Free House. Open 11-3, 6-11 (12-3, 7-10.30 Sun). Accommodation 15 bedrooms, 12 en suite, £47 (Single £36). Children welcome overnight (High-chair and cot available). Beer Courage Directors, John Smith's, Adnams. Garden, outdoor eating. Children allowed anywhere. Access, Diners, Visa.*

East Garston   **Queens Arms**

Tel 01488 648757	**B&B**

Newbury Road East Garston nr Newbury Berkshire RG16 7ET | Map 14a B4

Set in the heart of horse-country and frequented by an assortment of stable lads, well known jockeys and prominent trainers, this modernised and extended rural inn is a good base from which to explore the scenic Lambourn valley, or for those keen race goers attending the Newbury meeting. It is also a convenient stopover for M4 travellers, with J14 only 3½ miles distant. Bedrooms are clean and comfortable with simple limed fitted furniture, modern co-ordinating fabrics and an attractive pastel decor. Well-fitted, tiled bathrooms or compact shower rooms. All boast TVs, telephones, trouser presses and tea-makers for added comfort. Relaxing carpeted and wood-panelled bar and adjoining restaurant. *Open 11-11 (Sunday usual hours). Free house.* **Beer** *Wadworth 6X, guest beer. Garden, children's play area.* **Accommodation** *15 bedrooms, 13 en suite, £37.50-£47.50 (single £22.50-£35). Children welcome overnight (under-3s stay free in parents' room), additional beds and cots available. No dogs. Access, Visa.*

East Haddon   **Red Lion Hotel**

Tel 01604 770223 Fax 01604 645866	**B&B**

East Haddon Northamptonshire | Map 15 D1

Little hotel of golden stone in a country location seven miles from Junction 18 of the M1. Pleasant, relaxing lounge bar with a mix of furnishings, china and pewter, smaller, plainer public bar. Recommended for its cottagey, well-kept bedrooms (two twins, two doubles and a single) with a handbasin in each room. Sunday lunch (£13.95) offers a good choice, as does the bar food list. There are plans for all bedrooms to be converted to en suite soon. No dogs in rooms, but kennels may be provided. **Beer** *Charles Wells Eagle & Bombadier, Morlands Old Speckled Hen, Adnams Broadside, Mansfield Riding Bitter. Family room. Garden.* **Accommodation** *5 bedrooms, sharing 2 bathrooms, £39 (single £29). Children welcome overnight (under-4s stay free in parent's room, 5-12s ½-price), additional beds and cots available. Check-in by arrangement. No dogs. Access, Diners, Visa.*

East Ilsley   **The Swan**

Tel 01635 281238 Fax 01635 281791	**B&B**

East Ilsley nr Newbury Berkshire RG16 0LF | Map 14a C3

A well-run, friendly family pub at the heart of an attractive Berkshire village: turn off the A34 just 3 miles north of the M4, Junction 13. The Swan is operated by Morlands, the brewers from nearby West Ilsley, and by the bar is posted a record of their landlords, unbroken since 1865. The pub, however, was a coaching inn in the early 1700s and despite today's open-plan interior many original features remain within its many rooms and alcoves, alongside collections of brewery artefacts, cartoons, local photographs and miniature bottles which have been accumulated over the years. Residents overnight enjoy the best of the old building's charm in carefully modernised bedrooms, now all en suite and neatly equipped with beverage trays, colour TVs and direct-dial phones – two are non-smoking. In summer, the trellised rear patio is a picturesque spot where parents can sit while the children let off steam in the adjacent garden. **Beer** *Morland Original, Bombadier, Bass, guest beer. Family room, patio, garden and play area.* **Accommodation** *10 rooms, all en suite, £42 (single £32.50). Children welcome overnight, additional beds £5. Check-in by arrangement. Access, Visa.*

East Meon — Ye Olde George Inn

FOOD
B&B

Tel & Fax 01730 823481

East Meon Hampshire GU32 1NH

Map 15 D3

Originally two cottages, the oldest part of the Olde George dates back to the 15th century. Situated close to the church and beside the River Meon in the village centre, it has been welcoming customers for over 300 years. Four inglenooks, a wealth of heavy beams, bare brick walls and an assortment of sturdy scrubbed tables characterise the rambling bar and attractive adjacent restaurant. The unusual horseshoe-shaped bar dispenses well-conditioned ales and a selection of country wines, while the kitchen produces an interesting range of home-cooked bar food. The printed menu items include prawn pasta carbonara (£7.50), sardines in garlic butter (£5.95), fisherman's pie (£4.95) and the usual sandwiches and filled jacket potatoes. Daily specials listed on a board can feature up to four freshly-made soups, chicken and leek pie (£5.50) and seafood lasagne (£6.50). Good puddings. During the summer months it is open all day with afternoon teas proving very popular among the visitors. Upstairs, five simply-furnished, good-sized rooms are clean, light and airy with the usual comforts of TV, tea-making kits and standard en-suite facilities. *Pub open 11-11 May-Sep. Bar Food & Restaurant Meals 12-2.30, 7-10 (Sat to 10.30). Children allowed in bar to eat, children's menu. Free House. Beer Hall & Woodhouse Tanglefoot, Gales HSB, Boddingtons, Flowers Original. Patio, outdoor eating. Accommodation 5 bedrooms, all en suite, £50 (£40 in winter), single £30. Children welcome overnight (under-3s free in parents' room, 3-14s half-price). Additional beds available. Access, Visa.*

East Witton — Blue Lion

FOOD
B&B

Tel 01969 24273   Fax 01969 24189

East Witton nr Leyburn North Yorkshire DL8 4SN

Map 5 D4

Zzzz...

At the gateway to Coverdale and Wensleydale, East Witton stands on the A6108 just a mile from the Cover Bridge. The rather stern-looking, stone-built Blue Lion, originally a coaching inn in the 19th century, has recently been sympathetically restored to former glories, yet retaining its truly evocative mood. The single bar faces a huge stone fireplace where a log fire burns year round. Here the blackboards might offer chicken liver parfait wrapped in smoked bacon (£3.25), fresh oysters and sliced scallops poached in a light tomato and basil consomme (£4.95) to start, and for main course sautéed pigeon breast with calvados, apples and onions (£8.75) or fillet of monkfish, pan fried with basil and olive paste (£10.50). For residents, the dining room at night is candle-lit and intimate with variations on the theme extending to Provençal fish soup (£4.25) and pan-fried calf's liver in port and lime sauce (£11.95). Bedrooms are all individually furnished, with a mixture of period furniture and state-of-the-art additions such as remote-control TVs. En-suite bathrooms are more than adequate, while comfort and commensurate privacy are ensured by the lack of any telephones. *Open 11am-11pm (Sun 12-3, 7-10.30). Bar Food 12-2, 7-9.30. Restaurant Meals 7-9.30 Tue-Sat. Children allowed in bar to eat. Free House. Beer Theakston Best, XB and Old Peculier, Boddingtons. Garden, outdoor eating. Accommodation 9 bedrooms, all en suite, £60 (£35 single). Children welcome overnight. Access, Visa.*

Eastgate   Ratcatchers Inn

Tel 01603 871430	**FOOD**
Eastgate nr Cawston Norfolk NR10 4HA	**Map 10 C1**

A pleasantly old-fashioned free house, dating from 1861 and unusually
named, standing in a rural spot just off the B1149 one mile south of
Cawston. A warm and friendly atmosphere pervades the neatly
furnished bar and restaurant areas which are both laid up for diners,
for food is very much the thing here. The appeal is the extensive
range of home-cooked meals listed in a veritable tome
of a menu, a 14-page epic of jokily named dishes which in many
establishments would render the reader wary and sceptical of the
freshness and quality of the meals. However, additional imaginative
daily specials and a packed pub – it is advisable to book – instills
confidence in the enthusiastic kitchen. Use of fresh local produce is
clearly evident – fish from Lowestoft, shellfish direct from the North
Norfolk coast, produce from local smokehouses and naturally aged
cuts of meat from a nearby butcher. The 'home-made' policy extends
to freshly-baked bread, herb oils, chutneys, stocks and pickled
samphire plus the use of fresh herbs from the garden. Fish comes in a
variety of forms (monkfish in beer batter deep-fried with a caper and
gherkin sauce £8.95, Dover sole £11.95) and dipping into the menu
reveals steak and kidney pie (£5.95) served with either a short-crust
or puff-pastry top, moussaka (£6.25), salads (from £4.95), doorstep
sandwiches (from £1.95), at least 15 vegetarian options – vegetable
pie (£5.45), nut goulash (£5.95) – and grills and meats named after
film stars, such as Costner's garlic chicken (£6.95) and Heston's
massive rump (£16.85)! Specials may include thick ham and lentil
soup (£1.95) served with warm roll and a pot of butter, crab pancake
(£5.95) and peppered chicken (£8.95). Good vegetable choice. Turn
to page 13 of the menu for the range of home-made puddings with
Dickensian titles (from £1.95) – Faversham's Favourite is summer
pudding – or to the board for nursery puddings like jam roly-poly
(£2.65). Separate cheese menu listing twelve varieties, six of them
British. An ever-changing selection of real ales, plus an interesting list
of wines with at least eight available by the glass to complement your
meal. *Free House.* **Bar Food** *11.45-2, 6.30-10.15 (Sun 12-2, 7-9.45).*
Beer Hancock's Best Bitter, Wadworth 6X, Shepherd Neame Spitfire.
Garden, outdoor eating. Children allowed anywhere. No credit cards.

Eastling   Carpenter Arms

Tel 01795 890234	**FOOD**
	B&B
The Street Eastling nr Faversham Kent ME13 0AZ	**Map 11 C5**

The mellow redbrick Carpenter's Arms dates back to the 14th-century
and can be found on the edge of a sleepy village, eight miles southwest
of Faversham on the backslope of the North Downs. Character
interior with two inglenook fireplaces – one in the charming bar and
another in the cosy, brick-floored restaurant which has an old baking
oven; corn dollies decorate the old timbers and beams, and a host of
flowers and pot plants add a homely touch. The short and simple bar
menu lists a hearty home-made soup (tomato £1.50), steak and kidney
pie with vegetables and lamb casserole (both £4.50), and a few
standard snacks such as burgers, carpenter's lunch and countryman's
lunch (ploughman's with ½lb spicy Kent sausage £4.25). Next door in

a typically Kentish white clapperboard house, reached via its own old brick path, are three peaceful bedrooms, two of them rather on the small side with shower cabinets and toilets en suite. The best room is much more spacious with a full en-suite bathroom. All have the same floral curtains, which contrast rather oddly with abstract patterned duvets, as well as TVs and radio alarms. Good breakfasts are served in the restaurant. Children over 7 are welcome in the restaurant only. *Pub open 11-4, 6-11 (Sun 12-3, 7-10.30) all day in summer.* **Bar Food** *11.30-2.30 (Sun to 1.30) 6.30-10.30. No bar food D Sunday.* **Restaurant Meals** *as the bar. Children's menu. No under-14s allowed in bar under-7s in restaurant.* **Beer** *Shepherd Neame Master Brew, Bishops Finger, Spitfire, Masons. Lawned garden, outdoor eating area, summer barbecue.* **Accommodation** *3 bedrooms, all en-suite, from £45 (single £35). Children over 12 welcome overnight. No dogs. Access, Visa.*

Easton-on-the-Hill   Exeter Arms

Tel 01780 57503   **FOOD**

Stamford Road Easton-on-the-Hill nr Stamford Northamptonshire
PE9 3NS   Map 7 E4

Weather-worn, white-painted old inn set beside the A43, two miles south-west of Stamford. Charming open-plan interior, the single,knocked-through bar being tastefully decorated in deep terracotta and green with a good mix of wooden furnishings, quality watercolours and prints, plenty of greenery and light classical music enhancing the relaxed atmosphere. A twice-daily-changing blackboard menu lists the reliable and home-cooked fare on offer. Lunchtime sees a decent sandwich and ploughman's selection plus lasagne (£5.95), cream of courgette soup (£1.95), steak and kidney pudding (£6.50), gruyère and spinach fritters and perhaps decent cod and chips (£6.50). The evening fare steps up a gear with more imaginative choices that may include beef Wellington with red Burgundy sauce (£10.95), breast of chicken Madeira (£7.95), salmon en croute with a wine, cream and prawn sauce (£7.95) and roast sea bass with fennel, garlic and rosemary (£9.50). A separate board highlights chargrilled steaks. Sunday lunch (£4.95-£10.95) can be a family affair with a couple of high-chairs provided. **Bar Food** *12-2* **Restaurant Meals** *7-10. Children allowed in the bar to eat.* **Beer** *Courage Directors. Closed Sun eve, all Mon. No credit cards.*

Ebbesbourne Wake   Horseshoes Inn   **FOOD**

Tel 01722 780474   **B & B**

Ebbesbourne Wake nr Salisbury Wiltshire SP5 5JF   Map 14 B3

The Ebble valley and more especially the village of Ebbesbourne Wake seem to have escaped the hustle and bustle of modern day life, as it nestles among the folds in the Downs, close to the infant River Ebble. This peaceful unspoilt rural charm is reflected in the village inn which has been in the Bath family for the past 21 years. Its 17th-century brick facade is adorned with climbing roses and honeysuckle, while inside the traditional layout of two bars around a central servery still survives. The main bar is festooned with an array of old farming implements and country bygones and a mix of simple furniture fronts the open log fire. As in the past, in rural inns, well kept real ale – Adnams Broadside, Wadworth 6X and Ringwood beers – are served straight from the cask and both local farm cider and free-range eggs are also sold across the bar. Bar food is good value and homely, the best choice being the freshly prepared dishes that are chalked up on

☺

Zzzz...

the blackboard menu, featuring chicken and ham pie served with plenty of crisp vegetables, home-made ham quiche, venison sausage casserole and steak and kidney pie. The standard printed menu highlights the range of sandwiches, ploughman's and other hot dishes. The set 3-course Sunday lunch (£8.95) is superb value for money, extremely popular and served in the tiny adjoining restaurant – booking necessary. The flower- and shrub-filled garden is perfect for summer alfresco eating and safe for children, who also have access to view the four goats and pot-bellied pig in the pets area. Those wanting to explore this tranquil area further can stay overnight in one of the two modest bedrooms at either end of the inn. Both are decorated in a cottagey style with pretty fabrics and wallpaper and have TVs, tea-making kits and their own private facilities. A peaceful night's sleep is guaranteed. *Bar Food 12-2. Restaurant Meals 7-9.30 (except Mon eve). Children allowed in bar to eat. Free House. Beer Adnams Broadside, Wadworth 6X, Ringwood Best. Garden, outdoor eating, pet area. Accommodation 2 bedrooms, both en suite, £40 (single £25). Children welcome overnight, (under-2s stay free in parents' room, 3-12s by arrangement) additional beds and cots available. No credit cards.*

Eccleshall   St George Hotel

| Tel 01785 850300   Fax 01785 861452 | **B&B** |
| Castle Street Eccleshall Staffordshire ST21 6DF | Map 6 B3 |

A carefully restored 250-year-old coaching inn which enjoys a central crossroad position in Eccleshall. The site was also previously occupied, at various times, by a draper's shop, four cottages and an undertakers. The small room behind the inglenook fireplace is still referred to as the coffin room. The oak-beamed bar, which is open all day, has an opaque glass 'smoke room' panel and the red-brick inglenook, and there is also a relaxing little lounge. Cottage-style bedrooms, many with open fires, exposed beams with vaulted ceilings and canopied or four-poster beds, are thoughtfully equipped and all have private facilities. *Bar open 11-11, Sun 12-3, 7-10.30. Free House. Beer Tetley, Boddingtons, Burton, weekly guest beer. Accommodation 10 bedrooms, all en suite, £65, (single £45), weekend reductions. Children welcome overnight (no charge for under-8s sharing parents' room), additional beds and cots available. Access, Diners, Visa.*

Edburton   Tottington Manor

Tel 01903 815757 Fax 01903 879331	**FOOD**
	B&B
Edburton nr Henfield West Sussex BN5 9JL	Map 11 B6

A 17th-century Grade II listed inn-cum-hotel in its own grounds at the foot of the South Downs, with lovely views. The bar is simple and properly pubby with country furniture and an open fire and an adjacent comfortably furnished lounge is used for pre-dinner drinks and by residents. Good lunchtime bar food – by prior booking and residents only in the evenings includes an imaginative choice of sandwiches (from £2.50) and ploughman's (from £4), spinach, ricotta and wild mushroom cannelloni (£5), dim-sum (£5.90) and regularly changing specials like six Rossmore oysters (£5.40), beef and Guinness pie (£6), pan-fried pork loin steak with rosemary (£5.95) and a daily fish board selection – fresh squid Thai-style (£5.10) and a whole sea bass (£11). Emphasis in the evenings is on more elaborate restaurant fare, but residents should take advantage of the excellent 4-course table d'hote menu at only £14.50 a head. Traditional Sunday roast (£8.75) is served in the Downs Room. Bedrooms are pretty, with soothing

Zzzz...

colours and good sturdy furniture, and are gradually being updated and refurbished. All are neat and tidy with added touches like magazines, biscuits, mineral water and a box of tissues in each room. Clean en-suite facilities have proper guest toiletries. Under-5s not allowed in the restaurant. Good summer garden. No children under 5 allowed in the bar. *Pub open 11-3 (Sun to 2), 6-11. **Bar Food** 12-2. **Restaurant Meals** 7-9 (Sun to 8.30). Free house. **Beer** Fuller's London Pride, Bateman's XXXB, (weekly-changing guest beer). **Accommodation** 6 rooms, all en suite, from £60 (single £35). Children welcome overnight (under-3s stay free in parents' room, 4-12s £10). Check-in all day. Access, Diners, Visa.*

Egloshayle   Earl of St Vincent

Tel 01208 814807	**A**

Egloshayle Wadebridge Cornwall   Map 12 B3

Originally built as a boarding house for the masons who constructed the church and named after one of Nelson's admirals, the Earl is a most extraordinary pub hidden away in the old part of a rambling village. Lovingly rescued from being a run-down local, it is now a splendid, welcoming hostelry filled to the brim with Edward Connolly's personal antique collection. The relaxing atmospheric bar has heavy beams, some wood panelling, an open fire fronted by two comfortable armchairs, various sturdy tables and chairs, old paintings and prints and most noticeable of all an amazing collection of antique clocks – from grandfather clocks to unusual ball-bearing clocks – that fill every available surface. Unbelievably, all are in perfect working order and 'time' is called by a cacophony of chimes, bongs and cuckoos. A tiny intimate snug bar resounds with ticking clocks. Those with time on their hands can while away an hour or two in the award-winning garden, ablaze with flowers in summer. St Austell Brewery. *Beer St Austell Tinners Ale, HSD. Garden. No credit cards.*

Elkesley   Robin Hood Inn

Tel 01777 838259	**FOOD**

High Street Elkesley Nottinghamshire DW22 8AJ   Map 7 D2

The lounge bar and tiny dining room of this comparatively modest Whitbread pub are the setting for pub food that's better than one might expect. Pick rather carefully through the menu to unearth culinary compositions ranging from 'Not your average prawn cocktail' (£4.35) or roquefort cheese salad with grapes and cucumber (£5.60) to the authentically spiced daily curry with accompanying relishes (£5.25). The draw, though, is the daily blackboard compiled by landlord Alan Draper, who's an enthusiastic (if haphazard) cook; mushroom and Stilton soup (£1.80) and the likes of matelote normande (a mixed seafood stew served with copious amounts of fresh vegetables £8.50) reward diners of more adventurous choice. Though billed as Robin Hood Country, Elkesley is so close to the A1 that children might be discouraged from over-zealous ball games in the garden where the traffic thunders past. Parents meanwhile might be encouraged to spend rather more if ordering and service were better organised. *Open 11.30-11 Sat. **Bar Food** 12-2, 7-9 (Sat till 10, no food Sun eve). **Beer** Whitbread, Castle Eden, Boddingtons. Family Room. Garden, children's play area. Access, Visa.*

Ellerby   The Ellerby Hotel

FOOD
B&B

Tel 01947 8400342   Fax 01947 841221

Ellerby Saltburn-by-the-Sea Cleveland TS13 5LP

Map 5 E3

Zzzz...

☺

An imminent tenth anniversary here should be the cause of some
celebration for David & Janet Alderson, whose programme of steady
development from run-down village pub to refined country inn is
now virtually complete. A much-extended main bar and attendant
dining room provide plenty of space in which to enjoy a wide range
of substantial fare, of which a large proportion is changed daily and
posted on prominent blackboards. From starters encompassing onion
bhajis (£2.45) and sesame chicken (£3.45), progress to chargrilled
smoked gammon (£5.45), roast duck breast with black cherry sauce
(£6.95) or perhaps a cheese-topped vegetarian pancake (£5.45);
accompanying vegetables are fresh and plentiful. The fresh sandwiches
(from £1.95), children's options with beans and chips (£1.95) and
Sunday lunches (main course £4.95 in the bar; children £3.25) are all
pretty routine. Monthly Chinese banquets (£13.45) have
proven a highly popular addition. All nine bedrooms have been
furnished to a commendably high standard with varnished pine
furniture and bright floral drapes, and all are complete with colour
TVs, dial-out phones, trouser presses and hairdryers. Bathrooms are
fully tiled and carpeted (except two with WC/showers only). They
have large baths and separate shower stalls. Children under six stay
free in parents' room. *Free House.* **Bar Food** *12-2, 7-9.30 (Sat & Sun
11-11 in Summer).* **Accommodation** *9 bedrooms, all en suite (2 with
shower only).* **Beer** *John Smith's, Tetley Bitter. Garden, outdoor eating area.
Children allowed anywhere. Access, Visa.*

Ellisfield   Fox

FOOD

Tel 01256 381210

Green Lane Ellisfield nr Basingstoke Hampshire RG25 2QW

Map 14a C4

Tucked down a leafy lane in unspoilt countryside, this homely village
pub is a popular lunchtime venue for business people from
Basingstoke, four miles away. Its appeal (apart from its location)
is the excellent selection of seven well-kept real ales and the honest,
unpretentious home-cooked food that are served in the two
comfortable, pine-furnished and music-free bars. Exposed brick walls,
light-oak wood panelling, an open log fire and added touches like
fresh flowers on both bar and tables plus a few papers and magazines
help create a convivial eating atmosphere. The regularly-changing
blackboard menu lists a short selection of dishes, ranging from a 20oz
T-bone steak, and steak and kidney pie (£6.95) to a hot chili (£4.75)
served with garlic bread, and a hearty lamb and mint casserole,
accompanied by new potatoes and fresh vegetables. Selection of 18
malt whiskies at the bar. Four miles from the M3, Junction 6. *Bar
Food 12-2, 7-9.30 (except Mon eve, Sun to 9). Free House. Beer Gales
HSB, Marston's Pedigree, Wadworth 6X, Hall & Woodhouse Tanglefoot,
Old Peculier, King Alfred Bitter. Garden, outdoor eating. Access, Visa.*

Elsenham   Crown

FOOD

Tel 01279 812827

High Street Elsenham nr Bishop's Stortford Hertfordshire CM22 6DG

Map 10 B3

☺

Once a row of three 300-year-old character cottages, this attractive,
flower-decked and well-cared-for village inn has a traditional carpeted
and low-ceilinged interior complete with brasses, beams, open fires

and a relaxing atmosphere. Separate lively public bar offering a variety of games. Bar food relies primarily on an extensive and varied printed menu, featuring good pub favourites, as well as interesting home-cooked dishes, namely freshly-made Crownburgers served with home-made whisky relish (from £1.30), ham and mushroom pastry tartlet (£3.50), Shrewsbury lamb (£7.25), scrumpy chicken (£5.95), veal Oscar (£8.95), New Zealand grilled mussels (£4.50) and seasoned pork with peppercorn sauce (£6.25). Decent, well-cooked local vegetables or choose a selection of fresh salads from the self-service salad bar. Puddings (£2.85) include unusual home-made ice creams such as marmalade and gin and coffee, chocolate and brandy. South-facing front patio with benches and a beer garden to the rear (with children's play area). Not only a pub but also the headquarters of the Elsenham Cricket Club. Positive family welcome. The pub is actually in Essex, albeit with a Herts postal address. *Open 11-3, 6-11, Sun 12-2.30, 7-10.30.* **Bar Food** *12-2, 7.30-9.30. No food Sun evening. Children welcome in bar to eat.* **Beer** *Crouch Vale Millenium Gold, Tetley, guest beer. Garden, children's play area. Access, Diners, Visa.*

Elslack — Tempest Arms

Tel 01282 842450 Fax 01282 843331	**B&B**
Elslack nr Skipton North Yorkshire BD23 3AY	Map 6 B1

Just off the A56 near its junction with the A59 and only three miles from Skipton, the pub nestles in a verdant hollow with its own stream winding picturesquely round the garden. To the rear of the pub proper, and with its own secure entrance, a purpose-built block was added just five years ago whose bedrooms are well-appointed and fully equipped for the 90s with TVs, telephones and plenty of well-lit workspace for the business guest. En-suite bathrooms are a little small, but being fully tiled with strong over-bath showers they are more than adequate. Double-glazed and well back from the road, accommodation here promises less Tempest than midsummer night's dream. *Open 11-3, 6.30-11 (11-11 Sat, 12-10.30 Sun).* **Accommodation** *10 bedrooms, all en suite £52 (Single £44). Free House.* **Beer** *Youngers Scotch, Thwaites Best & Craftsman. Garden, outdoor eating area. Children welcome. Access, Diners, Visa.*

Zzz...

Elstead — Woolpack

Tel 01252 703106	**FOOD**
The Green Elstead Surrey GU8 6HD	Map 15a E4

On an old wool trading route, the tile-hung Woolpack was in fact originally built as a wool-bale store in the 18th century, and only later developed into a hostelry. Now comfortably countrified, various artefacts dotted about the place still hint at the pub's previous use: bobbins and spindles of yarn, a lamb's fleece, an ancient pair of scales and a partly woven rug. Today folk flock here (no pun intended) to enjoy the notably, famously generous portions of home-cooked dishes chosen from a long blackboard menu, which ranges from baked goat's cheese on toast with garlic and mango sauce (£4.25) to monkfish in Pernod fennel and cream sauce (£8.95) and a range of pies (steak and kidney, cod and prawn and chicken and ham (all £6.75)). Genuinely home-made puddings might include Mrs. Swayne's pudding (layers of a mix of cake and breadcrumbs, chocolate chips and cream £2.95) or apple strudel. Children can have smaller portions at smaller prices, or opt for baked beans and tinned spaghetti on toast. A children's room has nursery rhyme murals and bunches of flowers hung up to dry from the ceiling; there's also a slide, swing and climbing frame in the pretty garden. *Bar Food & Restaurant Meals* 12-2, 7-9.45 (Sun to 9). *Beer* Greene King IPA & Abbot. *Garden, outdoor eating, children's play area. Family room. Access, Visa.*

Elsted   Three Horseshoes

Tel 01730 825746	**A**
Elsted nr Midhurst West Sussex GU29 0JX	Map 15 D3

Bowed walls, terracotta-tiled floors, gnarled beams, mellow stained plasterwork and a good open fire in the vast inglenook all create an atmosphere of genuinely unspoilt charm in this popular 16th-century inn, originally built as a drovers, ale house. Evening candlelight enhances the romantic old-world atmosphere. Good range of real ales favouring local micro-breweries – Cheriton Brewhouse, Ballards – are dispensed straight from the cask. Well tended garden with rustic tables and benches and magnificent views over the South Downs. *Pub open 11-3, 6-11 (Sun 12-3, 7-10.30). Free House. Beer Ballard's Best Bitter, Cheriton Brewhouse Pots Ale, Fuller's London Pride, Flowers Original. Garden, lawn, outside eating area, tables in garden. Access, Visa.*

Elsted Marsh   Elsted Inn

Tel 01730 813662	**FOOD**
Elsted Marsh nr Midhurst West Sussex GU29 0JT	Map 15 D3

It would be very easy to drive past this unprepossessing Victorian roadside pub, but that would be to miss out on some good food and a warm welcome. It was built to serve the railway in the steam age, when there was a station here, but was later left stranded by Dr Beeching's 'axe' in the 1960s. This explains the old railway photographs that adorn the thankfully unmodernised and unpretentious bars, in what is very much a local community pub, free of background music and electronic games but with plenty of traditional pub pastimes like shove ha'penny, darts, cards, dominoes and even conversation. There are two small bars with lots of original wood in evidence, original shutters and open fires. A small dining room, candle-lit in the evening, boasts an old pine dresser and colourful cloths on a few dining tables surrounded by a motley collection of old chairs. Tweazle Jones and her partner Barry Horton produce varied menus – always home-made and based on good local produce. The likes of jumbo sausage (£4.50), king prawns in garlic or lemon butter (£10), home-cooked ham salad (£6.50), as well as door-step sandwiches (smoked salmon £3.15), baked potatoes and ploughman's (from £4) are available as bar snacks, whilst more elaborate fare on the daily menu might be crab and ginger parcels, fillet of beef stroganoff (£7.50) or chicken breast in cream and capers (£7.50), with dark chocolate mousse (£2.50) to finish. Children can have half portions at half price, and there's a car tyre hanging from a plum tree in the shady garden to keep them amused, plus pétanque for the adults. Dogs are welcome or at least tolerated by the house hounds, Truffle and Sam, and an area of the garden is fenced off to keep dogs and children apart. Steak nights and curry nights are a popular regular feature here. The pub is no longer owned by the local brewers, Ballard's, but their ales are still served here. B&B is now available – £30 for a double, no children under 12. *Bar Food & Restaurant Meals* 12-2.30, 7-9.30 (Sat to 10, Sun to 9). *Free House. Beer Ballard's, Fuller's London Pride, guest beer. Garden, outdoor eating, boules, children's play area. Access, Visa.*

Elterwater   Britannia Inn

| Tel 0153 94 37210   Fax 0153 94 37311 | **B&B** |

Elterwater nr Ambleside Cumbria LA22 9HP   Map 4 C3

Next to the tiny village green dominated by a magnificent maple tree, fronted by its own colourful window boxes, the black-and-white-painted Britannia is a summer picture. Ever-popular with the walkers who throng to Langdale valley are the garden chairs and slate-topped tables on the pub's front terrace as both front and rear bars are tiny. Residents have their own chintzy lounge with oak beams, antiques and an open log fire. Within the pub, six of the bedrooms have entirely adequate en-suite facilities while a seventh has its own private bathroom across the corridor. All have individually controlled central heating, colour TVs, telephones, hairdryers and beverage-making facilities. Alternative accommodation across the green at Maple Tree Corner is especially handy for family use and generously priced at a lower rate, which nevertheless includes a hearty Lakeland breakfast served back at the inn. *Open 11-11 (Sun usual hours). Free House.* *Beer Jennings, Bitter & Mild, Boddingtons, Marston's. Garden.* *Accommodation 13 bedrooms, 7 en suite, £62 (single £23.50). Children welcome overnight (3-6 years ½-price, 7-12 years 75% of adult price) additional beds and cots (£4) available. Accommodation closed 25 Dec. Access, Visa.*

Zzzz...

Emery Down   New Forest Inn

| Tel 01703 282329 | **FOOD** |
| | **B&B** |

Emery Down nr Lyndhurst Hampshire SO43 7DY   Map 14 C4

Prettily set in woodland, the building of the inn was the result of the first successful establishment of squatters' rights on Crown land in the early 18th-century. The original caravan that used to sell ale forms part of the front lounge porchway. Much extended since, it has a big, busy open-plan bar and fairly modern seating and style, with effective country touches and real fires. The reliable bar food available here aims to please all tastes, and the regular printed menu features old favourites and chips, as well as some interesting home-cooked dishes – fillet of pork in a green peppercorn sauce (£7.50). A daily-changing specials board increases the choice of freshly prepared meals such as sauté of lamb with raspberries (£6.50), rabbit in mustard sauce (£6.25) and venison in pear and cinnamon (£7.50), all accompanied with fresh vegetables. Home-made puddings (£2.75) like toasted lemon brulée, treacle and walnut tart and fruit Pavlova round off the meal. Bedrooms are clean, comfortable and homely, three having en-suite facilities, the fourth having its own private, but not en-suite, bathroom. The room above the kitchen can be unbearably hot and airless in summer. The three-level rear garden is a super summer spot for alfresco imbibing with benches and tables among the well-tended flower borders and mature shrubs and trees. Whitbread Wayside Inn. *Pub open 11-11 (except Sun). Bar Food 11-3, 6-9.30 (Sun 12-2, 7-9). Beer Flowers Original, Strong Country Bitter, Wadworth 6X, two guest beers. Garden, outdoor eating. Accommodation 4 bedrooms, 3 en suite, from £50 (single £25). Children welcome overnight (under-3s stay free in parents' room), additional beds and cots supplied. Access, Visa.*

Empingham — White Horse

Tel 01780 460221   Fax 01780 960521

2 Main Street Empingham nr Oakham Leicestershire LE15 8PR

FOOD
B&B

Map 7 E3

A stone's throw from serene Rutland Water, Roger Bourne's civilised pub (including newly refurbished bar area) is the centre of village life, a meeting-place for walkers and birdwatchers and convenient for access from the A1 at Stamford and the market town of Oakham. In attempting to be all things to most callers its day stretches from morning coffee and croissants through lunches and cream teas to late evening suppers. Central to the three eating areas, which include a family room, is the food counter displaying cold meats and home-made sweets backed by a blackboard of daily dishes offering fresh Rutland trout with almonds (£5.95), surf and turf (£5.95-£6.95) and spotted dick (£2.25), perhaps, plus quiche, self-served salads and junior pizzas. Home-made hoagies (£2), savoury fish pancakes (£5.75), Glastonbury lamb (£5.75) and Yorkshire puddings with a filling of your choice (£5.50) constitute substantial bar meals. A la carte Stilton paté (£3.55) and salmon and halibut terrine (£10.95) command heftier prices. The bedrooms are also popular. Fittingly, the best are in the stables, kitted out in varnished pine and each with its own well-appointed bathroom. In the main building, rooms are bright and neat though more modest, with shared bathing facilities. There's one four-poster and conference facilities for up to 60. *Open 10.30-11 (Sun usual hours)*. *Bar Food & Restaurant Meals 12-2 (Sat & Sun to 2.15), 7-10 (Sun to 9.30)*. *Beer John Smith's, Directors, Ruddles, Wadworth 6X. Garden, outdoor eating, disabled WC. Family room*. **Accommodation** *14 rooms, 9 en suite, £52 (four-poster £60, single £40). Children welcome overnight (under-2s stay free in parents' room, 2-8s ½ price), extra beds and cots available. Access, Diners, Visa*.

Eskdale Green — Bower House Inn

Tel 019467 23244   Fax 019467 23308

Eskdale Green Holmbrook Cumbria CA19 1TD

FOOD
B&B

Map 4 C3

Despite its out-of-the-way location, the Connors' informal, friendly inn continues to find favour with a faithful and returning clientele. Headquarters of the Eskdale cricket team, the bar has a distinctly clubby feel and opens on to an enchanting, enclosed garden of pine and shrub, with a tiny wooden bridge traversing the village stream. Children can play safely here. Bar menus more reflect the public demand for steak and kidney pie (£5.50) and scampi (from £5.25) than show off the kitchen's prowess; however, choices from the specials board may include devilled whitebait (£3) and pork loin in apple and Calvados (£6.25). Dinner, served at smartly polished mahogany tables, is the preferred choice of residents and might consist of cock-a-leekie soup (£2.50), escalope of veal with Gruyère (£9.75) and tiramisu (£3.50). This is a delightful place to stay for peace and quiet in the Eskdale valley; bedrooms are divided between the main house, where they are abundant in character, the converted stables and garden cottages, subtly extended and thoughtfully equipped to meet modern-day demands. Families are well catered for and there are three large rooms suitable for family occupation. After a restful night, it's traditional to tuck into a hearty Lakeland breakfast. *Open 11-11 (Sun usual hours)*. *Bar Food 12-2, 6.30-9.30 (Sun from 7)*. *Restaurant Meals 7-8.30. High Tea 5.30pm. Free House. Beer Theakston Best, Hartleys*

XB, Courage Directors. Riverside garden, outdoor eating. Family room.
Accommodation *24 rooms, all en suite, £56 (single £44). Children*
welcome overnight, extra beds and cots supplied (£6). No dogs.
Access, Visa.

Eton   Christopher Hotel

Tel 01753 852359 Fax 01753 830914	B&B
110 High Street Eton Berkshire SL4 6AN	Map 15a E4

Former coaching inn on the High Street. Some bedrooms are in the
main house, others in courtyard chalets. Leave the M4 at Junction 6
and follow Eton signs. The hotel is just beyond the College on the
right. Dogs in courtyard rooms only. *Free House.* **Beer** *Young's Special,*
Worthington, Bass, Wadworth 6X. Terrace. **Accommodation** *34 bedrooms,*
£81 (single £60). Children welcome overnight (family rooms £73.50).
Access, Diners, Visa.

Ettington   Houndshill

Tel 01789 740267	B&B
Banbury Road Ettington nr Stratford-on-Avon Warwickshire CV37 7NS	Map 14 C1

A friendly, family-operated roadhouse which includes children's play
areas and a licensed campsite in its extensive grounds. The clean, tidy
decor of the lounge bar and adjoining dining room is repeated in the
pine-clad bedrooms and compact bathrooms with over-bath showers.
Up-to-date direct-dial phones and remote-control TVs ensure a degree
of comfort commensurate with the price range. Very useful to know,
as it's beside the A422 Banbury road, four miles south of Stratford.
Free House. **Beer** *Theakston Best, XB. Garden, outdoor eating, children's*
play area. Family room. **Accommodation** *8 bedrooms, all en suite, £45*
(single £28). Children welcome overnight, additional beds (from £5), cots
(£5) supplied. Dogs by arrangement. Access, Visa.

Ewen   Wild Duck Inn

Tel 01285 770310	B&B
Drakes Island Ewen nr Cirencester Gloucestershire GL7 6BY	Map 14 C2

Lovely Cotswold village pub near the Water Park. The dimly-lit Post
Horn bar is nicely poised between traditional and smartened up; the
restaurant has red walls, candles in bottles, and simple pine furniture.
The recently refurbished bedrooms (particularly the two four-poster
ones in the oldest part of the building) are decent though the
extension-housed remainder might seem surprisingly modern in style.
The Grouse Room residents' lounge, a haven of peace overlooking the
pretty gardens, is also open to diners. *Open 11-11 Mon-Sat, regular*
hours Sun. Free House. **Beer** *Bass, Duck Pond Bitter, Theakston's XB and*
Old Peculier, 6X, Young's Special. Garden. **Accommodation** *9 bedrooms,*
all en suite, £65 (4-poster £75, single £48). Children welcome overnight
(under-4s free if sharing parents's room, 4-10s £10), additional beds and
cots available. Access, Visa.

ZzZz...

Exford   Crown Hotel

	FOOD
Tel 0164383 554 Fax 0164383 665	B&B
Exford Somerset TA24 7PP	Map 13 D1

Long a favourite among the huntin', shootin' and fishin' set, the 17th-
century Crown stands by the green in a lovely village. After a few
troubled years the hotel has recently undergone major refurbishment
under new owners and now offers country pursuit followers a touch
of luxury in the heart of Exmoor. Seventeen, very comfortable en-

ZzZz...

suite bedrooms have been tastefully furnished with quality pieces from
the Churchill Hotel in London and equipped with TVs, telephones
and hairdryers; room service for refreshments. Lots of traditional
charm in the lounge and rustic pubby bar, in which some above-
average bar food can now be enjoyed. Good snacks or starters include
spicy crab soup (£2.90), coarse pork terrine (£3.25), lightly baked
tomatoes filled with creamed goats' cheese (£3.75) and marinated
Scottish salmon (£4.25), with main course options ranging from
chargrilled leg of lamb steak with thyme, served with ratatouille
gratin and new potatoes (£7.75) to chargrilled salmon served with
soy, ginger and spring onion sauce (£6.75). To finish try the chocolate
mousse (£2.50) or pears gently simmered in a spicy red wine syrup
served with caramel ice cream (£2.75). Separate restaurant with set
menus – 3-course £22, 4-course £26. Stabling available for those
wishing to bring their own horses. *Bar Food* 12-2, 6.30-9.30 (*Sun
from 7*). Free House. *Beer* Brakspear Bitter, Flowers Original. Garden,
outdoor eating. Family room. *Accommodation* 17 rooms, all en suite, from
£80 (single £40). Children welcome overnight (under-10s stay free in
parents' room), extra beds & cots supplied. Access, Visa.

Eyam	**Miner's Arms**	**FOOD**
Tel 01433 630853		**B&B**
Water Lane Eyam Derbyshire S30 1RG		Map 6 C2

Sideways on to the village square, the pub is a row of white-painted
cottages fronted by a butcher's shop; drive gently up Water Lane to
find residents' parking at the rear. A tiny triangle of garden gives
access from the High Street, the croft adjoining having been a burial
ground at the time of Eyam's plague in 1665/6; no wonder the place
claims to be haunted. A balanced selection of bar lunches might
include carrot and lentil soup (£1.95), haddock mornay (£5.25),
lamb and mint sausages with onion gravy (£4.25) and a cauliflower
and Stilton quiche (£3.95); to follow, Bakewell tart and sherry trifle
(£1.95). The evening à la carte extends to the level of wild red
venison in Madeira sauce (£9.25) and English-style roast duckling
(£8.95); this is careful cooking, neatly presented, with service
supervised by the caring Nick Cook. The half-dozen bedrooms extend
through into the adjoining cottages; recently decorated, they are clean
and bright with adequate en-suite facilities (one single has WC/shower
only). Welcoming touches include mineral water and a selection of
books; rather more practical are remote-control TVs, clock radios and
a hot beverage tray. *Bar Food* 12-2.30 (*except Sun*) *Restaurant Meals*
(*Sun only 12-1.30*), 7-9 (*closed Sun & Mon eve*). Children allowed in bar
to eat lunchtimes only. Free House. *Beer* Boddingtons, guest beer. Patio,
outdoor eating (lunchtime only). *Accommodation* 6 bedrooms, all en suite,
£45 (single £25). Children welcome overnight (£5 in parents' room),
additional beds and cots available. Check-in by arrangement. No dogs. Pub
closed Sun nights and Monday lunchtime, accommodation closed 1st 2 weeks
Jan. No credit cards.

Eynsham	**Newlands Inn**	
Tel 01865 881486		**FOOD**
Newland Street Eynsham nr Whitney Oxfordshire OX8 1LD		Map 14a B2

A lost corner of the 16th century hides just off the A40 – devoid of
street lamps at night the setting can be magical. Unperturbed by the
two resident ghosts, Nick Godden charcoal grills one of the best steaks
around, and his barbecued hickory-flavoured spare ribs (£5.50) and

Cajun catfish (£7.25) have their fans also. The flagstone floors, candle-lit dining room and roaring log fires create the draw in winter; on summer evenings the rear patio with its canvas awning is a pleasant spot for a snack and occasionally there will be a barbecue in progress. Among the blackboard specials look for toad in the hole with gravy or smoked haddock au gratin (both £3.95) and pan-fried king prawns in garlic butter (£6.50). Phone beforehand on Sundays for a roast cooked to order (£6), in winter booking is also advisable on Fridays and Saturdays. Despite a lack of space, Christine Godden's motherly attitude towards children like her own is admirable – no chicken nuggets here. "If they can't be talked into a small portion of bangers or bolognese, someone can always manage to boil them an egg". **Bar Food** *12-2, 7-9.30 (no food Sun eve).* **Beer** *Greene King IPA, Bass, Worthingtons. Garden, outdoor eating, patio, children welcome in dining room. Access, Visa.*

Faccombe   Jack Russell Inn

Tel 0126487 315	B&B
Faccombe nr Andover Hampshire SP11 0DS	Map 14a B4

Faccombe is a tiny, out-of-the-way village signposted off the A343 north of Hurstbourne Tarrant. The present simple redbrick Jack Russell Inn is located opposite the pond and was built in 1983 after the previous building fell down while being renovated. It is quickly being mellowed by a spreading Virginia creeper and hanging baskets of flowers. A few rural artefacts grace the modest bar and the adjacent light and airy conservatory gives access to the large, totally secure garden with a children's play area. Three simple bedrooms, just one with en-suite bathroom, offer good clean accommodation with functional melamine furniture, poly-cotton bedding and the usual tea/coffee-making kit. There are televisions, but no telephones. *Free House.* **Beer** *Ringwood Best & Fortyniner, guest beer. Children's play area.* **Accommodation** *3 bedrooms, 1 en suite, £40 (single £23). Children welcome overnight (under-5s stay free in parents' room). Access, Visa.*

Zzz_z...

Farnham   Museum Hotel

Tel 01725 516261	FOOD
	B&B
Farnham nr Blandford Forum Dorset DT11 8DE	Map 14 C3

The Museum Hotel owes its name and its present existence to General Pitt Rivers who took over a Gypsy School nearby and housed one of his Museums in it, the most famous of which still exists in Oxford. The present 'curator' is John Barnes who for the past nine years has preserved a unique village inn that caters for all needs. The main bar – Coopers Bar – dates from Cromwellian times and occupies the original long and low cottage. It boasts a large inglenook fireplace, light oak and pine tables, tasteful green fabrics, local paintings and soothing classical music helps create the civilised dining atmosphere. Small intimate dining room and further tables in an airy conservatory extension. In complete contrast, the Woodlands Bar attached to the far side of the building, is simply furnished and houses an assortment of pub games. Home-cooked bar food is above average and reliable, but on recent inspection fell short of 'star' quality, with the main menu featuring firm favourites like steak and kidney and oyster pudding (£7.95), chicken curry (£5.25) and a choice of grills (from £5.95), as well as unusual salads and starters. Weekly-changing specials – scrambled eggs with smoked salmon (£4.75), fresh crab bisque (£3.50), wood pigeon casserole (£6.50), baked John Dory (£6.95) –

enhance proceedings at lunchtime, and evening additions may include breast of duck with black cherries (£10.50), fillet of turbot with grapes (£10.25) and loin of pork Dijon (£9.75). Fruits in season, warm apple strudel, Cointreau pancakes and treacle sponge may appear on the pudding list. A well-balanced and value-for-money wine list is world-wide and features at least 10 wines by the glass. Stable block accommodation comprises four rather compact bedrooms – one houses a four-poster – with modern pine, matching fabrics and spacious, well equipped and sparkling clean en-suite bathrooms. The usual added comforts are here, plus a stocked mini-fridge. Standard breakfasts. Sun-trap patio and sheltered walled garden. *Bar Food & Restaurant Meals* 12-1.45, 7.9.30. Free House. *Beer* Exmoor Ale, Wadworth 6X, Brakspear's Bitter, guest beers. Garden, patio, outdoor eating, children's play area. Children not allowed in the bar. *Accommodation* 4 bedrooms, all en suite, £50 (single £35). Children welcome overnight. Check-in by arrangement. No dogs. Access, Visa.

Faugh — String of Horses Inn

FOOD
B&B

Tel 01228 70297   Fax 01228 70675

Faugh nr Carlisle Cumbria CA4 9EG

Map 4 C2

Take the turning signed to Heads Nook from A69 at Corby Hill, just 4 miles from M6 Junction 43; a mile past the village stores and post office is the sharp left turn to Faugh (pronounced locally as "Faff"). Built in the late 17th century as a packhorse inn, nowadays its open fires and oak beams and an interior packed with antiques and prints, copper and brassware create an atmosphere of immediate warmth and welcome. Full family involvement of two generations of Taskers adds further dimensions, from Eric and Anne's long-standing personal attention through son Christopher's supervision of the kitchens to singer/songwriter Alan's regular weekend entertainments. Though there's no real ale cellar there's plenty of home cooking to be enjoyed, the daily specials boards promising salmon paté (£3.95), chicken Véronique or lamb rogan josh (both £5.95) and such home-made puddings as Viennese coffee cake or rhubarb crumble (£2.75). Traditional Cumbrian hospitality is reflected in the generous portions. Each bedroom is individually designed, their contrasting styles incorporating hand-painted furniture and bold-patterned fabrics, crowned canopies, brass bedsteads and four-posters. Ostentatious gold-tapped bathrooms include round and double hand-made Bonsack baths, several with built-in jacuzzis. Additional guest comforts include the mini-leisure centre with a sauna, solarium, whirlpool and ergometer, and a heated open-air pool and sunbathing patio. *Bar Food* 12-2, 6.30-10.45 (Sun 7-10). No real ales. Outdoor eating. *Accommodation* 14 bedrooms, all en-suite, from £68 (single £58). Children welcome overnight (under-16s stay free in parents' room), additional beds and cots supplied. Pub closed 25 & 26 Dec. Access, Diners, Visa.

Zzzz...

Fen Drayton — Three Tuns

A

Tel 01954 30242

High Street Fen Drayton Cambridgeshire CB4 5SJ

Map 15 F1

Characterful timbered old pub, originally housing the local trade or guild hall of Fen Drayton. The present bar is outside the original building, but brims with atmosphere: heavy moulded beams from the

15th century, inglenook fireplaces, oak furnishings, and lots of quality bric-a-brac. It gets extremely busy. *Beer Greene King IPA & Abbot, Rayments Special. Garden. Children's play area. Visa.*

Fenstanton   King William IV

Tel 01480 462467	**FOOD**
High Street Fenstanton Cambridgeshire PE18 9JF	Map 15 F1

Look out for the old clock tower as this attractive white-painted inn is next door. Once three separate cottages, it is very much the hub of village life with a lively bar area and a comfortably furnished dining area, including a rear, plant-festooned Garden Room. Food is reliable with home-cooked dishes appearing on the bi-monthly changing printed menu and the constantly varying blackboard list. Choose from stuffed mushrooms (£3.50), fresh grilled sardines (£3.25) or home-made soup (carrot and orange £1.75) to start, followed by a traditional steak and kidney pudding (£6.75), fillet of pork (£6.95) or fricassee of monkfish with lemon and ginger (£8.95). Good, separately plated vegetables. Vegetarians will always find two options on the board. Popular Sunday roast (£5.85) and a selection of six puddings (£2), notably hot chocolate sponge and treacle and walnut pie. Capability Brown is buried in the village churchyard. *Bar Food 11-2.15, 7-10 (Sun 12-2.15). Outdoor eating. Beer Greene King IPA, Abbot Ale, Rayments Bitter. Children allowed anywhere. Access, Visa.*

Fingest   Chequers Inn

Tel 01491 638335	**A**
Fingest nr Henley-on-Thames Buckinghamshire RG9 6QD	Map 15a D3

Charming 15th-century brick-and-flint pub located opposite a unique Norman church in a tiny hamlet set deep in the Chiltern Hills. Unspoilt and traditionally furnished interior – free from intrusive music and electronic games – boasting ceiling beams, an 18th-century settle, open fires and tastefully adorned with prints, horsebrasses, decorative plates, and a few guns and pistols. Sunny lounge area with French windows opening out on to a delightful sun-trap garden with colourful flower borders and rural views. Good walking country. Fingest is signposted off B480 Marlow to Stokenchurch road. *Pub open 11-3, 6-11 (Sun 12-3, 7-10.30). Beer Brakspear. Garden.*

Finstock   The Plough

Tel 01993 868333	**FOOD**
	B&B
The Bottom Finstock Oxfordshire OX7 3BY	Map 14a B2

A neatly refurbished, thatched pub at the foot of a gently sloping village. Inside, there's a benched seating area around a huge table facing a log fire and a separate, flagstoned games room (where breakfast is served for overnighters) set with sporting memorabilia (shotguns, rods, posters, albums of ancient photographs); all is kept in immaculate order by landlady Val Phillips who has been here since 1986. One menu is available throughout, with the room on the right as you enter set for dining. Daily specials are the best bet: perhaps Portuguese sardines (£3.75), faggots with onion gravy and new potatoes (£5.25), smoked duck or goose breast (£4.95), fisherman's pie (£8.95). The sole, delightful bedroom is in a converted weather-boarded barn with thatched roof and a separate entrance from the pub; within, it's beamed with bare stone walls, Laura Ashley decor, a four-poster bed and large, blue-and-white bathroom complete with

Zzz...

gold fittings. There's no bedside light, no bath mat and the running bath water may stop while one flushes the loo but that's all rather characterful – even the room key fob is from Raffles in Singapore; TV, radio alarm and coffee are provided. Breakfast is a feast, if you like, with soft white baps, soda farls, bilberry jam and marmalade all coming from local suppliers – typical of Val's attention to detail. Well-maintained garden with eight or so tables on neatly tended lawns bordered with flower beds; climbing frame, swings and Aunt Sally for children. *Pub open 12-2.30, 6-11.30 (Sat 12-11.30, Sun 12-3, 7-10.30).* **Bar Food** *12-2, 7-9.30 (Sun 12-2.30, 7.30-9).* **Beer** *Adnams Broadside, Hook Norton Best & Old Hooky, guest beer.* **Accommodation** *1 en-suite room, £45 (single £32). Garden, outdoor eating. Access, Visa.*

Fir Tree	**Duke of York**	**FOOD**
Tel 01388 762848		**B&B**
Fir Tree nr Crook Co Durham DL15 8DG		**Map 5 D3**

From whitewashed stone pub to extended and comfortable roadside inn (standing by the A68 one mile from Crook town), the grand old Duke – in landlord Ray Suggett's family for several generations now – is on the march again. When last we called the energetic Mr Suggett who personally raised his standard here in 1988 had achieved much the same for the pub by providing more-than-adequate ale and refreshment for a perceptibly discerning market. "Sauces of inspiration" remains his catchy catchword on voluminous blackboards offering chicken chasseur (£7.90), pork Zaccheroff and lamb fillet in hot pepper sauce (both £8.50) with, perhaps a salmon terrine (£2.75) to start and banana split or chocolate orange log (£2.25) to follow. Alongside are snacks (hot beef in a bun £3.25) and grilled steaks (sirloin £8.50) from an all-encompassing menu offered both in the lounge bar and dining room. On our most recent visit work was nearly finished on four en-suite bedrooms which promised a luxury standard with state-of-the-art facilities for the businessman. This, we're told, is the first phase of a·development which will, in stages, add up to 70 bedrooms and cater, no doubt, to a new army of camp followers. *Free House.* **Accommodation** *4 bedrooms, all en suite £59 (single £48). Children welcome overnight.* **Bar Food** *12-2.30, 6-10 (12-2.30, 7-10 Sun). Children's portions. Garden, outdoor eating.* **Beer** *Bass. Access, Visa.*

Firle	**Ram Inn**	**FOOD**
Tel 01273 858222		**B&B**
Firle West Firle nr Lewes East Sussex BN8 6NS		**Map 11 B6**

The road runs out once it eventually reaches Firle village at the foot of the Downs. It's a quiet backwater now, but this (almost unbelievably) was once a main stage-coach route and the Ram an important staging post. Built of brick and flint and partly tile-hung, the inn displays a fascinating mixture of periods. The Georgian part was once the local courthouse. Other parts are older, and the kitchen dates back nearly 500 years. The main bar is a simple, unpretentious affair with a motley collection of tables and chairs and old photos. A no-smoking snug bar is similarly modest. A daily-changing blackboard menu lists the selection of home-made food which makes use of good local produce. Choose from an excellent range of lunchtime ploughman's – cream cheese and asparagus paté, Sussex farmhouse Cheddar and Duddleswell soft sheep cheese – a deep bowl of vegetable soup (£2.35), smoked bacon roly-poly (£5.95), steak and kidney pie

(£7.95) and a short choice of freshly baked pizzas. Puddings (£2.85) include banana and toffee pie and apple, pear and other fruits crumble. Vegetarians are well catered for – mushroom and cashew nut loaf (£6.35). Among the short list of wines are three local wines, including Berwick Glebe and Breaky Bottom, available by the glass. Simple bedrooms are bright and fresh, with a variety of antique furniture. The largest and best room enjoys downland views and features a shower cabinet and en suite toilet; the remaining three rooms sharing a rather basic shower room. All rooms have tea and coffee-making kits but, as a matter of policy, no televisions or radios. When booking avoid the modest and cramped single room. Splendid flint-walled garden for peaceful summer drinking. *Pub open 11-3, 7-11 Mon-Fri & Sat in winter, (11-3, 6-11 Sat in summer, 12-3, 7-10.30 Sun).* **Bar Food** *12-2, 7-9. Free House.* **Beer** *Harveys Sussex Bitter, Charrington IPA, Otter Ale, Hop Back Summer Lighting. Harveys Old Ale in winter. Garden, outdoor eating, tables in garden.* **Accommodation** *4 bedrooms, 1 en suite, from £45 (en suite £60, single £25). No children under 14. Check-in by arrangement. Pub closed Christmas Day evening. Accommodation closed Christmas Eve and Christmas Day. No dogs. Access, Visa.*

Fittleworth	**Swan**	
Tel 0179882 429		**B&B**
Lower Street Fittleworth nr Pulborough West Sussex RH20 1EN		**Map 11 A6**

One can luxuriate in the peaceful beauty of the lovely award-winning garden of flowers and herbs of this 14th-century tile-hung inn, and see where the River Arun meets the Rother by taking a peaceful river walk. Inside, fresh flowers adorn the hallway and reception and the dark panelled picture lounge boasts a fine collection of early 19th-century paintings embedded in the upper panels. The main bar displays policeman's truncheons above the vast inglenook and brass and copper trinkets hang from the beams. Villagers enjoy darts in the small public bar. Spotless Laura Ashley-style bedrooms are comfortable and well-appointed – TVs, tea-makers, trouser presses, telephones, hairdryers – and feature modern pine furniture, although two rooms have fine mahogany 4-posters. Good en-suite facilities with three rooms sharing two smart bathrooms. A warm welcome awaits families. Children can eat with parents anywhere in the bar, choose from their own menu or request smaller portions of adult dishes and eat at any time of the day. A wooden climbing frame in the safe garden will keep the more active offspring amused on fine days. Under-2s are accommodated free overnight; older children are charged a nominal £6 if sharing a parents' room. Cots available. *Whitbread Wayside Inn. Open 11-11 (12-3, 7-10.30 Sun).* **Accommodation** *10 bedrooms, 7 en suite £55 (Single £25). Children welcome overnight (cot, high chair and extra child's bed if sharing). Garden, outdoor eating and playing area.* **Beer** *Flowers Original, Boddingtons, Wadworth 6X. Children allowed anywhere. Access, Diners, Visa.*

Fletching	**Griffin Inn**	**FOOD**
Tel 01825 722890		**B&B**
Fletching East Sussex TN22 3NS		**Map 11 B6**

The last real excitement in this sleepy Sussex village was in 1256 when Simon de Montfort's army camped outside the church prior to the Battle of Lewes. These days visitors with a more peaceful intent are made more than welcome at the 16th-century Griffin Inn, which

Zzzz...

is at the heart of Saxon Fletching's picturesque main street, and is everything a village local should be. The main bar has old beams and wainscot walls, a copper-hooded brick fireplace and a motley collection of old pews and wheelback chairs; the public bar provides a pool table and fruit machine for the amusement of the local youth and there's a pretty Laura Ashley-decorated restaurant. Good home-made food is a major attraction with a varied blackboard menu available in the bar and a short, more imaginative daily-changing à la carte menu on offer in the restaurant (more extensive Friday and Saturday evenings). An eclectic choice in the bar ranges from Nico's terrine of veal, bacon and herbs (£3.95), chicken liver parfait (£3.25), salmon and spring onion fishcakes (£5.95), whole roast red mullet and herbs (£7.50), lamb stew (£6.95) and sausage, mash and onion gravy (£4.95). Local organic produce grower, Francis Smith, supplies all the salad leaves that make up the imaginative accompanying salads to most meals. There are also chargrills, homely puddings – bread and butter pudding, apple and sultana pie – and ploughperson's large enough to cope with the sharpest of appetites. Regular theme evenings and dish night on Thursdays. An excellent wine list, featuring a special selection of vintage chateau bottled Bordeaux, owes a good deal to family connections with the Ebury Wine Bar in London. There are four charming, bedrooms, three with a four-poster purpose-built to counteract the sloping floors and to ensure a level night's rest. Tea- and coffee-making kits and TVs are provided and the substantial breakfast is worth getting up for. In summer the rear garden offers outstanding views across rolling Sussex countryside. An excellent stopover on the way to Newhaven, some sixteen miles distant, and the Dieppe ferry. *Pub open 12-3, 6-11 (Sun to 10.30).* **Bar Food** *12-2.15, 7.15-9.* **Restaurant Meals** *12-2.15 (Sun to 2), 7.30-9.30 (except Sun). Children allowed in the bar to eat. Free House.* **Beer** *Harveys Sussex Bitter, Hall & Woodhouse Tanglefoot, Fullers London Pride, Badger Best Bitter. Garden, 2 large lawns and patio, outdoor eating, Summer BBQ, tables in garden.* **Accommodation** *4 rooms, all en suite, from £45 (single £40). Children welcome overnight (free in parents' room), cot available. Check-in by arrangement. Pub closed Christmas Day. Accommodation closed Christmas Eve and Christmas Day. No dogs. Access, Visa.*

Fonthill Gifford   Beckford Arms

| Tel 01747 870385   Fax 01747 51496 | **B&B** |
| Fonthill Gifford nr Salisbury Tisbury Wiltshire SP3 6PX | Map 14 B3 |

Peacefully situated on a minor road (follow signposts to Fonthill Bishop from the A303), opposite Fonthill Estate and adjoining its vineyard, this 18th-century stone-built inn is a good base from which to explore the estate footpaths and the unspoilt scenery of the Nadder Valley. The modernised, yet attractive lounge bar with open fire and the airy Garden Room lead out on to a sun-trap patio and a delightful raised, flower and shrub-filled garden – ideal for summer alfresco imbibing. Complete refurbishment upstairs has resulted in seven compact and comfortable en-suite bedrooms, two of which boast four-posters. All are neat, clean and refreshingly decorated with matching floral wallpaper and fabrics, and are well equipped with TV, clock-radio, tea-making kit, hairdryer and good toiletries in the spacious bathrooms. Long-stay guests may find some of the rooms rather too cramped, with little luggage space. *Free House.* **Beer** *Courage Best, Wadworth 6X. Garden, outdoor eating. Family room.* **Accommodation** *7 bedrooms, all en suite, £49.50 (single £29.50). Children welcome overnight (under-5s stay free in parents' room, 5-16s £9.50) additional beds and cots available. Small dogs by arrangement. Access, Visa.*

Ford   Dinton Hermit

FOOD

Tel 01296 748379

Ford nr Aylesbury Buckinghamshire HP17 8XH

Map 15a D2

In an isolated hamlet and set back from the lane, this 15th-century
stone cottage pub is named after John Briggs, clerk to one of the
judges who condemned Charles I to death. Two small and homely
bars are well maintained, each having part exposed stone walls, brick
fireplaces and a mix of rustic furniture. Popular locally, both bars fill
quickly with customers seeking out the hearty home-cooked food –
steak and mushroom pie (£5.95), chicken curry (£5.75), chili
(£4.50), vegetarian hotpot (£4.95) and decent sandwiches and salads.
Additional, more elaborate dishes like duck in orange and ginger
(£11.50) and medallions of lamb with white wine and caper sauce
(£9.75) appear on the evening menu. Good vegetables, generously
served. Large, pretty garden with rural views – ideal for sunny days.
*Bar Food 12-2 & 7-9.30 (not Sun). Beer ABC Bitter, Tetley, Bass.
Pub closed 2 weeks at Christmas, 2 weeks in summer. No credit cards.*

Our inspectors *never* book in the name of Egon Ronay's Guides. They
disclose their identity only if they are considering an establishment for
inclusion in the next edition of the Guide.

Ford   Plough Inn

FOOD

B&B

Tel 01386 584215

Temple Gutting Ford Gloucestershire GL54 5RU

Map 14a A1

A gregarious pub in something of an agrarian setting on a bend in the
B4077. There's an old well in the walled garden and a mixture of
abandoned filling station and farmyard behind. The simply furnished
bars recall the pub's past days as a farmhouse with flagstone floors,
pine tables and high-backed settles, and diners move easily through to
a neatly-laid dining room which is cosily candle-lit at night. Food
starts at 9am and is available all day, the best of the day's choices
prominently displayed on ubiquitous blackboards. There's chilled
gazpacho or Stilton and celery soup (£2.35) followed by grilled
Donnington trout (£6.25) or steak, mushroom and Guiness casserole
(£6.50) to make a meal of, while all-in-one snacks might include dill
cured gravad lax (£6.25) or cauliflower cheese with tomatoes and
Stilton (£5.25). In increasing numbers regulars are leaving room for
the generously portioned, home-made, banoffi or pecan pies and
seasonal summer pudding (£2.35). Three simple bedrooms within the
pub share two bathrooms and are modestly appointed. We're assured,
however, that since our last visit, work has started on the long-awaited
courtyard conversion. These six annexe rooms will, on completion,
have en-suite WC and shower rooms and standard fittings will include
colour TVs and hot drinks-making facilities; telephones are planned.
*Open 9am-11pm (Sun 12-3 & 7-10.30). Bar & Restaurant Meals 9am-
9.30pm (Sun 12-3, 7-9). Beer Donnington BB & SBA. Garden. Outdoor
eating. Accommodation 3 bedrooms, none en suite, from £35. Children
welcome overnight (accommodated free in parents' room, meals charged as
taken), additional beds supplied. Pub closed 25 Dec. Access, Visa.*

Ford — White Hart

FOOD
B&B

Tel 01249 782213   Fax 01249 783075

Ford nr Chippenham Wiltshire SN14 8RP

Map 14 B2

Idyllically situated beside a babbling trout stream in the Wyvern Valley, this rambling, mellow-stone, 16th-century coaching inn offers both character and charm in its low-ceilinged bar and in the adjacent dining areas. The inn is well run by its owners, Chris and Jenny Phillips' who cater for all requirements, providing good ale, consistently reliable food and a high standard of accommodation. Subsequently the White Hart is a very popular and busy inn. The cosy, unspoilt half-panelled bar throngs with drinkers who are attracted by the continually varying selection of at least eight real ales that are drawn from the cellar, as well as some unusual malt whiskies. Discerning diners, seeking out imaginative and well-cooked food head next door into one of the two attractively decorated dining areas. Antiques, various rugs, an array of furniture and numerous paintings help create a convivial atmosphere in which to enjoy a meal, chosen from the sensibly short weekly-changing menu. To start there may be grapefruit with red onion and chicory and orange vinaigrette (£3.95), melon with fresh fruit coulis (£3.95), or salad of smoked salmon with sour cream dressing (£4.95) followed by a choice of seven meat dishes – chicken with braised leeks and wild mushrooms with raspberry and port and wine sauce (£7.95), entrecote steak on a bed of caramelised onions in brandy sauce (£9.95), tenderloin of pork in a spinach and mushroom pancake (£8.50) – and three fish and two vegetarian dishes. Puddings range from banoffi pie (£2.75) to gooseberry crumble and custard (£1.85). Lighter snacks like chicken and vegetable pie (£4.25), ploughman's and a range of sandwiches are available at lunchtimes. The final ingredient to this successful inn is the comfortable en-suite accommodation, most of the rooms being located across the lane in the converted stables. All are attractively decorated and furnished (some with four-posters) and equipped with TV, beverage tray, radio, telephone and trouser press. Residents have use of a swimming pool, and balloon flights, go-karting and clay pigeon shooting can be arranged. Five miles from Junction 17 of the M4. *Bar Food* 12-2, 7-9.30 *(Sun to 9). Children allowed in bar to eat. Free House. Beer Flowers IPA, Smiles Exhibition, Old Hooky, Wadworth 6X, Hall & Woodhouse Tanglefoot, Boddingtons, Theakston Old Peculier, Bass, Marston's Pedigree. Patio, outdoor eating. Family room. Accommodation 11 bedrooms, all en suite, £59 (single £43). Children welcome overnight, (under-12s £10 plus meals as taken) additional beds and cots available. Access, Diners, Visa.*

Fordcombe — Chafford Arms

FOOD

Tel 01892 740267

Fordcombe nr Tunbridge Wells Kent TN3 0SA

Map 11 B5

A blackboard outside this imposing rather than beautiful village tile-hung pub announces crabs (dressed crab with prawns £9.25) and Dover soles (14oz sole £11.95). Both are regular features on the menu and are served alongside a longish home-cooked menu which also offers more usual pub food – lamb chops Dijon (£5.80), steak and kidney pie (£4.80) and vegetarian quiche (£4.80). Service is particularly friendly and good-humoured and there is a sense of dedication and commitment in the cooking, even when the pub is exceptionally busy. Pleasant and somewhat wild garden with pub

tables. *Bar Food* 12.30-2, 7.30-9.45. *Children allowed in bar to eat.*
Beer *Whitbread, Fuller's Chiswick, Strong of Romsey. Garden.*
Access, Visa.

Forest Row — Brambletye Hotel

Tel 01342 824144   Fax 01342 824833   **B&B**

Forest Row East Sussex RH18 5EZ   Map 11 B6

Recently refurbished hotel located beside the busy A22 in the village
centre and close to the Ashdown Forest. The attractive building houses
a good locals bar, Black Peter's, dispensing a range of real ales, and
comfortable overnight accommodation in 25 en-suite bedrooms. Most
rooms occupy a rear extension that surrounds a pleasant courtyard,
and all are neatly furnished in modern style with light oak furniture
and good fabrics. Main building rooms have more charm and
character, but all have TVs, telephones and tea-makers for added
comfort. *Pub open 11-3 & 5.30-11 (Sun 12-3 & 7-10.30). Free House.*
Beer Harveys Best Better. Paved courtyard, outdoor eating area.
Accommodation 25 bedrooms, all en suite, from £69 (single £45).
Children welcome overnight, additional child's bed £10, cot and bedding
£3. Access, Visa.

Forty Green — Royal Standard of England

Tel 01494 673382   Fax 01494 523332   **A**

Forty Green nr Beaconsfield Buckinghamshire HP9 1XT   Map 15a E3

Granted its title and coat-of-arms in 1651 by Charles II who sheltered
here after the Battle of Worcester, this splendid pub is one of our
oldest free houses with a history dating back over 900 years.
Tremendous interior with many of the magnificent oak beams
having nautical origins, including the massive carved transom from
an Elizabethan ship, which now forms part of the entrance hall.
Amid a superb array of collectors' items and artefacts this is a truly
atmospheric setting for a drink, but unfortunately the food on offer is
a cheap and cheerful buffet-style operation. Hamlet signposted off the
B474 north of Beaconsfield. *Free House. Beer Marston's Pedigree &*
Owd Roger, Morland Old Speckled Hen, guest beers. Garden. Pub closed
25 Dec eve. Access, Visa.

Fotheringhay — Falcon Inn

Tel 018326 254   **FOOD**

Fotheringhay nr Oundle Northamptonshire PE8 5HZ   Map 7 E4

By night, the illuminated church starts as a golden beacon visible for
miles. Standing almost beside it in the main street of this historic
village, the Falcon is in many respects the perfect village pub – busy,
with a lively friendly crowd and charming staff. Their reputation for
offering good value food for lunch and dinner has spread far and
wide, so booking is advisable to avoid disappointment. Prices are
marginally cheaper at lunchtime though the choice remains the same –
changing daily. Some dishes such as roast duckling with apple and
rosemary (£7) or chicken in burgundy wine sauce with mushrooms
(£ 7.20) can run out – they only make a batch of 8 or so for each
sitting, helping to ensure the freshness of their produce. The menu
encompasses everything from a ploughman's lunch or supper (£3) and
baked spiced grapefruit (£1.80) to venison cutlets in port and orange
sauce (£8.20) and fresh Scotch salmon fishcakes. The food is generally
simple and unfussy reflecting the delightful informality of this inn.

Afternoon teas are served 3-5pm. *Open 10-11 (Sun 12-10.30). Bar Food (except Mon) 12.15-2, 6.45-9.30 (Sun 7-9). Children allowed in bar to eat. Free House. Beer Greene King IPA & Abbot, Adnams Southwolds, Cambridge, Ruddles County & Best. Garden, outdoor eating. Access, Visa.*

Fowey   King of Prussia

Tel 01726 832450	**B&B**
Quayside Fowey Cornwall	**Map 12 C3**

Pride of place on the tiny quay goes to this most unusual three-storey pink-washed building, which overlooks the perpetually busy quayside and river estuary and across to Pont Pill creek, a sheltered inlet filled with sailing craft. It was built by and named after the notorious smuggler John Carter, who operated from Prussia Cove. A clergyman by day and smuggler by night, his ill-gotten gains built the pub and his dual role in life is reflected in the unusual double-sided inn sign. Beyond the lively main bar, complete with juke box and a young crowd, are six delightful en-suite bedrooms, all of which have splendid river views. Neatly refurbished with co-ordinating colours, fabrics and friezes and furnished with modern pine, they are fresh, clean and very comfortable. Usual facilities include TVs and tea-makers, plus in summer months your own colourful window-box of flowers which spill into the room. Bathrooms are compact, well fitted-out and spotless. Breakfast is taken in the tiny pine-furnished restaurant. *Open 11-11, Sun usual hours. Beer St Austell. Accommodation 6 bedrooms, all en suite, £46 (single £23). Access, Visa.*

Zzzz...

Fowey   Ship Inn

Tel 01726 833751	**B&B**
Fowey Cornwall PL23 1AZ	**Map 12 C3**

Tucked away among the narrow streets and only 200 yards from the quay, the Ship dates from the 16th-century and is one of the oldest buildings in an attractive little fishing town. Local fishermen congregate in the main bar, which has exposed stone walls, comfortable wall bench seating and various nautical items. Of the six bedrooms, the most popular is the one located in what remains of the original building, which boasts an ornamental ceiling, fine panelled walls and a carved chimney-piece with the date 1570. Other rooms are modern in style with pastel walls and fabrics and simply furnished with new pine. Two overlook the town church. One room has en-suite facilities, the others washbasins in the room and all share two sparkling, spacious and fully-tiled bathrooms. Large residents' lounge. *Pub open 11-11 (except Sun) in summer, winter normal hours (except Saturday 11-11). Beer St Austell. Family room by arrangement. Accommodation 6 bedrooms, 1 en suite, from £37 per night. Children welcome overnight, additional beds & cots supplied. Accommodation closed 25 & 26 Dec. Access, Visa.*

Fowlmere   Chequers Inn

Tel 01763 208369	**FOOD**
High Street Fowlmere Cambridgeshire SG8 7SR	**Map 15 F1**

When Samuel Peyps spent a night here in 1659, the inn was already a popular travellers' rest. Its period charm largely survives and it still goes into many diaries as a good place for refreshment. Beyond the most appealing white painted facade a civilised, up-market ambience pervades the comfortably furnished and carpeted split-level bar area and the adjacent galleried restaurant. The convivial atmosphere is an ideal one in which to enjoy some good, reliable bar food. Choices are listed in a daily-changing blackboard menu and may feature white onion soup (£2.60), Stilton and walnut paté (£2.90) – both served with excellent warm French bread – pork and smoked sausage cassoulet (£4.95), mussels in white wine, cream and garlic (£3.90) and trout fillet in orange sauce (£5.20). Accompanying vegetables are crisp and salads imaginative. Vegetarian offerings include bean and vegetable crumble. Those venturing into the restaurant may find on the 3-monthly changing menu hot kiln roast smoked salmon (£5.40), noisettes of lamb served on spinach with a cream tarragon sauce (£11.10) or Oriental fish parcel of prawns, scallops and turbot (£10.60). Puddings may include crème brulée and treacle and orange tart. Specialities on the cheeseboard might feature Bonchester medium, Jersey Blue, Cornish Pepper and Irish Milleens. Daily 3-course table d'hote (£14.25). Good global wine list with at least seven wines served by the glass. Rear conservatory extension and delightful rear lawn with flower beds and shrub borders. *Free House.* **Bar Food & Restaurant Meals** *12-2 (Sun to 2.30), 7-10 (Sun to 9.30).* **Beer** *Tolly Original, Tetley. Garden, outdoor eating. Children allowed anywhere. Access, Diners, Visa.*

Fownhope   Green Man

| Tel 01432 860243   Fax 01432 860207 | **B&B** |

Fownhope Hereford & Worcester HR1 4PE   Map 14 B1

A fine old black-and-white, half-timbered inn at the heart of the village and less than a 10-minute walk from the banks of the River Wye, the 'Naked Boy' as it was once called, dates back possibly to the year of Henry VII's accession in 1485. Its historical associations continue through the Civil War to the 18th and 19th centuries when the Green Man became a petty sessional court and coaching inn on the Hereford to Gloucester route (now called the B4224). There is still plenty of timber and stonework extant in the succession of interconnecting rooms which surround the central bar servery. Residents perhaps get the pick in a comfortable lounge with armchairs set around an open log fire, and choice of dining areas including one for non-smokers. Accommodation is of a varying, though commendably high standard, divided between the inn and some smaller annexe rooms, with pride of place going to the old four-posters and former 'Judge's Room', well-equipped for family use, which overlooks an enclosed rear courtyard. Here there is also the Stable Room, ideal for residents who prefer to be on the ground floor. Appointments which run from TV and telephones to tea-trays, hairdryers and trouser presses are standard throughout. *Free house.* **Beer** *Samuel Smith Old Brewery, Marston's Pedigree, Hook Norton Best. Garden. Family room.* **Accommodation** *20 bedrooms, all en suite, £49 (single £31). Children welcome overnight (under 5 yrs £2.50, 5-12 yrs £10), additional beds and cots available. Access, Visa.*

Frampton Mansell   Crown Inn

| Tel 01285 760601   Fax 01285 760681 | **B&B** |

Frampton Mansell nr Stroud Gloucestershire GL6 8JB   Map 14 B2

Of 16th-century origin, the Crown stands at the heart of the village just off the A419 and just within the Cotswold district: its extensive acreage of ground falls steeply away through mature woods and orchard, to the Thames/Severn canal far below. Following a brief period of closure, the new landlords are breathing fresh life into the place with some interesting guest beers supplementing the real ale selection. While the bar areas are typically quaint, the pub opens out into larger rear extensions. The largest of these, some 12 years old, also houses a dozen spacious bedrooms uniformly fitted out with mahogany furniture, gold-tapped avocado bathrooms and close carpeting. The four ground-floor rooms, with access direct from the car park, are especially convenient for the less mobile, while it's the abundant peace and quiet amid restful panoramic views which proves to be one of the pub's greatest assets. *Pub open usual hours, all day Sat 11-11. Free House. Beer Oakhill Best, Wadworth 6X, guest beer. Garden. Family room. Accommodation 12 bedrooms, all en suite, from £45 (single £25). Children welcome overnight (under-8s stay free in parents' room), additional beds (£5) & cots supplied. Pub closed 25 Dec. Accommodation closed 24 & 25 Dec. Access, Visa.*

Freeland   Shepherds Hall Inn

Tel 01993 881256   **B&B**

Witney Road Freeland Oxfordshire OX8 8HQ   Map 14a B2

Once known as the 'Shepherds All' and originally a 13th-century shelter for shepherds and drovers, the green-shuttered inn today offers plain and practical accommodation. The bar is filled with antique furniture, copper and brass and wheelback chairs and a collection of plates adorns the walls. Five bedrooms (three of which are in an annexe) are clean, comfortable and modern in style, and include TVs, radios, telephones and tea-making facilities. The annexe rooms have neat, tiled shower rooms, and the pub rooms have private bathrooms. The patio and lawned garden with flowerbeds is safe for children, who also have their own purpose-built play area. On the A4095 half-way between Woodstock and Witney. *Free House. Beer Wadworth 6X, Flowers IPA. Garden, children's play area. Family room. Accommodation 5 bedrooms, all en suite, £38.50 (single £25). Children welcome overnight (under-2s stay free in parents' room), additional beds (£5) supplied. Access, Visa.*

Frilford Heath   Dog House Hotel

Tel 01865 390830   Fax 01865 390860   **B&B**

Frilford Heath nr Abingdon Oxfordshire OX13 6QJ   Map 14a C3

A ten-minute drive from Oxford, this pleasant 300-year-old tile-hung inn commands a lovely view over the Vale of the White Horse. The bar is spacious, and incorporates a central stone fireplace with a real winter fire. Eight bedrooms are non-smoking, all have en-suite facilities, TVs, telephones, hairdryers and pine furniture. Top of the range is the four-poster bridal suite. Greatly reduced weekend tariff. *Open 11-11 (Sun 12-10.30). Beer Morland. Garden, children's play area. Accommodation 19 bedrooms, all en suite, £69 (4-poster £80, single £60). Children welcome overnight, additional cots available. Access, Diners, Visa.*

Frilsham   Pot Kiln

| Tel 01635 201366 | A |

Frilsham nr Hermitage Berkshire RG16 0XX   Map 14a C4

A remote country pub on the Yattendon to Bucklebury lane, delightful in summer in the pretty sheltered garden with its soothing outlook across open fields to woodland. The name derives from this being the site of old brick kilns (abandoned after the war) and the building is, appropriately, of attractive redbrick construction. Inside is distinctively old-fashioned, with three simply furnished bars leading off a small lobby bar. Bare boards, sturdy wooden tables, cushioned wall bench seating and warming open fires characterise the good, relaxing atmosphere, with a successful mix of chatty locals and passing ramblers filling the unspoilt bars. Impromptu folk music some Sunday evenings. Good choice of well-kept local real ales. Well-behaved children who don't leave an "appalling mess" are welcome indoors. *Open 12-2.30, 6.30-11, Sun 12-3, 7-10.30. Free House.* **Beer** *Arkell's Best, Morland Original & Old Speckled Hen, Morrells Mild. Garden. Family room. No credit cards.*

Frithelstock   Clinton Arms

| Tel 01805 623279   Fax 01805 624006 | FOOD |
| | B&B |

Frithelstock Torrington Devon EX38 8JH   Map 12 C2

New owners have reversed the fortunes of this homely and unpretentious pub which nestles in a sleepy, affluent village two miles west of Torrington off the A386. Home-cooked bar meals and evening restaurant fare (also available in the bar) are attracting folk from far and wide, notably for the fresh fish dishes such as poached salmon with fennel, cucumber and sour cream sauce, stuffed haddock with prawn sauce (both £7.95), trout rolled in oatmeal and cooked with bacon (£9.50), all served with crisp fresh vegetables. Lighter bites are well-cooked pub favourites like steak and ale pie, fisherman's pie (both £4.25), lasagne (£3.95) and ploughman's (£2.95). Sunday roast lunch (£4.25, 3-courses £6.95). Upstairs accommodation comprises two spacious and pleasantly decorated bedrooms with equally good-sized en-suite facilities. One room overlooks the small village green. Delightful walled garden with tables and chairs, and numerous playthings to keep children amused. **Bar & Restaurant meals** *12-2, 7-10 (Sun to 9.30). Free House.* **Beer** *Draught Bass & guest beer. Garden, outdoor eating. Family room.* **Accommodation** *2 rooms, both en suite, from £36 (single £18). Children welcome overnight, additional beds & cots supplied. Check-in by arrangement. Access, Visa.*

Fulking   Shepherd & Dog

| Tel 01273 857382 | FOOD |

Fulking nr Henfield West Sussex BN5 9LU   Map 11 B6

In a truly glorious setting nestling at the base of the South Downs in a picturesque village, this 14th-century pub is named after the shepherds who farmed the surrounding downs and once served the travelling shepherds on their way to nearby Findon fair. It boasts inglenook fireplaces, polished oak tables, a low beamed ceiling and is decorated with numerous old artefacts, including a collection of shepherds crooks. A varied selection of bar meals ranges from tomato and orange soup (£3.15) and marinated feta cheeses and olive salad (£4.25) for starters, followed by beef and Guinness pie (£6.50), rack of lamb with rosemary sauce (£7.50) and pollack topped with a pesto

Frogget Edge - The Chequers   01433630231
£49 double b+b, £16 dinner

crust (£6.50). Lighter lunchtime snacks include a range of
ploughman's (£4) and salads (from £5.50). Rhubarb and apple
crumble, chocolate and coconut tart and Bakewell tart (all £2.95) are
among the home-made puddings. Idyllic terraced summer garden with
stream and play area. No children under 14 inside. *Bar Food &*
Restaurant Meals 12-2, 7-9.30 (*Sun* 12-2.30, 7.30-9.30). *Beer* Courage
Best Bitter, Directors, Harveys Bitter, Websters Yorkshire Bitter. Garden,
outdoor eating area, tables in garden. Access, Visa.

Fullers Moor   Copper Mine

Tel 01829 782293   **FOOD**

Nantwich Road Fullers Moor nr Broxton Cheshire CH3 9JH   **Map 6 A3**

Carpeted and pine-clad dining pub, interestingly adorned with mining
memorabilia and with a spacious summer garden and barbecue.
Sandwiches, open or closed, and filled baked potatoes won't much
challenge the imagination or the pocket. More substantially, look for
the daily pies and lasagne (£4.95) or chicken variations, tikka for
instance (£6.95), at any time, and trout with almonds (£6.95), roast
duck with cranberry sauce (£8.50) alongside multifarious steaks in the
evening (sirloin with pepper, cream and brandy sauce £9.50). Sunday
roast lunch (main course £4.95), theme-night Sunday suppers and
the 'Miner's Meal' on Monday evenings: three courses for £4.95.
Bar Food 12-3, 7-10. *Children's menu. Beer* Burtonwood, Bass.
Garden, outdoor eating. Family room. Patio. Access, Diners, Visa.

Fyfield   White Hart

Tel 01865 390585   **A**

Main Road Fyfield nr Abingdon Oxfordshire OX13 5LN   **Map 14a B2**

500-year-old ex-chantry house with a 30-foot-high gallery and four
family rooms. The landlord is also the cook. The very large garden
includes a children's play area. *Free House. Beer* Boddingtons, Hook
Norton, Wadworth 6X, Theakston Old Peculier, Gibbs Mew Bishop's
Tipple, Fuller's London Pride. Garden. Family room. Access, Visa.

Gedney Dyke   The Chequers

Tel 01406 362666   **FOOD**

Main Street Gedney Dyke Lincolnshire PE12 0AJ   **Map 7 F3**

Gedney Dyke lies off the A17, 3 miles east of Holbeach, isolated amid
vast open fenland. One can find this unassuming white-painted pub in
the heart of the village, but you will not be alone for this humble
establishment attracts diners from miles around, as well as having a
loyal local clientele. The homely carpeted bar has a chatty atmosphere,
an open fire and is simply furnished, a trend which continues into the
adjacent, unfussy dining area. Space is at a premium, especially during
busy times. The blackboard bar snack menu above the bar is rather
run-of-the-mill, but home-cooked options like bobotie (£6.50) and
leek and Stilton bake (£5.50) stand out. Most however order from
the more imaginative restaurant menu and daily-changing specials
board – also available in the bar – which features some interesting
dishes, for example, Cajun chicken (£7.95), sautéed pigeon breast
served on a pocket of onion marmalade with a mustard sauce (£6.95),
baked sea bass with fennel (£10-£12), sea bream with Provençal
sauce (£6.96) and guinea fowl with avocado and papaya salsa (£9.95).
A separate pudding board may highlight English walnut tart or St
Emilion au chocolate (both £2.50). Fresh fish is delivered from

Grimsby and all the crisp accompanying vegetables are locally grown.
Well-chosen global list of wines from Adnams at sensible prices. *Free
House.* **Bar Food & Restaurant Meals** *12-2, 7-9 (Thurs-Sat 7-9.30).
Children welcome anywhere.* **Beer** *Adnams, Southwold, Batemans XB,
Bass, Morland Old Speckled Hen. Garden, outside eating. Access,
Diners, Visa.*

Glemsford   **Black Lion**

Tel 01787 280684	**FOOD**

Lion Road Glemsford Suffolk CO10 7RF   Map 10 C3

On entering the Lion, it turns out to have a treasure of a Tudor
interior complete with half-timbered walls and rehabilitated timbers,
which today serve to frame and support the bar. With this noble
lineage is a mixed decor of distinctly Edwardian feel; quarry-tiled
floors, country prints, leather armchairs and bay-window seats, all of
which is at once both uncluttered and charming. Licensee Anne White
concentrates on producing good home cooking: lasagne ($£3.95$) and
chicken ($£3.50$) or beef and Guiness pie ($£4.50$) are good examples
on the bar food menu. There's a wider choice of dishes in the
restaurant but the cooking remains uncomplicated: garlic mushrooms
($£2.70$), mackerel and dill paté ($£1.95$), steak and kidney pie in
Abbot Ale ($£5$), grilled salmon ($£6.80$). Their fruit pies and toffee
apple tart are also home-made (all $£1.85$). There are four or five
vegetarian dishes on both menus and for those who favour a roast
the three-course traditional Sunday lunch is $£5.50$. **Bar Food &
Restaurant Meals** *12-2.30, 6.30-9.30 (no food Sun eve). Children
allowed in bar to eat, children's menu.* **Beer** *Greene King IPA, Abbot Ale.
Garden, outdoor eating, children's play area. No credit cards.*

Glooston   **Old Barn**

Tel 01858 545215	**FOOD**
	B&B

Main Street Glooston Leicestershire LE16 7ST   Map 7 D4

On the route of the Old Roman road called the Gartree, the Old Barn
stands at the centre of a tiny hamlet and just across the road from a
picture postcard row of stone terraced cottages; the pub's 16th-century
frontage of tiny leaded windows framed by flowering boxes and
hanging baskets also makes a summer picture. Within, the premises
readily divide into two separate sections, a postage-stamp-size cocktail
bar and restaurant to the front, its tables forming booths thanks to
high-backed pews and brass-ringed curtaining, and at a lower level to
the rear, a cellar bar largely devoted to snacks and bar meals, in which
stripped pine tables and kitchen chairs are gathered in front of a
winter log-burning fire. Prominently displayed blackboard specials
run from home-made soup through to roast duck in black olive sauce
($£9.25$), whilst the evening menu might include cauliflower mornay
($£2.95$) and rabbit casserole ($£6.75$). Puddings are home-made,
crumbles and fruit flans coming from the kitchen of the lady next
door. The bedrooms – two doubles and a twin, are well fitted out,
with duvets, trouser press and hairdryer, small televisions and bedside
radio. Much of the barn has been refurbished over the last six months.
Owing to lack of space, the modular fitted shower rooms are a
cramped, if practical, solution. Host Charles Edmondson-Jones and
chef/partner Stewart Sturge add a final ingredient of good service and
genuine friendliness which many could learn from; the Old Barn is
one of those pubs to which people keep going back. **Bar Food** *12-1.30
(Sat & Sun to 1.45), 7-9.30.* **Restaurant Meals** *12-1.30 (Sun only),*

*7-9.30. No food Sun eve. Children allowed in bar to eat, children's menu.
Free House.* **Beer** *Adnams, Bateman's, Theakston, guest beers. Garden,
outdoor eating.* **Accommodation** *3 bedrooms, all en suite, £49.50 (single
£39.50). Children welcome overnight, cot available. Check-in by
arrangement. Pub closed Sun eve & Mon lunch. Access, Visa.*

Goathland	**Mallyan Spout Hotel**	**FOOD**
Tel 01947 86486 Fax 01947 86327		**B&B**
Goathland nr Whitby North Yorkshire YO22 5AN		Map 5 F3

Zzz*z*...

Goathland village itself is tucked into a fold in the moors two miles
off the A159 and some 9 miles from Whitby. The inn's unusual name
derives from the waterfall which cascades down the wooded valley
just yards from the pub garden; hugging the valley's contours runs the
North Yorkshire Moors Railway. Lunchtime in the Spout Bar can be
a busy occasion with customers regularly overflowing into the hotel
lounge next door. Ever-popular are the Mallayan home-cured beef
(£4.95), deep-fried monkfish and chips (£8.50), pork and chicken pie
(£5.50). Puddings to follow are of the sticky toffee and summer fruits
varieties. Evenings see the hotel restaurant move up a gear, with bar
food restricted to the Spout. Residents and others (who should book)
encounter a three-course table d'hote dinner starting (before extras) at
£18 – for fillet steak add another £7.50. Bedrooms, indubitably
upmarket in a purely pubby context, are housed largely to the rear of
the Jacobean-style, ivy-covered hotel with splendid valley views; small
and cottagey in the coach house, spacious and balconied in a redbrick
extension. En-suite bathrooms are generally on the small side.
Negotiate, if you can, a larger room if arriving with a family; no
reduction for children's meals in the restaurant at dinner (when
children under 6 are not welcome); high-tea served from 6-7pm.
Some 120 wines and twenty malts to choose from. *Open 11-11, Sun
usual hours.* **Bar Food** *12-2, 6.30-9 (from 7 Sun). Children's menu.*
Restaurant Meals *12-1.45 Sun only, 7-8.30. Free House.* **Beer** *Malton
Double Chance. Garden, patio. Family room.* **Accommodation**
*24 bedrooms, all en suite, from £70 (from £35 single). Children welcome
overnight (under-2s stay free in parents' room), additional beds (£10) and
cots available. Access, Visa.*

Godstow	**The Trout Inn**	
Tel 01865 54485		**A**
195 Godstow Rd Lower Wolvercote nr Oxford Oxon OX2 8PN		Map 14a C2

This famous medieval pub situated on the River Thames at Godstow
on the outskirts of Wolvercote still attracts thousands of visitors every
year. In summer, the cobbled terrace beside the fast-running river
with its weir makes a restful place for a quiet pint while watching the
peacocks wandering round the terrace and catching a glimpse of the
chub in the clear water. The bridge across to the private island is now
sadly falling apart but it is still possible to see across to the island with
its famous stone lion, and on to the now ruined Godstow Nunnery
where the fair Rosamund (Henry II's mistress) was imprisoned. Inside
the pub you'll find flagstone floors, beamed ceilings and bare
floorboards, with welcoming open fires in winter. Be warned, the
Trout can get very busy in the summer. *Open 11-11 (Sun 12-10.30).*
Beer *Bass, IPA, guest beer. Riverside garden, children's play area. Family
room. Access, Diners, Visa.*

Goosnargh   **Bushells Arms**

Tel 01772 865235 Fax 01772 861837	**FOOD**
Church Lane Goosnargh Lancashire PR3 2BH	**Map 6 B1**

Just 4 miles from Junction 32 of the M6, this modernised Georgian building offers a splendid alternative to the expensive plastic food of the motorway service areas. To reach the pub, follow the A6 North and turn on to the B5269; once in the village, take the left turn opposite the post office, and you'll find the Bushells Arms about a quarter of a mile along on the right. It's run by the experienced David and Glynis Best, who have written a book on the business side of pub catering, using much of their own experience. Certainly the food at the Bushells is first rate; cooking is in the hands of Glynis, who produces a long, wide and cosmopolitan selection of specials, blackboard-listed behind the food counter, as well as those on the distinguished printed menu. A truly international menu includes spring rolls (£2) and falafel (£2) for starters with Greek stifado (£6), chicken Kiev (£6) or chili con carne (£5) to follow. British dishes aren't forgotten either: a steak, kidney and Murphy's pie (£5) is admirably handled. There are fine accompaniments, too, like O'Brien potatoes, a delicious mix of diced potato with cream, peppers, spices, garlic and Parmesan cheese. Great care and enthusiasm are evident throughout, and the wine list is constantly being reviewed. The interior of the pub itself is cleverly divided into a number of alcoves by using effective wooden screens and exposed sandstone columns and walls. There's also lots of greenery, not all of it real. Seating is mainly on plush red button banquettes and stools, arranged around unfussy wooden tables, and a couple of the areas are non-smoking. Brasses and watercolours in a real mix of styles hang on the walls, and there's piped music. To the rear is a well-maintained garden with white plastic patio furniture, useful in summer when the pub gets extremely busy. Staff are noticeably welcoming and friendly. The village, incidentally, is pronounced 'Goozner'. *Bar Food 12-2.15, 7-10. Children allowed in bar to eat. Beer Tetleys, Boddingtons. Garden, outdoor eating. Occasional bar closures on Sundays. No credit cards.*

Gosfield   **The Green Man**

Tel 01787 472746	**FOOD**
The Street Gosfield Essex	**Map 10 C3**

A rust-brick roadside pub on the A1017, 2 miles off the A131. The bar and eating areas are more or less one and the same, presided over by two tropical fish tanks. The day's dishes are displayed on the blackboard: mostly English as in perhaps tomato soup, beef casserole with dumplings, salmon cutlet, or liver and bacon, all accompanied by two vegetables and a choice of potatoes. Lighter snacks, including Welsh rarebit, soft roes on toast with bacon and sandwiches, are also available. The centrepiece, however, is the cold lunchtime buffet, laden with home-cooked ham on the bone, roast turkey, pork, beef and lamb joints, a whole salmon and a colourful selection of salads. Equally inviting are the delights on the sweet trolley, a rarity in pubs, with temptations such as Paris Brest, apricot and ginger charlotte, profiteroles, chocolate gateau, pear tart etc – most certainly none of your bought-in puds here! Landlord John Arnold keeps an eye on diners, making sure their needs are satisfied; the charming waitresses are efficiency personified. *Bar Food 11-3, 6-11. Beer Greene King. Access, Visa.*

Goudhurst   **Star & Eagle**

Tel 01580 211512	**B&B**
High Street Goudhurst Kent TN17 1AL	**Map 11 B5**

Behind the splendid timbered and gabled facade vintage charm and
modern comfort blend harmoniously in a fine 14th-century hostelry
owned by Whitbread. Beams, bricks, vaulted stonework and
inglenooks make great appeal in the public rooms, while creaking
floors and odd angles are the order of the day in the bedrooms. These
vary in size and shape and the majority are furnished in pine, though
the four-poster room has some antiques. In the public areas, period
appeal survives in exposed beams, open brick fireplaces and old settles.
Pub open 11-11 Mon-Sat, Sun usual hours. **Beer** *Flowers, Fremlins, guest
beer. Garden. Family room, children's menu.* **Accommodation** *11 bedrooms,
9 en suite, £45 (four-poster £50, single £32.50). Children welcome
overnight (under-3s free if sharing parents' room, 3-16s £15), additional
beds and cots available. Dogs by arrangement. Access, Visa.*

Grange Moor   **Kaye Arms**

Tel 01924 848385	**FOOD**
29 Wakefield Road Grange Moor West Yorkshire WF4 4BG	**Map 6 C1**

True family involvement has raised both expectations and results since
the Coldwell family bought the Kaye Arms from Tetley's Brewery,
and it goes from strength to strength. Arrive early for the table of
your choice (there are no reservations) and lunch at leisure from a
legion of choices. Top sellers include the cheese soufflé with Waldorf
salad (£3.95), a pesto, tomato and mozzarella tart (£3.15) and smoked
goose breast (£3.20). More substantial lunch and evening fare brings
into play the likes of chicken in filo pastry (£8.25), salmon fillets with
lime butter (£8.25) and some first-class char grilled steaks (from
£9.20). To the uninitiated (and the brewery, perhaps), the complaint
might be that this is no pub, as crisps and real ales are totally
overlooked; yet carefully chosen wines by the glass remain, in this
context, a better complement. A policy of three pounds added to the
cost price of any bottle (rather than a triple multiplication of it)
provides plenty of choice and value at a price which the average pub-
goer should appreciate. **Bar Food** *(no food Mon lunch) 12-2, 7.30-10
(Sat from 6, Sun to 9.30). Free House. Pub closed Monday lunchtime.
Access, Visa. No real ales. Access, Visa.*

Grantchester   **Rupert Brooke**

Tel 01223 840295	**A**
2 The Broadway Grantchester nr Cambridge	**Map 15 F1**

Named after the poet who immortalised this beautiful village of
thatched and lime-washed cottages in his poem "The Vicarage,
Grantchester". Brooke lived nearby and used the pub as his local
before the First World War. An interesting collection of memorabilia
relating to the poet adorns the walls of the comfortably refurbished
interior which boasts plenty of exposed brick, beams, standing timbers
and some cosy seating areas. The village can be reached from
Cambridge via a delightful footpath across Grantchester Meadows.
Whitbread Wayside Inns. *Open 11-11 (Sun 12-3, 7-10.30).*
Beer *Flowers IPA, Boddingtons, Wadworth 6X guest beer. Garden.
Access, Visa.*

Grayswood   Wheatsheaf Inn   ★

FOOD
B&B

Tel 01428 644440

Grayswood nr Haslemere Surrey GU27 2DE   Map 11 A6

Having run three successful pubs in West Sussex over the past decade
the Colman family have ventured into Surrey to this Victorian village
inn, located beside the busy A286 near the parish church, cricket pitch
and green (where there's a children's playground), for their next
challenge. Recent refurbishment has resulted in a neat and comfortable
bar area with older-style furniture, quality prints and fabrics, with the
adjacent spacious L-shaped restaurant sporting artistic plants, marble-
topped tables, a terracotta-tiled floor and cushioned rattan chairs,
creating a relaxing 'Italian-style' ambience. Quality of cooking and
food presentation matches the stylish surroundings, with both the
regularly-changing lunch and dinner menus listing imaginative pub
fare. Lighter lunch menu choices include warm salad of mushrooms
with pancetta ham and chili oil (£4.75), fusilli pasta with Provençale
sauce (£4.95) and fillet of cod on a bed of spinach with cheese sauce
(£6.25), as well as a range of sandwiches, salads (from £5.95) and
specials like steak and kidney pie with Parma ham and chicken terrine
with a basil vinaigrette followed by peppered medallions of monkfish
on a tomato compote with a chive cream sauce (£9.50) or roast rack
of lamb with chargrilled vegetables, tomato and basil sauce (£8.95),
both served with crisp, fresh vegetables. Lighter main dishes include
smoked salmon and scrambled eggs (£5.50) and mushroom and red
pepper risotto (£5.75). Round off the meal with a delicious lemon tart
with raspberry and mango coulis or a chocolate truffle slice (both
£3). Short global list of keenly priced wines. Seven comfortable
en-suite bedrooms are housed in a newish rear brick extension.
Uniformly modern in decor and furnishings they have clean marble-
floored bathrooms, as well as TVs, telephones and tea-makers for
added comfort. Conference facilities. *Open 11-3, 6-11, Sun 12-3, 7-
10.30.* **Bar Food & Restaurant Meals** *12-2, 7-9.45. Children allowed in
bar to eat. Free House.* **Beer** *Ballards Bitter, Wadworth 6X, Wheatsheaf
Bitter, Hall & Woodhouse Badger Best. Garden, outdoor eating.*
Accommodation *7 bedrooms, all en suite, £55 (single £35). Children
welcome overnight (under-5s stay free in parents' room), additional beds
(£5) and cots available. Check-in by arrangement. No dogs. Access, Visa.*

Great Chesterford   Plough

A

Tel 01799 530283

High Street Great Chesterford Essex CB10 1PL   Map 10 B3

Delightful 18th-century village pub with a traditional, unspoilt and
well-cared-for interior, despite the addition of a more modern rear
extension which houses the bar. Original cottagey bars feature exposed
standing timbers and ceiling beams, two warming winter fires in
inglenooks and neatly arranged tables. The airy extension leads out on
to an attractive patio and lawn for summer alfresco drinking. Children
enjoy the large adventure playground with its aerial runway, wooden
climbing frames and swings. **Beer** *Greene King. Garden, children's play
area. Family room. Access, Visa.*

Great Kimble   Bernard Arms

FOOD
B&B

Tel 0184434 6172/3

Great Kimble nr Aylesbury Buckinghamshire HP27 0XS   Map 15a D2

On the A4010 about 3 miles north of Princes Risborough. The
original early 19th-century core of a coaching inn has been much
modernised and extended to include a homely Victorian-style bar
decorated with plates and prints on the walls, currency from around
the world covering the bar shelves and three unusual old chimney
pots containing plants. Blackboard bar menus change seasonally with
all the inventive dishes being home-made using fresh herbs from their
own herb garden; warm goat's cheese salad (£3.75), Nile perch (£8),
loin of pork with sage sauce (£7.50), grilled chicken fillet with garlic
and herbs (£7.50), Bakewell tart or summer pudding (both £2.50).
A separate restaurant offers two table d'hote menus (2/3 courses
£16/£19) with choices such as warm salad of lamb's tongues in a
niçoise dressing or smoked mackerel soufflé with gooseberry sauce,
followed by saddle of venison with a timbale of wild forest
mushrooms or breast of Barbary duck on blueberries and gin, with
chocolate orange torte to finish. A 3-course traditional Sunday lunch is
also served (£16). Results on the plate are good, each dish served with
fresh, crisp vegetables; service is efficient and friendly. Lovely garden
in which to escape the noisy road. Five bedrooms with basins and
showers share two toilets; TV, tea-makers and telephones are standard.
Choice of 26 malt whiskies at the bar. *Bar Food & Restaurant Meals
12-3 (Sun to 2.30), 7-10. Children's portions. Beer Benskins Best, Tetley
Bitter, Marston's Pedigree. Garden, games room. Accommodation
5 bedrooms, £45 (single £35, triple £55). Children welcome overnight,
additional cots available. Access, Visa.*

Great Missenden   George

A

Tel 01494 862084   Fax 01494 865622

94 High Street Great Missenden Buckinghamshire HP16 0BG   Map 15a E2

A Grade-II listed ancient monument, the George still has its 15th-
century timbers intact; there are a dozen foot-thick beams on the bar
parlour ceiling alone. Six en-suite bedrooms (£61) have now been
added, with TVs, radios, telephones and tea/coffee making facilities;
these were not inspected in time for this year's Guide. A grass and
shingle patio/garden at the back is safe for children. *Beer Wadworth
6X, Adnams Southwold. Patio/garden. Access, Visa.*

Great Rissington   Lamb   ★

FOOD
B&B

Tel 01451 820388   Fax 01451 820724

Great Rissington Cheltenham Gloucestershire GL54 2LP   Map 14a A2

Dating back nearly 300 years, the oldest part of the Lamb was
originally a stone Cotswold farmhouse. Over the last 50 years one of
its more celebrated claims to fame lies in the memory of a ditched
wartime bomber which crashed in the garden, its propeller still
preserved above the stove in the bar. For 15 years now the Lamb has
been home to the Cleverlys whose extensions and improvements are a
tribute to the family name; there is master craftsmanship everywhere
here, to the extent that joins between the original and much newer
parts are virtually indistinguishable. Kate Cleverly's labours in the
kitchen have followed a similar pattern over the years as production
has reacted consistently to ever-changing circumstances; yet with
'home cooking' remaining the key these have conspired to create a rod

for her own back. The current situation, which is to run two menus
in parallel, still offers plenty of reliable and enjoyable food though at
times perhaps the pressure shows. Thus the admirable avocado and
crispy bacon salad (£4.75) seafood pasta (£4.25) and ever-popular
steak and kidney pie (£5.50) or liver and bacon (£4.65) served in the
bar are supplemented at lunchtime by filled jacket potatoes of tuna,
cheese or baked beans (£3.50). The restaurant offerings, by
comparison, are to be taken a mite more seriously with dependable
patés (tuna and anchovy, perhaps) and Cheddar or Stilton puffs (all
£3.95) preceding the likes of fillet steak with Stilton (£11.50) and
chicken breast with mushrooms, cream and garlic (£8.35). This is
truly ambitious for what remains essentially a chatty, informal village
local whose same informality draws so many returning guests for an
overnight stay to enjoy the Lamb's great tranquillity. Richard and
Kate's skills have combined in the creation of charming bedrooms
which include built-in wardrobes made with salvaged timbers, and
a splendid four-poster bed, testifying to his skills as a wood carver.
Kate's contribution is the pretty decor, each room highly individual
in style, with co-ordinating fabrics and wall coverings. Most of the
furniture is antique and all but two rooms, which share a shower
room, have en-suite bathrooms (five with showers rather than baths).
They make a virtue out of not having television or radios in the
rooms but addicts will find a television (and a log fire) in the cosy
residents' lounge, as well as in the best guest room, a quite luxurious
suite. A heated indoor swimming pool (Apr-Oct) in the delightful
garden is a luxury all residents can share in the summer months;
a separate beer garden is to one side of the pub. Several high-chairs
are provided and children are welcome. Dogs (£1.50 per night, not
including food) are only permitted in the bedrooms; over twelve
years visitors to the Lamb have contributed £25,000 to a Guide
Dog fund, providing 25 dogs. *Bar Food 12-1.45,7-9 (Sun to 8.30).*
Restaurant Meals as per bar meals except: 12-1.30 & 7-8.30 Sun.
Children's menu. Free House. Beer Morland Old Speckled Hen,
Hook Norton. Children allowed in bar to eat. Garden, outdoor eating.
Accommodation 13 bedrooms, all en suite, £48 (four-poster £55, suite
£72, 2-room family £76, single £30). Children welcome overnight
(under-2s free if sharing parents' room), additional beds (£8), cots available
(£3.50). Pub and accommodation closed 25 & 26 Dec. Access, Visa.

Great Ryburgh   Boar Inn

Tel 0132878 212	**B&B**
Great Ryburgh nr Fakenham Norfolk NR21 0DX	**Map 10 C1**

If you are looking for peaceful and quiet accommodation within
handy reach of the Norfolk coastline, the Boar Inn, a white-washed
pub nestling near the river Wensum in a sleepy village, is the place to
go. On chilly nights a log fire crackles in the huge inglenook fireplace
of the low-beamed bar and there are more beams upstairs in the
cottagey bedrooms. Each room has a washbasin, TV and tea-making
facilities and they share a shower and toilet. *Free House.*
Beer Tolly Cobbold Original, Wensum Bitter, Adnams Bitter. Garden.
Accommodation 3 bedrooms with shared facilities, £32.80 (single
£20.50). Children welcome overnight (charge depends on age), cots
available. Dogs welcome by arrangement. Access, Visa.

Zzzz...

Great Tew	**Falkland Arms**	**FOOD**
Tel 01608 683653 Fax 01608 683656		**B&B**
Great Tew Oxfordshire OX7 4DB		Map 14a B1

Great Tew has the inestimable advantage of being a bit out of the way and not on the main tourist trail. It must be one of the prettiest of Cotswold villages. Despite the ambition implied by its name, it's actually rather a small place, with barely a score of mostly thatched cottages, a small general store and, naturally, in its rightful place opposite the church, the village inn. Dating back to the 16th century, the creeper-clad Falkland Arms must be close to everybody's ideal country pub, with high-backed settles, a flagstone floor and a prized collection of hundreds of jugs and mugs hanging from the old beams. A pretty garden shaded by a large hornbeam tree is complete with dovecote, whose occupants seem to spend most of the day perched on the pub's stone-tiled roof cooing to each other. The regular real ales are supplemented by an ever-changing selection of guest beers (some 250 in a full year) and 50 malt whiskies and 14 country wines are also available. They sell snuff, and even clay pipes ready-filled with tobacco. Food is served at lunchtimes only from a short but varied blackboard menu that changes daily but always includes a vegetarian dish (the landlord John Milligan eats not of meat), along with ploughman's and perhaps a rook pie (well at least it wasn't dove). Everything is home-made, from a cod and prawn crumble (£4.80), pork and Stilton hot pot (£5), or duck and apricot pie (£5.50) to sponges and crumbles (£1.80). Four cottagey bedrooms, two with four-poster beds and two with old iron bedsteads, are furnished with antiques and decorated with pretty co-ordinating fabrics and wall coverings. The largest, under the eaves, has a pitched ceiling, exposed timbers and its own en-suite bathroom. Others have showers and, all but one, their own toilets. Televisions and tea /coffee facilities are standard, and you can help yourself to fresh milk from the kitchen. Breakfast is at 9 o'clock prompt (9.30 on Sundays) and they like the rooms vacated by 10.30 on the day of departure. Bookings must be confirmed in writing with a 50% deposit. *Bar Food* 12-2 (*except Sun & Mon*). *Free House. Beer Donnington Best, Hook Norton Best, Wadworth 6X, Hall & Woodhouse Tanglefoot, five guest beers. Garden, outdoor eating, children's play area. Accommodation 4 bedrooms, 3 en suite, £45 (single £25). Children welcome overnight (under 5s free if staying in parents' room). No dogs. Check-in by arrangement. Pub closed lunchtime Monday. No credit cards.*

Greta Bridge	**Morritt Arms Hotel**	**FOOD**
Tel 018336 27232 Fax 018336 27570		**B&B**
Greta Bridge Rokeby nr Barnard Castle Co Durham DL12 9SE		Map 5 D3

Just off the A66 three miles from Barnard Castle and invitingly floodlit after dark, the former coaching in beloved of Charles Dickens in *Nicholas Nickleby* stands right by the old stone bridge safely by-passed by today's highway. The Morritt Arms has carefully retained its 18th-century appeal in panelled lounges and deep, comfortable chintz armchairs. Food in the bar remains just as fiercely traditional – expect to find pea & ham soup (£1.80), braised lambs' liver and onions (£4.75), baked fillet of cod (£4.95) and hearty nursery puddings – treacle sponge and spotted dick with custard (£2.40). Bedrooms, though a touch utilitarian in decor, are nonetheless comfortable and well-equipped with remote control TVs, dial-out phones, radio alarms, trouser presses and hairdryers – spacious traditional bathrooms are carpeted throughout. **Accommodation** *16 bedrooms, all en suite, £68 (Single £45). Dogs welcome in rooms. Children welcome overnight.* **Bar Food** *12-2, 6-9 (12-2, 7-8.45 Sun).* **Restaurant Meals** *7-8.45 (12.30-1.15, 7-8.45 Sun).* **Beer** *Butterknowle Conciliation Ale. Garden, outdoor eating.* Access, Diners, Visa.

Gretna   Gretna Chase Hotel

| Tel 01461 337517   Fax 01461 337766 | **B&B** |

Gretna nr Carlisle Cumbria DG16 5JB   Map 4 C2

Patrons of the first marriage house over the Scottish border used the nearby Gretna Chase for stabling their horses. That function has long since ceased, but today's honeymooners can install themselves in a splendid four-poster suite. All rooms (with TVs, but discreetly phoneless) feature quality furniture and fabrics, and most overlook the award-winning garden of 2½ acres. There is a spacious Victorian reception hall, plenty of bar space and a little lounge. *Open 11-11 (Sun usual hours).* **Beer** *Theakstons. Garden, outdoor eating.* **Accommodation** *8 bedrooms, 6 en suite, £60 (four-poster £80, single from £38). Children welcome overnight (under-4s stay free in parents' room, 4-12 £5), additional beds & cots available. Check-in by arrangement. No dogs. Pub closed Sun eves and 2 weeks January.* Access, Visa.

Gretton   Royal Oak

| Tel 01242 602477 | **FOOD** |

Gretton nr Winchombe Gloucestershire GL54 5EP   Map 14 C1

Extensive gardens and playing areas (including a tennis court for rent) and regular summer visits by the steam train from Winchcombe, all contribute to the irresistible summer attractions of the Royal Oak. Low hop-hung beams adorned with pewter mugs and chamber pots and open log fires, whose glow is reflected in polished flagstones, make it equally appealing in winter. Add to this a good range of real ales and a vast blackboard menu and you have unravelled the secrets of this Cotswold pub's popular success. Sizzling potato skins with cheese (£2.75) and crab and mushroom pot (£2.95) can be either snacks or starters. Main courses run from Normandy chicken with apples and cider (£5.25) and baked ham with cauliflower cheese (£5.75) to popular omelettes Arnold Bennet (with smoked haddock or spinach and cheese both £4.50). Finish off, perhaps, with lemon cream torte or chocolate peanut crunch (£2.25). The old building does have a certain charm, its mellow stone and rickety porch seemingly held together by the creepers which flourish in the old oak's shadow. **Bar Food** *12-2, 7-9.30. Free House.* **Beer** *Cotswold Bitter, John Smith's, Wadworth 6X, Ruddles Country, guest beer. Garden, outdoor eating.* Access, Visa.

Grindleford   Maynard Arms Hotel

| Tel 01433 630321   Fax 01433 630445 | **FOOD** |
| | **B&B** |

Main Road Grindleford Derbyshire S30 1HP   Map 6 C2

Formerly proprietors here some years ago, Robert and Thelma Graham (who also own the *Chequers Inn* at nearby Calver), have set vigorously to work on restoration work at the Maynard Arms following their repurchase of the property in mid-1994. With their background they're helped enormously by an intimate knowledge·of innkeeping and have high aspirations for their work. As a case in

Zzzz...

point, the remodelled Longshaw Bar now exudes a stylish and comfortable ambience for the enjoyment of some simply conceived and reliably produced bar food. Pasta bows in a four-cheese sauce and pan-fried black pudding with English mustard (both £2.75), original Yorkshire puddings with fillings or vegetable and mushroom Wellington (both £4.50) are virtually meals in themselves. More adventurous choices may include flying fish in curried oil (£3.65) and sizzling chili beef with tagliatelle and stir-fried vegetables (£5.75). All comers are invited also to leave room for the traditional Bakewell pudding served hot with cream (£3.95) and which comes from the Grahams' own Bakewell shop – "it's loads for two and enough for four!". As befits an old coaching inn, the grand style, large, airy bedrooms overlook the Derwent Valley through elegant stone mullion windows. Suitably up-to-date accessories include direct-dial phones, remote-control TVs and trouser presses. As we went to press, however, further refurbishment was scheduled for early 1995, in which a meeting room next to the first-floor residents' lounge will be added, and remaining bedrooms with shower rooms only will be upgraded to include full en-suite bathrooms. The total number of letting bedrooms will be reduced by two as a consequence. *Open 11-3, 6-11, Sun 12-3, 7-10.30.* **Bar Food** *12-2 (Sun to 2.30), 6-9.30 (Sun from 7). Free House. Beer Whitbread Eden, Boddingtons. Garden, outdoor eating. Family room.* **Accommodation** *11 bedrooms, all en suite, £60 (single £45). Children welcome overnight, additional bed (£10) and cot available. Access, Diners, Visa.*

Guisborough Fox Inn

| Tel 0128 763 2958 | **B&B** |

10 Bow Street Guisborough Cleveland TS14 6BP   Map 5 E3

One of the two bars is decked out in green plush to complement the copper-topped tables, and the other is similarly furnished (in red), with mock beams and rough plaster walls. Bedrooms are simply furnished with lightwood units, TVs and tea-makers. Two public bathrooms and four toilets serve the rooms. Owned by Scottish & Newcastle. *Beer Marston's Pedigree & Exhibition, Theakston's, McEwan's 80/-.* **Accommodation** *7 bedrooms not en suite, £24.95 (single £19.95). Children welcome overnight, cots available. No dogs. Access, Visa.*

Guiting Power Ye Olde Inne

| Tel 01451 850392 | **FOOD** |

Winchcombe Road Guiting Power nr Stow-on-the-Wold
Gloucestershire GL54 5UX   Map 14a A1

The far end of the single lane running through this picturesque Cotswold village goes by the unlikely name of Th'Ollow Bottom. Here the Olde Inne nestles – a low, listed, 17th-century stone pub and a little hollowed out itself inside. Best of the three tiny rooms is the flagstone-floored dining room with its sandblasted ceiling timbers and a recently-exposed inglenook. The entire pub, however, has recently been spruced up, and food is on the up too, with enthusiastic new landlord Bill Tu overseeing the kitchen. Old favourites, including asparagus gratinée (£2·95), frikadeller (Danish pork rissoles £4.25) and curried nut roast (£5·50) predominate on the printed menu, with the more adventurous pigeon in red wine (£6.75) and fillet steak with salsa verde (£9.50) chalked up on the bar canopy. Look out, though, for some of Bill's native Burmese favourites like fish koftas or coconut chicken with noodles (£5.50) which make regular guest appearances to spice things up. Hearty, home-made puddings. Sunday lunches in winter and junior portions of Golden Tiddlers for toddlers (£2.50) ensure that there is something of good quality and value for all comers. *Bar Food 12-2, 6.30-9.30 (Sun from 7). Children allowed in bar to eat. Free House.* **Beer** *Theakston's Best, Hook Norton Best, guest beer. Garden, patio, outdoor eating. Access, Visa.*

Gunwalloe Halzephron Inn ★	FOOD
Tel 01326 240406	B&B
Gunwalloe nr Helston Cornwall TR12 7QB	Map 12 A4

Situated four miles south of Helston on the west coast of the Lizard peninsula, the Halzephron Inn commands an enviable position perched high up above Gunwalloe Fishing Cove, with spectacular views across Mount's Bay to Penzance and the Land's End peninsula. Its rugged stone exterior feels the full force of 2,000 miles of wild Atlantic weather, but inside there is a genuine warm welcome from amiable hosts, Cornish born and bred Angela and Harry Davy Thomas. They have utilised their vast experience in the trade in rejuvenating this 500-year-old smugglers' inn – a shaft still exists leading to a tunnel to the beach – which had been floundering in the doldrums for a few years. The two spick-and-span inter-connecting bars have been simply, yet tastefully refurbished, featuring attractive checked fabrics, scatter cushions on padded wall benches, warming winter fires, general fishing memorabilia, shining copper and brass and original watercolours of Cornish scenes. The intimate 'Captain's Table' dining room has a head-cracking low ceiling, stone walls, blue and white checked tablecloths topped with antique candlesticks and a cosy atmosphere, plus a charming sea view. Both lunch and evening printed menus offer a varied selection of dishes to please all tastes, from pub favourites to good home-cooked meals. However, the real emphasis is on the twice daily-changing blackboard menu which lists more imaginative fare using the best of local ingredients. Here everything is home-made from carrot and coriander soup (£2), smoked fish paté (£2.85), kedgeree (£5.80) and hot baked crab (£4.80) to lemon sole stuffed with salmon mousse (£7.50), chicken marengo (£5.90) and pork fillet with caramelised apples (£6). Vegetarians will not be disappointed with cheese and herb soufflé (£4.75) or vegetable strudel (£4.75). Accompanying vegetables are perfectly cooked and service impeccable from neatly attired staff. High standards extend upstairs to the two delightful bedrooms which have been kitted out with flair; they enjoy rolling country views. Notable features include old stripped-pine furniture, Laura Ashley fabrics and wallpapers, colourful cushioned director's chairs, hand-made quilts, original watercolours and nice added touches like fresh fruit, biscuits, mineral water and various books and magazines. Spotless en-suite facilities. Most enjoyable breakfasts. An excellent base from which to explore this unspoilt corner of Cornwall. No children under 14 overnight. *Bar Food & Restaurant Meals 12-2, 7-9.30. Free House.* **Beer** *Fergusons Dartmoor Best Bitter & Strong. Garden, outdoor eating.* **Accommodation** *2 rooms, both en suite, from £40 (single £20). Check-in by arrangement. Access, Visa.*

Hailey The Bird in Hand	FOOD
Tel 01993 868321 Fax 01993 868702	B&B
Hailey nr Witney Oxon OX8 5XP	Map 14a B2

A delightful 'residential country inn' in a rural setting surrounded by open fields, one mile north of Hailey on the B4022 between Witney and Charlbury. The small, neat, low-walled roadside garden gives an indication of the standards aimed for inside and the large, pebbled car park shows its popularity as a dining pub with a strong local following. A dozen or so picnic tables with umbrellas are set outside on a large patio by the side entrance. Inside, four stone-walled bar rooms include one with a long bar, sofa, pews and old tables, plus another with an inglenook where a wood fire burns during winter; the third is darker, leading down to the Dungeon room which this year has been refurbished to offer more lounge-style seating for residents with tables and old pews. The emphasis is very much on eating rather than drinking, with the printed menu supplemented by blackboard specials. Fresh fish is a feature of the latter, with the likes of mussel salad, fresh haddock (£6.45), fresh fillets of cod with prawn and coriander butter; other daily specials might include stir-fried chicken (£7.45) or rack of lamb with honey and sugar glaze and redcurrant sauce (£8.95). Regular choices include home-made soup (£2.95), chicken liver paté (£2.95), smoked salmon with citrus fruit salad and melba toast (£6.45) and a good selection of pasta dishes (£5.95 with garlic bread); home-made beefburgers with chips (£6.50), avocado, smoked chicken and almond salad with fresh coriander (£5.50), chicken and coconut curry with poppadoms (£6.75), and rump steak (£9.95) complete the picture. Sunday lunch includes a traditional roast (£5.95). 16 unusually spacious and comfortable, cottage-style rooms are in a U-shaped building on two storeys with wooden balconies and overlook a quiet, grassed courtyard. Two ground-floor twin rooms have facilities for the disabled; two large family rooms have a double and a single bed plus a double sofa bed and room for the wooden cot provided on request. Matching floral fabrics, pine furnishings, thoughtful touches like full-length mirrors and cotton wool plus good housekeeping bring all rooms up to an above-average pub standard. Good breakfasts put the icing on the cake. For families with babes in arms or children over five it's a good stopover, particularly for the outdoor tables and big family rooms; high-chairs are provided and a 'families welcome' sign is displayed outside; if junior diners require high tea before evening bar snack times, they should arrange such when booking. Residential weekday conferences are popular, with one of the dining rooms doubling as a conference room. *Open 11-11 Mon-Sat, regular hours Sun.* **Bar Food** *12-2, 7-9.45 (Sun to 9.30)* **Restaurant Meals** *12-2, 7-9.45 (Sun 9.45). Free House. Beer Boddingtons, Flowers Original, Bass. Patio, outdoor eating. Family room.* **Accommodation** *16 rooms, all en suite, £45 (single £38.50, family room £48 + £10 for each child over 2, max 5 people). Children welcome overnight, cot supplied. Check-in all day (except Sun afternoon). Dogs by arrangement. Access, Visa.*

Hallaton   Bewicke Arms

Tel 0185 889 217	**FOOD**
1 Eastgate Hallaton Leicestershire LE16 8UB	**Map 7 D4**

Neil Spiers's 400-year-old country inn stands above the Welland valley in the heart of fine Leicestershire countryside. Hallaton itself is locally renowned for the parish church's Norman tower, the conical butter cross on the village green – right across the road from the pub – and the tiny village museum which offers a unique insight into its rural past. The pub is a cracking good local and a predictable printed menu lists the usual steaks and grills, ploughman's and sandwiches – look to the specials board for more adventurous options. Starters typically include garlic mushrooms, deep-fried Camembert, and paté maison (£3.60), while top-sellers among the main courses include Somerset beef in dry cider (£6.80) and chicken Boursin (£7.60). Vegetarians get a good look in, too, with risotto, lasagne and a cauliflower, courgette and mushroom bake topped with Stilton crumble, and there's a fair choice of home-made puddings of the cheesecake, pavlova and treacle sponge and custard genre. Wines offered by the bottle are more interesting than the house beers; a printed, largely European list is backed by a wines of the month board, typically featuring Australian specials. The pub is consistently busy and the more recently added Bottom Room, stone clad with a bow window, Austrian blinds and an effective library theme, opens when demand dictates. At weekends it's almost certain to be full, so better book. B&B is no longer advertised. *Bar Food 12-2, 7-9.45. Children's menu. Free House. Beer Marston's Pedigree, Ruddles, Webster's Yorkshire Bitter. Garden, outdoor eating. Access, Visa.*

Haltwhistle   Milecastle In

Tel 01434 320682	**FOOD**
Military Road Haltwhistle Northumberland NE49 9NN	Map 5 D2

A mere 500 yards from the 42nd milecastle of Hadrian's Wall, the Paynes' neatly-kept inn stands on the B6318, 1½ miles out of town. Probably once a small farm with attendant drover's cottages, it would seem to have a long history of hospitality. Today's cosy, stone-lined interior is hung with a vast collection of brass ornaments and artefacts. The recently-extended bar nonetheless runs to no more than a half dozen tables. Daily menus are thus kept sensibly short with an emphasis on the hearty pies much favoured by a regular passing trade of wall-walkers. Of these, hot beef & venison or wild duck and boar, perhaps, (both £5.95) may be preceeded by leek & potato soup (£1.95) and followed by the popular banoffi pie (£1.65). There's a front patio and large, safe garden for leisurely enjoyment of the local Hexhamshire beers. Walkers in muddy boots, and children under 5, are not allowed in the bar. *Bar Food 12-2, 6.30-9 (7-9pm Sun). Restaurant Meals Lunch by arrangement, 7-9 (Tues-Sat). Children over 5 years allowed in the bar to eat. Free House. Beer Tetley Best, Hexhamshire Devil's Water and Whapweasel, guest beers. Garden, outdoor eating. Access, Diners, Visa.*

Hampstead Marshall   White Hart Inn

	FOOD
Tel 01488 658201	**B&B**
Hampstead Marshall nr Newbury Berkshire RG15 0HW	Map 14a B4

The splendid herbaceous borders around the neat lawn at the front of this 16th-century inn are very English, and the pride and joy of Dorothy Aromando, but inside the Latin influence of husband Nicola predominates in the White Hart's Italian menu. A few old beams, mingling with some newer ones, give clues to the age of the building, but the decor is basically simple: red plush in the bar, red cloths on the tables of the restaurant leading off it. The same handwritten menu serves for both bar and restaurant. Nicola makes his own pasta and consequently there's a selection of pasta dishes (from £6.50) alongside meat dishes. Two favourites are quadroni (ravioli) with wild mushrooms and spinach fettuccine with small lamb meatballs stuffed with mozzarella cheese in a wine, mushroom and cream sauce. Otherwise the menu offers soup of the day (£3.25), goat's cheese grilled with garlic and yoghurt (£5), Dover sole (£14.50), chicken

breast with ham and asparagus (£10.20) and spinach and ricotta
pancake. Amongst the home-made puddings, the crème caramel (£4)
is outstanding, freshly cooked and with the topping caramelised to just
the right degree; tiramisu and cassata might also appear alongside
sticky toffee pudding. An old barn to the rear of the pub has been
converted into six uncluttered bedrooms with pine furniture and good
cotton bedding. All have neat en-suite bathrooms with showers over
their bathtubs. Get one of the two large rooms under the eaves, if you
can, which have sloping ceilings and exposed timbers, as well as an
extra bed for family use. The two single rooms are very compact.
Good, freshly-cooked breakfasts set you up for the day ahead. *Bar
Food & Restaurant Meals 12-2, 6.30-10 (restaurant to 9.30). No food
Sun. Free House. Beer Hall & Woodhouse Badger Best, Wadworth.
Garden, outdoor eating. Accommodation 6 bedrooms, all en suite, £55
(single £40). Children welcome overnight, additional beds available (£5).
No dogs. Check-in by arrangement. Pub closed all Sunday and two weeks
in August. Access, Visa.*

Harberton   Church House Inn

Tel 01803 863707	**A**
Church House Inn Harberton nr Totnes Devon TQ9 7SF	Map 13 D3

Tucked away by the church in a sleepy village amid steep narrow
lanes off the A381 Totnes to Kingsbridge road, this fine building was
originally a chantry house for monks, one of whom is said to be still
lurking on the premises, and the Church House didn't pass out of
clerical hands until 1950. The carefully removed plaster of centuries
has revealed ancient fluted oak beams, a magnificent medieval oak
screen, a Tudor window frame and 13th-century glass. The open-plan
bar area was once the great chamber, and is now furnished with old
pews and settles. *Pub open 12-2.30, 6-11 (11.30-3, 6-11 Sat, 12-3, 7-
10.30 Sun). Free House. Beer Draught Bass, Courage Best, guest beers.
Pub closed 25 & 26 Dec eve, 1 Jan eve. No credit cards.*

Hare Hatch   Queen Victoria

Tel 01734 402477	**FOOD**
Blakes Lane Hare Hatch Berkshire RG10 9TA	Map 15a D3

This convivial, low-ceilinged 17th-century two-roomed local can be
found just off the A4 and is a popular refreshment spot between
Reading and Maidenhead. Simply furnished interior which still has
some of the original straw and dung walling, a collection of miniature
jugs hanging from the ceiling rafters, a real fire and a fruit machine.
Blackboards list a reliable selection of bar meals along with the usual
favourites. Choices may include hot fresh crab meat with brandy and
Parmesan (£4.95), sautéed chicken livers with bacon and granary toast
(£3.25), and main dishes like beef korma with wild rice (£4.40),
lamb and rosemary casserole (£4.40) and herb and vegetable pasta
with anchovy bread (£4.35). Well-cooked accompanying vegetables.
Colourful alfresco patio seating amid overflowing flower baskets and
tubs. *Pub open 11-11 (usual hours Sun). Bar Food 11.30-2.45,
6.30-10.45 (Sun 12-2.45, 7-10.15). Beer Brakspear. Garden, outdoor
eating. No credit cards.*

Harewood   **Harewood Arms**

Tel 0113 288 6566   Fax 0113 288 6064

Harrogate Road Harewood nr Leeds West Yorkshire LS17 9LH

B&B

Map 6 C1

Zzzz...

A fashionable address opposite the gates of Harewood House and convenient location on the A61 halfway between Leeds and Harrogate ensure particular mention for this elegant inn. Formerly a coaching house, with a history dating back to 1815, it has been meticulously restored by Samuel Smith, the brewers of Tadcaster. Though fully carpeted and rather studiously appointed, the three lounge bars retain an essentially pubby feel and are much frequented by a business, golfing and race-going fraternity. Nonetheless, temptation to over-price their best-selling Old Brewery Bitter (£1.20 per pint in October 1994) has been commendably resisted. Traditional oak bed frames and freestanding furniture have been used as a unifying theme in individually designed bedrooms, the majority of which are in the former coach-house wing overlooking the terrace, formal rose garden and rolling Yorkshire countryside. Four are conveniently located on the ground floor. A full range of room accessories – from remote-control TVs and trouser presses to bidets and over-bath showers – is impressive, a factor reflected in their rather higher-than-average room prices. *Open 11-10.50, Sun usual hours.* **Beer** *Samuel Smith Old Brewery Bitter. Family Room. Garden, terrace.* **Accommodation** *24 rooms, all en suite, £78 (single £65). Children welcome overnight (under-6s stay free in parents' room), additional beds and cots (both £12) available. Access, Diners, Visa.*

Harome   **Star Inn**

Tel 01439 70397

Main Street Harome nr Helmsley North Yorkshire YO0 5JE

FOOD

Map 5 E4

Virtually unchanged over the many years of our recommendation, the Star exhibits an ageless charm of thick, thatched roof and evocative low-beamed interior long-loved of the country set. Field sports and motoring magazines abound alongside the national dailies, and daily specials are headlined on the bar blackboard, in conjunction with a larger "carte" which has more notions of being a restaurant (as the adjacent larger dining room effectively is). Bar staples cover the range of steak and kidney pie, Cornish pastie and lasagne (from £3.95) with chips or baked potatoes. More snacky items might be scallops with mushrooms and bacon (£4.95) or chicken livers with cream and brandy (£3.95) while there's plenty of alcohol to hand in the Grand Marnier cream with rack of lamb and oranges (£7.95). To follow, huge nursery puddings (rhubarb crumble or blackberry and apple tart £2.25) are liberally sauced with custard. It's important to note that the pub's opening hours are much more restricted than once they were, so it may be wise to check before embarking on a long detour into the country. For the restaurant at night and for a formal Sunday lunch, booking remains essential. *Free House.* **Bar Food** *Closed Mon & Tues. 12-2, 7.30-9.30.* **Restaurant Meals** *Closed Mon & Tues. 7.30-9.30 (Opens for lunch by request, 12-2 Sun).* **Beer** *Theakston Best & Old Peculier, Timothy Taylor Landlord, guest beer. Garden, outdoor eating area. Family room. Pub closed Mon & Tues. Access, Visa.*

Hascombe   **White Horse**

Tel 01486 32258	**FOOD**

Hascombe nr Godalming Surrey GU8 4JA   Map 11 A5

Grade II listed, 16th-century pub nestling in a beautiful corner of
Surrey close to Winkworth Arboretum (NT). Charming and
immaculate interior comprising a rambling series of unspoilt, beamed
rooms, all tastefully decorated with Laura Ashley wallpapers and
kitted out with attractive pine in cosy alcoves, decent prints and open
fires. Neat restaurant area with linen-clothed tables and separate hop
and farming memorabilia-adorned public bar. Reliable bar food
choices are chalked up on a daily-changing blackboard and may
include home-made steakburger (£4.95), steak and kidney pie
(£5.65), Coronation chicken (£4.95), lamb and mint kebabs (£6.50)
and grilled calf's liver (£7.50). Also on offer are imaginative door-step
sandwiches (bacon and avocado £2.95) and a selection of salads, such
as dressed crab (£8.25). More elaborate evening fare appears on the
restaurant à la carte menu and the three-course set menu (£22).
Colourful summer terrace and pretty, extensive garden, ideal for fine
weather imbibing. Families with children are not encouraged (as per
the law), but tactfully served. *Open 11-11 Sat in summer, usual hours
at other times.* **Bar Food** *(Sat to 2) 12-2.20, 7-10.* **Restaurant Meals**
12-2.30 (to 2 Sun), 7-10 (not Sun eve). **Beer** *Marston's Pedigree, Friary
Mieux, Greene King IPA. Garden. Family room. Bar open lunchtime only
& restaurant closed on 25 Dec. Access, Visa.*

Haselbury Plucknett   **Haselbury Inn**

Tel 01460 72488	**FOOD**

Haselbury Plucknett nr Crewkerne Somerset TA18 7RJ   Map 13 F2

The distinct dining bias is an increasing draw at the Pooleys' spacious
village inn just off the A30 (Crewkerne 3 miles). Comprehensive
menus are on show for both the Country Bar and Stables restaurant,
candle-lit by night and set with lacy cloths and fresh flowers. Specials
boards supplement the bar offerings: beef stroganoff (£4.95), chicken
kiev (£6.50) and vegetable and cashew nut tikka (£4.50). Regular
features are a daily lunch brunch (£4.95) – except on Sunday when
roasts are substituted (£5.50) – and a celebrated barbecue selection
offered nightly (£15 for two). Fish, flesh and fowl all appear in
voluminous guises on the restaurant menu, a noticeably Spanish
influence in some of the food being reflected by much of the piped
music. While there is a clear reliance on the fryers, vegetables at least
are fresh and plentiful. Gooey, creamy desserts become something of a
high point, the toffee pecan cheesecake (£2.25) with butterscotch
sauce appearing to be especially popular. To end, there are plenty of
liqueur coffees and particularly good espresso. **Bar Food** *12-2, 7-10
(not Mon).* **Restaurant Meals** *12-2 (2.15 Sun), 7-9.30.* **Beer** *Hickelbury,
Butcombe, Exmoor Best, Wadworth 6X. Garden and play area. Children
welcome in bar to eat. Access, Visa.*

Hastingwood Common   **Rainbow & Dove**

Tel 01279 415419	**A**

Hastingwood Common Essex CM17 9JX   Map 11 B4

Charming old rose-covered pub dating from the 16th-century, its
name a reference to Noah's Ark (and it gets almost as crowded inside).
Despite its close proximity to the busy M11 (a quarter of a mile from

J7), the garden is a popular attraction on summer days with its adjacent 18-hole putting course and paddock. Escape the incessant traffic noise inside, within the three characterful and cosy, low-beamed rooms with open fires, rustic furnishings and collections of horse brasses and a few golf clubs. *Beer Ansells, Bass, Ruddles. Garden. Access, Visa.*

Hatherleigh   George Hotel

Tel 01837 810454 Fax 01837 810901	**B&B**

Market Street Hatherleigh nr Oakhampton Devon EX20 3JN   **Map 13 D2**

Dating from 1450, this ancient cob-and-thatch town-centre inn was once a rest house and sanctuary for the monks of Tavistock. In later years it became a brewery, tavern, a law court and a coaching inn before developing into what is now a most comfortable and historic small hotel. Off the central cobbled courtyard in the converted brewhouse and coachman's loft is the main bar and family area extension, while the original inn's bar oozes charm and antiquity with old beams, an oak-panelled wall, an enormous fireplace and an assortment of cushioned seats and sofas. It is now largely confined to residents or waiting diners, as the attractive restaurant is next door. The Farmers Bar across the courtyard opens only on Thursdays when the market is outside in the square. Sloping floors and low 'head-cracking' doorways lead to eleven individually furnished bedrooms with pretty chintz fabrics, pieces of old or antique furniture and generally good clean en-suite facilities. Three rooms have elegant four-poster beds. TVs, telephones and tea-making facilities are the added comforts and residents also have the use of a charming lounge and the outdoor swimming pool. Eight/ten wines available by the glass. *Free House. Beer Bass, Flowers Original, Devon Glory, Boddingtons. Cobbled outdoor eating area. Accommodation 11 bedrooms, 9 en suite, £65 (four-poster £75, single £48). Children welcome overnight, additional beds £6. Check in from noon. Access, Visa.*

Hatherleigh   Tally Ho

	FOOD
Tel 01837 810306	**B&B**

14 Market Street Hatherleigh Devon EX20 3JN   **Map 13 D2**

The exterior appearance of this market town-centre building belies the true age of this 15th-century inn which was 'discovered' by its present owners in 1983. During the intervening decade the Scoz family have regenerated and improved the Tally Ho by reviving the brewery (producing five real ales for the pub) and adding three elegant bedrooms to this well-run ship. The bar and intimate restaurant are charmingly rustic with a heavily beamed ceiling, part woodblock and part exposed brick floor; sturdy old furnishings and two upholstered easy chairs flank one of the two stone fireplaces, both with warming woodburners. Various plates and attractive paintings decorate the walls and the convivial atmosphere is enhanced by the classical music that fills this game-free bar. Food certainly has an Italian flavour, especially in the restaurant, where authentic and elaborate sauced dishes are featured. Bar food is simpler fare, the printed menu listing favourite snacks and a popular pasta dish of the day – bolognese, carbonara, lasagne or maybe al pesto. Further Italian food enlivens the bar on Tuesday evenings when pizzas are the speciality; on Thursday it's the 'grigliato evening', with the main menu being replaced by the blackboard and a set Italian menu. On Fridays at least a dozen fish dishes appear on the bar menu. Superior overnight accommodation is

good value and provided in three well-designed and comfortable
bedrooms. All are furnished with old pine and decorated with
attractive fabrics and quality prints, with added comforts including
TV, telephone, clock/radios and a complimentary miniature sherry
and a welcoming hand-written note from the proprietor on arrival.
Bathrooms are fresh and clean with expensive sanitaryware.
Continental breakfast is served with an extra charge for cooked items.
Dogs are not allowed in the rooms but they can be housed in a kennel
in the garden. *Free House.* **Beer** *Potboiler, Tarka's Tipple, Nutters,
Thurgia. Garden, outdoor eating area.* **Accommodation** *3 bedrooms, all en
suite, £40 (single £28). Access, Visa.*

Hathersage   Hathersage Inn

Tel 01433 650259 Fax 01433 651199	**B&B**

Hathersage Derbyshire S30 1BB

Map 6 C2

The ivy-clad, stone-built inn stands by Hathersage's steep main street
in the heart of the Peak District National Park; pub to the front
where the Cricketers' Bar is full of local memorabilia and quietly
residential to the rear with a lounge bar and cosy dining room.
Bedrooms are neatly kept, with plenty of extras from TV and radio-
alarm to drinks tray and fresh fruit. There are six executive rooms,
four-posters and a honeymoon suite. *Free House.* **Beer** *John Smith's,
Webster's Yorkshire Bitter, Courage Directors.* **Accommodation**
*15 bedrooms, all en suite, £54.50 (single £44.50). Children welcome
overnight (charge depends on age). Access, Diners, Visa.*

The Haven   The Blue Ship

Tel 01403 822709	**A**

The Haven nr Billingshurst West Sussex RH14 9BS

Map 11 A6

Hidden in the depths of the Sussex countryside along a tiny lane off
the A29 north of Billingshurst, this splendid rural gem is well worth
tracking down. An unassuming Victorian brick and tile-hung exterior
– festooned with a rampant climbing clematis – hides a charming
15th-century core, characterised by the classic main bar, which
features a worn red-brick floor, low heavy beams, a large inglenook
and scrubbed pine tables and sturdy wooden benches. Well kept King
and Barnes ales tapped straight from the cask are dispensed via a small
hatch servery. A flagstoned passageway leads to two further rooms
added in later years, a games room full of traditional pub games – no
music or electronic machines here – and access to the peaceful cottage
garden, a delight on warm summer days. *Pub open 11-3, 6-11 (Sun 12-
3,7-10.30).* **Beer** *King & Barnes Sussex Bitter, Broadwood, Old Ale
(winter), Summer Ale. Garden, lawn, patio, outdoor eating area. Family
room. No credit cards.*

Hawkshead   Drunken Duck Inn

Tel 0153 94 36347 Fax 0153 94 36781	**FOOD**
	B&B

Barngates Hawkshead nr Ambleside Cumbria LA22 0NG

Map 4 C3

Take the Tarn Hows turning at Outgate off the B5286 to find the
Drunken Duck, formerly the Barngate Inn, standing high in the hills
with spectacular views across distant Lake Windermere to its
backdrop of craggy hills. There's a healthy range of well-kept real ales
to accompany an impressive array of bar meals. A hard working
kitchen produces volumes of vegetarian fare from Brie and asparagus
or garlic mushroom paté (£2.95) to ricotta tortellini in tomato and

Zzzz...

herb sauce (£4.95) and vegetable chili with lentils and rice (£5). In addition to voluminous rolls and ploughman's at lunchtimes comes lamb with spinach and apricots (£5.95), Moroccan lamb tageen perhaps (£5.75) and Cumberland sausage casserole (£5.95). Treacle tart and jam roly poly are traditionally filling walkers' puds. Overnight guests are housed in stylish, individually designed bedrooms, some in stripped pine others with carefully chosen antique pieces. Fabrics feature soft restful shades, while the well-lit bathrooms have good over-bath showers, good towelling and quality toiletries. TVs, telephones and tea trays are all provided. *Bar Food 12-2, 6.30-9 (Sun from 7). Free House. Beer Yates Bitter, Jennings Bitter and Cumberland, Theakston's Old Peculier, Boddingtons. Garden, outdoor eating. Accommodation 10 bedrooms, all en suite, £69 (single £50). Children welcome overnight, additional beds (£12) and cots (£5) available. Accommodation closed 25 Dec. Access, Visa.*

Hawkshead   Queen's Head Hotel   **FOOD**

Tel 0153 94 36271 Fax 0153 94 36722	**B&B**
Hawkshead Cumbria LA22 0NS	**Map 4 C3**

The Queen's Head here is that of Elizabeth I; at the heart of this traffic-free village the black and white painted 16th-century frontage hides a cavernous pub within, full of period character and camaraderie. Food from the varied menus can be taken anywhere at lunch in the panelled bar areas and dining room, although at busy times it's certainly advisable to find a free table first! Main courses are typified by chicken biryani (£7.50), devilled lamb's kidneys (£6.75) and a vegetarian crespela Italiana (£6.50): on our latest visit, during Wimbledon fortnight, the "salmon and strawberries" special (£9.95) included a glass of bubbly. Residents and others wishing to eat in the dining room at night or for Sunday lunch (served all day) are advised to book in advance. Bedrooms within the pub have low beams, simple furnishings and compact en-suite bathrooms: two have old-fashioned four-posters and there are a couple of family rooms with bunk beds. The balance of the accommodation is in an adjacent cottage which is only yards away, and could conceivably be a good deal quieter. *Open 11-11 (Sun usual hours). Bar Food 12-2.30, 6.15-9.30 Restaurant Meals 12-2.30 (Sun only), 6.45-9.30. Beer Hartleys XB & Mild, Robinson's Bitter. Outdoor eating. Accommodation 14 bedrooms, 12 en suite, £59.50 (4-poster £70, single £45). Children welcome overnight (under-10s £12.50, 11-18 year olds £18.50). Access, Visa.*

Haworth   Old White Lion Hotel

Tel 01535 642313 Fax 01535 646222	**B&B**
Main Street Haworth West Yorkshire BD22 8DU	**Map 6 C1**

This Brontë village hotel goes back three hundred years. Formerly a coaching inn, part of the old building was a meeting room for masonics. An ongoing programme of refurbishment is now complete in the fourteen bedrooms, each having been individually decorated. They have en-suite bathrooms and are equipped with televisions, radio/alarms, telephones and tea/coffee-making facilities. Guests can relax in the oak-panelled residents' lounge. The restaurant was created from three weaver's cottages. *Early evening children's meals 6pm. Free House. Beer Webster's Yorkshire, John Smith's, Wilson's Original. Family room. Accommodation 14 bedrooms, all en suite, £46 (single £35). Children welcome overnight, additional beds and cots (£10) available. No dogs. Access, Diners, Visa.*

Hay-on-Wye   **Old Black Lion**

FOOD
B&B

Tel 01497 820841

26 Lion Street Hay-on-Wye Hereford & Worcester HR3 5AD   **Map 9 D5**

Owners John and Joan Collins have recently expanded the kitchen team to cater for the ever-growing popularity of this old coaching inn. On the bar menu starters range from ham and lentil soup (£2.50) to green lipped mussels (£3.75), whilst main courses on any given day may encompass venison bourguignonne (£9.95), medallions of prime veal (£11.85), or chicken in Calvados (£9.75). An entire menu section is devoted to steaks, sauced or plain, and another to vegetarian options. Bedrooms within the main building, of 17th-century origins, render the Black Lion justifiably famous. Refurbishment has generally enhanced the building's character and comforts of high degree include direct-dial phones, TVs, radios, beverage trays and bright duvets (traditional bedding provided on request). Rooms in the annexe are more modern, though no less comfortable; all rooms (with the exception of one single with a private bathroom) have entirely acceptable en-suite facilities. Families particularly enjoy the Cromwell Room with its gallery and two additional beds. The whole pub is candle-lit at night and there's no smoking in the restaurant. Not suitable for children under 5. *Bar Food & Restaurant Meals 12-2.30, 7-9.30 (In winter to 8.30, Sun 12-12.15, 7-9). Children allowed in the bar to eat. Free House. Beer Wye Valley, Flowers Original, Bass. Small patio. Accommodation 10 bedrooms, 9 en suite, £41.90 (single £18.95). Children welcome overnight (under-12s £10, over-12s £14), additional beds and cots available. Access, Visa.*

Haydon Bridge   **General Havelock Inn**

Tel 01434 684376

FOOD

Ratcliffe Road Haydon Bridge Northumberland NE47 6ER   **Map 5 D2**

The dark green exterior of the General Havelock certainly helps it stand out from neighbouring cottages. It was named after Sunderland-born General Henry Havelock, who relieved the Indian town of Lucknow in the late 1880s. The interior of the pub is also dark green. In the front bar area there are wrought-iron-legged tables, stripped wood and padded benches, and some brilliant wildlife photographs taken by a local photographer. The pub's main draw, though, is its dining room in the converted stables to the rear, a high-ceilinged room with exposed beams, natural stone walls, ready-set polished tables and watercolours of local scenes. The cooking is in the accomplished hands of self-taught chef Angela Clyde, who prides herself on using only fresh produce: meat comes from a local butcher in Hexham, and fish is delivered twice a week from North Shields. The short lunchtime menu includes soup like Stilton and onion or a terrine amongst the starters, followed by a daily roast and a fish dish (£5.95). In the evenings a set price four-course menu (£18.50) has a more upmarket feel with the likes of smoked North Shields cod or tarragon chicken. Cooking is of a high standard, and the puddings are also first-class: Danish chocolate bar and a splendid apricot tart (with very good pastry) are typical. Service is friendly and casual but efficient. To the rear of the dining room is a paved patio which runs down to a lawn and the River Tyne. Though the pub has its regulars who use the bar for a drink, this is really more of a dining pub, and people travel some distance to eat here. Weekends (including a popular Sunday lunch at £11.50) can be very busy, so booking is

advised. They close all day Monday and Tuesday. *Bar Food 12-2.30.*
Restaurant 7.30-9 (except Sun, Mon, Tues). Children allowed in bar to
eat. Free House. Beer Tetley. Riverside garden, outdoor eating. Closed all
Mon and all Tue, 1st 2 weeks Sept, 2 weeks Jan. No credit cards.

Haytor Vale	Rock Inn	**FOOD**
Tel 01364 661305 Fax 01364 661242		**B&B**
Haytor Vale nr Newton Abbot Devon TQ13 9XP		**Map 13 D3**

Dating back 200 years, this sturdy pub stands in a tiny Dartmoor
village below Haytor, the best known of the Dartmoor tors. A
characterful, traditional interior has sturdy old furnishings, plenty of
antique tables, settles, prints, a grandfather clock and various pieces of
china over the two fireplaces. Both the main bar and the attractive
adjoining rooms are popular settings in which to appreciate the
reliably good bar food, with a particularly strong list of light meals
and good hearty snacks, and the promise of fresh vegetables. After a
day on the moor healthy appetites can be satisfied with beef and
venison pie (£5.95), Dartmoor rabbit cooked in whole grain mustard
sauce (£5.25), and good steaks (from £8.95). Lighter snacks range
from salads (from £3.85) and sandwiches (from £2.35) to filled jacket
potatoes (from £3.45) and omelettes (£4.35). Fresh fish from
Brixham includes poached Devon salmon and monkfish with a
tomato and garlic sauce. To finish there may be tangy treacle and
lemon tart with clotted cream (£2.25) and lemon meringue pie
(£1.95), Sunday roast is £5.95 and there are six good West Country
cheeses on the board. The ten bedrooms are attractively decorated.
Four de luxe rooms and the refurbished Georgian four-poster room
are individually fitted out with quality fabrics, easy chairs and some
period pieces of furniture, with prices to match. All rooms are
spacious with clean en-suite facilities, and well appointed, with TVs,
tea-making kits, mineral water, fruit juices, radios and telephones.
Sheltered courtyard to the side and lawned area across the lane. *Open
11-11, 7 days a week. Bar Food 11-2.30, 6.30-9.30. Free House.*
Beer Eldridge Pope, Dartmoor Bitter, Hardy Ale, Royal Oak, Bass.
*Garden, Family room. Accommodation 10 bedrooms, 8 en suite, £65
(four-poster £81, single £39.95), children welcome overnight (under-5s
stay free in parents' room, 5-14s £8.55). Access, Visa.*

Heath	King's Arms	
Tel 01924 377527		**A**
Heath Common Heath nr Wakefield West Yorkshire WF1 5SL		**Map 6 C1**

Built in the early 1700s and converted to pub use in 1841, the King's
Arms has been operated by Clark's Brewery of nearby Wakefield
since 1989. It stands by the green in 100 acres of common grassland.
Genuinely unaltered and commendably unspoilt. Gas mantles still
burn in the three tiny flagstone bars which are lined with unique
carved oak panelling. Adjacent, the beamed 'Dining Chambers' serve à
la carte meals with an Italian bias, offering perhaps mixed salami
(£3.75) and bresaola napolitana (£9). Tuesday evening's 'Fish Special
Menu' is around £16. Don't expect miracles from the bar food;
rather, just soak in the unique atmosphere. Clark's Festival Ale is the
added bonus for beer drinkers. A conservatory has been added since
last year. *Beer Clark's Traditional Bitter & Festival Ale. Garden. Family*
room. Access, Visa.

Heathton The Old Gate

| Tel 01746 710431 | A |

Heathton Claverley Shropshire WV5 7EB Map 6 B4

A much-extended 17th-century inn down country lanes some five
miles from Bridgworth on the Staffordshire border. There's plenty to
amuse antiquarians in the parlour: hanging from the beams are
decorative Toby and water jugs, from the walls and lintels framed
watercolours, old prints and brass flat irons. The Old Stable snug
contains more suitable seating for families when the weather precludes
use of the garden's picnic tables and play area. Food quality rather
takes second place, and the mostly painted blackboards have an air of
permanence. Added daily specials might be a vegetable balti with nan
bread (£4.95) or chicken tikka (£4.95); for junior, the usual fish
fingers, burgers and nuggets at around £2.50. Outside, however, a
patio pit invites all to cook-your-own barbecues – a splendid idea for
large broods in the summer holidays. Eight miles from Junction 2 of
the M5 and near Halfpenny Green Airport. **Beer** *Holts, Tetley, Enville
ale, Stairway to Heaven, Timothy Taylor's Landlord, Wadworth 6X, guest
beers. Family room. Garden, children's play area. Access, Diners, Visa.*

Helford Shipwrights Arms

| Tel 01326 231235 | A |

Helford nr Helston Cornwall TR12 6JX Map 12 B4

Stunningly located on the banks of the Helford estuary, its approach
road is so narrow that in summer months it's restricted to pedestrian
use only. The picturesque walk through the village is well worth it
for this pretty thatched pub has a magical terraced garden, complete
with colourful flowers, palms and picnic benches on the water's edge.
The interior is quite special too, staunchly traditional, with rustic
simple furnishings, plenty of nautical bits and pieces and lots of
yachting types swapping unlikely stories. The pub and garden can get
extremely busy in the summer. **Beer** *Castle Eden, Flowers, IPA.
Garden. No credit cards.*

Helmsley Feathers

| Tel 01439 770275 Fax 01439 771101 | B&B |

Market Place Helmsley West Yorkshire YO6 5BN Map 5 E4

"Elmslac", a Saxon village on the river Rye settled in 600 AD was
listed in Domesday, and as Helmsley, renowned for its Norman castle,
had a well-documented history throughout the Middle Ages. Feathers
was once a merchant's house with the highest rent in town, later it
was split into two cottages and now, re-unified by the friendly Feather
family, offers some of the best-value accommodation in town. There
are, of course, two entrances, two bars – with a unifying theme of the
local "Mouse Man" furniture – two dining rooms and two stair-wells.
Two floors of bedrooms provide accommodation that is more
practical than luxurious; TVs and tea trays are provided, alarm clocks
and hairdryers available on request. Family rooms with en-suite
bathrooms offer good value, with under-12s accommodated free
(meals charged as taken). Several smaller rooms have en-suite
WC/shower rooms only, and the three remaining unconverted singles
share so-called public, but nonetheless, adequate, ablutions. *Open 11-11
(Sun 12-10.30) in high summer, usual hours other periods. Free House.*
Beer *John Smith's, Theakston Best, XB & Old Peculier, Morland Old
Speckled Hen, Worthington Best, two guest beers. Garden, family room.*

See over

Accommodation 17 bedrooms, 13 en suite, £53 (£36.50 single). Children welcome overnight (under-12s stay free in parents' room), additional cots available. Accommodation closed Christmas week and 27 Jan – 10 Feb. Access, Diners, Visa.

Henley-on-Thames   Argyll

Tel 01491 573400	**FOOD**
15 Market Place Henley-on-Thames Oxfordshire RG9 2AA	Map 15a D3

Behind its mock-Tudor facade the Argyll lives up to the Scottishness of its name with tartan carpet and prints of Scottish soldiers around the panelled walls along with the odd sporran, stag's head and battered breast plate. More a drinking than an eating pub – there's no food in the evening – but buffet lunches are popular. As well as sandwiches there's a small selection of traditional pub dishes that is likely to include steak pie, seafood lasagne and cottage pie plus a few salads (beef, gammon or quiche) and home-made fruit pies for puddings. Traditional Sunday roast lunch. *Bar Food* 12-2. *Beer* Morland. Patio, outdoor eating. Access, Visa.

Henton   Peacock Hotel

Tel 01844 353519 Fax 01844 353891	**B&B**
Henton nr Chinnor Oxfordshire OX9 4AH	Map 15a D2

This very pretty 600-year-old thatched, black and white timbered inn is in a sleepy village just off the B4009. The bar is comfortable and immaculately kept. 17 bedrooms are in the extension, which also houses the residents' lounge. There are now 20 in total and all are smart and well equipped. *Free House. Beer* Brakspear. Patio, outdoor eating. *Accommodation* 20 bedrooms, all en suite, from £62 (single £45). Children welcome overnight (rate depends on age), additional beds available. Dogs only welcome by arrangement. Access, Visa.

Zzzz...

Hermitage   Sussex Brewery

Tel 01243 371533 Fax 01243 379684	**A**
36 Main Road Hermitage nr Emsworth West Sussex PO10 8AU	Map 15 D4

A fresh carpet of sawdust is laid daily at this Grade II listed pub-brewery, and open fires are continually alight from October to Easter. No food recommendation here, but the remarkable selection of 36 different types of sausage on the bar menu deserves a mention. There's no jukebox or fruit machine, not even a cigarette machine. *Open 11-11 Mon-Sat, regular hours Sun. Free House. Beer* Badger, Wadworth 6X, Tanglefoot, Belhaven, Hard Tackle, Bombardier, guest beers. Garden, children's play area. Family room.

Hesket Newmarket   The Old Crown

Tel 016974 78288	**A**
Hesket Newmarket nr Caldbeck Cumbria CA7 8JG	Map 4 C3

A minor success story of the Dales, co-partner Jim Fearnley is now its Master Brewer in the converted Old Barn. Opened by Chris Bonnington by telex from Katmandu in 1988, the brewhouse now produces five uniquely named beers, for example the award-winning 'Doris' 90th Birthday Ale'. Dorothy's daughter, Liz Blackwood, runs front-of-house with a rod of general consensus; some Cumberland sausage sandwiches, famously spicy curries and vegetarian options somehow turning up in time to prevent a riot. Brewery tours take place on Wednesday evenings, followed by supper either in the tiny dining room or in a wayward garden, which doubles as headquarters of the village bottle bank. *Beer Own brewery: Skiddaw Special, Doris' 90th, Blancathra Bitter, Old Carrock Strong Ale, Great Cockup Porter, Catbells. Beer garden. Two bedrooms in adjoining cottage (from £15). Pub closed lunchtime Mon-Fri in winter. No credit cards.*

Hetton   Angel Inn   ★

Tel 01756 730263   Fax 01756 730363   **FOOD**

Hetton nr Skipton North Yorkshire BD23 6LT   **Map 6 C1**

Deservedly popular for bar food that is capable of scaling the heights of excellence, the Angel promotes a brasserie image by its smart attendants in ankle-length aprons. A dozen or more wines deserving of appreciation by the glass and tall bottles of chili dressing at every table help temper the traditionally pubby feel. Yet the country pub does remain in its central bar and progressive dining rooms – from no-smoking snug to smart restaurant; the food has a modern British accent with many Mediterranean overtones. Rustic fish soup with aïoli (£2.85) and terrine of chicken liver and foie gras (£3.95) share a lunch menu with chargrilled sirloin with Caesar salad (£9.75), salmon 'en croute' with lobster sauce (£7.75) and confit of duck (£7.95); dishes score highly for flavour, presentation and value. Sticky toffee pudding, crème brulée with strawberries (both £2.95) and warm apple strudel (£3.25) are the products of a reliable pastry department. Printed placemats in the bar areas invite customers to sample their table d'hote dinners (£21.95), but little further inducement appears to be needed as restaurant reservations at night remain a virtual necessity. Good selection of malt whiskies at the bar. Customers are requested to respect residents' considerations when parking. Winner of our 1995 Pub of the Year award for its outstanding pub food. *Bar Food 12-2 (Sat & Sun 12-2.30) 6-10. Restaurant Meals 12-2 (Sun only), 6-9.30 (except Sun). Free house. Beer Marston's Pedigree, Black Sheep, Boddingtons. Patio, outdoor eating. Bar closed two weeks in Jan. Access, Visa.*

Hexham   Dipton Mill Inn

Tel 01434 606577   **FOOD**

Dipton Mill Road Hexham Northumberland NE46 1YA   **Map 5 D2**

Less than a 10-minute drive out of town (follow Whitley Chapel signs off the B6531 past Hexham Racecourse), the Mill nestles by the stone roadbridge in a deep hollow. Conversion by Geoff and Janet Brookes of the tiny interior, knocking two minute parlour rooms into one has achieved a single bar of warmth and intimacy whose bonus is a brace of welcoming, open fires. If everything within is on a small scale, the daily lunch menus are no less accidental in concept. Home cooking of manageable proportions is limited on the blackboard to soup (minestrone £1.30), steak and kidney or beef and Guinness pies with generous portions of fresh vegetables (£3.50) commendable nursery puddings (bread and butter or apple and almond pie with cream or custard £1.25 on our last visit) and locally produced ice creams (£1). In addition to sandwiches – the only food now available at night – mature cheddar, Stilton and Wensleydale are available for ploughmen (£2.75), while vegetarians can tuck into a cheese and broccoli flan (£3.25). The most popular among real ales is the local Hexhamshire range from a local micro-brewery. Sheer size (and the law) restricts children from the bar: there's a tiny rear playroom when it's cold or wet, the fine weather benefit being a spacious walled garden complete with its own wooden bridge over the old mill stream – a splendid spot. *Two dozen malt whiskies available. Free House. Open 12-12.30, 6-11 (12-3, 7-10.30 Sun).* **Beer** *Hexhamshire Bitter, Devil's Water & Whapweasel, Hadrian Gladiator, Theakston Best Bitter, guest beers.* **Bar Food** *12-2.15 every lunch, sandwiches only at dinner. Garden. No credit cards.*

High Roding — Black Lion

Tel 01371 872847	**A**
High Roding nr Great Dunmow Essex CM6 1NT	Map 11 B4

Attractive black-and-white timbered Tudor roadside pub in a charming Essex village, full of character buildings. Landlord Osvaldo Ricci has made it his home for the past 22 years and the spick-and-span, intimate bar is full of old beams, standing timbers, a rustic collection of wooden furniture and a brick-built bar counter. Cosy atmosphere enhanced by piped light opera and classical music, and fresh flowers on each table. Small, separate dining room. **Beer** *Ridleys. Garden. Family Room. Access, Visa.*

Highclere — Yew Tree

	FOOD
	B&B
Tel 01635 253360 Fax 01635 254977	
Andover Road Hollington Cross Highclere Berkshire RG15 9SE	Map 14a C4

Just south of the village, on the A343. Jenny Wratten has managed the trick of improving the Yew Tree without detracting from its old-world character. Huge logs smoulder in the inglenook fireplace while old scrubbed pine tables and the odd sofa sit beneath ancient beams. Several interconnecting rooms comprise the more formal restaurant but the same menu is served throughout. Seasonally changing choices (plus dishes of the day) combine simple dishes like grilled South Coast plaice and steaks with more traditional and Old English items – homity cakes (potato cheese and onion coated in breadcrumbs - £7.30), tweed kettle tart (salmon in a pastry case with leek chive and parsley sauce – £8.95), hot crab ramekins, breast of duck, roasted pink, with white honey and orange sauce. Finish with rhubarb and champagne jelly and unpasteurised cheeses. To accompany there are at least nine wines available by the glass. Six cottagey bedrooms offer overnight accommodation with direct-dial telephones, remote-control TVs, beverage trays and little extras like books and magazines. All have en-suite bathrooms – half with shower and WC only. **Bar Food** *12-2.30, 6.30-10 (Sun 7-9.30). Free House.* **Beer** *Brakspear, Wadworth 6X, Flowers Original. Garden, outdoor eating.* **Accommodation** *6 bedrooms, all en suite, £55 (single £40). Children welcome overnight (under 5s stay free in parents' room), additional beds available. Dogs by arrangement. Access, Visa.*

Higher Burwardsley — Pheasant Inn ★

	FOOD
	B&B
Tel 01829 70434	
Higher Burwardsley nr Tattenhall Cheshire CH3 9PF	Map 6 A3

The Pheasant is best located by following signs to the candle factory from the A534. It is tucked into the hillside amongst the Peckforton hills, and on arrival, it's plain to see that the place was once a farm, and the more surprising, therefore, to find that there has been a pub here since the 17th century. The oldest part, a half-timbered sandstone farmhouse, is the venue for the bar, which claims to house the largest log fire in Cheshire. The adjacent Highland Room generally known as the Bistro, was once the kitchen and retains the old cast-iron range.

Zzzz...

The most recent addition is an imposing conservatory of striking modernity, which looks over a tiered patio and, beyond this, right across the Cheshire plain towards North Wales. The old barn has been skilfully converted into six very comfortable bedrooms, equipped to the highest pub standards, with televisions, clock radios, hairdryers, mini-bars and roomy, if poorly lit, bathrooms. Stonework interiors are eye-catching, and nights tranquil. Two further bedrooms, housed in the pub proper, boast original beams and brighter bathrooms, as well as memorable views. There are three quite distinct aspects to the food operation. At weekends, a self-service counter in the conservatory is useful for a quick lunch, perhaps of chicken provençale, mushroom stroganoff or a Sunday plate of roast beef and Yorkshire (all at about £5), with a special children's menu (£1.95 main course and pudding), and extended hours at weekends. In the bar, blackboards display a daily-changing list for those requiring a little more adventure: terrine of local venison with red cabbage (£2.95), fennel and watercress soup (£1.80), green-lipped mussels sautéed with fresh ginger and garlic (£3.25), Orkney salmon filled with baby leek and cheese (£6.50), local calf's liver with Dubonnet (£8.50) or Highland sirloin with Dijon cream (£9.50) typify the offerings here. The Bistro, meanwhile, comes into its own at night (and for Sunday lunch in winter). A further elaboration of the other menus, it offers more substantial fare (with more vegetables and fewer chips) in an informal and intimate setting. Space is limited; booking is advised. Landlord David Greenhaugh has an unusual and passionate interest, namely his prize-winning herd of pedigree Highland cattle. It's not surprising therefore to find a certain bias towards meat dishes, amongst which the steaks are outstanding (sirloin £9.95, fillet £11.20), especially when one of "the family" is on offer! The winter menu offers dishes of equal merit, including pheasant casserole (£5.50) or roast haunch of venison (£8.95). Among the home-made 'to follows' (all £2), the bread-and-butter pudding and banoffi pie come out tops, so, too, do a friendly bunch of staff who go out of their way to be pleasant and helpful. 40 malt whiskies at the bar. *Bar Food & Restaurant Meals* 12-2, 7-9.30 (*Sat to 10*). *Children's menu. Free House. Beer Bass. Garden, outdoor eating. Family room. Accommodation 8 bedrooms, all en suite, £70. Children welcome overnight (0-10 yrs free, over 10 yrs £10), additional bed & cot available. Dogs by arrangement. Access, Diners, Visa.*

Himley   Crooked House

Tel 01384 238583   **A**

Coppice Mill Himley nr Dudley West Midlands DY3 4DA   **Map 6 B4**

This is not a particularly attractive setting; turning off B4176 between Womborne and Dudley, the long lane runs down through woods past urban forest, landfill and quarry. Yet the sight at the lane's end is simply extraordinary. Once the Glynne Arms, the 250-year-old building was a victim of subsidence in Victorian times and teeters alarmingly from right to left. One bar door opens out at an oblique angle and instills an uneasy feeling of collapsing through it – and this is on the way in! Meanwhile, in the upper bar, (for a charitable donation) customers can watch a ball-bearing apparently roll upwards along the dado. Despite some recent levelling of the floor, many's the customer who appears all at sea with his legs. A more recent extension houses a family-friendly conservatory overlooking a small adventure playground, while through side windows into the cellar, Banks and Marston's ales are on view being electrically pumped back up to the crooked old bar. No children under 14 in the bars. *Pub open 11-11 Mon-Sat Apr-end Sept, 11.30-2.30, 6.30-11 Oct-end Mar, Sun 12-3, 7-10.30 all year round.* **Beer** *Banks's Mild & Bitter, Marston's Pedigree. Patio, children's play area. No credit cards.*

Hindon	**Lamb at Hindon**	**FOOD**
Tel 01747 820573	Fax 01747 820605	**B&B**
Hindon Salisbury Wiltshire SP3 6DP		**Map 14 B3**

Wistaria clings to one corner of this mellow 17th-century coaching inn. At its height, 300 post horses were kept here to supply the great number of coaches going to and from London and the West Country. Prime Minister William Pitt was apparently most put out to find no fresh horses available when he stopped off in 1786. But there have also been less reputable visitors: Silas White, a notorious smuggler said to be leader of the Wiltshire Moonrakers, used the Lamb as the centre of his nefarious activities. These days, things in Hindon are rather more peaceful and the Lamb limits itself to providing honest hospitality to modern travellers who bring their own horsepower in four-wheeled form. Inside, the long bar is divided into several areas and is furnished with some sturdy period tables, chairs and settles. A splendid old stone fireplace with log fire creates a warm, homely atmosphere, which is also enhanced by an ever-changing collection of paintings by local artists both here and in the smarter restaurant. The blackboard bar menu is sensibly not over-long, but still manages to offer a reasonable choice – smoked trout salad (£5.25) pork chop and mustard sauce (£5.25), cream of broccoli and potato soup (£1.95) and for pudding chocolate drambuie pie and fresh pineapple crumble (both £2.95). The emphasis is fishy on Tuesdays and Fridays, when the fishmonger calls, and in winter there's also plenty of game, from the estate of the local landowner who bought the inn a few years ago. In the non-smoking restaurant, an evening 3-course table d'hote menu (£18.95) is available with such choices as roasted duck breast with an orange marmalade sauce, pan-fried fillet of beef with oyster mushroom sauce or poached chicken breast with Stilton sauce, with similar fare on the à la carte menu at lunchtime. Upstairs, there are thirteen en-suite bedrooms, which are furnished and decorated to varying styles and standards. *Open 11-11 Mon-Sat, Sun usual hours.* **Bar Food** *12-2, 7-10.* **Restaurant Meals** *12-2, 7-9.30. Children allowed in bar to eat.* **Beer** *Wadworth 6X, Boddingtons, Oakhill, Ringwood. Garden, outdoor eating.* **Accommodation** *13 bedrooms, all en suite, £55 (four-poster £65, single £38). Children welcome overnight, (under-3s stay free in parents' room), additional beds (£10) and cots (£10) available. Access, Visa.*

Hinton St George	**Poulett Arms**	**FOOD**
Tel 01460 73149		
Hinton St George nr Crewkerne Somerset TA17 8SE		**Map 13 F2**

Homely hamstone local tucked away in the centre of an up-market and picturesque village. Original stripped stone walls and fireplace, heavy timbers and a small simply furnished anteroom characterise the dining areas, while drinkers can hold court in the rear public bar which boasts comfortable sofas and easy chairs. A fairly routine printed menu is enhanced by a few good value daily-changing specials, such as a decent home-made, creamy vegetable soup served with a warm roll (£2.20), chicken Cotswold, pigeon breast casseroled in red wine and sherry (both £6.95) and darne of salmon with hollandaise (£7.95). Generous portions of crunchy 'al dente' vegetables. Puddings

(£2.50) are made by a local lady and may include seven-fruit summer
pudding, lemon and lime mousse and sticky toffee pudding. Small
cottage garden with tressle tables. Not to be confused with the other
Poulett Arms two miles away on the A30 (previously the A303).
Bar Food *12-2, 7-9.30. Free House.* **Beer** *Wadworth 6X, Butcombe,
Boddingtons, guest beer. Garden, outdoor eating. Family room. Pub closed
25 & 26 Dec. Access, Visa.*

Holkham   Victoria Hotel

Tel 01328 710469	B&B

Park Road Holkham Norfolk   Map 10 C1

An imposing large brick building situated at one of the entrances (on
A149) to Holkham Hall, one of Britain's most majestic stately homes,
the estate owned Victoria makes a good base from which to explore
local walks, nature reserves and coastal villages. Built in the early
1800's to house the entourage to visiting aristocracy, it still offers
overnight accommodation in five comfortable, yet simply furnished
en-suite bedrooms. All are light and spacious with pretty fabrics, TVs,
beverage-making facilities and most have delightful rural outlooks.
The homely ambience is maintained downstairs in the large
lounge/dining area which is warmly decorated in green and furnished
in modern pine, with relaxing settees and easy chairs fronting a good
winter log fire. Pleasing views across the well tended garden and lush
coastal pastures. The traditional spartan tap-room is popular with
walkers. Holkham beach is only a short stroll away. No children
under 8 overnight. *Free House. Open 11-3, 7-11 (12-3, 7-11 Sun).*
Accommodation *5 bedrooms, all en suite, £50 (Single £27.50). Dogs
welcome by arrangement. Garden, outside eating. Children welcome
overnight.* **Beer** *Adnams Mild, Greene King IPA, Adnams Southwold,
Marston's Pedigree, guest ale. No credit cards.*

Holne   Church House Inn

Tel 013643 208	FOOD
	B&B

Holne nr Ashburton Devon TQ13 7SJ   Map 13 D3

Situated in an attractive Dartmoor village on the southern flanks of
the moor, this welcoming inn was built in 1329 as either a dwelling
house for the workers on the church, or as a resting place for visiting
clergy and worshippers in the church. It is still a popular meeting
place for locals, Dartmoor ramblers and car tourers alike. The appeal
inside the pleasantly rustic bars, furnished with a huge carved settle
and an assortment of simple tables and chairs, is the wholesome
country cooking that will satisfy the heartiest of moorland appetites.
With not a chip in sight, the freshest of local produce is used in
making such favourites as chicken and thyme pie, Devon lamb in
cider (both £5.25), steak, kidney and ale pie (£4.95), leek and
potato pie with locally-baked bread (£3.95) and lighter bites like
ploughman's (from £3.50), omelettes (from £3.75) and a good bowl
of soup (£1.75). A daily-changing board lists the pasta of the day
(from £3.95), a fish dish – grilled whole sole (£5.95) and a freshly-
made pudding such as treacle tart (£1.95). Local Devon ales feature
well behind the bar as does Gray's farm cider and a decent list of
world-wide wines (with a minimum of seven available by the glass)
supplied by George Piper wine merchants. A non-smoking restaurant's
table d'hote menu changes daily and is available to non-residents
(£12.50); 3-course Sunday lunch is £7.50. Most of the six upstairs
bedrooms have superb rural views. All are neat and comfortable and

Zzzz...

simply furnished, with four rooms having small clean bathrooms with showers. Added comforts of TV and tea-making kits are standard and residents have the use of a cosy, antique-filled lounge. **Bar Food** *12-2.15 & 7-9.15 (Sun from 7.15).* **Restaurant Meals** *12.15-2.15 (Mon-Sat bookings only), 7-8.30 (Sun bookings only). Family room, High Tea 5pm. Free House.* **Beer** *Dartmoor Best Bitter, Dartmoor Strong, Blackawton Bitter, Palmers IPA, guest beer.* **Accommodation** *6 bedrooms, 4 en suite, £50 (single £27.50). Children welcome overnight (under-2s stay free in parents' room, 3-5s £5, 5+ £10), additional beds available. Check-in from 2pm or by arrangement. Access, Visa.*

Holt — Old Ham Tree

FOOD
B&B

Tel 01225 785581

Holt nr Trowbridge Wiltshire BA14 6PY

Map 14 B3

Cleanly modernised, beamed and pleasant 18th-century inn near the village green. Reliably good, simple food in the form of steak and Guinness pie (£5.25), fresh bream Provençal-style (£6.95), chicken casserole (£4.95) or halibut steak with prawn sauce (£6.95). Bedrooms are centrally heated, clean and airy, white-painted with matching furniture, pretty floral fabrics, and a modern, shared bathroom. Residents' television lounge above the bar. **Bar Food** *11.30-2.30, 6.30-10. Children allowed in the bar to eat, children's menu. Free House.* **Beer** *Bass, Wadworth 6X, Marston's Pedigree, guest beer. Garden, outdoor eating.* **Accommodation** *5 bedrooms, 1 en-suite (family room), £42 (single £22.50). Children welcome overnight, additional beds available. Dogs welcome by arrangement. Access, Diners, Visa.*

Any person using our name to obtain free hospitality is a fraud.
Proprietors, please inform the police and us.

Holywell — Old Ferry Boat

B&B

Tel 01480 63227

Holywell St Ives Cambridgeshire PE17 3TG

Map 10 B2

A thousand years of history are behind this delightful thatched and wisteria-draped riverside inn, originally a monastic ferry house. Situated by the River Great Ouse where there is ample mooring, the Old Ferry boat has a particularly charming panelled alcove off the main bar, and good views from the sun terrace. It is haunted by Juliet, a young victim of unrequited love, so don't go on March 17th unless you want to join the ghost hunters! The seven neatly refurbished bedrooms are individually decorated with quality wallpapers and fabrics, but vary in size – minute to small – and standard of facilities. Two boast space for old pine four-posters and good-sized bathrooms, others are compact (to say the least) with beds against the wall and tiny shower rooms. Despite these drawbacks, two have delightful views over the river and a serene rural scene. Poor breakfasts. *Free House. Open 11-3, 6-11 (Sun 12-3, 7-10.30).* **Accommodation** *7 bedrooms, all en suite £49.50-£68 (single £39.50). Check-in by arrangement.* **Beer** *Courage Directors, Charrington IPA, Nethergate Old Growler, Webster's Yorkshire, Adnams Broadside, Fuller's London Pride. Garden, outdoor eating. Waterside location. Access, Visa.*

Holywell Green   Rock Inn Hotel

Tel 01422 379721   Fax 01422 379110   **B&B**

Holywell Green nr Halifax West Yorkshire HX4 9BS   Map 6 C1

Conveniently near Junction 24 of the M62 and yet enjoying a peaceful
rural setting, this pub (converted from a row of 17th-century cottages)
has a warmly welcoming air. Open fires, beams and original
stonework walls characterise the bars, while pine-ceilinged bedrooms
in a rear extension are contrastingly modern. All have mahogany
furniture and brightly tiled bathrooms, as well as TVs (free satellite
TV), radios, direct-dial telephones, tea/coffee-making facilities,
hairdryers, drinks trays and trouser presses. *Open 11.30-12 (Sat to 1am,
Sun 12-10.30). Free House. **Beer** Tetley, Theakston, Scottish & Newcastle
No. 3, Black Sheep, guest beer. Patio/terrace. Family room.*
***Accommodation** 18 bedrooms (3 with four-posters), all en suite, £69,
(single £59). Children welcome overnight (under-3s stay free in parents'
room), additional beds, cots supplied. Access, Diners, Visa.*

Hope   Poacher's Arms

Tel 01433 620380   **B&B**

Castelton Road Hope Derybshire S30 2RD   Map 6 C2

Gladys Bushells' much-extended roadside pub (on the A625) is as
popular as ever with walkers, cyclists and visitors to the Peak's
National Park. With eating and seating areas which include a family
room, rear conservatory and two dining rooms there's just one central
bar servery to cope with the crush. Amid the modern beamed decor
there's a limited degree of elegance and comfort; there are wider seats,
button-backed banquettes and copper-topped bar tables, some of which
are rather too small for comfortable eating. Bedrooms are rather more
generously sized, sporting a mixture of floral papers, curtains and
bedspreads. Freestanding pine or mahogany furniture, remote control
TV, clock radio, phone, hairdryer and hot drinks tray all combine to
fulfil the basic requirements of a comfortable and restful stay.
Patterned carpeting runs through to the en-suite bathrooms whose
fittings and decor are just a little basic. ***Beer** Courage Directors, John
Smith's. **Accommodation** 6 bedrooms, all en suite, from £52. Children
welcome overnight (under-4s stay free in parents' room), additional beds &
cots supplied. Access, Visa.*

Hopesgate   Stables Inn

Tel 01743 891344   **FOOD**

Hopesgate nr Minsterley Shropshire SY5 0EP   Map 8 D3

Debbie and Denis Hardings' tiny, secluded inn, set in glorious
countryside above the Hope valley, is signposted down country lanes
from the A488. It's a distinctly traditional pub, whose attraction, in
addition to the good food and beer, is an atmosphere in which good
company can be enjoyed, in the absence of intruding gaming machines
or juke boxes. The bar is L-shaped, its blackened oak beams hung with
pottery mugs, and the imposing open stone fireplace burns logs in
winter. The mood is intimate and friendly; summer talk may be of
cricket and the exploits of the pub's new team. Lunchtime choices,
posted on the blackboard, range from celery and Stilton soup (£2)
and hot local sausages (£3.80) to cheesy tomato and aubergine bake
(£5) and creamy smoked haddock pancake (£5.20). Evening eating
(Wed to Sat only) is a mite more serious. Booking is strongly advised
as there are only four tables in the dining room (so diners usually

overflow into the adjacent snug). Debbie's cooking makes the best use of local supplies and seasonal produce – mixed game pie (£7.85) or marinated Scotch salmon fillets with cream and chives (£8.50). They're substantial eaters in these parts, so there's no shortage of takers for puddings (all £2.50): treacle sponge with custard, the landlady's now celebrated bread-and-butter pudding, or seasonal fruit crumble served with local farm ice cream. **Bar Food** *12-1.30 (except Mon).* **Restaurant Meals** *7-8.30 (except Sun to Tue). Children allowed in bar to eat. Free House.* **Beer** *Wood's Special, Double Dragon, guest beers. Patio/terrace. No credit cards.*

Hopton Wafers   Crown Inn   **FOOD**

| Tel 01299 270372   Fax 01299 271127 | **B&B** |

Hopton Wafers nr Cleobury Mortimer Shropshire DY14 0NB   **Map 6 B4**

Zzzz...

The creeper-clad Crown in the Norman hamlet of Hopton Wafers is set in its own garden which slopes down to one of the many streams (crossed here by the A4117) that flow down to the Teme valley. Bounded on three sides by terraces of tables with their colourful summer parasols, it's a splendid spot for alfresco eating. Inside, the Rent Room, where once local villagers came to pay their rents, houses an atmospheric and intimate bar where talk is frequently of the shootin' and fishin' sort over a pint. Snacks and bar meals have a strongly fishy emphasis: seafood pancake (£3.95), mackerel paté (£3.95), poached salmon with oyster sauce (£7.50) and shark steak (£7.25). But meat-eaters are not forgotten, with hearty beef in stout pie (£6.25) or escalope of venison (£6.75). Nor are vegetarians neglected: decent meatless meals include celery and cashew risotto (£3.50), tagliatelle in Stilton cream sauce (£3.95). Puddings, home-made daily (£2.55) include treacle tart, bakewell tart or a banana and rum trifle. Behind a central stone chimney, in which huge log fires burn at both sides in winter, the Hopton Poacher restaurant serves a three-course dinner (£22.50, from Tuesday to Saturday) and Sunday lunch, for which you should book. Market-fresh fish, breast of duck with caramelised orange and Grand Marnier, pan-seared entrecote with peppercorn crust and rabbit casserole are typical main courses. The decor and character of the bedrooms are commendable. Unsuspecting overnighters are in for a treat of exposed rafters, sloping corridors and creaky floorboards – with which the automatic trouser press and bathroom telephone extensions seem faintly at odds; all, nonetheless, are assured a high degree of comfort, a warm welcome and the convivial company of a fine country inn. Children are offered their own menu or portions of anything. Three bedrooms are family rooms, there's one high-chair and the garden is large with trees, stream and pond. **Bar Food** *12-2.30, 6.30-9.30 (Sat to 10).* **Restaurant Meals** *12-12.30 (Sun only), 7-9.30 (except Sun and Mon). Children allowed in bar to eat/children's menu. Free House.* **Beer** *Flowers Original, Boddingtons, Marston's Pedigree. Riverside garden, outdoor eating.* **Accommodation** *8 bedrooms, all en suite, £60 (single £37.50). Children welcome overnight, additional beds (£10) and cots (£5) available. No dogs. Access, Visa.*

Horam   Gun Inn

Tel 01825 872361

FOOD

Gun Hill Horam Heathfield East Sussex TN21 0JU

Map 11 B6

Extended 16th-century tiled and timbered pub enjoying a peaceful
rural location just off the A22 northwest of Hailsham. Neat open-plan
interior with a series of comfortably furnished alcove seating areas,
several open fires, an old kitchen Aga, fresh flowers and various prints,
copper and brass artefacts. Head for the blackboard menu for the
daily-changing selection of home-cooked dishes, which supplements a
standard printed menu of pub favourites. Good reliable choices may
include decent pies – Sussex fidget, chicken, ham and leek and lamb,
apricot and rosemary (all £5.40) – fresh salmon and asparagus
pancakes (£6.30), lasagne of smoked haddock, mussels and spinach
(£5.60) and Sussex smokie in white wine and mustard sauce (£5.40).
Keen to cater for all tastes there is the choice of fresh vegetables, chips,
jacket potatoes or a selection of fresh, imaginative salads from the
regularly replenished salad bar. For a home-made pudding try the
treacle tart, apple crumble or summer pudding. Cream teas are
available each afternoon between April and October. Overnight
accommodation comprises three homely, simply furnished bedrooms
with TVs, tea-makers and rural views. One has en-suite facilities, the
others share a clean bathroom and two toilets. Continental breakfasts
are served in the room. Good summer lawn. *Pub open 11-2.30 Sun to
3, 6-11 Sun to 10.30. April-Oct 11-11. **Bar Food** 6-10, 7-10 Sun. April-
Oct all day. Children allowed in to the bar to eat before 9pm, children's
menu. Free House. **Beer** Boddingtons Bitter, Larkins Sovereign. Garden,
lawn, tables in garden. No credit cards.*

Horndon   Elephant's Nest

Tel 01822 810273

FOOD

Horndon Mary Tavy nr Tavistock Horndon Devon PL19 9NQ

Map 12 C3

Isolated 16th-century inn located on the flanks of Dartmoor and
reached via narrow, high-hedged lanes from the A386 Tavistock to
Okehampton road at Mary Tavy (signposted). Named after a portly
landlord with a bushy beard it is a character pub for wild winter
weather with its window seats, rustic furnishings, old rugs, flagstones,
heavy beams and open fires. The large garden has open views across
the moor and picnic tables for summer days. It is a busy dining pub
with an extensive blackboard menu listing popular pub favourites as
well as a range of home-cooked daily dishes – huntsman casserole,
liver and orange casserole, Tavy trout, steak and kidney pie, peanut
and lentil roulade (all about £5) – served with a choice of chips and
salad or vegetables (£1 extra). 'Pete's Puds' include treacle and walnut
tart and steamed apple and date sponge. ***Bar Food** 12-2, 7-10 (Sun to
9.30). Free House. **Beer** St Austell's HSD, Palmers IPA, Boddingtons,
guest beers. Garden, outdoor eating. No credit cards.*

Horndon-on-the-Hill   Bell Inn & Hill House   ★

Tel 01375 673154   Fax 01375 361611

FOOD

B&B

High Road Horndon-on-the-Hill Essex SS17 8LD

Map 11 B4

Located in the village centre a few doors from one another, John and
Christine Vereker's 500-year-old Bell Inn offers a blackboard menu
and a friendly rustic, pubby ambience including beams, unpolished
wood tables and flagstone floors; Hill House next door has more
formal dining in a pretty pastel-coloured room. A hot cross bun is

nailed to a ceiling beam at the Bell every Good Friday, and the collection of shrunken, fossilised old buns is now pretty spectacular. The Bell menu features both simple and more unusual dishes: perhaps mussel soup (£2.50), chicken livers with black pudding (£2.95) or red mullet with orange salad (£3.25) for starters, followed by chargrilled sirloin steak with tarragon béarnaise (£10.95), beef stew with pimentos (£4.25), lamb steak with tarragon (£6.35), braised lamb's liver casserole (£4.50) or poached salmon (£10.20). At Hill House the fixed-price menu does away with the simpler, more pubby items. 26-year-old chef Sean Kelly's cooking is imaginative, skilfully executed and produces very enjoyable results on the plate; a dish of seafood sausage with cream and leek sauce, and his personal favourite, lamb cutlets stuffed with haggis and baked in pastry. Chocolate pudding with vanilla custard, baby pineapple with lemon sorbet and lemon soufflé with almond biscuits among the bar menu desserts, plus British farmhouse cheeses. Diverse wine list and eight good wines served by the glass. Above and also to the rear of Hill House are ten pretty, cottagey en-suite bedrooms, each thoughtfully equipped and neatly maintained. A sporty, friendly community pub, free from music, gaming machines and pool tables. Booking essential in restaurant. Large courtyard with seating in summer. *Bar Food 12.15-2, 6.15-10. Restaurant Meals 12.15-2, 7.15-10 (no food Sat lunch, Sun 12.15-2.30, 7.30-10). Free House. Beer Bass Charrington & IPA, guest beers. Accommodation 11 rooms, all en suite, £55. Accommodation closed 24-30 Dec. Access, Diners, Visa.*

Horningsea   Plough & Fleece

Tel 01223 860795

FOOD

High Street Horningsea Cambridgeshire CB5 9JG

Map 10 B3

A Grade II listed building, built in the Dutch style so popular in the East Anglia of the late 18th century when Dutch engineers came to advise on the draining of the Fenlands. The generally very busy Plough & Fleece owes its great popularity to old-fashioned regional cooking, which is often given a modern interpretation. Come here for homely, comforting hot-pots (£4.85), cottage pie (£3.60) and cockles (with garlic £2.90), as well as more contemporary treatments of dinner-partyish food, like honey-roast guinea fowl (£7.75), or a perfect poached salmon (£9.75). Puddings (all £2.30) are suitably gorgeous and cream-laden; the Northamptonshire chocolate pudding in particular has an informal international fan club but there are at least seven others to choose from. All this means the pub can get crowded but the dining-room extension provides a welcome haven for non-smokers. In addition to the traditional roast on Sunday (£5.95 main course), the Romany rabbit (£7.25) proves equally as popular. The atmosphere is homely and traditional in feel, especially so in the unspoilt public bar, with its ancient settles, tiled floor, elm tables and custard-coloured walls. The lounge is comfortable rather than characterful and invariably packed with bar meal diners. Arrive early at lunchtime to beat the scrum. Children (minimum age 5) allowed in dining room only. *Bar Food and Restaurant Meals 12-2 (12-1.30 Sun), 7-9.30 (except Sun/Mon eves). Beer Greene King IPA & Abbot. Garden, outdoor eating. Access, Visa.*

Horringer   Beehive

Tel 01284 735260

The Street Horringer Suffolk IP29 5SD

FOOD

Map 10 C3

Genuine home-made food is served throughout the bar areas here, and
tables can be booked: the ratio of reservations to casual droppers-in is
usually about 50/50. A printed menu is much more imaginative than
most, and a specials board with delicious fresh fish makes the choice
even more difficult. The fish is cooked simply – grilled with butter
and wine (£7.95-8.95). Other choices are home-made taramasalata
(£3.95), scrambled eggs and smoked salmon (£4.95), leak and
mushroom tagliatelle topped with blue cheese (£6.95), chicken livers
flamed in brandy on a leaf salad (£6.95), pan-fried sweetbreads with
caper mayonnaise (£7.95) and eight home-made puddings (all £2.50):
banoffi pie, Beehive tart (sponge, butter and raisins), treacle tart.
Rambling, traditionally furnished little rooms radiate off a central
servery, warmed by a wood-burning stove. The terrace and established
garden overlooks the neighbour's farm – the animals keep children
amused. *Bar Food* 12-2, 7-9.30 *(except Sun eve)*. *Children allowed in bar
to eat.* *Beer* Greene King Abbot & IPA. Garden, outdoor eating.
Access, Visa.

Horsebridge   Royal Inn

Tel 0182287 214

Horsebridge Tavistock Devon PL19 8PJ

FOOD

Map 12 C3

Three excellent reasons for a detour to Terry and Julie Wood's
informal and relaxing pub: to look at the ancient Tamar Bridge, to
sample their own home-brewed ales (of which it is reported that no-
one has been able to drink more than five pints!) and to try the
landlady's cooking, including some herby home-made bread with the
ploughman's and imaginative salads. There are also sherried kidneys,
venison in wine, and beef in ale (all £5.95) and chicken, Stilton and
mushroom slice and nutters roast (£5.50); "no chips or fried food" –
all main courses are between £5.50 and £6.25. Children not allowed
indoors. *Bar Food* 12-2, 7.15-9 *(Sat to 9.30, no food Sun)*. Free House.
Beer Bass plus own home brews: Hella, Horsebridge Best, Tamar, Right
Royal. Patio, outdoor eating. No credit cards.

Horton   Horton Inn

Tel 01258 840252

Horton nr Wimborne Dorset BH21 5AB

FOOD

B&B

Map 14 C4

An imposing, yet attractively refurbished 18th-century country inn at
a crossroads on the B3078 between Cranbourne and Wimborne.
Rambling bar and spacious adjoining dining areas have been neatly
redecorated and furnished creating a convivial atmosphere in which to
relax over a meal. A routine printed menu tries to please everybody,
including juniors. However, the best options are the blackboard
specials – chicken soup (£1.80), grilled lamb cutlets (£5.95), steak and
mushroom pie (£4.95) and maybe poached salmon Bearnaise with
fresh vegetables (£6.30). Two-course evening menu (£10.95)
available in both bar and restaurant. Smartening up extends to the six
bedrooms (only two are en suite) which are bright and fresh and
extremely spacious, providing functional overnight accommodation;
one room has three beds. Lawned garden with trees and flowerbeds
and rural views. *Open 11-11 (Sun to 10.30)*. *Bar Food & Restaurant
Meals* 12-2, 7-9.30 *(restaurant menu available evenings only)*. *Small*

*children's menu. Free House. **Beer** Ringwood Best, Flowers, Courage
Directors. Garden, outdoor eating. Family room. **Accommodation**
6 bedrooms, 2 en suite, £50 (single from £17.50). Children welcome
overnight (family room £45), additional beds and cots available. Dogs
by arrangement. Access, Visa.*

Horton-in-Ribblesdale	**The Crown Hotel**	**FOOD**
Tel 01729 860209		**B&B**
Horton-in-Ribblesdale nr Settle North Yorkshire BD24 0HF		**Map 5 D4**

Sandwiched between two road bridges on the B6479 where Bransgyll
runs into the Ribble, the Crown is centrally located amid the Three
Peaks at the heart of the Ribble Valley. At the pub, three generations
now come into play. Landlady Norma Hargreaves moved here
exactly 30 years ago with her parents; now, daughter Helen has
returned home to take charge of the kitchen. Rapidly making a name
for her home-made pies and puddings, she has nonetheless extended
the range of offerings to include Provençal baked halibut, (£5.25)
turkey breast with mushroom and smoked bacon sauce (£5) and
apricot and courgette gratin (£4.95); to mention but three. In terms
of accommodation, to term the bedrooms modest is not to decry
them, as an absence of TVs and phones remains intentional. Internal
dimensions of this unaltered 17th-century inn dictate, though, against
much modernisation and there are but two rooms with en-suite
bathrooms and a further five with added shower stalls. Two adjacent
cottages offer self-contained private accommodation for larger parties.
Being an altogether family-run affair there's also a special promise that
"parents with children are welcome here to do exactly what other
normal people like to do". Longer opening hours in summer.
*Accommodation 9 bedrooms, two en suite £45 (single £22). **Bar Food**
12-2, 6-9 (Sun 7-9). Garden. **Beer** Theakston XB & Old Peculier. Family
room. No credit cards.*

Houghton Conquest	**Knife & Cleaver**	
Tel 01234 740387 Fax 01234 740900		**B&B**
Houghton Conquest nr Ampthill Bedfordshire MK45 3LA		**Map 15a E1**

Three miles from Ampthill and equidistant from Junctions 12 and 13
of the M10, opposite the medieval parish church in a sleepy village,
the Knife & Cleaver is more an inn than a pub. The accommodation
is especially pleasing, in spacious brick-built garden rooms standing
alongside a mature orchard. In addition to TVs, telephones, radio-
alarm clocks and beverage facilities, the mini-fridge in each room is
thoughtfully stored each day with fresh milk. The less mobile are
especially well catered for by wide, paved bedroom access and ramps
into the pub proper. *Free House. **Beer** Banks & Taylor Shefford Bitter.
Garden. Family room. **Accommodation** 9 bedrooms, all en suite, £53,
£41 single. Children welcome overnight (0-5yrs free in parents' room),
extra beds and cots supplied. Access, Visa.*

Hovingham	**The Worsley Arms Hotel**	
Tel 01653 628234		**B&B**
Hovingham North Yorkshire YO6 4LA		**Map 5 E4**

Built in 1841 as an adjunct to the unsuccessful development of
Hovingham as a spa, the inn has remained in the hands of the Worsley
family from that day to this. Described as "late-Georgian" in style, it
overlooks the green of this most unspoilt of North Riding villages.

Zzz_z...

The newly refurbished Cricketers' Bar, appropriately named as it's the headquarters of the local team, is hung with an unique photographic collection of the county's greatest in action, many of whom played at the Hovingham Hall ground. It's generally lively here, with some good Double Chance from the nearby Malton brewery, and substantial bar food (chicken and Guinness pie and beef or lamb hotpot, both £5.50). The inn itself has a more refined feel in its elegant lounges with deep armchairs and abundant reading matter. Sunday lunches (£14.50) and table d'hote dinner (£18.50) are served in the sedate dining room, heavy with fine 18th-century portraits. Spacious bedrooms echo the Georgian feel with large windows and sumptuous new drapes and co-ordinated fabrics. Bathrooms with large bathsheets and abundant toiletries are best described as traditional. *Free House.* **Beer** *Malton Ale, Tetley Best, Theakston Old Peculier. Garden, outdoor eating, patio, squash. Family room.* **Accommodation** *22 rooms, all en suite, £98 (single £62). Children welcome, extra beds (£15) and cots (£5) provided; baby-listening. Access, Visa.*

Hoxne   Swan

Tel 01379 668275

FOOD

Low Street Hoxne Suffolk IP21 5AS

Map 10 C2

A Grade II listed 15th-century inn built by the Bishop of Norwich as the guest quarters to his now defunct summer palace. It's been a hostelry since at least 1619 and the interior, which features high ceilings and fluted oak joists, is suitably evocative of centuries gone by. Some good bar food includes sandwiches and omelettes (fillings to order), mixed cheese ploughman's (£2.95), scampi (£4.30) and lamb cutlets (£5.60) on the hand-written menu; courgette and rosemary soup (£1.75), spinach and garlic terrine (£2.75), pork fillet in brandy cream sauce (£6.95) and cod and prawn gratinée (£5.95) might feature as daily specials, along with spinach, chickpea and cumin parcels in tomato sauce (£4.95) for vegetarians and chocolate pot or orange mousse (£2.25) for sweet. Outside, there's a large, tree-bordered garden where you can play croquet. The village is pronounced Hoxon (in case you want to feel like a local). **Bar Food** *12-2 (except Sun), 7-9 (except Sat & Sun). Children allowed in bar to eat.* **Beer** *Adnams Bitter, Old & Tally Ho, Greene King Abbot. Garden, outdoor eating. Pub closed 25 Dec. Access, Visa.*

Hurley   Dew Drop Inn

Tel 01628 824327

A

Near Hurley Berkshire SL6 6RB

Map 15a D3

Signposted off the A43, this is a tucked-away, well-loved and genuinely unpretentious cottage pub. The garden which backs on to National Trust woodland is delightful in summer. It's a real hideaway of a place in winter, when the twin log fires in the main bar are crackling. Miles of local walks make this rural retreat very popular with walkers and dog owners. **Beer** *Brakspear's Ordinary and Old. Garden, children's play area. No credit cards.*

Ibstone   Fox

Tel 01491 638289 Fax 01491 638873	**B&B**
Ibstone nr High Wycombe Buckinghamshire HP14 3GG	Map 15a D3

Much modernised and extended 300-year-old inn located on the
Chiltern ridgeway opposite Ibstone Common, and close to acres of
beechwood rambles. With the M40 (J5) only a mile away, this rural
inn is a handy overnight stop for travellers, for the nine en-suite
rooms are comfortable and well equipped. All rooms feature co-
ordinating fabrics, modern pine furniture, clean fully tiled shower
rooms and a full complement of added comforts – tea-makers, TVs,
direct-dial telephones, clock-radios, trouser presses and hairdryers. Rear
rooms have soothing views across fields and woodland. Relaxing,
simply furnished bars and a delightful sunny front terrace and well
tended garden. *Free House.* **Beer** *Harlow Brewery Rebellion, Greene King
Abbot Ale, Brakspear Bitter, guest beer. Garden. Family room.*
Accommodation *9 bedrooms, all en suite, from £76 per night (single
£58). Children welcome overnight, additional beds and cots supplied.
Dogs by arrangement. Access, Diners, Visa.*

☺

Zzzz...

Icklingham   Red Lion

Tel 01638 717802	**FOOD**
High Street Icklingham Suffolk IP28 6PS	Map 10 C2

Fine 16th-century village inn set back from the A1101 with a neat
front lawn and raised rear terrace overlooking fields. Sympathetically
restored and well refurbished two-bar interior featuring low "smoke"
brown ceilings with heavy, black-painted beams, an exposed brick
fireplace and an assortment of antique and sturdy tables, benches, pews
and chairs arranged on rug-strewn wooden floors. Relaxing ambience
enhanced by piped classical music, various newspapers and magazines
to read and evening candlelight. Increasingly popular, the appeal being
the reliable range of interesting home-cooked bar food using fresh
local produce. Blackboard lists may feature fresh asparagus soup
(£2.10), Newmarket sausages and mash (£4.05), lamb cutlets with
redcurrant sauce (£7.75), chicken and mushroom pie (£5.95) and a
huge wooden bowl of warm fillet of chicken and crispy pasta salad
(£8.45). Good accompanying vegetables – definitely no chips! Fish
fresh from Lowestoft may top 15 varieties on Thursday evenings,
including fillet of codling (£7,95), lemon sole and grilled plaice (both
£9.65), along with more unusual choices. Round the meal off with
sticky treacle tart, raspberry fool or ginger pudding with lemon sauce
(from £2.95). Well-kept Greene King ales and a good range of wines,
including country fruit wines. **Bar Food** *12-2.30, 6-10 (Sun 7-9).*
Beer *Greene King IPA, Abbot Ale, Rayments Bitter. Garden, outdoor
eating. Children allowed anywhere. Access, Visa.*

Ightham Common   The Harrow Inn   ★

Tel 01732 885912	**FOOD**
Common Road Ightham Common nr Borough Green Kent TN15 9ER	Map 11 B5

Coloured lights around the door offer a welcome at this Virginia
creeper-hung stone inn on a country lane. In the small front bar a
couple of stuffed birds in glass cases and old motor racing photos are
mounted above dado pine panelling, and there's a pair of old leather
armchairs and a pool table in the room next door; the whole effect
wobbles on the very fine line between characterful and seedy but
boxes of board games and newspapers laid out on a side table are a

nice touch, and the landlord and his friendly staff soon dispel any doubts. Gerard Costelloe has an impressive catering background, and the cooking is excellent. Well-balanced soups arrive in large tureens, from which one helps oneself (£2.10), along with a whole freshly baked rye loaf on its own bread board. There are always a couple of pasta dishes (from £3.95), at least one of them vegetarian, as well as the likes of baked red snapper (£6.50) and venison sausage (£4.50). It's worth saving a little space for dessert, like a classic summer pudding (£1.80), properly made, its bread thoroughly soaked in the juice of soft fruits. The bars are not really suitable for chidren but they are welcome (particularly for Sunday lunch) in the cottagey restaurant, its conservatory extension complete with grape vine. The menu here tends to be somewhat more adventurous. *Bar Food* 12-2 (*except Mon*), 7-9.30. *Restaurant Meals* 12.30-2 (*Sun to 3*), 7-10 (*except Sun eve*). Free House. *Beer* Fuller's London Pride, Greene King. *Garden, outdoor eating. Family room. Access Visa.*

Ilmington — Howard Arms

FOOD
B&B

Tel 01608 682226

Lower Green Ilmington nr Shipston-on-Stour Warwickshire CV36 4LN   Map 14a A1

For its location by the village green and setting in a mature orchard garden, the yellow stone Howard Arms falls into the "irresistible" category, a picture by day, romantically lit at night. Centuries-old connections with one of England's most illustrious families adds a touch of history to draw the crowds to its flagstoned bar and open-plan restaurant. Menus change daily, a single blackboard offering the same choices throughout, and all food orders are taken at the bar. Seasonal asparagus is a popular starter (£3.25) or there's lettuce and Brie soup, perhaps (£2); follow fishily with a seafood croissant (£6) or lemon sole with almonds (£6.95); for meatier choices the likes of lamb and rosemary pie (£6.50), chicken tarragon (£7.95), rib eye steak with bacon and red wine sauce (£8); for vegetarian's canneloni with ricotta & spinach (£5.25) and to follow lime crème brulée and Irish whiskey tart (£2.50). There have been two changes of landlord within the space of our last three editions: our hope must be that consistent standards are maintained. Just two bedrooms are let, a large twin with quite enough space for a family to stay, and the king-sized double for the more romantically inclined; en-suite facilities include both bath and shower, and there are no phones to impinge on the peace. Children under 5 stay free in parents' room. *Bar Food & Restaurant Meals* 12-2, 7-9 (*except Sun eve, Fri & Sat to 9.30*). Free House. *Beer* Boddingtons, Marston's Pedigree. *Garden, outdoor eating, children's play area. Accommodation* 2 bedrooms, both en suite £50 (*single £30*). Children welcome overnight, additional beds and cots available. Check-in by arrangement. No dogs. Access, Visa.

Zzzz...

Inkpen — Swan Inn

FOOD

Tel 01488 668326   Fax 01488 668503

Lower Inkpen nr Hungerford Berkshire RG15 0DX   Map 14a B4

Colourful window boxes and hanging baskets of flowers adorn the front of this long, low, white-painted 17th-century country pub. Inside, there are lots of old beams and timbers, some of them salvaged from a nearby barn, pew seating at one end and pink-clothed tables in the restaurant area at the other. After his return from 14 years out East, landlord John Scothorne thought Singaporean cooking and real ales would go well together; the experiment has proved a great success, and pints of good English bitter make fine partners for the spicy food. A new chef promised to integrate the traditional pub grub snack menu and Oriental offerings as we went to press. Drunken prawns, beef rendang, Singapore noodles, weeping tiger and nasi goreng are typical dishes; also vegetarian dishes with quorn. The choice on the extensive wine list is designed to accompany either the Singaporean or English dishes. **Bar Food & Restaurant Meals** 12-2, 7-9.30. Children allowed in restaurant and bottom end of bar to eat, children's menu. Free House. **Beer** Brakspear, Marston's Pedigree, Ringwood. Patio/terrace, outdoor eating. Access, Visa.

Ivy Hatch	**Plough**	★	
Tel 01732 810268			**FOOD**
Coach Road Ivy Hatch Kent TN15 0NL			**Map 11 B5**

Quite apart from its outstandingly good cooking, the Plough is the kind of pub just about everyone would love to have as their local. A large mid 18th-century roadside inn dominating this little hamlet, it's just enough off the beaten track, although well signposted. Within, it's peaceful and genuinely unspoilt, with dark pitch mahogany in the light of a crackling log fire, and candlelight by night. By way of contrast, the conservatory dining extension is light and fresh, with its soft pink linens, cane furniture and decorative greenery. The chef, Daniel Hamburg, has now also become the manager. The same menu applies throughout the pub and he continues to produce excellent food: choose an excellently flavoured soup (the fish soup is particulary good), perhaps salmon grilled with Cajun spices (£10.50) or a warm salad of scallops with ginger and coriander (£7.50), finishing with a classic, tangy tarte au citron. Or stick patriotically to some good old English specialities: a broccoli and Stilton soup, warming oxtail stew, jugged hare (£9.50), or liver and onions. Inspiration from further afield is shown in bresaola with roasted peppers and chili salsa (£5), mozzarella with red onion and plum tomatoes (£3.50). Puddings (£3.25) also cross the Channel and back: perhaps a delicate crème brulée, bread-and-butter pudding, sticky toffee pudding or strawberry tuile; all show a lightness of touch and substantial skill. Tables can't be booked in the bar, so be early, or be patient; tables are bookable in the conservatory. Pub open 12-3, 6-11 (Sun 7-10.30). **Bar Food** 12-2, 7-9.30. No bar food D Sun. **Restaurant Meals** as the bar. Children allowed in the bar to eat, no under-8s in restaurant for dinner. Free House. **Beer** Brakspear, Marston's Pedigree. Garden, outdoor eating. Access, Visa.

Ixworth	**The Pykkerell Inn**	
Tel 01359 230398		**FOOD**
High Street Ixworth Suffolk IP31 2HH		**Map 10 C2**

Don't be fooled by the unassuming brick exterior for it belies the true age of this rambling old coaching inn. Its medieval 15th-century charm has been carefully revealed throughout the series of rooms which ooze antiquity and atmosphere. Stripped ancient panelling, heavily carved beams, bare-boarded floors strewn with colourful Persian rugs, a library and a delightful mix of antique tables and chairs characterise this most civilised place. Added welcome touches include brass candle-holders on tables, soothing classical music and newspapers to browse. Food matches the ambience and decor in quality and style, with imaginative home-cooked dishes – using fresh local ingredients – in both bar and restaurant drawing a generally upmarket clientele from far and wide. Various blackboards list the day's fare, notably fresh fish from Lowestoft such as fillet of codling (£7.95). Further choices range from asparagus soup (£2.25), Tiger Bay prawns in garlic butter (£6.95) and Newmarket sausages and mash (£4.05) to pork chops with apple and cider sauce (£6.85), warm fillet of chicken and crispy pasta salad (£8.45) and delicious home-cooked Suffolk ham with Shrewsbury sauce, served with crisp fresh vegetables. More adventurous restaurant fare – spinach and salmon terrine on a redcurrant coulis (£3.75), sliced chicken breast with a cucumber and turmeric sauce (£9.75) – can also be ordered in the bar. Leave room for an excellent pudding (from £2.95) like luxury bread-and-butter pudding and ginger pudding with lemon sauce. Good range of wines, including country fruit wines. Rear courtyard seating for warmer days overlooks a fine timber-framed Elizabethan barn. Licensees also run the *Red Lion* at Icklingham (see entry). *Bar Food* 12-2.30, 6-10 (Sun 7-9). *Children's portions. **Beer** Greene King, Abbot Ale IPA, Rayments Bitter. Garden, outdoor eating. Children allowed anywhere. Access, Visa.*

Kegworth   Cap and Stocking

Tel 01509 674814	**FOOD**
20 Borough Street Kegworth Leicestershire DE74 2FF	**Map 7 D3**

Far from being either Leicestershire's oldest or most fashionable pub, today's high-flying 'Cap' is as evocative as its name, remarkable not least for its pétanque piste in the old walled garden and the ancient tradition of Bass-served-in-the-jug. Paddy and her kitchen crew produce customer-inspired dishes from meat and provisions bought in daily. The clamour is for ever-spicier curries, chicken tak-a-tan, wider vegetarian options and even more custard with the popular nursery puddings. Parking very limited. *Bar Food* 12-2.30, 6.30-9 (Sun from 7). *Beer Bass, 4 guest beers a week. Garden, outdoor eating, pétanque. Family room, children's portions. No credit cards.*

Kelston   The Old Crown

Tel 01225 423032	**A**
Bath Road Kelston nr Bath Avon BA1 9AQ	**Map 13 F1**

Standing alongside the old coaching route from Bristol to Bath (now the A431), with its car park across the busy road, the Old Crown is a gem of a place which has the carefully cultivated air of being by-passed by time. By day and by night flickering candles along the bar and mantleshelves, constantly highlighting strings of hops above the bar, are reflected in the glass of the pub's collection of framed prints and montages. The front rooms have shining, uneven flagstone floors, polished tables and carved oak settles. Beyond are two dining rooms, prettily appointed, where most of the serious eating goes on. Real ale buffs though, can enthuse over the authentic bank of four unaltered 1930s' beer engines which still dispense some fine Bass, Butcombe and regular guest brews. Children under 14 are permitted in the restaurant only, unless it's fine enough to use the picnic tables at the back, prettily laid out in a mature orchard. *Free House. **Beer** Bass, Butcombe, Wadworth 6X, Old Timer (winter) & Farmers Glory (summer), Smiles Best. Garden. Access, Visa.*

Kempsey   **Walter de Cantelupe Inn**

Tel 01905 820572	**FOOD**
Kempsey nr Worcester Hereford & Worcester WR5 3NA	**Map 14 B1**

In a modest former cider house on the A38 one and a half miles south of Worcester's city boundary, Martin Lloyd Morris has been plying his trade since late 1991. He provides a welcoming atmosphere, scrupulously-kept real ales and purposefully fresh food selections kept sensibly simple. Beside a lunch menu offering granary bread sandwiches (smoked trout £2.95), noodles with smoked ham and tomato (£4.90) and moist, three-egg omelettes (£3.20), there's a daily lunch special, perhaps beef sirloin, tarragon and white wine which, at under £3, is a clear loss-leader. There's both quality and value in the salmon supreme with samphire (£4.50) and courgette bake with garlic bread (£3.90). As evenings draw a hungrier crowd, the range then runs to smoked haddock mousseline (£3.25) and chicken korma salad (£2.75) as curtain raisers, perhaps, to tenderloin of pork with perry (£6.20), creamy leek croustade (£5.45) and the chef's fish dish of the day. Puddings are home made, many of them fruity and the hot English nursery puds (£2.50) particularly filling. Cafetière coffee is good, and service is relaxed and friendly. Parts of their three year plan are as yet incomplete (remodelled 'Gents' are planned) but landlord and crew clearly have their priorities right with their infectious enthusiasm and sense of fun. *Bar Food* *12-2, 7-9 (to 9.30 Fri & Sat). No bar food D Sun (except Sun before Bank Holiday Mondays). Free House.* *Beers* *Wood's Wonderful, Marston Best & Pedigree, guest beer. Outdoor eating area. Access, Visa.*

Keysoe   **Chequers Inn**

Tel 01234 708678	**A**
Pertenhall Road Keysoe Bedfordshire MK44 2HR	**Map 15 E1**

Dating back to 1520, the Chequers' one bar is divided into two by an unusual pillared fireplace; log fires in cold weather. The separate lounge opens on to a large, lawned garden complete with a Wendy House, playtree and swing. *Free House.* *Beer* *Hook Norton, Bass, Fuller's London Pride. Garden, children's play area. Family room. Pub closed all Mon (except Bank Hols). Access, Visa.*

Keyston   **Pheasant Inn**   ★

Tel 01832 710241 Fax 01832 710340	**FOOD**
Village Loop Road Keyston nr Bythorn Cambridgeshire PE18 0RE	**Map 7 E4**

Peacefully located near the church in this upmarket village and only a couple of miles from the busy A14 Huntingdon to Kettering road (if ever there was a pub worthy of a special detour then this is it), this long, low, whitewashed pub/restaurant with low, thatched roof and original timbers promises much in character and atmosphere, and the food lives up to it all in admirable fashion. Inside, you'll find heavy, dark oak beams and walls hung with old hunting photos, the odd stuffed pheasant and even a fox, too. Roger Jones, manager and head chef, oversees the fortnightly-changing menu – an extra daily dish or two may be added – which is available throughout the rambling, neatly-furnished bars and in the more formal restaurant area (where the only difference is larger tables, linen napkins and no smoking). Enthusiasm in the kitchen is evident in the comprehensive range of 13 starters (also suitable as a light snack), such as Tuscan bean soup (£3.25), chicken liver paté with toasted brioche and a Cumberland sauce (£3.85) and home-made noodles with smoked salmon, courgettes and fennel (£5.95). An equal number of imaginative main dishes may feature wild boar sausages with Dijon and onion sauce and mashed potato (£6.25), breasts of wood pigeon with a swede purée, bacon and haricot beans (£8.75), seared fillets of John Dory with stuffed baby peppers and a Sicilian pesto sauce (£9.35) and fillet steak with baked sweet onion, tomato confit and chips (£14.50). Finish with one of the dozen puddings – lemon soufflé cheesecake with an orange sauce (£3.85) – or a selection of Neal's Yard British cheeses (£4.25) served with apple and celery. Traditional Sunday lunch £9.95. Fresh fish is delivered daily from either Dorset or London, but most of the fine ingredients used here come from local suppliers less than two miles distant. The Pheasant remains at heart a well-kept friendly village pub, as deservedly popular for its range of cask-conditioned ales as for its superb, award-winning list of wines (unusually arranged by flavour not area), of which an even dozen may be ordered by the glass. Good, helpful notes are worth following. "The first Poste Hotel and now better than ever" – we concur! *Open 11-3, 6-11 (Sun 12-2, 7-10.30).* **Bar Food & Restaurant Meals** *12-2, 6-10 (Restaurant from 7). Free House.* **Beers** *Fuller's London Pride, Adnams Best, Courage, Directors, two guest beers. Garden, outdoor eating. Family room. Access, Diners, Visa.*

Kidmore End　　　**New Inn**

Tel 01734 723115	**FOOD**
Chalkhouse Green Road Kidmore End nr Reading Oxon RG4 9AU	Map 15a D3

This 300-year-old inn has just had one bar completely refurbished and the original beams and fireplace have been uncovered. Ordering a meal here is, however, a high-tech affair; having chosen from a regular printed menu, one orders at the bar where a 'light pen' is passed over a special bar-coded copy for the order to be automatically printed out in the kitchen. The food itself is rather more traditional: steak, mushroom and Murphy's pie (£5.45), Arbroath smokie bake (£6.7), mushroom goulash (£5.35) and entrecote steak platter (£9.90) plus more exotic monthly specials like chicken tikka (£7.60) and lamb cutlets in herbs (£7.85). Along with the good fresh vegetables go for the major 'chips' that are satisfyingly chunky, golden and arrive piping hot. On the snack front, French bread sandwiches start at about £2.45 and there are salad platters based on mature farmhouse Cheddar (£4.80) or Long Clawson Stilton (£4.95). Decor is typical of an English country pub with low beams and wheelback chairs. A large tree-shrouded garden provides for summer eating and drinking. **Bar Food** *12-2. 6.30-9.30 (Sun from 7). Children's menu.* **Beer** *Brakspear. Garden. Family room. Visa.*

Kilve　　　**Hood Arms**

Tel 01278 741210	**FOOD**
	B&B
Kilve nr Bridgwater Somerset TA5 1EA	Map 13 E1

Pristine 17th-century white village coaching inn at the front of the Quantock Hills, a mile from the sea, with log fires, a large collection of horse brasses and a complete set of a show harness above the fireplace. Modernised, comfortable interior, with wood-burning stove in the carpeted main bar, which is bistro-like in the evenings. The menu varies from prawn cocktail (£3), chicken and broccoli mornay (£4.95) and National Trust pie (£4.50) to Dover sole (£13), chicken Kiev (£8.50) or spinach and garlic lasagne (£4.95). Puddings are the

old favourites (all £2.50) – treacle tart, sherry trifle, rum tipsy cake.
Also smaller, cosy lounge. Pleasant garden. Friendly, welcoming
service. *Bar Food 12-2 (12-1.30 Sun), 6.30-10 (7.15-9.30 Sun).*
Restaurant Meals 7-9.30 (except Sun, Mon and Tue). Free House.
Beer Boddingtons, Flowers Original. Garden, outdoor eating.
*Accommodation 5 bedrooms, all en suite, £64 (single £38). Children
welcome overnight (minimum age 8). Access, Visa.*

King's Lynn   Tudor Rose

| Tel 01553 762824   Fax 01553 764894 | **B&B** |

**St Nicholas Street off Tuesday Market Place King's Lynn Norfolk PE30
1LR**   Map 10 B1

Located just off the main Market Place, this medieval timber-framed
merchant's house was built around 1500 with a brick townhouse
extension added in the 1640s. Beyond the medieval oak studded door
lies a good panelled pubby bar, a charming 15th-century beamed
restaurant and twelve neat and tidy bedrooms, some of which have
views of St Nicholas's Chapel. At present, accommodation is modest
with modern furniture, clean en-suite facilities and most of the added
comforts – TV, clock-radio, tea-makers, telephones and hairdryers.
Plans however are afoot, with the enthusiastic new owners planning to
gradually upgrade and refurbish each bedroom. *Free House. Open 11-
11 (Sun 12-3, 7-10.30).* **Accommodation** *12 bedrooms, 11 en suite £50
(Single £38.50). Children welcome overnight (free under 10, extra bed
£5).* **Beer** *Boddingtons, Bass, Woodforde's Wherry, Adnams May Day.
Garden, outdoor eating access. Access, Visa.*

Kingsand   Halfway House Inn

| Tel 01752 822279 | **FOOD** |
| | **B&B** |

Kingsand nr Torpoint Cornwall PL10 1NA   Map 12 C3

Attractive pink-washed inn tucked among the narrow lanes and
houses of this quaint fishing village, and only a few yards from the
seafront. Comfortably refurbished over the past two years by David
and Sarah Riggs it has become a popular place in which to dine and
more recently to stay. Relaxing, carpeted and stone walled bar
furnished with a mix of old pine and small copper-topped tables and
warmed by a good woodburning stove. A routine bar menu is
enhanced by an imaginative blackboard selection of dishes that are
served in both the bar and the small cosy restaurant. As one would
expect it is very fish orientated. Start with delicious crab puffs in a
pool of pesto sauce (£3.45), a selection of smoked fish (£4) or a
freshly made tomato soup (£1.80), followed by cassoulet of brill,
scallops and crab (£8.25), ragout of turbot and scallops with cream
and basil (£9.95) roast garlic monkfish with peppers (£7.65) or
chicken Basque with tomato, garlic and basil (£6.85) and lamb
noisettes with chasseur sauce (£7.95). Chocolate marquise with coffee
bean sauce and passionfruit mousse (both £2.75) may feature on the
pudding board. Co-ordinating Laura Ashley fabrics, wall friezes and
wallpapers grace the well kitted out, fresh and clean en-suite bedrooms
which are furnished with modern pine pieces, cane chairs, and
attractive prints with a seashore theme adorn the walls. Each window
has its own colourful and overflowing box of flowers in the summer.
A family room has bunk beds; children only allowed in restaurant
part of pub, though. Value-for-money overnight accommodation. *Pub
open 11-3, 6-11 (Sun 12-3, 7-10.30).* **Bar Food & Restaurant Meals**
12-2, 7-9.45. Free House. Beer Bass, Boddingtons, Young's Special, guest

beers. **Accommodation** *5 bedrooms, all en suite, from £39 (single £19.50). Children welcome overnight (under-7s stay free in parents' room), additional beds & cots supplied. Access, Visa.*

Kingscote	**Hunters Hall**	**FOOD**
Tel 01453 860393 Fax 01453 860707		**B&B**
Kingscote nr Tetbury Gloucestershire GL8 8XZ		Map 14 B2

Five miles from Tetbury on the A4135 Hunters Hall is an ideal spot for a family day out. It sports a lovely tree-lined garden with extensive play areas and assault course, while on wet days parents and little ones use the gallery room, almost hidden above the pub's interlinked beamed and flagstoned bars. Bar food is a safe bet with dishes changing daily, for example, lamb and red wine casserole (£5.45), smoked chicken and mayonnaise salad (£2.95), and rainbow trout with almonds (£6.25). A lunchtime buffet in the dining room remains ever-popular, while at night the à la carte rather points up the kitchen's limitations. Standing separately, a Cotswold stone block of recent construction houses the bedrooms, residents' lounge and a conference facility. With roomy en-suite bathrooms, remote-control TVs and dial-out phones, neither space nor comfort is stinted: one ground-floor room incorporates facilities for the disabled, and a large suite with two double bedrooms extends, for some lucky little ones, the day out into tomorrow. The lounge bar and bedrooms have recently been refurbished. Good selection of wines by the glass.
Bar Food *12-2, 7-9.45. Children allowed in bar to eat, children's menu. Free House.* **Beer** *Bass, Hook Norton Best, Wadworth 6X, Uley Old Spot. Garden, outdoor play area. Family room.* **Accommodation** *12 bedrooms, all en suite, £58 (single £44). Children welcome overnight (family room for 3 – £68, for 4 – £80). Additional beds (£10) and cots (£4) available. Access, Diners, Visa.*

Kingskerswell	**Barn Owl Inn**	**FOOD**
Tel 01803 872130		**B&B**
Kingkerswell nr Newton Abbot Devon TQ12 5AN		Map 13 D3

Look out for a sign on the A380 to the Barn Owl Inn, which offers decent food, good bedrooms and a friendly welcome. Lovingly restored by the Warners, the original 16th-century farmhouse has a neat if unremarkable exterior which makes its characterful interior even more of a surprise. Old beams, rough stone walls and flagstoned floors have been uncovered, and real log fires warm each of the three bars in winter. One room features an inglenook fireplace, another an ancient blackleaded range, while in the largest bar, oak panelling and an ornate plasterwork ceiling are rather grander than might be expected of a modest farmhouse. Fresh flowers on all the tables add to the general charm of the surroundings. A printed bar menu offers a standard choice of pub meals, from cold platters and filled jacket potatoes to steaks. Home-cooked daily specials listed on the blackboard improve matters significantly with such dishes as lamb en croute, steak and kidney pie, pork goulash (all £5.50), fisherman's casserole (£5.57) and pheasant and chicken with Cumberland sauce (£6.95), all accompanied by a decent selection of vegetables. Remember to bring your appetite; portions are generous. Separate restaurant with French-inspired à la carte menu. Six bedrooms within the original farmhouse combine considerable charm with conveniences like television and direct-dial telephones. Extensive sound-proofing effectively eliminates any noise from the bars below. Rooms are cottagey in style with black beams, white plaster walls, dark-stained pine furniture locally made in solid country style and their own individual floral fabrics, perhaps red poppy, honeysuckle or sweet pea. The 'signature' design is also used above dados in the bathrooms and in panels on the doors, the outsides of which are covered with old floorboards, thus cunningly concealing the modern fireproof doors within. Bowls of fruit, fresh flowers and mineral water add the final homely touch to the pristinely kept rooms. No children under 14 are permitted in either bars or bedrooms, but they are welcome in the small walled garden. *Bar Food 11.45-2 (Sun from 12), 6.30-10 (Sun from 7). Restaurant Meals 7-9.45 Mon-Sat. Free House. Beer Fergusons Dartmoor, Ind Coope Burton Ale, Wadworth 6X. Garden, outdoor eating. Accommodation 6 bedrooms, all en suite, from £60 (single £47.50). Pub & accommodation closed 3 days Christmas. No dogs. Access, Diners, Visa.*

Kingsteignton   Old Rydon   ★

Tel 01626 54624   **FOOD**

Old Rydon Road Kingsteignton Newton Abbot Devon TQ12 3QG   **Map 13 D3**

Hermann Hruby (pronounced Ruby) continues to maintain his high standards in producing some of the best pub food in the South West, and in that respect little has changed since the Hrubys bought the Old Rydon in 1978 except for the building of a splendid, and large, heated conservatory, leafy with vines, jasmine, bougainvillea and other plants. It's a Grade II listed former farmhouse, converted in the 1960s with an original old cider loft forming an attractive part of the bar, previously the farm stables. Underneath the plank and beam ceiling adorned with pewter mugs is a raised log fire; the whitewashed stone walls are hung with antlers and horns. Tables here are drinking style, too small and cramped for relaxed dining, and many of the seats are converted barrels. The place to dine is in the comfortable conservatory, or on warm sunny days at a table on the patio or in the sheltered walled garden – an ideal summer venue for lunch. Separate from the bar, a relaxing diners' lounge leads through to the charming little restaurant, in the oldest part of the building. Most visitors come for the delicious and interesting food which, in the bar, is listed on twice daily-changing blackboards and may include mushroom, bacon and parsley soup (£1.85), pork, chicken and herb terrine (£2.65), vegetable, lentil and coriander leaf curry in a cumin and ginger (£3.95), Mexican turkey hotpot with vegetables in a spicy tomato and chili sauce (£5.25), stir-fried vegetable chow mein (£3.95) and a memorable Italian-style seafood tagliatelle with cod, prawns, mushrooms, fresh spinach leaves and pesto sauce, topped with cheese (£5.85). Excellent puddings (£2.75) range from Swiss nut fudge and fruit frangipan to scrumpy bread pudding. Service is polite and very efficient. The restaurant menu embraces more elaborate fare, from fresh Brixham fish and seafood to local game and chargrilled steaks. Value-for-money 2-course menu (£10) served in the restaurant Monday to Friday. Children are welcome in the conservatory or upstairs. The pub is awkward to locate as it now hides within a modern housing estate, but it is best approached along Longford Lane off the A381, then take Rydon Road which lies on your left. *Bar Food 12-2, 7-10. Free House. Beer Wadworth 6X, Bass, guest beer. Garden, outdoor eating. Pub closed Christmas day. Access, Diners, Visa.*

Kingston   **The Juggs**

Tel 01273 472523 Fax 01273 476150	**FOOD**

The Street Kingston nr Lewes East Sussex BN7 3NT   **Map 11 B6**

Just off the A27, a short distance from Brighton, you will find this
picturesque little 15th-century inn made from two tiny cottages. The
name 'Juggs' originates from the leather jugs the women used to carry
on their heads to collect fish from the market. The main bar is
particularly characterful with its low ceilings, rough black timbers,
rustic benches and yellowing walls; there's also a small no-smoking
dining area (same menu in both). The home-made steak and kidney
puddings have a reputation for being enormous and good value
(£7.50), the Sussex bangers made by a local butcher and served
with chips (£2.95), and puddings are all home-made – chocolate
nutcake and butterscotch toffee with maple sauce (both £2.50).
*Bar Food 12-2 (Sun to 2.15), 6-9.30 (Sun from 7). Children's menu.
Free House. Beer Harveys Best, King & Barnes Broadwood Festive,
guest beer. Garden, outdoor eating, children's play area. Family room.
Pub closed 26 Dec & 1 Jan. Access, Visa.*

Kintbury   **Dundas Arms**

Tel 01488 658263 Fax 01488 658568	**FOOD**
	B&B

53 Station Road Kintbury nr Newbury Berkshire RG15 0UT   **Map 14a B4**

Reached via Halfway, past the Kintbury turnoff from the
Hungerford-bound A4, this well-loved, reliable old-fashioned
waterside inn, by the Kennet and Avon canal, has been run by the
Dalzell-Pipers since the 1960s. The civilised bar has a striking display
of blue patterned plates entirely covering one wall. The riverside patio
is very popular on summer lunchtimes. The comfortable dining room
with canal views is the stage for owner David's cooking. Fresh local
ingredients are prepared with skill, confidence and a notable lack of
fuss. These talents show up well in dishes like paté-stuffed quail with
peppered red jelly and grilled red mullet with a lively citrus sauce
which appear on the 3-course (£16.50) lunch menu. Dinner is à la
carte: smoked chicken and prawns with avocado (£6) or fresh pear
and gorgonzola salad (£4.90) as starters, baked halibut with lemon
butter sauce (£14) or roast breast of duck with mint and lemon sauce
(£13.50) as mains and the bread and butter pudding (£4.95) is moist
and well executed. The Dalzell-Pipers are proud of their particularly
interesting wine list, which admirably complements the fine British
cheeses. Food is also served in the small 'Cocktail' bar. Pleasant
bedrooms are in a converted livery and stable block, with French
windows opening on to a quiet private terrace, where garden
furniture is provided for each room. *Bar Food (No food Sun) 12-2,
7-9. Restaurant Meals 12-1.30, 7.30-9. Beer Morland Original, Charles
Wells Bombardier, Fuller's London Pride. Riverside patio/terrace, outdoor
eating. Accommodation 5 bedrooms, all en suite, £65 (single £55).
Children welcome overnight (under-4s stay free in parents' room, 5-10s
£6), additional beds available. Check-in by arrangement, dogs by
arrangement. Access, Visa.*

Kirkby Lonsdale   Snooty Fox Tavern

Tel 015242 71308   Fax 015242 72642   **B&B**

Main Street Kirkby Lonsdale Cumbria LA6 2AH   Map 4 C4

A smart Jacobean black and white painted inn adjacent to the town
square. Plenty of interest is revealed within the bars: period costumes
adorn the walls amid collections of post horns, farm implements and
old beer taps. Food throughout the dining room and three flagstoned
bars hits no heights of invention. A warm welcome is given to
children who can play safely in the enclosed rear garden. Overnight,
there's space in three larger rooms for a cot or an extra bed and there
are TVs for amusement. All five bedrooms are neatly furnished and
full of oak-beamed character; three only have full en-suite bathrooms.
A hearty English breakfast delivered to the room remains one of the
Snooty Fox's attractions. Twenty malt whiskies at the bar. *Open 11-11,
Sun usual hours. Free House. Beer Hartleys XB, Theakston Best, Timothy
Taylor's Landlord, guest beer. Garden, family room.* **Accommodation**
*5 rooms, 3 en suite, £46 (single £26). Children welcome overnight. For
under-10s, additional beds (£10 inc breakfast) and cots (£5 inc breakfast)
available. Dogs by arrangement. Accommodation closed 24, 25 & 26 Dec.
No credit cards.*

Kirkbymoorside   George & Dragon Hotel   **FOOD**

Tel & Fax 01751 433334   **B&B**

Market Place Kirkbymoorside North Yorkshire YO6 6AA   Map 5 E4

Agreeably fulfilling it's dual role of town-centre hostelry and quiet
country inn, the George and Dragon stands imposingly by the cobbled
square of picturesque Kirkbymoorside. There's a single bar in front,
with sporting prints and paraphernalia, where bar food is listed on
large blackboards and every available beam above the servery. Choices
here start with chicken liver, Stilton and walnut or smoked salmon
patés (from £2.75), progressing to seafood hotpot (£6.90), cheese
and spinach roulade (£4.95) and venison casserole (£6.90), with
voluminous puddings to follow (treacle tart and custard £2.50). Ever-
popular, however, remain the steak and kidney pie with red wine
onion and rabbit pie (£5.95), and 2-course Sunday roast (£8.50).
Housed in two detached rear buildings, one a former brewhouse,
the bedrooms overlook an enclosed wall garden. Remodelling and
refurbishment have been a priority here since Stephen and Frances
Collings took over in late 1992 and is just about complete. A
reduction in the number of rooms has made much more space in those
remaining, and artistic interior designs have greatly enlarged their
individual appeal. Features include remote-control TVs, dial-out
phones and hairdryers; revamped bathrooms have smart over-bath
showers and complimentary toiletries. Residents enjoy exclusive use of
the garden lounge, and evening restaurant menus produce the likes of
langoustines with hollandaise (£4.95) and Gressingham duck with
cassis and rosemary sauce (£10.90). Children under 16 accommodated
free in parent's room. *Open 11am-11pm Wed, regular hours other days.
Bar Food 12-2.15, 6.30-9.15. Free House. Beer John Smith's, Taylor's
Landlord, Theakston XB. Garden, patio, outdoor eating. Family room.*
Accommodation *19 bedrooms, all en suite, £68 (£44 single). Children
welcome overnight, additional beds and cots available. Access, Visa.*

Knapp   **Rising Sun**

Tel 01823 490436

FOOD

Knapp North Curry nr Taunton Somerset TA3 6BG

Map 13 E2

Directions here are hard to give and just as hard to follow. Meander down the lanes from the hamlet of Ham (six miles west of Junction 25 on the M5), right on the lip of the Somerset levels, and then keep a lookout for the arrows. Built as a Longhouse in 1480 and 'rediscovered' since the arrival of Tony Atkinson in 1991, the Sun attracts its fill of worshippers of fine, fresh fish these days, and diners should mark out their spot especially early at weekends. Separated by a lounge bar with deep sofas in front of a cast-iron stove, two cottage dining areas are now given over to some serious eating with top billing given to fresh fish from Brixham and elsewhere. Star quality is not far off in many of the dishes such as the chunky bouillabaisse (£3.50) and perhaps parrot fish in lemon with barbecue sauce (£12.50); so popular are the megrims (Torbay sole), lobsters and langoustines that availability cannot be promised to later arrivals. Half portions for children, popular Sunday lunch (from £4.50) with hot fishy bits on the bar and flowery summer patios are all added draws. In addition, they serve a fine pint of Exmoor Ale and two dozen or more quality wines, though some of these are on the pricey side. *Bar Food* 12-2. *Restaurant Meals* 12-2, 7-9.30. *Children allowed in bar and restaurant to eat before 8pm.* *Beer* Boddingtons, Bass, Exmoor Ale. *Patio. Family Room. Access, Visa.*

Knightwick   **Talbot Hotel**

FOOD

Tel 01886 21235   Fax 01886 21060

B&B

Knightwick nr Worcester Hereford & Worcester WR6 5PH

Map 14 B1

On the banks of the river Tewe, on which it has fishing rights, the Talbot stands by a disused road bridge and conveniently back from the new crossing on the busy A44. Dating in parts from the 14th Century, it retains an evocative interior of oak beams and blackened brick, the bar's finest feature being the back-to-back open fire and cast-iron, wood-burning stove which share a central chimney. One of the long-resident Clift family is a whizz in the kitchen and produces commendably varied home cooking on a daily menu that services both bar and dining room. For a snack, try the blue cheese pancake (£4.25), salmon quiche (£4.95) or substantial Hungarian bean pot (£7.95), while diners may satiate themselves on a three-course meal of hot and sour fish soup (£1.75), sweet and sour pork (£7.50), or medallions of venison (£11.50) with, to follow, a summer pudding or treacle 'hollygog' – "pastry rolled with golden syrup and baked in milk until it goes all caramelly" (both £3). The bedrooms' up-to-date amenities include colour TVs, tea trays and dial-out telephones with little other obeisance to ostentation or modernity. Furnishings and decor are generally modest and comfortable in a cottagey style – best employed in the newer bedroom extension. Above the bars, three bedrooms are larger and more characterful but share their bathing and toilet facilities. Over 20 wines available by the glass. *Open 11-11, Sun usual hours. Bar Food 12-2 (Sun to 1.45), 6.30-9.30 (Sun 7.30-9).* *Restaurant Meals* 12-1.45 (Sun only), 7.30-9.30 (except Sun). *Children allowed in bar to eat. Free House.* *Beer* Bass, Worthington's, guest beer. *Patio/terrace, outdoor eating. Family room.* *Accommodation* 10 bedrooms, 7 en suite, £52 (single £31). Children welcome overnight (charged according to age, family room £66), additional beds (£10) and cots available. Access, Visa.

Knowl Hill   The Bird in Hand

| Tel 01628 826622   Fax 01628 826784 | **B&B** |

Bath Road Knowl Hill Twyford Berkshire RG10 9UP   Map 15a D3

Set well back from the A4, the inn that exists today bears little
resemblance to the hostelry bestowed with a Royal Charter by King
George III in the late 1700s. Today's extensions to the lounge bar and
patio, with umbilical connections to a new 15-bedroom wing have
incorporated much of the old stonework on the inside. In places it's a
seamless join, elsewhere the stitch lines are visible. Leather armchairs,
wood panelling and a huge canopied open fireplace are the major
features of the sturdy oak lounge. Good ales are on handpumps and
buffet lunch served in the Old Forge is a popular weekday attraction.
The new wing is centred round a brick courtyard facing a secluded
and mature garden. Though light on decor, with blush walls and lined
fitted units, the bedrooms are fully equipped for today's executive
market, and priced accordingly (rates are reduced at weekends).
Trouser presses and hairdryers are added to the usual accoutrements
of direct-dial phones and remote-control TVs. Bright bathrooms are
three-quarter tiled with strong over-bath showers. Double glazing
throughout keeps noise from the busy road fully at bay. *Free House.*
Beer *Fuller's London Pride, Brakspear, Flowers. Garden, disabled facilities.*
Family room. ***Accommodation*** *15 bedrooms, all en suite, £90 (single
£70). Children welcome overnight (under-5s stay free in parents' room,
6-12s £10), additional beds and cots available. Accommodation closed
23-30 Dec. Access, Diners, Visa.*

Zzzz...

Knowstone   Masons Arms

| Tel 013984 231 | **FOOD** |

Knowstone South Molton Devon EX36 4RY   Map 13 D2

Thatched, 13th-century inn tucked away in a tranquil hamlet in the
foothills of Exmoor, in the sort of spot where dogs fall asleep in the
middle of the road. Grade II listed with a charming unspoilt interior
characterised by heavy black beams, sturdy old furniture, huge
inglenook with roaring winter log fire and a delightful chatty
atmosphere. Super spot to while away an hour or two with a pint and
play a traditional pub game. Those tempted to linger for something
to eat will find that the home-cooked food complements the
surroundings – rustic, hearty and value-for-money. Light snacks or
starters include freshly-made soups – vegetable (£1.50) – excellent
patés such as cheese, walnut and cider or cream cheese, wine and herb
(£2.25), salads (£3.50). More substantial daily-changing specials range
from salmon kedgeree (£3.95) and liver and bacon hotpot (£3.95) to
poussin in orange sauce (£3.95), good curries – 'beef kheema' (£5.25)
– and filling pies like cheese and onion or venison (£3.95). Puddings
may include sticky toffee (£1.75). On Thursday evenings the menu is
devoted to speciality curries. The adjacent tiny, beamed non-smoking
restaurant is where the set dinner (£11.75) and the three-course
Sunday lunch (£7.25) is served. To accompany the food there is a
good list of wines – eight are available by the glass – and real ales
dispensed straight from the cask. Standard of accommodation ranges
from basic to homely, the most acceptable room being en suite and in
the adjacent cottage. Peaceful rear patio and garden with rolling rural
views towards Exmoor. 1½ miles north of the A361 midway between
Tiverton and South Molton. *Bar Food 12-2, 7-9.30 (to 9 Sun).*

Restaurant Meals 7-9 (*not Sun & Mon*). *Free House.* **Beer** *Cotleigh Tawney Ale, Hall and Woodhouse Badger Best. Garden, outdoor eating, children's play area. Family room. Pub closed 24, 25 & 26 Dec. No credit cards.*

Lacock   George Inn

Tel 01249 730263	**FOOD**
4 West Street Lacock nr Chippenham Wiltshire SN15 2LH	Map 14 B2

The virtual epitome of the traditional village pub. The George could scarcely be in a more ideal spot than the National Trust village of Lacock. Starting life in 1361 as the *Black Boy* with its own brewery in farm buildings to the rear, its many modernisations have preserved and re-utilised many of the original timbers. Central to the bar is a unique mounted dog-wheel built into the open fireplace and used for spit-roasting in the 16th-century (the dog was not roasted, but trained to rotate the wheel). Today's pub lives well alongside such idiosyncrasy with its close-packed tables on odd levels set beneath a wealth of old pictures at many an odd angle. From a menu of firm favourites, traditional steak and kidney pie (£4.50) is always popular alongside fresh chicken breast in white wine, cream and garlic (£6.95), 14oz T-bone steak (£8.25), plaice stuffed with prawns and mushrooms (£4.75) and a vegetarian cheese, onion and potato pie (£4.50). Desserts include apple and blackberry pie and sticky toffee pudding (both £2.50). The large garden stretches out on both sides of the rear car park; beyond it is a safe play area for youngsters, close by an old stocks to restrain the most troublesome. True to its long-standing identity as a family concern, the licensees' family not only provides overnight farmhouse accommodation nearby but also lays on complimentary transport to and from the pub. Enquiries should be addressed to the pub. **Bar Food** *12-2, 6-10 (Sun from 7). Children allowed in the bar to eat, children's menu.* **Beer** *Wadworth. Garden, outdoor eating, children's play area. Access, Visa.*

Lamarsh   Red Lion

Tel 01787 227918	**A**
Lamarsh Essex CO8 5EP	Map 10 C3

Enjoying a peaceful locatioin overlooking the gently rolling landscape bordering the River Stour valley, this charming little tiled Essex pub is the place to frequent on a sunny summer's evening as the perfectly positioned front benches make the most of the view. Beams abound in the comfortable modernised interior with its rather ecclesiastical, carved and inscribed bar counter and welcoming winter log fire. The 16th-century barn is now a games room and popular with locals. *Open 11-11, Sun regular hours. Free House.* **Beer** *Greene King IPA, Courage Directors & Best, Wadworth 6X, Marston's Pedigree, John Smith's. Garden, children's play area. Family room. Access, Visa.*

Langdale   Three Shires Inn

Tel 015394 37215	**B&B**
Little Langdale nr Ambleside Cumbria LA22 9NZ	Map 4 C3

Little Langdale stands at a point in the Cumbrian mountains where the former three shires of Cumberland, Westmorland and Lancashire once came together. Built in 1872 entirely in Lakeland slate, the inn sustained those crossing the nearby Wrynose and Hardknott passes to and from the coast. Still a travellers' haven today, the Three Shires is notable for its tranquillity amid restful scenery whose only early morning intrusions are the birds and nearby brook. The slate bar and streamside patio are nonetheless very popular with walkers throughout the day, and the standard fare served up is decidedly for the heartier appetite. Residents enjoy use of their own lounge and flower-laden verandah from which to soak up the views and relax. Bedrooms are bright and spotless with generally floral-patterned decor. Though four of the rooms are on the small side, and only three are family-size, their perennial popularity is due in no small measure to an absence of TVs and telephones: as ever was, solitude here is king. Although a rather 'adult' pub, families are well catered for; there's a terraced garden to one side of the pub through which a stream runs, and the restaurant and one of the bars are designated non-smoking. *Feb-Oct open 11-11 (Sun usual hours).* **Beer** *Webster's Yorkshire, guest beers. Garden. High tea from 5.* **Accommodation** *10 rooms, all en suite, £66 (single £33). Children welcome overnight (under-4s free if sharing parents' room), additional beds and cots available. Accommodation closed Mon-Thu Dec & Jan. No dogs. No credit cards.*

Langley   The Brewery Inn

Tel 0121 5446467	**A**
91 Station Road Langley Birmingham West Midlands B69 4LW	**Map 14 C1**

Turn off the M5 at Junction 2 and head directly into the so-named industrial estate; just less than a mile later, Station Road bears left past Albright and Wilson. Though it can't be seen now, there's a Thomas Telford bridge over the canal, known here as "The Crow" which is the highest navigable waterway in Europe. By the bridge brewers Holt, Plant and Deakins' pub is an authentic restoration of the Telford era; the Victorian "snob windows" which separate the lounge bar servery from the "public" may be one of only two sets left in existence. A larger window, picture size, allows tipplers a view of the brew house where Holt's ever-popular "Entire" is brewed, and used here by legions of real ale afficionados to wash down a "Dibble Donker", whatever that may be. Landlord Tony Stanton feels, he says, more like the curator than a publican, there's such a wealth of history here, so many gallons of pure enjoyment, if not to say barrels of laughs. Classical music or big band jazz plays. *Open 11-2.30, 6-11 (Sun 12-2.30, 7-10.30).* **Beer** *Mild & Bitter Holts Traditional & Entire on premises (up to 75 barrels per week), Greenalls Original, guest beers. No credit cards.*

L-0.5

Langley Marsh   Three Horseshoes

Tel 01984 623763	**FOOD**
Langley Marsh Weliscombe Somerset TA4 2UL	**Map 12 E2**

Handsome 300-year-old red sandstone village inn with a homely old fashioned interior that is full of curiosities, from collections of banknotes and beermats to model aeroplanes and pictures of vintage cars – the landlords spare time passion. Lively 'locals' front room with traditional games and a comfortable back bar with piano, stone fireplace, a rustic mix of sturdy furniture and perhaps piped jazz music. Further attractions are the numerous real ales and Perry's farmhouse cider tapped straight from the cask, and the reliably delicious food which is a 100% home-cooked. You will not find chips or fried food on the constantly changing handwritten menu, just hearty freshly prepared dishes with interesting vegetarian options. Choices may include Somerset fish pie (£4.95), beef hot-pot (£2.95), pigeon breasts in cider and cream (£5.25), courgette and mushroom bake, mangetout and tomato au gratin (both £4.50) and haricot beans in Galliano (£3.45). Filling snacks include warming soups, filled rolls and jacket potatoes. If there's room finish with mincemeat, apple and brandy pancakes or raspberry and almond cream (both £2.10). Alfresco seating on the verandah or in the garden for warmer days. **Bar & Restaurant meals** *12-2 7-9.30 (Sun to 9). Free House.* **Beer** *Ringwood Best & 6X, Young's, Butcombe Palmers IPA, guest beers. Garden, outdoor eating. No credit cards.*

Langstone   Royal Oak

Tel 01705 483125	**A**
19 Langstone High Street Langstone Havant Hampshire PO9 1RY	**Map 15 D4**

Historic 16th-century pub with stunning views over Chichester Harbour. Right on the water's edge, the water reaches the front door when the tide's exceptionally high! Originally a row of cottages used in conjunction with the adjacent old mill, they later traded under a "tidal license" before the bridge to Hayling Island was built, allowing travellers a drink while waiting for the ebb tide. An individual rustic charm characterises the unspoilt interior. The neatly kept bars boast flagstone and polished pine floors, exposed beams, open fires and old wooden furnishings; a cosy haven on wild winter days. Warmer sunny days can be enjoyed with a drink on the front benches or in the secluded rear garden, which is a safe refuge for families and where a pet's corner runs the gamut from budgies to goats and a pot-bellied pig. *Open 11-11.* **Beer** *Flowers, Gale's HSB, Boddingtons, Marston's Pedigree, guest beer. Garden, outdoor eating, beside water's edge. Family Room, children welcome inside. Access, Visa.*

Lavenham   Angel Inn

Tel 01787 247388	**FOOD**
	B&B
Market Place Lavenham Suffolk CO10 9QZ	**Map 10 C3**

First licensed in 1420, the Angel looks on to the market place of one of the best preserved medieval towns in England. Inside, the bar has been opened up without losing any of its original charm, with half set up for eating and the other half well supplied with board games, playing cards and shelves of books. There are quiz and bridge nights and on Friday evenings Roy Whitworth (one of the partners) entertains with classical music at the piano. Carrot and coriander soup (£2.25), fresh grilled sardines (£3.25), lamb in paprika and cream (£7.25), duck breast in juniper sauce (£8.50) and steak and kidney pie (£5.95) are typical offerings from the daily-changing evening menu; lunchtime brings similar dishes (at slightly lower prices) plus some more snacky items like ploughman's (£3.95) and cauliflower cheese (£3.50). Good puds (all at £2.45) include excellent fruit pies served with custard in a separate jug. Bedrooms are all en suite (four with shower and WC only) and full of character with old beams, sloping floors and traditional freestanding furniture. All have TV, direct-dial phone and tea- and coffee-making kit. Children are made welcome with a couple of high-chairs, free cots and "put-u-up" beds and, although there is no special menu, resident youngsters can be provided with beans on toast, and all children can have small portions of suitable items from the menu. For summer there are tables in a secluded garden plus permanent tables. *Open 11-2.30, 6-11 (Sun 12-3, 7-10.30).* **Bar Food & Restaurant Meals** *12-2.15, 7-9.15 (to 9 Sun).* **Beer** *Nethergate, Adnams, Courage Directors, Webster's Yorkshire,*

Mauldons. **Accommodation** *8 bedrooms, all en suite, £47.50 (single £37.50), £57.50 at weekends. Children welcome overnight, extra beds £10, cots free of charge. Garden, patio, outdoor eating for up to 100. Family room. Closed 25 & 26 Dec. Access, Visa.*

Laxfield   Kings Head

Tel 01986 798395	**FOOD**
Gorans Mill Lane Laxfield nr Halesworth Suffolk IP13 8DW	**Map 10 D2**

This unspoilt thatched 600-year-old village pub is a rare Suffolk gem that oozes charm and character. Locals know it as the Low House because it lies in a dip below the churchyard, just off the B1117. Little has changed here over the past 100 years, the interior comprising four separate rooms – the front parlour boasting a magnificent three-sided, high-backed settle that fronts the warming open fire – narrow passageways and low ceilings. There's no bar – too new-fangled a feature, instead excellent Suffolk ale and cider are drawn from the cask in the rear tap room. Expect good hearty home-cooking as befits the rustic ambience. The blackboard list of dishes may feature onion and potato soup (£1.50), Stilton and Cheddar with Suffolk rusks (£2.75), buck rarebit (£3) and traditional hot dishes like a decent chicken pie or liver and bacon, both served with well cooked vegetables (£4.95). Homely puddings include rhubarb crumble, baked rice pudding and apple and clove pie (£2). Summer brings Morris dancers and there's often live folk music. Garden with bowling green. Note the unusual inn sign which is undecided which monarch to celebrate; one side shows Henry VIII, the other Charles I. *Free House.* **Beer** *Adnams Southwold Bitter, Mauldon Suffolk Punch & Porter, Greene King, Abbot Ale. Garden, outdoor eating. Family room. No credit cards.*

Ledbury   The Feathers

	FOOD
Tel 01531 635266 Fax 01531 632001	**B&B**
High Street Ledbury Hereford & Worcester HR8 1DS	**Map 14 B1**

Between Malvern and Ross-on-Wye, a classic timber-framed former coaching inn and corn exchange dating from 1564 with oddly-shaped, en-suite, double-glazed bedrooms (including one with a four-poster), original Elizabethan wall paintings, uneven, creaky floors and drunken staircases. Remote-control TV, bedside tea-tray and hairdryers are standard. Good lunchtime snacks in the hop-bedecked Fuggles bar: Fuggles home-made soup (£2.95), grilled mozarella crostini with salad (£4.60), fresh salmon with green peppercorns (£4.95), spinach and ricotta cheese filo tart (£7.50), grilled Herefordshire steaks (from £10.25) and for dessert passion fruit syllabub, chocolate and maple syrup pudding, hot rum and raisin cheesecake (all £3.25). A traditional three-course Sunday lunch (£12.95) is served in the restaurant. Annual real ale and cider festival on August bank holiday, music weekly on Tuesdays and small rear patio available in good weather. Four miles from the M50 Junction 2. *Bar Food 12-2, 7-9.30 (Sat to 10). Children allowed in bar to eat. **Beer** Bass, Directors. Small Patio.* **Accommodation** *11 rooms, all en suite £78.50, single £59.60. Children welcome overnight, additional beds, and cots available (£5). Access, Diners, Visa.*

Ledbury   Ye Olde Talbot Hotel

Tel 01531 632963	**B&B**
New Street Ledbury Hereford & Worcester HR8 2DX	Map 14 B1

A Grade II listed building, the historic Talbot dates back to 1596 and was the scene of a well-documented skirmish between the Cavaliers and Roundheads in 1745. The classic Oak Room panelling is complete to this day with the bullet holes to prove it; here also there are magnificent Jacobean carvings and overmantel. Past a vast carved oak door guests have their own use of a tiny first-floor lounge in a bow-fronted cantilever room which overhangs the street above the front door. Bedrooms, complete with exposed beams and creaking, uneven floors, are much in character. Three only have room for en-suite WC/shower rooms, the remainder sharing loos and a bathroom: all contain oil-filled radiators, TVs, beverage trays and clock radios. Two beamed, copper-hung bars, warmed by open winter fires, are intimate and convivial, and there's also a rear courtyard for summer drinking and occasional barbecues. *Free House. **Beer** Hereford Supreme, Wye Valley Bitter, Ruddles County, John Smith's. Courtyard. **Accommodation** 7 bedrooms, 3 en suite, £45 (single £25). Children welcome overnight (under-12s stay free in parents' room), additional beds and cots available. No dogs. Access, Visa.*

Ledsham   Chequers Inn

Tel 01977 683135	**A**
Claypit Lane Ledsham nr South Milford West Yorkshire LS25 5LP	Map 7 D1

Deep in the Don valley at the heart of a hidden village stands the old ivy-covered Chequers, complete with a low, roadside, bow-fronted window that lends the pub an almost Dickensian air. In recent years the place has been turned around, with entrance to the bar and first-floor restaurant round to the rear, while the servery now has its back to the village street. Tiered above a pebbled walkway are the colourful flower-filled patios which form the beer garden, so well frequented in summer. It's a popular, thriving local, with good Younger's and Theakston's ales; the food remains conservative, with home-baked ham (£6.25) and smoked salmon scramble (with eggs, of course, £4.25) the best hot lunch dishes. Unwary customers may be steered in the evening towards the higher-priced Hastings dining room. By a quirk of the local licensing laws, the Chequers still operates a six-day licence and closes on Sundays. *Open 11am-11pm Sat, usual hours Mon-Fri. **Beer** Younger's Scotch & No 3, Theakston Best & XB, John Smith's. Patio. Family Room. Pub closed Sundays. Access, Visa.*

Leeds   Whitelocks

Tel 0113 245 3950	**A**
Turks Head Yard Briggate Leeds West Yorkshire LS1 6HB	Map 6 C1

Lauded by the poet laureate, John Betjeman, as "the very heart of Leeds", this was the city's first-ever Luncheon Bar. Owned for nigh on a century up to 1944 by the Whitelock family (who were builders and piano tuners), it's virtually unchanged since its last facelift (it coincided with the arrival in Leeds of electricity). The bar top is copper and the sandwich servery marble; the whole bar is fronted by hand-finished ceramic tiles. The well-heeled may lunch in a panelled rear dining room while the more down-to-earth may encroach on the many park benches which stretch the length of Turks Head Yard. Today's Luncheon Bar offers little beyond sandwiches, a pie or two and the famed Yorkshire puddings served with mince and onion gravy (£1.60). Over a decent pint of Younger's ale customers hark back to the pre-war prices (Pie 2d; Cheese and Biscuits 1d) etched on the old servery mirrors – evocative reminders of the Whitelock's heyday. No children indoors. No adjacent parking. Look for the pub sign high above Briggate (a pedestrianised shopping street opposite Debenham's); the entrance to the yard is now a tunnel and can be easily missed. **Beer** *Younger's IPA, Scotch Bitter, IPA & No 3, Theakston Best. Terrace. Access, Visa.*

Leicester   **Welford Place**

| Tel 0116 947 0758   Fax 0116 947 1843 | **FOOD** |

9 Welford Place Leicester Leicestershire LE1 6ZH   Map 7 D4

This striking Victorian building, designed by Joseph Goddard in 1876, stands at a convenient city-centre intersection between the High Street, Cathedral, Castle Park and Granby Halls. Formerly home to the private members Leicestershire Club, Welford Place is operated by the Hope family, who have so successfully run Lincoln's now-famous *Wig & Mitre* (qv) for over twelve years. Their latest classy operation promotes itself both as a watering hole for the seriously intentioned and a haven of peace. There are no music noises and, they hope, no pretensions. It opens for breakfast and morning coffee, offers a Specials menu which purports to change twice daily, and promises its à la carte will be available all day throughout the premises until 11pm. Thus, in the bar – a striking semi-circular room with high windows overlooking Welford Place itself and furnished with leather armchairs and glass-topped tables – a light, relaxing lunch might start with avocado and smoked salmon, followed by roast duck with red cabbage and end with bread-and-butter pudding, all washed down with a creamy pint of Ruddles. Salmon fishcakes (£7.50), lasagne (£7.25) and chicken liver paté (£4) also feature. Across the grand parquet-floored hall, the restaurant, a stolid, square room in blues and russets, appears perhaps a little more formal than it's intended to be, with an à la carte menu extending to warm lobster and brill paté (£6.50), lamb cutlets (£10.50), sautéed calf's kidneys (£12), home-made sorbets (£3.25) and hazelnut gateau (£3.25). The new Welford Place adjoins the recently reconstructed Leicester magistrates courts, from which it appears destined to draw much trade, as a kind of laborious lawyers' canteen. *Open 11-11 (also from 8 for breakfast) Mon-Sun (drinks served Sun with meals only).* **Bar Food & Restaurant Meals** *all day. Free House.* **Beer** *Ruddles. Access, Diners, Visa.*

Lenham   **Dog & Bear Hotel**

| Tel 01622 858219 | **B&B** |

The Square Lenham Maidstone Kent ME17 2PG   Map 11 C5

This attractive coaching inn dates from 1602 and overlooks the pretty village square. Splendid oak beams combine with new up-to-date decor and comfortable seating in the bar, and there is a welcoming little foyer-lounge. Centrally heated bedrooms with darkwood furniture and bright contemporary fabrics all have direct-dial telephones, TVs, tea-making facilities and neatly kept en-suite bathrooms. Main building rooms have more charm and character, with the newer rooms beyond the rear courtyard offering more space. 10 minutes from Leeds Castle. Invicta Country Inns. *Pub open 11-3, 5.30-11 (Sat 11-11, Sun 12-3, 7-10.30).* **Beer** *Shepherd Neame. Garden,*

paved courtyard, outdoor eating. **Accommodation** *24 bedrooms, all en suite, from £45 (single £35 family rate £60). Children welcome overnight, additional beds available. Access, Visa.*

Leominster   Royal Oak Hotel

Tel 01568 612610   Fax 01568 612710   **B&B**

South Street Leominster Hereford & Worcester HR6 8JA   Map 14 A1

Modest accommodation in an early-18th-century coaching house on the corner of Etnam Street and South Street. Historic relics of its earlier glories are to be found in the Regency Room, complete with chandeliers and minstrel's gallery, and the brick-lined cellar bar which is a cosy spot in the evenings. The main Oak Bar boasts two enormous log fires and serves good real ales and guest beers (Woods Parish Best, perhaps). Bedrooms come in a mixture of sizes and styles with one or two smallish singles, six spacious family rooms and a fine four-poster suite. All have carpeted bathrooms, while room comforts run through TV and intercom (for baby listening and wake-up calls) to tea and coffee makers and electric blankets. *Open 10am-11pm Mon-Sat, Sun usual hours.* **Beer** *Hook Norton Best, Wood's Special, guest beer. Small patio, outdoor eating.* **Accommodation** *18 bedrooms, all en suite, £45 (4-poster £55, single £31.50). Children welcome overnight (under 12s stay free in family rooms), additional beds, cots and baby-listening available. Dogs welcome by arrangement. Access, Diners, Visa.*

Ley Hill   Swan

Tel 01494 783075   **FOOD**

Ley Hill nr Chesham Buckinghamshire HP5 1UT   Map 15a E2

Character 16th-century pub in the capable hands of Matthew and Terri Lock, opposite the golf course, village cricket ground and open common land. The charming low-ceilinged rambling bar with cushioned window and wall seats, an old cooking range and sturdy wooden furnishings, and the neat dining room extension have been completely refurbished over the past year (the editor of this Guide was 'amused' to find the pub closed and looking like a building site early in March 1994, having driven a considerable distance with his family for a weekend inspection!). Good home-cooking can, however, once again be found on the varied main menu and the daily blackboard list, with choices like country vegetable soup (£1.70), pork and cider casserole (£5.25), salmon en croute (£7.25), chicken, ham and mushroom pie with vegetables (£4.30) and evening specials like roast goose in plum sauce and fillet steak stuffed with paté in a red wine and mushroom sauce (£10.50). Home-made puddings range from Belgian chocolate and rum mousse (£2.65) to blackberry and apple pie (£2.20). Occasional curry nights (£8.50) and regular Sunday roasts (£5.70). Interesting Cygnets menu (even including peanut butter and jam sandwiches) for the under-12s who are still finding their gastronomic legs, and the family welcome extends into the very large, safe garden to the rear of the pub with a patio, barbecue, pets area and wooden play equipment. Inside, children are welcome everywhere except in the bar itself. Live Jazz Tuesdays. Many a condemned rogue is said to have supped his last ale here before being taken off to the gibbet at nearby Jasons Hill; if you hear the infamous cry of a highwayman – Stand and Deliver! – on his white charger you'll know that not all the spirits in the pub are alcoholic. *Pub open all day Bank Holidays and Saturdays during cricket season, normal hours other times.* **Bar & Restaurant Meals** *12-2, 7-9 (no food Sun eve).* **Beer** *Benskins, Ind Coope. Garden. Access, Visa.*

Lifton   **Arundell Arms**

FOOD
B&B

Tel 01566 784666   Fax 01566 784494

Lifton Devon PL16 0AA   Map 12 C2

Set in a valley of five rivers, close to the uplands of Dartmoor, this
upmarket old Devon inn is a favourite destination for those who enjoy
the country pursuits of shooting, riding, walking, birdwatching and
in particular fishing – the River Tamar flows past the bottom of the
garden and the inn has 20 miles of fishing rights along its length.
A truly civilised air pervades throughout its smart interior, from the
elegant lounge with deep comfortable sofas and armchairs, antique
furnishings, tasteful fabrics and hunting prints, to the refined hotel-like
bar where good-quality bar snacks are served. The short printed menu
may feature a salad of avocado, French beans and potato (£3.75) or a
soup with home-baked bread (£2.50) to start, followed by interesting
salads (from £7) and light, imaginative hot dishes such as roast salmon
with an herb crust (£7.50), mignon of beef fillet with griddled
vegetables (£9.25) or a Spanish omelette (£5.25). Various sandwiches
and ploughman's are available, as is the daily dessert choice. The
adjacent handsome restaurant offers an à la carte menu and a set lunch
(two-course £11.75, three-course £14.75) and set dinner (£21.50)
menus. The attached and independently-run Courthouse Bar is a very
pubby locals' bar serving real ale and basic bar snacks. Expensive decor
and furnishings extend upstairs to the 29 bedrooms, although some
have plainer wall-fitted units; road-facing rooms are double-glazed to
quell traffic noise. Bathrooms are well appointed with good toiletries
and, as one can expect at this level, all the usual comforts grace each
room. Choice of seventeen wines by the glass, restaurant non-smoking.
Open 11-10.50 (Sun 12-10.20). Free House. **Beer** *Up to six guest beers.
Garden, outdoor eating area.* **Accommodation** *29 bedrooms all en suite,
£75/90 (single £37.50/56). Children welcome overnight (under-17s stay
free in parents' room), additional beds and cots available. Accommodation
closed 25 & 26 Dec. Access, Diners, Visa.*

Lincoln   **Wig & Mitre**

FOOD

Tel 01522 535190   Fax 01522 532402

29 Steep Hill Lincoln Lincolnshire LN2 1LU   Map 7 E2

The Hope family's trendy city-centre pub is not the historic ale-house
it purports to be, but is nonetheless a classic. Its really rather ordinary
exterior, a glass shop front under a flower-laden cast-iron balcony,
stands between the Lincoln Vintner and Chantilly's bridal shop;
Lincoln cathedral is just a stone's throw away across cobbled streets
where once the Roman *via principalis* ran, and its echoing hourly
chimes are almost deafening. The pub's interior – which also has a rear
access from Drury Lane – won a Business and Industry Award in
1978 for the meticulous restoration of its genuine Tudor timbers,
between which sections of 13th-century daub and wattle walls are still
visible. Connected by three staircases, there's a warren of rooms in
which to eat, two bars dispensing Sam Smith's Old Brewery bitter and
oak-casked Museum ale, and a tiny rear patio, as well as a table from
which you can pick up the day's papers for a browse. The menu
encourages all comers to eat as little or as much as they'd like at any
time throughout the premises, thus encompassing every taste and
pleasing all pockets, and the catering is ambitious: breakfast starts at

8am with the papers and food's served through to 11pm. There are
two daily blackboard menus, one taking over from the other at
around 4pm. From this, perhaps minted pea soup (£3), tuna and
lemon paté (£4), lamb braised with chili, ginger and mixed peppers
(£6), or, stepping up a level, fillet of sole with salmon and spinach
mousseline on a dill and butter sauce (£12.95). In addition, an all-day
à la carte extends the selection, and there's a choice of ten wines by the
glass. Daily puddings could include chocolate biscuit cake, raspberry
crème brulée, warm banana and almond loaf with crème Anglaise.
Bar Food *8am-11pm. Children allowed in bar to eat. Free House.*
Beer *Samuel Smith Old Brewery & Museum Ale. Patio/terrace, outdoor*
eating. Access, Diners, Visa.

Linton	**Bull**	
Tel 01622 743612		**FOOD**
Linton Hill Linton Kent ME17 4W		**Map 11 C5**

If you love fresh fish, then this ancient, half-timbered building located
halfway up Linton Hill is the pub for you. Delivered regularly from
Rye, Hastings and Folkestone, the choice includes whole sea bass
(£12.50), huss (£6.75), haddock, cod, brill and plaice, grilled or fried
in a good light batter. Other dishes on the menu include lobster and
salad (£12), crab and prawn salad (£7.25) and darne of turbot (£12).
Lasagne, steak and kidney pie and ploughman's are on the menu for
non fish-fanciers. Delightful rear garden with far-reaching views across
the Kentish Weald. *Pub open 11.30-2.30, 6.30-11 (Sun 12-3, 7-10.30).*
Bar Food *12-2.30 (Sun to 2), 6.30-9.30.* **Restaurant Meals** *as the bar.*
Children allowed to eat in the bar. **Beer** *Harveys Best Bitter, Morland Old*
Speckled Hen, Wadworth 6X, Adnams Best Bitter. Garden, outdoor eating
area. Access, Visa.

Linton	**Fountaine Inn**	
Tel 01756 752210		**FOOD**
Linton nr Skipton North Yorkshire BD23 JHJ		**Map 6 C1**

An idyllic village green complete with stone bridge over a little
stream is the setting for this charming mid-17th century inn which
was recently restored in sympathetic style by Francis Mackwood.
Several interconnecting rooms (one for non-smokers and one where
children are made welcome) feature old beams (plus some false ones
but its hard to tell the difference) and built-in settles. On a short
printed menu there are various open sandwiches (small from £2, large
from £3.25), cold platters such as home-roast ham (£5.50), tuna
(£4.75) and chicken (£5.25) plus the likes of gammon and eggs
(£6.75), lamb cutlets (£5.25) and fresh local trout (£5.50), not
forgetting the Linton Yorker – a giant Yorkshire pudding filled with
gravy (£2.50), sausage (£4.25) or the casserole of the day (£5.50).
For the sweet-toothed there are some good home-made puds (all at
£2), while for those with more savoury tastes there's the local
Wensleydale cheese which comes either blue, smoked or in the
traditional white style. For children there are "turkey aeroplanes",
farmhouse sausages or "golden fishes" (£2.75-£3) plus a single high-
chair. The village green is well used in summer although the publican
is not allowed to put out any tables or chairs. *Open 12-3, 7-11 (to*
10.30 Sun). **Bar Food** *12-2.15 (to 2.30 Sun), 7-9.15. Free House.*
Beer *Black Sheep Best Bitter & Special, Jennings Bitter. Family room.*
No credit cards.

Linwood   High Corner Inn

| Tel 01425 473973   Fax 01425 480015 | **B&B** |

Linwood Ringwood Hampshire BH24 3QY   Map 14 C4

Much extended and modernised, early 18th-century inn set in seven acres of the New Forest and located along a quarter-mile gravel track off the narrow lane linking Lyndhurst and the A338 near Ringwood. A quiet hideaway in winter, mobbed in high summer, it is a popular retreat for families with numerous bar-free rooms, a Lego/Duplo room, an outdoor adventure playground and miles of Forest walks. Overnight accommodation comprises eight well-equipped bedrooms offering teletext TV, telephone, trouser press, hairdryer, tea-makers and en-suite facilities. However, the food was disappointing on our most recent inspection. *Open 11-2.30, 7-10.30 (winter), 11-3, 6-11 (summer), 11-4, 6-11 Sat, 12-3, 7-10.30 Sun. **Beer** Wadworth 6X, Boddingtons, guest beer. Garden, outdoor play area. Family room (three rooms), indoor play room. **Accommodation** 8 bedrooms, all en suite, £59 (single £37.50), weekend £69. Squash court, DIY stabling. Children welcome overnight, extra bed and cot available. Check-in by arrangement. Access, Diners, Visa.*

Little Bedwyn   Harrow Inn

| | **FOOD** |
| Tel 01672 870871   Fax 01672 870401 | **B&B** |

Little Bedwyn nr Marlborough Wiltshire SN8 3JL   Map 14a B4

Effectively owned and operated by Little Bedwyn's villagers, who purchased the abandoned property in 1991, the Harrow is run by husband and wife cooks Sean and Louize Juniper: accordingly the emphasis in this tiny three-roomed pub is strongly on the food. Daily snacks, lunch and evening, are prominently displayed on a blackboard behind the bar. Soup might be leek and parsley (£2); the main courses asparagus and smoked salmon platter (£4.50), and for vegetarians, cheese avocado tortilla chip melt (£3.95). Evening meals, from Tuesday to Saturday inclusive, and Sunday lunches (£6.50) are more elaborate and the cooking, too, is stylish. Start with hare and armagnac terrine (£3.75) followed by poussin with three sauces (£8.50) followed by a selection of home-made desserts ranging from grape crème brulée and chocolate to mascarpone and blueberry roulade. In addition to Hook Norton Bitter, there's always a guest ale or two; the house wines only are sold by the glass, but there's an interesting list of predominantly New World bottles. Decor is minimal in the open-plan bar and dining area which leads through to an enclosed rear garden: size, however, dictates advance booking at weekends. Those wishing to stay have choice of a single, twin or double bedroom, each with en-suite bathroom, TV and beverage tray – but mercifully free of telephones and traffic noise. *Bar Food 12-2, 7-9. **Restaurant Meals** 12-2 (Sun only), 7.30-9.30 (no food on bar or restaurant Sun or Mon). Free House. **Beer** Hook Norton, two monthly changing guest beers. Garden, outdoor eating. Family room. **Accommodation** 3 Bedrooms, all en suite, £37/45 (single £22). Children welcome overnight. Check-in by arrangement. No dogs. Pub closed Monday lunchtime. Access, Visa.*

Little Braxted   **Green Man**

Tel 01621 891659	**FOOD**
Kelvedon Road Little Braxted Essex CM8 3LB	**Map 11 C4**

Tucked away in a tiny hamlet signposted off B1389 near the A12
Witham bypass, this unspoilt little brick-and-tiled pub has a
comfortable lounge decorated with a large collection of horse brasses
and a traditional, tiled public bar off which is a games room. Newish
landlords are producing some good, wholesome home-cooked and
value-for-money food which is attracting a loyal clientele to this
secluded country destination. A printed snack and sandwich menu is
supplemented by a sensibly short, daily-changing blackboard list of
dishes, such as lasagne with bacon, red wine, garlic and onions
(£4.50), hot crab pot with salad (£4.50), Italian pork (£3.95), Green
Man pasta pot (£4.25) and turkey, gammon and mushroom pie
(£4.95). Vegetarian options may include baked stuffed aubergine and
cheese and vegetable loaf (both £3.95). Finish off with a tangy home-
made lemon soufflé or steamed date and coffee pudding (both £2.25).
Rear tree-shaded summer garden. *Open 11-3, 6-11, Sun 12-3, 7-10.30.*
Bar Food 11-2.15, 7-9.30 (Sun 12-2, 7-9). Children allowed in bar to
eat. Beer Ridleys. Garden. No credit cards.

Little Canfield   **Lion & Lamb**

Tel 01279 870257	**A**
Little Canfield nr Great Dunmow Essex CM6 1SR	**Map 10 B3**

On the A120 Colchester to Puckeridge road, three miles from
Junction 8 of the M11 (3 miles west of Great Dunmow), this large
family-dining pub is 200 years old in parts with more modern
extensions. Open brickwork, exposed pine and artefacts inside while
the fenced garden is ideal for children (bouncy castle on long
weekends and an old boat has been turned into a play area). Children
may eat in the restaurant and choose from their own menu. *Free
House. Beer Ridleys IPA. Garden, children's play area, disabled WC.*
Family room. Access, Visa.

Little Compton   **Red Lion Inn**

Tel 01608 674397 Fax 01608 674521	**FOOD**
	B&B
Little Compton nr Moreton-in-Marsh Gloucestershire GL56 0RT	**Map 14a B1**

David and Sarah Smith run their charming 16th-century village inn
with warmth and pride, offering good plain cooking to match the
simple surroundings of exposed stone walls, beams and sturdy wooden
furnishings. Follow thick, spicy mulligatawny soup (£1.95) or
mushrooms in garlic butter (£2.95) with a huge helping of chicken
chasseur (£6.25), roast duck with black cherry, peach and orange
curacao (£8.95), home-made lasagne (£5.50) or rump steak cut from
the joint to your own specification (£8.60). Ploughman's platters and
filled granary rolls make lighter bites and there are puddings like
chocolate truffito or pina colada ice cream. Upstairs, the three
bedrooms overlook the attractive garden and share a spacious carpeted
bathroom, and each has its own washbasin and tea-making facilities.
Two rooms feature original beams and two have open stone walls.
Garden and play area. *Bar Food & Restaurant Meals 12-2 (Sun to*
1.30), 7-8.45 (Sat to 9.30). Beer Donnington BB and SBA. Garden,
outdoor eating. Accommodation 3 bedrooms, share bathroom, £34 (single

*£22). Children welcome overnight (minimum age 8), additional beds
(£10). Check-in by arrangement. No dogs. No smoking in bedrooms.
Access, Visa.*

Little Cowarne	The Three Horseshoes	FOOD
Tel 01885 400276		B&B
Little Cowarne nr Bromyard Hereford & Worcester HR7 4RQ		Map 14 B1

☺

Zzzz...

Though not immediately obvious, one can still make out the remains
of a tiny two-roomed pub that once stood on this site: the newest
brick is an uneven match with the old and dormers have been added
to the frontage. The Shoes' interior is now a spacious dining pub, with
considerable thought given equally to the needs of children and the
elderly or disabled. The success of Norman and Janet Whittall in
attracting both in equal measure is to be commended. Kitchen
production is also prodigious from light bar snacks of haddock and
prawn smokies (£3.50) or devilled kidneys on toast (£3.50) through
to a carvery Sunday lunch (2 courses £6.95). Seasonally changing
main courses offer near endless variety, many flavoured with fresh
herbs from the garden: rabbit with lovage in cider (£6.95) and cutlets
of salmon in chive sauce (£7.95). Among the home-made desserts
apple pie and sticky toffee cake (both £1.95) are perennially popular,
and the home-made ice creams are outstanding: brown bread or
loganberry, and one made with damsons – fresh from trees in the
paddock, naturally. A pair of quiet country bedrooms (one double,
one a twin) are done in an appropriate country style with a lovely
rural aspect. Free from intrusive telephones, they're otherwise bang up-
to-date with colour TVs, clock radios, tea-making facilities and small
but effective WC/shower rooms. *Bar Food 12-2.30 (Sun 12-2),
6.30-10 (Sun 7-9.30),* **Restaurant Meals** *12-2, 6.30-10 (Sun 7-9).*
Beer *Webster's, John Smith's, Ruddles County. Garden/patio, outdoor
eating, barbecue, children's play area. Family room.* **Accommodation**
*2 bedrooms, both en suite, £32 (single £16). Children welcome overnight
(under-5s free, otherwise half-price), additional beds and cots available.
Check-in by arrangement. Access, Visa.*

Little Hampden	Rising Sun	
Tel 01494 488393		FOOD
Little Hampden nr Great Missenden Buckinghamshire HP16 9PS		Map 15a E2

Nestling among beech trees at the end of a sleepy village lane, this
smart brick-built pub has become a popular dining venue in this
peaceful part of the Chilterns. A central bar serves three neat and
simply-furnished interconnecting rooms, warmed by an open fire and
a woodburner during the winter. A few prints and some interesting
indentures decorate the plain walls. A short inventive selection of
dishes (rather than the standard range of pub fare) is listed on both the
printed menu and on the weekly-changing blackboards. For starters or
a light snack one might choose from deep-fried filo parcel with
spinach, Brie and Stilton (£4.45), hot croissant filled with prawns and
asparagus (£4.75) or chicken livers with bacon and raspberry
vinaigrette (all £4.45). Varied main courses may feature grilled fillet
of sea bass (£8.75), home-smoked roast pork with pineapple and
barbecue sauce (£7.95), salmon coulibiac (£7.95), plus specials like
rack of lamb with a rosemary and herb sauce (£7.95), all served with
fresh vegetables. The Woodman's lunch is a particularly good value
and hearty lunch – soup, roll and Stilton, Cheddar, Brie, pickles and
salad for £5.95. Walnut toffee tart and peach crème brulée may be

found on the pudding board. Walkers are welcomed, but their muddy boots aren't in the bar. *Bar Food* 12.30-2, 7-9 (not Sun). Free House. *Beer* Marston's Pedigree, Brakspear, Adnams Better. Garden. Pub closed Sun eve & all Mon except Bank holidays. Access, Visa.

Little Longstone   Packhorse Inn

Tel 01629 640471	**A**
Little Longstone nr Bakewell Derbyshire DE45 1NN	**Map 6 C2**

18th-century village cottage tavern, full of old-fashioned charm. Popular with walkers doing the Monsal Trail which runs between Bakewell and Millers Dale. Real fires, no music, animals in the steep little garden. *Beer* Marston's Pedigree and Best Bitter. Garden. No credit cards.

Little Odell   Mad Dog

Tel 01234 720221	**A**
212 High Street Little Odell Bedfordshire MK43 7AR	**Map 15 E1**

A one-bar-only thatched pub close to the Harrold-Odell country park. Real fire (and a ghost) in the inglenook, no music, and a roundabout for the children in the garden. The name comes from a supposed cure for the bite of mad dogs which 18th-century landlords took in payment of a debt. Children not allowed indoors (the pub is too small), so it's only suitable as a family pub in summer. *Beer* Greene King IPA, Abbot Ale and Rayments. Garden, children's play area. Access, Visa.

Little Stretton   Ragleth Inn

Tel & Fax 01694 722711	**A**
Ludlow Road Little Stretton Shropshire SY6 6RB	**Map 6 A4**

Laying claim to be one on the oldest brick-built pubs in the land, the Ragleth is tucked at the foot of Long Mynd (National Trust), a haven for walkers. Boots, dry dogs and well-behaved children are allowed in the walkers bar: here the juke box can intrude pretty loudly, too. The lounge is a more sedate setting for a quiet pint, the enclosed rear garden offering a summer alternative. A small rear dining room offers more of the same. *Free House. Beer* Marston's, guest ales. Garden. *Family room. Inn closed Sunday evening. No credit cards.*

Littlebury   Queens Head

Tel 01799 522251 Fax 01799 513522	**FOOD**
	B&B
Littlebury nr Saffron Walden Essex CB11 4TD	**Map 10 B3**

Occupying a corner site in the village centre, this attractive yellow-painted inn dates from the early 15th-century and welcomes visitors into its carefully refurbished bar and dining room, which preserve low beamed ceilings, some standing timbers, a rustic red-and-black tiled floor and two cosy snug areas, one with easy chairs and open fire, the other furnished with sturdy wooden tables and chairs and sporting attractive wall stencilling. Reliable home-cooked food is a popular attraction here, the short daily-changing blackboard menu featuring an imaginative choice of dishes that draw on fresh herbs, vegetables and fruit grown in their extensive kitchen garden. A typical menu may list cream of fish soup (£2.20), chicken liver parfait and baked avocado with Stilton butter (£2.80) among the starters, followed by fresh fish specialities – ling with orange and basil, haddock with mushroom sauce, herring in garlic (all £5.90) – plus Oxford lamb

steak with raspberries (£7.50), shepherd's pie (£5.50) and pork chop with greengages (£5.90). Extra evening dishes generally include game options like roast pheasant brigerade (£8). Home-made raspberry flan. Regular lunch special of soup and light main course (£5), set 2-course roast lunch (£7.50) and fish and chip supper on Sundays. Frequently rotating choice of six real ales and a short list of 14 wines available by the bottle or glass. Accommodation comprises six uniformly decorated and furnished bedrooms with clean, tiled en-suite bathrooms. Two family rooms and a rather compact single room with tiny shower room. All – except the quiet rear room – face the main road and with no secondary glazing they could well be noisy. TVs, telephones, clock/radios and tea-makers are standard. Continental breakfasts only (the price below, along with all the B&B prices in this guide, includes cooked breakfast – £6). Sheltered walled garden with play equipment geared for younger children. *Open 12-11 (Sunday usual hours).*
Bar Food 12-2, 7-9 (no food Sun except residents may eat Sun eve). Children allowed in restaurant only to eat, children's menu. Free House. Beer Worthington Best, Timothy Taylor Landlord, Marston's Pedigree, Bass, Innkeeper's Bitter. Garden, outdoor eating, children's play area. Accommodation 6 bedrooms, all en suite, £57 (single £36). Children welcome overnight, £5 extra, additional cots available. Access, Diners, Visa.

Litton   Red Lion Inn

Tel 01298 871458	**A**
Litton nr Tideswell Derbyshire SK17 8QH	Map 6 C2

The Hodgson family have run their pub in their inimitable way since the 1950s. The less the Red Lion changes all these years on the more special it becomes as there are so very few left like it. One secret is to find the pub open and pop in for a "Boddy" or a pint, for instance, of Lancaster Bomber from a firkin racked up on top of the bar. Yet to eat here remains an evening, or weekend lunch, to be planned well in advance, especially in view of the Red Lion's restricted opening hours (which we list below), and its total resistance to change (which, hopefully, will continue). *Pub open 12-2 Sat & Sun only, 7-11 Tue to Sat. Free House. Beer Boddingtons, guest beer. Pub closed all Mon, L Tue to Fri, Sun eve, 10 days end of September. Access, Visa.*

Liverpool   Philharmonic Dining Rooms

Tel 0151-709 1163	**A**
36 Hope Street Liverpool Merseyside L1 9BX	Map 6 A2

Extraordinary cathedral of Victorian confidence and excess. Built in 1896 as a gentlemen's club, this Grade A listed building has glorious tiling, carving, panelling and etched glass. The woodwork was handcrafted by the shipbuilders at the time. It's a social museum piece but with modern intrusions like a juke box and fruit machine. Remarkable Victorian toilets (ornate with marble and tiles)! *Pub open 11.30am-11pm Mon-Fri. Beer Jennings, Burton, Walker Bitter, Best Bitter, Cains. No credit cards.*

Llanymynech   Bradford Arms

Tel 01691 830582	**FOOD**
Llanymynech Oswestry Shropshire SY22 6EJ	Map 8 D3

Village pub (the building is in England, but entry is via Wales through the front door!) with above-average food in its spotless, comfortably traditional bar. It's an old coaching inn that's been

Victorianised. The bar menu ranges from leek and potato soup (£1.75), warm brioche filled with wild mushrooms in Madeira (£2.75) to chicken in garlic and bacon cream sauce (£5.50) and venison casserole in juniper and gin (£5.95). The à la carte restaurant menu may offer king prawns with asparagus with garlic butter (£4.75), baked eggs in chive and sour cream sauce (£2.50), loin of lamb with almonds and port sauce (£12.25) and salmon with white wine and prawn sauce (£11.25). Very good puddings – rum and walnut gateau, American peach pie (both £1.95). 12 tip-top "real" British cheeses are helpfully described on the menu (choice of three £2.95). The 80-strong wine list offers a good spread. *Bar Food* 12-2 *(Sun to 1.45), 7-10 (Sun to 9.30).* *Restaurant Meals* 7-10. *Free House.* *Beer Marston's Pedigree. Children allowed in bar to eat. Patio, outdoor eating. Pub closed Mondays (except Bank Holidays). No credit cards.*

Loders   Loders Arms

Tel 01308 422431

Loders nr Bridport Dorset DT6 3SA

FOOD

Map 13 F2

When Roger and Helen Flint took over this unassuming stone pub over two years ago, it was just another struggling village local trying to survive on little custom. With only a few months previous experience in the trade, helping their friends out in a successful Sussex pub, the challenge ahead seemed very great. However, local curiosity and a good 'gossipy' grapevine throughout the area heralded a steady flow of customers through the door, in search of the honest home cooking that was a notch or two above the rest in both imagination and value-for-money. Initiation into the business soon became a rapid one when national media coverage brought hordes of folk from far afield to this small humble establishment, all expecting a table in its tiny 20-seat dining room. Popularity is so great now, it is advisable to book for both lunch and dinner. The Flints have learnt very quickly and cope admirably with the pressure. Standard of cooking is high and the freshest of ingredients are used in preparing the short selection of dishes on offer. Those popping in for just a bar snack will not be disappointed with the choice of four hearty hot dishes that are generally available, such as lasagne (£4.95), chicken and parmesan bake (£4.95), mushroom and broccoli quiche (£4.95), a freshly prepared soup – leek and Stilton (£2.50) – plus generously filled French baguettes (from £2.50). More imaginative fare can be appreciated in the simply furnished dining room, where a short yet varied list of interesting dishes is chalked up on a blackboard. The menu changes regularly with seasonal availability of produce and when new ideas/recipes are introduced, although some firm favourites remain faithfully on the board. To start, there may be smoked chicken and mango salad, spinach and goat's cheese pancake, fresh crab and coriander parcel (all £3.50) and chilled watercress and almond soup (£2.50), followed by a choice of at least 8 well-presented main courses, for example fresh salmon fillet with cucumber and mint salsa (£8.25), venison steak flambéed in gin with juniper berries (£9.50), duck breast with anchovy sauce (£8.95) and whole baby guinea fowl with Dijon and rosemary sauce (£9.25). As well as new potatoes, each dish is accompanied by four or fives crisply cooked vegetables. Summer diners can wait for their table in the small rear garden which enjoys rural hillside views. *Bar Food & Restaurant Meals* 12-2.30, 7.30-9 *(no food Sun eves in winter). Beer Palmers IPA, Bridport Bitter, Tally Ho, Palmers 200. Garden, outdoor eating. Access, Visa.*

Lodsworth   Halfway Bridge

Tel 0179 85281   **FOOD**

Lodsworth nr Petworth West Sussex GU28 9BP   Map 11 A6

On the A272 midway between Petworth and Midhurst, the mellow,
red-brick Halfway Bridge was originally built as a coaching inn in
1740. Today, efficiently run by the friendly Hawkins family, it's still
catering to travellers with real ales and real food from an extensive –
if rather crowded – blackboard menu that may range from garlic
stuffed mussels (£3.95) and mushrooms in cream and tarragon to
steak, kidney and Guinness pie (£6.25), lambs liver and bacon
(£5.95), lamb in red wine and rosemary (£5.95) and fish stew
(£6.75). If you're really hungry go for the half roast duck and honey
(£8.95) or the quails with orange and pernod sauce (£7.75), both
served with fresh vegetables. Those with room for a pudding could
try the walnut and treacle tart or the banana toffee pie (both £2.50).
The same menu operates in both the neat country-style dining room
and throughout the series of cosy, tastefully furnished interconnecting
rooms that form the bar. Real fires (one room features an old kitchen
range) offer a warm welcome in winter; for the summer there are
tables out on the lawn and on the sheltered rear patio. For a
celebration, try a bottle of the local Gospel Green méthod?
champenoise cider. *Free House.* **Bar Food & Restaurant** *12-2, 7-10.*
Beer *Gales HSB, Brakspear Bitter, Flowers Original, Brewery-on-the-Sea
Spinnaker Classic, changing guest beers. Garden, outdoor eating.
Access, Visa.*

Long Crendon   The Angel Inn   ★

Tel 01844 208268   **FOOD**
                                                                      B&B

Bicester Road Long Crendon Buckinghamshire HP18 9EE   Map 15a D2

Restaurant or pub? The distinction becomes rather blurred here, and
really doesn't matter anyway. Whether having just a bowl of soup or
a full meal one can eat either in the bar area with its old sofas and
wooden settles or in one of the several eating rooms – one showing   Zzz_{z...}
some of the original wattle and daub construction, another a Lloyd
Loom-furnished conservatory – with soft floral cloths on the tables.
The same menu appears on blackboards above the bar and on
handwritten sheets – if eating 'restaurant-style' – with everything from
freshly-baked baguette sandwiches (£4.25), pasta dishes like bacon and
pesto or marinated Italian seafood (two sizes £4.95 and £6.75),
bangers 'n' mash (£5.95), steak frites (£7.25) and ploughman's (again
two sizes £5.25 & £7.50) to Provençal fish soup with rouille
(£3.75), rack of lamb with glazed shallots and a honey and rosemary
glaze (£9.95), confit of duck with beans (£7.50) and steak au poivre.
With deliveries direct from Billingsgate a couple of times a week it's
worth checking out the day's fish dishes too. Of the four appealing, en-
suite bedrooms (two with shower/WC only) two are particularly
characterful with old black beams. Furniture varies from old pine to
some more modern pieces and all rooms have TV, direct-dial phones
and tea/coffee-making facilities. **Bar Food & Restaurant Meals**
12-2.30, 7-10 (not Sun). Free House. Beer Brakspear Bitter, guest beer.
Accommodation *4 bedrooms, all en suite, £50 (single £35). Inn closed all
day Sun. Access, Visa.*

Long Melford   **Bull**

Tel 01787 378494 Fax 01787 880307	**B&B**
Hall Street Long Melford Sudbury Suffolk CO10 9JG	**Map 10 C3**

Situated in the heart of this attractive old wool town, this magnificent half-timbered inn was originally built for a rich wool merchant in 1450. It became an inn over a century later and boasts a wealth of impressively carved and moulded oak beams throughout the elegantly refurbished interior. Beyond the entrance hall are two relaxing and tastefully furnished lounges with huge inglenooks and a separate pubby bar serving real ale. Weary travellers will find that the civilised ambience and high standards extend upstairs to the comfortable and well appointed bedrooms, all of which have clean ensuite bathrooms. Added extras include TVs, clock-radios and telephones. 10 bedrooms are designated non-smoking. Splendid courtyard with wrought-iron furniture beneath the old weavers gallery. Forte Heritage Hotel. *Open 11.30-2, 7-11 (12-3, 7-10.30 Sun). **Accommodation** 25 bedrooms, all en suite £85-£110 (single £65). Check-in from 2pm onwards. Children welcome everywhere (to 5 free, under 16 half price if sharing parents' room). Children's portions.* **Beer** *Greene IPA, Adnams Southwold. Access, Diners, Visa.*

Longframlington   **Granby Inn**

Tel 01665 570228 Fax 01665 570736	**FOOD**
	B&B
Longframlington Northumberland NE65 8DP	**Map 5 D2**

On the A697, cosy, attractively modernised little 18th-century inn with colourful window boxes and a busy dining business. Food is served in the restaurant as well as the bar-and-lounge. For the latter, food is ordered at the bar and from then on, tables are waitress served. The menu is extensive (from moules marinière to lobster, and mushrooms on toast to steak chasseur) and helpings very generous, served on enormous oval plates; vegetarian options like mushroom stroganoff or broccoli and cream cheese pie are also offered. Good puddings might include deep-filled home-made apple pie or a homely and boozy sherry trifle (complete with fresh strawberries in season). Main building bedrooms are small, neat and modern. Three garden chalets (mobile homes) incorporate a small sitting area, fridge and bathroom, and standards of housekeeping are reliably high everywhere. Good breakfasts; try the kippers. ***Bar Food** 11-2 (Sun 12-1.30), 6-9.30 (Sun 7-9.30). **Restaurant Meals** 7-8.30. Children allowed in lounge at lunchtime if over 8. Free House.* **Beer** *Worthingtons Best Bitter.* ***Accommodation** 5 bedrooms, all en suite, £57 (single £28.50). Children welcome overnight. No dogs. Access, Visa.*

Longleat   **Bath Arms Hotel**

Tel 01985 844308 Fax 01985 844150	**FOOD**
	B&B
Horningsham nr Longleat Warminster Wiltshire BA12 7LY	**Map 14 B3**

This dignified, stone and creeper-covered inn has been licensed for over two hundred years and, like the rest of the village, it is owned by the Longleat estate and provides a convenient watering hole for visitors emerging from the safari park. Inside, the homely Bradley Room and comfortably furnished lounge bar, decorated with old local photographs, plates and horsebrasses, set the scene in which to enjoy the short selection of home-cooked dishes that are listed on three blackboards around the bar. Fresh fish is delivered three times a week and may feature darne of salmon with dill and cucumber sauce

(£8.50), scallops pastis (£10.50), grilled lemon sole (£7.50) and occasionally John Dory and Dover sole. A speciality here is wild boar from animals reared on 25 acres of woodland in Dorset, its meat used in making a delicious paté (£3.50) and a generous mixed grill (£10.50). Other simple dishes range from chicken stuffed with apple and cheese (£7.50) and vegetarian quiche (£4.25) to rabbit casserole (£5.75). Upstairs there are seven light and airy bedrooms with attractive co-ordinating fabrics and a variety of modern and period furniture. Most have clean and basic bathrooms and all are equipped with TVs and beverage trays. Two groups of lime trees grace the front patios of the inn; one set is pollarded and is known as the 'Twelve Apostles', the other as the 'Four Evangelists' and both provide shady areas in which to enjoy a summer drink. Whisky enthusiasts can choose from some 60 different malts at the bar here. *Open 11-11, Sun usual hours.* **Bar Food** *12-2, 7-10. Children's menu in bar.* **Beer** *Butcombe Bitter, Wadworth 6X, London Pride. Garden, outdoor eating area. Family room.* **Accommodation** *7 bedrooms, all en suite, £52 (single £35). Children welcome overnight (under-2s stay free in parents' room, 2-5s £5) additional beds available. Access, Diners, Visa.*

Longstock   Peat Spade

Tel & Fax 01264 810612   **FOOD**

Longstock nr Stockbridge Hampshire SO20 6DR   Map 14 C3

Unusual paned windows overlook the peaceful village lane and idyllic heavily thatched cottages at this striking, red-brick and gabled Victorian 'pub' that nestles in the heart of the Test Valley, only 100 yards from the famous trout stream. The uncluttered and neatly furnished bar/dining room is delightfully music-free and is more akin to a smart restaurant, with individual tables sensibly arranged around a central magazine- and book-laden table. Combined with tasteful fabrics, effective subtle lighting and a warm welcome, a relaxed convivial atmosphere ensues in which to appreciate some quality pub food. There is no room for an array of microwaves, freezers and fridges here, so landlady and cook Julie Tuckett prepares to order all the simply described dishes – listed on the two short blackboard menus and on the value-for-money set dinner menu. Chicken, lamb and beef will not be featured here so expect a well-thought-out choice of dishes that rely on game – especially hare, rabbit and venison in winter – fresh fish, imaginative salads and delicious quiches and savoury tarts, freshly made using feta and Gruyère cheese. The seasonally-changing menu may include shellfish soup (£3.25), salade 'Maison' (£6.50 – a surprise dish of mixed leaves, melon, avocado, topped with warm and smooth Sussex goat's cheese and a light oil dressing), breast of guinea fowl, breast of goose, roast fillet of salmon with samphire (all £10.25), and tarte 'Maison' – aubergine, tomato and feta flan served with salad, £6.50. The short set 3-course dinner menu offers a choice of two dishes per course for £16.50. Puddings may include a very light bread-and-butter with clotted cream, and tiramisu (both £3.50). To accompany your meal, there is an impressive choice of at least fifteen wines available by the glass from the comprehensive wine list. Outdoor summer eating can be enjoyed in the large and secluded rear garden. **Bar Food** *12-3, 7-10.30 (except Sun eve). Free House.* **Beer** *Pendragon, Lionheart. Garden, outdoor eating. Pub closed Sun eve, 25 & 26 Dec. Diners.*

Longworth   **Blue Boar**

Tel 01865 820494

FOOD

Tucks Lane Longworth Oxfordshire OX13 5ET

Map 14a B2

Pretty thatched pub covered with wisteria in the centre of a small village. Inside are two log fires and quarry tiles on the floors – lots of atmosphere with old wooden skis hanging from the ceiling. Good-value food: typical dishes include home-made asparagus soup (£2.45), vegetarian lasagne (£4.75), beef and Guinness pie (£4.90), spicy chicken salad (£4.95) and good steaks. Follow with sticky toffee pudding or rhubarb crumble (both £1.95). The rear garden, complete with weeping willow and roses, has picnic tables for outdoor eating, as well as a vegetable patch which supplies the kitchen. A annual pig roast takes place on Whitsun May Bank Holiday. *Bar Food 12-2, 7-10 (Sun to 9.45).* *Beer Morrells. Garden, outdoor eating. Family room. Access, Visa.*

Lostwithiel   **Royal Oak**

Tel 01208 872552

FOOD

B&B

Duke Street Lostwithiel Cornwall PL22 1AH

Map 12 C3

Popular, 13th-century inn just off the main road in the original capital of Cornwall and supposedly linked to nearby Restormel Castle by a smuggling or escape tunnel. Catering for all tastes, the lively, slate flagstoned public bar (complete with juke box, modern and traditional games) attracts a good local following who seek out the choice of well-kept real ales – at least six brews – and the interesting range of bottled beers available. In contrast, the comfortably furnished and carpeted lounge bar has tables with red and white checked cloths and is very much geared to a dining clientele at both lunchtime and dinner. Close inspection of a fairly standard printed menu and of the additional blackboard selection of meals will reveal some good home-cooked dishes, such as Fowey salmon with dill and cucumber sauce (£7.50), Mrs Hines' 'famous' cow pie (£4.95), fresh local plaice (£6.25), Dover sole (£10.95) and an authentic curry choice (£4.75). Chips may arrive with the lasagne (£4.75), but most main courses have the option of a full salad and in particular the fish dishes are accompanied by an excellent selection of four well-cooked vegetables, including dauphinoise potatoes. Plainer pub fare – steaks (from £8), grilled trout (£6.50), ploughman's (from £2.75) and salads (from £4.45) – is unlikely to disappoint in quality and presentation. To finish, clotted cream is served with a deliciously gooey treacle tart (£1.55). Those wishing to explore the area will find one of the upstairs bedrooms a most comfortable base. Spacious, well-decorated and furnished with a mix of period and pine furniture, they all have TV, radio/alarms, and beverage-making facilities, with four rooms boasting clean, en-suite bathrooms. *Bar Food & Restaurant Meals 12-2, 6.30-10 (Sun 7-9.30).* Free House. *Beer Flowers Original, Bass, Fuller's London Pride, Marston's Pedigree, guest beers. Outdoor eating area. Accommodation 6 bedrooms, 4 en suite, £51.50 (single £29.50). Access, Visa.*

Louth   **Masons Arms**

| Tel 01507 609525 | **B&B** |

Cornmarket Louth Lincolnshire LN11 9PY   Map 7 F2

Useful to know in an area not highly blessed with accommodation
pubs is the Masons, a former posting inn dating from the 18th
century. Right in the centre of the Cornmarket, the inn has been
given a new lease of life by resident proprietors Mike and Margaret
Harrison, who have refurbished throughout and created five new
bedrooms complete with well-equipped en-suite facilities. Two further
double bedrooms share a restored Victorian bathroom and separate
WC. Bars are open all day with fastidiously tended real ales on
handpump and seven wines available by the glass. A welcoming,
friendly inn. *Open 11-11 (Sun and bank holidays usual hours, summer
from 10am) Free House. **Beer** Bateman Dark Mild, XB, XXXB & Salem
Porter, Valiant, Marston Pedigree, Bass. **Accommodation** 10 rooms, 5 en
suite, £45 (single £20). Children welcome overnight, extra beds and cots
(£5) available. No dogs. Accommodation closed 25 & 26 Dec. Access, Visa.*

Low Catton   **Gold Cup Inn**

| Tel 01759 371354 | **A** |

Low Catton Humberside YO4 1EA   Map 7 D1

Five miles east of York, south of Stamford Bridge on the A166; can
also be approached from east of Kexby, off A1078. Modernised but
pleasant, relaxing and unpretentious pub run by Ray and Pat Hales;
there are two welcoming, real fires and high-backed wooden pews in
the rambling three-room lounge in contrast to a noisier back games
room. The beer garden/paddock at the rear of the building features
ponies, goats and geese and has access to the river
bank. *Free House. **Beer** Tetley, John Smith's. Garden, children's play area.
Pub closed Monday lunchtime (except Bank Holidays). No credit cards.*

Low Newton by the Sea   **The Ship**

| Tel 01665 576262 | **A** |

Low Newton by the Sea nr Alnwick Northumberland NE66 3EL   Map 5 D1

The 'village green' is just a grassy area enclosed on three sides by
fishermen's cottages, one of which is the pub, and on the fourth side
by the beach itself. As with so many coastal villages, public parking is
restricted to an area just away from the beach, leaving you a short
walk to the sand, green or pub – indeed popular with holidaymakers
and locals alike. The Ship is quite charming, largely as a result of the
Hoppers, who run it in a very friendly fashion. Outside, there are
picnic tables on the grass, while inside it has the air of somewhere
from the early part of the century – creels hang over the bar to
remind you of the seaside location. *Open 11-11 Mon-Sat Jun-Sep (Sun
and winter usual hours). Free House. **Beer** Webster's, Scottish & Newcastle
Exhibition, Courage Scotch. Garden. Family room. No credit cards.*

Lower Ashton   **Manor Inn**

| Tel 01647 52304 | **FOOD** |

Lower Ashton nr Christow Devon EX6 7QL   Map 13 D3

Small, traditional Teign Valley local with garden in front overlooking
fields and Valley. The welcome is friendly within the two homely and
simply furnished bars which are warmed in winter by open fires.
Good, unfussy, honest and home-cooked food prepared by the

landlady using fresh ingredients sees such hearty dishes as beef and apricot casserole (£5.75); lamb curry; pork, leek and prune pie; ragout of lamb; tuna and prawn bake (all £5.25) and vegetarian choices – mushroom provençale (£4.95), vegetable bake (£3.95) – on the daily specials board. This is also a chip-free zone! Real ale lovers have four brews to choose from plus regularly changing guest beers; 25 ales at the annual beer festival in September. *Bar Food 12-1.30, 7-9.30 (Sun to 9). Free House. Beer Wadworth 6X, Theakston XB, Bass, Cotleigh Tawny, guest beer. Garden, outdoor eating. Pub closed Mon (except Bank Holidays). No credit cards.*

Lower Beeding   Jeremy's At The Crabtree   ★

Tel 01403 891257 Fax 01403 891606	**FOOD**
Brighton Road Lower Beeding West Sussex RH13 6PT	**Map 11 B6**

Jeremy Ashpool relocated home three years ago (from *The King's Head*, Cuckfield) to the cream-painted Crabtree public house, which stands immediately alongside the A281 just south of Lower Beeding. The front of the building is Georgian and the rear section dates back to 1579 when it was a haunt for smugglers. Mentioned briefly in Hilaire Belloc's *The Four Men*, the pub is now tied to King and Barnes and features a good range of their beers including their new range of seasonal draughts. The bar is very simply furnished with just a few round tables and stools. One has to book to ensure a table in one of the restaurant's two rooms. The dining room is non-smoking or there's the characterful Smugglers, an ancient beamed room at the rear with an inglenook. In the evening the emphasis is very much on a three-course £19.50 (+10% service) menu and there's an additional, set, three-course menu for £9.50 (+10% service) midweek; the latter might feature a creamy mushroom and leek soup followed by baked cod with lemon and herb crust and end with strawberries and raspberries in cream. There is also a daily-changing, short à la carte lunch menu with dishes such as creamy fish soup with fresh haddock (£3.25), roasted Barbary duck salad with beetroot and orange (£4.25) mascarpone and asparagus tart with tomato dressing (£4.15); more substantial dishes might be ham and vegetable pie (5.95), wild rabbit with mustard sauce (£6) or grilled cod with mussels (£7.10). Delicious puddings to finish include an irresistible warm toffee pudding with butterscotch sauce (£3). Otherwise, there are simple sandwiches (prawn, smoked salmon) and ploughman's (from £3.25) with cheddar, Stilton, Tornegus or Shropshire blue for lunch only. *Bar Food & Restaurant Meals 12.30-2 (reduced bar menu Sun or £14.85 roast lunch), 7.30-9.45 (no eve bar menu, Monday gourmet nights, Tues-Thurs £9.50 midweek set menu special & 3-course à la carte £20.85). No food Sun eve. Beer King and Barnes. Garden. Access, Visa.*

Lower Brailes   George Hotel

Tel 01608 685223	**FOOD**
	B&B
Lower Brailes nr Banbury Oxfordshire OX15 5HN	**Map 14a B1**

On the B4035 four miles from Shipston on the Banbury road, the old George was a near-derelict property a mere two years ago. Things have changed rapidly under the Browns' experienced hands. Pine tables in the bright public bar and polished mahogany in the panelled lounge (opening through a French window into the picturesque flower garden) vie with one another as prime locations for a bar snack. Home cooking lies at the heart of everything, from the cream of celery and lentil soup (£2), rump steak and onion sandwich

(£3.50) and Thai recipe chicken curry (£5.95) to steak and kidney pie cooked in Old Hooky (£6.00). The former pool room and bottle store have been knocked through, the oak beams and splendid inglenook exposed and an intimate and romantic atmosphere created in the new dining room, though it's equally acceptable to have a less formal meal in the bar or lounge. Either way the prominent blackboards keep abreast of Peter Brown's latest shopping for bargains in Birmingham market. Typical results might be grilled darne of salmon served with warm basil dressing (£8.50) and escalopes of veal with white wine, mushrooms and cream (£9.75), appearing with generous portions of freshly-cooked vegetables, while Jane Brown lends her hand to the home production of such treats as jam sponge with custard and strawberry Bakewell tart (£2.80). Bedroom accommodation began to come on line, by stages, in September 1994, offering a high degree of comfort, style and amenities, including en-suite facilities with bath and shower, remote-control TVs, direct-dial phones, hairdryers and trouser presses. *Bar Food & Restaurant Meals 12-2, 6.30-9.30. Beer Hook Norton Mild, Best & Old Hooky. Garden, outdoor eating. Family room. Accommodation 6 bedrooms, all en suite, £48 (£35 single). Children welcome overnight (under-5s stay free in parents' room). Check-in by arrangement. No dogs. No credit cards.*

Lower Froyle   Prince of Wales

Tel 01420 23102	**FOOD**
Lower Froyle Hampshire GU34 4LJ	**Map 15a D4**

A rather modern and ordinary looking Edwardian-style village pub, built in the 1930s after the original thatched pub had burnt down. The modest open-plan bar and dining room is often busy with a dining clientele seeking out the reliably good home-cooked food that is on offer here. A regularly-changing blackboard menu, available lunch and evening, highlights the old favourites – chili (£4.20), lasagne (£4.80), grilled rainbow trout (£5.50) – and a few imaginative choices, such as duck breast in a green peppercorn sauce (£7.50) and a fresh fish list (mainly Thursday-Sunday) which may include roast monkfish with tarragon (£6.50), sea bass cooked with fresh ginger and spring onions (£10) and scallops wrapped in bacon (£7), all served with fresh crisp vegetables. In the evenings, a separate printed menu accompanies the blackboard and features beef Wellington (£12.85), veal cordon bleu (£11.80), chicken supreme with a Stilton and celery sauce (£7.70) and further fish dishes. A traditional 3-course Sunday lunch at £8.60 is good value and popular. Puddings are not so grand – strawberry flan, apple crumble and cheesecake. *Bar Food & Restaurant Meals 12-2, 7-10 (except Sun eve). Free House. Children allowed in the bar to eat. Free House. Beer Fuller's ESB & London Pride, Timothy Taylor Landlord, plus 2 guest beers. Garden, outdoor eating. Pub closed 25th Dec. Access, Visa.*

Lower Oddington   The Fox   ★

Tel 01451 870888 Fax 01451 870666	**FOOD**
Lower Oddington nr Stow-on-the-Wold Gloucestershire GL56 0UR	**Map 14a A1**

Tucked off the A436 just outside old Stow, this Cotswold hamlet is famed for its 11th-century church of St. Nicholas. Of rather more recent renown is The Fox, closed up until two years ago, now refaced in yellow stone and refitted internally with style and flair. Its balance between country brasserie and village pub has been carefully thought out in a succession of plainly furnished rooms with graduated colour schemes – from fresh, summery lemon, through magnolia to the rag-washed bar with 'designer nicotine overtones'. Food asserts its prominence in imaginative and colourful dishes that exhibit an equal attention to both flavour and balance. From Brie and broccoli soup (£2.25) or spinach soufflé with anchovy sauce (£3.95), progress to garganelle pasta with wild mushrooms, crème fraiche and fresh Parmesan (£4.95) or the popular salmon and potato fish cakes with parsley sauce (£6.95). There are peppered sirloin steaks (£8.95), a Sunday sirloin roast served rare (£7.95), yet there are also simpler snacks like French bread sandwiches with prawn mayonnaise (£3.25) or honey-roast ham and salad (£2.95). Among the desserts, the lemon crunch, treacle tart and 'Fox's chocolate challenge' (all £1.95) are all home-made, too. Excellent house wines by the glass are supplemented by a list of fine wines compiled by landlord Nick Elliot and his partner, Christopher Tatham. Their wholesale business, in an office adjacent to the car park, is already thriving. Since winning our Newcomer of the Year award last year The Fox is still ever-growing in popularity thanks, not least, to the pedigree and class of Vicky Elliot's work in the kitchen. Moreover it is abundantly evident that the whole team, in their own words 'run a pub because we want to run a pub' – and clearly do so to the satisfaction of all concerned! *Bar Food* 12-2, 7-10 *(Sun to 9.30). Free House.* **Beer** *Hook Norton, Marston's Pedigree, Taylor's Landlord, guest beers. Garden, terrace, outdoor eating. Family room. Access, Visa.*

Lower Peover	**Bells of Peover**	
Tel 01565 722269		**A**
The Cobbles Lower Peover nr Knutsford Cheshire WA16 9PZ		Map 6 B2

Recommended primarily for its atmosphere (although it's a popular local dining pub): originally a home for monks, a lovely, creeper-covered old pub by the church, at the end of a cobbled lane off the B5081. Toby jugs of all sizes and styles make amusing company in the snug, where the bar counter is to be found; the barless main room has a collection of copper and brass and decorative blue plates. Children are positively not welcomed. **Beer** *Greenalls. Patio/terrace. Visa.*

Lower Shiplake	**Baskerville Arms**	
Tel & Fax 01734 403332		**B&B**
Station Road Lower Shiplake nr Henley Oxfordshire RG9 3NY		Map 15a D3

Located 50 yards from the British Rail station (Paddington-Twyford-Henley service), the attractive garden of this red-brick pub near the Thames is a pleasant spot on sunny days for enjoying a traditional pint. Inside, the single bar is large and simply furnished, and a family room is available. For overnight guests, the three neat bedrooms have co-ordinated bed linen and curtains, TVs and tea-making facilities; they share a carpeted bathroom with separate shower unit. *Open 11-11 Sat.* **Beer** *Brakspear Special, Wadworth 6X, Boddingtons. Garden, children's play area. Family Room.* **Accommodation** *3 bedrooms, not en suite, £35 (single £20). Children welcome overnight (family room available, under-5s stay free in parents' room), additional beds & cots supplied. Check-in by arrangement. Access, Visa.*

Lower Wield   Yew Tree Inn

Tel 01256 389224

FOOD

Lower Wield nr Alresford Hampshire SO24 9RX

Map 14a C4

Isolated beside a narrow country lane off the B3046 Alresford-Basingstoke road, the Yew Tree acquires its name from the 300-year-old tree by which it stands. The local cricket pitch lies opposite and the sport is taken very seriously in these parts, the main, simply furnished, bar being particularly busy on summer Sundays. At other times, this welcoming rural retreat is a popular dining venue; the tables in the cosy, beamed restaurant are neatly laid with place mats, fresh flowers, linen napkins and are candlelit in the evenings. The attraction here is the reliable range of home-cooked food, from decent bar snacks like generously filled baguettes (from £3.50), baked potatoes (from £3.25), ploughman's (£3.25), ham salad (£5.95) and steak and kidney pie (£5.95) to a blackboard menu listing more inventive and ambitious dishes. To start, there may be rosette of avocado and fresh Cornish crab (£4.95), jacket potato with escargots (£3.95), followed by baked whole megrim with olive oil, lemon and herbs (£8.95), fillet of Angus beef with red wine and horseradish crust (£13.50) and roast breast of duckling with honey and peppercorns (£10.95), all served with a separate dish of fresh crunchy vegetables. To finish, try the steamed dark pudding or creme brulée (both £2.95). The simpler bar snacks are not available Friday or Saturday evenings. Traditional Sunday lunch features a choice of three roasts (2 courses £8.95), half price for children. Large peaceful garden with rural outlook. *Bar Food* 12-2.15, 7-9.45 (*Tue-Thu evenings only*). *Restaurant Meals* 12-2.15, 7-9.45 (*Tues-Sat evenings only*). *Children allowed in the bar to eat. Free House. Beer Diggers Gold, Cheriton Brewhouse Pots Ale. Garden, patio, children's play area. Pub closed Mon eve. Access, Visa.*

Loweswater   Kirkstile Inn

Tel 01900 85219

B&B

Loweswater nr Cockermouth Cumbria CA13 0RV

Map 4 C3

Stretching as far as the eye can see, the woods, fells and lakes are as much a draw today as they must have been in the inn's infancy some 400 years ago. The beck below meanders under a stone bridge, oak trees fringing its banks with mighty Melbreak towering above. The pub's interior retains the warm cosiness of interlinked rooms with an enclosed verandah, a TV lounge reserved for residents and the Little Barn housing a games room for wet days. Consistent with Lakeland tradition, lunches and afternoon teas are kept rather basic, with residents returning for table d'hote dinner (reservations only: £15). The oldest, and smallest bedrooms in the original cottage share bathroom and toilets, while those in the extension have more space and en suite facilities. All have background heating and Continental quilts; communal laundry and drying rooms are readily available for the droves of walkers who return nightly to make Kirkstile their home. *Open 11-11, usual hours Sun. Beer Jennings Bitter and Cumberland Ale. Garden. Family Room. Accommodation 10 bedrooms, 8 en suite, £50 (single £40). Children welcome overnight, additional beds (£12), and cots (£7) available. Bar closed 25 Dec. Access, Visa.*

Lowsonford   **Fleur De Lys**

Tel & Fax 01564 782431	A
Lowsonford nr Henley-in-Arden Warwickshire B95 5HJ	Map 14 C1

A long, low Whitbread pub with crooked chimneys and wrinkly roof
whose canalside position and outdoor tuck shop deservedly attract a
family clientele. A score or more picnic tables spread out along the
bank, from where parents can watch the longboats while the under-
12s master the climbing frames. The garden-side ketchup station of
plastic disposable packets suggests quite a lot about the food inside
(note table number before ordering); there are plenty of children's
meals and a galleried family room, complete with rocking horses and
high-chairs indoors. For parents, a toad-in-the-hole may just about fit,
without filling out, the bill. *Bar Food 12-9.30 (closed 3-6 in winter).*
Beer Boddingtons, Flowers Best & Original, two guest beers. Garden,
children's play area. Family room. Access, Visa.

Ludgvan   **White Hart**

Tel 01736 740574	A
Ludgvan nr Penzance Cornwall TR20 8EY	Map 12 A4

Dating from the 14th century and possibly older than the adjacent
church, this stone village local is well worth a trip inland, away from
the busy coast. The atmospheric interior has been carefully created in
old-fashioned style and is a most welcoming and relaxing place in
which to enjoy a drink, free from modern-day intrusions of piped
music and games machines that seem to feature in many of the pubs
in this touristy area. Ochre coloured walls, low beams, a rug-strewn
wooden floor and a motley assortment of rustic tables and chairs
characterise the main bar, and various jugs, mugs, books, prints and
bric-a-brac fill every nook and cranny around the room. An adjacent
small dimly-lit room boasts an old black kitchen range, a collection of
plates and two intimate boxed seating areas, one ideal for two people,
the other for a small private gathering. Real ale is tapped straight from
the cask and if visiting on a Monday evening you may find the local
male voice choir in full song. Greenalls. *Beer Flowers IPA, Cornish*
Original, Marston's Pedigree. Garden. No credit cards.

Ludlow   **Church Inn**

Tel 01584 872174	B&B
Church Street Buttercross Ludlow Shropshire SY8 1AW	Map 6 A4

One of the oldest sites in Ludlow, going back at least seven centuries,
the former 'Wine Taverne by the Cross' stands wedged between the
old Buttercross and St Laurence's church. A compact and convivial all-
day bar opens on to pedestrian Church Street; regularly changing
guest ales, landlord Stuart Copland's particular pride and joy, are a
feature here. Above, the bedrooms offer practical comforts, pastel-
coloured duvets, remote-control TVs and beverage faciliies. All are en
suite, though three have shower/WC only, and there's one spacious
family suite. The church clock may provide an early morning call,
though in the front rooms this may be interspersed with intrusive
traffic noise. Parking is difficult. *Open 11-11 Mon-Sat, regular hours*
Sun. Free House. Beer Ruddles, Webster's, guest Ales. Family room.
Accommodation 9 bedrooms, all en suite (3 with shower only), £40
(single £28). Children welcome overnight (meals charged as taken),
additional beds and cots supplied. Access, Visa.

Ludlow   Unicorn Inn

FOOD
B&B

Tel 01584 873555

Lower Corve Street Ludlow Shropshire SY8 1DU

Map 6 A4

Zzzz...

At the end of a row of 17th-century farmers' cottages stands this tiny half-timbered pub backing on to the river Corve, which flows into the Teme at Ludlow. Though dating from 1635, unbelievably only three years ago it housed a disco; today, under the impeccable guidance of Alan and Elisabeth Ditchburn, it's a jewel of a pub. The bar is all linenfold panels and original timbers in front of a vast stone-lined fire grate. Through to the rear, dining tables are neatly laid and cosily candle-lit at night. An eat-anywhere policy is sensibly applied to the main meals, chalked up daily on strategically hung boards. For starters, cream of broccoli soup (£2) or dim sum with spicy dip (£3.25); main courses of pork chop, apple sauce and onion gravy (£5.25) or venison with a port sauce (£7.75); and to follow, toffee pecan pie and lemon syllabub (£2). For those of lesser appetite are bar snacks of Evesham rarebit (£3.95), chicken tikka massala (£4.25) and fresh asparagus gratinée (£4.25). Additionally, a comprehensive vegetarian menu, regularly amended, offers Moroccan orange salad (£2), mushroom tikka (£5.25), savoury roast and jambalaya for vegans (£4.75). Not only is the food good, but the welcome is genuine and the service informal and friendly. Bedrooms are limited by space – and listed building constraints – from undergoing unsuitable alterations. Exposed roof trusses are certainly original and the creaking floors wholly in character. There are TVs available for those who can't endure the abundant peace and quiet. One bedroom only has a full en-suite bathroom – and it's tiny; two more have showers/WC only, while the remaining two bedrooms share adequate adjacent facilities. *Bar Food & Restaurant Meals* 12-2.15, 6-9.45 (Sun 7-9.30). *Free House. Beer* Bass, Worthington. *Garden, riverside terrace. Accommodation 5 bedrooms, 3 en suite, £40 (single £20). Children accommodated overnight by prior arrangement only, additional beds and cots available. No dogs. Access, Visa.*

Lurgashall   Noah's Ark

A

Tel 01428 707346

Lurgashall nr Petworth West Sussex GU28 9ET

Map 11 A6

450-year-old pub in a classic village green setting overlooking the cricket pitch. Perhaps best in summer when the tile-hung frontage is bedecked with flowers in hanging baskets and tables are set outside on the front grassed area; cosy in winter. *Beer* Greene King IPA, Abbot Ale & Rayments Special Bitter. *Family room. Garden. Access, Visa.*

Luxborough   Royal Oak

FOOD
B&B

Tel 01984 40319

Luxborough nr Dunster Exmoor National Park Somerset TA23 0SH

Map 13 E1

Nestling by a stream at the bottom of a steep-sided valley, deep in Exmoor's Brendon Hills, the recently re-thatched Royal Oak is a truly rural 14th-century inn. No piped music, no fruit machines and no posh fixtures and fittings have intruded here. In short, no attempt whatsoever to tart the place up for the holidaymakers, which is perhaps why so many flock here during the summer months. The several rooms have flagstoned or cobbled floors, low beams, old kitchen tables and hardly a pair of matching chairs. Besides uncontrived charm, another good reason for a visit here is the splendid

choice of well-kept real ales, with an ever-changing selection of guest
beers to supplement the regular names. An extensive menu ranges
widely, from sandwiches and jacket potatoes to home-made soups
(£1.95) partnered by great wedges of crusty bread, and substantial
main dishes like beef and Beamish pie (£4.95) with tender, lean meat
in a rich gravy cooked beneath a square of toothsome pastry. There's
always a vegetarian dish, and the ubiquitous fish fingers are offered to
children. Steaks and fish (Dover sole £10.95) and a few other extras
(fillet of pork £9.75) appear for the additional evening menu. It's still
very much a locals' pub: Tuesday night is quiz night, and every Friday
a folk club takes over the back room, which has a pool table (in
winter only). Two bedrooms are available for overnight guests but,
being above the bars, are probably not suitable for families with
children or others with an early bedtime. Rooms are perfectly clean
and respectable but this is not luxury accommodation: a bed and a
couple of sticks of old furniture is about it. The large, shared
bathroom is in good order. *Bar Food 12-2, 7-10 (Sun to 9.30).
Children allowed in rear bar to eat, children's menu. Free House.
Beer Flowers IPA, Cotleigh Tawny, Exmoor Gold, Bateman's XXXB,
guest beers. Garden, outdoor eating. Accommodation 2 bedrooms, £26
(single £20). No children overnight. Check-in by arrangement. No dogs.
Pub closed 25 Dec eve. No credit cards.*

Lyddington — The Old White Hart

FOOD

Tel 01572 821703   Fax 01572 821965

51 Main Street Lyddington nr Uppingham Leicestershire LE15 9LF   Map 7 E4

Truly a traditional local, standing by the village green with its honey-
coloured cottages and backdrop of the picturesque Welland valley.
Gatherings of the pétanque club are a regular feature of summer
evenings when the flower-filled beer garden is at its best. Menus
throughout the bars and restaurant are firmly British and equally
traditional. For lunch are the Anglesey eggs (baked in a ramekin with
leeks, bacon and cheese £2.95), Essex devilled whitebait (£3.25) or
mushrooms Lyddington (both £3.10) and the farmhouse recipe 'Hen
on her nest' (chicken, mushroom and herbs on a bed of sautéed
potatoes £6.25). More elaborate evening fare adds 'Trout the Welsh
way' (wrapped in bacon with leek and Caerphilly sauce – £5.70) and
fillet of lamb with apricot and thyme stuffing (£7.45). There's plenty
of choice for vegetarians on request and home-made desserts (£2.50)
show a bias towards fruit and cream. *Bar Food & Restaurant Meals
12-2, 7-10 (no food Sunday evening). Free House. Beer Greene King
IPA, Rayments Bitter, Abbot. Garden, outdoor eating. Ten flood-lit
pétanque areas. Access, Visa.*

Lydford — Castle Inn

FOOD
B&B

Tel 0182 282 242   Fax 1082 282 454

Lydford nr Okehampton Lydford Devon EX20 4BH   Map 12 C3

Just a stone's throw from open moors, the pink-washed, wisteria-
entangled Castle is certainly a pretty little pub, but it's not until you
go inside that you realise how old it is. Much is 12th-century, with
various later additions, and it just oozes atmosphere, with its slate floor
and low sagging ceilings turned a deep amber colour by time and
smoke. The place is literally crammed with bits and pieces collected
by landlords over the years, including several marvellous old high-
backed settles (some with little roofs), dozens of decorative plates,
numerous old photos and handbills and a fine collection of Hogarth

prints (not a fruit machine or juke box in sight). Seven of only 31 remaining Lydford pennies minted by Ethelred the Unready in the 10th century are on display, the rest being held by the British Museum. The Castle's reputation for good food and a friendly welcome is safe in the hands of owners Mo and Clive Walker. Mo controls proceedings in the kitchen producing an eclectic range of dishes that are listed on a daily-changing blackboard in the bar. Favourites are the Malaysian-style dishes – Thai chicken curry, beef rendang (both £5.75), Malaysian vegetable stew (£4.75) – and well cooked traditional dishes and home-made soups – ham and lentil, Stilton and asparagus (£2.20) – Dartmoor pie (£5.75), jugged hare (£6.75), salmon and trout fishcakes (£5.15) and pork and apple cobbler (£5.25), all served with fresh vegetables. At lunchtime, this menu applies throughout the inn, but at night it's limited to the smaller bar and snug, when the main bar becomes a restaurant offering a 3-course table d'hote menu (£14.50) and an à la carte choice. Six of the modestly comfortable bedrooms are en suite while the other two share a perfectly acceptable bathroom; antique furniture features in all rooms, the Castle Room sporting a four-poster bed. Special rates apply for 2-3 day stays. There is a lot to see in the vicinity of the pub. Immediately next door is the castle with its rather gruesome history; local folklore has it that even to this day the birds, sensing its evil, will not go near the place. Rather more welcoming, the church boasts some fine wood carving on no less than 69 pew ends, featuring all manner of birds, fish, flowers and animals as well as a very fine rood screen. Just a short walk away is the famously picturesque Lydford Gorge and its woodland walks. *Bar Food* *12-2.30, 6.30-9.30 (Sun from 7). Free House. Beer Dartmoor Best Bitter, Palmers IPA, Bass, guest beers. Garden, outdoor eating. Family room.* *Accommodation 8 bedrooms, 6 en suite, from £50 (single £37.50). Children welcome overnight (under-5s stay free in parents' room). Additional beds (£4-£15) & cots (£4) supplied. Access, Diners, Visa.*

Lympsham	**Batch Farm Country Hotel**	
Tel 01934 750371		**B&B**
Lympsham nr Weston-super-Mare Somerset BS24 0EX		Map 13 E1

Mr and Mrs Brown's hotel, with its 50-acre grounds, stands in open farmland through which the river Axe flows. Origins of the former farmhouse are evident in the beams which adorn the bar and residents' lounges, while the neat, practical bedrooms in an extension enjoy views of either the Mendip or Quantock hills. The adjoining Somerset Suite is a popular venue for functions up to 70. Lympsham is about 3 miles from Junction 22 of the M5. *Free House. Garden, coarse fishing.* *Accommodation 8 bedrooms, all en-suite, £54 (single £33). Children welcome overnight (rate depends on age), additional beds and cots available. No dogs. Access, Diners, Visa.*

Lynmouth	**Rising Sun Hotel**	
Tel 01598 53223	Fax 01598 53480	**B&B**
Harbourside Lynmouth Devon EX35 6EQ		Map 13 D1

Hugo Jeune has spent a great deal of money in lovingly restoring his 14th-century thatched pub and adjacent cottages which climb steeply up the slope from the Lynmouth breakwater. The bedrooms boast individual decor, stylish fabrics, pine furniture, colour TV, direct-dial phones and spotless bathrooms, and the top cottage, where Shelley spent his honeymoon in 1812, has been decked out for modern newly-

Zzzz...

weds: a double bedroom with four-poster bed, a sitting room and a private garden. There's another literary connection: R.S. Blackmore wrote part of *Lorna Doone* here. The inn owns a stretch of river for salmon fishing. *Free House. Beer Courage Directors, John Smiths. Garden. Accommodation 16 bedrooms, all en suite, £79 (cottage £110, single £44.50). No children under five, 5-12s half price, add beds (£10) and cots (£5) available. Dogs by arrangement. Closed January. Access, Diners, Visa.*

Macclesfield	**Sutton Hall**	**FOOD**
Tel 01260 253211 Fax 01260 252538		**B&B**
Bullocks Lane Sutton Macclesfield Cheshire SK11 0HE		Map 6 B2

Central to the building, a wood and stone-built 16th-century mansion in use as a nunnery until just 30 years ago, is the pub itself, which has a really stunning interior. The black oak beams, gnarled and knotted, which frame the bar, are certainly of much older origin than the rest of the structure (there having been a manor house on this site since 1093), and a unique atmosphere is created by the combination of oak panelling, exposed stonework, leaded windows and two large log-burning fireplaces, one of them guarded by a medieval knight in armour. The fiercely traditional bar menu is thus much in keeping with its surroundings. Starters and snacks are of the deep-fried button mushrooms stuffed with cream cheese (£3.25), home-made vegetable soup (£1.45) and home-made cannelloni (£3.45) variety, while the main dishes – goujons of lemon sole (£5.65), grilled sirloin steak (£9.25), spinach pancakes with ratatouille filling and sour cream dressing (£5.25) and perhaps a lasagne, all served with salad, chips or boiled potatoes are good value for money. The adjacent restaurant, kitted out in flock wallpaper with polished yew tables, takes itself a little more seriously, with a weekly three-course lunch at £10.95 (£12.55 on Sunday including an extra course) and a whole baby plaice or home-made steak and kidney pie are decidedly substantial, as are the cold desserts dispensed from the inevitable sweet trolley. Evening diners can enjoy a 4-course table d'hote menu (£19.95). Bedroom conversion by the present owners has seen the installation of bathrooms throughout, plus modern-day amenities like remote-control televisions, trouser presses, and hairdryers. The antique flavour, however, is well preserved in lace-covered four-poster beds and deep leather easy chairs, although (a penalty of antiquity) there's a distinct shortage of natural daylight through their leaded Gothic windows, further dimmed by heavily overhanging eaves. The Hall's immediate environs, backing on to a working farm at the rear, appear so close to ramshackle as to cause some initial concern, but the warmth of the interior and the casual tomfoolery between landlords Robert and Phyllida Bradshaw, staff and regulars suggest that such imperfection and incompleteness are not, perhaps, entirely accidental. *Pub open 11-11 Mon-Sat, usual hours Sun. Bar Food & Restaurant Meals 12-2.30 (Sun to 3), 7-9.45 (restaurant from 7.30). Free House. Beer Bass, Stones, Marston. Large garden, outdoor eating. Family room (weekend lunch). Accommodation 10 bedrooms, all en suite, £85 (single £68.95). Children welcome overnight (rate depends on age), cots available. Check-in by arrangement. Access, Visa.*

Zzzz...

Madingley   **Three Horseshoes**   ★

Tel 01954 210221 Fax 01954 212043	**FOOD**
High Street Madingley Cambridgeshire CB3 8AB	**Map 15 F1**

Built in the early 1900s, this neat white-painted, thatched pub with
tables outside and a pretty garden is all about eating. Young
chef/manager Richard Stokes's modern Mediterranean style of cooking
spills over from the smart restaurant menu (included in our Hotel and
Restaurant Guide) to an extensive blackboard menu for informal
eating in the bar. Risotto and oyster mushrooms (£3.50), tomato and
basil tart (£4), cottechino sausage with braised lentils (£5), fresh crab
salad with avocado, pink grapefruit, and ginger vinaigrette (£4.50),
daube of boeuf bourguignon (£8.50) and tandoori chicken with
spiced couscous (£7.50) all demonstrate how far this is from standard
pub fare. Puddings (at £3) are more familiar – crème brulée, sticky
toffee pudding, lemon tart – or there are some splendid unpasteurised
British cheeses from Neal's Yard Dairy. About 15 wines by the glass
(if one includes the dessert wines and a couple of vintage ports). *Bar
Food 11.30-2 (Sun 12-2), 6.30-10 (7-9.30). Free House.* **Beer** *Adnams
Southwold, Tetley, guest beer. Garden. Access, Diners, Visa.*

Maidensgrove   **The Five Horseshoes**

Tel 01491 641282	**FOOD**
Maidensgrove nr Stonor Henley-on-Thames Oxfordshire RG9 6EY	**Map 15a D3**

Well established with the country set as an eating house, this old brick
pub stands alongside the lane which winds past Russell's Water, off the
B481. Paper money from around the world frames the bar where
food is ordered, and there's little enough available, for two, for less
than a crisp bill or two. From a comprehensive list, where blackboard
chalk has been replaced by paint, are the likes of a prawn-filled baked
potato (with salad £5.50), pasta siciliana (£5.75) and baked avocado
with crab and prawns (£6.95). Daily dishes are nonetheless
prominent, with main courses of chicken supreme with creamy curry
sauce (£7.25) or scampi brochettes with Provençal sauce (£7.95)
being typical. Follow with home-made ice creams, crème brulée or
nutty treacle pie (£2.50). Barbecues in fine weather feature steaks and
lamb and chicken kebabs (£6.25) and there's patio seating under a
swaying octagonal awning. Hidden away to the pub's rear, the Café
Shoes attempts a little more adventure with main courses in much the
same price range. Individual tables, or the whole room for 20, are
bookable in advance. *Bar Food & Restaurant Meals 12-2, 7-9.30.*
*Beer Brakspear. Family Room, Barbecue patio and garden. No children
under 14 permitted in the bar. Access, Visa.*

Manchester   **Lass O'Gowrie**

Tel 0161-273 6932	**A**
36 Charles Street Manchester M1 7DB	**Map 6 B2**

A short walk from the city centre, right by the BBC, Lass O'Gowrie
is a must as much for Manchester's students of architecture as for
enthusiasts of real ale and micro-brewing. The building's facade is fully
tiled in brightly glazed browns and greens, quite literally shining as
a credit to the city's clean air. Inside, the cavernous neo-Victorian
recreation (somewhat gentrified for today's consumers) comes
complete with gas mantles, sanded floorboards and mock-antique
signboards. Above the bar are lined up some fine examples of the
ancient art of cooperage, while the lining of the pub's upper walls and

ceiling consists entirely of stretched hopsacks whose former contents have doubtless featured in many a brew. Central to the main bar is a glassed-in canopy through which the curious can gaze down into the cellar to see the vats. Lighter LOG 1035 and maltier LOG 1042 (indicative of their respective strengths) are the home brews hand-pulled up to the single servery and dispensed in staggering quantities. To temper a heavy lunchtime session cut sandwiches and the likes of bacon baps are on offer at very reasonable prices. Whitbread. *Pub open 11.30-11 (Sun usual hours)*. *Beer LOG 35 & LOG 42, Boddingtons, guest beer*. *No credit cards*.

Manchester   **Mark Addy**

Tel 0161-832 4080

FOOD

Stanley Street Salford Manchester M3 5EJ

Map 6 B2

Head for New Bailey Street where the old Albert Bridge crosses the River Irwell into Salford; on the Manchester bank opposite is the Pump House People's History museum. Once a jetty and waiting room for the river ferry, it is an imaginative and truly different pub that takes its name from the only civilian to be presented the Royal Albert Medal (VC) by Queen Victoria. Born on the banks of the Irwell, Mark Addy received this award for rescuing fifty drowning passengers from the river. Behind a waterside courtyard the single bar still sports the old flagstone floor and sandstone, barrel-vaulted brick ceiling encased behind full-length picture windows. Such is the range of cheeses on offer that it's best to visit in a sizeable party. Platefuls of tangy white Cheshire, Windsor Red and Sage Derby constitute a colourful display and are accompanied by baskets of freshly-baked granary bread. Shopping is meticulous: the blue Stilton comes only from Long Clawson Dairy in Melton Mowbray and the full-blooded Cricketer from Cricket Wallerby farm. As there are also several Belgian patés (including vegetarian varieties) to add to the feast, it's unsurprising – though undeniably generous – that take-away bags are also provided. *Pub open 11.30-11 (Sun 12-3)*. *Bar Food 11.30-8, Sun 12-3*. *Free House*. *Beer Boddingtons, Marston Pedigree, Pompey Royal*. *Outdoor eating*. *Pub closed Sun eve, 25 & 26 Dec*. *No credit cards*.

Manchester   **The New Ellesmere**

Tel 0161 728 2791   Fax 0161 794 8222

B&B

East Lancs Road Swinton Manchester M27 3AA

Map 6 B2

Very handy and decently priced accommodation, especially for families midway between the city centre and M62 (Junction 14) on the East Lancashire Road. "Per room" prices apply, including weekend discounts, with all the ground-floor doubles including fold-out sofa beds. Whilst remaining furniture and fittings are a mite utilitarian, up-to-date amenities include free satellite TV and radio channels, direct dial phones, hairdryers and trouser presses. Full en-suite facilities include heated towel rails and over-bath showers. Breakfasts, currently priced at £3.45 to include a full grill, are particularly good value. Children welcomed, with high-chairs, changing facilities, garden and play area all provided. Part of Greenall's chain of Premier Lodges. *Pub open 11-11 (usual hours Sun, 3-7 with food only)*. *Garden*. *Family room*. *Accommodation 27 bedrooms, all en suite, £46 (single £43); weekends £36/£33. Children welcome overnight, additional beds and cots supplied (no charge)*. *Access, Visa*.

Market Overton — Black Bull

Tel 01572 767677

FOOD

Market Overton Leicestershire LE15 7PW

Map 7 E3

Having bought a semi-derelict, part-thatched ale-house in 1985, John and Valerie Owen single-mindedly set about planning the conversion work needed to create what they were really after – a relaxed local pub with good-value dining. The bar's agreeable interior of red banquettes, polished tables, poker-back chairs and background popular music (there are speakers everywhere, even in the loos!) creates a chatty, relaxed atmosphere in which to engage in banter with the landlord and enjoy the beer. Across a central area of original flagstone floor is the dining room, converted from a garage, which offers the likes of sweet and sour chicken (£6.25), half a roast duck (£8.95), home-made soups (£1.75), seafood tagliatelle (£6.95) and blackboard specials like stuffed loin of pork (£7.50). Upstairs, one en-suite double and a twin bedroom (not inspected) are equipped with televisions and a tea tray. *Bar Food 12-2, 7-10. Beer Ruddles. Children allowed in bar to eat. Patio/terrace, outdoor eating. Access, Visa.*

Marsh Benham — Water Rat

Tel 01635 582017

FOOD

Marsh Benham nr Newbury Berkshire RG16 8LY

Map 14a B4

Kenneth Grahame's immortal *Wind in the Willows* was reputedly inspired by the countryside around here, and the book is also behind both the new name (it was formerly called the *Red House*) and decor of this recently reopened, thatched pub. The interior has been opened up into two rug-floored areas; one, with exposed brick walls, the other has walls covered with murals of riverside scenes; there is even an overgrown 'stream' (more of a pond, really) at the bottom of the garden where, with a little imagination, one might picture Ratty and his pals 'simply messing about in boats'. Foodwise, there is a nice varied selection on the one menu that is now served throughout; steak and mushroom pie (£6.25), variously-filled baguettes with salad and chips (£3.50), bouillabaisse (£3.95/£7.95), fillet of salmon in pastry with a creamy tarragon sauce (£8.95) and ploughman's (£4.35) are typical dishes. A few children's favourites are also offered. *Bar Food 12-2.30, 7-10 (to 9 Sun). Free House. Beer Brakspear, Toady's & Ratty's (Belcher's), Moley's (Mole's), Badger's (Hall & Woodhouse). Riverside garden, children's play area. Access, Visa.*

Marshside — Gate Inn

Tel 01227 860498

FOOD

Boyden Gate Marshside nr Canterbury Kent CT3 4EB

Map 11 C5

Delightfully set beside a lane in a tiny hamlet – 2 miles from A28 Canterbury to Margate road at Upstreet – and surrounded by farmland and marshes, this unpretentious rural retreat prides itself on still being "a talkers pub", in tandem with a thriving bar meal trade. Two welcoming and rustic inter-connecting rooms have quarry-tiled floors, a central brick fireplace with winter log fire and a selection of sturdy pine tables, chairs and old pews. Fresh, local produce is used to produce homely, honest English fare (spicy sausage hotpot £4), home-made vegetable flan (£3.65), hot bacon and mushroom torpedo (£1.75), along with home-made burgers and a famous black pudding sandwich (£1.35) served with mango chutney. Well-kept Shepherd Neame ales are dispensed direct from the barrel and free range eggs and local vegetables are also sold over the bar. Splendid summer garden with cottage flowers, stream and duckpond with resident ducks and geese – a constant amusement to children. Duck food 5p a bag. Live jazz every Tuesday, folk on Fridays and quiz night is Thursday night. *Pub open 11-2.30 (Sat to 3), 6-11 (Sun 12-3, 7-10.30).* *Bar Food* 12-2 *(Sat 11.30-2.30) 6-10 (Sun 12-2.30, 7-10). Children allowed to eat in the bar.* *Beer* *Shepherd Neame. Garden, outdoor eating area, summer barbeque. Family room. No credit cards.*

Marten   The Tipsy Miller

| Tel 01264 731372 | **FOOD** |

Marten nr Marlborough Wiltshire SN8 3SH   **Map 14a B4**

Formerly the 16th-century thatched "Nag's Head" which burned down at the turn of the century, this Victorian replacement stands right on the A338 6 miles south of Hungerford. In the same stable as the *Pheasant* at Shefford Woodlands and the *Royal Oak* at Wootton Rivers (qv), it has rapidly gathered a loyal following. A rather predictable blackboard menu produces such reliably cooked standards as home-made sausages with bubble and squeak (£4.95) or with onion gravy (£3.95); chicken stir-fry (£5.50) and trout wrapped in bacon (£5.75); feta cheese salad with black olives (£3.25) and ratatouille topped with melted Brie (£4.50) typify the healthy, meat-free alternatives. The pub has a convivial public bar and games room, a sheltered garden with swings and barbecue, and views over open country to Wilton Windmill on the hillside beyond. This is shared by a self-contained cottage by the car park which is available for up to three people on a bed and breakfast or self-catering basis. Management changes have, however, occurred since our last visit with the transfer of its popular managers Richard and Rachel Turner to a fourth pub in this expanding chain, the recently reopened *True Heart Inn* at nearby Bishopstone. *Bar Food* 12-2.30, 6.30-9.30 *(Sun 7-9). Free House.* *Beer* *Bass, Flowers IPA, Wadworth 6X. Garden, outdoor eating, summer barbecue. Access, Visa.*

Mayfield   Rose & Crown Inn

| Tel 01435 872200   Fax 01435 872200 | **FOOD** |
| | **B&B** |

Fletching Street Mayfield East Sussex TN20 6TE   **Map 11 B6**

Delightful 16th-century pub in a historic village pub, alongside what was the original London-Brighton road, now a quiet village lane. Unspoilt bars, particularly the two small front ones, have ochre walls, beams, and inglenook fireplace, two log fires, and an atmosphere in which shove ha'penny and cribbage are still keenly played. The same comprehensive menu featuring reliable home-cooked dishes applies both in the bar and cosy restaurant and there's an extensive global wine list. Start, perhaps, with crabcakes with ginger and spring onion chutney, or layered aubergine, leek, feta and walnut terrine (both £3.85), move on to Corsican chicken breast wrapped in smoked bacon and served with a garlicky sauce of shallots, olives and sun-dried tomatoes (£8.80), veal, wild boar, gammon and apple pie (£7.75) or Moroccan lamb Tajine with minted couscous (£7.50), followed by one of the home-made puddings (all £2.95) – treacle and walnut tart, exotic mixed fruit crumble, American baked apple cheesecake or lemon brulee. Upstairs are four quaint, beamed bedrooms each with antique pine furniture – one with a fine brass bed – a comfortable easy chair and are equipped with beverage-making facilities, TVs clock/radios, hairdryers and trouser presses. Excellent standard of

Zzzz...

housekeeping and spotless en-suite facilities. Breakfast is extra. Landscaped front terrace with village views. *Pub open 11-3, 5.30-11 (Sun 12-3, 7-10.30).* **Bar Food** *12-2, 6.30-9.30 (Sun 7-9).* **Restaurant Meals** *as bar. Free House.* **Beer** *Harveys Sussex Bitter, Adnams Southwold, Greene King, Abbot Ale, Felinfoel Double Dragon. Garden, paved terrace, outdoor eating, tables in garden.* **Accommodation** *4 bedrooms, all en-suite, from £48 (single £38), breakfast £13.90 for 2 extra. Children welcome overnight, additional child's bed £10. Check-in by arrangement. Small dogs welcome by arrangement. Access, Visa.*

Melksham   King's Arms

Tel 01225 707272 Fax 01225 702085	**B&B**
Market Place Melksham Wiltshire SW12 6EX	Map 14 B3

Across from Melksham's Market Place, the Bath stone former coaching inn with its cobbled forecourt and abundant flower displays is the old town's summer centrepiece. Residents here are well catered for with a quiet, cosy lounge leading through to an intimate dining room. By contrast, the lounge bar is functional, less private and appeared somewhat overdue for a face-lift when last we visited. Bedrooms vary between period, beamed style and the bright and more spacious, arched doubles favoured by those with work to do. Four smaller singles share two barely adequate public bathrooms, a fact reflected in their lower tariff. **Beer** *Wadworth, Bass, Henry's IPA: BX.* **Accommodation** *14 rooms, 10 en suite, £49 (single £45). Children welcome overnight (under-10s stay free in parents' room), additional beds and cots available. Access, Diners, Visa.*

Mellor   Devonshire Arms

Tel 0161 427 2563	**FOOD**
Longhurst Lane Mellor nr Stockport Greater Manchester SK6 5PP	Map 6 C2

A regular Devonshire drinker claims to have lived in Derbyshire, Cheshire and Greater Manchester without even having moved house, so close is the pub to this area's ever-changing boundaries. When Brian and Joan Harrison moved in here (he, weary of world travel, yet never world-weary), on to the menu came tiger prawns in filo pastry (£3.95), sardines Angola (£3.95) and Kung-Po chicken with sherry sauce (£4.95), thus extending the boundaries of good pub food. Authentic curries, however, remain Brian's abiding passion, with fresh spices and nan regularly ferried in from cosmopolitan Stockport. Kashmiri lamb; Raseda Jingha with prawns, ginger and yoghurt; buttered chicken Masala and Malaida Unday, the last word in curried eggs (all £4.95) are a representative sample. While the full menu is served only lunchtime at present, the Britannia Lounge, opening on to a rear patio, is available for evening 'entertaining', supplemented by jazz on Thursday nights. Cask-conditioned Robinson's, including the new brew 'Frederics', is electrically dispensed. *Open 11.30-11 Sat.* **Bar Food** *12-2.30, evening meals Mon only 7.30-9.30.* **Beer** *Robinson's. Garden, outdoor eating. Family room. Pub closed 25 Dec only. No credit cards.*

Mellor   **Millstone Hotel**

FOOD

B&B

Tel 01254 813333   Fax 01254 812628

Church Lane Mellor Blackburn Lancashire BB2 7JR

Map 6 B1

Daniel Thwaites, the Blackburn brewers, operate the Shire Inns chain; its original flagship, the Millstone remains true to its roots and is closest to the brewery. Pub first and foremost it has a thriving local trade and is consistently busy for bar food. Baked Queen scallops (£3.95/£6.90), salad niçoise (£3.50/£5.75) and smoked Scottish salmon (£5.20/£8.50) are offered as starters or main courses. More substantial offerings are the Cumberland sausage and Bury black pudding with creamed potatoes and brown onion sauce (£5.25) or a brochette of pork and peppers served with a salad (£6.95). By comparison, the à la carte restaurant and en-suite bedrooms are decidedly 'hotel' and priced accordingly. Rooms, in fact, come in both standard and executive grades with satellite TV, trouser presses and hairdryers throughout. Executive rooms receive rather more space, towelling bathrobes and top-drawer toiletries. Of great benefit to the less active is the wing of nine ground-floor bedrooms (there is no lift) which are also appreciated by parents of very little ones. *Open 11-11 Mon-Sat, regular hours Sun.* **Bar & Restaurant Food** *12-2, 7-8.45 (Restaurant till 9.30).* **Beer** *Thwaites Mild, Bitter and Craftsman. Patio. Family room.* **Accommodation** *21 bedrooms, all en suite, £74 (single £56). Children welcome overnight (under-16s free if staying in parents' room), additional beds and cots available. Access, Diners, Visa.*

Melmerby   **Shepherds Inn**

FOOD

Tel 01768 881217

Melmerby nr Penrith Cumbria CA10 1HF

Map 4 C3

After a dozen years as tenants here, Martin and Christine Baucutt have had the good fortune (and good sense) to buy from Marston's brewery the business for whose fine reputation they had worked so hard. Subsequent installation of Jennings beers from Cockermouth has proven an added bonus. At the heart of the operation, though, is Christine's cooking and it's no exaggeration that regulars cross and re-cross the Pennines simply to sample the variety on offer. On any one day, creamed mushroom soup (£1.80), Stilton and walnut pasta bake (£3.20), cheese, onion and courgette quiche (£3.95) and lamb's liver lyonnaise are just the 'Specials'; regular favourites, meanwhile, include bowls of chili (£3.40), lamb rogan gosht (£6.80) and chestnut and leek pie (£5.80). There's a traditional Sunday roast (main course £5.20). Up to a dozen sweets displayed on the counter (from £2.15) come with lashings of local Jersey cream, while cheese enthusiasts can choose from some twenty or more on offer, including interesting North Country varieties. A sensible, no-nonsense attitude towards the young enables grown-up meals as they'd like. No fish fingers here, but chips possible and scrambled egg, even, on request; high-chairs, too. A twenty-one bin wine list can be supplemented by 'tastings' from Martin's private cellar; less exotically, English country fruit wines are available by the glass, and there is a selection of at least 45 malt whiskies. **Bar Food** *11-2.30, 6-9.45. Free House.* **Beer** *Jennings Bitter, Cumberland Ale and Sneck Lifter, Marston's Pedigree, Greene King IPA. Family room. No smoking area and cobbled patio. Bar closed 25 Dec. Access, Diners, Visa.*

Meltham   The Will's O'Nat's

Tel 01484 850078   **FOOD**

Blackmoorfoot Road Meltham Huddersfield West Yorkshire HD7 3PS   Map 6 C2

For anyone deficient in map reading, this unusual name – "William's
(place), son of Nathaniel" – might topographically be described as
"Reservoir's (side) O'Meltham". Avoiding the village altogether it's
easiest to find off the A62 just south of Slaithwaite, passing
Blackmoorfoot reservoir, from where the pub's in full view. By the
same simple terms, the Schofields' food might be described as populist,
yet it's evidently fathered from a long-standing pedigree. Regular
instances of top-selling specials running out is, as ever, indicative of a
dedicated kitchen, and the constantly updated blackboards demonstrate
a downright determination to feed all comers. A plethora of
sandwiches runs from egg mayonnaise and rare roast beef (£1.40) to
bacon and black pudding (£1.95); snacks and salads galore include
green-lip mussels (£3.35), Greek feta and olive salad (£2.65) and
smoked salmon (£5.75). Some plentiful home cooking, straying
perhaps from quality towards volume, produces the likes of lamb,
potato and courgette bake (£4.20), chicken pieces in Stilton sauce
(£4.30) and admirable home-cooked tongue with mustard dressing
(£4.10). The majority of diners choose the upper eating area, away
from the central bar servery, where views are of the moorland and
surrounding hills. They're well served by friendly, hard-working
youngsters who wear their tabards proudly and make light at peak
periods of inevitable delays. *Bar Food* 11.30-2, 6-10 *(Sat from 6.30,
Sun 12-2, 7-10)*. *Beer* Tetley. *Access, Visa.*

Metal Bridge   Metal Bridge Inn

Tel 01228 74206   **B&B**

Floriston Metal Bridge Cumbria CA6 4HG   Map 4 C2

Pretty bed and breakfasting hostelry in a picturesque hamlet setting on
the Esk estuary. The exterior and bedrooms have experienced
complete refurbishments this year but the old bar (formerly a
fisherman's house) is still decorated with beamed bars, nets and rods.
The five bedrooms, four of which are en suite, are agreeably rustic
with pine furniture and nice views, and all have TVs – one is a single
with a separate but private bathroom. *Beer* Scottish & Newcastle Scotch,
Theakston's Traditional Ale. Riverside garden. Family room.
Accommodation 5 bedrooms, 4 en suite, £45 *(single £35). Children
welcome overnight (children stay free if sharing parents' room, family room
£50), additional beds & cots available. Access, Diners, Visa.*

Micheldever   Dever Arms

Tel 01962 774339   **FOOD**

Winchester Road Micheldever Hampshire SO21 3DG   Map 15 D3

Under threat of closure two years ago, this old Whitbread house has
been given a new lease of life by the enthusiasm of owner Michael
Penny, who has smartened the building up, totally refurbishing the
beamed interior. Three neatly furnished and carpeted interconnecting
rooms maintain a village local atmosphere, with a sensibly-placed bar
billiards table and darts board at one end, and for diners a comfortable
eating area close to the inglenook fireplace, plus a smart little adjacent
dining room. Popularity stems from the interesting selection of
freshly-prepared bar meals that are available here. A printed 'hearty
snack' menu is supplemented by daily-changing blackboard menus,

displayed around the fireplace, which may include for starters hot croissant with smoked turkey and melted Brie (£4.95), fresh wild mushrooms in white wine and tarragon (£3.50) or roulades of smoked salmon and cream cheese (£3.95). Main courses range from Dever game pie (£8.50) and chicken breast with port and cumin (£9.75) to baked swordfish on red pepper sauce (£8.50). On the short pudding list there is always a home-made ice cream (£3). A well-stocked bar boasts a good range of locally-brewed real ales, all of which can be sampled on summer days on the quiet patio to the rear of the pub. *Bar Food & Restaurant Meals* 12-2 *(Sun to 1.45)*, 7-10 *(not Sun eve). Children's menu in restaurant. Free House.* **Beer** *Hop Back Summer Lightning, Hall & Woodhouse Badger Best, XXXD Mild, guest beers. Garden, outdoor eating area. Family room. Access, Visa.*

Mickleham King William IV

Tel 01372 372590	**FOOD**
Byttom Hill Mickleham Surrey RH5 6EL	**Map 15a F4**

It's neither particularly easy to find nor to park at this old alehouse originally built for Lord Beaverbrook's estate staff; parts of the pub date back to 1790. Up a track above the *Frascati* restaurant (*before* the sign to Mickleham) on the main A24 heading south, north of Dorking; park at the foot of the hill and it's a short walk up it to the pub. Since the pub is on a steep slope it's rather rambly but the terraced garden is lovely, with splendid views across the Mole Valley, arbours, rambling roses and terracotta planters as a centrepiece; and there's even a serving hatch to the garden – handy for walkers with muddy boots. On a typical blackboard menu you might find a good selection of vegetarian dishes (perhaps up to five, and not all are equally successful, so get there early for the best choice – this pub is not a secret among vegetarians), ploughman's (£3.75), seafood pie (£5.95), jacket potatoes (around £4.75 with various fillings), breast of chicken with brandy and mushroom sauce (£6.75), jumbo sausage in French bread (£3.95) and cold poached salmon with salad and new potatoes (£6.95). Sandwiches are not served at weekends and there's not a chip in sight. Homely puds are all £2.50 or £2.75: bread-and-butter pudding with maple syrup, seasonal fruit crumble (rhubarb and apple) or treacle tart. Sunday lunch £6.95. No children under 12 in main bar area. Only suitable for families in summer. *Open 11-3, 6-11, Sun 12-3, 7-10.30.* **Bar Food** *12-2.15, 7-10. Free House.* **Beer** *Boddingtons, Adnams Best, Badger Best, monthly-changing guest beer(s). Garden. Family room. Pub closed Mon evenings. Access, Visa.*

Middleham Black Swan

Tel 01969 22221	**B&B**
Market Place Middleham North Yorkshire DL8 4NP	**Map 5 D4**

The stones that built this town-centre inn came from Middleham Castle at the time when Cromwell was punishing it for being on the Royalist side in the civil war. Today Middleham is a rather more peaceful and quite pretty little market town; the smallest in Yorkshire apparently. The comfortable bar comes complete with old beams and cushioned high-backed settles but it is the bedroom accommodation that we recommend here. The four rooms at the front are the most characterful (and the largest) with exposed ceiling beams but all are equally prettily decorated in co-ordinating, floral fabrics and wall coverings and most have French-style, sometimes fitted, furniture. All have neat carpeted bathrooms (the small single with shower and WC only) with showers over tubs; all rooms have TV, direct-dial phones and tea and coffee-making kits. The resident ghosts are reputedly quite friendly. *Free House.* **Beer** *John Smith's, Theakston Best, XB & Old Peculier. Garden, outdoor eating. Family room.* **Accommodation** *7 bedrooms, all en suite, £40/56 (single £25/28). Children welcome overnight (under-13s £12), additional beds & cots available (£5). Check-in by arrangement. Accommodation closed 24,25 & 26 Dec. Access, Visa.*

Middleton   Olde Boars Head

Tel 0161 643 3520	**A**
Long Street Middleton Greater Manchester M24 3UE	Map 6 B2

Established as a hostelry in 1632 and first licensed in 1753, this striking, timbered set of buildings is Elizabethan in appearance but arguably has even earlier origins; some remarkable remains of its original construction were unearthed and carefully preserved during restoration work by JW Lees's brewery in 1989. A small snug commemorates Middleton's favourite 19th-century son, the poet and radical Samuel Bamford. Elsewhere within a splendid building still divided by original timbers and oak partitions, the Fisherman's and Sessions room (the latter now given over to TV and darts) are careful recreations of former times. Tuesday evening discos and jazz every other Thursday drag the operation (almost) screaming into the 60s and 70s, while perhaps even more incongruously a 90s' closed-circuit TV screen behind the bar keeps a weather eye on any extra-curricular activity in the car park. No-smoking room at lunchtime (12-2). *Pub open 11-3, 5-11 Mon-Sat (usual hours Sun).* **Beer** *Lees. Paved rear patio. No credit cards.*

Middleton Stoney   Jersey Arms

Tel 01869 343234 Fax 01869 343565	**B&B**
Middleton Stoney nr Bicester Oxfordshire OX6 8SE	Map 14a C1

Small, family-owned and managed 17th-century Cotswold-stone inn, now a hotel and restaurant. Alongside the B430 (between Junctions 9 & 10 of the M40), it is well placed for Woodstock, Blenheim Palace and Oxford (even Silverstone race circuit). Unpretentious and cosy bars have a traditional feel. Cottagey bedrooms are divided between the main house (where wooden beams and creaking floors abound) and the courtyard, where they are a little more up to date; the Lily Langtry Suite has a four-poster bed and sitting room. Rooms are equipped with colour teletext TVs, direct-dial telephones and hairdryers; room service is also offered. Day rooms include a low-ceilinged bar warmed by an open fire and a new lounge with half panelling and comfortable seating. *Free House.* **Beer** *Youngers Scotch and Theakston. Children allowed in bar to eat. Garden, outdoor eating.* **Accommodation** *16 bedrooms, all en suite, £72 (single £59.50), suite £90, four-poster suite £110 (single occupancy £80). Children welcome overnight, additional beds (children under 15 free), cots supplied. No dogs. Access, Diners, Visa.*

Zzz_z...

Middleton-in-Teesdale   Teesdale Hotel

	FOOD
Tel 01833 40264	**B&B**
Market Place Middleton-in-Teeside nr Barnard Castle Co Durham DL12 029	Map 5 D3

At the centre of this rather austere stone-built village deep in the High Pennines the Streit family have been practising their own brand of hospitality for over seventeen years. If practice makes perfect they've little left to learn and offer much for others to learn from. Over the years the dayrooms have been carefully modernised throughout, tastefully furnished and immaculately kept. Audrey and her daughter handle the kitchen in a style which brings new respectability to the term "home cooking" while in the front-of-house former chef Dieter, in his own words, "helps to take the strain". Commendably varied bar menus, including an entire vegetarian section run from baked egg and asparagus gratinee (£3.00) for a snack, through to Hungarian goulash with noodles (£5.45) to poached salmon with potato and vegetable (£7.95). Residents are equally tempted to Table d'hote (£17.95) which changes nightly. Individually decorated bedrooms are for the most part full of colour and natural light, those on the first floor having neatly-kept, if rather basic, en-suite bathrooms. At the top level three new full tiled en-suite shower rooms have been carefully incorporated: the remaining rooms here, one of family size, share end-of-corridor facilities. In keeping with their own philosophy the Streits have resisted the provision of so-called "hospitality trays" (and room phones, too) in favour of a cheerily delivered early morning tea tray. But not *that* early! ***Accommodation*** *12 bedrooms, 10 en suite £50-60 (Single £38-50). Children welcome overnight.* **Bar Food** *12.30-2, 7.30-8.30. Outdoor eating.* **Restaurant Meals** *7.30-8.30 (12.30-2, 7.30-8.30 Sun).* **Beer** *Tetley Best. Access, Visa.*

Midhurst	**Angel Hotel** ★	FOOD
Tel 01730 812421 Fax 01730 815928		B&B
North Street Midhurst West Sussex GU29 9DN		Map 11 A6

Once a coaching inn dating back to the 16th century, the Angel is virtually plumb in the town centre. The plain white-painted Georgian facade gives no real indication of the warmth and welcome waiting within. Public rooms are largely centred around the two bars and restaurants with a relatively quiet residents' lounge area at the front. Furnishings throughout are a mixture of well-maintained polished antiques, deep relaxing armchairs and settees with paintings and prints on the walls – the usual traditional trappings that befit a well-cared-for establishment such as this. Bedrooms, all on upper floors, are either in the original building or in a purpose-built modern block to the rear. All are of a good size and comfortably appointed, offering all expected extras. Bathrooms too are up-to-date and kept in good order. Diners have a choice of two eating places, both offering the same food: the brasserie, adjacent to the bar is rustic in style and less informal in character and the dining room, in contrast, is spacious and classically elegant with large, well-spaced tables. Prices are cheaper in the brasserie. Peter Crawford-Rolt supervises and cooks, producing dishes as diverse as galantine of duck with a loganberry compote (£5.25), lobster, avocado and mango salad (£6.25), grilled Cornish monkfish with forest mushrooms (£12.50) and marinated chicken breast with polenta and aubergine relish (£8.50). The fish is particularly good here, the style of cooking is eclectic and the execution of the dishes first-rate. A banana tart, flamed with rum is a pyrotechnical then epicurean delight. Victorian walled garden. Eight wines by the glass. **Bar Food & Restaurant Meals** *12-2.30 (Sat to 3), 6-10 (Sun to 9.30, restaurant closed Sun). Children allowed in bar to eat. Free House.* **Beer** *Gale's HSB, BBB & Best Bitter, John Smith's. Garden. Children allowed in bar to eat.* **Accommodation** *21 bedrooms, all en suite, from £65 (single from £50). Children welcome overnight, additional beds (£20) available. No dogs. Access, Diners, Visa.*

Mill Green   Viper

Tel 01277 352010   **A**

Mill Green nr Ingatestone Essex CM4 0PS   Map 11 B4

Surrounded by woodland and common land a few miles north of
Ingatestone and the A12, the Viper is a popular, idyllically set little
country pub (formerly two cottages), best enjoyed after a wander
through the surrounding countryside. The charm of the environment
is enhanced by a peaceful, large garden full of shrubs and flowers
and the traditional, simply furnished interior of the two small bars.
A further draw since becoming a free house are the three regularly
changing and well-kept real ales. Simple snacks available lunchtime
only. No children inside. *Free House. **Beer** Regularly changing real ales.
Garden. No credit cards.*

Milton   Jolly Brewers

Tel 01223 860585   **A**

5 Fen Road Milton Cambridgeshire CB4 6AD   Map 10 B3

Painted cream and dark green with a picket fence around the front
garden roses and hanging baskets, from a distance the Jolly Brewers
resembles a cottage. Located 1½ miles from the A45, in the old part of
the village, it's appealingly unpretentious, with low-beamed ceilings,
pine and darkwood tables, and jugs of fresh flowers in the two bars.
The back garden has a slide and a swing. Children allowed in the bar
to eat lunchtime at weekends. The pub is said to "host a ghost".
***Beer** Flowers IPA, Tetley, Bass. Garden, outdoor play area. No credit
cards.*

Milton Abbas   Hambro Arms

Tel 01258 880233   **FOOD**
                                                             B&B

Milton Abbas nr Blandford Forum Dorset DT11 0BP   Map 14 B4

Crowning the top of this idyllic 'showpiece' village street, lined with
uniform thatched cottages and lawns, is the attractive long thatch of
the 18th-century Hambro Arms. Most days, especially in summer, the
attractively furnished lounge and dining room of this friendly inn are
busy with people seeking refreshment after a visit to Milton Abbey or
after climbing the long village street. Those who arrive early can
appreciate, on fine days, the picturesque village view from one of the
well-sited picnic benches to the front of the pub. Inside, there is a
comfortable collection of tables and chairs, two open fireplaces – one
with woodburner – and an assortment of plates, jugs, copper and brass
artefacts, as well as local prints decorating the walls. A separate livelier
and rather spartan public bar houses the juke box and pool table. A
choice of food runs from standard snacks to more substantial dishes
such as their speciality pies – steak and mushroom and beef and oyster
(both £7.25) – a range of steaks (from £7) and a selection of four
vegetarian meals. More elaborate and imaginative dishes are featured
on the daily-changing blackboard, which regularly lists fresh fish from
Weymouth – halibut steak in tarragon butter (£6.95) – and well-
sauced meat dishes like pigeon breast en croute in a redcurrant and
cognac sauce (£7.95) or medallions of beef in a mushroom and cream
sauce (£8.95). A carvery now operates Tuesday to Saturday evenings
and Sunday lunch – £7.45 for two courses and £9.95 for three
courses. Upstairs and overlooking the village street are two pretty
individually decorated bedrooms. Floral, chintzy fabrics abound with

matching curtains and bedcovers and as well as the usual comforts of TVs, clock-radios and tea-makers, there are thoughtful extras like a stocked mini-fridge, fresh flowers, pot pourri and biscuits. En-suite bathrooms are well equipped with good toiletries and are spotlessly clean. A further two en-suite rooms are available in a village house a few miles away, details of which are obtainable from the inn. No children in accommodation or pub. Greenalls. *Bar Food 12-2, 7-9.30 (Sat to 10, Sun to 8.30). Beer Flowers Original, Boddingtons. Patio, outdoor eating area. Accommodation 2 bedrooms, both en suite, £50 (single £30). No children overnight. No dogs. Access, Visa.*

Mithian   Miners Arms

Tel 01872 552375

FOOD

Mithian nr St Agnes Cornwall

Map 12 B3

Ancient inn located in a picturesque village and only a mile or so from the bustling beaches of the north coast. Built in 1577, the inn is delightfully unspoilt and typically Cornish in character for it retains its traditional layout, featuring low ceilings, wonky walls, woodblock floors and an open fire in the main bar. A cosy lounge displays a genuine Elizabethan ceiling frieze, half wood-panelled walls and shelves full of books, bottles and interesting ornaments. Also of note is the fascinating wall painting of Elizabeth I, the penance cupboard which at one time had a beautifully carved mahogany seat and a secret passage that led from the inn to the manor house across the village lane. The cellar bar/games room is ideal for families and leads out into the sheltered garden. Bar food choices are limited to a short printed menu and a few daily specials, but what is on offer is good and mostly home-made. Local crab is used in preparing the crab bake which is served with walnut and dill bread and soups are freshly prepared. Main-course dishes include a chunky steak and kidney pie (£5.25) accompanied by fresh vegetables or salad, beef curry (£4.95) and good ploughman's (from £3.65). Specials may range from green-lipped mussels (£3.50-£7) to lamb and apricot casserole (£5.45). Attractive front cobbled terrace with picnic benches. *Bar Food 12-3, 6.30-9.30. Beer Marston's Pedigree, Boddingtons Bitter. Garden, outdoor eating area. Children's play area. No credit cards.*

Molesworth   Cross Keys

Tel 01832 710283

B&B

Molesworth nr Huntingdon Cambridgeshire PE18 0QF

Map 7 E4

Skittles, darts and pool are all enjoyed by the locals at this unpretentious, 200-year-old pub which has a relaxed and friendly atmosphere. The bedrooms are warm, quiet and comfortable. All rooms offer en-suite bathrooms, TVs and tea-makers. *Free House. Beer Adnams, Bateman's XB, Sam Smith's, Flowers Best, McEwan's Export. Garden. Accommodation 10 bedrooms, all en suite, £36.50 (single £23.25). Children welcome overnight (rate depends on age), additional beds and cots available. Access, Visa.*

Monksilver   Notley Arms   ★

Tel 01984 56217

Monksilver Taunton Somerset TA4 4JB

FOOD

Map 13 E2

The experienced Sarah and Alistair Cade have brought inimitable flair to this white-painted roadside village pub and have built up a formidably good reputation. The interior is charmingly simple: an L-shaped bar with plain wooden furniture, black and white timbered walls, candles at night, and twin wood-burning stoves; a small but bright and cheery family room leads off, and there's a stream at the bottom of the trim, cottagey garden. The big attraction here, though, is the bar food, which roughly divides into three categories – the traditional, the Eastern or exotic, and the vegetarian – all given equal thought, the finest fresh ingredients, and cooked with sure-handed skill. Old favourites and four or five daily hot specials are chalked up on the blackboard: start with an excellent home-made soup (£1.75), like a well-balanced tasty tomato and fresh plum or carrot and carroway (served with French-flour bread). For a light but satisfying lunch, choose one of the delicious pitta bread sandwiches with garlic butter, tender meats and good crispy salad. Chinese red roast pork (£5.75) features well-marinated cubes of meat in a soy, five spice and hoi sin sauce, with stir-fried pimento and courgette. The fresh salmon and spinach strudel (£6.50), old fashioned lamb casserole with onion dumplings (£5.75), home-made fresh pasta dishes at £3.95, bacon, leek and cider suet pudding (£4.75) and the Janssen's delight (potato and anchovy pie with cream £4.25) are equally fine, as are puddings, with light pastry and good local cream. Try the lemon and cottage cheese cheesecake (£2.50), apricot bread and butter pudding or treacle tart (£2.25), or a locally-made ice cream. A few more restaurant dishes like steaks and trout are added to the evening menu. Local scrumpy cider in summer. Despite the crowds at peak times, all runs effortlessly smoothly and with good humour. *Bar Food 12-2 (Sun to 1.45), 7-9.30 (Sun to 9).* **Beer** *Courage Directors, Ushers Best, Wadworth 6X. Riverside garden, outdoor eating. Family room. Pub closed 2 weeks end Jan-early Feb. No credit cards.*

Montacute   King's Arms Inn

Tel 01935 822513

Montacute Somerset TA15 6UU

B&B

Map 13 F2

A 16th-century hamstone inn that was once an ale-house owned by the abbey situated in a very picturesque and unspoilt village about 30 minutes from the sea. Today's comfortable little inn offers characterful accommodation in 11 en-suite rooms, one with a four-poster bed. The Windsor Room is a relaxing lounge; the Pickwick Bar remains the centre of village life, with its real ales and bar snacks. Follow a peaceful night with a decent buffet-style breakfast and a walk on the National Trust's wooded St Michael's Hill behind the hotel. All rooms have TV, radio/alarm, tea and coffee-making facilities, drinks tray and telephone. *Free House.* **Beer** *Bass, Wadworth 6X. Garden.* **Accommodation** *11 bedrooms, all en suite, £64 (single (£46). Children welcome overnight, additional beds (£7), cots supplied. No dogs. Access, Diners, Visa.*

Moreton-in-Marsh — Redesdale Arms

| Tel 01608 650308 Fax 01608 651843 | B&B |

High Street Moreton-in-Marsh Gloucestershire GL56 0AW   Map 14a A1

Flagstone floors, some old pine panelling and exposed stonework and a real log fire in winter, give some character to the bars at this brewery owned, former coaching inn on the main street of town. There's also a small rattan-furnished conservatory to the rear. Recently redecorated bedrooms offer all the usual amenities – remote control TV, direct-dial phone, hairdryer etc – plus carpeted en-suite bathrooms, all with shower over the tub. Premier House. **Beer** *Wadworth 6X, Davenport, Thomas Greenall. Family Room.* **Accommodation** *17 bedrooms, all en suite, midweek £36.40 (family £65.90, single £32.95). Children welcome overnight (Under-10s stay free in parents room, £5 breakfast), additional beds and cots available. No dogs. Access, Diners, Visa.*

Moretonhampstead — White Hart Hotel

| Tel 01647 440406 Fax 01647 440565 | B&B |

The Square Moretonhampstead Devon TQ13 8NF   Map 13 D2

A fine traditional inn, one of the friendliest in the area, and formerly a Georgian posting house. This is due largely to likeable landlord Peter Morgan (here since 1977), who is very proud of his inn's 400-year history of hospitality. The oak-beamed bar, where an open fire adds its cheery glow, houses all sorts of copper and brass bric-a-brac, and there is a comfortable lounge. TVs, radios and phones are provided in the spotless bedrooms, which are comfortably furnished in old-fashioned style; all of the rooms have private facilities including power showers. There are 15 golf courses within 30 miles, plus fishing on the Teign and marvellous walks in Dartmoor National Park. *Open 11-11. Free House.* **Beer** *Boddingtons, Bass, Smiles. Family room.* **Accommodation** *20 bedrooms, all en suite, £63 (single £43). No children under 10. Garden. Access, Diners, Visa.*

Morwenstow — Bush Inn

| Tel 01288 83242 | A |

Morwenstow nr Bude Cornwall EX23 9SR   Map 12 C2

Set in an isolated cliff-top hamlet close to bracing coastal path walks, the simple, traditional and very unspoilt Bush makes an ideal resting place. Once a monastic resting house on the pilgrim route between Spain and Wales, it is reputed to be one of the oldest pubs in Britain with parts dating back to 950 when it was a hermit's cell. Further evidence of its antiquity is the Celtic piscina carved from serpentine stone and set into one wall of the bar. Flagged floors, ancient built-in settles, old stone fireplaces and rustic furnishings characterise the charming two-bar interior. No children indoors. No dogs. Signposted off A39 at Crimp. *Free House.* **Beer** *St Austell HSD, guest beers. Pub closed Mon Oct-Apr (except Bank Holidays). No credit cards.*

Motcombe — Coppleridge Inn

| Tel 01747 51980 Fax 01747 51858 | FOOD |
| | B&B |

Motcombe Shaftesbury Dorset SP7 9HW   Map 14 B3

The Coppleridge Inn is a splendid example of how to convert an 18th-century farmhouse and its adjoining farm buildings into a successful all-round inn. Set in 15 acres of meadow, woodland and gardens it enjoys a lofty position with far-reaching views across the

ZZzz...

Blackmore Vale. The old farmhouse forms the nucleus of the operation, comprising a welcoming bar with stripped pine tables, attractive prints and a small gallery with seating. There's a comfortable lounge with flagstoned floor and inglenook fireplace and a delightful light and airy restaurant with open country views. In the bar a comprehensive blackboard menu lists the daily selection of reliable home-cooked dishes that are on offer. Begin with a good choice of soups – carrot and coriander, celery and Stilton and a thick and hearty guinea fowl broth (£1.75) – or artichoke with lemon mayonnaise (£2.50) and smoked trout paté (£4), followed by an interesting and varied range of main courses – all at £4.50 – such as John Dory in Cambozola sauce, lamb rogan josh, venison and wild mushrooms in red wine, kidneys in cider and Dijon mustard or haddock and mushroom gratin. Accompanying vegetables are fresh and crisply cooked. Home-made pizzas are a speciality on Tuesday and Friday nights. Restaurant fare is more elaborate with dishes of the day – quail's eggs and smoked chicken with rouille (£4.25), grilled duck breast with orange and ginger sauce (£10), guinea fowl supreme stuffed with paté in Madeira sauce (£10.50) – featuring alongside the regular menu. Wines are supplied by the Yapp Brothers and include a good French selection with at least eight offered by the glass. Across the lawned courtyard with benches and fountain are ten well-appointed, en-suite bedrooms, all superbly incorporated into the single-storey old barns. Tasteful, attractive fabrics, pine furniture, mini-bars, TV, telephones, radios, sparkling clean bathrooms with bidet and rural views characterise these comfortable rooms. Also part of the complex is a hair salon and a magnificent 18th-century barn that has been converted into a conference and function room. *Free House.*
Beer *Fuller's London Pride, Hook Norton Best Bitter, guest beer. Garden, outdoor eating area. Children's play area.* **Accommodation** *10 bedrooms, all en suite, £55 (single £35). Access, Visa.*

Moulton   Black Bull Inn

Tel 01325 377289   **FOOD**

Moulton nr Richmond North Yorkshire DL10 6QJ   **Map 5 E3**

A mile south of Scotch Corner, this usually very busy retreat from the A1 is as popular as ever for its bar food. The lunchtime meals venue is the characterful, relaxing bar, warmed by a roaring fire in winter. Light meals include Welsh rarebit and bacon (£4.50), sandwiches (£2.50), home-made soup (£2), seafood pancake (£3.75) and spare ribs (£4.25). The side room has become an informal Seafood Bar (no booking) – shellfish from the west coast of Scotland and seafood from the east coast of England. There's also an attractive Conservatory (complete with huge grapevine) and one of the original Pullman carriages, vintage 1932, from the *Brighton Belle* for the evening trade, when the pub becomes a fish and seafood restaurant proper – Dublin Bay prawns (£12.50), lobster (£16.50) and salmon with asparagus (£14.50). The Black Bull pub & restaurant's reputation, nurtured by the Pagendam family for 30 years, extends far beyond North Yorkshire and is recommended in our *1995 Hotels & Restaurants Guide.* Pub not suitable for children under 7. **Bar Food** *12-2 (except Sun).* **Restaurant Meals** *12-2, 6.45-10.15. Free House.* **Beer** *Theakston Best, Tetley Best. Patio/terrace, outdoor eating. Access, Visa.*

Mousehole   Ship Inn

Tel 01736 731234

B&B

Mousehole Penzance Cornwall TR19 6QX

Map 12 A4

Delightfully unassuming little fishing pub, set on the harbour in this beautiful coastal village of pretty fisherman's cottages and attractive narrow alleyways. The plain stone facade shields a most characterful interior, which retains much of its original rustic charm with heavy black beams and panelling, granite floors, built-in wooden wall benches and as one would expect a nautical theme pervades the bars. Busy harbour scenes and the panorama over Mount's Bay can be appreciated by residents from two of the three homely bedrooms. Simply furnished and decorated with pastel shades and matching floral fabrics, all have en-suite shower rooms – one with its own loo next door – TV and tea-making facilities. The relaxing window seats and views make up for the basic facilities in the room. A small sun-trap terrace overlooks the village rooftops. *St Austell Ales.* **Beer** *St Austell Cornish Bitter, Tinners Ale, HSD. Garden, outdoor eating. Family room.* **Accommodation** *3 bedrooms, all en suite, £30-£40 (single £15-£20). No credit cards.*

Much Wenlock   Talbot Inn

Tel 01952 727077

FOOD
B&B

High Street Much Wenlock Shropshire TF13 6AA

Map 6 B4

The civilised interior of this ancient 'residential inn' (originally a 14th-century abbot's hall) mixes original beams with plush-covered banquette seating; good open fires and nice touches like fresh flowers. There are also seats in the old courtyard (dating back to 1391). Bar snacks are supplemented with specials such as Shropshire pie (£5.50), omelettes and jacket potatoes or breast of chicken with yoghurt, cucumber and mint sauce (£6.25). Interesting varieties of ploughman-style picnic lunches at under £5 are also on the lunchtime list. On the evening menu there are dishes like Talbot tartlets (£2.95), sautéed mushroom and Stilton gratin (£6.95), lemon sole meunière (£8.75) and a choice of puddings (all £2.25) that includes their famous bread-and-butter pudding or butterscotch flan. A 3-course traditional Sunday roast lunch costs £8.95. Bedrooms are divided between the inn and recent malthouse conversion with its own breakfast room; rooms are pristine and modern with white cotton duvet covers and are equipped with TVs, tea and coffee-making facilities and hairdryers. "Well-behaved children welcome" in the bar. **Bar Food & Restaurant Meals** *12-2, 7-9.30 (Sun to 8.30).* **Beer** *Ruddles, Webster's. Patio, outdoor eating.* **Accommodation** *6 bedrooms, all en suite, £90 includes dinner for two (single £45). Children welcome overnight (minimum age 12). No dogs. Access, Visa.*

Much Wenlock   Wenlock Edge Inn

Tel 0174636 403

FOOD
B&B

Hilltop nr Much Wenlock Shropshire TF3 6DJ

Map 6 B4

The somewhat austere look of this stone roadside pub on the B4371 belies the warmth of welcome you'll find inside. To find it, follow the road a good four miles up the edge from Much Wenlock and into the National Trust Park: from the large car park opposite is a pathway to the spectacular observation point at Ippikins Rock. Home to the Warnig family for ten years now, its reputation as one of the area's friendliest hostelries is well deserved – that's not as tall a story as some

Zzzz...

of those told at the monthly 'story-telling-Monday' gatherings. The menu, like the landlord, is also on the chatty side with winter's popular 'wedgie pie' (£6.80), 'oink and apple' or locally-farmed venison casseroles giving way to such summery delights as tomato and red pepper soup (£2.25), fresh salmon and leek flan (£5.20) and smoked chicken and broccoli gratin (£6.20). Stephen Warnig plays host from the bar, breaking the ice between diners who are virtually rubbing shoulders at closely-packed tables and insistently urging follow-up portions of treacle tart and chocolate chimney (both £2.25), or perhaps the hot tipsy bananas (£2.90). Demand for overnight accommodation is constant from talkers and walkers, conservation and conversationalists who, when the babble dies down, are assured of a quiet night's sleep. All three bedrooms are smart and comfortable, with pine furniture and plenty of thick winter bedding: they have en-suite WCs and pressure showers supplied from the pub's own spring. Detached from the pub proper, the cottage room is the most spacious, with a convenient hallway to house walkers' boots and canine companions. A hearty breakfast here is de rigeur. **Bar Food** 12-2, 7-9 (*no food Monday*). *Children under 14 allowed in the dining room only to eat. Free House.* **Beer** *Wood's Special, Webster's Yorkshire, Robinson's Best. Garden, outdoor eating. Family room.* **Accommodation** *3 bedrooms, all en suite, £55 (single £40). Children welcome overnight, additional beds and cots available. No dogs. Pub closed lunchtime Monday (except Bank Holidays). Access, Visa.*

We welcome bona fide complaints and recommendations on the tear-out pages at the back of the book for readers' comments. They are followed up by our professional team.

Mylor Bridge   Pandora Inn

Tel 01326 372678	**FOOD**
Restronguet Creek Mylor Bridge nr Falmouth Cornwall TR11 5ST	**Map 12 B3**

Yachtsmen are welcome to moor their craft at the end of the 140ft pontoon that extends out into the creek from this superbly sited and most attractive thatched 13th-century building – one of Cornwall's best-known inns. A boat is by far the easiest way to approach this creek-side inn which lies at the end of a series of narrow lanes off the A39 (from which it is signposted) and it is advisable to arrive early as the car park soon fills to capacity on fine days. Named after the naval ship sent to Tahiti to capture the mutineers of Captain Bligh's *Bounty*, the Pandora retains its unspoilt traditional layout and boasts low wooden ceilings, wall panelling, flagged floors, a good winter log fire, a black-painted kitchen range and many maritime mementoes. It is not only the pub's position, patio and pontoon that attract folk here; the range of bar food will not disappoint visitors. Good fresh seafood and local fish is the main emphasis, with dishes like shell-on prawns (£3.95), seafood platter (£7.75), Restronguet fish pie (£4.75), moules marinière (£4.50) and local crab thermidor (£7.25). Puddings include home-made treacle tart, apple and raspberry pie or apricot and almond Bakewell (£2.90). Very popular are the hearty sandwiches (from

£2.50), in particular the Pandora Club (£3.95) and chocolate spread (with chips! £1.50) for chocoholic children! Daily specials might be peppered steak in red wine casserole (£4.95) or ham, leek and pineapple au gratin (£4.75). The Andrew Miller restaurant upstairs serves more imaginative dishes, especially fish, and enjoys peaceful river views. During the summer Cornish cream teas are served every afternoon in the bar or on sunny days out on the pontoon. Over a dozen wines served by the glass. *Open all day (11-11, to 10.30 Sun) daily in summer, usual hours in winter. Bar Food 12-3 (to 2.30 in winter), 6.30-10 (Sun to 9.30). Restaurant Meals 7-10 (Sun 9.30). Children's menu and portions. Beer St Austell. Access, Visa.*

Nassington — Black Horse Inn

Tel 01780 782324	**FOOD**
2 Fotheringhay Road Nassington Northamptonshire PE8 6QB	**Map 7 E4**

The white-painted Black Horse is a fairly restaurantish pub with a couple of dining rooms, one with pine ceilings, but drinkers can sit on stools at the bar counter (constructed from old oak doors reclaimed from Rufford Abbey) or in the pink, plush, beamed lounge area in front of an old stone fireplace that may once have warmed Mary Queen of Scots as it was originally part of nearby Fotheringhay Castle. One can eat in any part of the pub from any part of the extensive menu that covers snacks: steak sandwich (£4.85), home-made lasagne (£5.45) – appetisers: Camembert (£2.95), Dublin bay prawns (£4.35) – house specialities: magret of duck Montmorency (£9.95), chicken zingara (£8.95) – fish dishes: poached lemon sole (£8.95) – vegetarian dishes: vegetable and cream cheese crumble (£6.25), aubergine Margarita (£6.25) – steaks from the grill and puddings like a chocolate cup and a delicious blackcurrant and lemon pudding (£2.75). Despite the large menu – supplemented by a blackboard of dishes of the day – everything is home-cooked by hardworking chef Darrell Belliveau, who must look forward to Sunday lunchtimes when the menu is limited to a traditional roast lunch at £9.95 for three courses. There's a very pretty walled garden for summer eating and drinking. Watch out for the frequent theme nights and events. *Bar Food & Restaurant Meals 12-1.45, 7-9.45 (Sun to 9). Children allowed in bar to eat, children's menu. Free House. Beer Bass, Tetley, guest beers. Garden, outdoor eating. Access, Visa.*

Needingworth — Pike and Eel

Tel 011480 463336	**B & B**
Needingworth nr St Ives Cambridgeshire PE17 3YW	**Map 10 B2**

Located at the end of a long and narrow country lane right on the banks of the River Great Ouse, adjacent to a marina, the Pike and Eel dates back to the 17th Century. The present owner, John Stafferton, has been here 20 years and in that time has gradually upgraded and enlarged the property. The whole place has a very homely, traditional atmosphere with polished, beaten copper tables in the huge, oak-beamed bar. Next door is a much smaller, quieter residents' lounge where there's a warming coal fire in the open fireplace in winter. Upstairs, there's a further residents' lounge – once the TV room but now used rarely as all the bedrooms have televisions. They are all decorated in an attractive and pretty style, some with old-fashioned pieces of furniture, all well co-ordinated. Tea and coffee facilities are provided. Carpeted bathrooms are neat, modern and of good size. However, the public rooms take a 'lived-in' look to the extreme, with upholstery due for replacement. *Open 11-11 Mon-Sat, regular hours Sun. **Beer** Fuller's London Pride, Bass, Greene King IPA, Adnans Broadside. Riverside garden. Family room. **Accommodation** 6 Rooms, all en suite £55. Children free under 2 years, cot supplied (no charge). Access, Visa.*

Nettlebed   White Hart

FOOD
B&B

Tel 01491 641245   Fax 01491 641423
Nettlebed Oxon RG9 5OD

Map 15a D3

The Worsdells have done a splendid job over the last 18 months in reviving this 16th-century coaching inn on the A423. The red-brick exterior belies its age but once inside, old timbers, low beams and the creaking floor boards of the bedrooms tell of its history. In more recent times, the White Hart was the unofficial 'Mess' for nearby RAF Benson with Douglas Bader a frequent visitor and scenes from the film of his wartime exploits, *Reach for the Sky*, were filmed here. Today, food is a major attraction with a blackboard list of bar meals including steak and kidney pudding (£6.75) and ratatouille with brie and hazelnuts (£4.95) plus sandwiches at lunchtime. The more sophisticated restaurant menu features the likes of duck liver and orange paté (£3.50), salmon and monkfish dip (£8.25), rack of lamb with rosemary garlic and mustard (£8.95) and an excellent summer pudding. Afternoon teas (£4.75) come with home-made scones and a beautifully moist fruit cake. Six characterful bedrooms offer good cotton bedding, feather pillows and carpeted en-suite bathrooms with large soft bath-sheets. All have remote-control TV and direct-dial phones and extras like fresh fruit and a welcoming glass of sherry. Five of the six rooms face the road so some traffic noise is unavoidable despite the secondary glazing. A neat garden and patio to the rear make a good spot for summer drinking and eating. ***Bar Food** 12-2, 2-6 (afternoon tea), 6.00-10 (Sun 7-9.30). Children's menu. **Beer** Brakspear's Pale Ale & Special. Garden, outdoor eating. Family room. **Accommodation** 6 bedrooms, all en suite, from £59.50 (single £49.50). Children welcome overnight, additional beds by prior arrangement. No dogs. Access, Visa.*

Nettlecombe   Marquis of Lorne

B&B

Tel 01308 485236   Fax 01308 485666
Nettlecombe nr Bridport Dorset DT6 3SY

Map 13 F2

Recently reopened after a period of closure, this modernised and extended 16th-century inn enjoys an isolated rural position at the base of Eggardon Hill, 5 miles north east of Bridport and best reached from the A3066 Beaminster to Bridport road. Comfortably refurbished bar areas with access to the extensive and well-maintained garden with children's play area and valley views across Powerstock village. Improvements will extend upstairs into the seven plain, yet comfortable bedrooms, four of which enjoy clean and compact shower rooms. All are neatly kept and kitted out with modern white furniture, TVs, telephones and beverage-making facilities; most enjoy splendid country views. One room has a double and bunk beds. Enthusiastic and welcoming landlords. ***Beer** Palmers BB, IPA, '200' Ale. Garden, children's play area. Family room. **Accommodation** 7 bedrooms, 4 en suite, £46 (single from £20). Children welcome overnight. Access, Visa.*

Nettleton   Nettleton Arms

| Tel 01249 782783 | B&B |

Nettleton nr Chippenham Wiltshire SN14 7NP   Map 14 B2

This old mellow Cotswold-stone inn dates from around 1500 and
enjoys a peaceful rural setting, yet it is only a few miles from the
tourist honey-pot of Castle Combe. It was once the Manor House for
the Codrington family and despite much modernisation over the
years, it still retains some ancient timbers on the fine minstrel's gallery
in its welcoming and neatly furnished bar. A quiet and comfortable
night's sleep is ensured in the four bedrooms that have been
incorporated into the medieval barn across the courtyard, complete
with original rafters and two-foot-thick walls. Each room has cottage-
style fabrics, practical modern furnishings, TVs, direct-dial phones, tea-
making kits and good en-suite bathrooms with tubs and showers.
Standard of housekeeping is good throughout. Bar Food & Restaurant
Meals 12-2.30, 7-10. Vegetarian dishes. Children's menu and portions.
Children not allowed in bar in evening. Free House. **Beer** *Bass, Archers
Village, Wadworth 6X, guest beers. Garden, outdoor play area.*
Accommodation *4 bedrooms, all en suite, £55 (single £37.50).
Children welcome overnight. Additional beds and cots available. Dogs
welcome by arrangement. No credit cards.*

New York   Shiremoor House Farm

| Tel 0191 2576302 | FOOD |

**Middle Engine Lane New York Newcastle-on-Tyne
Tyne & Wear NE29 8D2**   Map 5 E2

First to sing the praises of Shiremoor for its food in 1990, we take
encouragement from its sustained success. Historically, the Fitzgerald
group discovered and restored a set of derelict farmhouse buildings to
which they felt they could attract a discerning clientele of pub-goers.
Shiremoor remains unique, its circular gin-gang (a kind of horse-
powered threshing machine) forming the back drop to a bar from
which radiates a succession of eating areas, carefully broken up by
upturned barrels, easy chairs and an assortment of Britannia and
scrubbed pine tables. To a degree out-and-out quality is subordinated
to the demands of sheer volume, while there remains no doubt as to
the value given for money. A daily "Sizzle Dish", julienne of beef with
hoïsin Sauce perhaps (£5.95), beef stroganoff and rice (£4.35) and cod
with tarragon and lemon sauce (£3.95) amply illustrate the point. For
vegetarians, Oriental mushrooms and rice (£3.65), and for children
small portions of virtually anything (in addition to fish fingers on
request) cover almost any family's options. Outdoors are picnic tables
on the patios, a wooden pill-box seat for the hardy on windy days,
and plenty of safe space, albeit without play equipment, for roaming
about in. *Free House. Bar Food & **Restaurant** 12-2.30, 6-9 (12-9 Bar
Food Sat, 12-9 Restaurant Sun).* **Beer** *Theakston Best, Old Peculiar,
Stones Best, Bass, Timothy Taylor Landlord, Jennings Cumberland, various
guest beers. Outdoor eating on the terrace. 2 high-chairs available.
Access, Visa.*

Newcastle-on-Tyne   Cooperage

Tel 0191 232 8286	**A**
32 The Close Quayside Newcastle-on-Tyne Tyne and Wear NE1 3RF	**Map 5 E2**

Arguably the oldest pub in town, the timber-framed former brewery
teeters roadside by the "Long Stairs" on Newcastle's famed waterfront,
where a succession of high-and lower-level bridges criss-cross the
Tyne. For Real Ale buffs a single bar merits attention, resting on
halved wooden kilderkins and dedecked with pewter and pottery
mugs. Up to eight beers and two draught ciders are on tap at any one
time. When last we visited, however, the pool room to one side and
an upper eating area did somewhat tend to tarnish the image. 5 miles
from A194. *Free House. Open 11-11 (12-3, 7-10.30 Sun).* **Beer** *Tetley
Best, Buxton Ale, Marston's Best, Owd Roger, Hadrian Gladiator,
Hexhamshire Devil's Water, weekly changing guest beers. Access, Visa.*

Newnham   George Inn   ★

Tel 01795 890237	**FOOD**
Newnham nr Faversham Kent ME9 0LL	**Map 11 C5**

Fine rugs on polished wood floors, exposed beams, open fires, evening
candlelight, tasteful prints, pretty flowers and a piano are a sample of
the civilised ingredients at this lovingly cared for 16th-century tile-
hung village pub. The food is always imaginative and varied, and
takes over the whole interior at mealtimes, as there's no separate
dining or restaurant area. All needs are satisfied with the regular menu
listing popular lunchtime favourites from ploughman's and sandwiches
to interesting salads, decent pies – steak and kidney (£5.95) – and
pasta dishes. More substantial choices include a range of steaks, rack of
lamb with rosemary and salmon steak with hollandaise (both £8.50).
Beyond this, it is the short, hand-written list of daily-changing specials
that impressed on a recent visit. Inventive dishes using game, venison
or rabbit according to season, and fresh local produce may include
warm salad of duck breast with walnut oil dressing and leek and goat's
cheese tartlet to start, followed by pot roast shoulder of lamb with
apricot stuffing (£10.40), local rabbit in filo (£6.70), pan fried pork
fillet with cream and asparagus (£10.90) and fish brochette with
piquant sauce. Good accompanying vegetables (£1.30). Unusual
vegetarian choices range from aduki bean and chestnut loaf (£5.30) to
almond and aubergine fritters with creamy mint sauce (£3.50).
Puddings (£2.50) include rhubarb crumble, pecan and maple syrup
pie and chocolate roulade. Large peaceful garden backing on to sheep
pastures. *Pub open 10.30-3, 6-11 (Sun 12-2, 7-10.30).* **Bar Food** *12-2
(Sun to 1.30), 7.30-10. No bar food D Sun. Children allowed in the bar to
eat.* **Beer** *Shepherd Neame. Garden, outdoor eating area. No credit cards.*

Newton   Queen's Head

Tel 01223 870436	**FOOD**
Newton nr Cambridge Cambridgeshire CB2 5PG	**Map 15 F1**

For over thirty years now, the Short family have owned and operated
their tiny "fossilised" village pub which to this day resists change.
Simple home-made soup served in earthenware mugs and sandwiches
(good roast beef and smoked salmon) cut and filled to order in the
tiny bar servery have achieved near cult status over the years, while
the bitter, served direct from cask, is a flat yet flavourful beer. Village
tradition, preserved by skittles table and dilapidated dart board, is

echoed by pine settles, rickety chairs and old school benches. *Bar Food
12-2.15 (Sun to 1.30), 6.30-10 (Sun from 7). Free House. Beer Adnams.
Outdoor eating. Family room. No credit cards.*

Newton   Red Lion

Tel 01529 497256

FOOD

Newton nr Sleaford Lincolnshire NG31 0EE

Map 7 E3

In a quiet hamlet tucked away off the A52, this is a civilised, neatly
kept pub with shaded rear garden and play area. Popular unchanging
formula is the cold carvery/buffet of fish and carefully cooked cold
meats, from pink beef ribs on the bone to Lincolnshire sausages. Price
depends on size of plate and the number of meats chosen (small –
three choices £6.95, medium – four choices £7.95 and large with
unlimited choice £8.95): help yourself from a dozen or more
accompanying salads. Limited choice of starters (soup, home-made paté
£2.25, prawn cocktail £2.45) and ever-changing, similarly priced,
array of home-made desserts (£2.25). Children's prices and eating
areas; informal, easygoing atmosphere. *Bar Food 12-2, 7-10 (Sun to
9). Free House. Beer Bass, Bateman's XXXB, John Smith's. Garden,
outdoor eating, children's play area. Family room. Pub closed 25 Dec.
No credit cards.*

Newton-on-Ouse   Dawnay Arms

Tel 01347 848345

A

Newton-on-Ouse nr York North Yorkshire YO6 2BR

Map 7 D1

Turn off the A19, 5 miles north of York, for this pretty village with
its famous National Trust property at Beningbrough Hall and
impressive black-and-white Grade II listed pub. Fronting a sloping
garden down to the Ouse it comes into its own in summer with
moorings for boating enthusiasts and large tiered patios for al fresco
refreshment. Especially family-friendly, there's play equipment in the
garden, cartoon children's menus for colouring, birthday parties and
barbecues. Live entertainment on Fridays. *Free House. Open 11.30-3,
6.30-11 (12-3, 7-10.30 Sun). Beer John Smith's, Theakston Best XB &
Old Peculier. Garden, outdoor eating area. Children allowed anywhere.
Access, Visa.*

Newton on the Moor   Cook & Barker Inn

Tel 01665 575234

FOOD
B&B

Newton on the Moor Felton Morpeth Northumberland

Map 5 D2

Lynn & Phil Farmer's stone pub with a burgeoning reputation for
food stands just off, and literally overlooking, the A1 10 miles
North of Morpeth. From its elevated position superb views of the
Northumbrian coast are an added attraction for those who come
to stay. Those who do not book for lunch had best come early, as
ordering at the bar and finding an agreeable spot in the maze of
rooms can create a log-jam. Nevertheless the kitchen copes manfully,
working to a menu of gargantuan proportions supplemented by the
daily labour of blackboard specials. Adventurous flavourings are the
kitchen's hallmark:- Vegetable soup with Five Spices (£1.25), stir-fry
beef with ginger and spring onions (£3.25), cauliflower, broccoli and
mushroom pepper pot (£4.50), turkey casserole with black beans and
wild rice (£4.50) and Oriental chicken with cashew nuts (£9.50).
Barring a small selection on the blackboard in the snug meals at night
go up a gear in price and complexity; all of which is classy enough to

suggest that an overnight stay could be special. With its spa bath and romantic setting, the best of four new bedrooms certainly will not disappoint, and the rest aren't far behind with their en-suite baths and showers, TVs, beverage trays and trouser presses. Before turning in, though, join the night shift of locals protectively guarding the bar long after the legions of diners have departed. *Bar Food 12-2, 6-9 (same menu as restaurant), A la carte 7-9.30.* **Beers** *Theakson Best, Younger's No 3, Boddington, Newcastle Exhibition. Free House. Open 11-3, 6-11 (12-3, 7-10.30 Sun). Garden, outdoor eating.* **Accommodation** *4 rooms, all en suite £54 (single £30). Children welcome overnight (free under 10). Cots and bedding available. Access, Visa.*

Newton St Cyres · Crown and Sceptre

Tel 01392 851278	FOOD
Newton St Cyres nr Exeter Devon EX5 5DA	Map 13 D2

Alongside the A377 about two miles from Exeter, this simple roadside pub has had fresh life put into it by landlords, Graham and Carolyn Wilson (formerly at the *Royal Oak*, Meavy on the edge of Dartmoor). Many of their former favourite dishes are to be found on the blackboard scripted menu. For a snack, sandwiches might be an Oak Special (£1.95) with ham and Cheddar cheese or Brunch (£2.50) – toasted wholemeal bread filled with herby sausages and a fried egg on top. More substantial dishes could include cheesy aubergine bake (£4.25), beef and stout stew (£4.95) or fresh fish from Brixham – grilled plaice in herb sauce (£5.95). Puddings (£2.25) might include an apple and honey crumble or a treacle and walnut tart all served with clotted cream. One bar more for the locals includes a pool table and the large garden (over a footbridge across a fenced-off, safe stream) has a tree house, swings, slides and climbing frame. *Bar Food 12-2, 6.30-9 (Sun from 7). Children's menu.* **Beer** *Bass, Boddingtons, Marston's Pedigree. Garden, riverside patio, outdoor eating, children's play area. Family room. Access, Visa.*

North Dalton · Star Inn

Tel 01377 217688	B&B
Warter Road North Dalton Humberside YO25 9UX	Map 7 E1

The Georgian Star sits right next to the village pond, where the coach horses were watered at a stopping-off point on the old Minster Way. Inside, it has largely been remodelled in recent years with rough white plaster walls and exposed brick features in the cosy, welcoming bar and the creation of seven smart, comfortable bedrooms. All are of a good standard but vary a little; a couple have pine-boarded ceilings, one a splendid old brass bedstead; all have good solid wood furniture, neat, fully-tiled bathrooms – one with shower and WC only – direct-dial phone, remote-control TV and tea/coffee-making kit. *Free House.* **Beer** *John Smith's, Courage Directors. Garden, outdoor eating. Family room, children's menu.* **Accommodation** *7 bedrooms, all en suite, £39.50 (single £29.50). No dogs. Access, Visa.*

North Newton · Woodbridge Inn ★

Tel & Fax 01980 630266	FOOD
	B&B
North Newton nr Pewsey Wiltshire SN9 6JZ	Map 14a A4

Akin to a 20th-century staging post, with a warm welcome to every weary traveller extended all day, every day by landlords Lou and Terri Vertessy. As well as their abundant enthusiasm which has contributed so much to the rejuvenation of this pub, is the commitment and imagination which has brought to these parts some truly unusual pub food. Terry's worldwide experience in the kitchen leans towards the American Deep South for her fish creole (£6.95) and St Louis chicken (£7.85). Mexican food has become a hot favourite, represented by sizzling beef fajita (£10.15) and spicy chicken chimichangas (£6.50); from the Far East comes hoi sin yong yoke (Cantonese-style stir-fry lamb and vegetables in a hoi sin sauce with chili (£7.45) and balti curries – balti beef rhogan josh (£8.50). European offerings include Provençal pasta (£5.95), Bretagne pork (£8.25) and Stilton chicken (£8.05). Simpler bar food – sandwiches (from £1.65), steak and ale pie, woody vegetable pie (both £5.75), American-style burgers (from £3.40), Mexican burritos (£6.75) – are served all day, with the more serious restaurant fare (available throughout the pub) being served from 7pm. Daily blackboard specials may list navarin of lamb (£4.50) and broccoli and basil soup (£1.95). Prospective weekend diners are advised to book; a self-contained back room is available for parties up to ten. The comfortable and well-cared-for bar has a polished wooden floor, an assortment of furniture and is decorated with decent prints, plates and pieces of china. The Vertessys have converted three neat and tidy bedrooms for guests' use, all with cottagey wallpapers and fabrics, freestanding darkwood or pine furniture and fresh flowers. One has en-suite facilities, the others share an acceptable bathroom. Situated by the A345 bridge over the Avon, one and a half miles north of Upavon, it has a huge, colourful riverside meadow garden, part of which is fenced off to create an eating area where children can also play. Four pétanque pistes; trout fishing can be organised on the River Avon. "Well-behaved children are always welcome." *Open 11-11 Mon-Sat, Sun 12-3, 7-10.30.* **Bar Food** *11-10.30 (Sun 12-2.30, 7-10). Children allowed in bar to eat.* **Beer** *Wadworth Henry's Original IPA, 6X, Farmer's Glory, Old Timer in winter, two-weekly changing guest beer. Garden, children's play area.* **Accommodation** *3 bedrooms, 1 en suite, £35 (single £30), not en suite £30 (single £25). Children welcome overnight (under-5s free if sharing parents' room), additional bed (£10), cot supplied. Accommodation closed 25 Dec. No dogs. Access, Diners, Visa.*

North Perrott   Manor Arms

| Tel 01460 72901 | **B&B** |

North Perrott nr Crewkerne Somerset TA18 7SG   Map 13 F2

Charming 16th-century hamstone inn located opposite the village green with colourful, overflowing hanging baskets adorning its facade during the summer months. Inside, the series of well restored and refurbished bars maintain an old world charm with low-beamed ceilings, exposed stone, an inglenook fireplace and country furnishings. Five clean and tidy bedrooms are housed in the well-converted rear coach house. All are homely in decor and furnishings and each has a compact shower room, TV and a tea-making kit. Families with older children (10+) can make use of the two light and airy upstairs rooms which can be a self-contained unit – good value. Pleasant rear garden and interesting obstacle course/play area for children in adjacent field. *Free House.* **Beer** *Bass, Smiles Bitter, Ash Vine Trudoxhill, occasional guest beer. Garden, children's play area. Family room.* **Accommodation** *5 bedrooms, all en suite, £39 (single £26). Children welcome overnight (under-10s stay free in parents' room), additional beds and cots available. Check-in by arrangement. No dogs. Access, Visa.*

North Wootton   Crossways Inn

Tel 01749 890237	**B&B**
North Wootton nr Shepton Mallet Somerset BA4 4EU	Map 13 F1

The Crossways Inn overlooks Glastonbury Tor across the historic Vale
of Avalon. It is an 18th-century cider house enjoying a peaceful setting
amidst lovely unspoilt countryside. Well-kept bedrooms are pleasantly
decorated with floral fabrics and all have good thick carpets and
duvets as well as hairdryers, trouser presses, TVs and tea-makers.
Compact modern en-suite facilities throughout. There is a homely
little lounge for residents' use. Families are welcome, but there's no
garden. *Free House.* **Beer** *Wadworth 6X, Bass, Smiles, Morland Old
Speckled Hen, Brains SA, John Smith's, Worthington's Best, Toby, guest
beer. Patio.* **Accommodation** *17 bedrooms, all en suite, £38 (single £28).
Children welcome overnight (rate depends on age), additional beds available.
Dogs by arrangement only. Access, Visa.*

☺

North Wootton   Three Elms

Tel 01935 812881	**B&B**
North Wootton nr Sherborne Dorset DT9 5JW	Map 13 F2

Simple, old-fashioned local set beside the A3030 between Sherborne
and Bishop's Caundle, and whose L-shaped bar was extended several
years ago creating a country coffee shop feel in one area and more
pubby in the other. The focal point is landlord Howard Manning's
collection of over 1000 die-cast model cars, gathered over the years.
Added attractions include the range of nine real ales (local breweries
are favoured) and the far-reaching views towards Bulbarrow Hill
from the neat, lawned rear garden, complete with small play area.
Three neat and tidy, cottagey bedrooms sport pretty wallpapers and
fabrics, older-style pine furniture (including a four-poster bed) and
numerous books and ornaments. All share an attractive bathroom, but,
with the thoughtful addition of bathrobes behind each door, a
midnight trip will not be an embarrassing exercise. "All well-behaved
children welcome." *Free House.* **Beer** *Oakhill, Fuller's London Pride,
Boddingtons, Hook Norton Mild, Greene King Abbot, Summer Lightning,
Ash Vine, 2 guest beers. Garden, children's play area.* **Accommodation**
*3 bedrooms, £35 (single £20). Children welcome overnight (under-3s stay
free in parents' room), additional beds and cots available. Access, Visa.*

☺

Northleach   Wheatsheaf Hotel

	FOOD
Tel 01451 860244	**B&B**
West End Northleach Gloucestershire GL54 3E2	Map 14a A2

Quietly situated in the celebrated Wood Town (just off the A429) is
the Langs' people-friendly period coaching inn. Being family-run, it's
family-orientated as well, with plenty of minor diversions for the
young-at-heart in the bar while meals are ordered from a daily-
changing, all-embracing menu. Smoked chicken and orange salad
(£4.25) or smoked salmon and scrambled eggs (£3.95) are as opposite
for a snack as for a starter, while the substantial beef and ale pie
(£4.95) is a meal in itself. More adventurous scallops in lemon butter
(£9.50) and Provencal chicken (£8.25) are satisfying main courses.
If small portions here don't suit the youngsters, "sausages, eggs and
things?" can readily be rustled up. As a base for walkers and Cotswold
explorers, the Wheatsheaf offers bedrooms all individually furnished
to a high standard; two have king-sized beds, and while two of the

Zzzz...

en-suite bathrooms have wc/showers only, all the rooms have colour TV, beverage trays and dial-out phones. *Free House.* **Accommodation** *8 rooms, all en suite £45 (single £35).* **Beers** *Marston Best & Pedigree Hook Norton Best. Children welcome. Dogs welcome. Cot available. Garden. Access, Visa.*

Norton	**Hundred House Hotel**	**FOOD**
Tel 011952 71353 Fax 011952 71355		**B&B**
Norton nr Shifnal Shropshire		**Map 6 B4**

In the old 'hundred' of Brimstree, alongside what is today the busy A442, there's an unbroken history of there being a hostelry at Norton since the 14th century. The thatched barn which separates the car park from the road was once the local court and remains of the old stocks and whipping post are still to be found there. The main, creeper-clad redbrick inn, of Georgian origin, stands in its own mature orchard and garden in which all-comers are invited to wander at their leisure, and from which come the hand-dried flowers which hang from virtually every beam within the pub. All this is indicative of the personality Hundred House gains from the inimitable input of Henry and Sylvia Phillips and family (here since 1986). There's a particularly warm and intimate feel in the muted tones of the mellow-brick, tiled floors, stained-glass windows, colourful patchwork leather upholstery and festooned beams of the bar and dining areas, a setting to which the food has little trouble doing justice. Griddled black pudding and apple sauce (£2.95) and bruschetta with tapénade, dried tomatoes and basil (£3.95) typify the range of culinary skills and sources, while main courses may encompass salmon fish cakes with tomato and cumin sauce (£6), spiced chicken and bacon salad with mint vinaigrette, sausage, mash and onion gravy (£4.95), cassoulet of lamb and chorizo sausage (£6.50) and a savoury pancake of red peppers, mushrooms and coriander (£3.50/£6.50). To supplement both bar and à la carte menus, daily specials might include a ham and broccoli soup (£2.50), ravioli of crayfish with coriander (£5.50), roast saddle of hare with a summer fruits sauce (£11.50) and, to follow, perhaps a blueberry pie or summer pudding (£3.50) from the usually excellent desserts – the "ultimate dessert" (£7.50) brings a selection all on one dish with fresh fruit and home-made ice cream. Both names and colour schemes in the enchanting bedrooms return to the garden for their inspiration, incorporating pastel shades, brass bedsteads with patchwork covers, cane rocking chairs and even padded swing seats suspended invitingly from the rafters. From fresh flowers and pot-pourri to cotton buds and heart-shaped pin cushions, virtually every conceivable extra is contrived to make guests feel fully at home in cosy and cossetting surroundings; two superior rooms are very large. Throughout the day and evening there is room service of drinks and light snacks. Only slip-ups at breakfast and the lack of double-glazing (the road is often busy at night) let the side down. *Pub open 12-3, 6-11 (7-10.30 Sun).* **Bar Food & Restaurant Meals** *12-2.30, 6.15-10 (7-9 Sun). Free House.* **Beer** *Phillips Heritage and Old Ale, Ansells dark Mild, guest beer. Garden, outdoor eating.* **Accommodation** *9 Bedrooms, all en suite, £69 (single occupation £59). Children welcome overnight, additional beds and cots available (no B&B charge for children sharing parents' room). Dogs by arrangement only. Access, Diners, Visa.*

Norton St Philip   George Inn

Tel 01373 834224	**FOOD**

Norton St Philip nr Bath Somerset BA3 6LH   Map 13 F1

Certainly one of the oldest licensed premises in the land, the George
has been around since before liquor licenses were introduced! A
Carthusian guest house since its first building in the 13th century, it
has retained its present architectural features for over 700 years now.
Surviving to this day are the massive Gothic doorway, sloping
cobbled courtyard and unique timbered galleries. On 12th June 1668
Samuel Pepys and party dined here, while in June 1685 the Duke of
Monmouth occupied the whole village for a week prior to his defeat
at Sedgemoor. In this unique atmosphere, wonderfully steeped in
history, new landlords Andrew and Juliette Grubb have settled in
well, smartening the place up and introducing a reliable and varied
range of bar meals. Home-cooked dishes extend from a menu of good
pub favourites to blackboard specials, for example, smoked fish terrine
(£3.75), wild boar paté (£3.95), smoked fish and prawn pancakes
(£6.95), vegetable quiche (£4.95), pan-fried duck breast with plum
sauce (£8.95) and smoked pork loin cutlets in cider (£7.95), with
main courses accompanied by a huge dish of fresh and crisp vegetables.
Puddings (£2.75) include chocolate mousse, treacle tart and a
traditional fruit pie. Plans are afoot to utilise the historic charm of the
building by introducing ten en-suite bedrooms which should prove
very popular – watch this space! *Bar Food 12-2.30, 6.30-10 (Sun
7-9.30). Beer Wadworth. Outdoor eating. Access, Visa.*

Norwich   Adam & Eve

Tel 01603 667423	**A**

Bishopsgate Norwich Norfolk NR3 2RZ   Map 10 C1

Historic old tavern – the oldest in the city – located along Palace
Street close to the cathedral. Part 13th-century it was built as a
brewhouse to serve bread and ale to the workmen who built the
cathedral and later extended in the 14th and 15th-centuries, with the
addition of the Dutch gables which give this popular ale house a most
unusual appearance. Reputedly haunted by the ghost of Lord Sheffield
who was hacked to death here in 1549, the two bars and tiny snug
feature ancient carved benches and high-backed settles built into part-
panelled walls and old tiled floors. The lower bar is thought to be
over 700 years old. Good summer drinking patio and a handy pay
and display car park next door. *Open 11-11 (Sun 12-3, 7-10.30).
Beer Morland Old Speckled Hen, Ruddles Country, Wadworth, John
Smith's Bitter, Adnams Southwold, Mayday, guest beer. Garden, outdoor
eating area. Family room. No credit cards.*

Nosterfield   Freemasons Arms

Tel 01677 470548	**FOOD**

Nosterfield Bedale North Yorkshire DL8 2QP   Map 5 E4

A remarkable success story this, and an inspiration to legions of other
wannabies. The low, white-painted row of cottages and barn (planned
for later conversion into bedrooms) sparkles within, adorned in front
of a blazing log fire with a mish-mash of pub-associated artefacts from
pewter pots to miners' lamps and horse-tack. To this was added a
warmth of welcome and a confidence which suggests these young

publicans know that they are going places. Martyn Lea cooks up a storm, his recipe for success based on not trying to be a restaurant whilst serving good food from fresh ingredients of a quality that would not go amiss in one. His menus are no longer than they need to be and remain, in part, consumer-led. Thus alongside pan-fried plaice fillets in nut-brown butter (£5.50) and Thai beef with oyster sauce and egg fried rice (£6.50), diners will still find the Freemasons mixed grill (£7.95), steak pies and tagliatelli provencale (£5.50). Herbs from the pub garden contribute to the freshly-made soups (£1.50) while the home-made desserts and gateaux (all £1.95) are contributed by a commendable lady from the village. A hand-picked short list of wines is that, too, of an enthusiast, while both Theakstons and the irresistible Black Sheep Bitter are kept in fine condition in the rebuilt beer cellar. *Free House.* **Bar Food** (*No food on Mon*) 12-2.30, 6-11 (7-10.30 Sun. *Summer variation: 11-11 Sat & Sun*). *Children's portions.*
Beer Theakston BB, Tetley, Boddingtons, Black Sheep Bitter. *Access, Visa.*

Nottingham   Lincolnshire Poacher

Tel 0115 941 1584	**A**
161-163 Mansfield Road Nottingham Nottinghamshire NG1 3FR	**Map 7 D3**

A true pub-goer's "paraphernalia pub" is perhaps the best way to describe the former Old Gray Nag's Head, now leased by the Tynemill Group from brewers Batemans. A large obituary to the hundreds (they say) of independents swallowed up by one major brewer is displayed above the bar, whilst an eminently more sensible arrangement with their current landlords enables a wide range of popular and little-known guest ales always to be on offer. Yet anyone out for a tasting needn't stop there, as nigh on six dozen whiskies and single malts are an open invitation to the connoisseur to many more than a single session. From mid-evening and at weekends there's a livelier, merrymaking crowd amongst whom consumption of designer bottled beers "by the neck" appears to be more the norm. *Open 11-11* (*Sun usual hours*). **Beer** Batemans XB, XXXB, Dark Mild, Salem Porter, Victory, Bass, guest beers. *Patio. No credit cards.*

Nottingham   Ye Olde Trip to Jerusalem

Tel 01602 473171	**A**
Brewhouse Yard Castle Road Nottingham Nottinghamshire NG1 6AD	**Map 7 D3**

Built into the caves at the foot of Nottingham Castle's wall and formerly its brewhouse, Ye Olde Trip to Jerusalem (known as the Pilgrim in the 18th century) has been a pub for 800 years, "the oldest inn in England", a habitual resting place for crusading knights on their way to bash the heathen overseas. The present building is mainly 17th-century; the unique rock-face walls are most apparent in the spooky upstairs bar, which is opened only when the pub is busy. Downstairs has panelled walls, built-in cushioned settles, and exposed-rock alcoves; visitors' banknotes and coins litter the beams. In fine weather there are patios to the side and back, and extra seating in the cobbled yard opposite; souvenirs are available at the bar. Owned by Hardys & Hansens (the Kimberley Brewery). **Beer** Hardys & Hansons Kimberley Classic & Best Mild, Marston's Pedigree. *Patio/terrace. Access, Visa.*

Nuffield　Crown

Tel 01491 641335	**FOOD**
Nuffield nr Henley-on-Thames Oxfordshire RG9 5SJ	**Map 15a D3**

Pleasantly refurbished pub with beams and inglenook, now a popular
dining pub. Ann and Gerry Bean run it in a quietly civilised fashion
and offer food that covers a range from mushroom and cashew nut
paté (£3.95) to fine steak and kidney pie (£5.75) and a good choice
of homely puddings. Good-value house wines. No children in the
evenings. *Bar Food 12-2, 7-9.45 (Sun to 9.30). Beer Brakspear. Garden.
Family room. No credit cards.*

Nunney　The George at Nunney

Tel 01373 836458	**B&B**
11 Church Street Nunney Somerset BA11 4LW	**Map 13 F1**

White-painted, street-fronting coaching inn, its sign stretched right
over the road, opposite a brook and the 13th-century castle ruin in the
centre of this picturesque village. Rambling and much modernised
open-plan interior with winter log fire. Bedrooms of various shapes
are modestly furnished apart from the comfortable four-poster room.
Some overlook the pretty walled garden, some the castle; all have
private bath or shower, telephones, satellite TV and tea-makers.
Functional overnight accommodation. *Free House. Beer John Smiths,
Hancocks, Exmoor, Bass, Wadworth 6X. Garden, outdoor eating. Family
room. Accommodation 9 bedrooms, all en suite, £58 (single £42).
Children welcome overnight, additional beds (£5) and cots (£2.50)
available. Access, Visa.*

Nunnington　Royal Oak

Tel 01439 748271	**FOOD**
Nunnington nr York North Yorkshire YO6 5US	**Map 5 E4**

A laid-back and friendly local with a food bias at the heart of the
village, just up from a foot-bridge over the river Rye and hence a
short walk from the National Trust's Nunnington Hall. Stone jugs and
assorted farm implements hang from the beams while behind Tony's
one-man bar are suspended the blackboards of best-bet specials which
emanate from Bo Simpson's highly productive kitchen. Herb
dumplings with steak and kidney and tasty garlic bread with a crumb-
topped fisherman's pot (both £6.50) are well-conceived variations on
familiar themes: similarly chicken breasts are served with cheese and
mustard sauce, and sweet and sour vegetables (£6.50 also) come in a
crispy batter. Bright and crunchy accompanying salads can be
enlivened to taste from the preferred relish tray. To follow are a good
choice of puddings from rhubarb crumble to lemon mousse and
tiramisu (all around £2.50). A quiet dining room extension is
available for reserved tables (and families), though the same menus
hold good throughout. Light classical favourites provide a popular and
relaxing background to the general hubbub of appreciative diners. No
children under 8 in the bar. *Free House. Bar Food 12-2, 6.30-9 (7-9
Sun). Children's portions. Beer Tetley, Burton Ale, Theakston Old
Peculier. Access, Visa.*

Nunton   Radnor Arms

Tel 01722 329722	**FOOD**
Nunton nr Salisbury Wiltshire SP5 4HS	**Map 14 C3**

This welcoming ivy-clad village pub dates from the 17th century and
part of it once served as the village stores and post office. Locals come ☺
now purely for the well-kept ale and for the honest home-cooked
selection of meals that are served in its low-ceilinged and simply
furnished main bar and neat opened-out dining areas. Traditional
lunchtime favourites can be found on the printed menu, while the
changing blackboard menu advertises the lunch specials and evening
choices. Fresh fish dishes and rib-eye steak are regulars on the board,
which may also include smoked trout (£2.95), herrings in Madeira
(£3.95), pork fillet with Stilton and mushrooms (£7.95), rack of
lamb with port and redcurrant (£8.50) and brill fillets with prawn
and cream sauce (£7.95). Treacle and walnut tart (£2.50) and home-
made bread and butter pudding (£2.50) are popular puddings. The
large rear garden has fine rural views, plenty of picnic benches and
much to amuse energetic children. *Open 11-11 (Sun 12-10.30). Bar
Food 12-2 (Sun to 1.30), 7-9.30. Children allowed in side room away from
bar to eat, children's menu.* **Beer** *Hall & Woodhouse Tanglefoot & Badger
Best, Hard Tackle, Eagle IPA. Garden, outdoor eating, children's play area,
disabled facilities. Family room. No credit cards.*

Nuthurst   Black Horse

Tel 01403 891272	**A**
Nuthurst Street Nuthurst Horsham West Sussex RH13 6LH	**Map 11 A6**

Occupying an attractive row of 17th-century brick cottages, this
charming pub was, unbelievably, a coaching inn on the old Brighton
to Horsham road, now a quiet backwater off the A281 southeast of
Horsham. Beyond the raised front terrace, hanging baskets and
stripped pine doors lies a classic main bar featuring an old flagstoned
floor, a huge inglenook with winter log fire, heavy beams and rustic
pine furnishings. Character extends into the wooden floored snug bar
and beamed dining room with horsebrasses, hunting prints and old
photographs of local characters and village scenes. Good alfresco
seating on the peaceful front terrace and in the sheltered rear garden
complete with stream, shrubs and trees. Interesting local walks.
Pub open 11-3, 6-11 (Sun 12-3, 7-10.30). Free House. **Beer** *Eldridge
Pope Dorchester Bitter, Tetleys, Greene King Abbot Ale, Wadworth
6X. Garden, front terrace and lawn, outdoor eating, tables in garden.
Access, Visa.*

Oddington   Horse & Groom Inn

Tel 01451 830584	**FOOD**
	B&B
Upper Oddington nr Moreton-in-Marsh Gloucestershire GL56 0XH	**Map 14a A1**

A typically picturesque Cotswold inn with a flagstoned interior,
aglow in winter with real log fires and ablaze with summer colour in ☺
a sloping garden complete with ornamental pond and play area.
Balanced, rather than boldly original, bar menus ranging from crispy   Zzzz...
potato shells (£3.50) to surf'n'turf (comprising beef sirloin and crab
claws £6.25) are enlivened by daily shopping for fresh fish (grilled
whole plaice at around £5) and a traditional array of home-made
desserts (summer pudding and fruit crumble £2.25). Menus of similar
style and balance feature at night in the adjoining restaurant where
they command a higher price. Neatly-kept bedrooms give a taste of

village life, unencumbered by intrusive phones. Of four in the eaves above the bar, one has a full bathroom: two bright bedrooms, with wc/showers only, are in former stables across the yard; a family-size ground-floor bedroom was being prepared as we went to press. *Bar Food* 12-2 (*Sun to 3*), 7-9.30 (*Sun from 7*). *Restaurant Meals* (*Sun only 12-2*), 7-9. *Children allowed in bar to eat, children's menu. Free House. Beer Hook Norton Best, Wadworth 6X, guest beer. Garden, outdoor eating, play area. Family room. Accommodation 7 bedrooms, all en suite, £50 (single £33). Children welcome overnight, additional beds (from £13), cots (£2) available. Check-in by arrangement. No dogs. Access, Visa.*

Odell   Bell

Tel 01234 720254	**FOOD**
Horesfair Lane Odell Bedfordshire MK43 7AG	Map 15 E1

There's great virtue in being content with serving the very simplest of pub food when the circumstances demand it, and at the tiny Bell Inn they've got it just about right. From the front, it's a mellow-stone, thatched house, and the original two front rooms, connected by a single bar servery, can still be clearly seen. Round the back, a brick extension has brought a succession of little rooms at varying levels, their low tables and stools adding to the almost miniature feel of the place. Old beams and original mantels, framing a cast-iron range at one end, are hung with a collection of old brass beer taps; less traditional but rather more hygienic stainless steel engines are in active service now. Doreen Scott's stock-in-trade, in circumstances where the pub never appears less than full, is her single-dish flans of bacon vegetables or pissaladière (£3.55) and pizza (£3.50), and omelettes (from £3.55) which come with salad or chips or both, and appear designed to be eaten with fork only, in a confined space – which they are. Otherwise, there are cold platters, toasties and sandwiches (with commendable hand-sliced bread) (from £1.65) and a ploughman's (£2.70) which comes with a crock of home-made pickle. Added to these is a section honestly labelled "deep-fried" for lovers of scampi and other such things, and a routine dessert list with boozy chocolate mousse, rhubarb fool and yokel pie. A blackboard menu also materialises, offering turkey and mushroom pie (£5.25), seafood pasta (£4.55) or mango chicken casserole (£5.85) – positively prodigious output from space so confined. It gets extremely busy, overflowing on summer days into the garden under trees down on the banks of the Great Ouse. *Bar Food* 12-2, 7-9.30 (*except Sun*). *Children's menu. Beer Greene King IPA, Rayment Bitter, Abbot Ale. Garden, outdoor eating. Family room. No credit cards.*

Odiham   George Hotel

Tel 01256 702081 Fax 01256 704213	**B&B**
High Street Odiham nr Basingstoke Hampshire RG25 1LP	Map 15a D4

First granted a licence in 1540, the privately-owned George has kept a good deal of its period character. Timber framing can be seen throughout. Main-house bedrooms (including two four-posters) have creaking floors, low beams, and antique furnishings, while rooms in the converted coach house and former barn are modern behind original exteriors. Accessories throughout are thoroughly modern, and all rooms have private facilities. Farming artefacts decorate the flagstoned bar, while the residents' lounge features exposed stonework. One mile from the M3 (J5). *Open 11-11, Sun usual hours.*

Beer Courage Best, Directors & Wadworth 6X. Garden. **Accommodation**
18 bedrooms, all en suite, £72 (single £62). Children welcome overnight
(babies free in parents' room, otherwise under-14s £15), additional bed &
cot available. Access, Diners, Visa.

Old Dalby   Crown Inn

Tel 01664 823134	FOOD
Debdale Hill Old Dalby nr Melton Mowbray Leicestershire LE14 3LF	Map 7 D3

Tucked away down a lane in the village centre, this 300-year-old
converted farmhouse is today the home of some enjoyable, often
ambitious cooking. Cosy, antique-furnished bars are the setting for the
sampling of such home-made dishes as black pudding with fried apple
in cream of mustard sauce (£7.50), beef and oyster pie (£8.50), duck
breast with a cider and apple sauce (£10.50), stuffed salmon in
seaweed and puff pastry (£10.50), or stuffed aubergine and ratatouille
with crusty herb topping (£6.50). Local Colston Bassett Stilton
features amongst a good choice of cheeses. Eat in either restaurant or
bar where there is a constantly changing selection of draught bitters
(up to 14) always available. A large, pleasant and secluded garden
provides a haven for children and offers a terraced area for outdoor
eating from which guests can watch regular games of pétanque
organised by local enthusiasts. **Bar Food** 12-2, 6-10 (except Sun eve)
Restaurant Meals 12-2, 6-9.30 (except Sun eve). Free House. **Beer** up to
14 guest beers: Adnams, Marston's Owd Rodger, Kimberley, Morland's Old
Speckled Hen, Woodforde's Wherry, Green King Abbott Ale. Garden,
outdoor eating. Family room. No credit cards.

Old Heathfield   Star Inn

Tel 01435 863570	A
Church Street Old Heathfield East Sussex TN21 8AH	Map 11 B6

Not the easiest pub to find, but head for the village church and the
Star is right next door. Built for pilgrims in the 14th century, the
outside has gained a few creepers over the centuries and the inside has
mellowed nicely with its low beamed ceiling and large inglenook
fireplace surrounded by varnished copper and brass ornaments. A
major attraction is the peaceful, award-winning garden inhabited by
peacocks, rabbits, doves and the bantam cocks that strut about
amongst the tables showing off their fine plumage. New landlord and
a new menu. **Beer** Harveys, King & Barnes, Young's Special. Garden.
Access, Visa.

Oldbury-on-Severn   Anchor Inn

Tel 01454 413331	FOOD
Church Road Oldbury-on-Severn Avon BS12 1QA	Map 13 F1

The hamlet of Oldbury lies deep in the flatlands of the Severn estuary
two miles west of Thornbury and just half a mile from the water's
edge. Michael Dowdeswell's old pub has a flower-decked stone
frontage, a brick-lined pine-furnished rear dining room and extensive
streamside garden where a game of boules in the orchard is known
locally as "Petanchors". An extensive bar food menu, typed up each
day, relies on fresh local produce and regular favourites include grilled
Gloucestershire "snorkers" sausages (£4.95), an Oldbury "Flat 'At"
filled with roast beef and onion gravy (£4.20), and Oldbury mud pie
of coffee mousse with fudge topping (£2.35). The same menu serves
in all locations with orders taken at the bar: note here the Bass and

Theakston's Old Peculier drawn from cask as well as the traditional hand-pulled ales. Severn salmon baked with white wine sauce (£5.95) or cold with salad (£7.95) leads the more substantial main meals alongside chargrilled sirloin and spiced butterfly chicken breasts (£6.25), and there are both vegetarian (£4.35) and meat curries. Plenty of wines by bottle and glass: book for the dining room. *Bar Food* 11.30-2, 6.30-11 *(Sat 6-9.30)*. *Restaurant Meals* 12-1.30, 7-9. *Children are allowed in the dining-room to eat. Free House.* *Beer* Bass, Butcombe, Marston Pedigree, Theakston's XB & Old Peculier. Garden, outdoor eating. Access, Visa.

Ollerton   Dun Cow

Tel 01565 633093	FOOD
Chelford Road Ollerton Cheshire WA16 8RH	Map 6 B2

Set four-square on to the A537, two miles from Knutsford, and from the M6, the solid-looking Dun Cow enjoys a reputation just as squarely built around its food. The simpler bar menu (courgette and potato soup £1.50, breaded mushrooms with garlic mayonnaise £2.50), steak and kidney pie (£4.50) is supplemented by an eclectic choice of specials posted on the blackboard – gammon or salmon steak both in hollandaise sauce, Mediterranean fish stew and pork in peppers (all £4.75) could all feature in one day. An evening à la carte is served at pink-clothed tables in a cottagey side room: filleted Dover sole (£6.75), pork fillet in Madeira (£6.95) and chargrilled steaks set the tone here on Tuesday to Saturday evenings; tables are bookable, also for Sunday lunch (£8.50). In addition, there's a special 3-course £10 menu on Friday evenings. Several vegetarian dishes appear on all the menus. Locals mostly use a traditional tap room, families can enjoy the roadside garden in fine weather and senior citizens much enjoy the bonus of a fixed-price, mid-week, three-course lunch (£3.95). *Pub open 11-11 Sunday usual hours.* *Bar Food* 12-2.30, 6.30-9.30. *Restaurant Meals* 7-9 *(booking only, no food Sun & Mon eves)*. *Children's menu.* *Beer* Greenalls. Terrace, outdoor eating. Family room. Access.

Ombersley   King's Arms

Tel 01905 620315	FOOD
Ombersley nr Droitwich Hereford & Worcester WR9 0EW	Map 14 B1

A recent conversion at this wonderfully crooked-looking black-and-white timbered inn has provided space for 30 more seats in the restaurant and a spanking new kitchen! The bar sports thick blackened oak beams hung with agricultural implements, gleaming brasses and polished copper pans which reflect the huge open fires in winter. The Charles II and Devonshire lounges are predominantly designated for eating, with prompt service to your chosen table. From a single menu, the choice is wide, though more tried and trusted than bristling with novelty: home-made soup (£1.95), goose liver with white wine (£4.50) and deep-fried Camembert in sesame seeds (£4.95), grilled green-lipped mussels (£4.50); steak and kidney pie (£5.25), turkey pasta bake (£6.95) and sirloin steaks (10oz £8.95); vegetarian options – cheese and herb bread pudding (£4.95) – and a reasonable line of home-made puddings (£2.25). Owing to its popularity, unsuitable for children under 8, and 8-16s admitted for full meals only. There is, however, a sheltered rear patio to accommodate the unsuspecting and the hardy. Choice of 12 malt whiskies at the bar. Just off the A449 between Worcester and Kidderminster. *Bar Food 12.15-2.15 (Sun 12-10), 6-10. Free House. Beer Bass, Flowers Original, Boddingtons. Terrace, outdoor eating. Access, Visa.*

Onecote   Jervis Arms

| Tel 01538 304206   Fax 01538 304514 | **FOOD** |

Onecote nr Leek Staffordshire ST13 7RU

Map 6 C3

On the B5053, off the A523, and positioned just at the edge of the Peak National Park, the pub stands on one bank of the Hamps river: park on the opposite bank and cross a footbridge into the garden. While the picnic tables, play area and ducks are super, parents should be mindful of the littlest ones by this fast-flowing stream. Food has improved here, though the ordering and delivery systems appear faulty at peak times. (A tip, here: choose your table and stick with it!) Vegetarian and children's meals both feature prominently on the printed menu (curried nut, fruit and vegetable pie £4.50; egg, chips and beans £1.95), alongside pretty standard pub grub. A little more adventure emanates from the blackboard: peppered pork, chicken masala and vegetable rogan josh (all £4.50) spice things up a little – though not a lot. Adjacent to the pub is holiday accommodation in a converted barn. *Bar Food 12-2, 7-10. Children's menu. Free House. Beer Theakston Best, XB & Old Peculier, Bass, Marston's Pedigree. Riverside garden, children's play area. Closed 25 & 26 Dec. Family room. No credit cards.*

Osmotherley   Three Tuns

| | **FOOD** |
| Tel 01609 883301 | **B&B** |

Osmotherley nr Northallerton North Yorkshire DL6 3BN

Map 5 E3

A long-standing favourite, the Dysons' deserved reputation results in Three Tuns being referred to as "the Fish Pub". Choice is as diverse as the market allows: tempting platefuls of langoustines or moules; reliably cooked halibut and Dover soles, both plain or with classic sauces, served with crisp fresh vegetables and a personal bread board. Behind the single oak-framed bar a quietly elegant dining room is the popular place to enjoy a substantial meal, where the likes of Pig-in-a-Poke (£8.35) and chicken Valdostana (£6.95) are typical non-aquatic alternatives. Customers in the bar needn't be the poorer cousins: smoked salmon and scrambled eggs (£5.25) and seafood Thermidor (£6.50) can be enjoyed as a snack, and the equally popular doorstep sandwiches (from £2.50) are knife-and-fork affairs. Service here may, however, be suspended as the dining room fills up. Most recent developments have added three stylish, if compact, bedrooms under the eaves; with en-suite shower rooms, teletext TVs, dial-out phones and stylish towelling bathrobes they have gained overnight popularity with a discerning business clientele. *Family room. Bar Meal 12-2.30, 7-9.30 (12-2, eve Sun closed). Accommodation 3 bedrooms, all en suite £50 (Single £38.50). Check-in by arrangement. Children welcome overnight (extra child's bed avail if sharing). Free House. Beer Theakston Best & XB, Younger's No 3. Garden, outdoor eating area. Access, Visa.*

Over Haddon   **Lathkil Hotel**

FOOD

Tel 01629 812501

B&B

Over Haddon nr Bakewell Derbyshire DE45 1JE

Map 6 C2

The Lathkil scores with residents and visitors alike with its unparalleled views of the Peak National Park and spectacular Lathkil Dale several hundred feet below. Signposted from the B5055 White Peak scenic route, just two miles from Bakewell, it's been a pub since 1813 or earlier and extensions in the 1930s created a Victorian-style bar whose use of miniature-sized tables and chairs gives an illusion of space; there's also a post-war dining room extension with huge picture windows for making the most of the view. Local landscape photographer Ray Kenning has contributed a stunning set of portraits of Derbyshire's great houses, Haddon, Chatsworth, Hardwick and Kedleston among them. Lunch is served buffet-style from a hot and cold counter to the rear with standard bar food including soup, paté, steak and kidney pie, beef and mushroom casserole, lasagne and quiche. Dinner à la carte (for residents only on Sunday evening), and Sunday lunch produce melon with prawns and Marie Rose sauce (£2.95), soup (£2), crayfish with garlic mayonnaise (£3.40), goujons of plaice with tartare sauce (£3), chicken stuffed with leek in Stilton sauce (£8.50), hazelnut and brown rice roast with mushroom and nutmeg sauce (£6) or half a roast duck with orange sauce (£10.50). Puddings are home made and frequently change at peak times, cheesecake, walnut flan and treacle tart giving way to fruit crumble, Bakewell pudding or lemon meringue pie. Four bedrooms with en suite bathrooms (one a single with shower only), may be limited in space, but are comprehensive in facilities: all have colour television, clock radios and a personal bar and fridge. The best two, at the front, look across the dale to Youlgrave and the original village of Nether Haddon, now part of the Haddon estate. From the rear rooms, there are less edifying views, of fellow-patrons' wheel-hubs in the car park! **Bar Food** 12-2. **Restaurant Meals** 7-9 (not Sun). *Children's menu. Patio, outdoor eating. Family room (lunchtimes only)* **Accommodation** *4 bedrooms, all en suite, £60 (single £32.50). Children welcome overnight (rate depends on age), additional beds available. Check-in by arrangement. Access, Diners, Visa.*

Over Peover   **The Dog**

FOOD

Tel & Fax 01625 861421

B&B

Well Bank Lane Over Peover nr Knutsford Cheshire WA16 8UP

Map 6 B2

Frances and Jim Cunningham promote The Dog as a pub serving food, and so popular has it proved that these days table reservations are the norm. A well-tried formula invites choice of starters and main courses from the daily-updated blackboard, offering a range of soups (curried apple and parsnip £2.20), duck and orange paté and black pudding with mustard (£3.85) ahead of an equally wide range of main courses. Substantial dishes with vegetables and choice of potatoes are all under £6.95: rabbit pie, smoked haddock and prawn au gratin, smoked salmon and prawn pancake and rack of lamb with apricot and ginger exemplify the range. Desserts (£2.50) are selected from a groaning sideboard and cold cabinet replete with fruit pies, bread-and-butter pudding, pavlovas and gateaux. The Dog's identity as village local is retained in the Tap Room, while there's plenty of space for casual drinking on the front patio or in a rear garden where more limited snack service operates. In terms of its food, the pub could write North-Western appetites into folklore, the term "volume" being applicable equally to the portions as to the numbers who tuck into them. The individually decorated bedrooms are equally popular, their cottage appeal enhanced by the practical addition of spacious, carpeted bathrooms, colour TVs, trouser presses and beverage trays, thus attracting a clientele quite capable of providing their own telephones! *Bar Food 12-2.30 (bookings essential Sun), 7-9 (Mon-Sat). Free House. Beer Jennings Mild, Thomas Original, Flowers IPA, Tetleys. Garden, Outdoor eating. Accommodation 3 bedrooms, all en suite, £58 (single £38). Children welcome overnight (charge depends on age), additional beds available. Dogs by arrangement. Access, Visa.*

Over Stratton   Royal Oak

| Tel 01460 240906 | **FOOD** |
| Over Stratton nr South Petherton Somerset TA13 5LQ | Map 13 F2 |

This row of three 400-year-old thatched cottages merges with its neighbours in the main street of the village and, but for the pub sign, it would be easy to miss altogether; at the South Petherton roundabout (A303) take the old Ilminster town-centre road. Cottage atmosphere is still the secret of an interior with a real sense of style. Original features like old beams, hamstone and flag floors (as well as a couple of stone pillars that look to have been there for ever but were actually salvaged from the cellars of a nearby house a couple of years ago) blend successfully with dark rag-rolled walls, scrubbed wooden tables, a polished granite bar counter and extensive displays of dried flowers, hops and strings of garlic. The menu takes its inspiration from many sources: croissants from France, chicken and lamb sate from the Orient (£6.25), pears and Stilton (£2.75) and steak and kidney pie (£5.95) from Blighty and much else besides. A Booty Box (£2.95) is on the children's menu, full of goodies including a wholemeal sandwich, cheese, fruit, crisps and a Crunchy bar – all served in a special box that children can take away with them. Weather permitting, grills are cooked to order on the barbecue outside beyond which there are swings, a junior assault course and trampolines to keep the kids amused. *Bar Food 12-2, 7-10 (Sun 9.30). Restaurant Meals 12-1.45, 7-9.45 (7-9.15 Sun). Children allowed in the dining room to eat. Beer Tanglefoot, Badger Best, Hard Tackle. Garden, outdoor eating, children's play area. Access, Visa.*

Oving   Gribble Inn

| Tel 01243 786893 | **A** |
| Gribble Lane Oving nr Chichester West Sussex PO90 6BP | Map 11 A6 |

Set on the edge of a peaceful village three miles east of Chichester, this attractive 16th-century thatched cottage is named after one long-term occupant Rose Gribble. A pub since 1980 it retains much of its original charm with a low heavily beamed bar, a big log fire in a raised hearth and a good mix of country furnishings. Large comfortably furnished, no-smoking family room and adjacent skittle alley. Popular attractions here are the excellent range of home-brewed ales and the splendid cottage garden with climbing roses and rustic wooden tables and benches beneath apple trees; an ideal venue for summer alfresco imbibing. *Pub open 11-2.30, 6-11 (Sun 12-3, 7-10.30), Sat in summer 11-11. Beer Hall & Woodhouse Badger Best, Tanglefoot, home brewed ales: Gribble Ale, Reg's Tipple, Blackadder, Pig's Ear. Garden, lawn, outside eating, tables in the garden. Family room. Access, Visa.*

Ovington   Bush Inn

Tel 01962 732764	FOOD
Ovington nr Alresford Hampshire SO24 0RE	**Map 15 D3**

Located just off the A31 on a peaceful lane, this unspoilt 17th-century
rose-covered cottage enjoys an enviable picturesque setting, close to
one of Hampshire's famous chalk trout streams – the River Itchen.
Scenic riverside walks are very popular, as are the rustic bars and
bench-filled garden of the Bush, both of which are often crammed
with people replenishing their energy after a stroll, especially on fine
summer weekends. Three intimate, softly-lit bars boast dark-painted
walls, an assortment of sturdy tables, chairs and high-backed settles and
a wealth of old artefacts, prints and stuffed fish. On cold winter nights
the place to sit with a pint of traditional ale is in front of the roaring
log fire. On the eating side, food varies from routine bar meals listed
on a printed menu to a daily specials board highlighting a short, but
rather more interesting choice of dishes, such as home-made spicy
chicken royale soup (£1.95), grilled local trout (£6.50), chili con
carne (£5.95), summer vegetable pie (£5.75). The tiny bar boasts a
changing selection of at least five real ales, over eight wines served by
the glass and numerous country wines. *Pub open 11-11.* **Bar food** *12-4,
6.30-9.30.* **Beer** *Gales HSB, Wadworth 6X, Tanglefoot, Flowers Original,
guest beer. Riverside terrace, outdoor eating. Family room, children's menu.
Access, Visa.*

We welcome bona fide complaints and recommendations on the tear-
out pages at the back of the book for readers' comments. They are
followed up by our professional team.

Oxford   The Bear

Tel 01865 721783	A
Alfred Street Oxford Oxfordshire OX1 4FH	**Map 14a C2**

Just a step back from the High Street and claiming to be Oxford's
oldest pub (dating from 1242) the Bear is easily identified in summer
by its impressive display of hanging baskets. There's precious little sign
today of antiquity inside, bar its dimensions themselves – most of the
walls are modestly panelled and the beams and ceilings encased in
nicotine-enhanced ragwashed plasterboard. A medium-sized coach load
(not an uncommon occurrence) will virtually fill the bar. The Bear's
tie collection is nonetheless legendary: over 8,000 university,
regimental and sports club ties are displayed in glass cases on virtually
every wall and most of the ceiling. Though the beer is plentiful and
consistently good, be prepared to wait your turn at the tiny servery.
Food, at lunchtimes only, hardly ever strays beyond sandwiches,
ploughman's and fish'n'chips. Thankfully in fine weather there's space
to spread out into the paved beer garden under the beech trees. Don't
go looking for the pub by car, though, as parking is impossible. *Open
noon-11pm (Sun usual hours).* **Beer** *Tetley Best, Burton Ale, Royal Oak,
Hardy Country, Youngs Special. Patio. No credit cards.*

Oxford   Queen's Arms

Tel 01865 204060   **FOOD**

1 Park End Street Oxford Oxfordshire OX1 1HH   **Map 14a C2**

Following imaginative refurbishment in conjunction with the brewers, Morrells, Paul Daileys's oddly-shaped corner pub manages to make full use of its limited space. The former snug has been extended for dining and ends in a sliding picture window opening on to the wooden balcony cantilevered over Castle Mill Stream. Deep salmon walls are lined with voluminous blackboards set amongst a fine collection of framed 'Spy' cartoons. Setting a lunchtime trend are the ciabattas in guises such as tuna mayonnaise, avocados salad (both £3.25) or smoked salmon and cream cheese (£3.95). Alternative snacks include French onion soup with crusty bread (£2.95) and warm smoked mackerel salad served with pickled vegetables (£3.95). Main courses generally follow familiar lines from savoury mince (£5.25) and lemon peppered chicken (£5.50) through to Tayside salmon steak and beef stir-fry with oyster and plum sauce (£5.95), and cooking is consistent and reliable. Puds, though, appear largely to be bought in. The Queen's is a trendy and well-frequented pub with more than a little class. Thus it's not unusual for casual drinkers to be relegated to the old tap room, which has its share of pub amusements and games, and by day bears the brunt of the traffic noise. *Open 11-11.* **Bar Food** *12-2, 6-10, except Sun. Beer Morrells Mild, Bitter and Varsity. Riverside terrace, outdoor eating. Access, Visa.*

Our inspectors *never* book in the name of Egon Ronay's Guides. They disclose their identity only if they are considering an establishment for inclusion in the next edition of the Guide.

Padstow   Old Custom House

Tel 01841 532359   Fax 01841 533372   **B&B**

South Quay Padstow Cornwall PL28 8ED   **Map 12 B3**

Proudly set on the quayside with picturesque views across the bustling harbour with its colourful boats and beyond over the Camel estuary, the Old Custom House began life as the Customs and Excise building in the 1800s. St Austell Brewery have invested money in refurbishing the inn, resulting in spacious, well-decorated and neatly furnished public areas, which display a good collection of prints. A new light and airy conservatory added to the front of the building has a quarry-tiled floor and good cushioned cane furniture and is a popular spot from which to watch harbour life. Of the 27 tastefully furnished and well-equipped bedrooms, over half enjoy harbour and estuary views. Modern in style with fresh co-ordinating fabrics and wallpapers, they all have excellent spacious and sparkling bathrooms with good fixtures and fittings, plus fluffy towels and hairdryer. The honeymoon suite has an elegant four-poster, a double shower and a large deep jacuzzi set in the floor. Telephones, beverage-making facilities and satellite TV are standard throughout. *Open 11-11, Sun usual hours. Cream teas 3-5 in summer. Beer St Austell Bosun's Bitter, Tinners Ale.* **Accommodation** *27 bedrooms, all en suite, £76 (single £58). Children welcome overnight. Access, Diners, Visa.*

Pelynt   Jubilee Inn

Tel 01503 220312   Fax 01503 220920   **B&B**

Pelynt nr Looe Cornwall Pl3 2JZ   **Map 12 C3**

Originally called the Axe Inn, this attractive, pink-washed, 16th-
century inn patriotically changed its name in 1887 to celebrate the
first fifty years of Queen Victoria's reign. Ornate crowns top the front
pillars and various prints and portraits of the Queen and pieces of
Victorian china decorate the characterful lounge bar. Also furnishing
the smart public areas are a delightful collection of antique tables and
chairs, which front the fine fireplace with its gleaming copper hood.
There is also a simple, flagstone-floored public bar. There are fifteen
good-sized bedrooms which vary greatly in style and quality of
furniture. All are individually furnished, some are pleasantly furnished
in period-style with good antiques – one with a four-poster, another
with half-tester and matching chest of drawers – others are simply
furnished in modern style. All are either en suite or have their own
private bathroom, and telephone, TV, radio/alarm and beverage-
making facilities are standard. A homely lounge is available for
residents' use. Outdoor imbibing can be appreciated on the rear patio
and in the extensive garden with adjacent terrace and barbecue area.
*Free House. **Beer** Dartmoor Strong. Garden, outdoor eating area, children's
play area. **Accommodation** 15 bedrooms, 13 en suite, £60 (single £35).
Children welcome overnight. Access, Visa.*

Many establishments are currently on the market, so ownership could
change after we go to press.

Pembridge   New Inn

Tel 01544 788427   **FOOD**

Market Square Pembridge Hereford & Worcester HR6 9DZ   **Map 14 A1**

There is nothing new about this exceedingly old inn, one of England's
finest, standing at the heart of a picturesque medieval village of stone
and half-timbered houses. Opposite the old covered market (all of six
by twelve metres in dimension) and the 14th century Church
Approach. This is where peace was reportedly signed following the
battle of Mortimer's Cross in 1461. The inn itself probably pre-dates
this by some 150 years and is a treasure trove of massive oak timbers,
sloping flagstone floors and bulging walls: of two tiny bars the
"public" containing a huge open fire and massive settle is probably the
pick. Menus are sensibly scaled down to complement the limited space
available, though portions are hearty enough for today's trenchermen.
Home potted shrimps (£3.00), cheesy leek and potato bake and spicy
chicken crumble (both £4.50), can be preceded by tomato soup
(£1.75) or followed by baked bananas or apricot cheesecake (£2.25)
to satisfy any appetite. There is one front bedroom with an en-suite
shower, while two public bathrooms serve the remaining five rather
modest bedrooms. Children welcome overnight. No credit cards.
***Bar Food** 12-2, 7-9.30. Free House. **Beer** Ruddles County & Best, John
Smith's. Children allowed in bar to eat. Patio/terrace, outdoor eating.
No credit cards.*

Penelewey   **Punch Bowl & Ladle**

Tel & Fax 01872 862237

A

Penelewey nr Feock Cornwall

Map 12 B3

The idyllic exterior of rose-covered walls, heavy thatched porches and roof belie the true size of this much-extended 15th-century cottage, set sideways on to the road. Tacked onto the back is a vast dining area, but the main interest here is the warren of unspoilt rooms housed in the original cottage. Once used as a courthouse and a meet for Customs and Excise men, the charming series of interconnecting, low beamed rooms have a relaxing ambience in which to enjoy a pint and read some of the tourist literature and daily papers provided. There is much to catch the eye, from collections of rural bygones, plates, books, photographs and old tins to an array of rustic pine tables, sofas, easy chairs and some antique pieces of furniture. A handy stop for Trelissick Gardens (NT) and the King Harry Ferry across the River Fal. Greenalls. *Beer Boddingtons Bitter, Whitbread Best Bitter, Flowers Original, Bass, guest beer. Patio. Family room. Access, Visa.*

Penistone   **Cubley Hall**

Tel 01226 766086

FOOD

Mortimer Road Penistone South Yorkshire S30 6AW

Map 6 C2

The interior of this unusual conversion from Edwardian country house to what is almost a 'stately pub' is resplendent with oak panelling, mosaic floors and ornate ceilings. It echoes a bit when empty but hums along busily when full, and with sizeable parties accommodated in the conservatory, there can be a scrum for tables to eat at. Food follows generally predictable lines from beefburger and onions (£1.95) through to the steak and grill range (mixed grill £7.50), but the daily specials come to the rescue: lamb hot pot (£4.95), Cubley game pie (£4.95) and beef Mexican in spicy sauce (£4.95) are better indicators of a capable kitchen which also produces weightier weekend fare for the adjacent Workhouse Carvery (check opening times). The extensive gardens and grounds with play areas (even with the occasional bouncy castle) and drinking patios are a major draw for families through the summer. Beer festivals and events; no smoking in the 'Green Room'. *Bar Food 12-2, 6-9 (Sat to 10). Children's Menu. Free House. Beer Tetley Best and Imperial, Burton Ale, Barnsley Bitter, three guest beers. Large garden and patio, outdoor eating, children's play area. Family room. Access, Diners, Visa.*

Penn Street   Hit and Miss

Tel 01494 713109	**FOOD**
Penn Street nr Amersham Buckinghamshire HP7 0PX	Map 15a E3

200-year-old brick-built village pub with an attractive wisteria-clad facade and located opposite its own cricket pitch. Unpretentious and comfortably modernised interior with two neat, yet simply furnished bars, an open fire, a separate restaurant and a relaxing music and game-free atmosphere. A varied blackboard menu will suit all tastes, with a few standard favourites plus a selection of reliable home-cooked dishes and daily fresh fish specials. Typical bar fare ranges from filled jacket potatoes, cold meat salads, steak and kidney pie (£5.25), steak au poivre (£6.25), stuffed plaice (£5.95), ½ dozen fresh oysters (£4.50), and tagliatelle carbonara (£4.95). The restaurant à la carte menu can be ordered in the bar and offers more imaginative fare. Roast Sunday lunch is a popular affair (£6.95). Under the same ownership as *The Dove* (see entry) in Hammersmith, London W6. *Bar Food 11-3 (Sun from 12), 6.30-11 (Sun from 7). Children allowed in bar to eat. Free House. Beer Brakspear, Fuller's Chiswick Bitter & London Pride, Hook Norton Old Hooky. Garden, outdoor eating. Access, Visa.*

Perranuthnoe   Victoria Inn

Tel 01736 710309	**B&B**
Perranuthnoe nr Penzance Cornwall TR20 9NP	Map 12 A4

Pretty pink-washed village inn originally built to accommodate the masons who extended the church in the 15th century, and officially described as a safe house for the clergy. With the sea and a safe beach just down the road the comfortable typically Cornish stone-walled bar, adorned with various seafaring and fishing memorabilia, and the sheltered sun-trap rear terrace fill up early with visitors. A warm welcome is offered to families, who make use of the spacious games room. Two homely bedrooms are simply furnished and decorated and have their own WCs, showers and washbasins and a TV is provided in the adjacent lounge. A small kitchen complete with fully stocked fridge is available for those early risers catching the dawn ferry from Penzance to the Scilly Isles, the Victoria being a most convenient overnight halt. Breakfast will also be cooked for you on request. Ushers. *Beer Courage Directors, John Smith's Bitter, Ushers Best. Garden.* **Accommodation** *2 bedrooms, both en suite, £25 per room. Children welcome overnight by arrangement (under-3s stay free in parents' room, 3-12s £5). Check-in by arrangement. No dogs. Pub closed 25 Dec. No credit cards.*

Petworth   Angel

Tel 01798 42153 Fax 01798 44355	**B&B**
Angel Street Petworth West Sussex GU28 0BG	Map 11 A6

This inn dates from the 13th century and bowed walls, exposed beams, head-cracking doorways and wildly sloping floors all testify to its antiquity. The jumble of centuries is particularly apparent in the bedrooms. All rooms have either bath or shower facilities and TVs, tea-makes, hairdryers and trouser presses. Decorated in blue, they have co-ordinated floral bed linen and oak furnishings. In the bar, tapestry-covered stools and benches, Windsor chairs and horse brasses create a fairly standard old-world look, but the landlord's wit brings drinkers right up to date. *Open 10.30-3, 5.30-11 (12-3, 7-10.30 Sun).* **Accommodation** *9 bedrooms, all en suite £50-£75 (Single £30-£60).*

Dogs welcome by arrangement. Children welcome overnight (prices dep on age). **Beer** *Harvey Sussex Bitter, Fuller's ESB, Hall & Woodhouse Badger Bitter, Tanglefoot, Ballard Best, guest beers. Garden, outdoor eating area. Access, Diners, Visa.*

Petworth   **Welldiggers Arms**

Tel 01798 42287   **FOOD**

Pulborough Road Petworth West Sussex GU28 0GH   **Map 11 A6**

Once occupied by welldiggers as its name suggests, this 300-year-old roadside cottage can be located along the A283 Pulborough road, 2 miles east of Petworth. Two low-ceilinged bars furnished with a rustic collection of sturdy oak tables and benches are generally bustling with diners as this is very much a dining-orientated pub. Popular with enthusiasts of racing (Goodwood), shooting and polo (Cowdray Park), it is a useful rendezvous or stopping off point in which to enjoy some reliable bar food. Excellent seafood – fish soup £3.50) and mango and king prawn salad (£6.50), whole sea bass, whole Dover sole (both £12.50), seafood platter (£14) – and properly hung steaks (from £11.50). Alternatives on the blackboard menu may include Greek salad (£4.50), lamb's liver, onion and bacon (£6.50), braised oxtail (£7.50) or courgette cheesebake (£4.95). For pudding, try the home-made treacle tart or lemon meringue pie (£3.50). Sunday roasts (£6.50). Alfresco eating on the rear patio with views towards the South Downs. *Free House.* **Bar Food** *12-2, 6-10 (Closed Sun eve).* **Beer** *Young's Best Bitter & Special, John Smith's Courage Directors. Garden, outdoor eating. Access, Diners, Visa.*

Philleigh   **Roseland Inn**

Tel 01872 580254   **FOOD**

Philleigh Cornwall TR2 5NB   **Map 12 B3**

17th-century cob-built Cornish treasure peacefully positioned beside the parish church in an out-of-the-way village, two miles from the King Harry Ferry that crosses the River Fal. The front terrace is delightfully floral with colourful climbing roses and indoors there are old-fashioned seats, lovely old settles, worn slate floors, fresh flowers, low beams and a welcoming fire. Spotlessly kept and run with enthusiastic panache by Graham and Jacqui Hill, the Roseland is a popular rural destination for some reliable pub food. The menu and blackboard specials cover a range from home-made vegetable soup (£1.95), fresh cracked crab claws (£5.95), seafood tagliatelle (£4.75) and a 'proper' Cornish pasty (£2.20) to whole lemon sole (£8.75), turkey cordon bleu (£8.95) and swordfish steak hollandaise (£8.50). A slightly reduced à la carte menu operates on winter evenings. The garden is closed off from the road and has a rocking horse and slides for children. **Bar Food** *12-2.15, 7-9.* **Beer** *Marston's Pedigree, Cornish Original, Flowers Original. Garden. No credit cards.*

Pickering   **White Swan**

Tel 01751 472288   **FOOD**
                                                             B&B

The Market Place Pickering North Yorkshire YO18 7AA   **Map 5 E4**

In the ten years since coming here, Dierdre Buchanan has become The White Swan, and this charming town-centre inn becomes her, too. For her regulars and the casual drinker there's the traditional pubbiness of the oak-panelled bar and snug which overlook

Zzz_{z…}

Pickering's sloping main street. Residents both new and oft-returning enjoy privileged use of a quietly elegant lounge and a warm welcome from both Mrs Buchanan and her loyal staff which helps make them feel well at home. Bar food strays little from tried and tested favourites of a quality, however, which suggests a quietly competent kitchen. Lamb's liver and onions (£3.85), grilled Pickering trout (£4.25) and mushroom stroganoff (£4) are typical of daily updated offerings; for Sunday lunch as many as three roasts are available in the bar (£5.75). Desserts are generous and nicely presented (fruit Pavlova, bread-and-butter pudding and chocolate truffle torte all £1.95) or there's a Yorkshire cheeseboard available. Gradual yet continuous improvement of bedrooms has seen the addition of quality pine furniture and personally selected antique pieces where once there was hardwood and melamine. Rich floral borders and matching duvet covers add a touch of class add much-needed brightness and colour to the decor. *Free House.* **Bar Food & Restaurant** *12-2, 7-8/restaurant dinners 7.30-9 (Fri/Sat no bar suppers).* **Accommodation** *13 bedrooms, all en suite £76 (Single £55). Dogs welcome in rooms. Check-in all day. Children welcome overnight. Extra child's bed in shared room (£10), cot available free of charge. Garden, outdoor eating area.* **Beer** *Theakston Best, Cameron Lion Bitter. Access, Visa.*

Pickhill Nag's Head	FOOD
Tel 01845 567391 Fax 01845 567212	B&B
Pickhill nr Thirsk North Yorkshire YO7 4JG	Map 5 E4

Ever youthful and enthusiastic publicans Raymond & Edward Boynton will shortly celebrate their Jubilee at the pub which has become synonymous with Yorkshire hospitality at its best. Immaculately kept real ales, personally chosen monthly wine selections (offered also by the glass) and a 40-odd array of malt whiskies are the domain of one brother against which his sibling's kitchen output measures up admirably. Menu boards here do not so much proclaim daily specials as spell out the kitchen's entire repertoire. For starters, go for mackerel and smoked salmon paté (£3.50) or mushrooms stuffed with Stilton and York ham (£3.75). For a bar snack try seafood pancake mornay (£4.75) or tandoori chicken (£5.75). Main meals extend to veal escalope à la creme (£9.25) and halibut steak with herb butter (£8.25), plus traditional puddings such as Brown Betty, Highland Flummery and squidgy chocolate Roulade (all £2.50) to follow. As a place to stay, the Nag's Head is similarly above reproach. Well signed just off the A1, it was one of many 17th-century coaching inns which serviced the London to Edinburgh route; it is the best one to boast a genuine Yorkshire "weather-stone" which remains essential reading for the meteorologically credulous. Bedrooms, upgraded over the years, are divided between the pub and next door house standing in a neatly tended garden, and a self-contained cottage which can be let in its entirety. Remote-control TVs, dial-out phones and beverage trays are the standard appointments of rooms, the majority of which have plenty of desk space. Carpeted bathrooms are neat and well appointed, though three have WC/shower rooms only. Several rooms have space for an extra bed or cot, with children charged according to age and what they eat. For any anxious parents, baby listening is available, while for the entire family Yorkshire breakfast in the morning is irresistible. *Free House.* **Accommodation** *15 bedrooms, all en suite £45 (Single £32).* **Bar Food** *12-2, 6-10.* **Restaurant Meals** *7-9.30 (closed on Sun eve). Lunch by arrangement (Sun 12-2). Garden,*

outdoor eating. Children allowed anywhere. **Beer** *Hambleton Bitter,
Theakston Best XB & Old Peculier. Access, Visa.*

Picklescott   Bottle & Glass Inn

FOOD
B&B

Tel 01694 751345

Picklescott nr Church Stretton Shropshire SY6 6NR

Map 6 A4

Zzzz...

Follow well-signed lanes from the A49 at Dorrington, or the scenic
route over Long Mynd from the Strettons to happen on this epitome
of locals, complete with palm-reading gypsy (for ladies only!). Rear
extensions to the original two-roomed stone-built pub have been
sympathetically handled, the new dining area leading to a barbecue
terrace and rear garden. Food throughout stays with the safe options:
home-baked ham, grills of steak and fish supplemented by daily
specials (tomato and orange soup £1.40, turkey curry £4.95) and
lunchtime salads, sandwiches and savoury filled baked potatoes (spicy
beef £3.50). Sunday carvery with 8 fresh vegetables (2-course £7.75)
booking essential. Families are very welcome; there are picnic tables
on a sun-trap front patio and safe playing by the village stream
opposite. Comfortable, character bedrooms have been expertly created
in the roof space with brass bedsteads, coordinated fabrics and gold-
tapped bathrooms with over-bath showers. The temptation of
telephones has been resisted in favour of TVs, tea trays and trouser
presses. Well-balanced youngsters may be accommodated strictly
by prior arrangement. **Bar Food & Restaurant Meals** *12-2, 7-10.
Free House.* **Beer** *Bass, Worthington. Garden, patio. Family room.*
Accommodation *3 bedrooms, all en suite, £45 (single £30). Children
welcome by arrangement only. Check-in by arrangement. No dogs.
No credit cards.*

Piddlehinton   Thimble Inn

A

Tel 01300 348270

Piddlehinton nr Dorchester Dorset DT2 7TD

Map 13 F2

The Thimble is no longer thimble-sized nor is it the quaint, creeper-
clad village local that we once knew. The traditional two-bar layout
has disappeared and a splendid thatched extension has been built. This
curves along the tiny River Piddle with small bridges linking it to the
attractive summer flower-filled garden, which enjoys rolling country
views. Internally, it is very smart with tasteful decor, good prints and
subdued lighting and is furnished with an assortment of pub tables and
chairs throughout the now open-plan bars. A feature of the bar is the
27ft glass-topped well. *Free House.* **Beer** *Ringwood Old Thumper,
Badger, Hardy Country, Hard Tackle. Garden, outdoor eating.
No credit cards.*

Pilley   Fleur de Lys

FOOD

Tel 01590 672158

Pilley nr Lymington Hampshire SO41 5QG

Map 14 C4

This attractive thatched pub nestles in a tiny village right on the edge
of the New Forest. Originally it was a pair of foresters' cottages, the
tree roots and fireplace opening (an old New Forest Rights tradition)
can still be seen in the stone-flagged entrance passage. Beyond, three
interconnecting rooms are neat and tidy, boasting beams, a huge
inglenook, a comfortable mix of tables and chairs and various bric-a-
brac. Bar food remains reliable after a change of landlord and still
caters for all tastes by offering the old favourites – ploughman's

(£3.50), barbecue spare ribs and salad (£7.25) – plus grilled mussels with garlic and Parmesan (£4.85) and leg of lamb steak with red wine and rosemary (£7.45) on the printed scroll menu. Daily specials enhance the choice of dishes with fresh local fish featuring strongly: ling, herring, hake, mackerel, whole lemon sole (£8.50) and lobster thermidor (£10.50). Further blackboard-listed meals include home-made soup – celery and Stilton (£2.45) – Morrocan beef (£7.50), pork in ginger (£6.75), beef in Guinness, apricots and prunes (£7.25) and veal in black bean sauce with water chestnuts (£7.75). Good sheltered garden with weekend summer barbecues. Afternoon teas. *Pub open 11-11 (Sun 12-10.30).* **Bar Food** *11.30-2.30, 6-9.30 (Sun 12-2, 7-9).* **Beer** *Whitbread, Boddingtons, Flowers, Marston's Pedigree, Brakspear. Garden, outdoor eating, summer barbecue. Access, Visa.*

Pimperne   Anvil Hotel

Tel 01258 453431	**B&B**
Pimperne nr Blandford Forum Dorset	**Map 14 B4**

Set back from the busy A345 Salisbury to Blandford road, this pretty thatched cottage dates from 1535. Low ceilings, thick walls, old black beams and an inglenook fireplace characterise the tile-floored restaurant, while more modern plush wall-bench seating features in the neat and relaxing lounge bar and in the newly extended Forge Bar. Up a narrow, steep staircase and tucked beneath the thatch are nine clean and comfortable bedrooms. All are attractively decorated, furnished with modern telephones and tea-making facilities. Compact en-suite facilities – most with shower trays – are spotlessly clean. Delightful flower-filled front garden with a shady spot beneath a huge weeping willow. *Free House.* **Beer** *Wadworth 6X, Bass. Garden, outdoor eating area.* **Accommodation** *9 bedrooms, all en suite, £60 (single £40). Children welcome overnight. Additional beds and cots are available. No dogs.*

Pin Mill   Butt and Oyster

Tel 01473 780764	**A**
Pin Mill Chelmondiston nr Ipswich Suffolk 1RP 1JW	**Map 10 C3**

Classic riverside pub set in a tiny hamlet off the B1456 at Chelmondiston, south-west of Ipswich. Dating from the 17th-century, this old bargeman's retreat is still frequented by sailors and fishermen and on busy summer days it is chock full of tourists, all enjoying the simple charm of its old settles, tiled floors and fine views across Buttermans Bay, part of the River Orwell. Nautical artefacts and photographs adorn the wood-panelled walls of the main bar and the "smoke room" features a collection of model ships. Both bars are free of intrusive music and electronic games. Be early for the sought-after waterside window seats, or one of the sturdy benches adjacent to the slipway; it's an ideal spot to watch the setting sun on fine summer evenings. Traditional winter pub games are popular when the crowds have gone home. *Open 11-3, 7-11 (Sun 12-3, 7-10.30. Summer 11-11).* **Beer** *Tolly Cobbold Original & Bitter, Charrington IPA, Bass. Garden, outdoor eating. No credit cards.*

Pitton   Silver Plough

Tel 01722 72266	**FOOD**

Pitton nr Salisbury Wiltshire SP5 1DZ

Map 14 C3

The Silver Plough was a farmhouse until after the Second World War. Everything about the attractive long building is neat and well kept: the lawns at the front, full of white plastic tables and chairs for summer drinking, and the tastefully furnished main bar with its dust-free jugs, bottles and curios hanging from the ceiling timbers. Sturdy antique oak settles, various tables and quality paintings and prints characterise this bar and the snug bar with its neighbouring skittle alley – both popular with locals. It's very much a dining pub offering a good range of home-cooked bar meals using fresh local produce from reliable local suppliers, including Pitton's smokery. In the bar – part of which has smartly clothed tables – the daily-changing blackboards may list smoked trout paté (£3.95), chicken kebabs (£9.95), game pie (£8.95), and salmis of pigeon (£8.95). Pasta dishes and decent ploughman's are popular lunchtime choices. Vegetarians are well catered for, they have their own menu. Separate à la carte menu available in the neatly laid-up restaurant. There is an excellent global list of wines, with no less than eleven offered by the glass, and a raft of country wines. ***Bar Food*** *12-2.30, 7-9.30.* ***Beer*** *Wadworth 6X, Bass, Websters Green Label, Fuller's London Pride, Gale HSB, Courage Best. Garden, outdoor eating. Family room. Access, Diners, Visa.*

Pluckley   Dering Arms

Tel 01233 840371	**FOOD**

Pluckley nr Ashford Kent TN27 0RR

Map 11 C5

Located a mile from the village beside Pluckley Station, this impressive manorial building was once the Dering Estate hunting lodge and boasts curving Dutch gables, rounded triple lancet 'Dering' windows, and a rather spooky grandeur. Splendid interior to match with high ceilings, wood or stone floors, a tall exposed brick fireplace, stripped pine doors, various sturdy wooden tables, long Victorian benches and some old leather easy chairs. A relaxing atmosphere pervades in which to enjoy some good bar food listed on two sensibly short blackboard menus. Favourite snacks can be found on one; a range of interesting home-cooked dishes on the other. A typical choice may include gazpacho soup (£2.75), soft herring roes with crispy bacon (£3.85), mackerel grilled with capers (£4.95), grilled plaice (£4.95) and lamb, apricot and coriander pie (£5.95) with a decent shortcrust pastry top. Fresh fish from Hythe dominate the imaginative daily-changing restaurant menu. Good local Goachers ales and a Kentish farm cider are favoured here, and wine drinkers can choose from an interesting list of 82 wines. Regular gourmet evenings, summer barbecues and live jazz or classical music in the sheltered garden. *Pub open 11.30-3, 6-11 (Sun 12-3, 7-10.30).* ***Bar Food*** *12-2 & 7-10. No food Sun evening. Free House.* ***Beer*** *Goachers Maidstone Ale, Dering Ale, Dark Ale. Garden, outdoor eating. Pub closed Boxing Day & 27 December. Access, Visa.*

Plush   **Brace of Pheasants**

Tel 013004 357   **FOOD**

Plush Dorchester Dorset DT2 7RQ   Map 13 F2

Originally two cottages and a forge, dating from the 16th century,
this attractive collection of thatched, brick and flint buildings became
an inn in the mid-1930s and must surely be one of the prettiest in
Dorset. The location is idyllic, nestling in a peaceful rural hamlet,
surrounded by rolling downland. A brace of glass-encased stuffed
pheasants hangs above the main cottage door that leads into the
charmingly unspoilt bar, complete with huge inglenook (used for
seating), a further log fire and an assortment of traditional furniture.
Guns, prints and harnesses decorate the walls and the separate cosy
restaurant has tables neatly laid with linen cloths. The attraction here,
other than its setting, is the consistently good bar food. Separate
blackboards for both lunch and evening fare list the weekly-changing
specials which supplement an extensive printed menu selection. Lunch
features the usual ploughman's and salads, plus an excellent range of
lighter bites, including four patés – delicious Dorset herb (£3.25),
crab savoury and soft herring roes (both £3.50). Substantial home-
cooked lunch dishes may include steak, kidney and mushroom pie,
liver, bacon and onions and a good fish pie – crammed with salmon
and prawns (all £3.95). Evening fare is more adventurous; veal with
ginger and almonds (£10.95), venison in a mushroom and Madeira
sauce (£12.95) and of course pheasant Rob Roy (£9.25). Well-cooked
vegetables accompany each dish. Puddings, listed on a board, range
from raspberry pavlova to apple and plum crumble (all £2.75). There
is a delightful garden with mature trees and shrubs and a continental-
style vine-covered pergola with seating beneath. *Free House.*
Beer Greene King IPA, Flowers Original, Smiles Best. Garden,
children's play area. Family room. Access, Visa.

Plymouth   **The China House**

Tel 01752 260930   **FOOD**

Marrowbone Slip Sutton Harbour Plymouth Devon PL4 0DW   Map 12 C3

The China House has had many uses since being built as a quayside
warehouse in the mid-1600s, King's bakehouse, hospital for seamen,
porcelain factory (from which period it takes its name) and prison,
amongst others. Now cleverly rebuilt inside to reflect its warehouse
days with great bulks of timber, cast-iron pillars and sets of mock
cargo, it makes a most unusual hostelry with the added attraction of
some good bar food. The lunch menu is not large: about half-a-dozen
hot dishes like jacket potato with tuna and onion (£2.95), chicken and
broccoli pie (£4.95) and spaghetti carbonara (£4.35) plus open
'doorstep' sandwiches (from £2.25) with beef, prawn, local crab or
ham on great wedges of good granary. Puddings (all at £2.75) include
fruit pies and various ice creams (£2.25). At night, the sandwiches
disappear but there are a couple of starters and a few more main
dishes; lamb with cream and onion sauce (£9.95), pork satay with
cranberry sauce (£8.95) and fresh fish according to the market (from
£9.95). Full Sunday roast is £4.95. There is a no-smoking area and a
narrow verandah (no tables) jutting out over the water of the harbour.
Regularly held jazz and blues nights. *Bar Food 12-2.15, **Restaurant***
***Meals** 6.30-9.30 (Sun from 7).* *Beer Wadworth 6X, Dartmoor Best &*
Strong, guest beer. Terrace. Access, Visa.

Pocklington   **Feathers Hotel**

| Tel 01759 303155   Fax 01759 304382 | **B&B** |

5 Market Place Pocklington Humberside YO4 2AH   Map 7 D1

Popular with the locals, who enjoy a drink in the spacious, welcoming
bar, this pebbledash pub on the market place also has decent overnight
accommodation. The six main-house bedrooms of varying sizes have a
traditional appeal (one boasts a four-poster and another a half-tester),
while the remaining six, across the car park, are in chalet style. All
offer TVs, hairdryers, telephones, trouser presses, tea-makers and
smart private facilities. *Open 11-11 Mon-Sat, regular hours Sun.*
Beer Younger's, Theakston's. ***Accommodation** 12 bedrooms, all en suite,
£49.50 (single £39.50). Children welcome overnight, additional beds and
cots available. Guide dogs only welcome overnight. Access, Diners, Visa.*

Polkerris   **Rashleigh Inn**

| Tel 0172681 3991 | **A** |

Polkerris Fowey Cornwall PL25 3NJ   Map 12 B3

Literally on the beach in a tiny isolated cove and known locally as the
'Inn on the Beach', the Rashleigh is well worth seeking out for its
magnificent setting. Once the old lifeboat station, until becoming a
pub in 1924, it is a popular refreshment spot for coast path walkers
and for families using the beach in the summer. Summer alfresco
drinking is unrivalled in this area, for the table-filled terrace is a
splendid place from which to watch the sun set across St Austell Bay.
On cooler days the sea views can still be admired from the warmth of
the main bar, especially from the much sought after bay-window seats.
Parents enjoying a drink on the terrace can keep an eagle eye on their
children playing on the beach. *Free House. **Beer** Hicks Special & Best,
Dartmoor Best & Strong, Burton Ale. Outdoor eating area. Access, Visa.*

Pontefract   **Parkside Inn**

| Tel 01977 709911   Fax 01977 701602 | **B&B** |

Park Road Pontefract West Yorkshire WF8 4QD   Map 7 D1

A haunt of racegoers – opposite the racecourse – and a haven for
families with its enclosed gardens and play area, the Parkside appeals to
many tastes. In a layout reminiscent of a Western ranch, it contains a
host of bar areas with conservatory and sun lounge, a carvery and à la
carte restaurant. Accommodation has been carefully incorporated and
added to over the years. Of most character is the old farmhouse,
connected now by an arched walkway, where the old front door and
stairs can still be seen, and what is now a residents' lounge retains the
original kitchen sinks and shelves. A large family room and sets of
connecting twins are especially popular with weekending families;
baby-listening is all part of the service and family days are held
monthly. Accoutrements run through TV and phones to hairdryers
and trouser presses; ask, though, for a room with full bath, as some
of the shower rooms are, to say the least, cramped. Half a mile from
Junction 32 of the M62. *Free House. **Beer** John Smith's Best & Magnet.
Garden, children's play area. Family room. **Accommodation** 28 bedrooms,
all en suite, £62 (single £47). Children welcome overnight (under-5s stay
free in parents' room, large family room £50), additional beds (£10) and
cots (no charge) available. No dogs. Access, Visa.*

Port Gaverne — Port Gaverne Hotel

Tel 01208 880244	**B&B**
Port Gaverne Port Isaac Cornwall PL29 3SQ	Map 12 B3

Set in a sheltered cove 50 yards from the beach is this charming 17th-century inn; family-run for the last 25 years, Midge Ross is now single-handed at the tiller. The ship-shape, character pubby bar has a polished slate floor and the tiny snug bar features a collection of china, old local photographs, a genuine ship's table and carved chest, and an interesting diorama of the port years ago. Upstairs, along the warren of corridors lined with attractive paintings and watercolours lie nineteen cheerful, individually decorated bedrooms which boast pretty fabrics and wallpapers and attractive en-suite bathrooms. Antique furniture grace the older rooms in the main building, but all have thoughtful homely touches like pieces of china and ornaments, plus tissues, TVs, hairdryers and telephones for added comfort. Fresh, clean and comfortable accommodation, the best room affording a sea view. Self-catering cottages are also available. *Free House. Beer St Austell HSD (Hicks), Flowers IPA, Bass. Garden. Accommodation 19 bedrooms, all en suite, from £90 (single £45). Children welcome overnight (under-3s stay free in parents' room), additional beds & cots supplied. Accommodation closed early Jan-mid Feb. Access, Diners, Visa.*

Zzzz...

Porthleven — Harbour Inn

Tel 01326 573876	**B&B**
Porthleven nr Helston Cornwall TR13 9JB	Map 12 A4

Situated in an unspoilt fishing village, this old fisherman's pub enjoys good views across the colourful collection of fishing boats and dinghies that fill the picturesque little harbour twenty yards away. Inside, there is a comfortable lounge area and a much larger and livelier public bar area, while upstairs accommodation is offered in ten en-suite bedrooms, six of which have harbour views. Cottagey in style with pretty floral fabrics, wallpaper and matching duvet covers, they are neatly furnished with modern pine and the large, adequately equipped bathrooms have good overhead showers. Added comforts include TV, telephone, hairdryer and beverage-making facilities. Refurbishments to all rooms have now been completed. *Open 11-11, Sun usual hours. Beer St Austell. Accommodation 10 bedrooms, 8 en suite £54 (single £30.50). Access, Visa.*

Porthleven — Ship

Tel 01326 572841	**A**
Porthleven nr Helston Cornwall TR13 9JS	Map 12 A4

Set in the cliffside and perched on the harbour wall, this old fisherman's pub enjoys a magnificent position looking out across the quaint working harbour and out to sea. The view is best appreciated in summer from the series of terraced lawns that rise up the cliff behind the pub. On wild winter days, climb the flight of stone steps and savour the view from the warmth of a window seat in the nautical bric-a-brac adorned bar, complete with good log fires. Loud piped music, unfortunately, can spoil the effect of this superb location. The family room – the 'Smithy' – adjoins the garden, while the ground-floor cellar bar is used only in the summer. The tiny harbour is attractively lit by fairy lights at night. *Open 11.30-11 in summer, usual hours other times. Courage. Beer Ushers Best Bitter & Founder's Ale, Courage Best, Directors. No credit cards.*

Powerstock — Three Horseshoes Inn

FOOD
B&B

Tel 01308 485328

Powerstock Bridport Dorset DT6 3TF

Map 13 F2

'The Shoes' (as it is affectionately known locally) is a Victorian stone inn set in a sleepy village amid narrow, winding lanes and best reached from the A3066 north of Bridport. Rebuilt in 1906 after a devastating fire, but solidly old-fashioned in style with simple country furnishings in both the bustling bar and in the two pine-panelled dining rooms. People come from miles around to this reliable old favourite for the chef/licensee Pat Ferguson and Jason Williams's food; it's not cheap, certainly, but it is fresh and delicious, specialising in fish from local boats, Dorset lamb and seasonal game. The extensive daily-changing blackboard list of home-cooked dishes serves both bar and restaurant. Begin with salad of grilled goat's cheese (£4.50), fish soup (£4.95) or terrine of port and liver layered with chicken breasts and pistachio nuts (£2.75), and fish fanciers can continue with baked sea bream with garden herbs (£9.50), bourride (£13.50) or turbot fillet seasoned with crushed black pepper (£10.50). Meat and game dishes too: garlic studded rack of Dorset lamb (£10.95) and escalopes of venison marinated in red wine with garlic and herbs (£10.50) – all served with decent, well-cooked vegetables. Lighter bits include interesting fresh pasta dishes (from £3.50), salads and freshly baked and filled baguettes (from £2). Traditional puddings (£3-3.50) include summer berry tart, sticky toffee pudding and sunken chocolate soufflé. Must book for busy Sunday lunches (£12.50). Good Palmers ales and a choice of eight wines by the glass. Delightful terraced garden and rear patio with village and valley views for summer eating. Four simple, centrally heated bedrooms with traditional older-style furniture, TVs and tea-makers provide homely overnight accommodation. Two are spacious and comfortable with clean, en-suite bathrooms, the others are rather too compact and share a bathroom. *Bar Food & Restaurant Meals* 12-2, 7-10. *Children allowed in bar to eat, small children's menu.* *Beer* Palmers BB, IPA, '200' Ale. *Garden, outdoor eating, children's play area.* *Accommodation* 4 bedrooms, 2 en suite, £45 (single £24-£30). Children welcome overnight. Access, Visa.

Priors Dean — White Horse

FOOD

Tel 01420 588387

Priors Dean nr Petersfield Hampshire GU32 1DA

Map 15 D3

Also called the Pub with No Name; there is no sign. Fiendish to get to: leave Petersfield on the A272 Winchester-bound, turn right towards Steep, then after about 5 miles, take the East Tisted road at the crossroads, then immediate right down the second gravel track. It's worth the effort, for this is a quite wonderful 17th-century farmhouse pub of utterly simple (uncomfortable, some would say) charm and genuinely unspoilt by modernity, surrounded by 13 acres of fields belonging to the pub. The bar menu includes various dishes like beef and ale pie (£6.25), deep-pan lasagne (£3.10), farmhouse cottage pie (£3.75), spinach and mushroom lasagne (£4.50), and also in winter ("when the Aga is lit, as it is not the same on an electric stove"), thick country soup £2.95. First World War poet Edward Thomas wrote his first published work, *Up in the Wind*, about the pub; it's 750 feet up on the top of the Downs, with peaceful views on every side. There are 20 country wines. No children indoors but play area in garden.

Bar Food 12-2. *Free House. Beer Ballard's Best Bitter, Broadwood, Courage Best and Directors, Eldridge, No Name Bitter, Ringwood Fortyniner. Garden, outdoor eating, children's play area. No credit cards.*

Raby   Wheatsheaf Inn

Tel 0151 336 3416	A
The Green Raby Merseyside L63 4JH	Map 6 A2

Wedged amid a row of old farm buildings, the 'Thatch', as it is known, dates from around 1611 and is today just about the Wirral's last surviving rural pub. Notable within is a genuine snug, opposite the single bar, which is constructed from aged settles around a brick-lined inglenook fronted by a massive oak lintel. The wide choice of well-kept real ales is the main attraction, although lunchtime snacks are popular (no food Sunday lunch or any evening). Strictly no under-18s admitted. *Free House. No credit cards.*

Radwell   Swan Inn

Tel 01234 781351	FOOD
Felmersham Road Radwell Bedfordshire MK43 7HS	Map 15a E1

Quaint 17th-century thatched country pub located near the River Ouse within a delightful village. Rustic charm characterises the honely, simply furnished and tiny two-bar interior, and the recent arrival of enthusiastic new landlords heralds a positive new era for this friendly pub. An extensive and varied menu lists a few favourites, but predominantly features home-cooked fare using fresh local ingredients, especially fish and game, and is supplemented by good daily blackboard specials. Choices range from fish terrine and onion tart (both £2.95) for starters to venison in red wine (£6.95), medallions of pork in Calvados and cream (£7.50) and unusual Oriental dishes like teriyaki beeef (£4.95), kashmiri chicken (£5.25), lamb rogan josh (£6.25) and stir-fry chicken with bamboo shoots, water chestnuts and orange and green ginger sauce (£4.95). Vegetarian options. Puddings (£1.80) include lemon tart and apple pie. Plans for the large garden include a pets corner and children's play area. *Bar Food* 12-2, 7-9.30 *(no food Mon eve). Beer Charles Wells, guest beer. Garden, outdoor eating. Access, Visa.*

Ramsbury   Bell at Ramsbury

Tel 01672 20230	FOOD
The Market Square Ramsbury nr Marlborough Wiltshire SN8 2PE	Map 14a A4

The Bell's stock-in-trade remains the provision of good quality, carefully prepared bar food at affordable prices. Sensibly short and to the point, both the printed and daily-changing blackboard menus give equal billing to home-made soups and patés and single-course snacks such as medallions of beef fillet in red wine (£10.50) chicken breast with a Stilton sauce (£7.45) and duck breast roasted pink with a cassis sauce (£8.25), while fresh fish (monkfish, bream, lemon sole) and steaks, sauced or plain, are accompanied by plainly cooked fresh vegetables; Sunday roast is £6.45. To follow are plenty of traditional nursery puddings from Spotted Dick to rhubarb crumble and home-made ices and sorbets. This is not the 'Bell' of old but it is still worth a visit. Twenty malt whiskies, no-smoking area. *Bar Meals* 12-2 *(Sat and Sun to 2.30), 7-9 (Sat and Sun to 9.30). Free House. Beer Wadworth 6X, Hook Norton Best, IPA, two guest beers. Garden, outdoor eating. Family room. Access, Visa.*

Ravenstonedale   **Black Swan Hotel**

| Tel 015396 23204   Fax 015396 23604 | **B&B** |

Ravenstonedale nr Kirkby Stephen Cumbria CA17 4NG   **Map 5 D3**

Run by the Stuarts as a 'home-from-home', the Black Swan is a turn-of-the-century, Lakeland-stone inn, six minutes from the M6 (Junction 38) and a mere half an hour from Ullswater, useful as a base for walking and fishing. Main bedrooms in traditional style are supplemented by more modern additions in the old stables, where ramps and wide doorways offer good access for disabled guests; residents have a choice of sitting rooms. Relax in the quaint stone-walled bars with the locals or in the sheltered garden by the village beck. 26 malt whiskies. *Open 10.30-11 (Sun 12-10.30). Free House.* *Beer Hartleys, Theakston, Younger's, Robinson's, 2 guest beers. Garden, outdoor eating, lake and river fishing, tennis, children's play area.* *Accommodation 16 bedrooms, £60 (single £44). Children welcome overnight (under-3s free in parents' room), additional beds and cots supplied. Access, Diners, Visa.*

Ravenstonedale   **The Fat Lamb**

| Tel 015396 23242 | **B&B** |

Crossbank Ravenstonedale Kirkby Stephen Cumbria   **Map 5 D3**

Nine miles from Junction 37 of the M6, at a point where the Lake District just about meets the Yorkshire Dales, the Lamb stands right on the A683 just a couple of miles from Ravenstonedale. Originally built in the 17th century as a farmhouse the pub retains a winter warmth within its solid stone walls, where residents feel truly cosseted by the personable young owners. In summer there's a scenic patio and garden for an early-evening drink. Following a table d'hote (£16) there's a choice of the coffee and TV lounges before turning in. Several bedrooms are conveniently on the ground floor, in former outhouses, with wheelchair access. All have neat, if compact, bathrooms and tea-making facilities, and most have room for an extra bed (under-4s stay free). Panoramic views soak in every changing mood of the surrounding moorland. No smoking in restaurant. *Beer Mitchells Fortress. Patio and residents' garden, disabled facilities.* *Accommodation 12 bedrooms, all en suite, £54 (single £27). Children welcome overnight (under-6s stay free if sharing parents' room, 7-12s £6), extra beds and cots provided. No credit cards.*

Redmile   **Peacock Inn**

| Tel 01949 42554 | **FOOD** |

Church Corner Redmile Nottinghamshire NG13 0GA   **Map 7 D3**

Turn off the A52 at the signs to Belvoir Castle to find Redmile deep in the flatlands. Its pub, the Peacock, was rescued from dereliction some seven years ago. The interior is a tribute to the skills of landlord Colin Crawford whose restoration of its old fireplaces and former ships' timbers is commendable. His most recent work has enclosed the rear flagstoned patio to create a skylit Garden Room replete with wrought-iron tables and fanciful murals. Jean Louis supervises a busy kitchen: from the daily changing blackboard wild mushrooms in puff pastry (£3.95) and grilled sardines (£2.75) could precede such main courses as pan-fried salmon (£8.20) or rack of lamb with pistou sauce (£9.20) with a fromage frais cheesecake or chocolate and orange millefeuille (£3.50) to follow. A la carte dishes – a typical meal of seafood brochette (£4.50), fillet steak with Colston Bassett Stilton heart wrapped in bacon with Port sauce (£10.95) and aniseed iced mousse in chocolate shell with fresh fruit (£3.50) – come in less than authentic French translations. Fixed-price menus are also offered from £12.95. The atmosphere, however, remains one of the Crawfords' village local, for they were brought up here: their "locals" in turn have much to be grateful for. Booking advisable for bar and restaurant. The Crawfords also run the *Blue Ball* in Braunston, Leicestershire (*qv*). *Bar Food* 12-2, 6.00-10 (*Sun all day*). *Restaurant Meals* 12-2, 7-10 (*Sun lunch only 12-3*). *Free House. Beer Abbot Ale, Bass, Tetley, Marston's Pedigree. Garden, outdoor eating. Family room. Access, Diners, Visa.*

Reeth   Buck Hotel

Tel 01748 884210	·	B&B
Reeth Richmond North Yorkshire DL11 6SW		Map 5 D3

Boarded up little more than two years ago, it's tempting at this point to say that business has bucked up in a big way recently. Newly painted in brilliant white, the Buck is an imposing building standing at the head of this prettiest of Dales villages; the fascinating Swaledale Folk House inn is a short walk away across the green. Nigel Fawcett's friendly pub scores highly with families for its separate games room, safe back garden, children's menus and choices of family accommodation. All ten bedrooms have TVs and tea trays; the best have fabulous views of the surrounding hills. Under-8s stay free in their parents' room; while there is no baby listening, parents can watch TV undisturbed in an adjacent first-floor residents' lounge. *Free House. Open 11-3, 6-11 (Sat 6-12). Sun 12-3, 7-10.30. Accommodation 10 bedrooms, all en suite £44 (single £22). Children welcome overnight (under-8s stay free in parents' room). Cot, high-chair and child's bed available. Beer John Smith's, Theakston Best XB. Garden. Access, Visa.*

Reigate Heath   Skimmington Castle

Tel 01737 243100	A
Reigate Heath Reigate Surrey RH2 8RL	Map 15a F4

Pleasant old cottage pub in a delightful rural setting and reached via a pitted track (Bonny's Road) across the golf course off Flanchford Road on Reigate Heath, close to the A25. An odd looking front extension disguises the true age of the original cottage which houses two charming, partly-panelled and atmospheric rooms filled with an assortment of older-style furniture, collections of bottles, plates, copper and brass and a huge inglenook with open winter fire and bread oven. Front bench-filled patio for peaceful, fine-weather drinking. An abundance of well way-marked footpaths make this secluded pub a popular spot from which to explore the surrounding countryside. Large car park to the rear of the pub. *Open 11-2.30, 6-11, Sun 12-3, 7-10.30. Beer Greene King IPA, Burton Ale, two guest beers. Front patio. Access, Visa.*

Remenham   Little Angel

Tel 01491 574165	FOOD
Remenham nr Henley-on-Thames Oxfordshire RG9 2LS	Map 15a D3

Just over the bridge from Henley-on-Thames, on the Berkshire side of the river, the 17th-century Little Angel in Remenham (not to be confused with The Angel public house on the Henley side of the

bridge) is very much an eating pub. The same extensive menu
operates both in the pubby bar with its dark red ceilings and in the
beamed restaurant beyond with crisply clothed tables. There are also a
couple of function/private dining rooms. Eat outside and on summer
weekends you get the added attraction of being able to watch the local
cricketers, whose pitch is right next door. The same menu is offered
throughout the pub and may include deep-fried Brie parcels on a bed
of lettuce with a hot cranberry sauce (£4.50), salad of the day, perhaps
rare beef (£6.50), baked cod with garlic and herb crust with saffron
and parsley sauce (£8.50), sausage and mash (£4.95), beef stroganoff
(£11.95) and chicken and Stilton (£11.50), with the addition of
sandwiches (from £2.25) and ploughman's (from £3) served in the
bar area. To accompany there is a choice of twelve wines by the glass.
Smart young uniformed men and women provide efficient service.
*Bar Food 12-2.30, 7-10. Restaurant Meals 12.30-2.30, 7.30-10 (except
Sun eve). Children allowed in bar to eat. Beer Brakspears Bitter, Special,
guest beer. Terrace, outdoor eating. Access, Diners, Visa.*

Rennington   Masons Arms

Tel 01665 577275   Fax 01665 577894

Rennington nr Alnwick Northumberland WE66 3RX

B&B

Map 5 D1

Just one-and-a-half miles from the A1, the "Stamford Cot"
(as it's known locally) stands in open country well back from the
Northumbrian coastal resorts. There's a genuinely warm welcome
here from Frank and Dee Sloan to their skilfully converted single-
room bar, with open fires at each end, and cosy dining room. No
children under 14 overnight or in the bar. no infants in the dining
room, hence the reason for mentioning it! Guests should be aware,
however, that the pub does get very busy with quite an up-market
crowd, so that some participation in the convivial atmosphere thus
engendered is practically de rigeur. In addition to four standard
bedrooms, sharing facilites, in the main house, there are four new,
smart and fully equipped en-suite bedrooms in a former shipper
"out back", where the verdant grassland growing practically up to
the windows gives a whole new slant to country living. A hearty
Northumbrian breakfast is guaranteed, firmly setting up guests for
a day's exploring. *Free House. Open 12.30-2.30 6-11 (7-10.30 Sun).
Beer Courage directors, Ruddles Best, Jennings Dark Mild. Patio.
Access, Visa.*

ZZzz...

Richmond   The Orange Tree

Tel 0181-940 0944

45 Kew Road Richmond Surrey TW9 2NQ

A

Map 15a F4

Named after the first orange tree planted in Kew Gardens, the pub has
been around since 1870 and was the first in London to be granted a
theatre licence (in 1878). The building is large and airy with an
attractive ambience with dark wood and red velvet abounding.
Downstairs is a wine bar/restaurant and the theatre is upstairs.
Recommended for food in last year's Guide, but new landlords – Peter
and Jilly Cromack – took over as we went to press, with a promise
that the food "will change". *Open 11-11, Sun regular hours. Children
allowed in wine bar only. Beer Young's. Patio. Access, Diners, Visa.*

Richmond   **White Swan**

Tel 0181-940 0959	**FOOD**
25/26 Old Palace Lane Richmond Surrey TW9 1PG	Map 15a F4

The White Swan is secluded in a quiet cul de sac not far away from
the Thames and Twickenham Bridge. A charming pub, it combines
an old-fashioned intimate low-ceilinged bar with a modern
conservatory at the back. There is also a flowery paved garden.
A large selection of hot and cold food is piled up on the cramped
counter all prepared in-house and of a reasonable standard; ocean pie
(£3.75), chicken curry (£3.55) for main course, and varying desserts
including passion cake and lime crunch (all £2). *Pub open 11-3, 5.30-
11 (Sat 11-4, 6-11, Sun 12-3, 7-10.30).* **Bar Food** *'always available'.*
Children are allowed in the conservatory to eat. **Beer** *Courage. Terrace.*
No credit cards.

Rickling Green   **Cricketers**

Tel 01799 543210 Fax 01799 543512	**B&B**
Rickling Green nr Saffron Walden Essex CB11 3YE	Map 10 B3

Victorian redbrick-built pub enjoying a peaceful position overlooking
the village green and cricket pitch. Inside, the rather nondescript
public bar and lounge were due to be completely refurbished and
made open-plan as we went to press, but not the small and cosy side
room which has access to the delightful front terrace – a popular spot
in which to relax and watch an innings or two. People needing an
overnight stop close to Stansted aiport (ten minutes' drive away)
will find the five comfortable bedrooms, housed in a modern rear
extension, most convenient and acceptable. All are uniformly equipped
with reproduction darkwood furniture, decent fabrics and have clean,
tiled en-suite shower rooms. Added comforts include TVs, radio
alarms, telephones, trouser presses, hairdryers and tea-makers. Two
family rooms with extra beds. *Pub open all day Sat in summer. Free
House.* **Beer** *Flowers IPA & guest beers. Patio garden. Family room.*
Accommodation *7 bedrooms, all en suite, from £60 (single £50), family
room £75 (sleeps 3-5), weekend reductions. Children welcome overnight
(under-4s stay free in parents' room), additional beds (£10) & cots (£5).
Dogs by arrangement. Access, Diners, Visa.*

Ringlestone   **Ringlestone Inn**

Tel 01622 859900 Fax 01622 859966	**FOOD**
Ringlestone Harrietsham Wormshill Kent ME17 1NX	Map 11 C5

Splendidly atmospheric 16th-century inn, remotely tucked away
beside the Pilgrim's Way on top of the North Downs between
Harrietsham and Wormshill. An ale house since 1615 its three
charming inter-connecting bars boasts brick and flint walls and floors,
low beamed ceilings, a huge inglenook with winter woodburner and a
good assortment of rustic furniture, including carved settles and a
magnificent 17th-century oak dresser with the inscription 'A Ryght
Joyouse and welcome greetynge to ye all' etched into it. This still rings
true today with visitors attracted by the range of ales drawn straight
from the cask, local scrumpy ciders, the selection of 24 strong country
wines served by the glass and the reliable bar food on offer.
Lunchtime fare is help yourself buffet-style with a choice of casseroles,
curries and pies (all £4.25), or a range of salads. Arrive early for the
best of the food and to avoid the queues that form around the

cramped servery! Evening fare is more formal within the candle-lit bars and adjacent dining room with the home-made pies – ham, leek and cider, chicken and bacon, beef and beer (all £6.95) being the highlight of the printed menu. Vegetables are extra (£2.35). Puddings (£2.85) include brandy bread pudding and treacle and nut tart. Delightfully peaceful summer patio and garden. *Pub open 12-3, 6-11 (Sun to 10.30), from 6.30 in winter. **Bar Food** 12-2, 7-10. **Restaurant Meals** as the bar. Children allowed in the bar to eat. Free House.* **Beer** *Bateman's XXXB, Goacher's Maidstone Ale, Harvey's Sussex, Ringlestone Ale, Man O'War, regular guest beers. Garden, outdoor eating area. No food Christmas Day. Access, Diners, Visa.*

Ripley	**Boar's Head Hotel**	**FOOD**
Tel 01423 771888 Fax 01423 771509		**B&B**
Ripley nr Harrogate North Yorkshire H53 3AY		Map 6 C1

Dating back to 1830 when the Lord of the Manor rebuilt the village next to his castle (open to the public during the summer), this former coaching inn in the cobbled village square was refurbished by the present Lord (Sir Thomas Ingilby) some three years ago and turned into a hotel. Oil paintings and furniture from the castle help to create the country house feel in tranquil drawing and morning rooms and the individually decorated bedrooms, which favour plain walls and stylish matching fabrics. Antique furniture features in rooms in the main building and in the larger rooms in another house across the cobbled square, while those in the former stable block are furnished with white-painted wicker pieces. Service in the warm red, 38-seater dining room in one wing is rather less polished than chef David Box's accomplished cooking; a good-value set lunch is replaced by a menu of individually priced light dishes in high season. The excellent wine list has exceedingly kind prices. In another wing there is a pubby bar with snacks for the discerning: home-made soup (tomato and basil £1.95), sandwiches (from £2.50), filled jacket potatoes (from £2.75), broccoli, mushroom and Stilton quiche (£3.25), turkey and ham pie (£4.25), wild boar pie (£4.50), pecan pie (£1.95) and crème brulée (£1.95) are representative of the range on offer. Tea is served from 3 to 5pm in the two lounges – home-made sponges, fruit cakes and scones. Outdoor eating in the courtyard next to the bar. **Beer** *Theakston's, guest beer. **Bar Food** 12-2.30, 6.30-9.30 (Sun from 7). **Accommodation** 25 rooms, all en suite, £85 (single £70). Garden, tennis, coarse fishing. Access, Visa.*

Ripponden	**Old Bridge Inn**	
Tel 01422 822595 Fax 01422 824810		**A**
Priest Lane Ripponden nr Sowerby Bridge West Yorkshire HX6 4DF		Map 6 C1

Ancient pub (dating back to 1313) with medieval character, enormously thick stone walls and some nice old furniture in its three connecting bars. Probably originally a 14th-century monastic guest house. The modern world intrudes little into the finished interior; no machines, music or pool table, and pump clips are only tolerated for guest beers. There isn't even an inn sign. Children not allowed indoors. No garden but tables and chairs on cobbled front. Evening dining at the *Over the Bridge Restaurant*, literally over the bridge! Thirty malt whiskies at the bar. *Open 12-11 Sat. Free House.* **Beer** *Black Sheep Bitter & Special, Timothy Taylor Best and Golden Best, Ryburn Bitter, guest beer. No credit cards.*

Rochdale   Egerton Arms

Tel 01706 46183   Fax 01706 715343   **A**

Ashworthy Road Bamford Rochdale Lancashire OL11 5UP   **Map 6 B1**

This reputedly haunted pub, known locally as the Chapel House,
stands next to St James's chapel high on the moor above Rochdale.
Turn on the Ashworth road off the Bury and Heywood Road (A680)
by the Ashworth reservoir. Family dining forms an integral part of
the set-up with early evening suppers from 5pm and food served all
day on Sundays. For a table in the attractive Gallery restaurant
booking is advisable. Menus are too long and the catering operation
seemingly too large to provide much beyond the predictable, but the
Sunday lunch (main course £4.50) is generally perceived to be good
value. *Open 11-11 Sat, 12-10.30 Sun (drinks with meals only 3-7), usual
hours other days.* **Beer** *Ruddles Best & County. Patio. Children allowed in
bars to eat. Pub closed 1st week Jan. Access, Visa.*

Rockbeare   Jack in the Green

Tel 01404 822240   **FOOD**

Rockbeare nr Exeter Devon   **Map 13 E2**

A year or so ago even the most weary of A30 travellers would not
have given this roadside inn a second glance. Nowadays, rather than
accelerating away, the brake is applied, ready for the turning into the
car park of what has become a most welcoming refreshment stop. Paul
Parnell, who is part of the team who created the award-winning *Silver
Plough* at Pitton in Wiltshire (see entry), has transferred his enthusiasm
and verve into rejuvenating this white-painted roadside pub. The
smart exterior is bedecked with attractive flower tubs and baskets,
while inside the open-plan bar and dining areas have neatly arranged
darkwood furniture, church pews and a carved oak dresser. Tasteful
hunting theme paintings and prints decorate the walls and an open fire
warms the main dining area while a few easy chairs and comfortable
wooden-armed sofas are conveniently placed for waiting restaurant
diners. Choosing from the excellent-value set, but daily-changing,
menu (two-courses £9.95, three-courses £12.25) an imaginative and
well-presented meal may begin with avocado and smoked chicken
with tarragon vinaigrette or a puff pastry case of sweet and sour lambs
kidneys, followed by supreme of guinea fowl on leek and carrot
fondue or breast of chicken with a hazelnut mousse and light curry
sauce. Those travellers popping in for a quick, lighter bite will not be
disappointed by the interesting range of generously served bar meals,
all of which are under a fiver (except the fresh crab salad which is
worth the extra 50p!). Again, blackboards list the choice which may
range from beef and Guinness pie (£4.95), bubble and squeak with
Cumberland sausage (£4.95), or sausage and bean casserole with
crusty bread (£4.25) to lambs kidneys with Dijon mustard and a
range of eight ploughman's. Sticky toffee pudding and home-made
sherry trifle regularly feature on the pudding board £2.50. Those
eating on Sunday can expect to pay a reasonable £9 for a three course
lunch. A carefully-chosen selection of wines includes good-value wines
of the month and a choice of twelve served by the glass. Alfresco
imbibers wishing to escape the traffic noise can relax in the sheltered
rear courtyard or retreat to the splendid orchard garden and its open
rural views. Five miles from Junction 29 of the M5. Disabled WC.
Bar Food & Restaurant Meals *11.30-2 (Sat to 2.30, Sun 12-2.30),
6.30-10 (Sun 7-9.30). Free House.* **Beer** *Eldridge Pope Hardy Country,
John Smith's Bitter, Bass, Wadworth 6X, guest beer. Closed 25 & 26 Dec.
Garden. Access, Visa.*

Rockbourne   **Rose and Thistle**

Tel 017253 236	**FOOD**
Rockbourne nr Fordingbridge Hampshire SP6 3NL	**Map 14 C3**

Originally two 17th-century thatched cottages, this delightful, long
and low whitewashed pub enjoys a most tranquil location within one
of Hampshire's most picturesque and affluent downland villages.
Bought from Whitbread in 1991 – after a period of closure – by a
syndicate of local people, it is now a splendid village inn decorated and
furnished to a high standard. Country-style fabrics, dried flowers and
magazines are tasteful touches in the charming beamed bars, which
boast a collection of polished oak tables, carved settles and benches and
two huge fireplaces with winter log fires. Quality pub food, served in
the civilised, music-free lounge/dining area, is light and simple,
including a daily home-made soup (£2.45 served with fresh granary
bread and a dish of butter), soft herring roes on toast (£3.95), elegant
Welsh rarebit served with bacon and tomato (£5.25), scrambled eggs
with smoked salmon and prawns (£5.25) and ploughman's (from
£4.25). Evening fare is more elaborate: a monthly-changing menu
and a daily specials board that might feature fresh Portuguese sardines
(£4.25), home-made chicken liver paté laced with wild mushrooms
(£3.95) to start, followed by imaginative and well-presented main
dishes like roast rack of lamb (£8.95), pan-fried lemon sole fillet
(£7.95), duck breast with a mild mustard sauce, Normandy-style pork
or monkfish wrapped in bacon with a creamy prawn sauce. Interesting
and al dente vegetables accompany each dish. Mainly home-made
puddings are good, too. Traditional roast (£8.95) and many other
options at Sunday lunchtime (booking advised). To round off a good
meal, cafetière coffee comes with petits fours. A well-stocked
bar dispenses four real ales of varying strengths and offers some six
wines by the glass, from a worldwide list of 70 well-priced and
carefully-chosen wines. Children only in the 30-seater dining room
(minimum charge £8 during busy periods). *Pub open 11-3, 6-11 (Sun
12-3, 7-10.30).* **Bar Food & Restaurant Meals** *12-2.30, 7-9.30. Free
House.* **Beer** *Hop Back, Smiles, Butcombe Bitter, Courage, Gale's,
Wadworth 6X. Garden. Access, Visa.*

Roke   **Home Sweet Home Inn**

Tel 01491 38249	**FOOD**
Roke nr Benson Oxfordshire OX9 6JD	**Map 14a C3**

A row of low, stone white-painted former cottages (just off the
B4009) well befits its homely title and image following conversion
into a gentrified country pub. The pretty walled garden in front has
picnic tables and a pantiled wishing well. Popular lunchtime snacks are
notable more for their number than for any inherent quality, with a
vast selection of 30 sandwiches offered – from roast beef (£1.95) to
smoked salmon club-style (£3.95) – and 40 more variations on salad
and baked potato themes. Cooked lunches selected from the
blackboards may well include salmon fish cakes (£5.95), guinea fowl
with mushroom sauce (£7.95) or beef medallions with brandy, cream
and mushrooms (£8.95). A more extended menu selection in the
evening, served in either the bar or a prettily-appointed dining room
engages further flights of fancy based around grilled steaks and exotic

fish dishes: 'Surf'n'Turf' is £10.50. *Bar Food 12-2, 5.30-10 (Sun 7-9.30). Restaurant Meals 12-2, 7-10 (to 9.30 Sun). Beer Brakspear. Garden. Children welcome indoors to eat. Access, Visa.*

Romaldkirk   Rose and Crown   ★   **FOOD**

Tel 01833 650213   Fax 01833 650828   **B&B**

Romaldkirk nr Barnard Castle Co Durham DL12 9EB   **Map 5 D3**

Zzz₂...

Our British Meat Pub award winner from 1993 continues to go from strength to strength, worthily retaining its star status. Christopher Davy's cooking is a model of consistency, with his restaurant at the Rose and Crown now firmly established as an entry in our *1995 Hotels and Restaurants Guide*. Both at lunchtime and in the evenings meals served in the elegant lounge bar and Crown Room are not, however, overlooked to any degree. Traditional favourites, from port sausages with black pudding and onion confit (£3.95) to smoked Loch Fyne salmon with scrambled eggs (£4.75) are always cooked with flair; colourful presentation, with coleslaw and marinated mushrooms, turns a humble brown bread bap into a memorable repast: chicken pineapple, celery and walnuts (£2.95) constitute a typical filling. Best value of all, though, are the daily lunch specials which are rightly used as the showcase for a kitchen which is never slow to experiment and always actively evolving new dishes. Home-cured gravlax (£3.95) is a perfect curtain raiser to a hot confit of duck leg with lentils and salad (£5.95) or the locally renowned Whitby Woof topped with prawns and nut-brown butter (£7.50). Exemplary puds, typified by sticky toffee pudding and baked apple filo parcels (£2.50), and perfectly selected local cheeses (Cotherstone, Blue Wensleydale) provide an enviable choice of "afters". Creaking floorboards, beams, stripped stone walls, well-chosen antique furniture and contemporary fabrics feature in the refurbished and improved bedrooms, and duvets can be swapped for sheets and blankets. Front views overlook the village green. Five further rooms, in an outside annexe, are more uniform in size and design, with modern furniture and fittings. *Free House. Bar Food 12-1.30, 6.30-9.30 (7-9 Sun). Restaurant Meals 7.30-9 (Sun 12-1.30). Children's portions. Accommodation 12 bedrooms, all en suite, £74 (Single £52). Children welcome overnight (under-5s free if sharing), additional bed (£10) available. Beer Theakston Best & Old Peculier. Family room. Access, Visa.*

Rosedale Abbey   Milburn Arms   **FOOD**

Tel & Fax 01751 417312   **B&B**

Rosedale Abbey nr Pickering North Yorkshire YO18 8RA   **Map 5 E3**

Zzz₂...

Tranquil surroundings in the beautiful North Yorkshire moors are the big attraction of Terry and Joan Bentley's delightful country hotel which has parts dating back to the 1700s. Their brochure states 'we're also the village pub' and indeed, the spacious bar with its low beams does have a pubby atmosphere and comes complete with dart board and a couple of games machines but it's the extensive range of bar meals that is the big attraction; tiger tail prawns in garlic (£3.50), home-made Yorkshire pudding with local venison sausage and rich onion gravy (£4.50), grilled Farndale goat's cheese with salad (£2.95), home-made vegetable lasagne (£4.75), coq au vin (£5.25), sirloin steak (£8.95) and an excellent summer pudding (£2.25) demonstrate the range. The smart split-level Priory Restaurant offers an à la carte menu in the evenings. Bedrooms are individually decorated in a variety of styles – rich reds and blues, pale pink and yellow, pastel seersucker fabric – and furnished with a mixture of pine, freestanding darkwood and hotel unit-style furniture. All have good bathrooms (with showers over tubs) plus TV, direct-dial phone and beverage kit. A good spot in summer is the peaceful garden, opposite the village green, with tables set out under a splendid 150-year-old cedar. *Open 11.30-11, Sun usual hours.* **Bar Food** *12-2 (Sat & Sun to 2.15), 7-9.30.* **Restaurant Meals** *12-2.15 (Sun only), 7-10 (Sun to 9.30). Free House.* **Beer** *Bass, Stones, Theakston, guest beer. Garden, outdoor eating.* **Accommodation** *11 bedrooms, all en suite, £64 (single £42.50). Children welcome overnight (under-5s stay free in parents' room, 5-12s £10) additional beds and cots available. Dogs welcome in ground-floor annexe rooms only. Accommodation closed 23,24 & 25 Dec. Access, Diners, Visa.*

Rosedale Abbey   White Horse Farm Hotel   **FOOD**

Tel 01751 417239 Fax 01751 417781	**B&B**
Rosedale Abbey nr Pickering North Yorkshire YO18 8SE	Map 5 E3

The White Horse was a farm when Rosedale Abbey was a thriving mining village with a population ten times greater than it is now. As was then the practice, one end of the farmhouse was turned into a 'taps room' for the miners and its transformation into today's hotel had begun. The bar is full of interest with a couple of rough-hewn tree trunks acting as poles holding up the ceiling beams, stuffed birds, a fish in a glass case, horse harness and much besides decorating the walls, some of which are of rough exposed stone. Yorkshire fare features strongly on the bar menu: Yorkshire pudding either with onion gravy (£2.50) or with a filling like tarragon chicken (£4.50), Cropton Stoggies (casseroled wood pigeon £7.99), Rosedale rarebit made with Theakstons Bitter (£4.20), Whitby haddock pots (£3.99); along with a few dishes from further afield like chicken Satay (£4.50) and vegetable curry with fruit (£5.50). There are also various sandwiches and a short list of puds. Bedrooms, including two de luxe rooms with separate sitting areas, are prettily decorated with matching floral bedcovers (no duvets here), curtains and dado band around the woodchip walls. Even the en-suite bathrooms, half with showers and half with tubs, co-ordinate with their respective bedrooms. All rooms have TV and tea- and coffee-making equipment and some have wonderful views across Rosedale. 30 whiskies available at the bar. Take the A170 out of Pickering going north; after approximately three miles turn right – follow signs to Rosedale for seven miles and the pub is clearly signposted from the village. *Open 12-11 Sat, Sun-Thu usual hours.* **Bar Food** *12-2 (Sun to 2.30), 6.30-9.30. Children's menu.* **Beer** *Tetley Traditional, Theakston XB, Old Peculier. Garden, outdoor eating. Family room.* **Accommodation** *15 Bedrooms, all en suite, £60 (single £35). Children welcome overnight (under-5s £5, 5-14s ½ price) additional bed and cot available. No dogs. Accommodation closed 25 Dec. Access, Diners, Visa.*

Zzzz...

Rowde   George & Dragon   ★   **FOOD**

Tel 01380 723053	
High Street Rowde Wiltshire SN10 2PN	Map 14 B3

Inspired, inventive and realistically-priced cooking emanates from the kitchen of Tim and Helen Withers' village pub leased from Wadworth's brewery. A single bar has half a dozen Britannia tables and there are two dozen assorted bentwood chairs in the dining room set at plain, unclothed tables. Everywhere are blackboards proclaiming what's on offer. Dishes run from chard and saffron tart (£3) to well-presented main-course dishes such as grilled guinea fowl with lime (£10), pan-fried strips of calf's liver, avocado, lemon and parsley (£11.50), plus the freshest fish (fillet of turbot steamed with garlic – £12, ragout of John Dory, mullet and prawn -£10.50). A typical set lunch menu (£10) offers alternatives only at each course, perhaps crostini or brandade salad, then salmon fish cakes with hollandaise or chicken and lobster sausage, ending with brown sugar meringues and Jersey cream or rhubarb and ginger crumble (£4). Out of 40 names on the wine list a commendable 14 are available by the glass. Booking is always advised, at least one week in advance for tables at weekends, when good Sunday lunches offer a choice of four dishes at each course; fudge served with coffee. Tables in the walled garden during good weather. Wadworth's IPA and 6X are on hand pumps; the pub's 'English-only' policy is extended to the mineral water (Abbey Well and Malvern) and cheeses, of which Stilton, Allerdale, Sharpham and Cotherstone are a typical selection. *Bar Food Tues-Sat only 12-2, 7-10. Children allowed in restaurant to eat. Beer Wadworth 6X, IPA. Garden, outdoor eating. Pub closed 25, 26 Dec and 1 Jan. Access, Visa.*

Ruckhall	**Ancient Camp Inn**	**FOOD**
Tel 01981 250449 Fax 01981 251581		**B&B**
Ruckhall nr Eaton Bishop Hereford & Worcester HR2 9QX		**Map 14 A1**

The route from the A465 at Belmont Abbey to Ruckhall turns into a twist of narrow lanes. Once there, look carefully for signs to the Ancient Camp, so named because the site was once an Iron Age fort. Certainly, it must have been impregnable from the northern side, as the pub stands atop an escarpment overlooking a wide bend in the river Wye. In fair weather, there's a fine view across the fertile river valley from a front patio bordered by roses, the backdrop of the inn fronted by window boxes and hanging baskets. The interior decor of the pub retains the original stonework and flagstone floors, which results in an intimate atmosphere to which dried flowers and huge log fires add a special glow in winter. Doyenne of the kitchen is Nova Hague, and her production is prodigious. Bar meals are available at lunchtime and in the evening but greater emphasis is placed on her evening restaurant menu. Start with home-made soup (cauliflower and almond soup £2.25), or pears in roquefort and watercress salad (£4.25), followed perhaps by seafood provençale (£11.75) or poached supreme of chicken (£10.75). Tempting home-made puddings include chocolate roulade and iced coffee soufflé. It's not only the food that shines at the Ancient Camp: the inn's five-bedroomed accommodation is also quite special. At the rear are three neat bedrooms with en-suite showers; to the front, two superb bedrooms, one with a private sitting room, the other's en-suite bath elevated to maximise its river view. All are fully centrally heated, with telephone, television and bedside clock radio. No children under 8 in pub or accommodation. *Bar Food (no food all Mon) 12-2, 7-9.30 (except Sun eve). Restaurant Meals 7-9 (except Sun eve). Children allowed in the bar to eat. Free House. Beer Wood's Parish, West Country PA. Riverside garden, outdoor eating. Family room. Accommodation 5 bedrooms, all en suite, £58/£48 (single £45/£35). Children welcome overnight additional beds available (£15). No dogs. Access, Visa.*

Rudge   The Full Moon

Tel 01373 830936	B&B
Rudge nr Frome Somerset BA11 2QF	Map 14 B3

Conveniently located two miles from the A36 at its junction with the
A361, and equally close to the Woodland Park, is the sleepy hamlet of
Rudge. Its white-painted village inn of 16th century origins, whose
interior has been meticulously restored, reveals a wealth of interior
stonework, old fireplaces and uneven flagstone floors in a succession of
intimate nooks and alcoves whose focal point is a friendly locals' bar.
All manner of local history and memorabilia provides the starting
point for a tall story or two. There is now, though, a new extension
which threatens to dwarf the original, its ground floor given over to a
function room, Sunday lunch carvery and Country and Western
entertainments on Sunday nights. Above are the five en-suite
bedrooms, purpose-built and a little cottagey in style. All are neatly
equipped with TVs, radio alarms and tea- and coffee-making facilities:
there's one decent-sized family room. To the pub's rear the walled
garden is neatly kept and has some swings; from here, as from the
bedrooms, there are lovely rural views down to Broker's Wood. *Free
House. Beer Bass, Wadworth 6X, Butcombe. Garden, children's play area,
high teas 6pm. Family room.* **Accommodation** *5 bedrooms, all en suite,
£40 (£30 single, £50 family room). Children welcome overnight and stay
free in parents' room, additional beds and cots available. Check-in by
arrangement. Bar closed Mon lunch. Access, Visa.*

Running Waters   Three Horseshoes Inn

Tel 0191 3720286	B&B
Sherburn House Running Waters nr Durham Co Durham DH1 2SR	Map 5 E3

With fine views over open country and north-west towards Durham
(4 miles), the "Shoes" stands by the busy A181 fronted by old
ploughshares and farming implements; the "Running Waters" of its
location reflecting olden times when water was carried from its
underground stream by the monks of nearby Sherborne House. In
today's refashioned bedrooms, both hot and cold run abundantly,
though in the two oldest rooms this is confined to wash-hand basins
and shower cubicles, there being a shared WC and bathroom here.
Whilst none is particularly spacious, the rest have full en-suite facilities.
TVs, tea makers and radio alarms, and are decorated in a bright,
cottagey style. There's a small residents; lounge area and a fenced-in
rear garden: front double-glazing ensures that the morning traffic will
not become intrusive. Under 6s stay free in parents' room; cot and
beds provided. *Free House. Open 11-3, 6-11 (12-3, 7-10.30 Sun).*
Accommodation *6 bedrooms, 4 en suite £46 (Single £30). Children
welcome overnight. Check-in by arrangement. Beer Ruddles Best. Garden.
Access, Diners, Visa.*

Rusper   Star Inn

Tel 01293 871264	A
High Street Rusper West Sussex RH12 4RA	Map 11 A5

4 miles west of Crawley, close to the A24. Just south of the
Sussex/Surrey border, close (but not particularly convenient for)
Gatwick Airport. A heavily-beamed, traditional old coaching inn
dating back to 1460. The menu stays sensibly short and game dishes
feature in season. Landlord Derek Welton has been running the Star in
his own inimitable style for 10 years. Whitbread Wayside Inns.

Open 11-11. **Beer** *Fremlins, Brakspear, Marston's Pedigree, Morland Old Speckled Hen, guest beer. Garden. Family Room, children welcome inside. Access, Visa.*

Saddleworth   Green Ash Hotel

Tel 01457 871035 Fax 01457 871414	**B&B**
Denshaw Road Delph Saddleworth Greater Manchester OL3 5TS	**Map 6 C2**

Just a decade ago, one man saw this burned-out Co-Op warehouse and barn as an unrivalled investment opportunity; today, Terry Ogden's civilised country inn is the realisation of that dream. Rebuilt and extended entirely in handsome Derbyshire stone, it stands proud on the A640 above Delph village enfolded by the woody moors. Each of the bedrooms enjoys a share of the view; they possess in common a high degree of comfort and practical up-to-date accoutrements with satellite TV, radio alarms, direct-dial phones and trouser presses. Included in executive standard rooms are mini-bars and towelling robes; all bathrooms are bright, fully-tiled and have over-bath showers. This is decidedly more inn than pub; there's Tetley bitter on hand pump to enjoy in the bar or on the scenic, sun-trapped patio. Choice of eating is between an à la carte restaurant or the popular pizzeria in the basement. "Small well-trained" dogs in rooms only. Nearest motorway junctions: 21 & 22 of the M62. *Free House.* **Beer** *Tetley, 3 guest beers. Garden. Family room.* **Accommodation** *15 bedrooms, all en suite, £52/62 (single £39.50). Children welcome overnight (under-2s stay free in parents' room, 3-9s £5), additional beds (£5) and cots available. Access, Visa.*

Zzzz…

Saffron Walden   Eight Bells

Tel 01799 522790	**FOOD**
18 Bridge Street Saffron Walden Essex CB10 1BU	**Map 10 B3**

A newly refurbished, solidly traditional pub whose bar is partitioned by ancient wall timbers into two smaller rooms, complete with old furniture and exposed timbers and brick. The old barn restaurant has been extended to include a central gallery and the walls are hung with tapestries and flags. The bar and restaurant menus offer reliably good food: home-made soup (£1.90), fresh Cromer crab (£4.75), roast duckling with orange sauce (£8.45), home-made lasagne (£5.75) plus a large selection of fresh fish – prawn thermidor (£6.50), whole grilled plaice with parsley butter (£5.45), with hot toffee-apple fudge cake, or Morello cherry cheesecake (both £2.35) for pudding. The restaurant and bar serve food all day Sunday from noon to 9.30. **Bar Food & Restaurant Meals** *12-2.30, 6.00-9.30 (Sun 12-9.30).* **Beer** *Adnams, Burton, Friary Meux, Tetley. Garden, outdoor eating. Family room. Access, Visa.*

Saffron Walden   Saffron Hotel

Tel 01799 522676 Fax 01799 513979	**FOOD**
	B&B
High Street Saffron Walden Essex CB10 1AY	**Map 10 B3**

Formerly a coaching inn with origins in the 16th century, the Saffron Hotel is more hotel than pub today but the green plush bar still welcomes all and offers real ale and bar snacks. The printed bar menu includes pie of the day (£5.95), minute steak with Stilton (£5.75), skate wing with caper, prawn and nut butter (£5.95) as well as baked potatoes with different fillings (£2.95-£4.50). The blackboard menu changes daily – Lincolnshire sausage casserole, Essex oysters Florentine.

The more formal restaurant has a table d'hote menu at £14.95 for three courses plus à la carte; we recommend the bar food only. Bedrooms come in all shapes and sizes, some with head-threatening beams. The best and largest have been recently refurbished with stylish fabrics and smart new veneered furniture, the worst are cramped singles that share a shower room. All have telephone and TV. *Pub open noon-11pm Mon-Sat, usual hours Sun.* **Bar Food & Restaurant Meals** *12-2, 7-9.30. Children's portions. Free House.* **Beer** *Greene King IPA, Adnams. Terrace. Family room.* **Accommodation** *17 bedrooms, all en suite, £65 (4-poster £85, single £45). Children welcome overnight (0-3 yrs free if sharing parents' room), additional beds (£20) and cots available. Access, Diners, Visa.*

St Agnes   Driftwood Spars Hotel

Tel 01872 552428	B&B
Trevaunance Cove St Agnes Cornwall TR5 0RT	Map 12 B3

Constructed in the 17th century of huge ship's timbers and spars (hence the name), with stone and slate, the hotel – once a marine chandlery and tin miners trading post – is located just 100 yards from one of Cornwall's best beaches, making it an ideal family destination for a holiday. Accommodation comprises nine neat and tidy en-suite rooms – one family room with bunk beds – featuring attractive co-ordinating fabrics, and a mix of furnishings that ranges from comfortable new pine to modern-style white furniture. Rooms are well equipped and two afford peaceful sea views. Guests are treated to the sound of waves on the beach and live music on Fridays and Saturdays. *Pub open 11-11 (except Sun, Fri & Sat to 12). Free House.* **Beer** *Tetley, Burton, Bass, guest beers. Family room.* **Accommodation** *9 bedrooms, all en suite, from £29. Children welcome overnight (under-2s stay free in parents' room), cots supplied. Accommodation closed 25 Dec. Access, Diners, Visa.*

St Albans   Garibaldi

Tel 01727 855046	FOOD
61 Albert Street St Albans Hertfordshire AL1 1RT	Map 15a F2

Popular old town centre pub located down a narrow back street not far from St Albans Abbey. Pleasant Victorian style interior with a central servery, a few alcove seating hidey-holes and a piney, café-style conservatory dining room leading to a narrow patio with tables and chairs. Food servery displaying salads, plus a sandwich, ploughman's and filled jacket potato list and a blackboard listing home-cooked hot specials, such as cauliflower and Stilton soup (£1.75), spicy vegetable couscous (£3.50), steak and ESB pie (£4.20) and chicken in a mulled wine sauce (£3.80). This is a chip-free zone so expect fresh vegetables or salads. Mexican dishes (from £2.50) and three-course Sunday roast (£7.50). Puddings (£1.50) are mainly of the bought-in variety. *Pub open 11-11 (except Sun).* **Bar Food** *12-9.* **Beer** *Fuller's. Garden, outdoor eating. Pub closed 25 Dec & Good Friday. No credit cards.*

St Albans   Rose and Crown

Tel 01727 851903	A
St Michael's Street St Albans Hertfordshire AL3 4SG	Map 15a F2

This is a pleasingly simple, woody and traditional 300-year-old pub located in the upmarket St Michael's 'village' suburb of the town, close to Verulamium Park and the Roman Museum. Classic public bar with heavy beams, huge fireplace, sturdy furnishings and a chatty atmosphere free from intrusive music and games. Simple, unadorned and comfortable lounge bar and flower-decked side patio for fine weather imbibing. Renowned locally for its imaginative and unusual range of American-style 'gourmet' sandwiches available at lunchtimes. Regular live folk and blues music, barbershop singing and quizz nights. *Beer Greenalls. Garden. No credit cards.*

St Austell   White Hart

Tel 01726 72100 Fax 01726 74705	B&B
Church Street St Austell Cornwall PL25 4AT	Map 12 B3

Attractive and comfortable accommodation is offered in this three-storey town-centre hotel, dating from the 16th century and located opposite the church. All the well-looked-after bedrooms have smart darkwood furniture, quality floral fabrics, pink and plum decor and the usual comforts of TVs, telephones, tea-making facilities and hairdryers. Modern carpeted bathrooms are spacious, fully-tiled and clean. Public areas include the well-furnished Admirals Bar and the more pubby Captains Bar, complete with pool tables, darts and other games. Decent prints decorate the walls throughout the inn. Note: nearby parking is difficult. *Open 11-10.55, Sun usual hours. Afternoon teas served. Beer St Austell Tinners & HSD. Accommodation 18 bedrooms, all en suite £63 (single £40). Children welcome overnight (under-12s stay free in parents' room), extra cots available. Access, Diners, Visa.*

St Briavels   George Inn

Tel 01594 530228	B&B
High Street St Briavels nr Lydney Gloucestershire GL15 6SP	Map 14 B2

A moody old part-medieval pub whose sombre stonework and blackened beams yet create intimate nooks and crannies warmed by real log fires in winter. In full view of the ruined castle, rooks and royalty joust on an inlaid patio chessboard. Modest yet comfortable accommodation provided in four en-suite bedrooms (with WC/showers only) is housed under the eaves with an outlook either up the village street or down over the castle. Recent improvements under owners, the Bennett family, include an added old world dining room, though the over-long blackboard menus follow a well-trodden path, and the music may not always appear sympathetic to the pub's historic surroundings. Choice of 25 malt whiskies at the bar. *Free House. Beer Spitfire, Wadworth 6X, Marston's Pedigree, Courage Directors. Patio, outdoor eating. Family room. Accommodation 3 bedrooms, all en suite (WC/shower only). £40 (single £25). Children welcome overnight, additional bed (£20), and cots (£10) available. No credit cards.*

St Kew   St Kew Inn

Tel 01208 84259	A
St Kew nr Wadebridge Cornwall PL30 3HB	Map 12 B3

Well off the beaten track, amid tiny lanes in a small hamlet in a splendid wooded valley, the 16th-century St Kew Inn is a peaceful spot in which to savour a relaxing summer drink in the large attractive garden, which looks towards the parish church. Inside, the atmospheric main bar has a slate floor laid with high-backed settles and Windsor chairs; a popular window seat overlooks the cobbled courtyard, resplendent with summer flower tubs and baskets. A fine black-painted kitchen range burns logs and warms this bar in winter, old meat hooks hang from the ceiling and generally a good chatty atmosphere prevails. There is a further stone-walled bar and a small dining room. Local ales are served in the traditional way, straight from the barrel. St Austell Brewery. *Beer St Austell. Garden, outdoor eating area. No credit cards.*

St Mawes   Rising Sun

FOOD
B&B

Tel 01326 270233

The Square St Mawes Cornwall TR2 5DJ

Map 12 B4

Popular and lively little hotel that occupies a splendid position overlooking the quaint harbour and its 19th-century quay. The busy, simply furnished 'locals' bar has a good pubby atmosphere, and is a favourite among the gig rowers. More refined is the small cane-furnished conservatory which houses the lounge bar and has access to the harbour-view terrace that attracts the crowds when the sun shines. Highlights on the routine bar menu are the fresh seafood dishes (a speciality), for example fish and chips (£3.85) and daily specials like avocado and seafood mornay (£3.75), calaloo soup – a West Indian recipe with curry, spinach and crab (£2.25) – crab salad (£7.50), lobster salad (£13.95) and seafood pasta mornay (£4.25). Bedrooms are smart with attractive wallpapers and fabrics, modern pine furniture, TVs, tea-makers, telephones and all bar one have immaculate en-suite bathrooms. Front rooms enjoy peaceful harbour and headland vistas. *Pub open 11-11 (except Sun) in summer season.* *Beer St Austell Brewery. Terrace, outdoor eating. Accommodation 11 rooms, 10 en suite, from £64 (single £32). Children welcome overnight (under-10s stay free in parents' room), additional beds supplied. Access, Visa.*

Zzz_z...

St Mawgan   Falcon Inn

A

Tel 01637 860225

St Mawgan Newquay Cornwall TR8 4EP

Map 12 B3

In the heart of the holiday land where good unspoilt traditional pubs are an endangered breed, the Falcon survives and is a haven for the discerning pub-goer. Nestling in a most attractive village, deep in the Vale of Lanherne and a stone's throw from its tiny stream, this 16th-century wisteria-clad inn is a popular summer destination with those escaping the bucket-and-spade brigade on the beach. Inside, the main bar is neatly arranged and decorated with pine farmhouse tables and chairs, trellis wallpaper and decent prints and is thankfully music and game-free. The adjacent dining room has a rug-strewn flagged floor, a pine dresser and French windows leading out into the bench-filled cobbled courtyard. Beyond a rose-covered arch there is a splendid terraced garden, ideal for enjoying some summer refreshment. *Beer St Austell Tinners Ale, HSD & XXXX Mild. Garden, outdoor eating area. Access, Visa.*

St Neots   Chequers Inn

FOOD

Tel 01480 472116

St Mary's Street Eynesbury nr St Neots Cambridgeshire PE19 2TA

Map 15 E1

A lovely old English country pub, where you can sit in the main bar with its roaring winter fires and highly-polished dark furniture or at tables with green tablecloths for bar food, or in the dining area for more substantial meals. The changing blackboard bar menu offers home cooking by landlord David Taylor: cauliflower and broccoli soup (£2), steak and mushroom pie (£5.50) or steak and ale pie (£5.50), a substantial ploughman's (£3.95), mushrooms with garlic butter and croutons (£5.50), pasta with chicken (£5.25). The restaurant proposes a selection of prawn dishes, pork tenderloin with Madeira and sauce au poivre (£11.50), hazelnut and brown rice roast (£8.25), lamb's liver and diced bacon in Marsala sauce (£8.50). Children are kept amused in the outdoor play area in the fenced off garden. *Bar Food 12-2, 7-9.45 (Sun to 9.00)*. *Restaurant Meals 12-1.30, 7-9.30 (Sun to 9)*. *Free House*. *Beer Hook Norton, Wadworth 6X. Garden, outdoor eating, children's play area. Access, Diners, Visa.*

St Neots   Eaton Oak

Tel 01480 219555 Fax 01480 407520	**B&B**
Crosshall Road Eaton Ford St Neots Cambridgeshire PE19 4AG	**Map 15 E1**

The completely renovated Charles Wells brewery's Eaton Oak is located at the junction of the A1 and A45 but the bedrooms are happily undisturbed by traffic – you can expect a comfortable overnight stay. The rooms in the motel extension are large and warm, with fitted units, colour TVs, tea-makers, direct-dial telephones and well-fitted bathrooms. In the main building (once a farmhouse) the bar has been extended along with the restaurant and a conservatory added which leads on to the garden. Families are well looked after (even a free kiddies menu) and an outdoor play area is provided. *Beer Adnams, Charles Wells Eagle Bitter & Bombadier. Accommodation 9 bedrooms, all en suite, £50 (single £40). Children welcome overnight (rate depends on age), additional bed available. Check-in by arrangement. Access, Visa.*

Salisbury   Haunch of Venison

Tel 01722 322024	**A**
1-5 Minster Street Salisbury Wiltshire SP1 1TB	**Map 14 C3**

Antiquity and charm ooze from this ancient and tiny city-centre pub, which dates from 1320 when it was built as a church house for nearby St Thomas's Church. Three rooms, usually busy with tourists, radiate from the minuscule pewter-topped bar and are affectionately known as the 'horsebox', a tiny snug off the entrance lobby; the 'House of Commons', which features a chequered stone floor and plenty of wooden panels, beams and carved oak benches; and the upper room or 'House of Lords', boasting a 600-year-old fireplace with a small side window displaying a mummified hand holding a pack of 18th-century playing cards, which was discovered here in 1903. 146 malt whiskies. Children allowed upstairs only. *Open 11-11, Sun usual hours. Beer Courage Best, Directors, guest beer. Pub closed 25 & 26 Dec. Access, Diners, Visa.*

Salisbury   King's Arms Hotel

Tel 01722 327629 Fax 01722 414246	**B&B**
7a-11 St John's Street Salisbury Wiltshire SP1 2SB	**Map 14 C3**

The half-timbered, wattle and daub facade of this historic city inn, located opposite the Cathedral Close, dates from the early 1600s, while the main core of the inn was built at least ninety years before the first foundations were laid for the magnificent cathedral. Oak panelling and beams abound in the log fire-warmed bars and in the clean and

comfortable en suite bedrooms, two of which have four-posters,
and reached by a winding staircase plus a series of sloping-floored
corridors. The converted stable across the courtyard houses three
bedrooms decorated in a light, modern style. A high standard of
comfort is guaranteed with all rooms having TVs, telephones, tea-
making kits and trouser presses. This year a residents' lounge has also
been added. *Open 11-11 (Sun 12-10.30). Free House.* **Beer** *Flowers
Original, Castle Eden, Boddingtons. Courtyard.* **Accommodation**
*15 bedrooms, all en suite, £68 (single £45). Children welcome overnight
(under-6s stay free in parents' room, 6-14s £6). Additional beds and cots
available. Access, Diners, Visa.*

Satwell   The Lamb Inn

Tel & Fax 01491 628482	A

Satwell nr Shepherds Green Henley-on-Thames Oxon RG9 4QZ   Map 15a D3

An untypically tiny Thames Valley inn, tucked away off the B841,
two miles south of Nettlebed. Beneath a weird agglomeration of
unevenly pitched roofs, it contains only two small rooms within;
floors are quarry tile and the tables are assorted. Every nook and
cranny seems taken up with collectables: old beer bottles (glass and
earthenware) dating back to the last century; an old dog grate, butter
churn and mangle. There's extra room to spread out in the garden,
while very little ones can frolic on a swing or a slide. Young tenant
licensees, less than sartorially elegant in appearance, seem otherwise
eager to please. Minimum of six wines by the glass. **Beer** *Brakspear
Best, Special, Old Ale. Garden, children's play area. Family room.
No credit cards.*

Saunderton   Rose and Crown Inn

Tel 01844 345299 Fax 01844 343140	B&B

Wycombe Road Saunderton Princes Risborough Buckinghamshire   Map 15a D2

Located beside the A4010, this large pub dates back to 1840 and has a
spacious, neatly-furnished bar and lounge area. Business-orientated
accommodation comprises modest, functional bedrooms with built-in
units and compact en-suite facilities. Two superior bedrooms are
furnished and decorated to a good standard. TVs, tea-makers,
telephones and radio-alarms are standard. Double-glazing helps to
reduce traffic noise on road-facing rooms. Attractive sun-trap terrace
reached through French doors leading off the Beechwood Restaurant.
Open 11-3 & 5.30-11 (Sun 12-3 & 7-10.30). Free House.
Beer *Brakspear Bitter, Morrells Varsity, Morland Bitter. Garden.*
Accommodation *17 bedrooms, 4 en suite £57.95 (single £52.95).
children welcome overnight, extra bed and cot supplied (£5-£10).
Accommodation closed 1 week at Christmas. Garden. Access, Diners, Visa.*

Sawley   Sawley Arms

Tel 01765 620642	FOOD

Sawley Fountains Abbey Ripon North Yorkshire HG4 3EQ   Map 6 C1

A fine old-fashioned dining pub whose immaculate upkeep and
enduring popularity are a tribute to the devotion of June Hawes,
celebrating this year a quarter century at the Sawley Arms. The
garden, her pride and joy, is a recent Britain in Bloom winner, while
the pub inside is flower-filled and homely. In a succession of alcoves
and tiny rooms (two being non-smoking), legions of regulars find
their chosen spots and order at the bar from a varied menu amply

supplemented by truly tempting daily specials. Pride is taken equally in June's range of fresh soup (£2.10) which on any one day might be cauliflower, seafood and a leek and apricot; pancakes, another popular item, may be filled with salmon and herbs (£3.95) ham, spinach and almonds (£3.50), or hot cherries and cream for pudding (£3.50). The range of food is further extended by night when one end of the pub becomes rather more restaurant and choices will include steak pie with buttercrust pastry (£7.20) and half a duckling with Curacao sauce (£12.50). Further puddings include apple pie (£3) and chocolate brandy mousse (£3.20) or there's a plate of English cheeses (£3.50). Capable, friendly service in a warm atmosphere. No children under 8. *Free House.* **Bar Food** *12-2, 7-9 (closed Sun eve).* **Beer** *Theakston Best. Garden, outdoor eating. Access, Visa (only over £10).*

Scales   White Horse

Tel 017687 79241	**FOOD**
Scales nr Threlkeld Cumbria CA12 4SY	Map 4 C3

Set back from the A66 between Keswick and Penrith and 1000 feet above sea level, the whitewashed White Horse is surrounded by stunning Cumbrian countryside and is within easy reach of splendid walking country. Immaculately kept, the interior has a strong hunting and sporting theme, its uneven whitewashed walls covered with horsey prints, photographs of local meets, and caricatures, while a large hanging backs up the white horse theme. The low beamed ceiling, slate fireplace (customers put coins between the gaps and the money is later collected for charity), well-polished copper pans, stuffed birds and animals, and lots of plants all add to the rustic atmosphere. Local produce features strongly on the short lunchtime bar menu which includes their delicious Cumberland sausages served with apple sauce, mushrooms and port jelly (£7.95). There might also be smoked salmon roulade (£3.95), chicken and mushroom filo parcels with salad (£4.95), or peach halves filled with herb cheese paté (£4.25). Baked strawberry pudding with cream (£2.75) to finish. Evenings bring candlelight and a more restaurant menu; booking is essential, as it gets extremely busy. Potted shrimps with garlic bread (£3.95), rainbow trout filled with prawns served with lemon ad parsley butter (£7.95) and steaks served with different sauces testify to first-rate fresh produce (local butcher chooses the meat on the hoof). **Bar Food** *12-2 (Mon-Fri in winter to 2.30), 7.30-9. Free House.* **Beer** *Jennings Best and Cumberland Ale. Patio, outdoor eating at lunchtime. Family room. Pub closed 25 Dec. Access, Visa.*

Scole   Scole Inn

Tel 01379 740481 Fax 01379 740762	**B&B**
Ipswich Road Scole nr Diss Scole Norfolk IP22 4DR	Map 10 C2

Built in 1655 by a wool merchant, this grand-looking red brick inn is Grade 1 listed for its architectural interest. Splendid brick gables front and rear show a Dutch influence. Bedrooms in the Georgian stable block are quieter and more modern than those in the main building, which face a busy lorry route. These rooms, though, are full of character, many having carved oak doors, old timbers and fireplaces plus four-poster or half-tester beds. The beamed, pubby bar is also full of atmosphere with a vast brick fireplace, dark oak furniture and an 'old English Inn' ambience. *Lyric Hotels.* **Open** *11-11 (Sun 12-3, 7-10.30).* **Accommodation** *23 bedrooms, all en suite £63-£79 (single £49). Children welcome overnight (under 12 free).* **Beer** *Adnams Southwold, Broadside, Bass, M&B Mild. Garden. Access, Diners and Visa.*

Seahouses	**Olde Ship**	**FOOD**
Tel 01665 720200 Fax 01665 721383		**B&B**
9 Main Street Seahouses Northumberland NE68 7RD		**Map 5 D1**

Perched above the small harbour with splendid sea views out to the Farne Islands, the Olde Ship began life as a farmhouse in 1745 and was first licensed in 1812. It has been in present licensees Alan and Jean Glen's family since 1910, each generation, beginning with Alan's grandparents, introducing its own improvements. Behind the grey stone exterior there lies a real treasure trove of nautical paraphernalia collected over 80 years; the saloon bar is quite something and must be a nightmare to clean! The whole room is full of objects hanging from ceiling, walls and bar; a ship's figurehead, oars, diving helmet, brass lamps, ship's wheel, baskets, model boats, pictures, barrels, fishing gear and more besides. The smaller cabin bar has panelling, royal blue upholstered seating and even more collectibles, while a small area to the rear (where children can sit) features stuffed seabirds in cases. Good bar food is generously priced and ranges from rich crab soup (£1.50) and generously-filled sandwiches (around £1.25/£1.50) to wonderful, old-fashioned English desserts (raspberry pie, golden sponge, gooseberry crumble, Brown Betty, sticky toffee meringue gateau – all £1.25). Main courses might include lamb korma, beef stovies, beef in stout, liver and onions or a roast rib of beef with Yorkshire pudding (all £4). The dinner menu (served 7-8.15) offers a good choice at a price for four courses of £13; booking advised at weekends. Upstairs, the nautical theme continues, with a fine collection of large model boats in one of the first-floor hallways. The bedrooms, including three in outside annexes, are clean, neat and unfussy, with plain painted walls and cottagey bedspreads; furniture varies from modern fitted units to more traditional freestanding pieces; two rooms have four-poster beds. Direct-dial telephone, television (with satellite) and mineral water (local of course) are standard, and every room is en suite, though half have shower only, and some are on the small side. The pub also has its own lawn and summerhouse overlooking the harbour and enjoying fabulous views. In the evenings, the bars fill with the locals and fishermen who mix well with visitors. ***Bar Food*** *12-2.30 (sandwiches only in evenings).* ***Restaurant Meals*** *12-2, 7-8.15. Free House.* ***Beer*** *Theakston Best, XB, Longstone. Garden, putting, outdoor play area. Family room.* ***Accommodation*** *15 bedrooms, all en suite, £66 (single £33). Children welcome overnight (minimum age 10). Check-in after 2pm. No dogs. Closed Dec & Jan. Access, Visa.*

Seaview	**Seaview Hotel**	**FOOD**
Tel 01983 612711 Fax 01983 613729		**B&B**
High Street Seaview Isle of Wight PO34 5EX		**Map 15 D4**

A small early Victorian hotel, charmingly and efficiently run by Nicholas and Nicola Hayward; the hotel's two pubby bars are at the very heart of this small seaside town's life and the simple bar meals are always popular. Just yards from the seafront with its pebble beach and pretty assortment of sailing dinghies bobbing in the Solent, the hotel has enormous charm, starting with the small front patio complete with flagpole, and the little rear courtyard which heaves in season with youngsters. Both bars have a nautical theme, one (where children can wreck the atmosphere if left to run around) with a myriad of photos of old ships and small round tables, the other more rustic in style with bare floorboards, dado pine panelling and, more unusually, part of an old ship's mast. Try a pint of the particularly good Goddard's, brewed on the Island. Eat in the cosy, smoke-free restaurant under table lamps set on crisply-clothed tables (two sittings in high season), or choose from the bar menu served both inside and outside on the terrace; gazpacho, hot crab ramekin (£3.95), herring roes on toasted muffins (£3.60), plaice and chips (£4.30) or local lobster (£10.95/£17.95) usually feature and crab (when available) and prawn crusty rolls are also always popular. Traditional Sunday lunch (£9.95, children £5.95 in the restaurant, £5.95 in other areas) served 12.30-1.30 (ring to check availability). Pretty, individually decorated bedrooms – blues and yellows are the favoured colours – are most appealing, with lots of pictures, books and objets d'art. The best, and largest, rooms feature antique furniture; others have simple white-painted built-in units. Two of the rooms have small patios (unfortunately overlooking the small rear car park) and on the top floor there's also a family suite, its two bedrooms separated by a sitting room. Two cosy lounges (that on the first floor is non-smoking, the one to the rear of the back bar is rather dimly lit and cosier) are reserved for residents and restaurant diners. Recommended in our 1995 *Hotels & Restaurants Guide*. **Bar Food** *12-2 (Sun to 1.45), 7-9.30.* **Restaurant Meals** *12-1.30, 7.30-9.30 (not Sun eve). Children allowed in bar to eat, children's menu, high tea 5.45pm. Free House.* **Beer** *Flowers, Goddard's. Patio/terrace, outdoor eating.* **Accommodation** *16 bedrooms, all en suite, from £60 (single from £40). Children welcome overnight (ring for prices – high season exceptions), additional beds and cots (£2.50) available. Access, Diners, Visa.*

Sedgefield   Dun Cow Inn

Tel 01740 20894   **B&B**

43 Front Street Sedgefield Stockton-on-Tees Cleveland TS21 3AT   Map 5 E3

A splendid old inn – in this village of near a dozen pubs – which received Civic Trust awards for its bedroom conversions in 1974. Roof beams and black and white timber-framed walls have been exposed and restored, skilfully set off by the tapestry-weave fabrics used for the bed-heads, counterpanes and curtains. There are no en-suite bathrooms, though the three which are shared (including one fully tiled with a modern pulse shower) do enter into the spirit with splendidly evocative, yet up-to-date, bathroom fittings. Teletext TVs, fresh fruit and bedside boiled sweets greet the overnight visitor – breakfast orders placed the night before are cheerfully served at guests' chosen hour next morning. On our last visit however, we felt, sadly, that the food was not up to the standard such a fine pub deserves. **Beers** *Theakston BB& XB, Newcastle Exhibition, Village Brewery Bull Bitter, several weekly-changing guest beers.* **Accommodation** *6 rooms, not en suite £45 (single £36.50). Children welcome overnight, additional beds and cots available. Access, Diners, Visa.*

Sellack   Loughpool Inn

Tel & Fax 01989 730236   **FOOD**

Sellack nr Ross-on-Wye Hereford & Worcester HR9 6LX   Map 14 B1

A popular dining pub and an equally pleasant spot for summer drinking around picnic tables under the weeping willows. The generally unspoilt interior features flagstones, log fires and two dining rooms whose cloths and candles create a rather more sedate setting than in the previous owners' time. Menu boards proclaim the range of bar snacks and dining fare: though the choice is wide, it varies little from day to day. Cumberland sausage (£3.50), spicy pork ribs (£5.75) and deep fried plaice (£6.50) typify bar offerings. Herefordshire steaks are prominently featured among main meals which also include salmon steak (£8.45), steak and kidney pie (£5.95) and, perhaps, Greek style goat casserole (£8.50). Not suitable for children under 14. *Bar Food & Restaurant Meals 12-2, 7-9.30. Free House. Beer Bass, Hereford Supreme. Garden. Family room. Access, Visa.*

Selling   White Lion

Tel 01227 752211	FOOD
The Street Selling nr Faversham Kent ME13 9RQ	Map 11 C5

Surrounded by tubs of flowers, this charming 300-year-old village pub is decorated inside in traditional Kentish-style with swags of hops. Half set up for eating and half for drinking there are wheelback chairs, an inglenook fireplace, dressers loaded with plates and tureens and lots of fresh flowers and plants. The menu always includes a traditional beef suet pudding and steak and kidney pie plus steaks (sirloin £8.75, rump £9.75), and ploughman's lunches (three cheeses with apple, £3.75) along with the likes of potted crab in butter (£4.75), mushrooms provençale (£5.95) and a few more exotic items such as spicy Indian samosas with a tamarind dip (£5.95) and black-eyed bean curry (£5.25). For those with particularly spicy tastes Monday night is curry night. A good selection of puds (at £2.50) of which about half are brought-in. 48 malt whiskies at the bar. Live jazz Monday evenings. *Bar & Restaurant Food 12-2.15 & 7-9.30 (Sat to 10, Sun to 9). Children's menu. Beer Shepherd Neame Spitfire Ale, Master Brew & Mild. Garden, outdoor eating. Family room. Access, Visa.*

Semington   Lamb on the Strand

Tel 01380 870263 Fax 01380 870815	FOOD
99 The Strand Semington nr Trowbridge Wiltshire	Map 14 B3

Over the past three years the Flaherty family have spent much time and energy in carefully refurbishing this fine ivy-clad old farmhouse, set beside the A361 between Devizes and Trowbridge. Original features and fireplaces have been revealed and a tasteful collection of old darkwood furniture, farmhouse high-back chairs, a carved oak corner cupboard, quality fabrics and prints have created a relaxed and upmarket air in both the neat bar and small intimate dining room. The latter, painted dark green and candle-lit, is particularly popular in the evenings and the soothing tones of light classical music enhance the overall atmosphere and charm of a really civilised pub. Quality bar food is the main emphasis at the Lamb, the daily-changing blackboard menu offering a pleasing variety of home-made dishes, all of which make use of fresh local produce. Start with herrings in a Madeira sauce, sauerkraut with chorizo sausage, mushroom in a Stilton sauce (all at £2.95), followed by well-presented main-course dishes such as lamb casserole with apricot (£6.50), noisettes of lamb (£7.75), breast of Barbary duck (£7.50) and crusty chicken (£6.50). Fresh fish – salmon with a wine and cream sauce (£6.75), goujons of plaice (£5.95) – and good vegetarian dishes – chick pea hotpot, hazelnut and vegetable loaf – feature on the menu. To round off a meal, inviting puddings may include bread pudding in whisky sauce, kissel with ice cream and chocolate truffle cake (all £2.75). A competitively priced wine list includes at least eight house wines served by the glass. To the side of the pub is a delightful garden with shrubs, trees and wrought-iron tables and chairs, from which there are fine views over open countryside. Pub may be closed on Sunday evenings Nov-Mar. *Bar Food 12-2.30, 6.30-9 (Sat to 9.30, Sun 7-8.30, bookings only). Children's menu and portions. Free House. Beer Eldridge Pope, Hardy Ale, Dorchester Bitter. Garden, outdoor eating. Access, Visa.*

Semley   **Benett Arms**

Tel 01747 830221	**FOOD**

Semley nr Shaftesbury Dorset SP7 9AS   **Map 14 B3**

This unusually tall, white-painted building enjoys an enviable rural location on the edge of the village, opposite the green and overlooking the isolated church. Inside, a warm welcome is ensured in the rustic, split-level and simply furnished bar, which is warmed in winter by an open fire. The printed bar menu covers the standard items – steak and kidney pie, lasagne and Wiltshire ham, egg and chips (all at £4.95) – while a daily-changing blackboard menu displays the more interesting and unusual dishes that are on offer. Fresh fish features well – delivered on Tuesdays and Thursdays from Poole – and may include herrings in mustard sauce (£4.95), baked salmon John Tovey (£7.95), and grilled cod fillet served with vegetables (£5.95). The unusual comes in the form of chorizos served with sauerkraut (£4.95). Home-made puddings (all at £2.75) usually include the popular treacle and walnut tart and lemon crunch. On Sunday a traditional roast lunch is served (2-courses £7.95, 3-courses £8.95). An above-average selection (about 15) of worldwide house wines is served, by both bottle and glass. *Bar Food & Restaurant Meals 12-2, 7-10. Children allowed in bar to eat. Beer Gibbs Mew Salisbury Best, Deacon & Bishop's Tipple. Garden, outdoor eating, children's play area. Family room. Access, Diners, Visa.*

Sennen Cove   **Old Success Inn**

Tel 01736 870232 Fax 01736 871457	**B&B**

Sennen Cove by Whitesands Bay Cornwall TR19 7DG   **Map 12 A4**

Located off the A30, next to the huge expanse of Whitesands Bay and only a mile north of Land's End, the 17th-century inn has been well refurbished to provide accommodation in twelve comfortable bedrooms that have impressive sea views. Especially popular are the rooms that capture the famous sunset sinking into the sea, the most attractive being the spacious honeymoon suite with its four-poster bed. All rooms have pretty floral curtains and print wallpaper, solid modern pine furnishings and good clean en-suite facilities. Added comforts include satellite TV and tea-makers and residents have use of a stylish lounge complete with picture window and sea view. The pubby 'Charlies Bar' is modern and open-plan in layout with a mix of pub furniture, stools and high-backed benches and various local seafaring photographs of bygone days decorate the walls. *Free House. Beer Bass, Tinners Cornish Ale. Outdoor eating area. Accommodation 12 bedrooms, 10 en suite, £44 (single £22). Children welcome overnight (½-price). Access, Visa.*

Sevenoaks   **Royal Oak**

FOOD
B&B

Tel 01732 451109   Fax 01732 740187

High Street Sevenoaks Kent TN13 1HY

Map 11 B5

A former coaching inn with abundant atmosphere and character.
Rich, bold colours perfectly complement the fabric of the building.
Traditional or antique furniture is used in the bedrooms, which are
decorated in individual, often striking style. Neat, bright bathrooms.
Among the day rooms are a cosy pub-like bar (where imaginative bar
snacks are served in a candle-lit section with scrubbed pine tables and
comfortable, well-upholstered seats), a beautifully furnished drawing
room and a conservatory. The charming and comfortable restaurant
comprises several rooms that are partially panelled and cleverly lit,
creating a relaxing atmosphere. Chef James Butterfill manages to
include something for everyone on his à la carte, and the three-course
fixed-price menus (dinner – £13.95) offer particularly good value.
Outdoor eating in good weather on a creeper-clad patio. Wine list
features eight house wines available by the large glass. *Bar Food
12-2.30, 7-10.30 (Sun to 10).* *Restaurant Meals 12.30-2, 7.30-10 (Sun
to 9.30). Set L £11.50 Set D £18.50. Patio, outdoor eating, tennis.
Accommodation 37 rooms, all en suite, £70 (single £60). Children
welcome overnight (under-10s stay free in parents' room), additional beds
(£15) and cots (£10) available. Access, Diners, Visa.*

Shaldon   **Ness House Hotel**

B&B

Tel 01626 873480   Fax 01626 873486

Marine Drive Shaldon Devon TQ14 0HP

Map 13 D3

The Ness House Hotel overlooks the Teign estuary and across to the
town of Teignmouth. Built in 1810, it has retained its Regency
exterior and is set in 22 acres of parkland. The twelve rooms (1 bridal
suite, five apartments, 2 family suites, 3 doubles and 1 single) all have
en-suite facilities and are equipped with modern facilities. Room
service is available. There is a spacious open-plan bar with a no-
smoking area and, at the back, a small, simple lounge. *Open 11-11,
Sunday usual hours.* *Beer Royal Oak, Palmers. Garden, outdoor eating.
Family room.* **Accommodation** *14 bedrooms, all en suite, from £80 (single
from £40). Children welcome overnight (under-5s stay free in parents'
room 5-14s £15), additional beds (£15), cots supplied (no charge).
Access, Visa.*

Shamley Green   **Red Lion Inn**

FOOD
B&B

Tel 01483 892202   Fax 01483 892788

Shamley Green Surrey GU5 0UB

Map 15a E4

Listed, 300-year-old building overlooking the village green and cricket
pitch, with a smart and well-cared-for interior boasting three open
fireplaces, a pleasant mix of modern pine and antique furnishings,
tasteful prints and fresh flowers and candles on tables. Reliably good,
homely food listed on the blackboard in the bar – tagliatelle with
seafood and mushrooms (£5.85), Dijon peppered chicken breast
(£8.45), steak and mushroom, artichoke and green olive crepes (both
£5.85) – with printed restaurant menu fare (also served in the bar)
offering more substantial main courses such as wild salmon steak with
prawn and dill sauce (£11.45) and calf's liver Marsala with grapes and
bacon (£11.95). Fresh and al dente accompanying vegetables. Popular
puddings (£2.95) include deep lemon pie and home-made grapefruit
ice cream. Fresh, chintzy, antique-furnished bedrooms upstairs – one

has a four-poster – all with en-suite facilities. *Open 11-11.30, Sun 12-3 & 7-11.* **Bar Food** *11-10.30.* **Beer** *K&B Sussex, Greene King Abbot Ale, Flowers Original, guest beer. Garden, outdoor eating.* **Accommodation** *4 bedrooms, all en suite, £35 (single £30). Children welcome overnight (family room £40/45), cot supplied. Access, Diners, Visa.*

Shardlow   The Old Crown

Tel 01332 792392	**FOOD**
Cavendish Bridge Shardlow Derbyshire DE72 2HL	Map 7 D3

Signed just of the A6, Cavendish Bridge was the old road crossing of the Trent into Derbyshire, now mercifully a dead end, where the old bridge collapsed, some thirty feet above the river. The Old Crown, recently rescued from a possibly similar fate, now breathes new and vibrant life within stone walls hung with old tobacco and brewery posters and beams hung at every conceivable point with pottery water jugs. A high turnover of real ales draws the locals and high-piled plates of food almost everyone else. Landlord Peter Morton-Harrison operates his own inimitable food-ordering system on his note pad (cometh the man, cometh the menu) while the best food bets on the Specials Board are equally idiosyncratic. Upside-down fish pie (£5.75) has reached Mark II phase (laced with pernod), while the beef and chicken hotties (£5-£5.75) are generously fired up with tabasco. The balance of a conservative menu places volume, perhaps, above variety though no one seems to care that much. Good ale and a genial atmosphere more than paper over the cracks. **Bar Food** *12-2. Free House.* **Beer** *Marston Pedigree, Bass, 6 guest beers. Garden, outdoor eating. No credit cards.*

Shave Cross   Shave Cross Inn

Tel 01308 868358	**A**
Marshwood Vale Shave Cross Dorset DT6 6HW	Map 13 F2

Once a busy resting place for pilgrims on their way to Whitchurch, as well as monastic visitors, who frequently had their tonsures trimmed while staying, hence the name. This charming old cob-and-flint inn in beautiful Marshwood Vale has a stone floor, inglenook fireplace, beamed ceiling, rustic furnishings, and a delightful suntrap garden. Through the skittle alley, there's a children's play area. *Free House.* **Beer** *Bass, Eldridge Pope Royal Oak, Hall & Woodhouse Badger Best. Garden, children's play area. Family room. Closed Mondays (except Bank Holidays). No credit cards.*

Shefford Woodlands   Pheasant Inn

Tel 01488 648284	**FOOD**
Baydon Rd Shefford Woodlands nr Hungerford Berkshire RG16 7AA	Map 14a B4

On the lip of Lambourn Downs, just a quarter of a mile from the M4 Junction 14 (turn on to the B4000), the Pheasant stands in view of the motorway. A new brick wall, sporting colourful flower troughs, enhances the white-tiled frontage, and in view of the traffic noise the double-glazed conservatory porch is a welcome addition. Despite an unaltered public bar and somewhat primitive toilets in a lean-to, the body of the pub has been made over to dining, with prodigious choices chalked up on ubiquitous blackboards; kitchen output is dependable rather than inspired. Good home-made tomato soup (£1.75) and prawn and celery cocktail (£2.75) are typical starters; seafood pie (£6.50) and venison and black cherry casserole (£7.50)

Zzzz...

make a one-course lunch; chicken breast with garlic and herb sauce
(£6.50), salmon with lemon butter (£7.50), rich beef casserole
(£6.50) and peppered fillet steak (£9.50) constitute more substantial
dinners. Hot and cold sweets are home-made and gooey; treacle tart
or banana split are both £2.50. Sunday roast is £9.95 for three
courses. There are picnic tables in the garden for fine weather and
regular summer barbecues. *The Royal Oak* in Wootton Rivers (see
entry) is under the same ownership. *Bar Food* 11.30-2, 7-9.30 (*Sun
12-2, 7-9*). *Free House.* *Beer* Wadworth IPA & 6X, Brakspear Bitter,
Speckled Hen, Eagle Bitter, Hard Tackle, guest beers. Garden, outdoor
eating, family room. Access, Visa.

Shelf   Duke of York

Tel 01422 202056 Fax 01422 206618	**B & B**
West Street Stone Chair Shelf Halifax West Yorkshire HX3 7LN	Map 6 C1

The 17th-century former coaching inn, right by the A644, is pub
in front and flooring factory to the rear. Local foundries have
contributed over the years to the collection of brassware and blow-
torches which adorn the interior, alongside the whisky jugs, chamber
pots and jam pans which hang from its blackened oak beams.
Bedrooms, meanwhile, attract a mid-week business clientele in an area
not over-blessed with comparable competition. In addition to five en-
suite bedrooms in the pub, there are six self-contained rooms in a row
of weavers' cottages across the road. These retain the old stone walls
and fireplaces, and on the ground floor, it's plain to see that the
bathrooms (with shower/WC only) were once the kitchens. A return
to the bar for breakfast finds it in altogether less atmospheric mode.
Whitbread. *Open 11-11, Sun usual hours. Free House.* *Beer* Boddingtons
Mild & Best, Trophy Bitter, Castle Eden, Timothy Taylor Best. Patio.
*Accommodation 13 bedrooms, all en suite, (most with shower/WC only),
£45 (single £30). No dogs. Access, Diners, Visa.*

Shelley   Three Acres Inn   ★

Tel 01484 602606 Fax 01484 608411	**FOOD**
	B & B
Roydhouse Shelley nr Huddersfield West Yorkshire HD8 8LR	Map 6 C1

Set high in the Pennines above Huddersfield, the Emley Moor
television mast (red-lit at night) provides a useful landmark for finding
the unassuming, greystone Three Acres, which is on the Emley road,
off B6116 at Shelley village. Central to the inn is a long bar counter
framed in darkwood panelling beneath solid oak beams, lent further
character at night by candle-lit tables and lively accompaniment from
the grand piano. After 25 years' consistent performance at the top
level, Neil Truelove and Brian Orme still attract the crowds for bar
food which is commendable for its unswerving quality and simplicity.
Among the comprehensive range of unusually good sandwiches (£2-
£4.95), a BLT (£2.60) of crispy bacon, firm, ripe tomatoes and
home-made mayonnaise typifies attention to every detail in this
department; a pan-fried sirloin steak version (£4.95), served on crusty
bread with onions and chipped potatoes that are genuinely home-
made, becomes a meal in itself. For a full meal, main courses ranging
from liver and onions with bubble and squeak (£5.95) to smoked
salmon with dill scrambled egg (£7.25) and Gruyère-topped Spanish
omelette (£4.95) vie for prominence alongside roasts of the day
(£6.95), shortcrust-topped steak, kidney and mushroom pie (£6.25)
and Whitby haddock (served with traditional mushy peas – £5.95).
From the specials blackboard, a croustade of chorizo with sun-dried

tomatoes and Parmesan laid over baby spinach leaves was rated by one inspector as "outstanding". To follow are the justifiably memorable desserts such as a chocolate and rum mousse or raisin and curd tart served with a rich raspberry coulis. At either end of the bar are two more formal dining rooms offering an evening à la carte and traditional 3-course Sunday lunch (£10.95, £6.95 roast dish in the bar). Booking here is essential, and as may be inevitable (given the inn's popularity), service may become ragged. The quality, however, of this dedicated team's food is beyond question, and anyone looking for such adveturous flavours – and not a little conviviality of atmosphere – will surely not be disappointed. The Three Acres bridges the gap between small hotel and country inn with a choice of quality accommodation. Bedrooms in the main building are spacious and airy, and furnished in traditional-style natural pine with colour co-ordinated fabrics. Much smiliar decor has been used in the newer annexe, housed in much older stone cottages across the lane, where the rooms are that good bit smaller and single rooms are equipped with WC and showers only; those businessman with work to do may find these last a little cramped. Three rooms are large enough for families and one pair connect. All are nonetheless immaculately kept and equipped with TVs, direct-dial phones, trouser presses and plenty of toiletries. *Open 12-11 Mon-Fri, Sat 7-11.30 only, Sun 12-3, 7-10.30.*
Bar Food & Restaurant Meals *12-2 (not Sat), 7-10. Free House.*
Beer *Mansfield Riding Traditional Bitter, Dark Mild & Old Baily, Adnams Extra, Timothy Taylor's Landlord, regular guest beer.*
Accommodation *20 bedrooms, all en suite, £57.50 (single £47.50), weekend reductions. Children welcome overnight, additional bed and cot available. Pub closed Saturday lunchtime. Access, Visa.*

Shenington   **Bell Inn**

Tel 01295 670274	**FOOD**
Shenington nr Banbury Oxfordshire OX15 6NQ	**Map 14a B1**

Just five miles west of Banbury (turn off the A422) Shenington is a comfortable, sleepy village boasting a celebrated Norman church. By the three-acre green, the Bell is very much at the heart of village life. Don't miss the locals' bar down one side of the pub if you're in search of a fine pint of Hook Norton – the originating brewery is only six miles away. To the front, the two dining rooms with attendant log fires are cosy and intimate. Here Stephen Dixon supervises food ordering (with sweets chalked up on Scotty, the itinerant cut-out dog) while Jennifer is the genius behind a regularly-evolving range of seasonal food. A typical starter would be mushrooms in cream and paprika (£3.25), followed by lamb and lime casserole (£6.95), cod in celery sauce (£7.25) or an almond celery and cashew bake (£5.75). Super puddings follow the lines of raspberry crumble (£2.25) and banoffi pie (£2.75). The Bell has four bedrooms, two of them en suite (£15 per person), which are offered on a strictly casual basis.
Bar Food *12-3, 7-9.* ***Beer*** *Boddingtons, Hook Norton. Pub closed Sun eve Oct-Mar. Access, Visa.*

Shepperton   **Anchor Hotel**

Tel 01932 221618 Fax 01932 252235	**B&B**
Church Square Shepperton Middlesex TW17 9JZ	**Map 15a F4**

A favourite haunt of Charles Dickens, the historic Anchor has dominated Shepperton's tiny square for over 400 years. Despite serious fire damage some years ago, the Disraeli Room retains original linenfold oak panelling, and the evocative Anchor Bar has been meticulously restored. Bedrooms, of which only 7 are doubles and all but one have shower/WCs only, all offer TVs, tea-makers and direct dial telephones. The best front doubles overlook the tiny square where once illegal prizefighters stood toe to toe; when the Bow Street runners were spied approaching, they would escape across the Thames to open country. *Pub open 11-2.30, 5.30-11 (Sun 12-3, 7-10.30).* *Free House.* **Beer** *Eldridge Pope Royal Oak and Hardy Country.* **Accommodation** *29 bedrooms, all en suite, £72 (single £56). Children welcome overnight (under-12s stay free in parents' room), additional beds and cots available. Access, Diners, Visa.*

Shepperton   King's Head

Tel 01932 221910	A
Church Square Shepperton Middlesex TW17 9JY	Map 15a F4

Across the square from the *Anchor*, the name of Nell Gwynne is most commonly associated with the King's Head. Although the two front bars have recently been made one, the traditional feel of its interior remains unchanged; floors are flagstoned, connecting doorways and alcoves are tiny and in winter log fires burn in an impressive inglenook. To the rear, a summer gazebo and enclosed patio are conducive to sociable drinking, though just as many may meander down from the square, glasses in hand, to take in a view of the river. *Open 11-11 Wed-Sat, Sun-Tues usual hours.* **Beer** *Courage Best, Wadworth 6X, Ruddles. Patio/terrace. Family room. No credit cards.*

Shepperton   Warren Lodge

Tel 01932 242972 Fax 01932 253883	B&B
Church Square Shepperton Middlesex TW17 9JZ	Map 15a F4

Arguably the least pubby of Shepperton's hostelries, it nonetheless enjoys the choicest location. Riverside terrace and garden are shaded by a handsome old walnut tree, and there's comfortable seating both in the spacious beamed bar and panelled reception lounge. Most bedrooms, both in the main 18th-century house and two wings of later additions, share serene river views: all have TVs, tea-makers and hairdryers. No real ales. *Open all day. Free House. Garden.* **Accommodation** *50 bedrooms, 47 en suite, £74 (single £57) tariff reductions at weekends. Children welcome overnight (under-16s stay free if sharing parents' room), additional beds and cots available. Accommodation closed 5 days at Christmas. No dogs. Access, Diners, Visa.*

Shepton Mallet   Kings Arms

Tel 01749 343781	B&B
Leg Square Shepton Mallet Somerset BA4 5LN	Map 13 F1

Check directions when booking at this 1660 stonebuilt pub, as it is set in a quiet corner of town. Locally known as the 'dusthole' from the days when it was a haunt of quarry workers, it contains low beamed bars with open stone walls and some photographs of the area past and present. The bar and restaurant area (no food Sat lunch) were recently refurbished, and the bedrooms are all en-suite, with TVs and tea-makers. **Beer** *Ansells Traditional, Thomas Hardy, Burton. Patio. Family room.* **Accommodation** *3 bedrooms, all en suite, £33 (single £25). Children welcome overnight (rate depends on age), additional beds available. Check-in by arrangement. Dogs welcome by arrangement. Access, Visa.*

Sherfield English   **Hatchet Inn**

Tel 01794 322487	**FOOD**
Sherfield English Romsey Hampshire SO51 6FP	Map 14 C3

Set back from the main road, this homely 17th-century pub is a
popular stopping-off point for A27 travellers between Salisbury and
Romsey. Refreshment is provided in two simply furnished and
carpeted bars, the larger lounge/dining room housing the blackboard
menu which lists the daily-changing bar snacks and the twice-weekly-
changing choice of more substantial main meals. Food is freshly
prepared, generously served – a chicken and ham pie filled with
chunks of tender meat in a creamy sauce and served with a selection of
vegetables (£4.50) – and good value. Other lighter meals include steak
and kidney pie (£4.75), curry (£3.95), home-cooked ham, egg and
chips (£3.95) and a range of ploughman's and salads. Main courses
feature up to six fresh fish dishes – fillet of sea bream with cream and
dill sauce (£8.95), seafood platter (smoked trout, crab, king prawns,
cockles, mussels, squid and octopus at £10.95) – as well as rack of
lamb with a rosemary and redcurrant sauce (£8.95) and supreme of
chicken with a leek and Stilton sauce (£8.25). Sunday is a busy day
here: the traditional roast (£4.50) draws a full house, booking
essential. *Bar Food* 12-2, 7-9.30. *Beer Directors, Wiltshire Stonehenge
Bitter, Bass. Garden, outdoor eating. Family room. Access, Visa.*

Sherston   **Rattlebone Inn**

Tel & Fax 01666 840871	**A**
Church Street Sherston Wiltshire SN16 0LR	Map 14 B2

Only 6 miles from the M4 this busy old Cotswold-stone pub still has
its original stone roof intact, and lots more exposed stone, oak beams
and open fires inside. Boules competitions in the fenced garden. Well-
behaved children allowed in the bar to eat. Choice of over 40 malt
whiskies. *Pub open all day Sat 11.30-11, usual hours other days. Free
House. Beer Smiles Best, Wadworth 6X, Rattlebone Pale Ale, guest beers.
Garden. Pub closed bank holidays. Access, Diners, Visa.*

Shifnal   **Oddfellows**

Tel 01952 461517	**FOOD**
	B&B
Market Place Shifnal nr Telford Shropshire TF11 9AH	Map 6 B4

What was once the Star Hotel close to the railway station is now part-
pub, part-brasserie in a novel ground-floor conversion which utilises
wood-block flooring and a pine-clad bar canopy to balance the trendy
installation of assorted pine and cast-iron tables, sofas, banquettes and
pews which form the tiered quartet of eating areas. An assorted age
group seems as at home with a mixture of 1960s' and 70s' pop classics
as they are with menu concepts as diverse as club sandwiches of sirloin
steak (£3.95), asparagus, mange tout and bean salad (£3.75), spicy
chicken and almond curry (£4.25) and pork brochettes with peanut
sauce (£6.95). Some of the better fare appears towards the top of this
wide price range: grilled sea bass with leeks (£8.95), scallop, prawn
and monkfish salad or duck breast with plums and coriander (both
£8.50): but rather more care could be taken in preparation of
the salad items, and the mostly bought-in desserts are decidedly
disappointing. There is still overnight accommodation available in
four pine-furnished en-suite bedrooms above; but it appears to be on a
rather random basis with Continental breakfast obtainable from a
communal kitchen. The best we can suggest is that one phones ahead

for clarification. *Bar Food 12-2.30, 6-10 (Sun from 7). Free House.*
Beer Boddingtons, Timothy Taylor's Landlord, guest beer. Accommodation
4 bedrooms, all en suite, £35 (single £25). Check-in by arrangement.
Access, Visa.

Shipton-under-Wychwood	**Lamb Inn**	**FOOD**
Tel 01993 830465		**B&B**

High Street Shipton-under-Wychwood Oxfordshire OX7 6DQ   **Map 14a B2**

Tucked away down a quiet side road, the Lamb is a typical 17th-
century Cotswold building, complete with honey-coloured stone walls
and stone tiled roof, and its neat little patio with parasol-shaded tables
makes an ideal spot in summer. Inside, all is equally immaculate.
The beamed bar has a polished woodblock floor and mostly antique
furniture: a settle here, a pew there, and attractive old oak tables. At
lunchtimes, the cold buffet displayed in the bar offers cold cuts like
salmon, ham and beef, a vegetarian tart and hot dishes of the day. In
the evening an extensive blackboard menu offers the choice of a full
three-course meal or perhaps just a light snack. Main dishes like guinea
fowl (£8.95) or roast leg of lamb (£7.50) come in generous portions
with good simply-cooked fresh vegetables; as a bonus, someone in the
kitchen has the cool, light hand needed to produce
a melt-in-the-mouth pastry for the home-made fruit pies. For more
formal dining there is a cosy low-beamed restaurant with similar fare
on a set price (3-course, £19.50) dinner menu. The owner's interest in
wine is evident from a well-chosen wine list, four or five of which are
available by the glass. The Lamb's five bedrooms are all as neat as
a new pin, with cream-coloured melamine furniture and spotless
modern bathrooms. Three of the rooms boast some old beams and
these help lend a little extra character. Televisions, radio-alarms and
tea and coffee making kit are standard, with mineral water and bowls
of fruit as welcoming extras. The convivial hubbub from the bar
below is quite audible in some rooms, which might be a problem if
you want an early night. Good hearty cooked breakfasts are worth
getting up for. *Bar Food 12-2, 7-9.30. Restaurant Meals 7-9.30 (closed
Sun). Children's portions. Beer Hook Norton, Wadworth. Patio/terrace,
outdoor eating. Accommodation 5 bedrooms, all en suite, £65 (single
£48). Access, Visa.*

Shipton-under-Wychwood	**Shaven Crown Hotel**	**FOOD**
Tel & Fax 01993 830330		**B&B**

High Street Shipton-under-Wychwood Oxfordshire OX7 6BA   **Map 14a B2**

Originally a 14th-century hospice to Bruern Abbey, this is a charming
medieval building constructed around a delightful courtyard garden
(complete with goldfish pond), where you can eat in good weather. In
addition to lunch and dinner, visitors are offered breakfast, morning
coffee and afternoon tea. Choices on the Buttery Bar's blackboard
menu include Toronto-style potato skins (£3.25), smoked haddock
mousse (£3.95), gateau of crepes (£4.25), mushroom terrine (£4.25),
poached salmon (£5.95), curried prawns (£5.55) and tomatoes stuffed
with blue cheese and walnuts (£3.95). Delicious desserts (£1.95)
feature fruit pies, sticky toffee pudding, lemon soufflé and home-made
ice-creams (£1.40). A 2/3-course Sunday lunch (£11/£14.50) is
served in the no-smoking restaurant where a table d'hote dinner menu
(£14.95/£18.50) operates in the evenings – salmon in filo pastry with
ginger, coriander and lime, or pork with prunes, juniper berries and
Pernod are two choices of main course. Charming service. The newly

refurbished bedrooms vary in size, some smaller than one might expect for the price. *Bar Food* 12-2, 7.30-9.30 (*Sun to 9*). *Restaurant Meals* 12-1.30 (*Sun only*), 7.30-9.30 (*Sun to 9*). *Children allowed in bar to eat.* **Beer** *Hook Norton, guest beers. Garden, outdoor eating. Family room.* **Accommodation** *9 bedrooms, 8 en suite, from £68 (four-poster £82, single £33). Children welcome overnight (charge depends on age). Check-in by arrangement. Guide dogs only. Access, Visa.*

Shobdon   **Bateman Arms**

Tel 015668 708374	**FOOD**
Shobdon nr Leominster Hereford & Worcester HR6 9LX	Map 14a A1

The Williams family have returned to take over the running of an historic pub which they've actually owned for some years: the black and white timbered former farmhouse stands on the B4362 at the heart of the village. They've smartened it up greatly, moving the bar to a more central position, extending the dining area to the lower-level former function room and carpeting throughout to create a more conducive ambience for eating, (even if the piped music is sometimes rather loud). Young Gary Williams looks after the bar and the business of eating while Tracy keeps a watchful eye on the kitchen. Production here is now on something of a larger scale than before with the long, printed menu of "overfilled" sandwiches and ploughmans platters (£3.95), grills and vegetarian selections (broccoli and courgette strudel £4.95) supplemented by some varied and imaginative daily specials. Spicy meatballs with pasta (£3.50), Cajun chicken with tarragon cream sauce (£6.50) and chunky Mediterranean fish casserole (£7.95) are indicative of the choices. Nevertheless, a top seller remains the "Elegant fish and chips"; haddock in beer batter with chips and mushy peas all served up in pages of the Financial Times. Since our last edition, the Bateman Arms has ceased to offer bed and breakfast. *Bar and Restaurant Meals* 12-2, 7-9.45. *Free House.* **Beer** *Bass, Stones Bitter. Garden. Pub closed Sun eve, all Mon. Access, Visa.*

Shroton   **Cricketers**

Tel 01258 860421	**FOOD**
Shroton nr Blandford Forum Dorset DT11 8QD	Map 14 B4

Homely village local, situated opposite the village green and close to the unique sloping cricket pitch, which is superbly sited beneath Hambledon Hill. Thirsty cricketers (this pub is their HQ), walkers refreshing themselves along the Wessex Way and local drinkers fill the simply furnished bar that includes, to one side, a pool table and various cricketing memorabilia. Diners complete the cross-section of people that frequent this humble establishment. They seek out the honest home-cooked food, especially the unusual fresh fish selection – red snapper, grouper and other tropical varieties – that are on the menu here. A no-frills bar snack menu is supplemented by freshly prepared daily blackboard specials such as pasta twists in courgettes and mushroom sauce (£3.95), turkey, ham and leek pie (£4.75), rump steak (£5.25) and gammon steak (£5.25). Restaurant fare changes seasonally to include good local game, as well as beef Wellington (£9.25), stuffed quails (£7.95) and wild salmon with lime butter (£8.35). Featured fish that may be on offer are monkfish tails in tomato and basil (£6.95) and plaice fillets meunière (£5.20). All main dishes are accompanied by crisply cooked selection of vegetables.

Generally there are five wines available by the glass, selected from a short list that always feature a good-value end-of-bin wine. Well-maintained and sheltered rear garden with flower beds and a trellis of climbing roses is ideal for outdoor eating. It is worth noting that Shroton is still referred to as Iwerne Courtney on some maps. *Bar Food & Restaurant Meals 12-2, 7-9.45 (Sun to 9.15, rest to 9). Children allowed in bar to eat. Free House. Beer Flowers Original, Bass, Smiles, Wadworth 6X, Theakston, guest beers. Garden, outdoor eating. Access, Visa.*

Sibford Gower   The Wykham Arms

Tel 01295 78351   **FOOD**
Sibford Gower Banbury Oxon OX15 5RX   Map 14a B1

Yellow stone, mature thatch and a blaze of flowers and hanging baskets are picture-postcard material here in summer. In winter the interior is warmed by real fires and the tiny dining room with low beams and exposed stone walls takes on an altogether more cosy air. The newly renovated bars are fully carpeted and quite sedate, their best feature being an old stone well, now glass-covered to form an unusual bay-window table. The Hook Norton ales are nicely kept and bar food can be relied upon. Recent specials included parsnip and potato soup (£1.85), chicken satay (£2.85), cheese-topped cottage pie and spinach and mushroom lasagne (both £4.95). Children are made very welcome and there are swings under the trees in a pretty back garden. *Bar Food 12-2 (Sun to 2.30), 7-9.30 (Sun to 9). No food Mon. Beer Hook Norton Best & Old Hooky, Morland Old Speckled Hen, guest beer. Garden. Family room and patio. Pub closed Mon lunch. Access, Visa.*

Silverton   Silverton Inn

Tel 01392 860196   **FOOD**
Silverton Devon EX5 4HP   Map 13 D2

Don't be put off by the rather run-down exterior appearance of this pub which is situated along the main village street. Equally unpretentious and rustic inside with just a few scattered scrubbed pine tables on bare board floor and a collection of arty 'ads' for Gitanes around the walls. It looks anything but a foodie place yet talented chef Matthew Mason (who spent two years with Shaun Hill when he was at *Gidleigh Park* in Chagford) comes up with some above-average pub food for under a fiver. A very short blackboard menu might include bangers and mash (£3.95), liver and bacon casserole (£3.95), chargrilled chicken and baked avocado, venison stew (both £4.95) – all served with an imaginative selection of vegetables – and fish 'n' chips using beer-battered wild River Dart salmon (£3.95). Welsh rarebit and BLTs are lunchtime favourites. Delicious desserts (£2) may include chocolate marquise, summer fruit gratin and fruit delice. On Thursday, Friday or Saturday night, there may not be any bar food available if the restaurant upstairs (recommended in our *1995 Hotels & Restaurants Guide*) is busy. *Bar Food 12-2, 7-10. No bar food Sun eve. Restaurant Meals 7.30-10. Free House. Beer Burton Ale, Exe Valley Dob's Best Bitter. Access, Visa.*

Skidby   **Half Moon Inn**

Tel 01482 843403	**FOOD**
16 Main Street Skidby Humberside HU16 5TG	**Map 7 E1**

Chips with everything is not the stuff of the Half Moon; its speciality
is home-made Yorkshire puddings – eight different combinations
(£2.60-£4.90) including one with vegetarian gravy. They are almost
big enough to obscure the waitress. The half-acre garden has its own
'Sproggies Bar' for children, together with the only huge suspended
spiral climbing frame in the country. The pub itself is not without
idiosyncrasies, having four little bars and wooden pillar supports.
More home-made pies (£3.80), soups (£1.60), chilis, curries (£2.90)
and burgers (£2.55-£3.40) are also available. *Open 11-11 Mon-Sat,
regular hours Sun.* **Bar Food** *12-10 (Sun 12-2.30, 7-10). Children
allowed in the bar to eat.* **Beer** *John Smith's, Marston's Pedigree. Garden,
outdoor eating, children's play area. Access, Visa.*

Skirmett   **Old Crown**

Tel 01491 638435	**FOOD**
Skirmett nr Henley-on-Thames Oxfordshire RG9 6TD	**Map 15a D3**

Set by the village lane overlooking open fields, this charming, 350-
year-old pub has an unspoilt and restful atmosphere that pervades
throughout its two cottagey rooms and adjacent old-fashioned tap
room. Beams, quarry-tiled and flagstone floors, an inglenook fireplace
and an assortment of rustic sturdy furniture – from pine pews to
trestle tables – characterise the traditional interior. A vast collection of
bric-a-brac clutters every available space. There is no music, no games
machines and no counter; the well-conditioned Brakspear ales are
dispensed straight from the cask in the old still-room beyond the tiny
serving hatch. Bar food is reliable and home-cooked and although the
varied menu rarely changes – except for the occasional extra starter or
the addition of fresh crab – the tried and tested formula is a successful
if not a cheap one. To start, perhaps a freshly-prepared soup such as
tomato and herb (£2.95), a rich home-made paté like Stilton and
walnut (£4), or creamy garlic mushrooms (both £3.85), followed by
well-presented pub favourites: steak, kidney and mushroom pie,
lasagne (both £7.35, the latter served with chips or salad) and more
inventive main dishes like Dutch calf's liver pan-fried in butter
(£9.75), medallions of pork with apricots and cream (£9.50) and
poached salmon with dill sauce (£9.50), all served with good
vegetables. To finish, there are various ice creams, cheesecakes, toffee
pudding or chocolate truffle torte (around £2). Those popping in for
just a snack will find ploughman's (£3.65, lunch only) and a range of
filled jacket potatoes (from £4.25 with salad). Splendid secret summer
garden with benched areas surrounded by mature shrubs, willows and
flower-beds. No children under 10 either inside or out in the mature
cottage garden; no draught lager, either, for that matter. 5 miles north
of Henley. **Bar Food** *12-2, 7-9 (Sun to 8.30) possibly closed for food
Nov-Feb.* **Beer** *Brakspear. Garden. Pub closed all Monday (except Bank
Holiday lunchtimes). No credit cards.*

Slaidburn **Hark to Bounty Inn**

| Tel 01200 446246 | **B&B** |

Slaidburn Clitheroe Lancashire BB7 3EP

Map 6 B1

Zzz_z...

The rather sombre stone village of Slaidburn stands in a deep vale at the heart of the Forest of Bowland. Almost feudally, the village constitutes just a small part of a vast private estate, with many houses of medieval origin remaining; the romantically-named Hark to Bounty traces its origins back to the 13th century. Its exterior stone staircase leads to a splendid oak-beamed upper floor which housed the local stipendiary court until 1937; the jury benches and witness box are clearly intact in what is now a function room. By comparison, the ground-floor bars are rather shorter on character and spartan in style, with rough-painted walls and rustic tables and chairs facing an open fireplace adorned with polished brass and copperware. There are plenty of oak beams and creaky floors in the cottage-style bedrooms in some of which the melamine furniture strikes one as oddly out of place. All have en-suite bathrooms (one with WC and shower only) which could do with a little smartening up. There's also a decent-sized family room: children are welcome overnight. Notwithstanding the age and character of the building, we felt on our last visit that more attention could be paid to its upkeep, though we gather that this is all planned by the new tenants who were just installed as we went to press. There are no private room for residents. The village stream runs along the bottom of the garden. *Beer Theakston Best & Old Peculier, Matthew Walker's Dark Mild. Garden. **Accommodation** 8 bedrooms, all en suite, £45 (single £25). Children welcome overnight, additional beds supplied. Access, Visa.*

Slapton **Tower Inn**

| Tel 01548 580216 | **FOOD** |

Slapton nr Kingsbridge Devon

Map 13 D3

Tucked up a narrow driveway within this unspoilt Devon village, the ancient ivy-clad tower (which gives this charming 14th-century inn its name) looms hauntingly above the pub. It is all that remains of the old College of Chantry Priests. Apart from its peaceful location, the main appeal of the Tower is the excellent range of real ales – up to ten in the summer – that are dispensed in the atmospheric bars and the unusual pub food that is served. As one might expect with an Italian owner the food has a distinct Mediterranean flavour, with good authentic pizzas that are made to order and served on a large metal dish. Fresh pasta with various sauces – tomato £5.50, bolognaise £4.95, al tonno £5.20 – maintain the style, as do more substantial dishes such as steak pizzaiola (£11.50) and fish pie (£7.95). Other standard snacks are of the filled jacket potatoes, ploughman's and salad variety, plus generally good home-made soups. The rather gloomy stone-walled interior filled with rustic darkwood tables, old pews and a fine stone fireplace comes into its own in the evenings, when candle-light and firelight create a warm cosy ambience. Poor accommodation. Parking is extremely difficult. *Bar Food 12-2.15 & 7-9.15. Free House. Beer Exmoor Ale, Palmers IPA, Eldridge Pope Royal Oak, Gibbs Mews Bishop's Tipple, Hall & Woodhouse Tanglefoot, Wadworth 6X. Garden, family room. No credit cards.*

Smallburgh Crown

FOOD

Tel 01692 536314

B&B

Smallburgh Norwich NR12 9AD

Map 10 D1

Thatched, beamed 15th-century village inn set beside the busy A149 Great Yarmouth to Cromer road with a peaceful, well-tended rear beer garden, complete with flower borders and picnic benches. Homely, simply-furnished bar areas with barrel furniture, a large open fire and blackboard menus listing reliable, home-cooked daily specials. Choices may include a well-flavoured soup (£1.95) served with a warm roll, Cromer crab and salad (£4.50), a decent minced beef and onion pie (£4.25), chicken breast with Stilton and mustard (£5.25) and baked cod fillet with tomato, onion and garlic sauce (£5.50), all served with fresh vegetables. Routine printed bar menu. Sunday roasts (£4.75). Upstairs in the roof space are two freshly painted, clean and tidy bedrooms with attractive fabrics, sturdy furniture and dormer windows in the sloping roof. TVs, radios and tea-makers are standard. Both share an adequate, good-sized bathroom. *Free House.* **Bar Food** *12-2, 6-9 (Sat eve 7-9.30. No food Sun eve). Children allowed anywhere.* **Accommodation** *2 bedrooms, neither en suite £35 (Single £20). Children welcome overnight. Check-in by arrangement.* **Beer** *Greene King Abbot Ale, guest beer. Garden, outdoor eating. Pub closed Sun eve in winter. No credit cards.*

Smarden Bell

Tel 01233 770283

FOOD

Bell Lane Smarden Kent TN26 8PW

Map 11 C5

Tiled and rose-covered medieval Kentish inn in peaceful countryside (take the road between the church and Chequers pub, then left at the junction). Rambling and rustic interior full of character with low, hop-festooned oak beams, inglenook fireplaces and a motley mix of old wooden furnishings in three flagstoned bars that are candelit in the evenings. Adjacent games/family room with pool table. Bar food is reliable, especially the hearty range of home-made daily specials such as fish pie (£3.75), Kentish liver and bacon casserole (£4.95), coq au vin (£5.75) and beef stroganoff (£5.45). Well-stocked bar dispensing nine real ales on hand pump, the heady Biddenden scrumpy cider and eight wines by the glass. Children welcome inside but no under-14s in the Cellar Bar or Monk's Bar. Good summer garden. **Bar Food** *12-2 (Sun to 2.30), 6.30-10 (Sat to 10.30, Sun 7-10). Free House.* **Beer** *Fremlins, Flowers, Fuller's London Pride, Shepherd Neame, Goacher's, Old Thumper. Garden, outdoor eating. Family room. Access, Diners, Visa.*

☺

Smarden Chequers Inn

FOOD

Tel 01233 770217

B&B

1 The Street Smarden Kent TN27 8QA

Map 11 C5

14th-century weatherboarded pub located close to the church in the heart of this most attractive village. Charming Chequers Bar with light oak woodblock floor, sturdy wooden tables and chairs and an exposed brick fireplace. Separate, neatly furnished lounge bar and dining area with open fire. No intrusive games or music. Decent bar food listed on a regularly changing menu runs from the simplest snack to more restaurant-style dishes that might include cream of cauliflower soup (£1.95), fisherman's pie (£4.75), monkfish in red pepper sauce

(£6.95), navarin of lamb (£5.95) and salmon en croute (£6.95). Separate dish of good, well-cooked fresh vegetables. Five homely and cottagey bedrooms upstairs feature exposed beams and wall timbers, simple decor with Laura Ashley fabrics and a few older pieces of darkwood furniture. Two have en-suite facilities, the other share a spacious and clean bathroom. On-going upgrading will result in a third en-suite room. Good choice for breakfast. *Bar Food & Restaurant Meals 11.30-2.30 (Sun from 12), 6.30-10 (Sun 7-10). Free House. Beer Bass, Worthington Best, Charrington IPA, Young's Special, Morland Old Speckled Hen. Children allowed in bar to eat. Garden, outdoor eating. Accommodation 5 bedrooms, 2 en suite, £36 (single £20). Children welcome overnight (under-5s stay free if sharing parents' room), additional beds (£5) and cots available. Pub closed 25 Dec, accommodation closed 24 & 25 Dec. Access, Visa.*

Smarts Hill   Bottle House Inn

Tel 01892 870306 Fax 01892 871094	**FOOD**
Smarts Hill Penshurst Kent	**Map 11 B5**

Well-modernised 15th-century pub remotely situated on a country lane 2 miles south-west of Penshurst off B2188. Low beams, a good inglenook fireplace and sturdy pub furniture characterise the friendly and welcoming bar and attractive dining room. The varied bar menu is the main attraction here and it can get very busy early on with eager diners. Beyond a fairly standard selection of starters an extensive, daily-changing main course menu hide some interesting and reliable dishes such as chicken supreme and tiger prawns, spinach and port sauce, grilled monkfish with garlic and pepper sauce (both £9.95), a decent steak and kidney pie (£6.95) and chicken breast in cream, brandy and mustard sauce (£7.95). Portions are generous and accompanying vegetables well cooked. Sunday lunch £6.95/£13.95. Peaceful front lawn and patio with country views. *Open 11-2.30, 6-11 (Sun 12-3, 7-10.30). Bar Food 12-2, 7-10. Children allowed in bar to eat. Beer Larkins Bitter, Adnams Bitter, Ind Coope Burton Ale. Garden, outdoor eating. Access, Visa.*

Snape   Golden Key

Tel 01728 688510	**FOOD**
Priory Road Snape Suffolk IP17 1SQ	**Map 10 D3**

A delightful and tasteful 15th-century, cottage-style pub close to Snape maltings Concert hall, with a colourful summer hanging-basket festooned facade and alfresco front patio. Inside the main bar has a quarry-tiled old fashioned public end and a carpeted lounge end, with neatly arranged scrubbed pine tables and some fine old settles fronting one of the two open fires. The blackboard menu holds few surprises, but the food is carefully prepared and home-cooked. Choose from sound favourites such as home-made samosas with a yoghurt and mint dip (£3.75) and a decent soup – tomato and parsnip – followed by sausage and onion pie (£4.95), smoked haddock quiche (£4.95), whole lemon sole (£8.95) and a steak selection (from £8.95). There's roast beef on Sundays (£6.50) and several wines are served by the glass. Puddings (£2.75) are popular, including the home-made chocolate brandy cake and hot lemon cake. Children welcome in the dining area. *Bar Food 12-2.30, 6-9.30 (7-9.30 Sun). Beer Adnams Southwold, Broadside (summer), Old & Tally Ho (winter). Patio, eating area. No credit cards.*

Snettisham   Rose and Crown

Tel & Fax 01485 541382	B&B
Old Church Road Snettisham Kings Lynn Norfolk PE31 7LX	Map 10 B1

☺

Tucked away in the village centre this splendid white-painted 14th-century inn was originally built to house the craftsmen who built the beautiful local church. Beyond the attractive flower-decked facade lie a warren of rooms linked by a twisting, tile-floored corridor. Heavy oak beams, old uneven red-tiled floors, inglenook fireplaces and comfortable settles characterise the traditional front bar and locals' bar. A collection of old farm implements decorates the charming front bar. Overnight guests are accommodated in three neat, cottagey upstairs bedrooms and reached via a very steep staircase. Rooms are light, spacious, prettily decorated and all have TV and tea-makers. Only one room has ensuite facilities – clean and smart – the others share an equally attractive bathroom and separate toilet. Beware of the head-cracking low doorways! The pub can become very crowded when busy. Families are welcome here with open arms and the delightful extension, children's room and garden can be brimming with contented children. After feasting on the under 12's menu – toddlers have the use of highchairs – youngsters can escape into the safe walled garden and clamber around the play area which boasts swings, wendy house, wooden fort and a climbing frame on a soft wood-chip floor. Less active children may find the aviaries with budgerigars, exotic finches, rabbits and guinea pigs more entertaining. There is a mothers' changing area in the ladies. Families staying overnight can make use of the small kitchen area which has a fridge, hob, sink and oven for preparing food or alternatively early evening meals can be requested for children downstairs. *Free House.* **Accommodation** *3 rooms, 1 en suite, £40 (Single £25). Check in by arrangement. Children are welcome overnight.* **Beer** *Bass, Adnams Southwold, Greene King Abbot Ale, guest beer. Garden, outdoor eating, children's play area. Family. Access, Visa.*

Somerby   The Old Brewery Inn

Tel 0166 477 866	A
High Street Somerby Leicestershire LE14 2PZ	Map 7 D3

Those to whom the quaffing of fine ale is akin to the staff of life will rejoice at the life the Old Brewery Inn has restored to the quiet village of Somerby. Closed and derelict a mere six years ago, it now houses brewer Barrie's commendable Parish brewery whose products already have a burgeoning reputation. In the bar, by the 40-foot well (to be used one day, it is hoped, in further beer production) samples of Parish Special (still £1 per pint), Somerby Premium and Poachers Ale hold more than their own alongside ever-changing guest brews – 16 hand pumps in total. For those in bolder mood, Baz's Bonce Blower, at 11% ABV, is probably the country's strongest ale. Food ranging from beefburgers to steaks ensures that there are plenty of foundations to lay under a sampling session. Increasingly popular are the brewery tours, for twelve or more, at a price inclusive of food and all you can drink. For those who may find the experience totally overwhelming, there's bedroom accommodation in the old stables where three twin rooms share the necessary ablutions. Monthly jazz nights and beer festivals. **Bar Food** *11.30-2.30, 6-11 (Sun 12-3, 7-10.30). Free House.* **Beer** *Parish Special Bitter, Somerby Premium, Mild, Porter, Baz's Bonce Blower, guest beers. Garden, outdoor eating, BBQs. Children's play area.*

Family Room. **Accommodation** *3 double bedrooms, £25 (single £15).*
Children welcome overnight (under-5s stay free in parents' room). Check-in
by arrangement. Access, Visa.

Sonning Bull

| Tel 01734 693901 | **A** |

High Street Sonning Berkshire RG4 0UP | **Map 15a D4**

Quintessentially southern English traditional pub, its ancient black and
white exterior covered with plants and flowers – you can sit outside
and admire them and the view across the peaceful parish churchyard
opposite – while in its two linked rooms there are sturdy old beams,
gleaming brass, quarry tiles, barrel chairs and an inglenook fireplace,
alive with logs in winter, ablaze with flowers in summer. Not a
family pub. *Open all day Sat in summer. Free House.* **Beer** *Wethered,*
Flowers, Brakspear Special, Boddingtons, guest beer. Patio/terrace.
No credit cards.

South Harting Ship Inn

| Tel 01730 825302 | **FOOD** |

South Harting West Sussex GU31 5PZ | **Map 15 D3**

This white-painted mid-17th-century inn in the centre of the village is
adorned with hanging flower baskets and a wisteria is getting
established. Mind your head once through the door, as the beams are
rather low. The interior furnishings are a mixture of varnished rustic
tables, banquettes and wheelback chairs with hunting prints on the
walls. The main bar is largely given over to eating, with an extensive
menu of mostly home-made dishes; soup is popular, perhaps celeriac
and apple (£2.40), and the steak and kidney pie combines chunks of
lean beef with a crisp pastry lid (£5.65). Fresh seafood is a speciality
and fish starters feature strongly on the menu – crevettes Provençale
(£4.95), gravad lax (£4.85), marinated herrings (£3.95) or potted
shrimps (£4.05) whilst the comprehensive list of main dishes offers
plenty of variety: salmon fishcakes (£5.90), game pie (£6.60), rack of
lamb (£7.25), lemon sole (price by weight) and fish pie (£7). Leave
room for splendidly traditional puddings like treacle tart (£2.60) to
round things off. It's usually wise to book for meals but at lunchtime
snacks are also offered, like sandwiches (from £2.05) and jacket
potatoes (from £3.75). Diverse, carefully chosen wine list. A small
public bar has a dartboard and fruit machine. Children under 14 years
are not allowed inside, but in fine weather are welcome in the small
garden, which boasts an aviary with cockatiel and quail amongst other
birds. *Open 11-11, Sunday usual hours.* **Bar Food** *12-2.30, 7-9.30 (Sat*
all day, Sun to 9, no food Sun eve Oct-Mar). **Beer** *Palmers. Fuller's ESB,*
Arundel Stronghold, monthly changing guest beers. Garden, outdoor eating.
Access, Diners, Visa.

South Harting White Hart

| Tel 01730 825355 | **FOOD** |

High Street South Harting West Sussex GU31 5QB | **Map 15 D3**

Pleasant village pub with three beamed bars, wooden tables, polished
wood floors, log fires and a decent choice of good, fresh food. Known
for their traditional country recipes, the licensees display their menu
on a blackboard where three specials appear daily – gamekeeper's stew
(£4.95), chicken and broccoli baked in pepper sauce (£4.95) are
typical choices. On Thursday, Friday and Saturday evenings the

restaurant, formerly an old scullery, with flagstone floors and open inglenook fireplace, features dishes such as stuffed local trout (£10.50), roast local duck (£12.50) or baked lamb with orange and ginger (£9.75); good vegetables are served with main-course dishes. Vegetarians may wish to try the corn and avocado bake (£4.95) or chestnut and red wine paté. Desserts are the old favourites: bread-and-butter, treacle tart or fresh fruit puddings (all £2.25). In fine weather, families may wish to venture into the beautiful garden overlooking the South Downs where children can safely play around the pond and waterfall. *Bar Food 11-2 (Sun from 12), 7-9.30 (except Mon eve, Sat & Sun to 10). Restaurant Meals 7-10 (except Sun-Wed, except by arrangement). Children's menu. Free House. Beer Gales HSB & BBB, Burton, Friary, guest beers. Garden, outdoor eating, children's play area. Family room (with toy box). No credit cards.*

South Leigh — The Mason Arms

Tel 01993 702485	**A**
South Leigh nr Witney Oxfordshire OX8 6XN	Map 14a B2

A short distance from the A40 (East Witney turn-off), families and alfresco diners can enjoy the spacious garden with peacocks of this large thatched pub in the centre of a small village. Flagstoned bar with a multitude of coppers and brasses. Sowlye (the old name for South Leigh) is specially brewed for the pub. Generous Sunday roasts. The lovely old church nearby features 14th- and 15th-century murals, for which a restoration appeal has been launched. *Free House. Beer Theakstons, Sowlye. Garden. Pub closed Mondays. Access, Visa.*

South Pool — Millbrook Inn

Tel 01548 531581	**FOOD**
South Pool nr Kingsbridge Devon TQ7 2RW	Map 13 D3

Opening hours at this white-painted, 400-year-old pub vary somewhat according to the state of the tide in the creek that extends into the heart of the pretty village and brings a number of the Millbrook's customers by boat. Inside it is small and cosy with tapestry cushions on the wheelback chairs and ceiling beams decorated with old clay pipes, horse brasses, old bank-notes and hundreds of visiting cards. To the rear a tiny terrace overlooks a small stream which is home to a family of ducks. The menu includes something to suit most tastes from filled jacket potatoes (with chili £3.85), cheese & broccoli quiche (£3.75) and smoked mackerel (£3.25) to cottage pie (£3.75), fisherman's pie (£5.25), Devon pasty (£2.25) and cheesy leek and potato bake (£4). Puds such as Devon apple cider cake and treacle tart (both £2.25) provide a sweet conclusion. *Bar Food 12-2, 6.30-9. Free House. Beer Bass, John Smith's, Ruddles Best. Forecourt & streamside terrace, outdoor eating. Family room. No credit cards.*

South Zeal — Oxenham Arms

Tel 01837 840244 Fax 01837 840791	**B&B**
South Zeal Devon EX20 2JT	Map 13 D2

Just off the A30, 17 miles west of Exeter this ancient, romantically fronted, creeper-covered inn is in the centre of rural South Zeal. Genuinely unspoilt inside too, with worn flag floors, vast open fires, original beams, rough plaster walls, spooky passageways, solidly traditional drinking areas, and a relaxing clubbish lounge. Isolated garden overlooking Dartmoor at the back. Nice, old-fashioned bedrooms (one with four-poster) offer discreet modern comforts; delightful place to stay. *Free House.* **Beer** *Dartmoor Best, guest ale. Garden. Family room.* **Accommodation** *8 bedrooms, 7 en suite, £50 (single £40). Children welcome overnight – extra cots £3, and beds £5.50 (both inc. breakfast) provided if sharing parents' room. Access, Diners, Visa.*

Southwold	**Crown**	★	**FOOD**
Tel 01502 722275 Fax 01502 724805			**B&B**
High Street Southwold Suffolk IP18 6DP			**Map 10 D2**

Local brewers, Adnams, take the credit for the stylish restoration of Southwold's central Georgian inn. While not without fault in attempting to be most things to all comers, the Crown is to be applauded for its success in bringing straightforward food, prime-condition beers and excellent wines to the average spender. The nautically themed rear bar is complete with binnacle and navigation lamps; the bar's curved and glassed-in rear panel gives the entirely fitting impression of being the flagship's bridge. To the front, facing the High Street, the Parlour serves as lounge and coffee shop; the front bar and attendant restaurant, decked out with green-grained panelling and Georgian-style brass lamps, has a refined air, yet is totally without pretension or stuffiness. Menus are produced daily with an accent on fresh fish, and simpler dishes are the best bet. Off the bar menu, choose perhaps cream of celery and Stilton soup (£1.75) or baked fillet of mackerel with spiced crust (£3.85), followed by steamed wing of skate Roger Vergé (£7.50) or supreme of chicken filled with leeks and mushrooms (£7.50), and finish with a banana fool with mango couli or dark chocolate and rum pot (both £2.75). In addition to the fine wine list (winner of our 1992 Wine Cellar of the Year East of England Regional award) chosen by Simon Loftus, there's a splendid supplementary list of 20 or so wines, available by both glass and bottle, which changes monthly. The non-smoking restaurant has interesting fixed-price menus (lunch £12.75 for two courses, £14.75 for three; dinner £16.25, and £18.50): start with aromatic chicken livers baked in filo with tomato and basil or oak-smoked Scotch salmon and proceed to steamed king scallops and oriental-style prawns or poached supreme of brill with fresh asparagus and Chablis sauce and finish with choux buns filled with vanilla cream and a nutty caramel sauce. A simple old-fashioned roast beef and Yorkshire pudding (£6.85) is served on Sundays. Bedrooms are well equipped, with antique or decent reproduction pieces and bright fabrics and furnishings: all have private bathrooms though three are not strictly en suite (the bathroom is across a corridor); one family room has a double and two single beds (£82). Pleasant staff offer a warm welcome and good but informal service. A light breakfast is served promptly in the bedroom along with the morning paper. **Bar Food** *12.15-1.45, 7.15-9.45.* **Restaurant Meals** *12.30-1.30, 7.30-9.30. Children allowed in bar to eat (High tea 6-6.30).* **Beer** *Adnams. Patio, outdoor eating.* **Accommodation** *12 bedrooms, 9 en suite, £58 (single £38). Children welcome overnight, additional beds (£10) & cots (£5) available. Check-in from 1pm onwards. Pub and accommodation closed 1 week Jan. No dogs. Access, Diners, Visa.*

Sowerby Bridge   **The Hobbit**

Tel & Fax 01422 832202	**B&B**
Hob Lane Sowerby Bridge West Yorkshire HX6 3QL	**Map 6 C1**

Standing on the very lip of the moor (follow directions, below, carefully), the Hobbit enjoys panoramic views over the Pennines and Sowerby Bridge far below. A relaxed and welcoming place, it's a haven for families, with Bilbo's bistro open all day, every day: youngsters receive a fun pad on arrival. For grown-ups there are menus of awesome variety, to which notions of quality are somewhat subordinated. Connecting bedrooms are available for families, with special weekend rates, while a thoughtful array of accessories appeals equally to the mid-week business traveller. Satellite TVs, for instance, include a video channel and fresh milk is conveniently kept in a corridor fridge. A cottage annexe across the road contains a pair of splendidly-furnished executive bedrooms which also benefit from the finest views down the valley. No-smoking areas in bistro and restaurant. Watch out for the many and varied theme nights and special children's events. Take the A58 to Sowerby Bridge by the Railway Viaduct, turn onto Station Road, then right at the police station, left at the T-Junction, continue up the hill and then right at the crossroads. *Open 11.45-11 (up to 2am with meals). Beer John Smith's, Courage Directors, Ruddles Best. Garden, two patios. Family room. Accommodation 22 rooms, all en suite (15 with shower/WC only), £60 (single £41). Children welcome overnight (under-6s stay free in parents' room, 6-12s £10). No dogs. Access, Visa.*

Sparsholt   **Plough**

Tel 01962 776353	**FOOD**
Sparsholt nr Winchester Hampshire SO21 2NW	**Map 15 D3**

A delightful flower- and shrub-filled garden complete with children's playhouses, wooden garden chalet, chickens and donkeys is a popular summer feature at this much-extended 200-year-old cottage, located on the edge of the village. It has been smartly refurbished by the new tenants, the old 'pub-style' furniture being replaced by pine tables, a dresser and comfortable cushioned chairs, with plenty of attractive prints brightening up the walls and an open brick fireplace for cooler days. Plans are afoot for more improvements to both bars and garden. The bar food on offer is promising as well: a weekly-changing blackboard menu lists some 12 interesting dishes that are freshly prepared to order, such as goat's cheese and basil croutons (£4.95), cauliflower, sweetcorn and cheese oaty crumble (£4.50), curried fish and onion puff (£5.50), gingered pork with Chinese noodles (£6.75) and Malayan beef rendang (£5.95). Also freshly-baked baguettes or brown doorstop sandwiches (£2.25-£3.75), jacket potatoes (£2-£4), omelettes (£2.95-£4.95) and ploughman's (£3.75-£4.50) – something for everyone. Short choice of children's favourites includes Marmite sandwiches £1.50). *Open 11-2.30, 6.30-11 (from 7 Sat between Sep and end Apr), Sun 12-3, 7-10.30. Bar Food 12-2, 7-9 (to 9.30 Sat). Free House. Beer Wadworth, guest beer. Garden, children's play area. No credit cards.*

Speldhurst Hill   George & Dragon

Tel 0189 286 3125

FOOD

Speldhurst Hill nr Tunbridge Wells Kent TN3 0NN

Map 11 B5

Set back from the village lane, this magnificent black and white timbered inn is thought to be one of the oldest pubs in southern England, dating as it does from 1212. Inside, a wealth of ancient features exist, from an enormous inglenook, heavy carved ceiling beams, vast flagstones, antique cushioned settles and wall panelling in the main bar to the huge original roof timbers in the charming Oak Room restaurant. A good range of real ales, local Chiddingstone cider and an impressive global list of wines all complement the extensive range of home-cooked bar food on offer. Highlights of the daily printed menu and the interesting specials board may include broccoli and almond soup (£2.95), fishcakes with lobster sauce (£5.95), beef stroganoff (£5.50), spicy Moroccan lamb with apricots and almonds (£6.50) and lamb steak with green pepper sauce (£7.95). Chips and salad accompany pub favourites and good fresh vegetables are generously served with main dishes. Standard selection of puddings. Value-for-money table d'hote (3-courses £12.50) and a separate à la carte menu can be enjoyed in the character restaurant. Front lawn and patio for fine weather imbibing. *Open 11-11 (Sun 12-10.30).* *Bar Food 12-2, 7-10. Restaurant Meals 12-2 (except Sat), 7-10. No food Sun evening. Children allowed in bar to eat, children's menu. Free House Beer Harveys Best & Armada, Fuller's London Pirde. Garden, outdoor eating. Access, Visa.*

Spreyton   Tom Cobley Tavern

Tel 0164723 1314

B&B

Spreyton Devon EX17 5AL

Map 13 D2

This peaceful white-washed village local draws plenty of visitors in the summer months due to its name and associations with 'Widecombe Fair'. It was in 1802 that Tom Cobley and all left the village for Widescombe and his cottage still stands opposite the pub. The unspoilt main bar has an open fire, cushioned settles and dispenses some good Devon ale straight from the cask. Those on the historical trail can be accommodated in one of the four homely and comfortably furnished bedrooms which have attractive fabrics and bedcovers. None are en suite, but the adjacent bathroom facilities are spotlessly clean. Summer alfresco drinking can be enjoyed on the pretty flower-bedecked gravel terrace or in the rear garden with its far-reaching views. *Free House. Beer Cotleigh Tawny, Exe Valley Dob's Bitter, two guest beers. Accommodation 4 bedrooms, £36 (single £18). Children welcome overnight (under-6months stay free in parents' room, under-2s £6, 2-6 £12). Additional cots available £6. Check-in by arrangement. Garden, outdoor eating area. Pub closed Mon lunchtime. No credit cards.*

Springthorpe   New Inn

Tel 01427 838254

FOOD

16 Hill Road Sprinthorpe Lincolnshire DN21 5PY

Map 7 E2

Created from a row of brick cottages over 100 years ago, this homely off-the-beaten-track village local enjoys a peaceful position close to the parish church and overlooking the small green. An unpretentious and welcoming atmosphere awaits visitors in the comfortable carpeted lounge and in the separate, spartan locals bar. Along the corridor is a neat and cottagey dining room, which bustles with set Sunday lunch (4-courses £7.50) diners. A short and simple printed bar menu features mainly standard dishes, but standing out from the rest are the landlady's traditional home-cooked specials, such as a hearty soup (£1.40) served with warm rolls, sausage, bacon and liver casserole, steamed steak and kidney pudding, smoked haddock fishcakes or fresh large cod and plaice (all £4.95). Puddings (£1.85) include bread and butter pudding and syrup and sultana sponge. *Free House.* **Bar Food & Restaurant** *12-2, 7-10. Children allowed anywhere.* **Beer** *Bateman XB, Marston's Pedigree, Whitbread Castle Eden Ale. Garden. Access, Visa.*

Sproughton   Beagle

Tel 01473 730455   **FOOD**

Old Hadleigh Road Sproughton Suffolk IP8 3AR   Map 10 C3

About half a mile out of the main village (on the left, down a T-road and not signposted) along the Old Hadleigh Road going towards the A12, the ever-popular Beagle is an old wooden-beamed establishment converted from four farm cottages. Inside, there are two neatly-furnished bars and an attractive, airy conservatory off the lounge bar which overlooks the herbaceous borders in the splendid sheltered garden. Particularly popular with local business people, the short, daily-changing blackboard menu lists some reliably good bar food – asparagus quiche and salad (£3.75), game pie or pork and apricot pie (both £4.25), chicken casserole (£4.80) and three home-made soups (such as vegetable, courgette and brie and minestrone £1.65). A dish like vegetable and Stilton crumble (£4.50) will not disappoint vegetarian customers. Good puddings (£2) include chocolate tart and gooseberry and strawberry crumble. Children over five allowed in the family room. *Free House.* **Bar Food** *12-2 only (Mon-Sat, no food Sun).* **Beers** *Adnams, Greene King IPA. Garden, outdoor eating. Family room. Access, Visa.*

Stalisfield Green   Plough

Tel 01795 890256   **FOOD**

Stalisfield Green nr Faversham Kent ME13 0HY   Map 11 C5

Splendid 15th-century Kentish hall house nestling by the green in an unspoilt hamlet high up on the North Downs north of Charing, and enjoying far reaching views across the Swale estuary and the Isle of Sheppey. Two well-maintained and welcoming beamed bars, furnished with a mix of old and new pine and warmed by two open log fires. Cosy dining room and an airy garden room – ideal for families – with access to a peaceful patio and side garden. Look beyond the standard pub snack menu for reliable home-cooked fare with main menu dishes – served with a choice of chips and salad or decent vegetables – ranging from steak and kidney pie (£5.95) and rack of lamb with Cumberland sauce (£7.95) to pork Normandy and chicken margarita (both £7.95). Fish delivered fresh from Hythe is the highlight of the daily-changing specials board with such choices as sea bass in soya and ginger (£12.50), hake creole (£6.95) and skate in cider and orange sauce (£5.95). In season the board will also feature local game. Average selection of puddings. **Bar Food & Restaurant Meals** *12-2.30, 7-9. Free House.* **Beer** *Adnams, Harveys Sussex Bitter, Shepherd Neame Master Brew. Garden, outdoor eating. Family room. Pub closed all day Monday (except Bank Holiday lunch). Access, Visa.*

Stamford   **Bull and Swan**

Tel 01780 63558   **B&B**

High Street St Martins Stamford Lincolnshire PE9 2LJ   **Map 7 E3**

Opposite the former house of Lady Wingfield, who in 1643 persuaded
Cromwell not to raze the town, today's Bull and Swan is wonderfully
preserved; its inheritors should be truly grateful to their erstwhile
neighbour for its survival. Its stone facade and mullion windows house
an intimate pub within, its plain two-tiered timbered bar hung with
horsebrasses and bric-a-brac. Bedroom accommodation is modest with
five of the simply furnished rooms sporting en-suite showers (only one
has a bath), some of which are very cramped indeed. The best and
biggest room takes character from its sloping floor, angled ceiling and
the bright duvets and light paintwork. Other rooms are looking
rather dated and in need of some investment. All have TV, clock-
radio and tea-makers. *Pubmaster. Open 11.30-2.30, 6-11 (12-3, 7-10.30
Sun). **Accommodation** 7 bedrooms, five en suite £45 (single £35).
Check-in by arrangement. Children welcome overnight. Dogs welcome in
rooms, not in bar. **Beer** Tetley Bitter, Charrington IPA. Garden.
Access, Visa.*

Stamford   **The George of Stamford**

Tel 01780 55171   Fax 01780 57070   **FOOD**
                                                            B&B
71 St Martins Stamford Lincolnshire PE9 2LB   **Map 7 E3**

Arguably the finest and grandest (and, it has to be said, the most
expensive) of England's old coaching inns, the George is a fully
modernised hotel (recommended in our *1995 Hotels & Restaurants
Guide*) that retains some wonderful period atmosphere. It's believed
that there's been a hostelry of sorts here since the Norman period,
originally as a stopping place for pilgrims on their way to the Holy
Land, and a crypt under what's now the cocktail bar is certainly
medieval, while much of the present building, which dates from 1597,
remains in the veritable warren of rooms which makes up the public
areas. Facing the High Street, the oak-panelled London Suite and York
Bar were once waiting rooms for the "twenty up and twenty down"
stages which passed this way, but for the modern pub-goer this bar is
probably the least attractive, being solidly masculine in its appearance.
The Garden Lounge, however, which is exotically bedecked in
orchids, palms and orange trees, provides a fine setting for informal
eating throughout the day (7am-10pm): lunch includes a fine cold
buffet, with which, incidentally, up to 20 wines are offered by the
glass. Next door, and by far the most picturesque spot, is the enclosed
courtyard. Surrounded by the ivy-covered hotel buildings, hung with
vast flowering baskets and illuminated by old street lamps, it makes
an ideal venue for morning coffee and afternoon tea, as well as
barbecues on mid-summer evenings. Restaurant dining, in an elegant,
chandeliered hall sporting silver urns, duck presses, and domed carving
wagons (daily roast joints) and serving trolleys (smoked salmon,
cheese, desserts) still in daily use, runs along traditional (and
comparatively pricey) lines with adventurous touches; gentlemen are
'respectfully' requested to wear a jacket and tie. The super wine list is
keenly priced, expertly compiled and simple to use. Accommodation
at the George is strictly hotel, which is fine if you're prepared to pay.
A liveried porter shows you to the room and there's a full, cosseting
night service; not too many pubs today recall this part of our
heritage! But the comfort of plushly draped bedrooms, close-carpeted

through to the bathrooms fitted out with bespoke toiletries, generous towels and rather wonky telephone showers is all quintessentially British and not to be sneered at. A morning tray of tea appears at the appointed time with folded daily paper, and a traditional English breakfast down in the Garden Lounge sets well-rested residents up for the day. *Open 11-11.* **Bar Food** *All day.* **Restaurant Meals** *12.30-2.30, 7.15-10.30; Set Lunch £15.50 (Mon-Sat) children allowed in bar to eat. Children's portions. Free House.* **Beer** *Adnams.* **Accommodation** *47 bedrooms, all en suite, £99-£154 (single £66-£81). Children welcome overnight, additional beds (£10) and cots available. Garden, outdoor eating, beautician, hair salon, bookshop. Access, Diners, Visa.*

Stanford Dingley · The Bull Country Inn

Tel 01734 744409	**FOOD**
Stanford Dingley nr Reading Berkshire RG7 6LS	Map 14a C4

The pretty redbrick Bull has its origins genuinely in the 15th century and its sturdy oak pillars mid-bar are certainly load-bearing. They divide the beamed lounge bar into two intimate areas which are primarily made over to eating, and their refined air is augmented by light classical background music. With only half a dozen or so tables to service, and a tiny kitchen from which to work, menus are kept sensibly short while the service shines by being so friendly and obliging. For a snack are filled baked potatoes (from £2.30) and wholemeal sandwiches cut to order (beef £1.95); daily specials are typified by leek, cheese and potato pie (£4.60), creamed chicken with avocado (£6.60) and a rich, dark chocolate mousse (£2.10). More substantial dinners might start with a creamy Stilton soup (£2.45) or creamed mushrooms on toast (£2.95), with turkey almond (£6.45) and grilled steaks to follow; while chips are readily available, those in the know will go for the excellent 'pommes Dauphinoise'. There's a fairly-priced choice of wines by the bottle (though house white wines are on draught) and both the Bass and Brakspear ales are kept in fine condition. Six miles from Junction 12 of the M4 – follow the A4 west to the second roundabout, turn right on the A340 towards Pangbourne, take the first left to Bradfield, then left again after which you will find Stanford Dingley signposted on the right. *Bar Food 12-2.30, 7.30-10. Free House. Children allowed in saloon bar to eat up to 8.30pm (except Sat eves).* **Beer** *Bass, Archers Village, Brakspear. Garden. Family room. Pub closed Mon lunchtime, except Bank Holidays. No credit cards.*

Stannersburn · Pheasant Inn

Tel 01434 240382 Fax 01434 240024	**FOOD**
	B&B
Stannersburn Falstone nr Hexhan Northumberland NE48 1DD	Map 5 D2

Just a mile from Kielder Water in the Northumberland National Park stands the four centuries old farmhouse which now houses the Pheasant. The Kershaw family's conversion of the former Crown Inn has been painstaking and purposeful. The carpeted Lounge Bar is in muted tones and in the warm mellow pine dining room traditional pub food is served from a kitchen reliably run by Irene and son Robin. Always available are the likes of Lasagne, haddock fillets and steak and kidney pie (all £5.75): daily specials encompass sweet pickled herrings (£3.35), chicken breast with lemon sauce and baked trout stuffed with prawns (£7.95). Follow with sticky toffee pudding or meringue nests filled with ice cream and summer berries (£2.50). There are no chips here; rather, the kitchen's reputation rests firmly on freshly cooked vegetables and roast prime sirloin for a commendable Sunday lunch. In the Barn and Hemmel, bedroom conversion is, for now, complete; furnishings are colourful and TV, hairdryers and beverage trays the standard fittings. Fully en suite, the family room and three larger twins have full-size bathtubs with showers: remaining doubles have WC and showers only. All are smartly tiled and brightly lit. All bedrooms and the dining room are non-smoking areas. Children are welcome overnight/under-5s (stay free in parents' room). *Free House.* **Beers** *Theakston Best, Newcastle Exhibition. Open 11-3, 6-11 (12-3, 7-10.30 Sun).* **Accommodation** *8 rooms £52 (£30 single). Family room. Access, Visa.*

Stanton St John   Star Inn

Tel 01865 351 277

Stanton St John nr Oxford Oxfordshire OX9 1EX

FOOD

Map 14a C2

☺

A former 18th-century butcher's shop and abattoir (now owned by Wadworth) with lots of period feel in the two original little bars, both low-beamed, one brick-floored, the other carpeted and furniture-crammed. Families can eat in a separate no-smoking room and children can use the outside play area. Reliably good food is offered on a simple menu – soup (£1.85), cheesy tuna bake (£5.05), lamb and apricots (£5.05), fisherman's platter (£8.25) and such puddings (from £2) as Bakewell tart or bread-and-butter pudding served with clotted cream. A separate vegetarian menu with a choice of six dishes is always available. Landlords the Tuckers now also own the Sparkford Inn, Somerset (Tel 0963 440218). **Bar Food** *12-2, 7-10 (7-9.30 Sun). Vegetarian dishes. Children's menu.* **Beer** *Wadworth Old Timer (in winter) and Farmers Glory (summer), 6X and IPA, Hall and Woodhouse Tanglefoot. Garden, outdoor eating, children's play area. Access, Visa.*

Stanton Wick   Carpenters Arms

Tel 01761 490202

Stanton Wick Pensford nr Bristol Avon BS18 4BX

FOOD

B&B

Map 13 F1

🍷

The Carpenters Arms is all one would expect of a country inn, complete with roses clambering up the walls and tubs of colourful flowers. It was converted from a row of 17th-century miners' cottages in the tiny hamlet of Stanton Wick, which overlooks the Chew valley. Inside, there are low oak beams, natural stone walls and warming log fires; at one end of the building is a restaurant for formal eating, at the other, the less formal Coopers Parlour. The printed menu here includes grills (T-bone steak £10.95), home-made soup (£1.75), devilled lambs kidneys (£4.65) and a good choice of vegetarian dishes (vegetable bake with crispy topping £4.95). There are also daily specials on the short blackboard menu. The restaurant menu has a more elaborate choice: trilogy of salmon (£5.50), terrine of chicken and wild mushrooms (£3), poached darne of salmon with toasted hollandaise (£10.95), medallions of veal with herb, mushroom and cream sauce (£12.75). Traditional sweets include bread and butter and summer puddings, and the speciality ice creams are home-made (all £2.75). There are some ten wines available by the glass from a good realistically-priced wine list and a handful of real ales to wash down the eats. Immaculate bedrooms are appropriately cottagey in style, with pine furniture and pretty co-ordinating fabrics and wall coverings. Modern conveniences are included and there are smart, modern carpeted bathrooms. *Open 11-11 Mon-Sat, regular hours Sun.* **Bar Food** *12-2.15, 7-10* **Restaurant Meals** *12-2, 7-10 (closed all Mon &*

*sun eve). Free House. **Beer** Bass, Butcombe, Wadworth 6X, guest beer. Terrace, outdoor eating. **Accommodation** 12 bedrooms, all en suite, £59.50 (single £45.50). Children welcome overnight (rate depends on age), additional beds (£10) available. No dogs. Access, Visa.*

Staple Fitzpaine   Greyhound Inn

Tel 01823 480227	A
Staple Fitzpaine nr Taunton Somerset TA3 5SP	Map 13 E2

Built as a hunting lodge by the local lord of the manor in 1640, the creeper-clad Greyhound has since been extended a number of times. The result is a series of rambling, connecting rooms, some with flagstone floors, some with old timbers or natural stone walls and stools made out of old barrels. The gravelled terrace garden has a play area with a splendid rustic climbing frame and slide; children allowed in bar to eat. Music on Thursdays. *Free House. **Beer** Exmoor, Flowers Original, Boddingtons, guest beer. Terrace, outdoor eating, children's play area. Family room. Access, Visa.*

☺

Starbotton   Fox & Hounds   ★

Tel 01756 760269 Fax 01756 760862	FOOD
	B&B
Starbotton North Yorkshire BD23 5HY	Map 5 D4

A typical 400-year-old stone-built, white-painted Yorkshire pub the inside of which is quite unspoilt, with flagstone floors, a few plates on the wall for decoration and a motley collection of jugs, pots and mugs hanging from the ceiling beams, plus a real fire in the stone fireplace in winter. In summer there are a few tables outside. What is untypical about the Fox & Hounds is Hilary McFadyen's excellent cooking with an ever-changing blackboard menu offering the likes of chicken and leek crumble (£5.75), Moroccan-style lamb with apricots, prunes and almonds (£6.50), pork and sage burger (£4.65), spinach and mince lasagne (£5.50), vegetables Provençal with a crunchy cheese topping (£5.25) and mixed bean casserole (£4.65). Lunchtimes there is also a ploughman's (three cheeses) that comes with an apple and Hilary's own home-baked granary bread (£3.75), Yorkshire pudding with various fillings (from £3.50) and crusty French stick sandwiches. Two single, charming bedrooms with en-suite shower rooms offer comfortable overnight accommodation with TV and tea and coffee-making kit. **Bar Food** *12-2, 7-9 (except Mon). Children's menu. Free House. **Beer** Theakston's Old Peculier, XB, Black Sheep. Terrace, outdoor eating. Family room. **Accommodation** 2 bedrooms, both en suite, £46. Children welcome overnight. No dogs. Pub closed Monday evening, and all day Mon Oct-Mar. Accommodation closed mid Dec-mid Feb. Access, Visa.*

Staverton   Sea Trout Inn

Tel 01803 762274 Fax 01803 762506	B&B
Staverton nr Totnes Devon TQ9 6PA	Map 13 D3

A warm welcome heralds a pleasant stay at the Sea Trout, a country inn that is a particular favourite of fishermen. The fishing theme runs through the pub, some specimens mounted in showcases, others depicted in paintings or on plates. There's a conservatory leading from the restaurant to the patio-style garden complete with pond and fountain. All rooms have TVs, telephones and tea-makers and are decorated in a cottagey style. Pub is not suitable for children under six. *Free House. **Beer** Fergusons Dartmoor Best, Wadworth 6X, Bass, guest beer. Garden. **Accommodation** 10 bedrooms, all en suite, £54 (single*

£39). Children welcome overnight (under-5s stay free in parents' room, 5-16s £8.75), additional beds and cots available. Access, Visa.

Steep   Harrow Inn

Tel 01730 262685

FOOD

Steep nr Petersfield Hampshire GU32 2DA

Map 15 D3

The 400- to 500-year-old Harrow is a modest little pub tucked down a sleepy country lane that dwindles into a footpath by a little stream. The tenancy has been in the same family since 1929 and in 1992 landlord Edward McCutcheon finally managed to buy the inn from the brewery and keeps it very much as it must have been in the last century (earlier, even). Two small rooms have boarded walls, an old brick inglenook fireplace, scrubbed wooden tables and a hatch-like bar, behind which barrels of beer sit on racks, with bundles of drying flowers hanging above. There's a small cottagey garden to one side, and some old sloping rustic benches and tables out at the front. Toilets are in a separate brick building on the other side of the lane. The food is limited to a few wholesome snacks, a split-pea- and ham-based soup (£2.40) full of fresh vegetables served with great chunks of bread; a few salads and ploughman's of beef, cheese or home-cooked ham – Ellen cooks about 20 gammons a week; home-made Scotch eggs (£1.30), and perhaps, home-made quiche or lasagne (both £4.90). Apart from the beers, there's a good selection of fruit wines. The new Petersfield Bypass on the A3 has drastically changed the road layout round these parts, so here we go: heading south or north on the A3, take the A272 turning to Midhurst & Petersfield, follow exit road to roundabout, take first left on to A272 Midhurst road (old A3); at bottom of hill (about 350yds) take first turning on the left (opposite the garage); follow this road to Sheet church (about 350yds), take the road on the left opposite the church signposted Steep ½ mile – this will take you via the level crossing and the motorway bridge to the Harrow Inn. Directions courtesy of the landlord, who will be waiting to serve you a well-deserved ale or two! *Bar Food 12-2, 6.30-9.30 (Sun 7.30-9.30). Free House. Beer Flowers, Boddingtons, County Bitter. Garden, outdoor eating. No credit cards.*

Steeple Aston   Red Lion

Tel 01869 340225

FOOD

South Street Steeple Aston Oxfordshire OX6 3RY

Map 14a C1

Colin and Margaret Mead run this pretty 330-year-old village pub, just off the main Oxford-Banbury A4260. A small flower-filled terrace leads into a comfortable beamed bar to the left and a small dining room to the right. Very well kept beer, a multitude of malt whiskies and an extensive wine list all complement Margaret's cooking. Home-made hot-pot in winter (from £4.75), rare roast beef sandwiches (£1.80) and ploughman's (£3.30) made with local cheeses are specialities in the bar, while a more creative and imaginative small menu (3-course meal with coffee is priced according to main dish – roast saddle of English spring lamb – £19, fillets of brill – £18.70, roast breast of duck normande – £18.70) is offered in the dining room at night, making use of game in season and local produce. Home-made puddings include Craigellachie cream (Scottish syllabub made with syrup of marmalade and malt whisky). *Bar Food 12-2 (except Sun). Restaurant Meals 7.30-9.15 (except Sun and Mon). Free House. Beer Tanglefoot, Hook Norton, Wadworth. Garden, outdoor eating. Access, Visa.*

Stiffkey   **Red Lion**

Tel 01328 830552	**FOOD**
44 Wells Road Stiffkey Wells-next-the Sea Norfolk NR23 1AJ	**Map 10 C1**

Nestling in the Stiffkey valley amid rolling Norfolk countryside, this peaceful village once boasted three pubs, but all became victims of the Watney revolution in the 1960s. After 27 years as a private house the Red Lion, a fine 16th-century white-painted brick and flint cottage on the main coast road, was resurrected in 1990 as a free house and has been thriving ever since attracting a loyal local clientele. Inside, three charming rooms have bare board or quarry-tiled floors, three warming logs fires – one in a splendid inglenook – and a simple rustic mix of wooden settles, pews and scrubbed tables. Apart from the ambience, it is the good home-cooked food that draws people here. The short, regularly changing blackboard menu lists a choice of ploughman's, salads and generously filled sandwiches, as well as a hearty soup – leek and celery (£2.20) – or maybe chicken terrine (£3.25), soft herring roes on toast (£2.75) and smoked trout paté (£3.25) for a snack or starter. Main meals, served with fresh crisp vegetables include brill with basil sauce (£7.20) and a decent steak and kidney pie (£5.95). For pudding try the apple and rhubarb crumble or banana and yoghurt cheesecake (both £2.50). More imaginative fare is featured in the rear mock-baronial restaurant (Wednesday to Saturday evenings only); a typical meal being salad of asparagus and sesame chicken (£8.95). Good range of East Anglian beers and a short list of wines from Adnams. After a day on the beach or strolling the Peddars Way, this is a good stop for families, who have use of a large and airy rear conservatory with access to the terraced garden. On cooler days children are welcome in the fire-warmed bars and restaurant to eat and smaller portions of adult meals are willingly prepared. *Bar Food 12-2, 7-9. Children welcome anywhere.* **Beer** *Greene King Abbot Ale, IPA, Woodfordes Wherry, Phoenix 3X, Mardlers Mild. Garden, outdoor eating. Access, Visa.*

Stilton   **Bell Inn**

	FOOD
Tel 01733 241066 Fax 01733 245173	**B&B**
Great North Road Stilton nr Peterborough Cambridgeshire PE7 3RA	**Map 7 E4**

Reputedly the oldest coaching inn on the Great North Road, the Bell boasts a Roman well in its courtyard and an impressive 15th-century stone frontage. Discreetly concealed from the road are two wings of en-suite bedrooms whose 20th-century trappings include telephones, satellite television and whirlpool baths, while tokens of the past are confined to the odd four-poster bed. This is a pity, as the rest of the building is simply splendid. The village bar retains its stone-flagged floor and cosy alcoves huddled round the great log fire; this is where the original Stilton cheese was sold to travellers in the 1720s. Today it's served on its own with plum bread (£3.95), or in a celery soup (£1.95), or in a lamb casserole with Stilton dumplings (£6.85). For the less single-minded, there's zucchini and seafood creole (£4.95), ham hock served with coarse grain mustard sauce (£5.95) or sweet and sour fried vegetables (£5.95). More serious food is on offer in the galleried restaurant, where linen-covered tables are widely spaced in two sections under gnarled oak beams and a vaulted ceiling with original exposed rafters. Here, one can eat from either the weekly table d'hote menu (3 courses £15.50, 4 courses £21.50) which offers perhaps the best value: warm sautéed chicken livers in a brioche loaf with tarragon vinaigrette salad preceding seafood quenelles beurre blanc and followed by one of the home-made traditional puddings (Spotted Dick and custard, summer berry). **Bar Food & Restaurant Meals** 12-2, 6.30-9 (Sun 7-9). Free House. **Beer** Marston's Pedigree, Ruddles County, Tetley. Garden, outdoor eating. **Accommodation** 19 bedrooms, all en suite, £59 (single £50). Children welcome overnight (under-5s stay free if sharing parents' room), extra beds available (£10), cots supplied. No dogs. Access, Diners, Visa.

Stockland	**Kings Arms Inn**	**FOOD**
Tel 01404 881361 Fax 01404 881732		**B&B**
Stockland nr Honiton Devon Ex14 9BS		**Map 13 E2**

Well signposted from the Chard-Honiton stretch of the A30 this cream-faced thatched village pub dates from the 16th century, became a coaching inn in the early 18th century and is now Grade II listed. Although the building has been considerably renovated and extended in recent years it retains a marvellously unspoilt interior, especially in the beamed Cotley Bar dining area. Divided by a medieval oak screen, it has a vast inglenook, padded wall benches, high-back settles and good sturdy refectory tables. With added touches like fresh flowers on tables and piped light classical music, it is a most relaxing room in which to dine. The daily-changing blackboard menu is popular with local diners, the dishes and sauces carefully explained by the restaurant manager, if required. Simple starters like Brie in filo, garlic mushrooms and chicken liver paté (all £3) can be followed by Cotley rack of lamb (£8.50), sirloin of beef roulade (£9.50), seafood in filo pastry (£8.50) or fillets of dab with crabmeat (£9.50). Booking is advisable at all times. A separate snack menu is available at lunchtimes only and features a selection of omelettes, pancakes, curries, steak and kidney pie (£4.50), steaks (from £7.50) and the usual sandwiches and ploughman's. As well as local ales there is a good choice of German bottled beers, a tremendous range of Island malt whiskies and an interesting wine list, with at least eight offered by the glass. This rambling pub also has a public bar, a further dining room and the Terrace Room, which can be reserved for functions and skittle matches and is the venue for live music on Sunday evenings. Three neat and comfortable bedrooms are traditionally furnished and offer TV, phones, beverage-making facilities and clean, older-style bathrooms. No children under ten in the dining room. **Bar Food** 12-1.45 (except Sun). **Restaurant Food** 12.1-45, 6.30-9 (Sun 7-9). Free House. **Beer** Exmoor Ale, John Smith's, Badger Best, Ruddles County. Garden, outdoor eating. Family room. **Accommodation** 3 bedrooms, all en suite, £30, (single £20). Children welcome overnight, additional beds available £10. No food Christmas lunch, accommodation closed 24 & 25 Dec. No credit cards.

Stockport	**Red Bull**	**FOOD**
Tel 0161 480 2087		
14 Middle Hillgate Stockport Cheshire SK3 4YL		**Map 6 B2**

Modest little pub with good home-cooking – pea and bacon soup, large open sandwiches (£2.50), gammon and egg (£3.80), fish and chips (£3.50), treacle sponge and custard. **Bar Meals** 12-2.45. **Beer** Robinson's Best. No credit cards.

Stoke St Gregory — Rose & Crown

FOOD
B&B

Tel & Fax 01823 490296

Woodhill Stoke St Gregory Somerset TA3 6EW

Map 13 E2

In the hamlet of Woodhill, the Rose & Crown is a 17th-century
cottage pub with a delightful patio and, indoors, a fairly subtle horsey
theme, lots of nooks and crannies, timbers and brasses aplenty. The
centrepiece of the bar area is the 60ft well which is decorated with
plants. Landlady Irene Browning's wildlife pictures hang on the walls.
Diners are still travelling miles for the famous scrumpy chicken
(£4.95) and cherry cheesecake (£2.25), just two of their good home-
made dishes. Other popular dishes include grilled skate (£4.95) (fresh
fish from Brixham harbour), or on the fixed-price menu (£11.50):
California salad, hot peppered mackerel or grilled trout with almonds,
and a choice of home-made ice cream specialities. The granary bread
is home-made. There is a 3-course traditional Sunday roast lunch
(£7.50). Bedrooms are modest with modern fittings and equipped
with TVs, radios, tea & coffee making facilities and hairdryers.
Bar Food & Restaurant Meals 12-2 (*Sun to 12.30*), 7-10. *Free House
Beer Exmoor, Eldridge Pope Royal Oak & Thomas Hardy Country.
Terrace, outdoor eating. Family room.* **Accommodation** *5 bedrooms, sharing
a bathroom, £36 (single £22.50). Children welcome overnight, additional
beds available. No dogs. Access, Visa.*

Stoke-by-Nayland — Angel Inn   ★

FOOD
B&B

Tel 01206 263245   Fax 01206 37324

Stoke-by-Nayland nr Colchester Suffolk CO6 4SA

Map 10 C3

Soft lamplight glows invitingly in the window of this solid,
beautifully restored 16th-century inn which can be found beside the
B1068 in the village centre. Eight years of careful renovation and
conversion by owners Peter Smith and Richard Wright have revealed
the true charm of this fine building. Inside, the delightful bar divides
into two; a comfortable lounge bar with exposed carved beams, tiled,
polished brick and carpeted floors, a brick fireplace, log-burning stove
and wooden furnishings, and a real relaxing sitting room with deep
sofas, wing chairs and a grandfather clock. Tasteful touches like fresh
flowers and candles on tables, quality prints and paintings, a few
antique pieces and a warming dark green and cream decor enhance the
overall ambience. The Angel fills early with discerning diners seeking
out the imaginative, twice daily-changing blackboard menus which
feature predominantly fresh fish – delivered daily from Billingsgate –
as well as well sauced meat dishes, including local game, and unusual
vegetarian choices. A typical meal may start with home-made green
pea and ham soup (£2.45) or smoked trout fillet with a mango and
mint dressing (£4.25), followed by grilled whole pink snapper
(£10.25), supreme of chicken stuffed with goat's cheese served with
a grape coulis (£8.25) or guinea fowl in its own mousseline with a
mushroom sauce (£8.25), with baked brioche pudding, thick orange
and lemon tart (£3) to finish. Traditional Sunday lunch (£6.25).
Well priced selection of global wines. The same menu applies in the
charming Well Room restaurant – once the old brewhouse – with its
high-vaulted ceiling, 52-foot well and green linen covered tablecloths.
Tables can be booked here (£1 cover charge). Reached via a small
gallery above this room are five decent-sized, individually decorated
bedrooms, all with stylish co-ordinating wallpaper and fabrics,
comfortable easy chairs and spotlessly clean ensuite facilities.

A further room is housed in an annexe across the rear courtyard. Winner of our Bed & Breakfast Pub of the Year 1995 award. No children in the bar, no under-10s overnight. Wheelchair access. *Free House.* **Bar Food & Restaurant Meals** *12-2, 6.30-9.* **Beer** *Greene King, Abbot Ale, IPA, Nethergate Bitter (summer), Old Growler (winter), Adnams Southwold. Patio, outdoor eating.* **Accommodation** *6 bedrooms, all en suite £55 (single £42). No dogs. Access, Diners, Visa.*

Stokenham   **Tradesman's Arms**

Tel 01548 580313   **FOOD**

Stokenham nr Kingsbridge Devon   **Map 13 D3**

Tucked in the heart of a picturesque old village, this 14th-century cottage takes its name from the tradesmen who once used the coastal bridle path between Kingsbridge and Dartmouth, using the inn as their first night's lodging. With so many pubs catering for the hundreds of visitors that crowd this area in the summer, it is refreshing to find this small, refined village local doing just the opposite, even refusing to let children inside. Inside, you will find few tradesmen in the quaint, beamed and simply-furnished main bar, which has an upmarket ambience with tasteful classical music, 'Harrods' bar towels and a clientele to match. More rustic than smart, the bar enjoys fine views from the three small windows across the valley to the church. The adjacent dining room has a collection of modern settles and light oak tables topped with red and green gingham tablecloths, candles and dried flowers. The draw here, other than the genuinely warm welcome, is the honest home-cooked food. There are no frills and pretence to the short blackboard menu which features regularly changing fresh fish, chicken with tarragon sauce, pork steak with cider and rosemary, rack of lamb with red wine and redcurrant, tagliatelle with courgette and tomato sauce (£5.25) and a selection of freshly prepared patés served with warm toast and salad. Fish is delivered daily from Plymouth and, rather than a roast on Sundays, authentic Indian curries make up the menu and are extremely popular – booking advisable. The well-stocked bar dispenses, over 100 malt whiskies and a list of only eight wines, which surprisingly includes a Chateau Latour 1958 at £150. **Bar Food** *12-2, 7-9.30. Free House.* **Beer** *Hook Norton Best, Bass, Adnams, Greene King IPA, up to 10 guest beers. Garden, outdoor eating. Pub closed Mon-Wed Oct-Easter. No credit cards.*

Stony Stratford   **Cock Hotel**

Tel 01908 567733   **B&B**

High Street Stony Stratford nr Milton Keynes Bucks MK11 1AH   **Map 15a D1**

In the heart of town, this former coaching inn dates from 1300 and was rebuilt after a fire in 1750. 'Ride a cock horse to Banbury Cross' – the horse was apparently from the Cock Hotel stables and with its neighbour the Bull gave rise to the phrase 'Cock and Bull story'. Recent investment in the building has seen the comfortable pubby bar and adjacent lounge refurbished with modern wallpaper and deep sofas, the addition of a function marquee to the sheltered walled garden and the upgrading of the 28 en-suite bedrooms. All are well furnished, the superior rooms (housed in a converted ballroom) having lightwood furniture and clean bath/shower rooms, some with bidet. Handy for racing at Silverstone, but supplements may apply during busy periods. *Free House.* **Beer** *Hook Norton Best, Morland Old Speckled Hen. Walled garden, outdoor eating.* **Accommodation** *28 bedrooms, all en suite, £57.50-£69.50 (£47.50-£59.50 single), reduced rates most weekends. Children welcome overnight. Access, Diners, Visa.*

Stourton Spread Eagle Inn

Tel 01747 840587	**B&B**
Stourhead Stourton nr Warminster Wiltshire BA12 6QE	Map 14 B3

Fine 18th-century brick inn owned by the National Trust and peacefully located within a neat complex of buildings – tea room and National Trust shop – close to the tiny parish church and Stourhead House with its magnificent landscaped gardens, enchanting lakes and woodland walks. As one would expect the interior of the inn has been tastefully refurbished, the bars sporting sturdy wooden furnishings, good prints and paintings and warming open fires. High standards extend to the five charming en-suite bedrooms which retain architectural details, including Georgian and Regency fireplaces, and boast quality co-ordinating fabrics, antique and older-style furniture, easy chairs and various ornaments, clocks and pieces of china adding a homely touch. Each room has a TV, telephone, beverage-making kit and spotless bathroom. The pub can get busy in the summer months with Stourhead visitors, but out-of-season this is an idyllic rural retreat. *Open 11-11 (Sun usual hours). Free House.* **Beer** *Ash Vine, Bass, guest beer.* **Accommodation** *5 bedrooms, all en suite, £59 (single £37). Children welcome overnight, additional beds and cots available (£10). No dogs. Access, Diners, Visa.*

Stow Bardolph Hare Arms

Tel 01366 382229	**FOOD**
Stow Bardolph nr Downham Market Norfolk PE34 3HT	Map 10 B2

A picturesque country pub in a delightful Norfolk village nine miles south of King's Lynn off the A10. Inside is pleasantly refurbished and immaculately run, with a cosy bar, elegant restaurant, popular conservatory extension (also the family room) and an intriguing coach house in the garden for children. The pub gets its name, not from the animal, but from a prominent local family, still found in these parts. Good bar food ranges from a fairly routine printed menu listing home-made curries, lasagne and grills alongside standard favourites with chips; daily-changing blackboard specials include excellent pies – steak and kidney or pigeon (both £5.25) – or more imaginative dishes like pork steak in peppercorn sauce (£5.25) and plaice fillet rolled and stuffed with spinach (£5.75), all served with ready-plated vegetables. Puddings include Mississippi mud pie and lemon lush pie. A bi-monthly changing table d'hote dinner menu (£16.25) is offered in the restaurant as well as a seasonally changing a la carte choice. **Bar Food** *12-2, 7-10.* **Restaurant** *7.30-9.30, closed Sun.* **Beer** *Greene King. Gardens, outdoor eating. Children allowed anywhere. No credit cards.*

Stratfield Turgis   **Wellington Arms**

FOOD

B&B

Tel 01256 882214   Fax 01256 882934

Stratfield Turgis nr Basingstoke Hampshire RG27 OAS   **Map 15a D4**

Hard by the A33 between Basingstoke (M3 Junction 6) and Reading
(M4 Junction 11), behind a handsome white Georgian facade, a
charming old inn with a mix of the old and the new. The cosy, pubby
L-shaped bar features a polished flagstone floor, a characterful mish-
mash of wooden tables and chairs laid for bar snacks, stained-glass
detail around the bar itself and swagged heavy drapes above the tall
windows; it leads directly round into a friendly drawing room in
country-house style with open fire, sunken-cushioned sofas, gilt-framed
oil portraits and glass-cased stuffed birds. French windows open on to
a small lawned area where bench picnic tables are set. Light meals and
snacks include sandwiches and ploughman's (four cheeses – £5.25)
scrambled eggs with smoked salmon (£5.50), venison sausages
(£6.95), home-made pies (£6.95) cooked to order, pasta served with
salad (£6.25) and daily blackboard specials (cajun chicken £4.75,
venison stroganoff £5.25) complete the picture. The traditional
restaurant (where breakfast is also served to residents) offers a table
d'hote (£14.50) and à la carte, both with a good choice; beef
Wellington features, of course and to finish Waterloo and Wellington
(from the nearby Stratfield Saye Estate) are among the exceptionally
large range of British cheeses on the board (available in the bar or
restaurant – £3). Fifteen bedrooms in the original building include
two 'luxury doubles' (one a suite with a heavily-carved four-poster
and spa bath, the other with a pastel green, highly decorative suite of
furniture); 20 further rooms are in a two-storey modern extension to
the rear, uniformly decorated with Laura Ashley pastel blues and
yellows plus modern light oak furniture suites, and overlook a grassed
area; hotel room facilities like a comfortable armchair, remote-
controlled TV, powerful showers and tea/coffee making facilities are
standard. A couple of modern suites serve as both small meeting
rooms and family rooms with pull-down additional beds. Next door
to the Duke of Wellington's estate (Stratfield Saye House, where river
fishing can be arranged) and close to Wellington Country Park (ideal
for family outings). Busy Mon-Thurs with workers from nearby
Basingstoke and travelling businessmen; restful at weekends, when
greatly reduced rates apply. Badger Inns. *Open 11-11 (Sun usual hours).*
Bar Food & Restaurant Meals 12-2.30 & 6.30-9.30 (Sat to 9 in bar,
restaurant closed Sun eve). Children allowed in bar to eat. **Beer** *Hall &*
Woodhouse Badger Best, Tanglefoot. Garden, outdoor eating.
Accommodation 35 bedrooms, all en suite, £70 (single £60), weekend
£48 (single £35). Children welcome overnight (under-12s £10),
additional cots & beds available. Access, Diners, Visa.

Stratford-on-Avon   **The Dirty Duck**

A

Tel 01789 207312

Waterside Stratford-on-Avon Warwickshire CV35 6BA   **Map 14 C1**

This "theatre of the gastronomic arts" once went by the name of the
"Black Swan", the traditional "Mucky Duck" of English pub folklore.
Today's crowds are drawn more in hopes of meeting a theatre type
than a gastronome, the panelled and wood-block Theatre Bar
containing a gallery at autographed photographs of RSC stars down
the years which will keep many a theatre-goer long a-guessing.
Standing above and back from the Waterside with its crazy-paved

patio, it's the closest pub to the Royal Shakespeare theatre, with one of the town's most peaceful river views framed by massive horse chestnut trees. Just 50 yards down the road the hand-operated chain-link ferry (20p) conveys foot passengers back across the Avon to the playgrounds, amenities and long-term car parks. Whitbread Wayside Inns. **Beer** *Flowers IPA & Original, Boddington. Patio/terrace, outdoor eating. Access, Diners, Visa.*

Stratford-on-Avon   **Slug & Lettuce**

Tel 01789 299700

FOOD

38 Guild Street Stratford-on-Avon Warwickshire CV37 6QY

Map 14 C1

A long-established formula, which despite the self-mocking nature of its name, still succeeds in producing a commendably diverse range of untainted pub food at prices that appeal. The setting is one of panelled walls, stone and plain board floors with scattered rugs, daily newspapers for perusing and a menu that's equally up to the minute. On any given day, half a dozen starters from leek, potato and sweetcorn soup (£2.35) to smoked mackerel pate (£4.25) may be supplemented by up to twice as many light meals (all £5.45) ranging from pork and chive sausages, through fusilli carbonara to turkey and mushroom crepes with salad garnish. Main meals take in chicken breast with avocado and garlic (£9.25) and huss fillets with smoked salmon and herb butter (£9.95); lemon flan, baked bananas (£2.95) or a plate of cheese (£3.75) to follow. It's hard, though, to escape the fact that this is essentially a young persons' pub which can get crowded to the point of discomfort. The music is, simply, inescapable. Ansells. **Bar Food** *11-3, 5.30-11 (11-11 Sat, 12-3, 7-10.30 Sun).* **Beer** *Ansells Slug & Lettuce Bitter & Best, Tetley Best, Burton Ale. Access, Visa.*

Strinesdale   **Roebuck Inn**

Tel 0161 624 7819

FOOD

Brighton Road Strinesdale nr Oldham Greater Manchester OL4 3RB

Map 6 B2

A family welcome from Sue, Mark, John, Mary and Peter, and a prodigious choice from the menu await those who venture up the moor to the Howarth and Walters families' imposing hillside pub; the pub's not easy to find on a map – it's about a mile off the A672, taking Turfpitt Lane south of Denshaw. While the little ones can choose from fish fingers, beefburgers or sausages (£2), a specials board can help buck the otherwise chip-and-peas mentality. Go, perhaps, for avocado with cottage cheese and crabmeat (£1.70), beef braised until tender in a pint of 'Boddies' (£5.75) and cream-soaked sticky toffee pudding (£2). From bookable tables by the picture windows, views down the moor's edge end in an urban skyline; in the foreground a paved yard beckons animal-loving youngsters whose parents don't mind them getting mucky. *Pub open 12-2.30, 6-11 (Sun 12-10.30).* **Bar Food** *12-2.30, 6.30-10 (Sun 12 noon-10). Children allowed in the bar to eat, children's menu.* **Beer** *Oldham, Boddingtons, Castle Eden. Garden, outdoor eating, children's play area. Access, Visa.*

Stroud   **Old Nelson**

Tel 01453 765821 Fax 0453 765964	**B&B**

Stratford Lodge Stratford Road Stroud Gloucestershire GL5 4AF   Map 14 B2

From the M5 Junction 13 follow the Superstore signs when coming into Stroud on the A419 to find this pub where a block of bedrooms (part of the Premier Lodge chain) were added a little more than a year ago. Family rooms with sofa beds offer good value with inexpensive breakfasts. There's a spacious non-smoking conservatory and safe garden, but no play area. *Pub open 11-11.* **Beer** *Tetley Best, Greenall Original, Wadworth 6X, guest beer. Garden. Family rooms.* **Accommodation** *32 bedrooms, all en suite, from £46.50 (single £43). Children welcome overnight (accommodated free in parents' room), additional beds & cots supplied. Access, Visa.*

Sturminster Newton   **Swan Inn**

Tel 01258 472208	**B&B**

Market Place Sturminster Newton Dorset DT10 1AR   Map 14 B4

Pride of place in the market place of this busy little town goes to the Swan, a fine, brick 18th-century coaching inn that offers a warm welcome to both locals and visitors alike. Completely refurbished four years ago it has a comfortably furnished open-plan main bar with brick fireplace and open fire, and an adjacent attractively decorated dining room. Tasteful fabrics and furnishings extend upstairs to the five individually styled en-suite bedrooms. one of which has a four-poster bed. Relaxing pastel shades of colour, quality wallpaper, co-ordinating fabrics, decent prints and good modern pine furniture ensure a comfortable stay. Added comforts include remote-control TVs, clock-radios, telephones and tea-making equipment. Bathrooms are rather on the compact side. All bedrooms overlook the bustling market place and housekeeping is of a high standard. *Open 10.30-11pm (Sun 12-3, 7-10.30, tea 3-5.30).* **Beer** *Hall and Woodhouse, Badger Best. Garden, outdoor eating.* **Accommodation** *5 bedrooms, all en suite, £49.20 (single £36). Children welcome overnight. Additional beds and cots available. Dogs welcome. Access, Diners, Visa.*

Sulgrave   **Star Inn**

	FOOD
Tel 01295 760389	**B&B**

Manor Road Sulgrave Oxfordshire OX17 2SA   Map 14a C1

A cosy, creeper-clad village pub, created out of a 300-year-old former farmhouse, where Andy Willerton provides the bonhomie and partner Caroline Shoebridge the home cooking. Blackboard menus provide something for most tastes and appetites from double-decker sandwiches (ham £2.25, Norwegian prawn £2.95) and humus on toast (£2.50) via duck and vegetable broth (£2.50) and filo-wrapped tiger prawns (£3.95) to chicken Madras (£4.95), swordfish steak (£6.50) and a mixed grill (£8.95). Sunday lunchtimes the menu includes a traditional roast at £5.75. For afters try lemon fudgecake, toffee crunch cheesecake or pecan pie (all at £2.50). A small patio and lawn to the rear of the car park provides for summer eating and drinking. Three spotless bedrooms, all with en-suite shower rooms, feature old timbers and modern comforts like remote-control TV and tea and coffee kits but no telephone. *Bar Food 12-2, 6.30-9.30 (Sun 7-9, no food Sun eves in winter).* **Beer** *Hook Norton, Old Hooky, guest beer.* **Accommodation** *3 bedrooms, all en suite, £37 (single £25). Children welcome overnight (cot age stay free in parents' room). No dogs. Accommodation closed 25 Dec. No credit cards.*

Zzz$_z$ ...

Surbiton   **Fox & Hounds**

Tel 0181 390 3408	**FOOD**
60 Portsmouth Road Surbiton Surrey KT6 4HS	**Map 15a F4**

A short blackboard menu of simple home cooked dishes attracts a host
of regular customers here at lunchtime. There are no chips on offer,
but always a soup (£2.25) and a daily-changing selection of hot dishes
– turkey and mushroom pie (£3.55) made with an excellent short-
crust pastry, lasagne (£3.55), pasta bake (£3.25) – plus ploughman's
with Dijon mustard-baked ham, cheese or cheese filled potatoes (all at
£2.95) or served as salads (£3.95). A couple of traditional puds like
bread and butter pudding, treacle tart or peach and raspberry crumble
(at £1.75) provide the finale. The atmosphere is that of a friendly
'local' and the smart decor has something of a Victorian feel. There
are a few tables outside on a roadside terrace. *Bar Food 12-2.30.*
Beer Young's IPA, Wadworth 6X. Terrace, outdoor eating.
No credit cards.

Sutton   **White Horse Inn**

Tel 017987 221 Fax 017987 291	**B&B**
Sutton nr Pulborough West Sussex RH20 1PS	**Map 11 A6**

In a sleepy village tucked beneath the South Downs and amid a maze
of narrow lanes – signposted off the A285 Petworth to Chichester
road – the 250-year-old White Horse offers peaceful overnight
accommodation in six ensuite bedrooms. All rooms are well fitted out
with dark mahogany furniture, pale floral fabrics and spotlessly clean
tiled bathrooms. Added comforts include TVs, beverage-making
facilities, telephones and hairdryers, with mineral water, a basket of
fruit and magazines being welcoming touches. Reached via its own
path across the rear garden, the Gardners Cottage room is ideal for
those seeking isolation, although a handy brolly by the door will
encourage a trip to the bar on rainy nights. Good standard of
housekeeping. If follows that public areas are smart and well looked
after with attractive prints, carpets and fabrics, fresh flowers and
traditional darkwood furniture. *Free House. Open 11.2.30, 6-11 (11-3,
6-11 Sat, 12-3, 7-10.30 Sun). Accommodation 6 bedrooms, all en suite,
£58 (Single £48). Check-in all day. Children welcome overnight (Cot,
high-chair, and extra child's bed in parents' room. Beer Batemans XB,
Young's Bitter, Courage Best, Directors Arundel Best Bitter. Garden,
outdoor eating. Children allowed anywhere. Access, Diners, Visa.*

Sutton Courtenay   **The Fish**   ★

Tel 01235 848242	**FOOD**
4 Appleford Rd Sutton Courtenay Oxfordshire OX14 4NQ	**Map 14a C2**

Behind the very unassuming brick facade of this late 19th-century
village pub lies, surprisingly, a distinct dining ambience, where mats,
linen table napkins, quality cutlery and candles grace neatly arranged
tables in two relaxing dining areas, one of which is a no-smoking
room. Framed collections of fishing flies and a selection of attractive
watercolours of flies brighten up the plain walls. A chatty atmosphere
fills the bar area where local drinkers mingle with intending diners,
who enjoy a pre-prandial drink and a pick at the deep bowls of herby
olives on the bar while perusing the conveniently placed blackboard
menu and wine list. Attentive and efficient staff take the orders before

showing you to your tables. A discerning clientele frequent The Fish as landlord/chef Bruce Buchan produces some serious pub food from his kitchen, using quality local produce from good, reliable suppliers. Meat is hormone-free and fresh fish is delivered direct from Brixham and Penzance. The short blackboard menu changes daily and features a choice of four starters such as crispy duck with five spices (£4.95), gateau of smoked chicken and avocado (£6.95), open ravioli of scallops and artichokes (£6.95); eight imaginative, well-executed and well-presented main dishes follow: for example, fillet of sea bass with Nicoise salad (£13.50), whole cracked Cornish crab with sherry mayonnaise (£13.50), chargrilled John Dory with chili vinaigrette (£12.95), rare breast of duck with rosti and blackberry vinegar (£12.50). A generous selection of crisp vegetables and maybe dauphinoise potatoes accompany each dish. To round off your meal, try the selection (7-8) of unusual farmhouse cheeses (£5.75), or the feuillette of Apricots with caramel ice cream or gratin of strawberries (£3.95). Hand-made truffles appear with the good, strong coffee. The same menu is available at lunchtime and on Sundays there is also a good-value, set lunch (3-courses £13.95). To complement your meal there is an ever-changing blackboard list of 40 wines, the four house wines being available by the glass. There are plans for a conservatory and patio to the rear. *Bar Food* 12-2.15, 7-9.30 (Fri-Sun to 10, no food Tue eve). Children allowed in the bar to eat, children's portions. *Beer* Morland Original & Old Speckled Hen. Garden, outdoor eating. Access, Visa.

Sutton Gault   Anchor Inn

Tel 01353 778537   Fax 01353 776180

FOOD

Bury Lane Sutton Gault nr Ely Cambridgeshire CB6 2BD

Map 10 B2

Deep in Fen country, just off the A142 at Sutton village, the Anchor is protected from the 'hundred foot drain' (built by the Dutch in 1650 to drain the Fens and now called the New Bedford River) by a veritable rampart of earthworks. Descend, then pass a new riverside patio into the low, brick-built pub. Beer jugs hang from hooks in the low-beamed bar, racked Burton Ale is served direct from cask and landlord Robin Moore's preference for classical music seems entirely apposite to the setting. A long menu which relies heavily on fresh produce indicates careful shopping. The daily-changing menu starts with local game salami with home-made chutney (£3.95) and grilled dates wrapped in bacon on a mild mustard cream sauce (£3.95) and progresses to fresh seafood bourride (£8.95), aubergine and ricotta cannelloni (£7.95) and rack of lamb with redcurrants and rosemary sauce (£12.95), wild rabbit braised in cider with prunes and herbs (£8.75), chicken, leek and bacon crumble (£7.25) and pan-fried pigeon breasts with rich Burgundy sauce (£9.95). Home-made puddings, from £3.45-£3.75, served with clotted cream, include Baileys Irish cream cheesecake, tarte au citron and pecan nut and maple pie. A medley of unusual British cheeses with warm bread (£4.50) is another option. Those with children or particularly favouring the non-smoking Inglenook Room are well advised to book; it's virtually essential at weekends. In addition to the beer and a 60-plus wine list from Lay and Wheeler, other beverage choices include freshly squeezed orange juice and cups of cappuccino, chocolate or speciality teas. *Bar Food* 12-2, 6.30-9.30 (Fri & Sat to 10, Sun 7-9 Easter-end of Sept – phone to confirm). Free House. *Beer* Greene King IPA, Burton Ale. Garden, outdoor eating. Family room. Pub closed Sun eves end Sept-Easter. Access, Visa.

Sutton Poyntz   Springhead

Tel 01305 832117	**FOOD**

Sutton Poyntz nr Weymouth Dorset DT3 6LW   **Map 13 F3**

The pub takes its name from the nearby spring and waterworks,
which actually incorporates one of the funnels from Brunel's
steamship, the *Great Eastern*. Owned by Devenish, the inn has an
interior that's largely the work of brewery designers, with its high
shelves of contrivedly casual piles of old books and brass plates but
managers Jim and Julie White have successfully individualised things
with the help of a bar billiards table, magazines, the daily papers to
read, and their own relaxed friendliness. The longer-standing residents
of the village have furnished the walls of the pub with old photos of
the village. The food side is down to Julie, who cooks everything
herself. The restaurant serves a wide variety of dishes including home-
made chicken liver cognac and cream paté (£3.25), crispy mushrooms
in breadcrumb and herbs (£3.95), whole roast poussin (£8.25), stir-
fried fresh vegetables in a pancake (£5.95), tenderloin of pork in
cream, garlic and lemon sauce (£8.25) and puddings include banana
and cream profiteroles with butterscotch sauce (£2.50) or a spicy
apple meringue pie. To accompany there are nine wines available by
the glass and for a snack there are also plenty of sandwiches (good
ham) and French sticks (£2.50), ploughman's (£2.50), jacket potatoes
(£2.50) and salads; for the children there are fish cakes or jumbo
sausages, and they will always boil an egg. They're looked after in the
garden, too, where an extensive play area has rustic swings, a slide and
a climbing frame, as well as splendid views of the Dorset Downs and
the huge chalk-cut figure of a mounted George III. One of the pub's
outbuildings has been turned into a shop where genuinely locally
made craft goods and pictures by local artists are on sale throughout
the summer and at weekends in winter. *Bar Food & Restaurant
Meals 12-2, 7-9.30. Children allowed in the restaurant to eat.
Beer Greenalls. Riverside garden, outdoor eating, children's play area.
Access, Visa.*

Swanton Morley   Darby's

Tel 01362 637647	**FOOD**
	B&B

Swanton Morley nr Dereham Norfolk NR20 4JT   **Map 10 C1**

A "family" free house converted from two brick cottages in 1986 by
the licensee – John Carrick – a local farmer, after the local mega-
brewery closed the village's last traditional pub. A rustic ambience has
been created in the main bar with beams, exposed brick walls, open
brick fireplace with log fire, sturdy wooden furnishings and old and
unusual farming implements. Both here and in the neatly laid out
dining area visitors can enjoy reliable, home-cooked meals. Main
menu choices include popular favourites, plus a mixed garden salad
with smoked cheese, cashew nuts and pesto vinaigrette (£2.50), beef
and oyster pie (£5.95) and vegetarian dishes like tomato, spinach and
Brie bake (£4.75). Daily blackboard specials may feature shellfish
chowder (£2.25), lamb casserole with red wine and rosemary
(£5.75), chicken ham and mushroom pie (£5.50) and braised sausages
with an onion and beer gravy; all served with good sauté potatoes and
a crisp vegetable selection. Puddings (£2.25) may include lemon
crunch flan and white and dark chocolate mousse. Sunday roasts
(£5.25). Younger diners have their own menu (Peter Rabbit – small

ham salad) which is served in the dining area or in the small children's room, complete with a box of toys for impatient toddlers. Those seeking overnight accommodation will be surprised when directed ¾ mile along the narrow lane to Park Farm, a fine farmhouse peacefully located in open countryside. Five fresh, airy and spotless en-suite bedrooms are housed in a splendid cattleyard conversion offering exposed ceiling timbers, free-standing pine furnishings, TVs, clock-radios and beverage-making facilities. One room is geared to accept wheelchair visitors. Overflow accommodation in the farmhouse is more modest; four bedrooms, including two character attic rooms share two bathrooms. Guests wishing to venture to the pub have use of a free taxi service and sleeping children will be well looked after if parents want a night out. The welcome attributed to visiting children extends beyond the menu, children's room and toy box into the garden, where a vast enclosed play area – Darbyland – on a soft wood-chip floor boasts a swing, see-saw, climbing net and frame. Down on the farm there is a connecting family room, provision of further beds and cots, high-chairs at breakfast, a kitchen area for mums to prepare food and numerous animals to keep youngsters amused. 3 to 14-year-olds are charged £1 per year old per night. *Free House.* **Bar Food** *12-2, 7-10 (12-10 Sat, 12-2.30, 7.30-9.30 Sun).* **Accommodation** *9 bedrooms, 5 en suite £38 (single 19). Dogs and children welcome overnight (cots and high chairs available).* **Beer** *Adnams Southwold, Broadside and Extra, Woodfordes Wherry, Mardlers Mild, Hall & Woodhouse, Tanglefoot, Morland Old Speckled Hen, Centurian Best Hadrian. Garden, eating outside, children's play area. Access, Visa.*

Swavesey   Trinity Foot

FOOD

Tel 01954 230315

Huntingdon Road Swavesey Cambridgeshire CB4 5PD   Map 15 F1

Fairly modern pub next to the A604, named after Trinity College's hunt (Colonel Whitbread was Master of the Trinity Beagles), or rather more specifically, its horse-less followers. Parts of the building go back to 1870. The fish shop on the corner (which is also owned by the pub) supplies the superb fish for the many dishes on the menu – from oysters to baked salmon, grilled Dover sole and monkfish in Pernod and cream (£9). A more standard menu of pub favourites offers omelettes, ploughman's (£3), grills to fillet steak, sandwiches, salads and a small selection of sweets – banana split, apple and blackberry sponge £2. Airy conservatory. *Whitbread.* **Bar Food** *12-2, 6-9.30.* **Beer** *Flowers Original, Boddingtons. Patio, outdoor eating. Access, Visa.*

Talkin Village   The Blacksmiths Arms

FOOD

B&B

Tel 016977 3452

Talkin Village Brampton Cumbria CA8 1LE   Map 4 C2

At the heart of this immaculately kept village just 9 miles from Carlisle and only 6 from the M6 at Junction 43, the revitalised Blacksmiths Arms is the pub all and sundry are talkin' about. The Bagshaws, Pat and Tom, run it very much as a family concern with quiet good humour and nothing appears too much trouble for them. Pat's kitchen tries not to overextend itself while offering a wide range of fare from the "Hot and Simple" steak and kidney pie (£4.85), leg lamb chop (£5.95) and fresh haddock in her own beer batter (£3.95) through to some more adventurous daily specials such as chicken provençal, beef teriyaki and crispy garlic and herb prawns (all £5.95).

Simplicity has also remained the key to careful conversion of the bedrooms, all of which now boast full en-suite facilities. Decor follows a country theme without being overly cottagey, furniture and fittings are of durable quality and colour TVs and tea- and coffee-making kits ensure an entirely adequate degree of guests' comfort. *Bar Food 12-2, 7-9. Beers Boddingtons, Theakston's Best. Garden, outdoor eating. Family Room. Accommodation 5 bedrooms, all en suite, from £38 (single £28). Children welcome overnight (accommodated free in parents' room), additional beds supplied. Pub closed 24 & 25 Dec. Access, Visa.*

Tangley   Fox Inn

FOOD
B&B

Tel 01264 70276

Tangley nr Andover Hampshire SP11 0RU

Map 14a B4

Well worth the diversion off the A343 north of Andover, the Fox is a remote white-painted brick and flint cottage pub with a welcoming atmosphere in its tiny, rustic bars and homely restaurant. Reliably good food from the landlady cook (Gwen Troke), her daily-changing blackboard menus listing value-for-money lunchtime snacks – decent vegetable soup (£1.60) served with basket of warm bread, cassoulet (£4.25), steak and kidney pie (£5.15), chili bean pot (£3.25) and tagliatelle with blue cheese, celery and bacon (£3.50). More imaginative evening restaurant fare (also available in the bar) may include tenderloin of pork with calvados, mustard and cream (£8.75) and marinated leg of lamb with a redcurrant and spring onion sauce (£9). Home-made ice cream, summer pudding or chocolate roulade (all £1.80) are some of the puddings. The landlord, John Troke, has a comprehensive wine list, eight of which are available by the glass. Accommodation comprises one spacious and comfortable twin-bedded room which is furnished in modern pine and has a spotless ensuite shower room. TV, tea-maker, mini-fridge and continental breakfast. *Bar Food & Restaurant Meals 12-2, 6.30-10 (Sun from 7). Children allowed in the bar to eat. Free House. Beer Bass, Royal Oak, Courage Best. Garden, outdoor eating. Accommodation 1 en suite bedroom, £40. Children welcome overnight, additional beds available.*

Tarporley   Rising Sun

FOOD

Tel 01829 732423

High Street Tarporley Cheshire CW6 0DX

Map 6 B2

High street pub strictly for eating rather than drinking in; very popular in the area and with the local cricketers. Forty-plus item 'Specials Board', scarcely aptly named, runs the gamut of choices from steak bordelaise (£8.95) down to spaghetti bolognaise at £5. Evening grills are supplemented by duck with cherries (£7.20), beef stroganoff (£6.75) and veal cordon bleu (£5.25). *Bar Food 12-2.30 (Sun to 2), 7.30-9.45. Beer Stones, Bass, Marston's. Garden. Pub closed Sun eve. Access, Visa.*

Tarporley   Swan Hotel

FOOD
B&B

Tel 01829 733838   Fax 01829 732932

50 High Street Tarporley Cheshire CW6 0AG

Map 6 B2

Formerly a coaching-house of reknown, the Swan was destroyed by fire in 1735 and rebuilt with its unusual Georgian frontage around 1769. Within, however, the flagstoned kitchen bar containing heraldic insignia of the Fettered White Swan, dates back to 1565. Here is a relaxing spot for carefully cooked light lunches and evening bar

snacks, which range in complexity from smoked mackerel fillets
(£2.95) and a chef's salad (£3.50) to daily specials typified by baked
avocado with mushrooms, broccoli, and Gruyère (£5.25) and stir-
fried beef with oriental vegetables (£6.95): chocolate éclairs or treacle
sponge to follow (£2.25). A three-course table d'hote (£12.95) in the
newly-decorated, airy restaurant offers very fair value, with the
seasonal carte contributing, perhaps, fresh asparagus with hollandaise
and salmon fillet with lobster sauce (£7.25). Stylish modern design
and patterned, matching fabrics lend the bedrooms a distinctly classy
feel, to which the TV, tea tray and trouser press add suitably up-to-
date comfort. En-suite bathrooms may be looking a little dated,
though heated towel-rails, smart towels and toiletries keep them well
up to scratch. Premier House. *Bar Food & Restaurant Meals* 12-2,
7-9.30 (Sat and Sun to 10). *Beer* Greenalls Best & Original. Garden.
Accommodation 14 bedrooms, all en suite, £51.95 (single £46). Children
welcome overnight, additional beds (£5) available, cots provided free. Access,
Diners, Visa.

Tatenhill   Horseshoe Inn

| Tel 01283 64913   Fax 01283 511314 | **A** |

Main Street Tatenhill nr Burton-on-Trent Staffordshire DE13 9SD   Map 6 C3

A splendid summer spot just two miles from the A38 Burton-on-
Trent by-pass, in the village once owned by Lady Godiva. So busy
does it get that the staff run their little socks off, though generally the
fun stops about there as, more restaurant-style than pub, there's
waitress service to all interior tables. The garden, though, is pretty
special in the summer months with loads of play equipment, a
Norman castle and Wendy house. Children's menu lunchtimes only
and regular barbecue events. Long hours on Bank Holiday weekends;
long games of dominoes to while away the winter evenings.
Marston's. *Open 11.30-3, 5-11 (Sun 12-3, 7-10.30). Beer Marston's Iron
Founders & Pedigree. Garden, outdoor eating. Children are welcome.*
Access, Visa.

Temple Grafton   Blue Boar Inn

| Tel 01789 750010 | **FOOD** |

Temple Grafton nr Alcester Warwickshire B49 6NR   Map 14 C1

The oldest part of the Blue Boar dates back to the 17th century and
includes a well, now glassed over and illuminated, set into a flagstoned
floor which is home to some goldfish – the water reaches to within a
few feet of floor level. Elsewhere is furnished in typical pub style with
red carpet, tapestry, upholstery and Britannia tables, set with red paper
napkins in the restaurant area. The menu, hand written in a
copperplate hand indicating that it doesn't often change, covers all
the standard items like steak and kidney pie (£4.95), gammon steak
(£4.95), pint of prawns (£4.95), jacket potatoes, ploughman's and
sandwiches plus devilled roes (deep-fried herring roes with tartare
sauce £2.75), a couple of pasta dishes and several vegetarian dishes;
vegetable curry (£4.75), mushroom stroganoff (£4.75). The
restaurant menu (from which one can also eat at the bar) is in similar
vein including steaks and salads. *Bar Food & Restaurant Meals* 12-2,
6.30-10 (7-9.30). Free House. *Beer* Flowers, Wadworth 6X, Donnington
SBA, Hook Norton Best, Boddingtons Mild. Garden, outdoor eating.
Access, Visa.

Testcombe   Mayfly

Tel 01264 860283   **FOOD**

Testcombe nr Stockbridge Hampshire SO20 6AZ   **Map 14 C3**

Idyllically situated right on the banks of the swiftly flowing River
Test, this beamed old farmhouse (dated 1808) has a traditional bar, a
bright conservatory and a splendid riverside terrace. Unrivalled
tranquil river scenes, complete with ducks and swans, make the
Mayfly a popular drinking spot, but on fine sunny days the whole
place can be unbearably crowded, so arrive early to appreciate its
superb position. Children can be considered a nuisance at times. The
food operation tries hard to cater for the volume of people. A daily
hot dish such as chicken tandoori (£3.60), supplements the selection of
cold meats – rare roast beef (£3.60), Test trout (£3), home-cooked
ham (£3.40) – and for £2.95 three cheeses from a choice of 30 or 40!
Along with vegetarian quiche (£2.95) and harvester pie (£4.25), all
can be accompanied by a selection of freshly prepared salads, but at
70p a spoonful, it can get pricey! Standard puddings are generally of
the bought-in variety. Be prepared to queue for the food and then be
patient for a seat at peak times, especially in the summer. Whitbread
Wayside Inns. On the A3057 Stockbridge-Andover road. *Pub open
11-11 Mon-Sat.* **Bar Food** *11-9. Free House.* **Beer** *Flowers Original,
Boddingtons, Wadworth 6X, plus guest beers. Riverside garden, outdoor
eating. Family room. Access, Visa.*

Thame   Abingdon Arms

Tel 01844 260116   **FOOD**

21 Cornmarket Thame Oxfordshire OX9 2BL   **Map 15a D2**

Known locally as 'The Abo', this 18th-century, former coaching inn
offers a fairly modest face to the main street of town but inside several
rooms have been opened up to each other to create a long bar with
rug-strewn, bare board floors, some exposed brickwork, magazines
and newspapers to read and a lively, friendly atmosphere that comes
courtesy of manager Roger 'Dodge' Clark and his young staff. To the
rear an old barn, used for functions at night, is about to become a
lunchtime steak bar and beyond this a beer garden comes with rustic
tables (some with rustic baby seats attached), slide, swing and climbing
frame. Features of the menu are hugely thick 'doorstep' sandwiches
(from £2) and bowls of homemade tagliatelle with various toppings
(garlic and herb butter £2.65, chili £2.95, bacon and tomato £3.75).
Other items range from home-cured gammon and fried eggs (£5.25),
chicken, ham and leek pie (£4.95), soup, paté, and a selection of
pizzas (£2.85). A short children's section includes fish fingers and
beefburgers. *Pub open 11-11.* **Bar Food** *12-3 (to 2.30 Sun), 6-9.30
(to 8.30 Fri & Sat, to 9 Sun). Free House.* **Beers** *Wadworth 6X, Hook
Norton, Brakspears, Tetley, guest beers. Garden, outdoor eating area.
Pub closed 25 Dec. Access, Visa.*

Thaxted   Farmhouse Inn

Tel 01371 830864   Fax 01371 831196   **B&B**

Monk Street Thaxted Essex CM6 2NR   **Map 10 B3**

Surrounded by open fields and farmland, 1 mile south of the village
off the B184, this former 16th-century farmhouse has been much
extended and modernised in recent years and provides overnight
accommodation in eleven ensuite rooms. Located around a courtyard,

bedrooms are standard and functional with built-in furniture, TVs, telephones, tea and coffee making facilities and adequate bathrooms. Ideal for a peaceful, rural stopover en route to a flight out of Stansted Airport, only 8 miles away. *Free House. Beer Wadworth 6X, Greene King IPA, Adnams Southwold. Open 11.30-11pm (11.30-4.30, 6-11 Wed. 12-3, 7-10.30 Sun). Accommodation 11 bedrooms, all en suite £39.50 (single £29.50). Garden, children's play area. Access, Visa.*

Thelbridge   Thelbridge Cross Inn

| Tel 01884 860316   Fax 01884 860316 | **B&B** |

Thelbridge nr Witheridge Devon EX17 4SQ

Map 13 D2

Three miles west of Witheridge on the B3042 this attractive, white-painted inn is isolated high up in a very rural part of Devon with views across to Dartmoor. The much modernised interior is carpeted and open-plan in layout with some comfortable settees, a couple of log fires and is delightfully free of live music, juke box or pool table. The bar offers some good local cider, country wines and some sixty whiskies including twenty malts. The adjacent barns have been well converted to provide a comfortable block of seven bedrooms and a large self-catering apartment. Bedrooms are rather compact with pretty matching fabrics, modern units but room is found for a telephone, TV, tea-makers and a small fully-tiled shower room. Housekeeping is of a good standard. An occasional attraction is the original 'Lorna Doone' stagecoach which brings extra Sunday lunch trade. *Free House. Beer Bass, Butcombe Bitter, Wadworth 6X. Garden, outdoor eating, children's play area. Accommodation 8 Bedrooms, all en suite, £60 (single £35). No dogs. Access, Diners, Visa.*

Thompson   Chequers Inn

| Tel 01953 483360 | **A** |

Griston Road Thompson Thetford Norfolk IP24 1PX

Map ?

Well off the beaten track, this splendid, long and low, thatched 14th-century inn is worth finding – 1 mile off the A1075 Watton to Thetford road along a tiny lane on the edge of the village – for its peaceful location and unspoilt charm. Beneath the steep-raked thatch of this ancient ale house, once a row of several cottages, lies a series of low-ceilinged inter-connecting rooms served by a long bar. Wonky wall timbers, low doorways, open log fires, a rustic mix of old furniture and collections of farming implements, brass and copper characterise the well-maintained and atmospheric interior. Good rear garden with rural views and children's play area. Handy for excellent local woodland walks. *Free House. Open 11-3, 6-11 (Sun 12-3, 7-10.30). Beer Adnans Southwold, Broadside, Fuller's London Pride, Bass, Morland Old Speckled Hen, guest beer. Access, Visa.*

Thornham   Lifeboat Inn

| Tel 01485 512236/512297   Fax 01485 512323 | **FOOD** |
| | **B&B** |

Thornham Norfolk PE36 6LT

Map 10 B1

A perennial classic: the Lifeboat is a charming, whitewashed, 16th-century smugglers inn, ideally set for weekend escapes on the edge of an expanse of salt marsh: wake up to the sound of the sea or of doves cooing in the cote. The characterful ramble of old rooms boast low-beamed ceiling, rug-strewn quarry-tiled floors, low doors, half-panelled walls and a rustic array of furniture, including sturdy oak tables, antique settles and pews. Antique oil lamps suspended from the ceiling partly light the main bar and various pieces of china and old farming implements adorn the walls, enhancing the charm. The pub also features "penny-in-a-hole", a rare pub game built into an old wooden bench. Food is reliably good, especially the fresh fish, crab, mussels and cockles bought from local traders, and the regularly changing specials list, which may offer home-made soup (£2.25), game pie (£6.25) and tandoori chicken (£5.95). Standard printed menu fare includes ploughman's (£3.95), sandwiches (from £2.25), fish pie (£6.50) and fish and chips (£5.95). Summer sees a buffet and barbecue in the garden and hearty hot dishes like beef pepperpot and rabbit and leek pie appear in the winter. Venture into the restaurant for more elaborate à la carte fare and a keenly priced set dinner menu (£17.50). A tastefully converted barn houses the majority of the bedrooms which are comfortably furnished in warm pine with pretty fabrics, all the added comforts – TV, direct-dial telephone, tea-maker, hairdryer – plus the added bonus of open views across the salt marsh and out to sea. Fresh and clean en-suite facilities with showers over tubs. Enjoyable breakfasts served in the attractively decorated restaurant. Well placed for coastal walks and locally renowned bird reserves. Families are warmly welcomed; children are allowed in the bars to eat and at other times in the side conservatory which leads out into the safe rear courtyard and patio, complete with a slide and small climbing frame. Toddlers have use of two high-chairs and young appetites are satisfied with either the children's menu choice or half-portions of parent-sized meals. *Free House. Open 11-11 (12-3, 7-10.30 Sun). Accommodation 13 bedrooms, all en suite £65 (Single £37.50). Children welcome overnight (Cot and extra child's bed available in parents' room). Beer Woodfordes Wherry, Greene King Abbot Ale, IPA, Adnams Southwold, Woodfordes Baldric, Felinfoel Double Dragon, guest beers. Children allowed anywhere. Garden, outdoor eating, children's playing area. Access, Visa.*

Thornham Magna   **Four Horseshoes**

| Tel 01379 71777   Fax 01379 718134 | **B&B** |

Thornham Magna nr Eye Suffolk   **Map 10 C2**

Affectionately known as the 'Shoes', this fine 12th-century inn lies in a delightfully unspoilt village half a mile off the main A140 Norwich to Ipswich road, 3 miles southwest of Eye. Although much extended over the years it still maintains a magnificent Norfolk reed and straw thatched roof and preserves much of its timber-frame and mud-and-daub walls. Accommodation comprises eight neat en-suite rooms, four of which are tucked beneath the thatch in the original building and ooze charm and antiquity with wonky floors, a wealth of beams and tiny dormer windows. Cottagey in style, all boast attractive solid pine furniture, TVs, beverage-making facilities, telephones and compact shower rooms. Public areas, despite being sadly open-plan in layout, still retain head-cracking low beams, upright timbers, a large inglenook fireplace, a well and collections of rural bygones and farming memorabilia. Thornham Country Park – good walks – and the beautiful thatched church at Thornham Parva are worth exploring. *Free House. Beers Courage Best, Directors, Adnams Southwold, guest beers. Garden. Family room. Accommodation 10 rooms, all en suite, from £55 (single £37). Children welcome overnight, additional beds and cots supplied. Access, Diners, Visa.*

Zzz...

Thornton   Ring O'Bells

Tel 01274 832296 Fax 01274 831707	**FOOD**
Hilltop Road Thornton Bradford West Yorkshire BD13 3QL	**Map 6 C1**

Up on a windy, woody moor just 3 miles from Bradford, the Ring O'Bells is firmly established as one of the area's top dining venues. Over the last two years the combined talents of Clive and Ann Preston at the helm and daughter Michelle Bone in the kitchen have provided the pub with that extra degree of quality that earned it the British Beef category award in this Guide's 1993 British Meat competition. Behind some jokey names on the menu there are substantial Yorkshire offerings: for 'Bully Beef' read 'roast topside of beef with rich gravy and Yorkshire pudding' (£5.50), while the 'Ring O'Bells Reviver' produces mountainous steak, kidney, potato and vegetables (£4.95). Michelle's daily blackboards, however, eschew such flippancy and much of what she produces is seriously good. Avocado bound in a dill mayonnaise garnished with melon balls and lightly poached prawn and seaweed fish sausage typify the starters (both £3.50). The day's fish special might be smoked cod fillet grilled with a prawn and mussel sauce (£7.95); no less popular is a daily game dish: perhaps partridge with cherry sauce (£8.95), or traditional braised rabbit (£6.95). Similarly inventive sweets include 'Snap Dragon', a brandy snap basket filled with a home-made fruit sorbet (£2.75). Nonetheless Ring O'Bells remains essentially a pub, with well-spaced tables set away from the bar and a restaurant area (booking advised) providing the same food and waitress service with just a little more comfort. Choice of 8 wines by the glass. No smoking area in restaurant. **Bar Food** *12-2, 5.30-9. Children allowed in bar to eat.* **Beer** *Webster's Yorkshire, Ruddles County, guest beer. Family Room. Pub closed 25 Dec. Access, Visa.*

Threshfield   Old Hall Inn

Tel 01756 752441	**FOOD**
Threshfield Skipton North Yorkshire BD23 5HB	**Map 6 C1**

A lovely stone-built Dales inn, based on a Tudor hall from which comes its name, the Taylors' pub gains further character from its idiosyncratic individuality. An eccentric mix of flagstone floors, classical music and chamber pots suspended from the ceiling is accentuated by the "Brat Board" at ankle height by the fireplace: chicken nuggets and chips followed by two scoops of multi-flavoured ice creams (£2.75) seem fairly brat-proof. Adult choices mix steak and mushroom pie (£5.50) and jumbo fish and chips (£5.95) with the likes of Dales sausage with onion gravy (£5.25), Wensleydale ploughman's (£3.25) and wild boar and pheasant pie with a Cumberland sauce (£6.25). In the daily specials line, notably fresh market seafood predominates, as in sweet and sour king prawns (£6.45) and fillet of haddock with herb crust in a tomato and basil sauce (£6.45); for a spicier palate, perhaps, chicken tikka (£5.95) or for vegetarians mushroom and spinach crepe (£5.95). A perennially hectic place; ordering and paying at the bar can be a little chaotic, though for a little peace and quiet the garden is a delightful alternative. **Bar Food** *12-2, 6.15-9.30 (no food all day Mon and Sun eve). Children's menu. Free House.* **Beer** *Younger's Scotch, Theakston XB, Timothy Taylor Best. Garden, outdoor eating. Family rooms. Inn closed all day Monday & Sun eve. No credit cards.*

Thursley   Three Horseshoes

Tel 01252 703268	A
Dye House Road Thursley nr Godalming Surrey GU8 6QU	Map 15a E4

One minute off the A3 between Milford and Hindhead, a characterful, 300-year-old beamed local with Thursley Common and the Devil's Punchbowl nearby. 1½ acre garden. No juke box or games machines. Children only welcome if over 5 and eating at lunchtime – it's too small a pub! *Free House. Beer Gale's HSB and BBB, guest beer. Garden. Access, Visa.*

Tichborne   Tichborne Arms

Tel 01962 733760	FOOD
Tichborne nr Alresford Hampshire SO24 0NA	Map 15 D3

Heavy thatch predominates throughout this idyllic hamlet nestling in the peaceful Itchen Valley and also cloaks the local pub, making it a popular attractive destination for both lunch and supper. Over the years, a series of fires have destroyed the pub here, but the present structure, built in 1940, survives and is very much the hub of village life, being the venue for the village carol service, harvest supper and the polling station – a good turn out is generally guaranteed! At other times, locals and visitors alike are attracted here to sample the range of real ales dispensed straight from the cask and to taste the reliable home-cooked food that is served in both the small comfortable panelled bar and in the larger and livelier 'locals' bar. Home-made soup, generously filled jacket potatoes (from £3.50) and salads are supplemented by a good range of daily specials such as liver, bacon and onion casserole (£4.95), chicken breast with apricots and brandy (£5.75), and steak and mushroom pie (£5.25), with home-made raspberry jam sponge and custard (£1.75) to finish. The well tended and sheltered rear garden is a perfect spot for warm weather imbibing. No under-14s allowed in the pub. Six miles from the M3 Junction 9. *Bar Food 12-1.45, 6.30-9.45 (Sun 7-9.30). Free House. Beer Wadworth 6X, Flowers IPA & Original, Boddingtons. Garden, outdoor eating. No credit cards.*

Tideswell   George

Tel 01298 871382	B&B
Commercial Road Tideswell Derbyshire SK17 8NU	Map 6 C2

Market town coaching inn dating from 1730. Small snug, traditional locals' noisy tap room, dining lounge and dining room proper. Shaded courtyard garden with goldfish pond, creeping vines and flowers. Beautiful parish church known as 'Cathedral of the Peak' next door. The four-poster and double rooms have en-suite shower rooms, the other two have their own basins and share one bathroom and toilet. Live music every Fridya evening. *Beer Hardys & Hansons Kimberley Classic, Best Bitter & Mild. Courtyard. Accommodation 4 bedrooms, 2 en suite, £46 (£56 four-poster) (single £20). Children welcome overnight (rate depends on age), additional beds available. Check-in by arrangement. Access, Diners, Visa.*

Tillingham   Cap & Feathers

Tel 01621 779212 **A**

8 South Street Tillingham nr Southminster Essex CM0 7TH   Map 11 C4

Crouch Vale Brewery's only tied house – a delightfully unspoilt,
classic white-painted, weather-boarded Essex village inn dating from
1600. A timeless, old-fashioned atmosphere remains within the warm
and woody low-ceilinged interior with its eclectic mix of traditional
furnishings, board floors and a real open fire. Several distinct areas
ramble about, including a small rear carpeted area with woodburner
and dresser, and a section housing time-honoured pub games (table
skittles and an ancient bar billiards table that still operates on shillings).
Home-cooked blackboard specials feature locally-smoked fish and
meats and look promising. Modest bed and breakfast accommodation,
the three rooms sharing a shower room. *Beer Crouch Vale. Garden.
Family room. No credit cards.*

Tillington   Horseguards Inn

FOOD

Tel 01798 42332 **B&B**

Tillington nr Petworth West Sussex GU28 9AF   Map 11 A6

Charming 300-year-old inn peacefully positioned opposite the parish
church just off the A272 Petworth to Midhurst road. Raised up from   **Zzzz**...
the village lane it was originally three cottages and enjoys good views
towards the South Downs. Inside, a rambling series of relaxing and
tastefully refurbished rooms feature exposed stripped beams, original
pine panelling, open fires, various antique and pine furnishings and
collections of hunting prints, brass blow lamps and polo mallets.
Beyond the small bar area each table is neatly laid with fresh flowers
and candles, as this is very much a dining pub attracting an upmarket
clientele from miles around for the imaginative, twice-daily changing
menu available. Lighter lunchtime fare includes cottage pie (£5.95),
venison sausages (£5.50), sandwiches (from £2.25) and ploughmans
(from £3.95). In the evenings the atmosphere remains informal, but
the cooking moves up a gear with maybe goat's cheese in filo pastry
(£3.75), courgette and cheddar mousse or terrine of pigeon and rabbit
with Cumberland sauce (both £3.95) for starters. Main course options
range from well presented pork fillet with a sage and onion sauce
(£8.75) and eye fillet of venison with a redcurrant sauce (£10.50) to
red sea bream with Cajun spices (£8.50) and poached salmon with a
lemon sauce (£8.95), all served with a dish of decent fresh vegetables.
Good home-made puddings (£3). Global list of wines plus a
connoisseur's blackboard list of vintage wines at £25 a bottle. Sunday
roast (£6.95). Large secluded rear garden and front terrace for fine
weather alfresco imbibing. Overnight accommodation comprises two
attractive and cottagey upstairs bedrooms and a further comfortable
room in a converted outbuilding. All have TVs, tea- and coffee-
making kits and clean en-suite facilities. *Pub open 11-3, 6-11 (Sun 12-3,
7-10.30).* **Bar Food** *12-2, 7-10.* **Restaurant Meals** *as bar. Children
allowed in the bar to eat. Children's portions. Free House.* **Beer** *Hall &
Woodhouse, Badger Best, King & Barnes Sussex Bitter. Garden, tables in
the garden.* **Accommodation** *3 bedrooms, all en-suite, from £46 (single
£35). Children welcome overnight, additional bed. Access, Visa.*

Titchfield **Fishermans Rest**

Tel 01329 842848	**A**
Mill Lane Titchfield Fareham Titchfield Hampshire PO15 5RA	Map 15 D4

Mill Lane is a turning north off A27, 3 miles west of Fareham (take J9 off M27). An attractive brick country inn, ideally located opposite the entrance to the impressive ruins of Titchfield Abbey and on the banks of the idly flowing River Meon. Inside, the well refurbished series of rambling rooms feature flagstones, exposed brick walls and an interesting variety of fishing paraphernalia adorns the walls. Good spot to relax as the bars are devoid of intrusive electronic games and background music. Large waterside garden for sunny summer days. Whitbread Wayside Inns. *Open 11-11.* **Beer** *Wadworth 6X, Brakspear, Flowers, guest Beer. Garden. Access, Visa.*

Tivetshall St Mary **Old Ram**

Tel 01379 676794 Fax 01379 608399	**B&B**
Ipswich Road Tivetshall St Mary Norfolk NR15 2DE	Map 10 C2

Conveniently situated beside the A140 between Norwich and Ipswich, this old 17th-century inn positively bustles with people all day with travellers and locals seeking refreshment within the rambling and carefully refurbished series of rooms. Road-weary visitors in need of overnight accommodation will not be disappointed with the five "luxury" en-suite bedrooms built into the eaves with sloping roofs and exposed timbers. Tastefully decorated with Laura Ashley wallpaper and co-ordinating fabrics and kitted out with quality modern lightwood, each boasts satellite TV, direct-dial telephone, tea-maker, trouser press and hairdryer. Two are mini-suites with comfortable easy chairs and all gain top marks for their spotless bathrooms with gleaming tiles, fluffy towels and robust, powerful showers over tubs. Breakfast is extra. Staff are particularly friendly and efficient, but the food was disappointing on our most recent visit. *Free House. Open 7.30-11 (Sun 10.30pm).* **Accommodation** *5 bedrooms, all en suite £50.55 (single £35-40). Guide dogs only. Children welcome overnight.* **Beer** *Ruddles County, Adnams Southwold, Wadworth 6X, Ram Bitter (brewed by Woodforde's). Garden, outdoor eating. Access, Visa.*

Toot Hill **Green Man**

Tel 01992 522255	**FOOD**
Toot Hill nr Ongar Essex CM5 9SD	Map 11 B4

Early 19th-century coaching inn located in a tiny hamlet amid a web of lanes between Ongar and Epping, and efficiently run by the Roads family for the past 28 years. Unpretentious exterior enhanced each summer by a magnificent, award-winning floral display in its sheltered courtyard. Equally simple interior with a pleasant carpeted bar with open fire and an adjoining comfortably furnished dining area. Popular locally for home-cooked bar food set out on a blackboard: choices might range from light lunchtime snacks to a short daily-changing evening selection of dishes such as vegetable soup (£2.50), prawn and crab pancakes (£3.95), steak and kidney pie (£6.50), pork steak in a rich plum sauce, chicken breast with ham and basil (both £7.50), whole grilled lemon sole (£9) and pink trout with leeks and fennel (£7.50), all main courses served with fresh vegetables. Home-made puddings (£2.75) such as peach flan and rhubarb crumble. The Longbow restaurant is across the courtyard, but it's the bar food that we recommend. Good range of real ales and a list of over 100 wines that includes 20 half bottles and numerous champagnes. No children under 10 inside. *Bar Food 12-2, 7-9.45 (Sun to 9.30). Beer Adnams Bitter, two interesting guest beers. Garden, outdoor eating. Access, Visa.*

Topcliffe   Angel Inn

| Tel 01845 577237   Fax 01845 578000 | B&B? |

Long Street Topcliffe Thirsk North Yorkshire YO7 3RW   Map 5 E4

At the junction of the A167 and A168, the pre-Norman village of Topcliffe is convenient for, and equidistant from, both the A19 and A1 (3 miles). the 17th Century Angel, once a coaching inn, has been sympathetically remodelled and extended by its present owners. Three bar areas, games room, residents' lounge and a large garden complete with rockery and ornamental fish pond allow a multiplicity of choices for guests' relaxation. The purpose-built wing of bedrooms (above a self-contained functions suite) is tastefully furnished in varnished pine, and facilities in all rooms include satellite TVs and mini-bars as well as dial-out phones, hair dryers and trouser presses. Residents have their own entrance, allowing them free access and security 24 hours per day, and effective double glazing ensures a completely restful night. *Free House. Open 11-11 (12-3, 7-10.30 Sun). Family room. Accommodation 15 bedrooms, all en suite £50 (Single £35). Dogs welcome in rooms. Children welcome overnight (Cot, high-chairs and extra bed available). Garden, outdoor eating. Beer John Smith's, Boddingtons. Children allowed anywhere. Access, Visa.*

Torcross   Start Bay Inn

| Tel 01548 580553 | FOOD |

Torcross nr Kingsbridge Devon TQ7 2TQ   Map 13 D3

Arguably the 'best pub fish and chips in Devon' can be found at this 14th-century thatched inn, which is superbly situated between the beach at Slapton Sands and the freshwater lagoon and nature reserve of Slapton Ley. Landlord Paul Stubbs is a keen diver and fisherman and his catch of fresh seafood contributes to the vast amount of fresh fish that is delivered daily to this extremely popular seaside inn. The modest bar and dining areas are simply furnished with a mix of tables and chairs and various old photographs of the storm-ravaged pub adorn the walls. Every available seat is taken soon after opening, especially in the summer, and this year the kitchen has been extensively upgraded in order to cope with the rush. Fish and chip connoisseurs come eager to sample the delicious battered cod, haddock and plaice of which three sizes are available – medium (£3.70), large (£4.80) and jumbo (£5.70), the last served on a huge plate, and all accompanied by good plump chips. Blackboards outside inform you that only polyunsaturated oils are used for frying. Also on the menu are daily fish specials such as whole lemon sole, monkfish tails, skate wings (£4.95) and scallops in garlic butter or batter. The freshest of crab is cooked and dressed on the premises and used in their platters (from £6.75/£7.75) and sandwiches (£3.25). The rest of the menu lists standard pub fare that will not disappoint meat eaters. Although the service is fast and efficient, be prepared to wait a little while as the fish is cooked to order. *Bar Food 11.30-2 & 6-10 (Sun from 12). Children's menu. Beer Flowers IPA and Original, Bass. Garden, outdoor eating. Family room. No credit cards.*

Tormarton   **Compass Inn**

Tel 01454 218242	**B&B**
Tormarton nr Badminton Avon GL9 1JB	Map 13 F1

Creeper-clad in summer, the oldest part of the inn dates back to the late 17th century and the not entirely unspoilt bars boast some old timbers and exposed stonework. The Orangery, a sort of glass-roofed courtyard, is a good spot in summer. Most of the generally good-sized bedrooms are in a newer wing. Darkwood fitted furniture is the norm with wing armchairs and the usual amenities – beverage tray, trouser press (some with iron and ironing board attached), hairdryer etc. Most of the well-kept bathrooms have tubs (just a few have shower and WC only), many with shower above. There are also several meeting rooms. Less than ½ mile from M4 Junction 18. *Free House.* **Beer** *Bass, Smiles, Archers. Garden, terrace.* **Accommodation** *31 bedrooms, all en suite, £79 (single £63). Children welcome overnight, additional beds and cots available. Access, Diners, Visa.*

Totnes   **Kingsbridge Inn**

Tel 01803 363324	**FOOD**
9 Leechwell Street Totnes Devon TQ9 5SY	Map 13 D3

Located at the top of the town, this is the oldest inn in this historic borough, dating from the time of the Domesday Book. The rambling, low-beamed and exposed-walled bar boasts a 1,000-year-old Saxon fireplace, rustic tables, carved benches and is delightfully unspoilt, being music- and game-free. Magazines and daily newspapers are provided for quieter entertainment. An adjoining room has an ancient spring bubbling up into a small stone trough, which links to the Old Leper's Well nearby, known for its healing properties in medieval times. It is not only the charm of this building that draws folk here, it is the good value and reliable bar food that can be enjoyed throughout the week. Menu boards are chalked up twice daily with an interesting well-balanced selection of home-cooked dishes that rely on fresh local produce from good local suppliers. Lunchtime sees a variety of sandwiches, filled French sticks, various platters (one featuring up to four Devon cheeses), lemon soup (£1.50 and £2.50) and locally smoked mackerel fillets (£2.95). More substantial snacks may include fennel goulash on rice (£4.95), peanut slice with spicy barbecue sauce (£4.95), whole Brixham plaice (£8.25), or garlicky chicken with tarragon cream sauce (£6.75). Evening fare is similar with the addition of a few meat dishes such as steaks, gammon and lamb chops in various sauces. Home-made puddings include summer pudding and honey and walnut tart (both £2.30). Local Devon allegiances run to Dartmoor Best Bitter among the range of five real ales, Luscombe scrumpy cider and the very local Diptford wines; the short main selection of wines (of which 12 may be sampled by the glass) is acquired from reputable merchants – Yapp and Piper. The upstairs Leechwell suite features live music on Wednesday evenings. *Bar Food 12-2 & 6-10 (Sun 7-9.30). Children's menu. Free House.* **Beer** *Courage Best, Theakstons Old Peculier, Bass, Dartmoor Best Bitter, guest beer. Family room. Pub closed 25 Dec. No credit cards.*

Tregadillet   Eliot Arms (Square & Compass)

| Tel 01566 772051 Fax 01566 773010 | A |

Tregadillet nr Launceston Cornwall PL15 7EU   Map 12 C3

This pretty, creeper-covered Eliot Arms was built in the 14th century
as a coaching inn. Once inside, it's like being in the 'old Curiosity
Shop', as every inch of wall space is littered with a host of
memorabilia. Pride of place goes to the splendid collection of some 66
clocks, including seven grandfather clocks, as well as paintings, plates,
books and ornaments. Unspoilt layout with lots of rambling little
rooms with rug-strewn slate floors and nice old furniture freely and
successfully mixing with modern seating. Sheltered garden with
children's play area. *Free House.* **Beer** *Marston's Pedigree, Flowers
Original, Wadworth 6X, guest beer in summer. Garden. Pub Closed
25 Dec. No credit cards.*

Trent   Rose & Crown

| Tel 01935 850776 | FOOD |

Trent nr Sherborne Dorset DT9 4SL   Map 13 F2

Nestling in a sleepy village deep in rural Dorset, Charles & Nancy
Marion-Crawford's thatched pub is refreshingly unpretentious within
with its rug-strewn stone floors, roaring winter log fires and simple
furnishings. No pub games, fruit machines or music to disturb the
peace, but children's play things can be found in the garden, which
enjoys open country views. Emphasis is on good fresh food making
excellent use of local gardens, farms and sensibly short, weekly-
changing blackboard menu which is served throughout the pub,
especially in the attractive and airy 40-seat conservatory dining room.
Interesting main courses may include medallions of monkfish on a red
pepper coulis (£8.25), poached fillet of halibut with a raspberry and
sage sauce (£7.95) and breast of duck with a mango confit (£8.95),
with chocolate and banana roulade (£2.50) or a decent West Country
cheeseboard (£3.25) to finish. Families are well catered for – it's an
ideal venue for a family outing on a summer's evening. *Pub open for
drinks from 6.30pm in summer.* **Bar Food** *12-2, 7-9.30 (no food Sun eve).
Free House.* **Beer** *Shepherd Neame's Spitfire Ale, Oakhill Best. Garden,
outdoor eating, children's play area. Family room (no smoking).
Access, Visa.*

Troutbeck   Mortal Man Hotel

| Tel 015394 33193 Fax 015394 31261 | FOOD / B&B |

Troutbeck Windermere Cumbria LA23 1PL   Map 4 C3

A hotchpotch of antique seating, gleaming copper-topped tables,
beams, horse brasses, pewter tankards, hunting horns and views of a
gentle green valley through the windows give the Mortal Man plenty
of rustic charm. It's a bright, well-kept inn of 17th-century origins,
with an established reputation for hospitality. One of the bars is kept
mainly for residents, but it provides an overspill when the public bar
is full. There is a plentiful supply of food on offer such as home-made
soup (£1.50) home-cooked ham, lovely fresh summer salads,
Cumberland sausage, plaice goujons (£5.50), whilst the restaurant
offers a set menu dinner (5 courses £19) of more substantial dishes –
tronçon of halibut with Vermouth Hollandaise sauce, supreme of duck
with orange and kumquat sauce. Roast Aberdeen Angus beef features

on Sunday lunch. The bedrooms are clean and comfortable, with attractive, homely decor in co-ordinated colours and well-cared-for furniture. A sunny lounge overlooks the Troutbeck Valley. All have smart, clean, en-suite bathrooms, TVs and entrancing views. Housekeeping is excellent. Half-board terms only. *Bar Food 12-1.45, 6.30-8.45 (Sun from 7).* **Restaurant Meals** *1-2 (Sun only), 7.30-8. Free House.* **Beer** *Theakston Best, Scotch Bitter. Garden.* **Accommodation** *12 bedrooms, all en suite, half-board £100 (single £50). No children under 5. Pub closed Jan-mid Feb, accommodation closed mid Nov-mid Feb. No credit cards.*

Trusham	**Cridford Inn**	★	**FOOD**
Tel 01626 853694			**B&B**
Trusham nr Newton Abbot Devon TQ13 0NR			Map 13 D3

In search of a new challenge and a smaller, less demanding pub, David and Sally Hesmondhalgh sold their 10-bedroom hotel in Cumbria to take on this Devon village inn, hidden in the Teign Valley between Exeter and Dartmoor. Little did they know that they had bought the oldest domestic dwelling in Devon dating from 1081, and that it would cost dearly in terms of money, time and energy over a two year period to sympathetically renovate and refurbish this ancient longhouse to its full potential. A medieval mud and thatch roof was found beneath the old tin roof, a mosaic datestone discovered in the original Saxon floor in what is now the dining room, and in the bar one can see the earliest example of a domestic window in Britain. Freshly painted white under a new thatched roof the charming interior displays original huge beams, stone fireplaces and floors in the low-ceilinged lounge/dining room, which has relaxing easy chairs and sofas, tasteful pictures and five mahogany tables topped with fresh flowers, gleaming cutlery and glassware. Rustic stone floors characterise the two interconnecting bars with woodburner, and pew and settles in cosy partitioned seating areas. David Hesmondhalgh is in charge of the kitchen, producing a varied range of good home-cooked dishes that use fresh local produce and are listed on regularly-changing boards above the bar. As well as popular pub favourites, interesting daily choices may include courgette and onion soup (£1.95), chicken liver and brandy paté (£3.75), pork fillet with calvados and cream (£7.50), lamb steak marinaded in mint and garlic (£6.50) and fish fresh from Brixham, such as monkfish with pernod (£8.50) and plaice with brandy American sauce (£6.25). Home-made puddings (£3) range from banoffie pie to plum and apple crumble with freshly-made custard. Excellent value-for-money 3-course table d'hote restaurant menu (£15.75). Short list of wines from Christopher Piper wine merchants, with two good value wines of the month and helpful tasting notes. Character upstair bedrooms are individually decorated to a high standard with pretty co-ordinating cottagey fabrics in floral designs and all are comfortably furnished. Fresh and well equipped, en-suite bathrooms. Homely touches include fresh flowers, pot pourri, tissues, china tea service and magazines to read. No children overnight. Joint winner of our 1995 Pub Newcomer of the Year award. *Bar Food 12-1.45 (Sun to 2), 6.30-9 (Sun to 7). Pub closed Mon. Free House.* **Beer** *Cotleigh Old Buzzard (in summer), Trusham Ale, Exmoor Ale, Bass, Adnams Broadside. Garden, outdoor eating. Family room.* **Accommodation** *4 rooms, all en-suite, £50 (single £35). No dogs. Visa.*

Tuckenhay   Floyd's Inn (Sometimes)

B&B

Tel 01803 732350   Fax 01803 732651

FOOD

Bow Creek Tuckenhay Totnes Devon TQ9 7EQ

Map 13 D3

Gastronaut Keith Floyd's delightfully rusticated pub dates back to
1550 and enjoys an idyllic location on the quayside of a very pretty
wooded creek. The menu in the bar (at road level) divides between
'Canteen Snacks' (where caviar sits alongside corned beef hash and
cheese and pickle salad) and 'Floyd's Food' – from fish and chips
(£10.50), and canteen soup (£6.50) to Mexican fish (£11.50),
Bourride (£13.50), cod with red peppers and pancetta (£13.50) and
'Floyd's rare roast beef monster' (£8.50), as well as some even more
unique and eclectic changing menus. In the newly opened restaurant
an elaborate (and expensive, 2-courses for £37.50) table d'hote is also
offered. Lunchtimes in summer, weather permitting, there's a 'cook-
your-own' barbecue with tables down on the quayside. 'We do not
serve half portions' proclaims the menu. The inn has recently added
three bedrooms all with the most up-to-date facilities – prices include
the use of sauna, sunbed and works club. The name may be jokey, but
the intentions are serious; nevertheless, its popularity can push service
and standards to the limits of acceptability – arrive early or expect a
long wait! This used to be called the *Maltster's Arms* – one of several
in the neighbourhood, causing confusion. Cheap it ain't, but
everything's home-made and carefully prepared and Floyd's inimitable
style – love it or hate it – is writ large upon the place. Recommended
in our 1995 *Hotels & Restaurants Guide.* ***Bar Food*** *12-2.30, 6-9.30
(Sun from 7).* ***Restaurant Meals*** *12.30-1.30, 7.30-8.30 (No restaurant
food Sat lunch and all Sun). Free House.* ***Beer*** *Dartmoor Best Bitter,
Cotleigh Tawny Bitter, Bass, Blackawton, Exmoor Gold. Garden, summer
barbecue.* ***Accommodation*** *3 Rooms, all en suite £125 or £175, not
suitable for pets or children. Access, Visa.*

Zzzz...

Tunbridge Wells   Sankeys

Tel 01892 511422

FOOD

39 Mount Ephraim Tunbridge Wells Kent TN4 8AA

Map 11 B5

Reached via a flight of steps from the street, this informal cellar wine
bar/bistro is the place to come for enjoyable seafood dishes, or just for
a relaxing glass of wine or pint of real ale, especially sitting out on the
very Continental, sun-drenched summer terrace. A good pubby
atmosphere fills the stone-floored bar area, topped with rustic pine
tables, kitchen chairs and pews. Excellent daily-changing bar meals
range from fishy dishes like Mediterranean crab soup (£3.50), ocean
pie, fresh cod and chips and home-made fishcakes (all £6.50) to a
selection of pates and terrines (£4), and Hungarian goulash (£6.50).
Puddings (£3) may include strawberries with crème brulée, lemon
ginger crunch and apple pie. Imaginatively filled baguettes (£2.75) are
available all day. Restaurant fare normally available in the neatly laid
upstairs rooms can be ordered in the cellar bar. Interesting list of
wines with at least 12 available by the glass. *Open 12-11.* ***Bar Food &
Restaurant Meals*** *12-2.30 (Sat and Sun to 2), 7-10 (Sun to 9.30,
restaurant closed Sun). Free House.* ***Beer*** *Harveys Pale Ale. Terrace,
outdoor eating. Access, Visa.*

Turvey   Three Cranes

Tel 01234 881305	**B&B**

High Street Loop Turvey Bedfordshire MK43 8EP   Map 15 E1

Enjoying a peaceful village setting adjacent to the parish church and
close to an interesting abbey, this predominantly Victorian stone inn
offers comfortable and good-value overnight accommodation in five
cottagey bedrooms: attractive and welcoming, with modern pine
furnishings, tasteful wallpaper and contrasting fabrics and clean en-
suite facilities; TV, radio and tea-making kits are standard. The spick
and span feeling extends downstairs into the neatly-furnished and well-
decorated, open-plan bar which displays plenty of plants, decent
framed prints, plates and other pieces of china. The front of the
building is a real picture in summer with hanging baskets, flower
borders and virginia creeper, while to the rear is a sheltered garden.
Free House. **Beer** *Fuller's London Pride & ESB, Bass, Hook Norton Best
Bitter, Morland Old Speckled Hen, Timothy Taylor Landlord. Garden,
children's play area.* **Accommodation** *5 bedrooms, all en suite, £40 (single
£30). Children over 6 welcome overnight, price by arrangement, additional
beds available. Check-in by arrangement. No dogs. Access, Visa.*

Turville   Bull & Butcher

Tel 01491 638283	**FOOD**

Turville Buckinghamshire RG9 6QU   Map 15a D3

Back in the 1700s, some workmen on the local church went on strike
for want of a village pub, prompting an enterprising cottager to turn
his home into one; thus the Bull & Butcher was born. Inside the
attractive black-and-white timbered building are two unspoilt, low-
ceilinged bars with cushioned wall benches and settles, open fires, a
collection of horse brasses and a welcoming atmosphere. New
landlords since our last edition have maintained the style and standard
of home-cooking that has proved so successful here over the years. A
daily-changing blackboard generally lists a choice of patés – garlic or
smoked salmon (£3) – good pub favourites like cottage pie (£4.75),
moussaka (£4.95), spinach lasagne (£4.25) and steak and oyster pie
(£6.45), as well as balti curries (£6.95), salads and the ever-popular
Brakspear pie (£5.25). Good puddings (£2.75) include chocolate and
cherry roulade and Aunt Nancy's treacle tart – prepared by the 93-
year-old lady who lives across the lane. Winter Sunday roasts (£5.95).
Excellent local walks, quaint village and an impressive white windmill
on the hill opposite. No children indoors. *Pub Open 11-3, 6-11, Sun
12-3, 7-10.30.* **Bar Food** *12-2, 7-9.45.* **Beer** *Brakspear. Garden, outdoor
eating. No credit cards.*

Tushingham   Blue Bell Inn

Tel 01948 662172	**A**

Bell O' Th' Hill Tushingham Whitchurch Cheshire SY13 4QS   Map 6 B3

"Bell O' Th' Hill" is the sign to look for by a new stretch of the A41,
four miles north of Whitchurch. Standing in extensive grounds on a
bend in the old road is this remarkable building of 14th-century
origins with a black and white painted timbered frame, massive oak
doors and a wealth of original timbers, oak panelling and memorabilia
within. There's a single bar, the pub's focal point, where the ales are
real (and well-kept) and the welcome's a mite unusual. Landlord
Patrick Gage hails from California, while his wife Liz is Russian. This
somehow matches the mild eccentricity of an establishment which lists

amongst its claims to fame the presence of a ghost duck and the more physical presence of a pair of resident Great Danes. Wooden benches in front for an alfresco drink look suitably ancient, while "paddock" rather than garden would describe the safe outdoor allocated to youngsters who are particularly welcome to play with the Gage children (and Great Dane dogs). *Free House.* **Beers** *Tetley Best, Dramwell Bitter. No credit cards.*

Tutbury Ye Olde Dog & Partridge Inn

Tel 01283 813030   Fax 01283 813178

High Street Tutbury nr Burton-on-Trent Staffordshire DE13 9LS

B&B

Map 6 C3

Zzzz...

With parts dating back to the 15th-century, this resplendent half-timbered inn on the high street is as popular today as it was in the 18th century when it was extended to accommodate passengers on the busy Liverpool-to-London coaching route. Successive extensions and improvements over the centuries can be traced within. Tapestries adorn the main bar with its thatched servery, and residents enjoy use of a restful timber-framed lounge well away from the populous self-serve Carvery restaurant. The oldest accommodation, with creaking floors and oak pannelling, remains in the original buildings, while the adjacent Georgian house, built around an impressive central spiral staircase contains the bulk of bedrooms which are more routinely up-to-date. Accoutrements which run to satellite TV, mini-bars and forceful over-bath pulse showers are all decidedly up-market for a pub, and tend to be priced accordingly, though the weekend rates are something of a bargain. *Free House.* **Beer** *Marston's Pedigree, Jennings Sneck Lifter. Garden, outdoor eating.* **Accommodation** *17 bedrooms, all en suite, £72.50 (single £52.50). Children welcome overnight, additional beds available. Access, Visa.*

Ulcombe Pepper Box Inn

Tel 01622 842558

Fairbourne Heath Ulcombe Maidstone Kent ME17 1LP

FOOD

Map 11 C5

The Pepper Box is a cottagey pub with low eaves and white-painted stone walls, surrounded by fields of corn and affording views across the expanse of the Kentish Weald. Dating back to the 15th-century, it was once the haunt of smugglers and takes its name (apparently unique) from their favourite weapon, the Pepper Box pistol. A three-piece suite takes pride of place in front of an inglenook fireplace in the beamed bar and old pewter mugs hang above the bar counter along with decorative hopbines. A Shepherd Neame-owned house, the tenancy has been in the same family since 1958 with Sarah and Geoff Pemble currently providing the hospitable welcome. Highlights of a reliable bar menu include steak and kidney pudding (£5.90), home-made fish pie (£5), and daily dishes such as lamb steak Dijonaise (£6), chicken stuffed with asparagus and roast duck with honey sauce (both £8). Good value roast (£4.95) plus ploughmans' and sandwiches replace the regular menu at lunch on Sunday. The same menus are available in the small dining room, with its oak table and wood-burning Aga. There's a short list of wines, and the Shepherd Neame ales are drawn direct from the barrels behind the bar. No children inside, but they are welcome in the large, pretty garden. *Pub open 11-3, 6.30-11 (Sun 12-3, 7-10.30).* **Bar Food.** *12-2 & 7-9.45 (no food D Sun). Children's menu.* **Beer** *Shepherd Neame. Garden, outdoor eating area. No credit cards.*

Ulverston   **Bay Horse Inn**

FOOD
B&B

Tel 01229 583972   Fax 01229 580502

Canal Foot Ulverston Cumbria LA12 9EL   **Map 4 C4**

1½ miles from Ulverston (from the A590, follow the signs for Canal
Foot), this is an old pub with sympathetic conversion that includes an
intimate conservatory restaurant with picturesque views over the
Leven estuary. Chef Robert Lyons gives full rein to his wide-ranging
repertoire; once the protégé of John Tovey at Miller Howe, he's
equally at home with the deceptively simple bar food such as home-
made soup (£1.85), cheese and herb paté with cranberry and ginger
purée (£4.50), venison sausage with sage and apple stuffing (£6.75) or
prawn and avocado pear salad (£7.50) as he is in the more elaborate
offerings in the restaurant. Lunch offers a limited choice of two dishes
per course plus a few more sweets; set lunch is £14.50; dinner pushes
the boat out (starters £2.25-5.25, main courses from £12.50, desserts
£3.95). There are two wine lists, though customers tend to choose
mainly from the outstanding New World list (80+), which features
many gems at keen prices. No children under 12. No smoking. Of the
six bedrooms, five open out on to a small terrace with a view of the
estuary; half-board terms only. Recommended in our *1995 Hotels &
Restaurants Guide*. Open 11-11 *(Sun 12-10.30)*. **Bar Food** 12-2 *(except
Mon)*. **Restaurant Meals** 12-1.30 *(except Sun & Mon)*, 7.30 for 8. Free
House. **Beer** Mitchells, Adnams, Fullers, Marston's, guest beers. Riverside
terrace, outdoor eating. **Accommodation** 6 rooms, all en suite, £140+10%
service charge *(half-board only, single £110)*. Access, Visa.

Upper Benefield   **Wheatsheaf Hotel**

FOOD
B&B

Tel 018325 254   Fax 018325 245

Upper Benefield nr Oundle Northamptonshire PE8 5AN   **Map 7 E4**

Situated beside the A427 Corby to Oundle road, this stone inn was
originally built as a farmhouse in 1659 and subsequently became a
coaching inn with the addition of stables to the rear. These have been
neatly converted to house eight functional en-suite bedrooms,
featuring modern pine furnishings, built-in wardrobes and good
writing space for visiting businessmen. TVs, tea-makers, telephones
and radios are standard throughout. Beyond the routine printed bar
menu offered in the Game Keepers Room is a list of simple home-
made blackboard specials, such as sweetcorn and orange soup (£1.95),
sauté of chicken in mushroom suace (£4.75), steak and kidney pie,
Hungarian goulash (both £5.25) and poached salmon in lemon butter
(£6.95), followed by almond bread-and-butter pudding or baked
Alaska (home-made desserts £2.50), which are served in the homely
open-plan bar. Separate restaurant (Garden Room), where a pianist
plays on Saturday nights; we recommend the bar food. Children's
facilities include high-chairs, board games and garden toys. *Pub open
11-11 (Sun usual hours)*. **Bar Bar & Restaurant Meals** 12-2, 6-10 *(Sun
7-9)*. Family room. Free House. **Beer** Directors, guest beer. Garden, outdoor
eating. **Accommodation** 9 bedrooms, all en suite, £55 *(single £45)*;
weekend reductions *(£48/£38)*. Children welcome overnight, additional
beds *(£5)* and cots *(£2)* supplied. Dogs by arrangement. Access,
Diners, Visa.

Upper Sheringham **Red Lion**

Tel 01263 825408	**FOOD**
Holt Road Upper Sheringham Norfolk NR26 8AD	Map 10 C1

Converted from three rather plain, 300-year-old brick and flint cottages, this homely village inn is popular locally for its above-average home-cooked food. Two friendly bars are filled with a rustic mix of sturdy country pine tables and chairs and high-backed settles on quarry-tiled and bare boarded floors, and are delightfully music- and game-free. The smaller snug bar is also a no-smoking room. Reliable bar food is listed on a sensibly short, often twice-daily-changing blackboard menu, which averages a choice of only eight interesting dishes. Begin with a well flavoured soup – parsley and cauliflower (£1.85) – served with a basket of fresh bread or tomato and basil salad (£2.75) and follow it with a decent ham and vegetable pie (£5.25), beef in black olive sauce (£5.90), local rabbit with red wine and mushrooms (£5) or chicken breast poached in bacon, tomato and onion (£5.70), all accompanied by crisp fresh vegetables; no chips here! Puddings (£1.95) include apricot and apple crumble and treacle tart. Fresh Cromer crab (£3.95) is always on the board and special meals include 3-course Wednesday evening supper (£7.50), seafood night on Thursdays and on Saturdays their mustard-glazed ham lunch attracts folk from miles around. Sunday roasts (£5.75). Well-kept Adnams Southwold, a guest ale on draught and a choice of over 70 malt whiskies. *Free House.* **Bar Food** *12-2, 7-9.* **Beer** *Adnams Broadside, Greene King Abbot Ale, guest beer. Garden, outdoor eating. Children welcomed. No credit cards.*

Upton **French Horn**

Tel 01636 812394	**FOOD**
Main Street Upton nr Southwell Nottinghamshire NG23 5SY	Map 7 D3

Plenty of good things are to be found within the Carters' almost self-effacing local. A single bar where the majority of tables are pre-laid for diners, dispenses the range of Wards ales, bottled beers and ciders from around the globe and a fair choice of wines by the glass. Behind the bar hangs the polished French horn, albeit little blown, and they don't make a great song and dance about their competently cooked bar food either. Fresh fish predominates on the blackboard, the daily choices including, perhaps, skate wings (£5.50), trout with prawns and almonds (£5.25) and monkfish kebabs (£5.95). Meaty alternatives are along the lines of lamb chops and minted gravy (£5.95) and pork in ginger (£5.95) whilst a separate vegetarian menu offers the likes of brie and broccoli crepes in mushroom sauce (£4.25). Upstairs in a rear pantiled former barn the restaurant opens on Sunday for lunch (traditional three-course £8.25) and in the evenings when the accent is on steaks, grills, and game – booking is advised. *Open 10.30-11pm, winter and Sunday usual hours.* **Bar Food** *11.30-3, (Sun 12-4.30), 7-10.30 (light snacks only 3-6).* **Restaurant Meals** *12-2.30 (Sun only), 6-10 (Sun from 7). Children under 14 allowed in bar to eat.* **Beer** *Wards Best, Thorne Bitter, Vaux Special. Garden, outdoor eating. No credit cards.*

Upton Bishop The Moody Cow

Tel 01989 780470	**FOOD**
Upton Bishop nr Ross-on-Wye Hereford & Worcester HR9 7TT	**Map 14 B1**

South Herefordshire pub-goers will remember this one (just off the
M50 from Junction 3 or 4) as the Duke of Wellington. Extension of
the old stone building to incorporate a formerly derelict barn and a
new kitchen in the old living quarters have produced an entirely
different animal. Creature comforts have certainly been improved in
an ambience enhanced by wall-to-wall carpeting and candle-lit tables.
In the hands of a trio of enthusiastic young leaseholders there's a lot of
promise in menus which cover a full range from bangers with bubble
and squeak to Chateaubriand with béarnaise. This is not all cow pie:
interspersed in the daily menus are their unusual soups (smoked cheese
and cauliflower or smoked salmon and champagne £2.35); warm
pigeon salad (£3.95); pasta carbonara (£3.25) and seafood pancake
(£4.50) among the starters or snacks and main courses from aubergine
bake (£5.95) or savoury strudel (£7.50) through chargrills of steak or
salmon (£7.20) to pork fillet stuffed with spinach and apricots
(£8.40) and chicken curry served up in half a pineapple (£5.95).
The atmosphere of a chummy village local lives on. There's a food
takeaway service, live jazz on Thursday nights and monthly cookery
demonstrations; mood swings which are indicative surely of
a conscious effort to do more than just fill the old Duke's boots.
*Bar Food 12.30-2, 7-9.30. Free House. Beer Worthington Best,
Herefordshire Wye Valley Best & Dorothy Goodbody's, Bass. Outdoor
eating. Access, Visa.*

Upton Grey Hoddington Arms

Tel 01256 862371	**FOOD**
Upton Grey nr Basingstoke Hampshire RG25 2RL	**Map 15a D4**

Licensees, Ian and Irene Fisher, are also the cooks at this warm and
welcoming local dating back to the 18th century. The daily-changing
blackboard menu might include moules marinière (£4.25), celery and
Stilton soup (£1.85), Thai-style pork and peanut curry (£4.95),
spinach and bacon salad (£3.75) Dijon mustard and apple sauce
(£3.50) seafood special (half a fresh lobster, prawns and mussels in a
creamy wine and saffron sauce £10.50) and summer pudding,
raspberry roulade or treacle sponge and custard (all £2). The
traditional Sunday roast is £5.25. On a fine day you can eat on the
small rear patio or on benches in the long, pleasant garden, at the top
of which is a children's swing and activity playground. Five miles
from the M3 Junction 5. *Bar Food 12-2, 7-9.30 (Sun to 9). Children's
menu. Beer Morland Old Speckled Hen and Original, IPA. Garden,
outdoor eating, children's play area. Family room. Access, Visa.*

Ventnor Spyglass Inn

Tel 01983 855338	**FOOD**
	B&B
The Esplanade Ventnor Isle of Wight PO38 1JX	**Map 15 D4**

Stephanie and Neil Gibbs are both native islanders (or Calk Heads, in
the vernacular) who have done a marvellous job of totally rebuilding
the Spyglass Inn after the disastrous fire of just a few years ago.
Wandering around the several interconnecting rooms, which include
two reserved for non-smokers and several where children are
welcome, it is difficult to believe that the pub is not hundreds of years
old. The bar counter is built of old pews and the whole place is full of

old seafaring prints and photographs, as well as numerous nautical antiques, ranging from a brass binnacle and ship's wheel to old oars and model ships in glass cases. The setting could not be better, at one end of the seafront with a front terraced area stretching right to the edge of the sea wall. In winter, the waves break right over the wall and more than one customer has been known to get a soaking by mis-timing their exit from the pub. In summer, there's an outside bar and kiosk selling shellfish and ice cream. Inside you might try hot chicken with a peanut dip (£4.50) or home-made cottage pie (£5) but the thing to look out for is the local seafood: crab served out of its shell in generous bowlfuls with salad (£6.50), and locally caught whole lobsters (£11.75). In winter, there are home-made soups from a blackboard menu, and on Saturday nights a candlelit dinner, for which booking is advisable, complete with pianist. There is live music nightly (less frequently in winter) from a small group who might play country, folk or jazz. Three neat little flatlets with upholstered rattan furniture and a sea-facing balcony offer accommodation for up to two adults and two children. A public car park is just 50 yards away, but check your brakes before venturing down here – the road to the seafront has hairpin bends and a gradient of 1 in 4. *Open 11-11 Mon-Sat Jun-end Sept, regular hours Sun and other times. **Bar Food** 12-2.15, 7-9.30. Children's menu. Free House. **Beer** Burton, Benskins, Black Rock house beer, guest beers. Patio/terrace, outdoor eating. Family room. **Accommodation** 3 en-suite flatlets, sleeps 4, from £35 (discounts for week-long stays). Children welcome overnight. No credit cards.*

Waddesdon	Five Arrows Hotel	★	**FOOD**
Tel 01296 651727	Fax 01296 658596		**B&B**
High Street Waddesdon Buckinghamshire HP18 0JE			Map 15a D2

A delightful Victorian confection built by the Rothschilds to house the architects and artisans working in nearby Waddesdon Manor (NT) – itself worth a visit. The name comes from the family crest with its arrows representing the five sons sent out by the dynasty's founder to set up banking houses in the financial capitals of Europe. Recently restored from top to toe and bedecked with flowers (there's a fine garden to the rear) the hotel/inn is now run in a friendly, family-orientated fashion by Gaynor Hitchcock and Terence Jackson. One enters straight into the bar from which open several rooms with antique tables, colourful upholstered chairs plus the odd settee and armchair with pictures from Lord Rothschild's own collection on the walls along with numerous photos of old Waddesdon – charmingly un-pub-like. Food is important (and good) here with the likes of mousseline of salmon with basil butter sauce (£5.95), Roquefort salad (£3.50), sautéed lamb with honey and garlic (£6.95), oyster mushroom tart with fresh herbs and sour cream (£4.95) and lovely desserts like fresh raspberry tart (£2.95) supplemented at lunchtimes by more snacky items – mature Cheddar or Stilton ploughman's (both £3.50), burger topped with grilled goat's cheese (£4.50) or sandwiches (from £2.50). Afternoon teas (£2.50 per person) are served at weekends. Terence's passion for wine is reflected in a fascinating list that includes offerings from the various Rothschild wine interests that extend to Portugal and Chile as well as the famous Chateau Lafite; there are always at least a dozen wines available by the glass, and many, many more if Terence is behind the bar! Six good-sized bedrooms are individually decorated with matching en-suite bathrooms (two with shower and WC only) and boast extra large

Zzz*z* …

beds (with pure Egyptian cotton sheets) and antique Victorian washstands along with modern comforts: remote-control TV, direct-dial phones and tea/coffee-making facilities. No smoking in the bedrooms. *Open 11-3 & 6-11, Sat 11-11, Sun 12-3 & 7-10.30.* **Bar Food** *12-2.30, 7-9.30 (to 10 Fri & Sat). Afternoon teas 3-6 Sat & Sun. Free House.* **Beer** *Fuller's London Pride, Hook Norton Old Hooky & Hock Mild, guest beer. Garden.* **Accommodation** *6 bedrooms, all en suite, £65 (single £45). No dogs. Access, Visa.*

Wall   Hadrian Hotel

Tel 01434 681232	**B&B**
Wall nr Hexham Northumberland NE46 4EE	**Map 5 D2**

A handsome Jacobean-style 16th century house standing in its own attractive gardens by the A6079, about a mile from Hadrian's Wall and only three from nearby Hexham. The best feature for residents is the welcoming, if small, foyer lounge with deep sofas set around the open fire. Unopposed in this tiny village, the bar is a convivial place for meeting the locals. Four bedrooms boast full en-suite facilities. In the remainder are wash-hand basins and free-standing plastic shower cubicles whose practicality, like the water pressure, is limited. Colour TVs and beverage trays are standard. At the time of our last visit, the Wall's future was uncertain, with a change of ownership pending. *Open 11-3, 6-11.30.* **Beer** *Vaux Sampson and ESB Bitters.* **Accommodation** *9 bedrooms, 4 en suite, £49 (single £35). Check-in by arrangement. No dogs. Access, Visa.*

Walliswood   Scarlett Arms

Tel 01306 627243	**A**
Walliswood Surrey RH5 5RD	**Map 11 A5**

Originally a pair of 17th-century labourers' cottages, this attractive white-painted and red-tiled roofed village pub preserves a splendid unspoilt interior. Four small rambling rooms have low ceilings, sturdy wooden furnishings on either carpeted or flagstoned floors, various country prints and old photos, and a good open fire to sit in front of on cold winter days. Relaxing chatty atmosphere and the full complement of well-kept King and Barnes real ales. Benches and brollies fill the front lawn for peaceful summer alfresco drinking. No children under 14 indoors. **Beer** *Kings & Barnes Festive, Broadwood, Sussex & Mild plus Old Ale in winter. Garden. No credit cards.*

Waltham-on-the-Wolds   Royal Horseshoes

Tel 0166478 289	**B&B**
Melton Road Waltham-on-the-Wolds nr Melton Mowbray Leicestershire	**Map 7 D3**

A compact, thatched and ivy-covered pub with a cottagey interior, on a corner of the busy A607 by the sign to Belvoir Castle. Melton Mowbray is about 5 miles. Stands opposite the old village church built in sandstone with a distinctive spire. The patio to the rear is a sun trap in which to enjoy a summer ale. Plenty of parking beyond. *Free House.* **Beer** *John Smith's, Bass, Marston's Pedigree, plus two guest beers.* **Accommodation** *4 bedrooms, all en suite, £49 (single £25). Children welcome overnight. Additional bed. Check-in by arrangement. No credit cards.*

Wansford-in-England   The Haycock   ★

FOOD
B&B

Tel 01780 782223   Fax 01780 783031

Wansford-in-England Peterborough Cambridgeshire PE8 6JA   Map 7 E4

Zzzz...

A lovely 17th-century honey-coloured stone coaching inn in 6 acres
of grounds next to the junction of A1 and A47. It has been much
extended, in sympathetic style, the most recent additions being a large
conference/ballroom (a lovely setting for functions with its soaring
oak beams, enormous fireplace and private garden, catering for up to
200) and the stone-walled Orchard Room with all-day bar and coffee-
shop menu (7am-11pm with a fine lunchtime buffet). Other day
rooms include a pubby bar and two traditional lounges. Bedrooms in
the older parts of the building are full of character, but all have been
decorated with great style and flair by Julia Vannocci using high-
quality fabrics and furnishings; one ground-floor twin room has a
wide door and handrails for disabled guests. Bathrooms are equally
luxurious. Last year there were extra special B&B deals for those who
ate 3-course dinners in the restaurant (around £70 for two including
wine) on Sunday nights (and at Easter). Extensive grounds include
award-winning gardens which stretch along the banks of the river
Nene and the village cricket pitch. The variety of food on offer in
both bar (excellent bar snacks – grilled salmon fillet with thyme and
parsley butter £9.45, sautéed pasta shells baked in a triple cheese sauce
£6.95, pork satay £4.95, deep-fried supreme of chicken filled with
Stilton £9.95), Orchard Room (one room is non-smoking) and
restaurant caters for all tastes and pockets; outdoor barbecue daily in
summer with seating for 100 in a courtyard. Candelabras and highly-
polished silver add to the mellow, traditional atmosphere of the twin
dining rooms. The menu is pretty traditional too, with the likes of
'cheffy's' steak and kidney pie and jugged hare with sausage meat balls
(both considered a speciality), plus the daily roast sirloin of prime
English beef that always features on the silver trolley. A wine list
doesn't need to be long to be considered outstanding, if, as is the case
here, it has been carefully compiled to complement the style of
restaurant and offers both helpful notes and giveaway prices! There's
also a good selection of wines served by the glass. Part of Ivo
Vannocci's Poste Hotel group; hotel, inn and pub all rolled into one.
Graded as a 70% hotel in our *1995 Cellnet Hotels & Restaurants Guide*;
we also award the Haycock a star for its outstanding bar food. *Bar
Food* 12-10.30 7 days. *Accommodation* 50, all en suite, from £85 to
£98 (single from £68 to £85), four-poster £120, suite £130. *Garden,
croquet, fishing, pétanque, helipad. Access, Diners, Visa.*

Wardlow   Bull's Head

Tel 01298 871431

FOOD

Wardlow nr Tideswell Derbyshire SK17 8RP   Map 6 C2

A friendly village local with a dining emphasis only three miles from
Ashford-in-the-Water: the B6465 passes scenic Monsal Head on the
way. The Wetheralls' bar menu stays sensibly short, though the
portions can be massive – a 1lb rump steak, chips and vegetables
selling for £12.45! Illuminated specials boards probably present the
best options: mushroom soup £1.50; potted shrimps with toast
£2.95; chicken curry £4.75; steak au poivre £8.95; rhum baba
£1.95. Plenty of other desserts, including Bakewell pudding (£2.25),
and Hartington blue Stilton for those of less sweet persuasion. Family
dining in the Loose Box; picnic tables in a small but scenic garden.

Two bedrooms available overnight, sharing facilities; children welcome. **Bar Food** *12-2.15 (except Mon & Tue in winter), 6.30-9.30 (Sun 7-9). Free House. **Beer** Wards Bitter. Garden, outdoor eating. Family room. Pub closed Mon & Tue lunchtime in winter. No credit cards.*

Warenford   Warenford Lodge   ★

Tel 01668 213453	**FOOD**
Warenford nr Belford Northumberland NE70 7HY	Map 5 D1

There's a wonderfully eclectic range of good bar food on offer at the rather un-pubby Warenford Lodge, a solid stone building on the village loop road off the A1; there's no sign outside so you'll have to look hard for it. Inside, it's a handsome old place, with exposed thickset stone and a modern air which blends well with the atmosphere of an old-fashioned private house. There are little mullion windows, polished light pine tables and cushioned benches in the split-level bar, a big stone fireplace in the lower part, and a woodburning stove in the upper area, which has armchairs and sofas just made for relaxing; the bar area is probably more attractive an area in which to eat than the restaurant. Menus change here twice yearly, in spring and autumn, reflecting seasonal produce and appetite, but a random selection of favourites might well feature marinated seafood salad with herbs (£4.25), Lindisfarne oysters (£4.25), Northumbrian fish soup – a delicious and generous equivalent of the French bouillabaisse – £7.60) or baked halibut (£7.20). Other dishes on last year's Spring/Summer menu included port royal lamb (flavoured with cinnamon and orange £6.50), and cold roasted pork stuffed with fruit (£5.20). Not all puddings are home-made, but those that are, such as a baked lemon pudding, are wonderful. The menu is clever, well presented and most unusual – a shining star in the firmament of pubs! The unifying factor behind it all, exotic or homely, is the instinctive, hearty cooking of the landlady, Marion Matthewman, at work in the kitchen while Ray tends to the bar where he has introduced a choice of unusual bottled beers. Owing to the popularity of the Warenford you need to book for weekend evenings (or any time in summer). **Bar Food** *12-2 (Sat & Sun only), 7-9.30 (Tue-Sun).* **Restaurant Meals** *7-9.30.* **Beer** *Newcastle Exhibition, McEwan's Scottish. Garden. No outdoor eating. Pub closed Tue-Fri lunch. Access, Diners, Visa.*

Warham All Saints   The Three Horseshoes

Tel 01328 710547	**FOOD**
	B&B
Warham All Saint Wells-Next-The-Sea Norfolk NR23 1NL	Map 10 C1

Warham is a sleepy rural backwater situated only a mile or so from the North Norfolk coast. At its heart, close to the church, lies the Three Horseshoes, a timeless gem of a village local, comprising a row of 18th-century brick and flint cottages and the Old Post Office which closed 14 years ago. Owned by nearby Holkham hall until 1960 it is a rare survivor, remaining delightfully unchanged internally since the 1930's. An old-fashioned ambience pervades throughout the three unspoilt rooms with numerous gas-lights, nicotine yellow walls, scrubbed deal tables, plain wooden chairs and red leatherette one-arm bandits and a 1930's pianola which performs on alternate weekends. Unlike most humble country hostelries a good choice of home-cooked food is served, especially traditional Norfolk dishes using fresh local produce, including fish and game. Local ladies prepare the meals that appear on the interesting main menu – smokie hotpot (£3), Ann's soused herring (£2.50), Warham mushroom bake (£4.50), Brancaster cream mussels (£3.70), roast Norfolk duck (£6.25) – and the hearty dishes on the daily specials board, for example curried parsnip soup (£2), Warham baked crab (£5.20) and liver, onion and sausage casserole (£4.60). Fresh vegetables are the order of the day; definitely no chips. For dessert try the steamed jam sponge or Bakewell tart (both £2.20). Well conditioned ales are drawn straight from the cask and home-made lemonade is served in the summer. Four homely bedrooms in the adjacent Old Post Office accommodate overnight guests. Simply furnished with old darkwood furniture – some antique pieces – washbasins and latch-doors, all except one which is en suite, share a clean bathroom. Added touches include a box of tissues, cotton wool, a range of teas and a dressing gown. Residents have use of a sitting room with TV and easy chairs. No under-14s overnight. *Free House.* **Bar Food** *12-2, 7-9.* **Accommodation** *4 bedrooms, 1 en suite £40 (single £18).* **Beer** *Greene King Abbot Ale, IPA, Woodfordes Wherry Bitter. Garden, outdoor eating. Children welcome. No credit cards.*

Warnham   Greets Inn

Tel 01403 265047	A
Friday Street Warnham West Sussex RH12 3QY	Map 11 A6

Tucked along Friday Street on the western edge of the village – off the A24 north of Horsham – this attractive tile-hung and timbered old farmhouse dates from 1450. Preserved inside is the original layout of a series of charming rooms radiating out from a central bar which boasts a highly polished stone floor, a vast inglenook with log fire, a fine high-backed settle and sturdy tables. Part stripped pine and oak furnishings and gleaming copper and brass artefacts characterise the unspoilt rooms and traditional local's bar. Good alfresco seating in the sheltered rear garden among the roses, flower beds and apple trees. *Pub open 11-2.30, 6-11 (Sun 12-3, 7-10.30).* **Beer** *Wadworth 6X, Flowers Original, Strongs Country Bitter. Garden, lawn, outdoor eating area. Access, Visa.*

Warren Street   The Harrow

Tel 01622 858727 ·	FOOD
	B&B
Hubbards Hill Warren Street Lenham nr Maidstone Kent ME17 2ED	Map 11 C5

Once a rest home for Canterbury pilgrims, now a converted and refurbished downland inn not far from the A20 above Lenham (signposted) and the M20. Simple cushioned chairs and stools around little tables in the open-plan lounge, much used for dining and warmed in winter by a good log fire. Separate, neatly laid up conservatory restaurant but it's the bar food that we recommend overlooking the sun-trap courtyard and garden with waterfall and pool – access for residents and restaurant diners only. Standard range of bar snacks supplement by decent home-made specials, such as spicy pan-fried marinated chicken (£8.25), seafood lasagne with salad and garlic bread (£7.50), and a generous portion of steak and kidney pie accompanied by six fresh vegetables. Good bed and breakfast too, the fifteen spacious bedrooms being kitted out with neat darkwood furniture, clean bathrooms with showers over tubs, and cluttered with added comforts. Five family rooms. *Pub open 11.30-2.30, 7-11 (Sun 12-3, 7-10.30).* **Bar Food** *12-2, 7-10.* **Restaurant Meals** *12-2, 7-9.30. Children allowed in the bar to eat. Free House.* **Beer** *Shepherd Neame, guest beers. Water garden, patio, outdoor eating area.* **Accommodation** *15 bedrooms, all en-suite, from £45 (single £35). Children welcome overnight (under-5s stay free in parents' room, 5-14 years olds £5). Access, Visa.*

Wasdale Head   Wasdale Head Inn

Tel 019467 26229   Fax 019467 26334   **B&B**

Wasdale Head Gosforth Cumbria CA20 1EX   Map 4 C3

At the head of Wasdale, in a setting of romantic grandeur, with steep
fells by way of backdrop, this is a famous traditional mountain pub   Zzzz...
popular with walkers and climbers. Ritson's Bar, named after its first
landlord (the world's biggest liar) has high ceilings, a polished slate
floor, wood panelling, and cushioned old settles. Food is largely
traditional. There's a residents' bar and a relaxing lounge. Bedrooms
are comfortable and unfussy with telephones and beverage trays
provided. 9 self-catering cottages right next to the pub are available
from between £240 and £360 per week. *Open 11-11 in summer
(Easter-end of Sept), normal hours during winter (see closures below).*
Beer *Jennings, Yates, Theakston Best & Old Peculier, guest beer in
summer. Riverside garden, outdoor eating. Family room.* ***Accommodation***
*6 bedrooms, all en suite, £58 (single £29). Children welcome overnight
(0-2 free), additional beds & cots available. Dogs £3. Pub and
accommodation closed mid Nov-28 Dec, mid Jan-mid Feb. Access, Visa.*

Wass   Wombwell Arms   ★   **FOOD**

Tel 01347 868280   **B&B**

Wass North Yorkshire YO6 4BE   Map 5 E4

This whitewashed village inn dates from the 18th century and sits in
the shadow of the Hambleton hills, just a couple of miles from the   Zzzz...
A170, east of Thirsk. The interior consists of four connecting rooms
with stylish fabrics and furnishings. The first room to the left of the
entrance has lightwood floorboards, stripped pine tables and chairs,
and half-panelling. This room is especially good for families. The bar
and its adjoining dining area have a mix of flagstone and red-tiled
flooring, some exposed stone walls, more panelling and original
beams. Some walls have attractive Laura Ashley wallpapers, while
farmhouse kitchen-style tables are covered with colourful cloths. The
final room is similarly appointed. Throughout the pub, there are
splendid fresh and dried flower displays, watercolours of chickens,
foxes and other country subjects, magazines and books. Over the bar is
an original drawing of TV's Captain Pugwash, drawn for the landlord
by its creator John Ryan, an old boy of nearby Ampleforth College.
A huge blackboard displays the day's choice of interesting bar food.
Rather bistro in style, this is the preserve of Lynda Evans, who is a
more than competent cook. Only fresh, mostly local produce is used,
and the choice is extensive and varied: perhaps cauliflower and
almond soup (£1.95), local venison and redcurrant (£7.95), minted
lamb (£7.25) and tipsy chicken with red wine (£7.25). There are
good vegetarian dishes too, Wensleydale mushrooms (£2.75) or
tomato and basil flan (£5.25). Desserts are well up to standard, with
sticky toffee pudding, chocolate truffle and hot nut sundae (£2.75).
There's also a selection of lighter lunch dishes. The three bedrooms are
equally impressive. Two doubles and a twin are kitted out in colourful
Laura Ashley wallpapers, with matching curtains and duvet covers,
and stripped pine furniture. They're impeccably kept and offer a
selection of magazines as well as televisions and radio alarms. Each
room is en suite, one with a shower, two with baths. To immaculate
housekeeping is added a sense of fun: plastic ducks are provided. Alan
Evans looks after the bar and is an extremely jovial host. A quite

exceptional country pub, well worth a detour. *Bar Food &*
Restaurant Meals (*no food Sun eve or all day Mon in winter except bank*
holidays and Christmas week) *12-2, 7-9.30. Free House.* *Beer* *Cameron*
Traditional, Timothy Taylor Landlord, Black Sheep, guest beer. Family
room. *Accommodation* *3 bedrooms, all en suite, £49 (single £24.50).*
Children over 8 years welcome overnight (8-10 yrs free if sharing parents'
room), additional beds available. Check-in by arrangement. No dogs. Pub
closed on Mondays in winter and 1 week January. Access, Visa.

Waterhouses   George Inn

Tel 01538 308228	**FOOD**

Waterhouses nr Leek Staffordshire ST10 3HW   Map 6 C3

Now a second Free House for the industrious Graham and Ann Yates,
the rehabilitated George has rocketed from closure to celebrity in just
a few short months. On the busy A523 midway between Ashbourne
and Leek, and very handy for the Alton Towers turning, its recently
extended kitchen hours are no common coincidence. The George also
promotes itself as "not a restaurant but a pub serving food" which is
admirably reflected in prices that uniformly give good value for
money and service which is, as promised, both casual and friendly.
In addition to the full range of standard items, look out for some
imaginative additions ranging from the all-day breakfast (£4.95) to
splendid Cantonese stir-fry prawns (£7.95) served on a sizzling platter.
The daily curries, such as our lamb and apricot (£5.95) are tasty, well-
cooked and come with generous accompaniments. With additional
menus for vegetarians and children, a non-smoking room and play
equipment in a safe-side garden, there's truly something for all the
family – with hours to match. As we went to press work was due to
start on bedrooms scheduled to come into use over the winter:
completion promises en-suite bathrooms and all "mod cons". The
Yates's impeccable pedigree suggests that nothing less would be good
enough. *Pub open 10-11 (except Sun).* *Bar Food* *10-10 (Sun 12-2,*
7-9.30). Free House. *Beer* *Marston's Pedigree. Garden, outdoor eating.*
Pub closed 25 & 26 Dec. Access, Visa.

Waterley Bottom   New Inn

Tel 01453 543659	**B&B**

Waterley Bottom North Nibley nr Dursley Gloucestershire GL11 6EF   Map 13 F1

Ruby Sainty's friendly, idiosyncratic pub takes some driving to down
the country lanes from North Nibley on the B4060, yet cyclists and
walkers find it unerringly from their maps. The setting is serene, the
garden a blaze of colour shaded by beech, silver birch and horse
chestnut; for the youngsters, swings and a terrestrial tree house are a
safe distance away. Overnight guests are assured the tranquillity of this
hidden valley quite undisturbed. The two bedrooms share a single
bathroom, and breakfast is worth getting up for; book well in
advance. *Free House.* *Beer* *Cotleigh WB & Tawny, Smiles Best &*
Exhibition, Theakston Old Peculier, Greene King Abbot Ale.
Accommodation *2 rooms, £35 (single £20). Garden, outdoor play area.*
No credit cards.

Wath-in-Nidderdale   Sportsman's Arms

FOOD
B&B

Tel 01423 711306

Wath-in-Nidderdale Pateley Bridge nr Harrogate N Yorkshire HG3 5PP   **Map 6 C1**

Zzzz...

Nestling in a wooded valley just 2 miles from Pateley Bridge, the
Sportsman's is prominently signed across a tiny stone hump-backed
bridge over the Nidd. A carpeted lounge bar with its own side
entrance suggests at once that this is no pub for the beer-swilling
brigade – there are no real ales, instead a connoisseur's collection of
malt whiskies and Russian vodkas. As one would expect from an inn
whose restaurant is recommended in our *1995 Cellnet Hotels &
Restaurants Guide* the food, too, has an identity all its own. Rich black
pudding with tomatoes and mushrooms (£4.50) and moules marinière
(£4.80) can be starters or just a snack; Scarborough Woof with a
garlic crust (£6.80) and pork loin with prunes, orange and ginger
(£6.80) are decidedly main meals. Alongside ever-present sticky toffee
pudding with fresh cream, there's a scrumptious "tarte au citron" (£3)
which is definitely not to be missed. Stripped pine doors are the
unifying theme of the single corridor of bedrooms which are of
modest size and appointment: returning guests appreciate rather the
total peace and quiet and an absence of room telephones. Whilst all are
equipped with wash basins only two from seven have full en-suite
facilities; two WCs and two separate bathrooms are shared by the
rest. A long, leisurely and very large breakfast is served at 9 am.
Free House. **Bar Food & Restaurant** 12-2, 7-9.30 (Sun 12-2.30).
Accommodation 7 bedrooms, 2 en suite, £50 (Single £30). Children
welcome overnight (cot and extra bed if sharing parents' room). Dogs
welcome in rooms. No real ale. Garden, outdoor eating. Access, Visa.

Watlington   Chequers

A

Tel 0149161 2874

Love Lane Watlington Oxfordshire OX9 5RA   **Map 15a D3**

A useful stop, less than two and a half miles from Junction 6 of the
M40. It's a characterful, rambling old pub with a lovely summer
garden and covered patio. Unprepossessing exterior, cosy interior with
an eclectic mix of paraphernalia – from dried flowers to an unusual
collection of bottles and paintings. Not a family pub – no children
under 14. *Beer Brakspear. Garden. No credit cards.*

Watton-at-Stone   George & Dragon

FOOD

Tel 01920 830285

High Street Watton-at-Stone Hertfordshire SG14 3TA   **Map 15 F1**

The George & Dragon is popular with everyone, from OAPs to
business class, and its well-balanced bar menu attracts a fair number
of locals. On any one day, the menu could offer George & Dragon
smokie (gratinéed flaked, smoked haddock with tomato concasse
£4.50), lambs kidneys in cream wine and mustard (£6.85) or
matelote normande (whitefish and scallops in cream £7.85), white
anchovy fillets marinated in olive oil and garlic served with mixed
leaf salad (£3.85), roast breast of duck with rich red wine sauce
(£4.55). Fish is delivered daily and prices never exceed £10 – grilled
hake with garlic butter £7.75. In addition, traditional roast lunch is
served on Sundays (beef £6, other £5). Desserts such as summer
pudding start at £2.20. Reasonable house wines are available by the
carafe. The bars are usually bustling with diners, some of whom travel
some distance to eat here. The public bar is a locals' spot, though, with

keen cribbage players, black and white photographs of the pub and
village in days gone by, and furnishings similar to the main bar, in the
oldest part of the building, which has a wonderfully homely
atmosphere enhanced by jovial management and welcome touches like
fresh flowers and the day's newspapers. There are also exposed beams,
open fireplaces, yellow stained walls hung with a mixture of framed
oil and watercolour paintings, and two large bay windows admitting
lots of natural light. Furnishings are a mixture of blue upholstered
bench seating and simple wood chairs around oak tables topped with
candles. There is one modern regulations though, singlet tops are
prohibited in the bars. This is a difficult pub to miss, as it dominates
the centre of the village, and is of pink-painted pebbledash. There's a
small flower-filled garden and patio for kinder weather. Children are
welcome in the dining room only. *Bar Food & Restaurant 12-2,
7.15-10 (except Sun).* **Beer** *Greene King. Garden, patio/terrace, outdoor
eating. Access, Diners, Visa.*

Well   Chequers

Tel 01256 862605	**FOOD**
Well nr Odiham Hampshire RG25 1TL	**Map 15a D4**

Deep in the heart of the Hampshire countryside, this 17th-century pub
provides a retreat from the modern world and an opportunity to
enjoy the old-world charm. A flourishing vine covers the patio
outside, and inside, the homely rustic bar features low wooden
ceilings, panelled walls, bare floorboards, plenty of beams and a mix of
old scrubbed tables, chairs and church pews. Shelves of books and old
photographs and prints adorn the walls. Bar food is reliably good with
the emphasis being on interesting and light home-cooked meals. The
daily-changing selection of dishes is chalked up on a blackboard in the
bar and the good value choice ranges from freshly-prepared soup
(celery and apple £2.50) to chef's pasta (£4.95), cajun chicken with
Caesar salad (£5.50), open steak sandwich (£5) and ratatouille au
gratin (£4.95). Home-made puddings include lemon torte, banoffi pie
and apple strudel (all £2.50). The adjacent pine-panelled restaurant is
neatly arranged with tables laid with linen clothes and fresh flowers. A
peaceful drink or meal can be savoured in the attractive rear garden,
which affords rural views across fields. On Friday nights the pub can
get a bit '*urbe in rus*'! Five miles from the M3 Junction 5. *Bar Food
12-2.30, 7-10. Free House.* **Beer** *Boddingtons, Flowers Original, Fremlins.
Garden, outdoor eating. Family room. Access, Visa.*

Wells-next-the-Sea   Crown Hotel

Tel 01328 710209 Fax 01328 711432	**FOOD**
	B&B
The Buttlands Wells-next-the-Sea Norfolk NR23 1EX	**Map 10 C1**

Outward appearances are sometimes deceptive, the facade of the
Crown being a case in point. It stands at the foot of a tree-lined village
green, the Buttlands, where medieval marksmen once practised their
archery. Compared to the elegant Georgian terraced houses which
surround the green, the Crown's black and white painted exterior
(genuinely Tudor, as it turns out) has the rather care-worn look of a
modest town pub. But what a jewel it is inside! The bar progresses on
three levels from front to back, where a family-friendly conservatory
of high-backed settles opens on to the rear patio and stableyard.
Within, there's an open log fire, high bar stools and low copper-
topped, barrel-shaped tables, the walls throughout covered with
portraits and memorabilia of Horatio Nelson – born in a nearby

village and whose sister reputedly lived on the Buttlands. The beer's good and the bar menu is extensive. Single-course meals of pasta dishes and omelettes come in generous portions at under £5, and grills from a mini 'steakwich' through to a full mixed grill at £12.50. Plenty of salads, sandwiches, and sausage-burger-fishfinger combinations for the children complete the picture. The adjoining restaurant, continuing the interior's Victorian theme, is neatly decked out with pink cloths and fresh vased pinks, and offers more adventurous dining. Lunch is available daily (booking essential on Sunday), and there is an evening choice of table d'hote or à la carte, on which locally landed fish and shellfish feature prominently. Local mussels in filo with Provençal sauce and wild salmon hollandaise are prettily presented and reveal much skill in their saucing, without the pretence of haute cuisine nor the pretension of 'moderne'. Roast duck with garlic honey (£11.75), tournedos Rossini and wiener schnitzel are equally appealing, without taking any undue risks, and the cream-heavy desserts carefully made. To describe the bedrooms as modest is not to decry them: they are simply but adequately furnished and even the smallest offers a view of the charming old town, across the Lion Yard where the London mail coach once pulled in, and over pantiled roofs to the sturdy Norman church below. The seal is set on an enjoyable stay by a tranquil night's rest in these evocative surroundings, a hearty and enjoyable English breakfast, and the friendly service and warm hospitality of the Foyers family and their youthful staff. *Bar Meals* 12-2, 6-9 (restaurant 7-9.15, winter to 8.30). Children's menu. Free House. *Beer* Adnams, Marston's Pedigree, Tetley. Patio/terrace, outdoor eating. *Accommodation* 15 Bedrooms, 10 en suite, £65 (single £34). Children welcome overnight (under-10s £10, 10-15s £15), cots available (£3). Access, Diners, Visa.

Weobley   Ye Olde Salutation Inn

Tel 01544 318443   Fax 01544 318216
Market Pitch Weobley Hereford & Worcester HR4 8SJ

FOOD
B&B
Map 14 A1

Dedication and sheer hard work have been the key to Chris and Frances Anthony's success at this wonderfully evocative 14th-century ale and cider house. It commands the view down picturesque Broad Street to Weobley parish church, and is at once village local, congenial food pub and bespoke country inn. Frances supervises a hard-working kitchen which daily produces both traditional and imaginatively different bar meals: diners feast equally well on salmon and broccoli gratin (£5.95), sauté of lamb's kidney flavoured with red wine and herbs (£5.50) and steak and Guinness pie (£5.75). Vegetarian specials might be lentil and apricot terrine or pasta and blue cheese bake. Also for a lighter meal try a hot filled roll (cheese, bacon and mushroom or steak – £3.95) made with bread baked freshly on the premises. Popular desserts, prepared to order, include lemon soufflé with pistachio nuts (£3.35) and traditional bread-and-butter pudding (£3.25). The non-smoking Oak Room restaurant serves a full à la carte (gravad lax £4.50, roast duck with blueberry sauce £10.40) and highly popular 3-course Sunday lunch (£8.25), for which booking is essential. Victorian furniture, cast-iron bedsteads and brass-topped bathroom fittings set the unifying theme. The three larger rooms (one with a four-poster) have en-suite WC/shower rooms, while two smaller doubles which share a vast Victorian bathroom are let at a realistic economy price. To follow the most restful of nights, a splendid country breakfast is served in the recently added conservatory. Due to the building's age, guests are requested not to

Zzzz...

smoke in their rooms, though smoking is permitted in the residents' lounge. (An adjacent self-contained cottage with lounge, kitchen/diner, bathroom and two double bedrooms accommodates up to 5 people in the first timber-framed building to be put up in Weobley since the 17th century). Choice of 20 malt whiskies and eight wines by the glass. Premises unsuitable for children under 14 (unless very small in which case there is a baby-listening service) – call first to check. *Bar Food* 12-2, 7-9.30 (*Sun to 9*). *Restaurant Meals* 12-2 (*except Mon*), 7-9 (*except Sun & Mon*). *Free House. Beer* Boddingtons, Hook Norton, Bass, Westons Old Rosie Cider. *Garden, outdoor eating. Family room. Accommodation* 4 bedrooms, all en suite, £54 (single £32). *Children over 14 years welcome overnight, also babies by prior arrangement. Accommodation closed 25 Dec. Access, Diners, Visa.*

West Bexington   **Manor Hotel**

FOOD

Tel 01308 897785   Fax 01308 897035

B&B

Beach Road West Bexington nr Bridport Dorset DT2 9DF   **Map 13 F2**

Old manor house just a short walk from Chesil Bank, with stone-walled cellar bar, leafy conservatory and residents' lounge. Books, magazines and dried flower arrangements add a homely, welcoming touch to simply furnished but well-equipped bedrooms, which come complete with tea and coffee kits, TVs, direct-dial phones, sherry, elderflower water and goodnight chocolates. They offer an £11.85 set Sunday lunch, and a special £7.95 three-course children's menu. Food is typified by monkfish au poivre (£11.95), rabbit pie (£6.95), fish thermidor (£8.05) and sticky toffee pudding (£2.95). *Open 11-11 Mon-Sat, regular hours Sun. Bar Food* 12-2, 6.30-10 (*Sun from 7*). *Children allowed in the (no-smoking) conservatory to eat, children's menu. Free House. Beer* Palmers Bridport, Eldridge Pope Royal Oak, Wadworth 6X. *Garden, outdoor eating, children's play area. Family room. Accommodation* 13 bedrooms, all en suite, £76 (single £44). *Children welcome overnight, additional beds (£7.50) and cots available. Check-in after noon. No dogs. Accommodation closed 24 Dec. Access, Diners, Visa.*

West Bromwich   **The Manor House**

Tel 0121 588 2035

A

Hall Green Road Stonecross West Bromwich West Midlands B71 2EA   **Map 6 C4**

This is arguably the finest pub building anywhere in England and as such we are reluctant not to give it space in the Guide. The 13th-century Great Hall, North and South wings, chapel and gate house were revealed behind a tenement facade by its unwitting owners, Sandwell Council, in 1987 and are now leased to Banks's Brewery. We can't recommend the food, nor are there any real ales to try – clearly due to cellar limitations in a building of this nature. However, some wooden casks racked behind the bar would be more in keeping than electronic tills, glass-fronted fridges and piped reggae music. Just go, then, for the building, to view this most remarkable piece of restored British heritage. *Free House. Open 11.30-2.30, 6-11 (Sun 12-3, 7-10.30). Garden. Access, Visa.*

West Camel   **Walnut Tree**

| **FOOD** |
| **B&B** |

Tel 01935 851292

West Camel nr Sparkford/Yeovil Somerset BA22 7QW

Map 13 F2

Smartly modernised and extended 100-year-old village inn located
half a mile off the A303 between Sparkford and Ilchester, and named
after the magnificent walnut tree that stands in the pretty shrub filled
garden. Pristinely kept carpeted bar, lounge and separate restaurant
featuring lots of plush chairs and benches, some comfortable easy
chairs and sofas and attractive silk flower arrangements. Good relaxing
ambience in which to enjoy reliable, above-average bar food. Fresh
local produce is used in compiling the value-for-money, twice-daily-
changing blackboard menu which may list Crewkerne goat's cheese
salad with walnut oil dressing and Dorset crab gateaux among the
starters, followed by Mendip lamb casseroled in red wine with herbs
(£6.95), beef braised in ginger and pineapple (£5.95), West Country
seafood salad (£6.50) and fresh fish from Poole – cod fillet pan-fried
with prawns and beansprouts (£8.75) and skate wing oven-baked
with capers and garlic (£7.95). Excellent accompanying vegetable
selection – definitely a chip-free zone! Puddings (£2.25) include
lemon tart with fruit syrup and white chocolate cream crunch.
Imaginative set menus – 3-courses (£19.95), 4-courses (£22.95), 5-
courses (£25.00) – available in the restaurant. Four en-suite bedrooms
are pretty basic, on the small side for the size of some of the furniture
and lack many necessary homely touches, especially in the spartan
shower rooms; however, upgrading is due to begin over the winter –
check before booking. *Pub open usual hours, inc Mon-Sat from 5.30pm.*
***Bar Food** 12-2, 6.30-9.30 (Sun 7-9). Restaurant closed Mon. Children
allowed in bar to eat, children's menu. Free House.* ***Beer** Butcombe Bitter,
Worthington, Oakhill Best. Garden, outdoor eating, children's play area.
Family room.* ***Accommodation** 4 bedrooms, all en suite, £49 (single £32).
Dogs by arrangement. Access Visa.*

West Hoathly   **Cat Inn**

| **FOOD** |

Tel 01342 810369

West Hoathly nr East Grinstead West Sussex

Map 11 B6

Homely, half tile-hung pub overlooking the parish church in this
sleepy, off-the-beaten-track Sussex village. Beams, panelling, a fine
inglenook fireplace with ancient carvings and comfortable cushioned
bench seating in cosy alcoves characterise the old fashioned interior,
which remains free of intrusive music and games. Reliable bar food –
listed on a changing blackboard menu – may be pricey, but portions
are generous and the quality of the home-cooked dishes most
acceptable. Typical choices include crab pate, fresh anchovies and
French bread (both £4.55) to start, followed by home-made
hamburger with green peppercorn sauce (£6.75), steak and kidney
pie (£5.95), kidneys in red wine (£6.95) and fillet of sole Bretonne
(£8.95), all served with crisp vegetables. Banana cheesecake and
chocolate mousse (both £2.95) may feature on the short list of
puddings. Peaceful summer seating on the front terrace with village
views. ***Bar Food** 12-2, 7-9.30 (except Sun eve). Children allowed in bar
to eat.* ***Beer** Harveys Best, 3 guest beers. Garden, outdoor eating. Family
room. No credit cards.*

West Huntspill   Crossways Inn

Tel 01278 783756	**B&B**
West Huntspill nr Highbridge Somerset TA9 3RA	Map 13 E1

Popular proprietor-run 17th-century inn located beside the A38 and a handy overnight stop for travellers using the M5 (3 miles from Junctions 22 and 23). Simple old-fashioned interior comprising a series of inter-connecting low-ceilinged rooms, featuring exposed beams, winter log fires, a mix of sturdy furniture and a welcoming atmosphere. Clean and comfortable accommodation in three neat, modern pine-furnished upstairs bedrooms. Two boast compact en-suite facilities, the third's bathroom is private but not en-suite, and all have TV's and beverage-making kits for added comfort. Picnic tables among the fruit trees in the rear garden. *Free House.* **Beer** *Flowers IPA & Original, Royal Oak, Butcombe Bitter, Blakes Bitter. Garden, outdoor eating, children's play area. Family room.* **Accommodation** *3 bedrooms, 2 en suite, £34 (single £24). Children welcome overnight (under-12s stay free in parents' room), additional beds and cots available. Check-in by arrangement. Access, Visa.*

West Ilsley   Harrow Inn   ★

Tel 01635 281260	**FOOD**
West Ilsley nr Newbury Berkshire RG16 0AR	Map 14a C3

A mile from the Ridgeway footpath on the edge of the Berkshire Downs, in a lovely village green setting, complete with lazy ducks on the pond, there are many good reasons to visit the ever-popular Harrow Inn. Within, antique furniture and several country settles create a smartly rustic but simple and old-fashioned atmosphere. There's plenty of space in which to relax and enjoy an excellent pint of Morland (who founded their brewery in this village in 1711, but are now based in Abingdon) and some tip-top food, which is as good as always – the consistency of approach and cooking is admirable. The menu changes seasonally and is supplemented by a daily-changing specials board (broccoli and Stilton tart with walnut pastry £4.85, beef and king prawn kebabs with risotto rice £5.25, macaroni cheese with vegetables £4.50, pork chops with sage, apple and onion rings £4.85, twice-baked cheese soufflé, lamb with redcurrant sauce, chicken with cider and apples) – a variety wide enough to suit all tastes and pockets. Soups, salads, bread and puddings are reliably good, the home-made puddings (pineapple upside down cake, home-made almond ice cream, treacle tart, sticky toffee pudding, 18th-century creamed apple flan with unpasteurised local Peasemore cream from a Guernsey herd) especially, and a fine selection of constantly varying British cheeses puts the seal on a splendid bill of fare. Portions are generous and vegetarians are thoughtfully catered for (perhaps aubergine and sweet potato africaine); all in all, a properly pubby combination of the imaginative and homely, which keeps people coming back. You can even take home one of their particularly good pies. Regular 'pie nights' (Tue as we went to press). A good garden for children has playthings and animals (donkey, ducks, geese, goat, chickens). *Bar Food 12-2.15, 6-9.15 (Sun 7-9). Children allowed in the bar to eat, children's menu.* **Beer** *Morland. Garden, outdoor eating, children's play area. Access, Visa.*

West Pennard — The Lion at Pennard

FOOD
B&B

Tel 01458 832941

Glastonbury Road West Pennard Somerset BA6 8NH

Map 13 F1

A comfortable informality exudes from the central stone-flagged and
low-beamed bar, where easy chairs sit around a huge inglenook that
boasts a roaring log fire in winter. Radiating off are the neatly-set
dining room and a cosy parlour which doubles as both family and
breakfast room. There's local praise for some well-kept Oakhill and
Ash Vine bitters, and for the pool room and skittle alley. Wilkins cask
cider in summer. Menus run from burgers (£1.95) to steaks (£9.50),
with daily specials such as beef and Stilton pie (£4.95), toad-in-the-
hole (£3.50), and home-made pasties with herb pastry (£1.95) added
on the blackboard. A la carte are breaded garlic prawns (£4.50),
Somerset pork chop with apple, cream and brandy (£6.25) and lamb
steak with cranberry and rosemary sauce (£9.25). Sunday lunch is
priced according to the number of dishes (one course £5, three
courses £7). Bright duvets have smartened up the bedrooms in the
adjacent former stable block. Bathrooms are neat, clean and carpeted,
while extras include colour TVs, dial-out phones and radio alarm
clocks. Formerly the *Red Lion*. ***Bar Food & Restaurant Meals***
12.30-2, summer 6.30-9 (Sat to 9.30, Sun from 7). Free House.
***Beer** Oakhill, Wadworth 6X, Bass. Garden, outdoor eating. Family room.*
***Accommodation** 7 bedrooms, all en suite, £45 (single £30). Children
welcome overnight (under 10 free if sharing parents' room), additional beds
(£12). Check-in by arrangement. No dogs. Access, Diners, Visa.*

West Stafford — Wise Man Inn

FOOD

Tel 01305 263694

West Stafford nr Dorchester Dorset DT2 8AG

Map 13 F2

With Thomas Hardy's birthplace at Bockhampton close by, this
homely, thatched village pub is a very popular refreshment spot.
Virginia creeper and a variety of colourful hanging baskets and
flower-troughs adorn the rendered facade. Also on the front wall is a
poem hymning the virtue of ale, attributed to Hardy: 'health lies in
the equipoise', apparently. Inside, the traditional two-bar layout and
central off-sales remains intact, with the public bar sporting a wood-
block floor; a toby jug collection and simple darkwood furniture plus
padded wall-bench seating characterise the modest interior throughout.
If planning to eat, go for the home-made specialities that are
highlighted on the comprehensive printed menu. These may
vary from a freshly prepared soup – potato and onion (£1.50) –
chicken tikka (£4.95) and chili (£3.95) to steak and mushroom
pie (£4.75), chicken en croute (£6.75) and a daily fresh fish dish.
Zoomamadooma, a red kidney bean stew, is the vegetarian choice
available. ***Bar Food** 12-2, 6.30-9. **Beer** Flowers Original, Boddingtons
Bitter. Garden, patio, outdoor eating. Access, Visa.*

West Witton — Wensleydale Heifer

FOOD
B&B

Tel 01969 22322   Fax 01969 24183

West Witton Wensleydale North Yorkshire DL8 4LS

Map 5 D4

The signs of good breeding which abound at John and Anne Sharp's
well-tamed heifer are manifest. At the heart of every good pub is the
bar:- here it holds no more than four tables and attracts a healthy
mixture of residents and locals and dispenses a hearty pint of
Theakstons. To one side a snug room and chintz foyer lounge are

Zzz...

available for sitting out, while to the other the bistro daily pushes out the fatted calf with quite serious intent. Goats cheese served in filo pastry with walnut vinaigrette (£3.25) and prawns a la Pil Pil (£4.50) are typical precursors to lamb's kidneys with Dijon mustard and cream (£7.95) and tagliatelli carbonara (£4.95). Sandwiches are served in the bar at lunchtimes only along with a Yorkshire Cheese lunch (£3.75) of three varieties of Wensleydale of course. Accommodation comprises traditionally furnished and comfortable en-suite bedrooms not only in the pub itself but also in the Old Reading Room, standing in its own garden over the road, and East View House some 50 yards away, also with its own walled garden and housing a small conference facility. All rooms have radio, TV and beverage trays with telephones providing a baby listening facility. *Free House.* **Accommodation** *19 bedrooms, all en suite £70 (Single £49). Dogs welcome in rooms. Garden.* **Bar Food & Restaurant** *12-2, 7-9 (7-9.30 Fri/Sat eve).* **Beer** *John Smith's, Theakston Best & Old Peculier. Access, Visa.*

West Wycombe   George & Dragon

Tel 01494 464414 Fax 01494 462432	FOOD
West Wycombe nr High Wycombe Buckinghamshire HP14 3AB	Map 15a D3

Set in a National Trust village beside the A40, this imposing Tudor coaching inn is due for some much-needed refurbishment, as its rather grubby facade seems to indicate. Despite the run-down air, there are still some reasonable bar snacks on offer. Beyond the fine cobbled archway entrance (one of several surviving original features) lies an appealing period bar with large oak beams, settles and Windsor chairs by a roaring fire. Friendly staff offer a promising menu ranging from potted Stilton (£3.25) and cream of broccoli and bacon soup (£1.75) to decent home-made pies filled with chicken and asparagus, sole and grape or rabbit (from £5.25) and reliable specials like game pastie with sloe and crab apple sauce (£7.25). Follow with a rich, gooey treacle tart or fresh fruit crumble (both £1.95). Investment and structural improvements will extend up the haunted staircase into the nine bedrooms (not recommended until the promised work has been carried out). Peaceful rear garden with a play area for children. *Open 11-2.30, 5.30-11 (Sat 11-11), Sun 12-2.30, 7-10.* **Bar Food** *12-2 (Sun to 1.45), 6-9.30 (Sun 7-9).* **Beer** *Courage Best & Directors, guest beer. Garden, outdoor eating, children's play area. Family room. Access, Diners, Visa.*

Westleton   Crown

Tel 0172 873777 Fax 0172 873239	B&B
Westleton Saxmundham Suffolk IP17 3AD	Map 10 D2

Guests have been accommodated on the site of the Crown since the 12th-century when a priest in charge of Sibton Abbey lived here and took in travellers. Over the years this attractive brick-built pub, located opposite the parish church, has evolved through careful renovation and refurbishment into a well-appointed inn. Public areas are spacious, comfortably furnished and decorated with old local photographs and farm tools and a splendid no-smoking conservatory leads out onto a delightful sunny patio and landscaped garden, complete with aviary. Nineteen ensuite bedrooms are divided between the main building and the converted stables. Standard rooms feature floral fabrics, relaxing easy chairs and free-standing pine furniture, while six luxury rooms boast antique furniture, half-tester or four-poster beds, bidet and jacuzzi baths. Added comforts in all rooms include remote-control TV and video channel, telephones, clock-radios, tea-making equipment and a welcome tray of fruit juices and chocolates. The inn is popular with visiting birdwatchers as the RSPB reserve at Minsmere is close by. Wheelchair access. *Free House. Open 11-2.30, 6-11 (12-2.30, 7-10.30 Sun). Beer Adnams Broadside, Southwold, Marstons Pedigree, Greene King IPA, Abbot Ale, Morland Speckled Hen. Accommodation 19 bedrooms, all en suite £69.50-£89.50 (£49.50-£58.50). Children welcome overnight (price varies depending on age). Garden, outdoor eating. Access, Diners, Visa.*

Weston   Otter Inn

Tel 01404 42594	**FOOD**
Weston nr Honiton Devon EX14 0NZ	**Map 13 E2**

Situated 400 yards off the busy A30 and beside the River Otter, this much-extended 14th-century cottage is a popular refreshment stop en route to and from the West Country, and a particular favourite with families. The original old cottage interior is delightfully unspoilt with a vast inglenook fronted by comfortable armchairs and old tables. Plenty of prints, books and various bric-a-brac make this a cosy and relaxing spot in which to sit. The main bar extension is very much in keeping with heavy beams, a real assortment of old sturdy tables and chairs, an unusual chamber pot collection hanging from the beams and the added touch of fresh flowers on each table. Beyond some double doors is a skittle alley and games room. A printed bar menu highlights many of the usual snacks such as salads (from £5.95), ploughman's (£3.95), filled jacket potatoes (from £2.35) and steaks (from £6.95); main course specialities include honey roast chicken (£4.15), Barnsley lamb chops (£9.65) and monkfish, red sea bream and halibut in banana and mustard sauce (£9.85), all accompanied by fresh vegetables and potatoes. Daily dishes chalked up on a board may feature a hearty portion of home-cooked lasagne served with a generous salad and the freshly-prepared soup – spicy tomato and herb (£1.85). The evening blackboard always lists a choice of fish and meat specials and a vegetarian dish of the day. Children who have been cooped up in the car for long periods will relish the space in the splendid riverside garden, which offers youngsters the chance to paddle in a very safe shallow section of the river. In one corner there is an animal enclosure, with a notice on the gate inviting children in to study and learn about the rabbits and guinea pigs that live in this wild and peaceful part of the garden. There is also a swing and in summer months supervised children's archery is a well-attended event. Children will also be entertained by the resident ducks and chickens. *Free House. Bar Food 12-2 & 6.30-10 (Sun 7-9.30), children allowed in bar to eat. Beer Eldridge Pope Hardy Country, Boddingtons, Worthingtons, guest beer. Garden, outdoor eating, indoor and outdoor play area. Access, Visa.*

Whitchurch   White Swan

Tel 01296 641228	**A**
High Street Whitchurch Buckinghamshire HP22 4JT	**Map 15a D1**

500-year-old, partly-thatched building which has been an inn since the mid-17th century, and still has the unspoilt atmosphere of an old-fashioned country pub with two bars. There's piped music and traditional pub games, but no intrusive modern gaming machines.

Nice old furnishings and fresh flowers. Large variety of snacky food items (not Sun eve). Huge garden to the rear, overlooking fields. *Beer Fuller's. Garden. Family room. Pub closed Sunday evenings. No credit cards.*

Whiteleaf	**Red Lion**	
Tel 01844 344476		**B&B**

Upper Icknield Way Whiteleaf nr Princes Risborough Buckinghamshire HP27 0LL   **Map 15a D2**

Cream and red-painted 17th-century village pub, set back from the lane in a quiet, attractive village. Inside, the two homely and cosy interconnecting rooms and adjacent dining room are neatly arranged with a pleasant mix of polished pine and antique settles, a good log fire and various brasses, sporting prints and dried flower arrangements. Reached via stairs behind the bar are four simply-furnished bedrooms with modern dark-patterned fabrics, TV and tea makers and compact en-suite facilities (only one with bath). Front-facing rooms enjoy good rural views. *Open 11.30-3 & 5.30-11 (Sun 12-3 & 7-10.30). Free House. Beer Hook Norton Best, Wadworth 6X, Morland PA. Garden, outdoor eating. Accommodation 4 bedrooms, all en suite, £39.50 (single £29.50). Children welcome overnight, extra bed supplied. Check-in by arrangement. No credit cards.*

Whitewell	**Inn at Whitewell**	**FOOD**
Tel 01200 448222		**B&B**

Whitewell Forest of Bowland nr Clitheroe Lancashire BB7 3AT   **Map 6 B1**

Set amid the wild beauty of North Lancashire, well away from the hurly burly, the Whitewell Inn stands next to the village church, overlooking the River Hodder (and owns eight miles of fishing rights) in the beautiful, unspoilt countryside of the little-known Forest of Bowland. Back in the 14th century, the inn was home to the keeper of the King's deer, and the Queen still owns the building as part of the Duchy of Lancaster. Inside, it's wonderfully relaxed, laid-back, even mildly eccentric, with a haphazard arrangement of furnishings and bric-a-brac. In the main bar there are wooden tables, old settles, roundback chairs, a stone fireplace, log fire in cold weather, and heavy ceiling beams. An entrance hall has colourful rugs, more settles, even a piano, and a selection of magazines, papers and books for some serious loitering. A wide variety of pictures, dotted about the building, come from the Inn's own art gallery; there's also a small wine merchant business, as well as expensive sweaters and hunting gear in the shop. Food is served in both the bar and restaurant, which overlooks the river; the bar meal selection follows the tried and trusted from mostly fresh local produce, and is decently rather than excitingly cooked. More ambitious cooking is at work in the restaurant, where local ingredients include fish from this very river. The à la carte menu features dishes like potato and wild garlic soup (£2.20), hare casserole (£9) and a combination of poached seafoods (fresh salmon, scallops, prawns and mussels – £10.50). Calorific desserts like sticky toffee pudding (£2.50); a good wine list. There are nine bedrooms, seven of them refurbished with antique furniture, peat fires and Victorian baths. Unusual extras include video recorders and superb Bang and Olufson stereo systems, as well as books, magazines, and a set of binoculars; the best and largest rooms overlook the river and the country beyond. Everything is usually immaculately clean. On sunny days the attractive rear lawn furnished with simple benches is an ideal

spot to relax and soak in the view. **Bar Food & Restaurant Meals**
12-2, 7.30-9.30. Children allowed in bar to eat. Free House.
Beer *Marston's Pedigree, Boddingtons. Riverside garden, outdoor eating.*
Accommodation *9 bedrooms, all en suite, £67 (single £49.50). Children welcome overnight, sofa bed or cot and breakfast £10. Access, Diners, Visa.*

Whitmore   Mainwaring Arms

| Tel 01782 680851 | A |

Whitmore nr Newcastle-under-Lyme Staffordshire ST5 5HR   Map 6 B3

Close to the site of the Manor of Whitmore, which was listed in the
Domesday Book, the same families, Mainwarings and Whitmores,
have run a hostelry here since time immemorial. Today's version, in
cream-painted brick and creeper-clad with an ivy-covered porch, plays
host to a wide cross-section of locals in congenial surroundings.
Timber cross-beams frame the single mahogany bar and access to three
large yet cosy rooms, each with its own log fire in winter. For
summer evening entertainment, tiered patios to the rear are the setting
for regular barbecues. Sundry sandwiches and the likes of deep-fried
fish at lunchtimes only. Three miles from Junction 15 of the M6.
*Open 12-3, 5.30-11 (Fri & Sat 12-11, Sun 12-3, 7-10.30). Resident
ghost. Free House.* **Beer** *Bass, Boddingtons, Marston's Pedigree. Patio.
No credit cards.*

Whitney-on-Wye   Rhydspence Inn

| Tel 01497 831262 | FOOD |
| B&B |

Whitney-on-Wye nr Hay-on-Wye Hereford & Worcester HR3 6EU   Map 9 D4

Set in the heart of Kilvert country, on the A438 about a mile out of
Whitney-on-Wye, this is a well-loved, reliably entertaining inn with a
delightful timbered interior, two attractive bars with real fires, old
furniture and beams aplenty. Nice touches include magazines and
newspapers, creating an atmosphere in keeping with the old library
chairs. The charming dining room and restaurant overlook the garden.
Five comfortable bedrooms have beams, sloping floors, plus an
armchair at the least; some rooms are more romantic; one has a four-
poster. Bar food suggestions include mushroom provençale (£5.25),
spiced chicken and tagliatelle caponata (£5.50). The longer restaurant
menu is as varied: warm seafood salad (£5.95), gravad lax (£5.50),
garlic roasted monkfish (£12.95) and supreme of chicken with oyster
mushrooms (£11.95), plus an excellent choice of farmhouse cheeses.
A 3-course traditional Sunday lunch is available in the restaurant
(£11.95). Summer lunchers can enjoy the view over the Wye Valley
from the terraced garden. **Bar Food & Restaurant Meals** *11-1.45
(Sun from 12), 7-9.45. Children allowed in bar to eat. Beer Bass,
Robinson, Hook Norton. Garden, outdoor eating. Family room.*
Accommodation *5 bedrooms, all en suite, £55 (single £27.50, 4-poster
£75). Children welcome overnight (under-2s stay free in parents' room),
additional beds (£12.50). No dogs. Access, Visa.*

Zzzz...

Whitwell   Noel Arms

| Tel 01780 460334   Fax 01780 460531 | B&B |

Main Street Whitwell Rutland Water Leicestershire LE15 8BW   Map 7 E3

A modest pub very much of two halves, the thatched original
building with a tiny village bar standing sideways on to the road
(A606). Hidden behind is landlord Sam Healey's labour of love, a
stone extension, tucked into the hillside, containing lounge bar, dining

rooms (one with a fish tank), and, above, the wing of dormer-windowed bedrooms. Neatly appointed with colourful duvets and freestanding furniture, all enjoy the benefit of colour TV, radios, phones and beverage trays, though only four have en-suite bathrooms. The remainder share facilities along the tiny corridor. Barely a long cast from the banks of Rutland Water, the bar's a base for fishing stories late into the night, and the hearty fisherman's breakfast makes a fine start the following morning. *Open 10-11 (Sun 12-10.30). Free House.* **Beer** *Tetley Bitter, Burton Ale, Ruddles County. Patio, outdoor eating. Family Room.* **Accommodation** *9 bedrooms, 4 en suite, £49 (single £40). Children welcome overnight (under-12s stay free in parents' room). Access, Visa.*

We welcome bona fide complaints and recommendations on the tear-out pages at the back of the book for readers' comments. They are followed up by our professional team.

Widecombe-in-the-Moor — Rugglestone Inn

Tel 013642 327

FOOD

Widecombe-in-the-Moor Devon

Map 13 D3

Unspoilt gem of a rural pub set beside moorland within walking distance of the picturesque village. Named after the Ruggle Stone, a huge mass of granite nearby, this rustic stone inn comprises two tiny rooms, one a delightful, old-fashioned parlour with beams, open fire and simple furnishings and both are devoid of modern-day intrusions. Excellent Bass and Butcombe Bitter are tapped straight from the cask and served with one of the hearty, home-made 'one-pot' meals – chicken pie (£3.05), steak and kidney pie (£3.45), cauliflower cheese, cottage pie (both £2.75) – that make a satisfying meal. Puddings (£2.25) include blackcurrant tart and walnut and syrup tart with clotted cream. Across the babbling brook to the front of the pub lies a lawn with benches and peaceful moorland views. No children under 14 inside. **Bar Food** *L only 12-2 (till 2.30 Sat & Sun). Free House.* **Beer** *Bass, Butcombe Bitter. Garden, outdoor eating. No credit cards.*

Wigglesworth — Plough Inn

Tel 01729 840243

FOOD
B&B

Wigglesworth nr Skipton North Yorkshire BD23 4RJ

Map 6 B1

For over fifteen years now the Goodall family have operated, enlarged and improved their 18th-century country inn which was once the farm buildings and ale house of a vast Dales estate. This being quite the last place one would expect to find an "American-style Diner", its new found success is all the more remarkable. A rapidly expanding food operation is now based largely on the output of a wood-burning pit barbeque whose contents can be hot- or cold-smoked over hickory, mesquite or oak chippings. Around the resultant rack of ribs (£5.95), hickory chicken (£4.95) and smoked halibut steak (£6.50) is a menu full of Yankeeisms from potato skins with sour cream and hickory dips (£2.75) "thro'" Caesar salad and smoked chicken (£4.75) to "steak and prawn combo" (£9.25). More traditionally, there are still bar snacks served in the original village bar and evening meals in a bright, new conservatory. Accommodation offered is either Standard (over the original pub) or Superior in a carefully conceived extension which blends in immaculately with the original timbered black-and-white frontage. Within are all the trappings of modern-day comfort from TV and radio to direct-dial phones and tea and coffee trays: all the rooms are of a decent size with well-kept en-suite bathrooms and effective double glazing. While the front rooms look across a village street where practically nothing happens from day to day, those to the rear soak in the ever-changing moods of the twin Dales peaks of Ingleborough and Pen-Y-Ghent. *Free House.* **Accommodation** *12 bedrooms, all en suite £47 (Single £33). Cot available at no charge.* **Bar Food & Restaurant** *12-2, 7-10 (restaurant only eve). Children's portions.* **Beer** *Tetley Best, Boddingtons. Children welcome overnight. Garden, outdoor eating. Family room. Access, Diners, Visa.*

Wilmcote   Mason's Arms

Tel 01789 297416	FOOD
Wilmcote nr Stratford-upon-Avon Warwickshire CV37 9XX	Map 14 C1

Just off the A3400 three miles north of Stratford, Wilmcote is the former home of Mary Arden. The home of "pub grub" in the village is to be found at the Mason's, though any journey through its voluminous menus should be trodden with care. There's much to be said for the various sandwiches, and ploughman's with crusty bread and pickle (from £3), but rather less for some uninspired vegetables which accompany the steak and kidney pie (£4.60) and halibut steaks with parsley sauce (£6.90). Look to a specials board for the likes of beef stir-fry with vegetable fried rice (£3.80). Largely unaltered since the gentry's coaches pulled in to water their horses, the Mason's front rooms are evocatively those of a village inn. Twin conservatories to the rear provides refuge from the 52-seater restaurant and offer views of polished motors, potting sheds and rambling pub gardens. *Free House.* **Bar Food** *12-2, 6.30-9.30 (7-9 Sun).* **Beer** *Hook Norton Best, Boddingtons, Wadworth 6X. Garden. Access, Visa.*

Winchcombe   Old White Lion

Tel 01242 603300 Fax 01242 221969	B&B
37 North Street Winchcombe Gloucestershire GL5H 5PS	Map 14 C1

A reminder that good things come in very small packages, the hitherto unsung, 400 year old, Old White Lion is a rare find. Only the tiny enamelled inn sign and black oak door distinguish it from the other listed buildings in North Street. With a minescule front room, tiny rear parlour easy chairs and varnished tables, the whole place has a relaxed and homely air. Six small bedrooms, restored with great care and good taste, also have a special feeling of closeness to antiquity with many of their original features unaffected by careful and unobtrusive addition of the requisite televisions and clock radios, though phones have not been added. While five rooms (including just one single) have en-suite WCs and showers only, there's a roomier 4-poster bedroom with both a corner bath and separate shower en-suite. New owners took over in early August 1994. *Free House.* **Beer** *Marston Best*

& Pedigree, guest beer. Garden. Family room. **Accommodation** *6 rooms, all en suite, from £50 (single £35). Children welcome overnight, additional beds supplied. Access, Visa.*

Winchester   Wykeham Arms   ★   FOOD

Tel 01962 853834 Fax 01962 854411	B&B
75 Kingsgate Street Winchester Hampshire SO23 9PE	Map 15 D3

Tucked away in the narrow back streets of Winchester, immediately south of the Cathedral Close (by Kingsgate on the junction between Canon Street and Kingsgate Street), Graeme and Anne Jameson have turned the mellow, redbrick, 250-year-old 'Wyk' into one of the finest hostelries in the land. The main bar, which is mostly for drinkers, has old-fashioned schoolroom desks with integral seats, some authentically carved with the initials of inattentive pupils from years gone by. Collections of hats, mugs and fascinating old prints and cartoons adorn the bar and no less than six other interconnecting rooms, all set up for eating, with a special dining area for non-smokers. The old pine, candle-lit dining tables each have a brass money slot to collect donations for the upkeep of the cathedral. Much patronised by the Dons from Winchester College, and barristers attending the local courts (among many others), this is probably the best place to eat in town, and booking is essential. A blackboard menu at lunchtime changes daily, offering unusual but successful combinations of flavours like Stilton and quince paté (£3.65), 'Wyk' cottage pie served with crusty bread (£4.75), pork, sage and apple casserole (£5.25). Main course suggestions on the evening menu are fillets of smoked haddock poached in Dijon mustard and caper sauce, filo parcels of rabbit and celery set on a lentil, bacon and tarragon sauce, chicken breast with caramelised onions and celeriac with a chervil jus (all £10.75). A separate pudding menu offers mouth-watering choices like carrot and ginger pudding with fudge sauce and white chocolate and Drambuie mousse with bananas (both £2.95). Twenty names on the well-chosen wine list are also available by the glass, and for summer eating and drinking there is a neat walled garden. Individually decorated bedrooms have stylish matching bedcovers and curtains and mostly honeyed pine furniture. All have mini-bars, television and telephone, plus homely extras like fresh flowers, books, magazines and pot-pourri. Modern en-suite bathrooms, all with showers over tubs, boast quality Woods of Windsor toiletries. First-rate cooked breakfasts, with freshly squeezed orange juice, are served in a charming period breakfast room on the first floor. No children under 14 overnight or in restaurant, three non-smoking rooms. **Bar Food & Restaurant Meals** *(no food Sun) 12-2.30 (sandwiches served till 6), 6.30-8.45.* **Beer** *Eldridge Pope. Garden, outdoor eating.* **Accommodation** *7 bedrooms, all en suite, £75 (single £65). Children over 14 welcome overnight. Access, Visa.*

Wineham   Royal Oak

Tel 01444 881252	A
Wineham nr Haywards Heath West Sussex BN5 9AY	Map 11 B6

Partly tiled and black and white timbered cottage dating back to the 14th century and located on a country lane between the A272 and B2116 near Henfield. It is a classic ale house, a true rural survivor that has been serving the locals for over 200 years and is delightfully traditional and unspoilt in every way. Head-cracking low beams, huge inglenook with warming winter fire, part wooden and part stone flagged floor topped with sturdy wooden furnishing characterise the charming bar and tiny rear room. Old corkscrews, pottery jugs and mugs, old photographs and other old artefacts adorn the walls. Ale is drawn straight from the cask in a rear room and in keeping with ale house tradition food is limited to good freshly-made sandwiches – smoked salmon, cheese, home-cooked ham and beef – and a thick soup served on cold winter days. The pub has been in the same family since 1945. Extensive summer gardens and adjacent children's/function room with TV and books. *Pub open 11-2.30, 5.30-10.30 (Fri & Sat to 11), Sun 12-2.30, 7-10.30.* **Beers** *Whitbread Pompey Royal, Boddingtons, Wadworth 6X, Harveys Best. Garden, lawn, outside eating, tables in garden. Family room. No credit cards.*

Winforton   Sun Inn   ★   FOOD

Tel 01544 327677   B&B

Winforton Hereford & Worcester HR3 6EA   Map 9 D4

Just three miles inside England on the A438 Wye Valley Road, the Sun was our British Meat Pub of the Year award winner in 1992. Tireless and enthusiastic as ever, Wendy Hibbard is, however, rather less an award-seeker than she is dish-crazy. Her seemingly endless stream of inventiveness produces something different and exciting whenever we visit, whatever the season. Her winter regular, the hearty stockpot soup (£1.95) and summer's latest addition, a lettuce and lovage version are a typical case in point: winter's speciality pigeon pie (£7.54), made to Brian Hibbard's "secret recipe" is likely replaced, perhaps, by monkfish medallions (£8.59) with ginger and coriander as the warmer weather approaches. Thai chicken starters (£3.25) now appear in filo pastry with tangy lemon sauce and the new Singapore steamboat prawns are sensationally hot and spicy. Ever-popular, the braised oxtails (£8.94) in cider sauce with root vegetables are salt-free slow-cooking perfected for the traditionalist's palate; those with more adventure enthuse equally over the Kashmiri lamb shoulder (£7.50) in a mildly curried sauce. Carefully cooked and neatly presented dishes of vegetables, lightly honeyed carrots, caraway-seeded cabbage, are the embellishments, rather than mere accompaniments, which serve to point up the star quality of Wendy Hibbard's cooking. Her puddings, conceived both to amuse and satisfy, are equally up to this benchmark – tipsy bread and butter pudding, a nuts-upon-nuts tart (£2.95) and the dangerously moreish figgy ice cream clearly illustrate the point. The three en-suite guest bedrooms are new this year; they share a private entrance and unfussy decor of commendable quality, their accoutrements including TVs, radios, beverage trays, and hairdryers; a private phone is located in the hall. With Wendy and Brian's warm hospitality to look forward to, they are indeed a welcome addition: how refreshing to report on two such progressive publicans who are forever looking to their laurels rather than merely resting on them. **Bar Food & Restaurant** *(except all Tue Nov-May and Tue eve Jun-Oct) 12-2, 7-9.30 (Sat & Sun to 9.45). Children allowed in bar to eat. Free House.* **Beer** *Woods Parish, Jennings Cumberland Bitter. Garden, outdoor eating. Access, Visa.*

Winkton   Fisherman's Haunt Hotel

Tel 01202 484071   Fax 01202 478883   B&B

Salisbury Road Winkton Christchurch Dorset BH23 7AS   Map 14 C4

The river Avon is just across the road from this well-kept, wistaria-clad hotel, which stands on the B3347 Christchurch-Ringwood road about 2 miles from Bournemouth (Hurn) Airport. Stuffed fish and an old well with running spring water are unusual features of the characterful beamed bars, and there is an airy conservatory. The good bedrooms, which are in the main 17th-century building, extended coach house and nearby cottage, blend pretty fabrics with a mixture of modern and traditional furnishings. All offer TVs, telephones and tea-makers and two rooms also boast four-poster beds. *Free House.* ***Beer*** *Ringwood Best & Fortyniner, Bass, Wadworth 6X. Garden. Family Room.* ***Accommodation*** *20 bedrooms, 16 en suite, £59 (single £37.50). Children welcome overnight (under-2s stay free in parents' room, 2-10s £7.50), additional beds, and cots available. Access, Diners, Visa.*

Winsford   Royal Oak Inn

FOOD
B&B

Tel 0164 385 455	Fax 0164 385 388

Winsford Exmoor National Park Somerset TA24 7JE

Map 13 D2

A lovely 12th-century thatched inn (now a hotel) in a sleepy picture-postcard Exmoor village resistant to street lighting and noise. Despite the hotel status, Steven's cosy inn doubles as both village local and celebrated haunt for the hunting and fishing folk who throng the place, especially in winter. The hotel waters run through the village and additional beats, fishing tuition and the hire or purchase of fishing tackle can be arranged. In the pleasantly refurbished, semi-smart and relaxing interior, a large selection of home-made food is available in the form of bar snacks and restaurant meals. In the bar, suggestions include pasties (£2.95), jacket potatoes with various fillings (£2.95), sandwiches with ham or roast beef (£2). For a more substantial lunch in the restaurant, choose perhaps leek and potato soup, followed by a local fresh trout and finish with a sweet from the trolley. In the evening, the dinner menu (3-course table d'hote (£22.50) or à la carte) may offer button mushrooms stuffed with Stilton paté or fresh crab and asparagus wrapped in filo pastry, followed by strips of fillet steak sautéed with mushrooms, granary mustard, wine and cream sauce or half a fresh, locally bred Gressingham duck with pear and orange sauce. Bedrooms (five are in a modern annexe around the rear courtyard) are individually appointed, with pretty floral fabrics and freestanding furniture; those in the main house are cottagey and some nestle under the thatched eaves. Get up in time for breakfast – the poached haddock is marvellous. A family can be accommodated in a converted cowshed (sleeps two adults and three children). The inn's also notable for its unusually good vegetarian choice – an entire menu in the restaurant: mushroom and nut casserole, pancakes filled with vegetables with a gouda sauce. Children can eat in the back bar only. *Pub open 11-11 (Sat 12-10.30)* ***Bar Food*** *12-2, 7.30-9.15 (6.30-9.30 summer, 7-9 or 9.30 Sun).* ***Restaurant Meals*** *12.30-1.30 (Sun only), 7.30-9.30. Children under 10 allowed in bar to eat. Children allowed in bar to eat (High tea 6pm).* ***Beer*** *Whitbread Flowers Original, IPA. Riverside garden, outdoor eating.* ***Accommodation*** *15 bedrooms, all en suite, £85 (single £60). Children welcome overnight (£15 in family cottage) additional beds (from £5) and cots supplied. Check-in before 6pm. Garage. Access, Diners, Visa.*

Zzzz...

Winslow   Bell Hotel

B&B

Tel 01296 714091	Fax 01296 714805

Market Square Winslow Buckinghamshire MK18 3AB

Map 15a D1

Handsome Georgian coaching inn that proudly overlooks the market square in this pleasant small town. After a period of uncertainty new owners have over the past year reversed the fortunes of this welcoming establishment, which features a good pubby bar with heavy beams and inglenook fireplace, and comfortable lounge areas with oak and leather furniture, easy chairs, attractive prints and plates. There are seventeen bedrooms, two designed for the disabled, all spacious with floral fabrics, reproduction darkwood furniture – one with a four-poster – clean, tiled bathrooms and added extras like TVs, telephones, tea-makers, hairdryers and trouser presses. *Free House.* **Beer** *Green King. Garden. Family room.* **Accommodation** *17 bedrooms, all en suite, £39.50 (single £34.50). Children welcome overnight. Access, Diners, Visa.*

Winster   The Brown Horse

Tel 015394 43443	**FOOD**
Winster nr Bowness-on-Windemere Cumbria LA23 3WR	**Map 4 C3**

Hosting a once-beleaguered Lakeland pub only five miles from Bowness (on the A5074), the Dohertys have quickly established an identity all their own by producing what is, without doubt, uncommonly good pub food. Stephen Doherty's prowess at the stove is founded in a pedigree which might intimidate many an untrained amateur. Yet his success in these totally untried surroundings is firmly rooted in sound common sense; his kitchen provides meals of genuine quality at affordable prices. At lunchtime the roast loin of pork served with crackling, savoury stuffing and apple sauce (at £5) and a same-day dinner special of beef fillet with creamy white wine sauce with green peppercorns (£7.50) challenges many a "country house" kitchen's ability to compete, while a sensibly short seasonal menu offers choices as simple as aubergine and polenta (£4.50) and fillets of prime plaice (£6) alongside neatly-crafted "ragout fin" of chicken, mushrooms, and Parmesan (£3.50) and excitingly flavoured Thai prawns in crispy beignet batter with rémoulade sauce (£6.50). With such overwhelming appeal for his food, we strongly advise that you book, and for any special event book early. There will be few boozers in heavy boots venturing to this sturdy pub in any great numbers but there already exists a carefully trodden path to the Dohertys' door by a well-heeled clientele. *Free House.* **Bar & Restaurant Meals** *12-2, 6-9.* **Beers** *Jennings Bitter, Marston Pedigree. No credit cards.*

Winterton-on-Sea   Fisherman's Return

Tel 01493 393305	**FOOD**
	B&B
The Lane Winterton-on-Sea Norfolk NR29 4BN	**Map 10 D1**

Small it maybe, but this prettily-kept row of former fishermen's cottages is an ideal hang-out for locals and visitors alike, be they fishermen or not. Built in traditional brick and flint, the buildings are probably 16th-century, and unaltered over the last quarter century or more. The public bar is lined in varnished tongue-and-groove panelling and hung with sepia photographs and prints of Lowestoft harbour, the Norfolk Broads and the pub itself. Some of these, movie buffs will note, are not as old as they seem. Centrestage, the cast-iron wood-burner opens up in winter to add a glow of warmth to an already cheery atmosphere. A smaller and possibly older lounge, low-ceilinged, with a copper-hooded fireplace and oak mantel, is carpeted these days and ideal for a quick, if cramped, snack. Families will more likely head to the "Tinho", a timbered rear extension of pool table and games machines which leads mercifully quickly to a lovely enclosed garden and adventure playground. The menu's pretty comprehensive.

Individual savouries and omelettes, generously garnished, are the popular choices; there are pasta dishes at £4.75 and sea trout with herb dip and new potatoes at £5.75. Overnighters, too, are in for a treat. A tiny flint-lined spiral staircase leads up under the eaves to three cosy bedrooms, which share the house television (propped up on a seaman's trunk) and two bathrooms (one with shower only). The largest, family room also has a sitting area with its own television. Modest comforts, maybe, but entirely adequate for a brief stay, a stone's throw from the beach and long walks over the dunes. Visitors are made truly welcome by John and Kate Findlay, and seen on their way with the heartiest of seafarer's breakfasts. *Bar Meals 11.30-2, 6-9.30 (winter from 7). Children's menu. Beer Adnams. Garden, outdoor eating, children's play area. Family room. Accommodation 3 bedrooms, sharing 2 bathrooms, £40 (single £28). Children welcome overnight. Check-in by arrangement. No credit cards.*

Withypool	**Royal Oak Inn**	**FOOD**
Tel 0164 383 506 Fax 0164 383 659		**B&B**
Withypool Somerset TA24 7QP		Map 13 D1

A stylish, friendly and thoroughly laid-back country inn, well-beloved of hunting and shooting parties in season. The Royal Oak was a favoured haunt in the 1860s of 'Lorna Doone's' author, R.D. Blackmore. Despite modern-day bedroom comforts, little enough appears changed today: hunting trophies adorn the Resident's Bar, while the Red Room Bar is dedicated more to angling memorabilia. Here the blackboard menu of scampi and prawn brochettes, lamb casserole with lentils and poached local salmon supplements a bar menu all-encompassing from sandwiches to grilled steaks. At dinner, table d'hote menus in the restaurant start at £19.50 for 3 courses with main courses à la carte (supreme of chicken stuffed with spinach; grilled fillet of haddock with tarragon sauce) priced around £14. The comfortable, recently refurbished, bedrooms have a comprehensive range of facilities – though a couple of bathrooms have shower/WC only – while by night the peace and quiet are total. Withypool is just off the B3223 from Dulverton. Not suitable for children under 10. *Bar Food 12-2, 6.30-9.30 (Sun from 7). Restaurant Meals 12-2, 7-9. Free House. Beer Wessex Bitter, IPA, Flowers. Accommodation 8 rooms, 7 en suite, £72 (single £32). Access, Diners, Visa.*

Woburn	**Black Horse**	
Tel 01525 290210		**FOOD**
1 Bedford Street Woburn Bedfordshire		Map 15a E1

Located in the main street of this small upmarket town and close to the Safari Park, the 16th-century Black Horse is renowned far and wide for their excellent steaks and fresh fish cooked on a Forge Grill which is the centre-piece between two well-maintained, pine-furnished rooms. Prime English meat, Billingsgate fish and Abbotsbury oysters are displayed on the 'Butcher's Shop' counter. Steaks are cut in front of you to your requirements and charged by the ounce – rump 90p, fillet £1.20, salmon and halibut £1 – then cooked on the grill and served with a jacket potato and salad. Various marinaded steaks can be ordered and there is a choice of some 14 different mustards to accompany your meat. Other choices on the menu include oysters (£1.35 each), lobster (£12-£20), sea bass (£12-£15) and duck breast in gin (£9.50), with lighter options ranging from cold fish, meat and quiche salads/ploughman's to three hot dishes like Mexican lamb, venison pie and coconut chicken (each around £5). Only the Grill is in operation on Saturday and Sunday evenings, and just the normal bar fare is available on Saturday lunchtimes. Country Style Inns. *Pub 11-2.30, 6-11 (Sun 12-3, 7-10.30).* **Bar Food** *12-2.15 (to 2 Sat & Sun), 6.30-10 (note Grill times above).* **Beer** *Wadworth 6X, Theakston's Old Peculier, Ruddles County, guest beer. Access, Visa.*

Wolterton	**Saracens Head**	**FOOD**
Tel 01263 768909		**B&B**
Wolterton nr Erpingham Norfolk NR11 7LX		Map 10 C1

To locate this isolated and very individual rural inn follow signs for Erpingham off the A140 Aylsham to Cromer road, then pass through Calthorpe before bearing left on to a narrow lane, signposted Wolterton; your efforts will be well rewarded. Only 250 yards from the main gates to Wolterton Hall, this most unusual red-brick inn was built in 1806 by Lord Walpole as a coaching inn for the main house and was modelled on a Tuscan farmhouse. Inside, the ambience is decidedly civilised and upmarket with high ceilings, soothing terracotta painted walls with friezes, stylish patterned clothed tables, open log fires and an eclectic mix of built-in leather wall settles and wicker chairs. Scatter cushions, magazines, newspapers and evening candlelight enhance the relaxed atmosphere. Landlord/chef Robert Dawson-Smith produces an interesting, short selection of dishes that are listed on a twice-daily changing blackboard menu. No chips or scampi are served here, so expect well-above-average pub fare and book a table! Imaginative choices may begin with Stilton and orange pate (£3.50), crispy aubergines and red pesto mayonnaise (£3,25), Morston mussels in cider and cream (£3.95), followed by braised local pigeon in masala (£7.25), stir-fry white fish with ginger and orange (£6.95), all accompanied with a dish of well-cooked vegetables. Finish with a traditional pudding (£2.50), such as sticky brown bread and butter pudding or upside down apple tart. Popular events are the roast Sunday lunch (£5.60), the special Sunday 2-course supper (£5.50), a weekday "two choice" lunch (£4.50) and the monthly "feast" nights (£11.50) – French, seafood and Old English for example. Short list of well chosen wines. Individual charm extends to the top floor of the inn into the three attractive ensuite bedrooms, each furnished with free-standing pine – one with brass bed – wicker chairs and quality fabrics. TV, hairdryer, and beverage-making facilities are standard, but fresh milk and earthenware jars of tea and coffee are a welcome touch, as are the excellent breakfasts which are well worth getting up for. Sheltered courtyard garden and delightful walled garden for sunny days. *Free House.* **Bar Food** *12.15-2.15, 7-9.30.* **Accommodation** *2 bedrooms, both en suite £45 (Single £35). Children welcome overnight. Check-in by arrangement.* **Beer** *Adnams, Hook Norton Old Hooky, guest beer. Garden, eating outside. Access, Visa.*

Wooburn Common	**Chequers Inn**	**FOOD**
Tel 01628 529575 Fax 01628 850124		**B&B**
Wooburn Common nr Beaconsfield Buckinghamshire HP10 0JQ		Map 15a E3

The charming 17th-century Chequers Inn lies midway between the M4 and M40, perched on the rolling Chiltern Hills and has been carefully and lovingly developed over the years by Peter Roehrig. Find him chatting to the locals in the convivial beamed bar, where quality wines by the glass are supplemented by simple but stylish lunchtime snacks. Choose from open sandwiches (£3), ploughman's, celery and Stilton (£2.35), tossed salad of avocado, smoked salmon and prawns with hazelnut dressing (£5.85) or mignons of pork fillets with a Dijon mustard and red wine sauce (£6.95). Two 3-course table d'hote menus (lunch £14.95 and dinner £17.95) are available in the restaurant as well as à la carte dishes. The evening menu offers four choices in each category – perhaps chicken liver and veal paté, then ragout of monkfish in a tomato and cream sauce with strips of smoked salmon, followed by summer pudding with fruit coulis. Home-made petits fours and good coffee to finish. The cottagey bedrooms all have en-suite facilities and are equipped with TVs (plus Sky), telephones, clock-radios, trouser presses, tea/coffee making facilities. One room has a four-poster. *Open 11-11 Mon-Sat, regular hours Sunday.* **Bar Food** *12-2.30.* **Restaurant Meals** *12-2.30, 7-9.30. Free House.* **Beer** *Eldridge Pope Thomas Hardy, Dorchester, Royal Oak & Blackdown Porter, Fuller's ESB, Cotleigh Rebellion, Blackdown Porter. Garden, outdoor eating.* **Accommodation** *17 bedrooms, all en suite, £77.50 (single £72.50). Children welcome overnight, additional beds available. No dogs. Access, Visa.*

Woodbastwick   Fur & Feather

Tel 01603 720003	A

Woodbastwick Norwich Norfolk NR13 6HQ   Map 10 D1

Nestling within an unspoilt estate village on the edge of the Norfolk Broads, this picturesque thatched brick building was converted from two farm cottages into a pub as recently as 1992. Owned by Woodforde's brewery, who established their brewhouse in the farm buildings behind some eight years ago, the Fur and Feather serves as the "Brewery Tap" dispensing their full range of eight award-winning cask ales. As one would expect, tip-top Wherry Best Bitter, Nelson's Revenge, Porter, Baldric, the champion beer Norfolk Nog and the deceptively strong Headcracker can all be enjoyed in the traditionally refurbished bars or on the peaceful front lawn on fine weather days. *Open 11-3, 6-11 (Sun 12-3, 7-10.30).* **Beer** *Woodforde's. No credit cards.*

Woodchester   Ram Inn

Tel 01453 873329	A

South Woodchester nr Stroud Gloucestershire GL5 5EL   Map 14 B2

One of Gloucestershire's more way out pubs both in clientele and location – a splendid spot above the A46 (follow signs uphill to South Woodchester). Visitors are rewarded with fine views back down the valley and across to Minchinhampton Common. Niceties are kept to a minimun with picnic tables on a tarmac patio, assorted pine tables and bentwood chairs in the L-shaped bar and plain floorboards surrounding the single stone-built box counter. Three log fires are a great draw in winter. The Ram's pride and joy, however, is its selection of real ales – (any nine are on tap at any one time) – running through the alphabet from Archers and Boddington to Smiles Exhibition and Uley Old Spot. These are devoted drinker's ales, to be savoured somewhat seriously: in our recent experience the food was rather less satisfying. *Free House.* **Beer** *Uley Bitter & Spot, Archers, Boddington, Smiles (Bristol), Butcombe, Morland Old Specked Hen, Websters Green Label. Garden. Access, Visa.*

Woodnewton   White Swan

Tel 01780 470381	**FOOD**
Main Street Woodnewton Northamptonshire PE8 5EB	Map 7 E4

When the White Swan was closed and bought by a developer in 1988 the villagers thought they had lost their pub, but after a campaign which involved residents lobbying council planning meetings, the White Swan was saved and reopened, after extensive renovations, in 1990. Simple, single oblong room, one end focusing on the bar and a wood-burning stove, with the other end neatly set up as a dining room. New favourites for the bar – chicken curry Madras, a decent steak and kidney pie (both £4.50) – with the emphasis being on the 'Continental' restaurant menu (also served in the bar), which covers a world-wide selection of dishes quite admirably. For example, under the Mexico heading there is beef Mexican (£8.50) and stuffed peppers (£7.95) and Italy is represented with steak Italiano (£8.95) and lasagne (£7.25). Further choices include Greek meze for two (£14.95 each), Moroccan couscous (£11.95) and Turkish lamb kebab (£8.25). Appropriate dishes are served with excellent, well-cooked vegetables. Various 'country' nights – Egyptian (£15.95) – and occasional summer barbecues. *Bar Food 12-2, 7-10. Children allowed in bar to eat, children's menu. Free House.* **Beer** *Greene King IPA, Fullers, London Pride. Garden, outdoor eating. Access, Visa.*

Woodstock   Feathers Hotel

Tel 01993 812291 Fax 01993 813158	**FOOD**
	B&B
Market Street Woodstock Oxfordshire OX7 1SX	Map 14a B2

Eight miles north of Oxford, within walking distance of Blenheim Palace. Situated in the heart of a historic village, behind a 17th-century Cotswold-stone frontage, the Feathers offers a comfortable range of superior accommodation with bedrooms differing in price by size (suites are particularly attractive). All have elaborately draped curtains and a useful range of extras that includes mineral water, chocolates, fresh flowers, magazines and tea on arrival. Some rooms have draped awnings over the beds, while the best have four-posters. Bathrooms are luxuriously fitted in marble throughout, with bathrobes and an abundance of toiletries provided. The upstairs drawing room with a library and open fire is the most inviting of the day rooms and a cosy bar has flagstone flooring and an open fireplace. During warm weather the courtyard garden is a delightful spot for light meals (which are also served in the bar). A quiet, sophisticated air pervades the dining room, where à la carte and fixed-price menus provide a choice of interesting options. Recommended in our 1995 *Hotels & Restaurants Guide.* Lighter eating in the Whinchat Bar – from pickled quail's eggs with saffron mayonnaise (£4.50) to baked forest mushrooms and goat's cheese with sweet peppers (£5.25), honey-baked ham with new potato salad (£7.35), and toasted marshmallow with berry compote (£4.25). Service is courteous and efficient. *Bar Food & Restaurant Meals 12.30-2.15, 7.30-9.15 (no bar food Sat or Sun eve; open Bank Holidays). Beer Wadworth 6X. Courtyard garden. Family room.* **Accommodation** *17 rooms, 16 en suite, £99-£145 (single £75/£98). Children welcome overnight, additional beds (£20) and cots available. Access, Diners, Visa.*

Woolhope   **Butcher's Arms**

Tel 01432 860281

FOOD

B&B

Woolhope Hereford & Worcester HR1 4RF

Map 14 B1

The infectious enthusiasm of the Power family and a commendable
reliance on local produce bring customers from far and wide to their
pub which is not easily found down the narrow country lanes. A
black-and-white timber frontage, copiously hung with flower baskets,
and the neat, colourful brookside garden and patio induce an
anticipation more than adequately fulfilled by the food. Leek and
hazelnut terrine (£3.25), mushroom biryani (£5.50) and Woolhope
wild rabbit and cider pie (£5.25) head the bar menu, while on
weekend evenings (bookings advisable) the restaurant menu extends to
snails in garlic butter (£3.75), wild Scottish salmon with fennel and
hollandaise (£9.75) and Herefordshire beef fillet with peppered sauce
(£11.95). Plenty of home-made sweets – almond pudding (£2.25),
chocolate brandy refrigerated cake (£2.25). The three bedrooms are
small and cosy: decor is in an appropriate cottage style, and they share
a bathroom. There's abundant peace and quiet in this hidden valley,
and a substantial breakfast, come the morning. *Bar Food 12-2, 7-9.30.*
Restaurant Meals 7-10 (Fri & Sat only). Free House. Beer Hook Norton
Best & Old Hookey, Marston's Pedigree, guest beer. Garden, outdoor eating.
Accommodation 3 rooms £39 (not en suite), £25 single. Check-in by
arrangement. Children welcome overnight (under-10s stay £10).
Accommodation closed 24 & 25 Dec. No credit cards.

Zzzz...

Woolley Moor   **White Horse**

Tel 01246 590319

FOOD

White Horse Lane Woolley Moor Derbyshire DE5 6FG

Map 6 C3

Bill and Jill Taylor are celebrating their tenth year as landlords of the
smart, friendly and very popular White Horse. Approached from the
A61 at Stretton, Woolley Moor is a tiny hilltop hamlet above the
river Amber at the point where it flows into Ogston reservoir. The
large paddock and garden have a sandpit, swings, and small adventure
playground to help keep the youngsters happy and there's a newly
built boules pitch. There are at least two dozen trestle tables outside;
bag one for a summer lunch, but remember the number before going
inside to order. Within there's restaurant seating for around 60 people,
and it fills up quickly, so booking is recommended. This dining area,
reached through a stone archway, was originally the pub lounge, a
cottagey, carpeted area in two sections, with large picture windows
and attractive lace-clothed tables. On the printed menu, dishes such as
beef Italienne (£3.40), game pie (£3.95), or mushroom stroganoff
(£3.95) are offered. Desserts could include treacle and walnut tart or
lemon and ginger crunch (£1.75). Blackboard specials may include
garlic prawns (£1.95) or kidneys provençale (£4.50). It's substantial
stuff, nicely cooked and presented and, above all, tasty. Half a dozen or
so New World wines now feature on the short wine list. The Smoke
Room still remains the village local, with is quarry-tiled floor, red
leather banquettes, Britannia tables and prominent dartboard; Monday
night dominoes are played in a seriously competitive spirit. This is
where a good drop of ale comes in. In addition to draught Bass, a
healthy rotation of guest beers is publicised well in advance, a good
proportion of them from independent breweries. Piped music, when
playing, is of the restful kind. This is a smart and impressive pub,
professionally managed, and it runs like clockwork. *Bar Food &*

*Restaurant Meals 11.30-2 (Sun 12-2.30), 6.30-9 (except Sun, Sat to
11). Children allowed in bar to eat. Children's menu. Free House.
Beer Bass, Worthington Best, Highgate Dark, two weekly guest beers.
Garden, outdoor eating, children's play area. Family room. Pub closed Sun
eve. No credit cards.*

Woolverton   Red Lion

Tel 01373 830350	FOOD
Woolverton Somerset BA3 6QS	Map 14 B3

Set back from the busy road and fronted by neat lawns, this smart pub
has flagstone floors, exposed stone walls, and open fires, plus a
pleasingly informal approach to good eating. Hearty portions of
interesting salads (from £4), attractively presented, and a variety of
filled baked potatoes, priced according to which of the twenty fillings
you choose (£1.20-£3.95), dominate the bar menu. New on the
menu this year are a range of grill steaks (from £8), burgers (from
£3.95), carbonnade of beef pie (£4.50), seafood mixed grill (£6.25)
and scampi (£5.95). The extensive garden with flowerbeds and a large
walnut tree is lovely for a summer lunch. *Open 11.30-11 (Sun-Tue to
10.30). Bar Food 12-2.30 (Sun to 2.15), 7-10. Children allowed in bar to
eat. Beer Bass, Wadworth 6X & IPA, John Smith's. Garden, outdoor
eating. Family room. Access, Visa.*

Wootton Rivers   Royal Oak

Tel 01672 810322	FOOD
	B&B
Wootton Rivers nr Marlborough Wiltshire SN8 4NQ	Map 14a A4

Situated only 100 yards from the Kennet and Avon Canal in one of
Wiltshire's most picturesque villages, this 16th-century, black and
white timbered, thatched pub offers visitors an old-world charm in its
low heavily beamed and comfortably furnished bars and dining room.
Plates and prints adorn the walls and atmosphere in which to enjoy
well-kept ale – Wadworth 6X drawn from the wood and Brakspear's
– and a wide choice of bar food. The comprehensive printed menu
features standard snacks and favourites, including a good range of
steaks, while the photocopied handwritten menu advertises the freshly
prepared daily specials. Begin with home-made mushroom and garlic
soup (£1.75) or avocado, mozzarella, tomato and basil salad (£3.75)
followed by a hearty steak and Guinness pie – full of chunky meat in
a rich gravy – fillets of pork in green peppercorn sauce (£7.75), all of
which are served with a selection of fresh vegetables. Popular
puddings (all £2.75) include treacle and almond tart and Greek
yoghurt with honey and kiwi fruit. Six fresh, clean and comfortable
bedrooms – four with en-suite or private facilities – are located in a
large modern house to the rear of the pub. Guests have the use of
communal tea and coffee making facilities in the TV lounge and for
early risers their own breakfasts, the ingredients of which are supplied,
with the washing-up being attended to later. Breakfast can also
be taken in the pub. Pub areas are less suitable for children under
four. *Bar Food & Restaurant Meals 12-2.30, 7-9.30 (Sun to 9).
Children over 4 allowed in bar to eat, High Tea 6.30pm. Free House.
Beer Brakspear Bitter, Wadworth 6X and IPA, 2 guest beers. Patio,
outdoor eating. Family room. Accommodation 6 bedrooms, 4 en suite,
£40 (single £27.50). Children welcome overnight, (under-2s stay free in
parents' room, 2-5s £5, 5-10s £10s), additional beds available. Dogs by
arrangement. Access, Visa.*

Wootton Wawen · The Bull's Head

Tel 01564 792511

Stratford Road Wootton Wawen Warwickshire B95 6BD

FOOD

Map 14 C1

A smart, black-and-white timber-framed pub just a mile or so from the picturesque village of Henley-in-Arden (A3400) with flagstone floors and low, gnarled oak beams. Determined emphasis on fresh fish attracts an ever-increasing clientele, the iced seafood platter (£17.50pp min two) proving a tempting indulgence on a hot summer's evening. Notable equally for size and variety, hearty portions of moules marinière (£4.95), lemon sole in caper sauce (£8.95), whole red snapper with orange sauce (£9.75) and sea bream with spinach sauce (£8.50) tempt diners choosing from the daily-updated blackboards. The less fishy, meanwhile, may plump for calf's liver, bacon and onion marmalade (£10.50) or escalope of turkey with avocado and mozzarella (£7.75). A fair and generously-priced selection of wines by the glass is supplemented by good-value bin-end bottles. *Pub open 12-10.30.* **Bar Food & Restaurant Meals** *12-2.30, 7-10.30 (Sun to 9.30). Children allowed in bar to eat. Free House.* **Beer** *Marston's Best & Pedigree, Morland Old Speckled Hen, Wadworth 6X, Greene King Abbot Ale & Fuller's London Pride. Garden, terrace, outdoor eating, barbecue. Children under 14 in dining room, garden and terrace only. Access, Visa.*

Worth · St Crispin Inn

Tel 01304 612081

The Street Worth nr Sandwich Kent CT14 0DF

B&B

Map 11 D5

Zzzz...

Peacefully located along the village street just off the A258 south of Sandwich, this attractive and pleasantly refurbished local has a single character bar, which is full of heavy timbers, brick walls, a big log fire and a collection of rustic pine tables and chairs. Interesting range of eight real ales tapped straight from the cask behind the bar. Spacious rear terrace with an all-weather retractable awning and an excellent summer garden with benches among the flower borders and trees. Four charming upstairs bedrooms – one with a fine half-tester bed – have stripped pine doors, a good mix of older/antique style furniture and clean en suite facilities with showers over tubs. Three further rooms are housed in a converted outbuilding and feature modern built-in furniture and compact bathrooms. All have satellite TV and tea-makers. The pub is a handy base for golfers playing the Royal links courses at the end of the lane. *Pub open 11-3, 6-11 (Sun 12-3, 7-10). Free House.* **Beer** *Mansfield Bitter, Shepherd Neame Master Brew, Gales HSB, Marston's Pedigree. Rear garden and courtyard, summer barbecue, outdoor eating area.* **Accommodation** *7 bedrooms, all en suite, from £50 (single £35). Children welcome overnight (under-2s stay free in their parents' room), additional beds available £5. Check in by arrangement. Access, Visa.*

Wybunbury · Swan Inn

Tel & Fax 01270 841280

Main Road Wybunbury Cheshire CW5 7NA

FOOD

Map 6 B3

Few signs remain here of the 18th-century farmhouse with an unusual bow-front opposite St Chad's church, where only the 15th-century leaning tower survives today. The Church was abandoned in 1972, and the tower's last vertical correction occurred in 1989. Even more recent straightening-out of the Swan divides the interior into alcoves separated by curtains, brass rails and banquettes, and warmed by real fires in winter. The menu is equally traditional and unchanging, supplemented by daily specials boards: filled baguettes of steak and onions (£3.30), steak and kidney pie (£4.10) and home-made summer fruit pavlova (£2.50) are not untypical. Outside in summer are a 'Pop Shop', and plentiful new children's play equipment and neatly-spaced picnic tables on a lawn by the lych gate. *Bar Food 12-2, 7-9.30 (except Sun eve). Children's menu. Beer Boddingtons, Jennings, Tetley, guest beers. Garden, children's play area. Family room. Pub closed Sunday evening. No credit cards.*

Wye   New Flying Horse Inn

Tel 01233 812297	B&B
Upper Bridge Street Wye Kent TN25 5AN	Map 11 C5

With a 400-year-old history, this well maintained village centre inn is characterised by low ceilings, black beams, open brickwork and a large open fireplace. The spick and span main bar has gleaming, copper-topped tables and simple chairs while the neat lounge bar boasts some comfortable armchairs and access to the splendid sun-trap patio and extensive lawned garden. Six main building bedrooms – including one four-poster and one spacious family room – have been smartly refurbished with attractive pastel colours, quality fabrics and some decent individual pieces of furniture. Good well kitted out bathrooms with showers over tubs. Upgrading in similar style is due to begin on the four uniform, en-suite stable block rooms. Invicta Country Inns. *Pub open 11-9.15 (Sun 12-9.15). Beer Masterbrew, Spitfire, Bishops Finger, Masons Pale. Garden and patio, outdoor eating area, summer barbeque. Accommodation 10 bedrooms, all en suite, from £45 (single £35). Children welcome overnight (under-5s stay free in parents' room). Dogs by arrangement. Access, Visa.*

Zz_{zz…}

Wykeham   Downe Arms Hotel

Tel 01723 862471 Fax 01723 864329	B&B
Wykeham Scarborough North Yorkshire YO13 9QB	Map 5 F4

An imposing stone building at the roadside (A170) just five miles from Scarborough, the hotel has remained part of the Downe family estates since its conversion into a coaching inn some 120 years ago. A century later the Orangery, designed by Sir Martin Beckett on an 18th century theme, was added to provide extensive function facilities. The rather less-than-pubby bar and lounge nonetheless remain suitably comfortable and intimate for the resident guest, and there's a spacious garden and patio for family use in summertime. En-suite facilities were added to the bedrooms just seven years ago, although the listed nature of the original structure limited several to WC and shower rooms only. All are kept, however, in apple-pie order with bright matching fabrics adding a welcome splash of colour. *Free House. Open 11-11 (12-3, 7-10.30 Sun). Family room. Accommodation 10 bedrooms, all en suite £35 (Single £25). Children welcome overnight. Cot and high-chair available, extra child's bed if sharing (£17.50). Garden. Beer Tetley Best. Theakston XB & BB. Access, Diners, Visa.*

Zz_{zz…}

Wyre Piddle   Anchor Inn

Tel 01386 552799   **FOOD**

Main Street Wyre Piddle nr Pershore Hereford & Worcester WR10 2JB   Map 14 B1

Standing low and white-painted at the roadside, bedecked with fairy
lights and flower baskets, the Anchor reveals its wealth of talents on
further investigation. This is one of the region's premier summer pubs
with its grassy terraces and rolling lawn graduating down to the Avon
river bank where holidaymakers may moor their narrowboats. Views
across the river take in the verdant Vale of Evesham whence come the
asparagus and strawberries that enrich the summer menus. Menus
change daily in any case: popular for snacks are the home-made soup
(£1.95), and home-made chicken, mushroom and brandy paté
(£2.10). Home-made steak and kidney pie (£4.90), spinach canneloni
(£4.60) and vegetable Dauphinoise (£4.90) are substantial bar meals,
with spotted dick or chocolate pudding and chocolate sauce (£1.85) to
follow. An elevated dining room has possibly the best view; the
restaurant menu offers reliable steaks with fowl and fishy alternatives
and a family Sunday lunch (3-course £10.95). Watch out for the
theme nights, live music and ten real fruit wines. *Bar Food &*
Restaurant Meals 12-2.30 (Sun to 2), 7-9.45 (Sun to 9 in bar, no food
Sun eve in restaurant). Children allowed in bar to eat, children's menu.
Beer Marston's Pedigree, Flowers, IPA, Boddingtons and one guest beer.
Garden, children's play area. Family room. Access, Visa.

Wytham   White Hart

Tel 01865 244372   **A**

Wytham Oxfordshire OX2 8QA   Map 14a C2

This famous old creeper-clad pub in the centre of the pretty village of
Wytham has a part-panelled bar with a flagstone floor, open fire and
high back settles. Outside is a very pretty courtyard garden, popular
for barbecues in the summer beyond which extra seating has been
provided by converting the loose boxes in the old stables into booths.
Beer Ind Coope. Garden. Family room. Access, Visa.

Yarmouth   The Bugle Hotel

Tel 01983 760272   Fax 01983 760883   **A**

The Square Yarmouth Isle of Wight PO41 0NS   Map 14 C4

Lively seaside pub in the town's main square. A warren of rooms
offers a choice of drinking areas with a nautical theme throughout.
Pleasant paved rear beer garden with picnic tables. Regular live music
twice a week. Car parking behind the building, entrance to left of
pub. Accommodation (not inspected) in ten rooms upstairs.
Convenient for the Lymington ferry. *Open 10.30-11, Sun regular*
hours. Beer Wadworth 6X, Flowers Original, Boddingtons, Morland Old
Speckled Hen, guest beers. Paved beer garden. Family room. Access, Visa.

Yattendon   Royal Oak

Tel 01635 201325   Fax 01635 201926   **FOOD**
                                                              B&B
The Square Yattendon nr Newbury Berkshire RG16 0UF   Map 14a C4

Dating back to the days of Oliver Cromwell, the creeper-clad Royal
Oak is only ten minutes' drive from Junction 13 of the M4, at the
heart of a pretty Berkshire village. Food continues to be the main
attraction in both the busy beamed bar (where all tables are set for
diners). A door leads straight out from the tiny bar counter into a

ZZZz...

walled garden where a few tables nestle under vine-clad trellises; in summer this is a delightful spot for a drink – at other times of the year almost every visitor has come to the pub comes for the food (although the quality continues to vary following several changes in chef and management over the last couple of years). Nevertheless, prices are kinder than in recent years for dishes like home-made pasta with smoked salmon and fresh basil (£4.75/£7.95), baked spinach and Gruyère tart (£7.25), fish and chips (£6.95), lemon tart (puds £3.75/£4.50). Sunday lunch is £12.50/£20. Upstairs, three of the five bedrooms have smart en-suite bathrooms (the other two have their own private bathrooms across the hallway) and feature king-size beds and generous towelling. Some rooms overlook the small garden, others the quiet village centre. Now run by Regal Hotels. **Bar Food** *12-2.30, 7-10 (to 10.30 Sat, 9 Sun). Free House. Garden, outdoor eating.* **Accommodation** *5 rooms, 3 en-suite, £80, single £70. Children welcome overnight. Access, Diners, Visa.*

Yealand Conyers — New Inn

Tel 01524 732938

FOOD

40 Yealand Rd Yealand Conyers Carnforth Lancashire LA5 9SJ

Map 4 C4

Signed off the A6 north of Carnforth, and just a mile or two short of the Cumbrian border, the village attracts its fair share of visitors both to Leighton Hall and the nearby Leighton Moss Nature Reserve. An added attraction, conveniently located between the two, is Ian and Anne Dutton's ivy-clad listed pub, acquired on lease from Hartleys just a year ago. Cumbrian foodies connect the Dutton name with the Miller Howe Café in Windermere and this by association with John Tovey, whose proteges pepper the Lake District. Here the village's only pub bar is newly gentrified with carpeting and marble-topped tables and regularly doubles as the overflow to a 40-seat dining area, daily filled to capacity. Food-wise the legacy, if not the hand of Tovey remains; the ubiquitous side salad bowls are forcefully flavoured not only with orange, fresh pineapple and grapes but also dried banana and candied walnuts beneath a cream cheese dressing and mustardy vinaigrette. All-day snacks include home-made soup (carrot and coriander, perhaps (£1.60) filled baps and snacks which include the "Miller Howe cheese and herb paté" (£3.25). Look to the blackboard for main courses which may include Indian mushrooms (£5.50), haddock fillet with tomato and cream sauce (£5.95) and lambs' liver with onion marmalade and red wine gravy (£5.95). Puddings (at £2.50) include sticky toffee and tipsy trifle. Expansion now looms with an 80-seat restaurant in the adjacent barn and overnight accommodation above it at an advanced stage of planning.
Open 11-11. **Bar Food & Restaurant Meals** *11-9 (Fri-Sat to 9.30).* **Beer** *Hartleys XB, Robinson Best Mild, Bitter & Old Tom. Garden, outdoor eating. Access, Visa.*

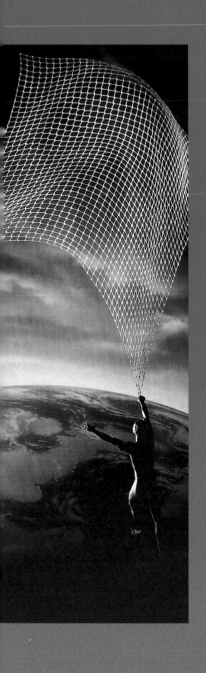

BIG
on choice.

Choosing the right tariff is important if you're to get the best value from your mobile phone.

Cellnet offers a wide tariff choice so you can choose the best combination of affordability and network features.

What's more, we make it easy to identify the tariff that is ideal for your needs.

For further information call
0800 214000

If you need...

- National network coverage
- Lower call costs – business hours
- Advanced call handling services
- Business information lines
- Large choice of handsets

...you need

primetime ™

Cellnet's premier TACS business service..Ideal for the business user needing to make more than 2 calls a day during working hours.

If you need...

- Special call rates within M25
- Access to national network
- All services supported by Cellnet Primetime
- Large choice of handsets

...you need

citytime ™

Ideal for frequent business users who make most of their calls from in and around London, but who still need to be able to make and receive calls from anywhere in the country.

If you need...

- Low cost off-peak calls
- National network coverage
- Callback intelligent messaging

...you need

lifetime ™

Ideal for less frequent users (1 or 2 calls per day) – personal or business – who are likely to receive more calls than they make.

cellnet

If you need...

- **International Roaming**
- **Optimum call quality**
- **Enhanced security**

...you need

primetime™
plus

Cellnet's new digital service.
Ideal for business users who travel
extensively in the UK and abroad, and
who need to keep in touch – and be
contactable – at all times.

For further information call
0800 214000

Using your mobile overseas.

In addition to superb
voice quality, and
enhanced call
security, Cellnet's
digital service
enables Primetime
Plus subscribers to
keep in touch, not
only throughout the
UK, but also while
travelling overseas.

primetime™
plus

For further information call
0800 214000

Scotland

Aberdeen   **Prince of Wales**

Tel 01224 640597	**FOOD**
7 St Nicholas Lane Aberdeen Grampian AB1 1HF	Map 3 D4

By a modern shopping centre (St Nicholas) in the heart of the city the Prince of Wales dates back to the middle of the last century ('est 1850') and still has a very Victorian feel with bare board floor, old flagstones, panelled walls, some booth seating and the longest bar counter in town. Good plain cooking is available at lunchtimes only from a self-service counter. There are always salads, jacket potatoes (from £2.60), a soup (the likes of Scotch broth or lentil), and pies (chicken and ham £3.50, steak and kidney £3.30) made properly with the short pastry actually cooked on the pie, plus a changing selection of other items like fresh haddock with cheese sauce (£3.50), spaghetti carbonara (£2.90) and a single home-made dessert of the day. In addition a pile of filled baps (all at 80p) are made and served over the bar until they run out – usually at about tea time. *Open 11am-11pm (to midnight Thu, Fri & Sat, Sun 12.30pm-11pm).* **Bar Food** *11.30-2 Mon-Sat only. Free House.* **Beer** *Bass, Caledonian 80/-, Theakston Old Peculier, Orkney Dark Island, guest beers. No credit cards.*

Almondbank   **Almondbank Inn**

Tel 01738 583242	**FOOD**
Main Street Almondbank Tayside PH1 3NJ	Map 3 C5

☺

Just off the A85 to the west of Perth, on the village main street, the whitewashed Almondbank Inn enjoys fine views over the River Almond from its small well-kept rear garden. It's not a quiet pub: a juke box in the bar regularly pumps out the latest hits, and there's a pool table on the first floor. Food is taken fairly seriously, however, and the Birdcage Bistro, despite some rather gimmicky, tacky descriptions ("our birds of paradise", "have an ice day" and "salad days are here again") produces generally pleasing food, the majority of it from fresh produce, including some first-rate home-made chips. All the beef used is Aberdeen Angus from the licensee's own family butcher, and even the scampi is fresh and crumbed on the premises. The menu itself is long, running from first courses like "name that tuna" and deep-fried Camembert with cranberry sauce (£2.75), to main courses such as steak and onion pie (£3.95), oriental of chicken (£4.85), and a whole list of Angus minute steaks with a variety of sauces (all £4.85). All come with fresh vegetables, as well as the aforementioned chips. Puddings are largely ice-cream based and there's good cappuccino (80p) and espresso coffee. On Friday and Saturday evenings, a slightly different menu is heavy on steak (Western sizzler Mexicano sirloin £9.50) and chicken dishes (supreme of chicken Carvoeiro laced in a banana demi-glaze with peaches and bananas £6.95), and prices throughout are very reasonable. The uniformed staff are friendly and approachable and the locals, gathered on stools at the bar, are also only too willing to chat. Pub not suitable for children under 11. *Open 11-11.30 Fri & Sat, 12.30-11 Sun, regular hours other days.* **Bar Food** *12-2.15 (Sun from 12.30), 5-8.30 (Fri/Sat 6.30-10). Children's menu. Free House.* **Beer** *Greenmantle Ale. Riverside Garden (River Almond), outdoor eating. Access, Visa.*

Anstruther   Dreel Tavern

Tel 01333 310727	A
16 High Street Anstruther Fife KY10 5DL	**Map 3 D5**

Attractive, traditional three-storey 16th-century stone pub with a
garden overlooking Dreel Burn. Real fires. *Open 11-11 (Sat to 12,
Sun from 12.30). Free House.* **Beer** *Alloa Beers, Tetley Bitter, Caledonian,
guest beers. Garden. No credit cards.*

Applecross   Applecross Inn

Tel 015204 262	FOOD
	B&B
Shore Street Applecross Highland IV54 8LR	**Map 2 A3**

If you don't fancy going over the highest pass in the British Isles (and
it's a bit hairy in parts) take the equally glorious 'shore' route to find
this most unpretentious of pubs that looks out across Raasay to the Isle
of Skye beyond. Run by expatriate Yorkshirefolk Berni and Judith
Fish, with Bernie looking after the bar while Judith makes good use of
excellent seafood in the kitchen. The blackboard menu includes the
likes of local cod in batter (£4.25), steaks and chicken roasted with
garlic and herbs (£4.75), but the things to go for are the queen
scallops cooked in wine and cream with mushrooms (£5.95), squat
lobster cocktail (£3.25), dressed crab salad (£5.95) perhaps, or a half-
pint of shell-on prawn tails with a dip (£4.95). Homely puds like
rhubarb crumble and raspberry cranachan (both £1.95) and a good
cheeseboard follow. Five modest bedrooms are clean and cosy and
share a shower room and more appealing pine bathroom. A peat fire
warms the small lounge that is also used by the owners. No smoking
in the bedrooms, but the large garden by the shore is a puffer's retreat.
Thirty to fifty malt whiskies on offer. *Open 11am-12pm (to 11.30 Sat,
from 12.30 Sun), closed 2.30-5 Tue-Fri, Sun eve and Mon lunch in
winter.* **Bar Food** *11-9 (from 12.30).* **Beer** *McEwan Export, 80/-.
Seashore garden.* **Accommodation** *5 bedrooms, £40 (single £20).
Children welcome overnight (under-5s stay free in parents' room, 5-14s
£10). Accommodation closed 25 Dec and 1 Jan. Access, Visa.*

Ardentinny   Ardentinny Hotel

Tel 0136981 209 Fax 0136981 345	FOOD
	B&B
Ardentinny Loch Long nr Dunoon Strathclyde PA23 8TR	**Map 3 B5**

35 miles from Glasgow, this west-coast droving inn lies on a small
promontory in Loch Long surrounded by the Argyll Forest Park. The
Viking and Lauder Bars have stunning views and access to the gardens

Zzzz...

☺

and beach. Lots of local produce – particularly strong on venison,
lamb, salmon, lobster and crab. Popular dishes from the bar are West
Coast clam chowder (£2.25), crab cakes (£3.95), venison sausages
with onion sauce (£4.25), and lemon sole on the bone (£8.50). The
restaurant table d'hote menu (£19.50) offers the likes of seafood crepe
with cream and herb sauce, Musselburgh pie or poached fillet of
salmon Glayva and a choice of Scottish cheeses or puddings (boozy
bread and butter pudding or McCallum – shortbread, ice cream and
jam sauce). Good wine list. Popular with Clyde yachtsmen at
weekends and fishermen. Bedrooms are good-sized, neat and bright,
with white units or period furniture; some have showers only. The
hotel has a guest boat to journey up Lochs Long and Goil. *Pub open
11-11 all week.* **Bar Food** *12-2.30, 6.30-9.30 (Sat & Sun noon-11).*
Restaurant Meals *7.30-9. Children's menu, children allowed in bar to eat.
Seaside garden, outdoor eating. Family room.* **Accommodation** *11*

bedrooms, all en suite, £86 (single from £45), reductions in Spring.
Children welcome overnight, additional beds (£8), cots supplied (£3).
Hotel closed 1 November to 15 March. Access, Diners, Visa.

Ardvasar   Ardvasar Hotel

Tel 0147 14 223	**B&B**
Ardvasar Sleat Isle of Skye Highland IV45 8RS	**Map 3 A4**

Bill and Gretta Fowler's handsome, white-stone coaching inn dates
back to the 18th century, and is a mile from the Armadale ferry (from
Mallaig), in the wooded Sleat peninsula (often referred to as the
Island's Garden). Not far from the shore, it has superb views across the
Sound of Sleat to the mountains beyond. Good choice of whiskies, as
one might expect! Accommodation in ten room, all en suite. Open all
day in summer months. Car hire in Broadford (17 miles away, closer
to the Kyle of Lochalsh-Kyleakin ferry). *Beer* Tennent's. *Patio/terrace.*
Accommodation 10 rooms, all en suite £60. Accommodation closed late
December to March. Access, Visa.

Brig O'Turk   Byre Inn

Tel 01877 376292	**FOOD**
Brig O'Turk by Callander Central FK17 8HT	**Map 3 B5**

With a lovely wooded setting deep in the Trossachs, this former, now
somewhat extended, cattle byre has a sort of hotchpotch Victorian
flavour (*pace* the piped music) in both the rough-walled original byre
with its iron 'tractor seat' stools at the bar counter and in the carpeted
eating room beyond with antique and reproduction dining chairs.
During the day, it operates very much as a regular pub with a bar
lunch menu including various sandwiches (all at £3.55) along with
haddock in batter (£5.55), Carrick cream and damson wine paté
(£3.55), deep-fried spicy mushrooms (£2.95), beef steak and oyster
pie (£5.95), and the like. While at night, it becomes more of a
restaurant (although one can still have just a drink) with formal à la
carte menu only served throughout: main dishes (all under £10)
might include grilled halibut with dill, sirloin steak filled with haggis
and topped with Islay sauce, guinea fowl with tarragon and white
wine sauce – there's also always a vegetarian dish of the day. Just 24
wines on the list but 20 of them available by the glass. Tables outside
for drinking and lunchtime eating. Lots of newly created parking
space. *Open 12-11 May-Sep. Bar Food 12-2.30, 6-9. Free House.*
Beer Greenmantle Ale, Broughton Special. Garden, outdoor eating. Visa.

Burrelton   Burrelton Park Hotel

Tel 0182 87206 Fax 0182 87676	**FOOD**
	B&B
High Street Burrelton Tayside PH13 9NX	**Map 3 C5**

A long, low roadside inn in typical Scottish vernacular style, as neat
outside in its brown and cream livery as it is well-kept within. An
extensive all-day menu of home-cooked fare ranges from lentil soup
(£1.30), Lancashire hot pot (£3.95) and steaks to gravad lax (£3.75),
whole peppers stuffed with ratatouille (£3.25) and schnitzels of pork
with apples, onions and cider (£5.95) plus good home-made fruit pies
(£2.20) amongst the puds. Eat either in the bar with its green stained-
pine cladding and tile-topped tables or (until 6.30 pm, after which it's
reserved for the à la carte menu) the smart restaurant which features
some fine oriental rugs on the walls. Six spotless, low-ceilinged
bedrooms have TVs but no phones, and good en-suite bathrooms, each

with thermostatically-controlled shower over the tub. Efficient double glazing effectively cuts out the traffic noise. Note that credit cards are not accepted for bills of less than £20. *Open 12-10.45 (Sat & Sun to 11.15)* **Bar Food** *12-10.30.* **Restaurant Meals** *6.30-10. Free House.* **Beer** *Theakston's, McEwan's 80/-. Family room.* **Accommodation** *6 bedrooms, all en suite, £45 (single £30). Children welcome overnight, additional cots available. Dogs by arrangement. Pub closed 1 Jan. Visa.*

Busta   **Busta House Hotel**

Tel 0180622 506   Fax 0180622 588

Busta Brae Shetland Islands ZE2 9QN

FOOD
B&B
Map 2 D1

ZZz_z... Zzz_z...

This 16th-century former laird's home overlooking the sea is a tremendously civilised hotel in a wild place, simply furnished in Scottish rural style. Open to non-residents for good home-cooked bar lunches and suppers – smoked Shetland salmon (£3.95), pork and pepper terrine (£2.95), stuffed courgettes with tomato and fresh chili sauce (£4.85), peppered chicken and pork fillet with rice (£5.95), followed by bramble Cranachan or orange and lemon cheesecake (both £2.05). The restaurant offers a 5-course daily-changing fixed-price menu (£20.50) which could include deep-fried fresh local squid with spicy tomato sauce, roast breast of duck with hazelnut and orange sauce, followed by home-made toffee and Malibu ice cream. All fresh vegetables, and Raven Ale from 'nearby' Orkney. 136 malt whiskies on offer! Four acres of walled garden, small private sea harbour, and holidays arranged of the fly/sail and drive kind too. P&O ferries sail to the Shetland Islands from Aberdeen. **Bar Food** *12-2 (Sun 12.30-2), 6.30-9.30 (6.30-9 winter, except Fri & Sat).* **Restaurant Meals** *7-9. Children are allowed to eat in the bar.* **Beer** *Orkney Raven Ale. Garden, outdoor eating.* **Accommodation** *20 bedrooms, all en suite, £80 (single £60). Children welcome overnight (if sharing parents' room £10), additional beds and cots available. Bar and accommodation closed 22 Dec-3 Jan. Access, Diners, Visa.*

Canonbie   **Riverside Inn**

Tel 013873 71512

Off A7 Canonbie Dumfries & Galloway DG14 0UX

FOOD
B&B
Map 4 C2

ZZz_z... Zzz_z...

This pristine white-painted Georgian country inn is in a quiet spot overlooking the river Esk, just over the Scottish border, some twelve miles off the top of the M6. Within, it's authentically rural rather than rustic in style, neat, clean and simple with a definite and individual charm which is, however, not the nicotine-stained creaky timbered gloom of the classic English alehouse. The carpeted bar has simple country chairs, some cushioned, some not, around sewing machine tables, and a stone fireplace and bar front; a few discreet decorations line the plain cream walls, framed fishing flies, the odd old cider jar, but there are otherwise few frills. The dining room is similar, but with proper eating-height tables and chairs, and the small, cosy residents' lounge, which has the air of a private-house sitting room, has a chintzy three-piece suite and a few other chairs arranged around a log-effect fire. Bedrooms are the prettiest feature of the inn, two of them with draped bedheads, another with a four-poster bed, and all individually styled with good-quality fabrics and thoughtful little extras, electric blankets among them. Bathrooms are spotless, with decent toiletries. Bar food is never less than satisfactory, occasionally excellent, and takes particular care with first-rate fresh ingredients – local fish (some of it from the river only yards away), local suppliers, an increasing use of organic and farm produce, vegetables from their own garden, and a fine range of unpasteurised British cheeses (selection £3.50). The long-standing hosts share the cooking duties, producing as starters home-made soups (often intriguing combinations like carrot and sage £1.50); light but well-flavoured terrines and patés – especially the fishy ones, a smoked mackerel and horseradish, smoked haddock and egg mousse and mushroom and cream cheese terrine (all £3.95). Main courses offer casseroles like venison in red wine with green peppers and wild rabbit in cider (£6.25-£6.95), home-made salmon fishcakes with hollandaise (£6.25) or chargrilled Aberdeen Angus steak (£10.95), proper fish and chips, and the fish kebabs (£5.95) are always worth a try. Bread comes from the renowned Village Bakery at Melmerby. Gorgeous and often unusual puddings too; they use their own ice cream in the profiteroles. There's also a daily-changing 5-course table d'hote restaurant menu (£22) – baked garlic oysters, roast crispy duck with soft peppercorn and strawberry sauce. Satisfying, hearty breakfasts. *Bar Food 12-2 (except Sun), 7-9. Restaurant Meals 7.30-8.30 (except Sun). Free House. Beer Yates and guest beer. Children allowed in bar to eat. Garden, outdoor eating. Accommodation 6 bedrooms, all en suite, £72 (single £55). Children welcome overnight (cot age free if sharing parents' room). Dogs by arrangement. Pub and accommodation closed 2 weeks February and 2 weeks November. Access, Diners, Visa.*

Carbost   Old Inn

Tel 01478 640205	**B&B**
Carbost Isle of Skye Highland IV47 8SR	Map 2 A3

On the shores of Loch Harport, and near the Talisker distillery, a charming, chatty little island cottage, popular as a walkers' base. Accommodation is now offered in six rooms, all en suite; one family room has a connecting bunk room for children. Occasional entertainment in summer. *Open all day in summer. Family Room. Lochside patio/terrace, children's play area. Children welcome overnight. Access, Visa.*

Castlecary   Castlecary House Hotel

Tel 01324 840233 Fax 01324 841608	**B&B**
Castlecary Village by Cumbernauld Strathclyde G68 0HD	Map 3 C5

The original private house has been extended to incorporate a large lively bar with fruit machines, a large selection of draught beers and a more peaceful, partitioned-off 'snug' with plush seating. Good modern bedrooms, popular with the commercial trade, are mostly in a couple of newly-built 'cottage' blocks set motel-style around the car park. Comfortable beds have crisp cotton sheets and feather pillows and all rooms have direct-dial phones, remote-control TV, beverage tray, trouser press and fully-tiled bathroom (about half with tub and half with showers). Four single rooms in the main building share a shower room and come at a considerably reduced rate. *Pub open 11-11 Sun-Wed, 10-11.30 Thurs-Sat. Free House. Beer Belhaven, Caledonian, Bass, John Smith's Magnet, Worthington, Stones. Accommodation 40 bedrooms, 35 en suite, £45. Children welcome overnight (0-12yrs free if sharing parents' room), additional beds (£10) and cots available. Access, Diners, Visa.*

Clachan Seil   Tigh-an-Truish Inn

Tel 01852 300242

Clachan Seil by Oban Seil Strathclyde PA34 4QZ

FOOD

B&B

Map 3 B5

18th-century inn right on the sea by the Atlantic Bridge. Boarded
nicotine yellow ceiling, old pine bar counter and twin dartboards;
popular with locals. Limited winter menu (perhaps only soup and
sandwiches), but recommended for high-season bar food – home-made
soup (£1.50), venison in Drambuie and cream (£6.50), beef and
mushroom pie (£5.30), locally caught prawns (£6.50), roast lamb and
pork, followed by such home-made sweets (all £1.80) as chocolate
biscuit cake and sticky toffee pudding. Bed and breakfast is available in
two good-sized bedrooms, one with bath, the other shower only, but
breakfast is still a self-service affair. The inn has its own petrol station
"across the way". *Open all day in summer, usual hours in winter.* **Bar
Food** *12-2.15, 6-8.30. Vegetarian dishes. Children's portions. Free House.*
Beer *McEwan 80/-, Tartan. Garden, outdoor eating. Family room.*
Accommodation *2 bedrooms, both en suite, £40 (single £25). Children
welcome overnight, additional beds (£5). Accommodation closed
December/January. No credit cards.*

Clachan Seil   Willowburn Hotel

Tel 01852 300276

Clachan Seil by Oban Seil Strathclyde PA34 4TD

FOOD

B&B

Map 3 B5

Zzzz...

Although an island, Seil is joined to the mainland by a single-span
stone bridge built in 1792 and locals will enjoy telling you that it is
still the only such "bridge across the Atlantic". Delightfully situated on
the shore of Seil Sound, the Willowburn is not really a pub or inn but
a small cottage hotel built in the '60s. There is, however, a somewhat
pubby bar with pine ceiling, wood-burning stove, bar counter built of
local slate and a blackboard menu of good bar snacks that feature local
seafood like squat lobsters with lemon mayonnaise dip (£5.95) and
half-a-pint of prawns (£3.65) along with spicy bean and vegetable hot
pot (£4.40), chicken in a basket (£4.40), gammon steak with
mushroom and onion sauté (£4.90), sandwiches, steak and home-made
puds such as hot toffee sponge and rum and apple meringue (all at
£2.45). Tables outside on the lawn that runs down to the edge of the
water are popular when the weather and the midges allow. Both the
comfortable residents' lounge and dining room enjoy fine views across
the sound as do all but one of the neat, well-kept bedrooms all of
which have TVs, tea-making kit and modern, en-suite bathrooms
(four with shower and WC only). Half-board terms only. Credit cards
for restaurant meals and accommodation only. *Bar Food 12.30-2.*
Restaurant Meals 7-8. Children allowed in bar to eat. Free House.
Beer *Tartan Special, Younger's 60/-. Garden, outdoor eating.*
Accommodation *6 bedrooms, all en suite, £60 (single £30). Children
welcome overnight (under-5s stay free in parents' room, 6-13s half-price).
Hotel closed Nov-Easter (open for New Year). Access, Visa.*

Crail   Golf Hotel

Tel 01333 450206

4 High Street Crail Fife KY10 3TB

B&B

Map 3 D5

Neat old black and white inn in the centre of town with a choice of
bars, one modestly comfortable in red plush, the other more
characterful with exposed stone walls and beamed ceiling. Upstairs,
five immaculate bedrooms have pretty duvets with matching curtains,

pine furniture and neat en-suite shower rooms with WC. All have remote-control TVs and tea/coffee-making facilities but no phones. A further TV with satellite channels is to be found in the comfortable and appealing residents' lounge. No real ales. *Open 11-12 (Sun 12-12). Family room.* **Accommodation** *5 bedrooms, all en suite, £40. Children welcome overnight (Under-5s stay free in parents room, 5-12s half-price), additional beds and cots available. Dogs by arrangement. Access, Visa.*

Cromarty   **Royal Hotel**

Tel 01381 600 217	**B&B**
Marine Terrace Cromarty Highland IV11 8YN	**Map 2 C3**

Formed out of a row of 18th-century coastguards' cottages facing the Cromarty Firth, the black and white painted 'Royal' is now under the hospitable Morrisons, and is a hotel of considerable charm. Except in the warmest of weather a real fire burns in the homely lounge off which a Lloyd-Loom-furnished sun lounge looks across the road to the water beyond. The lounge bar features armchairs along with banquettes or you can challenge the locals to a game of pool or darts in the Public Bar. Immaculate, individually decorated bedrooms, each with a sea view, have traditional furniture and crisp pure cotton bedding. *Bar open 11-11 (Sat to 11.30pm, Sun to 12.30). Free House.* **Beer** *Belhaven Best. Garden, children's play area. Family room.* **Accommodation** *10 bedrooms, 8 en suite, £53 (single £30). Access, Visa.*

Zzzz...

Dundee   **Mercantile Bar**

Tel 01382 225500	**A**
100-108 Commercial Street Dundee Tayside DD1 2AG	**Map 3 C5**

A large, reconstructed, family-run Victorian bar in an old converted haberdashery shop setting. Over 500 photos and prints with a trading or drinking theme adorn the walls and over 150 malt whiskies are on offer. Reasonable Dundee prices throughout. *Open 11-11 (Sat 11-midnight). Free House.* **Beer** *McEwan's 80/-, Maclay's 80/-, Burton Ale, Belhaven's St Andrew's Ale, Theakston's Best & Bitter, Greenmantle, Younger's No.3. Pub closed Sundays 25 Dec and 1 Jan. Access.*

Dysart   **Old Rectory Inn**

Tel 01592 651211	**FOOD**
West Quality Street Dysart Fife KY1 2TA	**Map 3 C5**

Just a few hundred yards off the main road from Kirkcaldy to Leven, in the pretty village of Dysart, is the imposing single-storey Rectory Inn, resplendent on its corner site perched above the fishing harbour, and with a delightful walled garden. The main bar is beamed, while a second room is served by a large hatch, and there's a third small room through the dining area. Furnishings are a mixture of old solid wood tables and chairs and more modern upholstered bench seating. Dining is very much the thing, and tables are pre-set with mats (no cloths). Fresh flowers and free-range butter are plus points. An extensive menu is supplemented by daily specials listed on a blackboard in the main bar. At lunchtime: potted beef (£2), lamb goulash with yoghurt (£4.55), haggis Drambuie (£2.95), smoked ham shank (£4.35), venison and mushroom casserole (£4.85); at suppertime vegetable mulligatawny (£1.80), boiled leg of ham and asparagus with Stilton sauce (£5.25). Delicious fresh cream pavlova (£1.90) or bread & butter pudding (£1.25) are bar favourites for puddings. Salads are of the help-yourself sort, from around eight different selections at the hatch. Real coffee with accompanying cream is a bonus and of the bottomless sort. Many fellow-lunchers are evidently regulars, on first-name terms with the owner-licensees, who are, however, commendably uncliquey and friendly to strangers. It's also a popular business lunch venue in a small local way. The menu's quite different in the evening in the dining room, with lots more meat and fish dishes – chilled courgette and rosemary soup with hot mustard bread (£2.70), duck and port terrine (£3.25), 8oz prime Aberdeen Angus steak with a whisky sauce (£12.30), salmon off-the-hook in Vermouth and white wine sauce (£11). There's a variety of steaks – one dish features three medallions with three different sauces (£15). A whole Stilton is renewed each week and at least seven wines are served by the glass. Vegetarians are not left out, a choice of four dishes includes rice and vegetable stuffed pancakes with a cheese sauce (£4.70). *Bar Food & Restaurant Meals 12-2, (Sun 12.30-2.30), 7-9.30 (except Sun). Children over 8 allowed in bar to eat. Free House. Beer McEwan's 80/-. Garden, outdoor eating. Pub closed Sun night and all Mon, 1 week mid-Jan, 2 weeks mid-Oct. Access, Visa.*

Edinburgh   Doric Tavern Wine Bar & Bistro

Tel 0131-225 1084   **FOOD**

15-16 Market Street Edinburgh Lothian EH1 1DE   Map 3 C6

Wine bar style upstairs, particularly as the first encounter is with the little bistro-style eating area; the separate little bar is at the back, often crammed with students and other trendy types. But there's no mistaking it's a pub downstairs, in the spartan public bar, complete with dartboard by the door (watch out when entering). Start with the 'Doric kebab' (£4.95) or mixed seafood chowder (£3.95), followed by Szechuan-style beef (£9.50), aubergine and mozarella grilled with cheese (£6.95), or haggis, whisky, neeps and tatties (£10.25). Tremendous atmosphere in the evenings, with deep reds and blues, and candlelight. Twelve wines available by the small or large glass, parking difficult. *Open noon-1am (Thu-Sat to 2am, Sun closed except during Edinburgh festival). Bar Food 12-10.30. Children allowed in bar to eat, children's menu. Beer Bass, Caledonian, Maclay 80/-, McEwan 80/-, Worthingtons, Bellhaven Best. Pub closed 25 & 26 Dec, 1 & 2 Jan. Access, Visa.*

Edinburgh   Fishers

Tel 0131-554 5666   **FOOD**

1 The Shore Leith Edinburgh Lothian EH6 6QW   Map 3 C6

Fishers is a jewel cast up from the sea, an outstanding seafood speciality bar which serves full meals all day, noon 10.30 pm. It's taken root in a renovated corner building at the end of The Shore, at the foot of what looks like an ancient bell-tower or lighthouse. The bar area, in which you can also eat, groups high stools around higher-still tables. Up a short flight of steps, the main eating area features light-wood panelling with night-sky blue tables and chairs, windows half of frosted glass, half giving a view to the harbour and beyond, and all presided over from a great height by a bejewelled mermaid figure. The pricing structure and the variety of food on offer are admirably suited to most appetites and pockets, whether for serious eating or quick snacking. It's worth going the full three rounds from starter to pudding, and make an evening of it, when it's also wise to book; word is spreading. In addition to the photocopied-handwritten menu, a blackboard of daily specials offers a host of starters and main courses which should appeal

to more than fish fans alone. The creamiest, most deeply delicious
salmon soup (£2.75) competes for attention with fish patés and
oatcakes (£2.85), mussels in white wine, garlic, tomato and herbs
(£3.50), seafood platter (£10.75) or one of the day's specials; a sheep's
cheese and olive salad (£6) in a creamy sauce fills a whole platter,
with little room left for the new potatoes, garnished with mint. Salads
are crunchy, fresh and in plenty – endive, Chinese leaves, tomatoes,
radishes, mangetout and spring onions. Chose your dressing from a
piquant selection of onion, hazelnut or raspberry vinaigrette, or mix
your own combination from the bottles of Spanish olive oil and
French champagne vinegar thoughtfully provided on each table. If any
room remains, there are simple home-made fruit flans, pies and
crumbles (£2.95). Altogether excellent quality and value for money.
Open all day 11am-10.30pm (winter to 10). **Bar Food & Restaurant
Meals** *12-10.30 (from 12.30 Sun). Children allowed in bar to eat. Free
House.* **Beer** *Caledonian 80/-, guest beer. Riverside, outdoor eating. Family
room. Pub closed 25 Dec, 1 Jan. Access, Visa.*

Edinburgh   Stockbridge Bar

Tel 0131-220 3774	**FOOD**
44 St Stephen's Street Edinburgh Lothian EH3 5AL	**Map 3 C6**

A well-known pub in a trendy part of town which, on Sunday
mornings, becomes a bolt-hole for morning-after blues and can usually
provide a friendly opinion on the day's rugby and golfing prospects.
The two-part eating area sits 18 comfortably in appropriately relaxed
surroundings. Don't be put off by the numerous framed rugby
pictures decorating the walls: scrumming is only necessary for the bar
stools. Service is casual but prompt, and ever-respectful of the sanctity
of your Sunday paper. This is a place for big, filling breakfasts (£4):
the full, traditional line-up of bacon, eggs, sausages, beans, black
pudding and potato scones, all remarkably low on the grease and black
bits so often expected from a fry-up. Practically everything on the
menu (even the toast and marmalade) could be prefixed with
"mansize" and is at, £4, including tea or coffee; exceedingly good
value for money. Some popular typical bar snacks and meals include
potato and leek soup (85p), mushrooms on toast (£1.20), pork chop
and cider (£3.10) and macaroni cheese (£2.95). *Open 11am-12.30pm
(Sun 12.30-11).* **Bar Food** *12-2.30 (10.30-1.30 Sun brunch). Children's
portions. Children allowed in bar to eat at lunch only. Free House.*
Beer *Caledonian 80/- and 70/-, McEwan 80/-, Timothy Taylor's
Landlord. Garden. No credit cards.*

Edinburgh   Tattler

Tel 0131-554 9999	**FOOD**
23 Commercial Street Leith Edinburgh Lothian EH6 6JA	**Map 3 C6**

To step into the Tattler is to step several decades back into the
subdued splendour of Scottish Victoriana – fringed table lamps, some
of smoked glass, a bird cage in the window, green velvet bar stools, a
chaise longue by the bar and, most charming of all, attentive and old-
fashioned courtesy from the bar staff. The bar is popular itself – a
gentlemanly local for unhurried chat – but most come to eat. The
Tattler restaurant, another creature altogether, is reached through the
snug and has a different menu, though there are a few overlaps. Music
is speakeasy 1920s, with live piano some evenings. The walls are
adorned with humorous antique prints and an intricately-carved dark
wood fireplace with inset tiles completes the picture. From 11.30am

on Sundays, a full cooked breakfast is served (£4.95). Starters include mulligatawny soup (£1.10) or a portion of paté (£2.50). The main course list strikes a good balance between fish and meat dishes: a Dunbar crab salad (£4.25), grilled swordfish steak (£4.95), roast beef or lamb on Sundays (£4.95) and the homely seafood haddie (£4.95) is an enduring favourite, combining smoked haddock and prawns in an egg and cheese cream sauce topped with piping-hot potato. Portions are generous. Likewise, a doorstep-thick braised pork chop à l'orange (£4.95) assumes hunger of a serious kind, and comes with huge helpings of potatoes and salad. Little room is left to indulge in the huge coupes of ice-cream (£2.95). Blackboard specials change daily. It's truly first-class value for money: an opportunity to splurge without overspending. *Open all day 11-midnight. Bar Food 12-2.30, 6-10 (12-10 Sat & Sun). Children's portions. Free House. Beer Tetley Bitter, Caledonian 80/-, Maclay's. Family Room. Access, Diners, Visa.*

Edinburgh   Waterfront Wine Bar

Tel 0131-554 7427 Fax 0131 555 6060	**FOOD**
1c Dock Place Leith Edinburgh Lothian EH6 6LU	Map 3 C6

The Waterfront's plain, redbrick exterior gives little indication of what lies within – this is one of Edinburgh's favourite food and drink spots. By the entrance there are about 23 wines served by the glass, as well as unusual beers. Through the first doorway is a low-ceilinged room lit by low lamps, nautical maps and wine-crate panels doubling as wallpaper. Further back, the romantically-sited conservatory ("always fully booked") is attractively overhung by a growing vine, and looks out over the water; beyond this, a narrow pontoon seats a few summer tipplers. Service is casual but friendly, waiters often identifiable only by the speed at which they move; music is kept low and is usually classical or light jazz. Ashtrays are changed with unfailing regularity. There are no fixed or printed menus, and the dishes of the day are all listed on a blackboard: a rich and creamy fish soup served with plenty of chunky bread, baked crab in a Jamaican rum and fresh basil sauce (£3.50) and Polish stuffed cabbage with spring vegetables and light soy dip (£3) makes a substantial starter in winter weather. Dishes with wild mushrooms are regularly featured and they have their own smokehouse. Well above the usual pub grub dishes are, however, surprisingly more basic than they sound – there's roast monkfish tails (£9.50), aubergine, courgette and capsicum terrine (£6), brochette of pigeon, venison and duck (£9.50) and to finish chocolate and strawberry roulade (£3). Coffee is fresh and good (no cappuccino). A very reasonable set-price menu (£6.50) runs along the same lines in winter. Over 110 wines on the list, including some very old Madeiras and pre-war brandies. Book well in advance for a weekend evening. No children under 5 in the pub. *Open 12-11 (Sat to midnight, Sun from 12.30). Bar Food 12-2.30 (Sat & Sun 12-3), 6-9.30 (Sat to 10). Children's portions. Children allowed in bar to eat (minimum age 5). Free House. Beer Caledonian 80/-, Deuchar's IPA. Riverside pontoon, outdoor eating. Access, Visa.*

Elie   Ship Inn

Tel 01333 330246	**FOOD**
The Toft Elie Fife KY9 1DT	Map 3 C5

When the Ship (part of a terrace of old cottages down by the harbour) was rebuilt not long ago the original bar was left, much to the relief of the locals, very much as it was before with wooden benches around

the dark-painted, boarded walls, beamed ceiling and back room with
booth seating. What was added was a pair of restaurant rooms with
old dining tables, sturdy kitchen chairs and, on the first floor, a small
balcony with coin-operated binoculars for scanning the harbour.
Limited snacks – soups, burgers and toasted sandwiches – are served in
the bar while more substantial meals are available in the restaurant
where one can have just a single dish from the printed menu – soup of
the day (£1.35), scampi thermidor (£8.25), collops of venison
(£8.95) plus children's portions – or twice-daily changing blackboard
specials which at night feature local seafood like lobster (£15.95),
lemon sole with a lemon and lime sauce (£6.95) and seafood Calypso
(£8.95). Cakes and biscuits are served with tea and coffee throughout
the day. In July and August, tables on the sea wall opposite the Ship
are served by an open-air barbecue. When the tide is out a vast
expanse of sand is revealed where, twice a year, the Ship's own cricket
team plays a match against a visiting side. *Open 11am–midnight, Sun
12.30-11.* **Bar Food** *11am-12pm (12.30-11 Sun).* **Restaurant Meals**
6-9.30 (Sun to 9). Children's menu. Free House. **Beer** *Belhaven 80/-,
Boddingtons, Courage Directors. Family room.
Pub closed 25 Dec. Access, Visa.*

Fochabers   Gordon Arms

| Tel 01343 820508   Fax 01343 820300 | **B&B** |

High Street Fochabers Grampian IV32 7DH   Map 2 C3

Antlers decorate the exterior of a former coaching inn standing
alongside the A96 and a short walk away from the River Spey, while
the public bar sports a variety of fishing bric-a-brac – including stuffed
prize catches. Simple overnight accommodation is provided by 13
well-equipped bedrooms (TVs, tea-makers, hairdryers and direct-dial
telephones), which include both older rooms with large carpeted
bathrooms and a number of smaller but quieter ones in the extension.
Open all day 11-11. Free house. **Beer** *Theakston's. Garden. Family room.*
Accommodation *13 bedrooms, all en suite, £70 (single £43). Children
welcome overnight, additional beds (from £10), cots supplied. Access, Visa.*

Garve   Inchbae Lodge

| | **FOOD** |
| Tel & Fax 0199 75 269 | **B&B** |

Inchbae by Garve Highland IV23 2PH   Map 2 B3

A few miles north of Garve on the A835 this is really a hotel, but
with a very pubby bar popular with locals, with blue cushioned
banquettes around the panelled walls, rustic tables and some exposed
stonework. Construct a full meal or just have a snack and you will do
equally well from Les Mitchell's kitchen. The day's soup (£1.85) will
come with home-made bread rolls, the salmon (£5.95) is locally
smoked and the ham salad (£5.75) is made with home-baked
gammon. There's always a casserole and pasta dish of the day plus
omelettes (£4.25), steaks, filled baked potatoes (£3.25), triple-decker
sandwiches and a selection of Charlotte's home-made puds. Bedrooms,
half in the main house and half in an adjacent red cedar chalet, are
modestly appointed (no TV, radio or telephone and all but three have
shower and WC only) but are well kept and quite attractive with pine
furniture and a plum and pale green colour scheme. Breakfast choices
include locally smoked haddock. Approximately 40 malt whiskies at
the bar. *Bar Food 12-2, 5-8.30, (Sun 12.30-2, 6.30-8.30). Children
allowed in bar to eat. Free House.* **Beer** *Belhaven Best.* **Accommodation**

*12 rooms, all en suite, £56 (single £33). Children welcome overnight
(under-16s stay free in parents' room). Garden. Pub and accommodation
closed 25 & 26 Dec. No credit cards.*

Gifford   Tweeddale Arms

FOOD
B&B

Tel 01620 810240   Fax 01620 810488

High Street Gifford Lothian EH41 4QU

Map 3 D6

Probably the oldest building in the village, the black and white
Tweeddale Arms lies alongside a peaceful village green. The
comfortable, mellow lounge features some old oil paintings while the
bar has tapestry-style upholstery and baskets of dried flowers hanging
from the old beams. The bar menu, which changes every few weeks,
offers a good selection of carefully cooked dishes ranging from some
excellent garlic bread (£1.25), quenelles of paté with oatcakes (£3.25)
and cream of cucumber soup (£1.25) to curried lamb Madras
(£5.75), lasagne al forno (£5.50) and salmon in leek and cream sauce
(£6) with a few home-made puds at about £2. Good clean bedrooms
have either light or darkwood freestanding furniture and modern en-
suite bathrooms. All have TV, direct dial phone and a tea/coffee-
making kit. A nice old inn, family run in friendly fashion. *Open 11-11
(Sat & Sun to 12). **Bar Food** 12-2, 7-9. Free House. **Beer** Burtons,
Speckled Hen, Greenmantle. Garden, children's play area. Family room.
Accommodation 17 bedrooms, all en suite, £60 (single £47.50). Children
welcome overnight (under-12s stay free in parents' room). Access, Visa.*

Glasgow   Babbity Bowster

FOOD

Tel 0141-552 5055   Fax 0141-552 5215

16/18 Blackfriars Street Glasgow Strathclyde G1 1PE

Map 3 C5

A renovated Robert Adam town house in the city's business district is
the setting for the splendidly informal and convivial Babbity Bowster
(named after a dance), which is not exactly a pub, rather, a light and
stylish café-bar, with a restaurant and hotel attached. The café-bar is on
the ground floor, and there is an outdoor patio with a covered awning
that is pulled back when the weather permits. Food of all kinds is
served all day – haggis, neeps and tatties (£3.35), home-made nut loaf
£3.95), spiced chicken (£3.95), sausage casserole (£3.95) and a choice
of barbecued dishes in the summer. On the first floor, the Schottische
Restaurant (also named after a dance) provides lunch, light meals and
supper. Choose from a variety of Scottish dishes from two fixed-price
menus (£11.50 and £14.50) or à la carte *terrine de la mer* (£3.65),
mignons of Perthshire venison on a whisky sauce (£11.50), stuffed
rosettes of Scottish lamb on Madeira sauce (£10.85) and home-made
puddings (from £2.95). **Bar Food** 12-11. **Restaurant Meals** (except
Sun) 12-3, 6.30 till late. Free House. **Beer** Maclay's 80/-, 70/-, Oat Malt
Stout, Kane's Amber Ale, guest beer. Patio/Terrace, outdoor eating.
Access, Visa.

Glasgow   Upstairs at the Ubiquitous Chip

FOOD

Tel 0141-334 5007

26 Ashton Lane Glasgow Strathclyde G12 8SJ

Map 3 C5

A former Victorian coach house and stables in a cobbled lane near the
university. Busy bar above famous Glasgow restaurant; famously
trendy and Bohemian. Impressive bar food of a resolutely simple kind.
Eating here is largely a vehicle for some serious people-watching and
supping from the fine wine list. Try the cold poached leek with egg

vinaigrette (£1.85), vegetarian haggis, neeps and tatties (£2.75), grilled grey sole with Howgate cheddar sauce (£4.25), Finnan haddies with bacon (£4.25), beef and butter bean stew (£4.05) and local cheeses including Mull of Kintyre Truckle cheddar and Inverlochy goat's cheese. On Sundays, breakfast is served from 12.30pm. Downstairs, there's a 2-course set lunch menu for £10 with a patio for outdoor eating. *Open 11-11 (Fri & Sat to midnight), (Sun 12.30-11).* **Bar Food** *11-11 (Sun from 12.30).* **Beer** *Caledonian 80/- & Deuchars India Pale Ale. Closed 25 Dec, 1 Jan. Access, Diners, Visa.*

Glendevon	Tormaukin Hotel	**FOOD**
Tel 01259 781252 Fax 01259 781526		**B&B**
Glendevon by Dollar Tayside FK14 7JY		Map 3 C5

Just south of Gleneagles, on the A823, and surrounded by glorious hill country, this ruggedly handsome old white-painted inn is remarkably peaceful, except when it's busy, which is apparently often. The warm and welcoming interior consists of several communicating rooms, all with lots of exposed stone, rough whitewashed walls and ceiling beams. Old settles (one of them beautifully carved), upholstered stools and roundback chairs surround heavy iron-legged tables. Old black and white photographs, colourful plates and pictures adorn the walls, and a splendid open fire makes the Tormaukin an ideal retreat from the chill Scottish winter. Food's a major attraction, to the extent that the bar menu makes a plea for patience at busy times; this printed list is supplemented by a daily specials board. Begin with perhaps deep-fried 'tattie skins' (£2.45), or herring fillets marinated in sherry and dill (£2,85) followed by venison sausages in port wine sauce (£5.75), supreme of salmon (£7.95), and then hot summer fruit crepe (£3.10). Cooking is competent, if unspectacular; fresh local produce makes all the difference. To the other side of the entrance, an exposed stone and beam-laden restaurant features smartly laid polished tables, candle-lit in the evening. The printed menu is not without interest: Scottish seafood chowder (£4.25), puff pastry vegetarian sausage (£10.85) and roast saddle of 'Maukin' (hare) (£13.25) stand out from the list. A roast is available on Sundays. Scottish cheese is featured on the board and all the puddings are home-made. Recently refurbished bedrooms are extremely comfortable and appropriately styled in keeping with the inn's age. Original features include yet more exposed stone and a generous sprinkling of beams. Floral fabrics match with pretty wallcoverings, furniture is pine and freestanding, beds are comfortable, sheets crisp. Nice local toiletries and plenty of towels compensate for slightly cramped sizes. Four of the rooms, in a converted stable block, are more contemporary in style, and all the bedrooms are named after whiskies (a theme continued in the bar where a fair selection of malts are available). Service is admirably efficient and friendly from a young, mostly female staff, who take most things in their stride. *Open 11-11, Sun 12-11.* **Bar Food** *12-2, 5.30-9.30 (Sun 12-9.30).* **Restaurant Meals** *6.30-9.30. Free House.* **Beer** *Burton Ale, Harvistoun 80/-. Patio, outdoor eating.* **Accommodation** *10 bedrooms, all en suite (7 with baths, 3 with showers), £66 (single £47). Children welcome overnight (rate depends on age), additional beds, cot supplied. Hotel closed 2nd and 3rd week January. No dogs. Access, Visa.*

Glenelg   **Glenelg Inn**

FOOD
B&B

Tel 0159 982 273   Fax 0159 982 373

Glenelg by Kyle of Lochalsh Highland IV40 8JR

Map 3 B4

Zzzz...

With an idyllic location on the shore of Glenelg Bay, the inn combines a rustic bar with civilised restaurant and, created out of the old stable block, six spacious bedrooms which have been individually decorated and charmingly furnished with antiques. All have good bathrooms but that with the master bedroom is particularly sybaritic. The bar menu, for residents only on Sunday, offers main dishes as varied as oriental chicken stir-fry, seafood chowder and pork stroganoff (all at £4.50 lunchtime and £5 at night, when only main courses are served) with the addition of soups (£1.50), sandwiches (£1.50) and pastries (scones 50p) at lunchtime. In the restaurant, the fixed-price dinner menu (£19 for non-residents – residents' terms are half-board only) majors on the loch-fresh seafood along with hill-bred lamb or local venison perhaps. After dinner, residents repair to the comfortable, antique-furnished 'morning room' (the first to arrive puts a match to the log fire on cool evenings) where the atmosphere lends itself to conviviality. Trips can be organised in either the inflatable boat or the inn's motor yacht. A large, walled and fenced-in garden overlooks the sea and is safe for children. Baby-sitters on hand.
Bar Food (no food end-Sept-Easter or Sun in season for non-residents) 12-2.30, 7-9. Restaurant Meals 12-2.30, 7.30-9. Free House. Garden. Accommodation 6 bedrooms, all en suite, half-board terms only £110 (single from £60). Children welcome overnight (rate depends on age), additional beds and cots available. Dogs by arrangement. Check-in by arrangement. Accommodation closed 21 Oct-Easter. No credit cards.

Glenfarg   **Bein Inn**

FOOD
B&B

Tel 01577 830216   Fax 01577 830211

Glenfarg Tayside PH2 9PY

Map 3 C5

By the A912 to the south of Perth, this pebbledash former drovers' inn is now under new ownership. Just to the north-east of Glenfarg, it stands on its own just five minutes' drive from Junction 9 of the M90 in front of the river Farg. Inside has an unfussy and homely feel. There are old, well-worn wing chairs aplenty and a grandfather clock in one corner. The small, uncluttered bar has red plastic upholstered banquettes, wooden chairs and walls littered with clan coat of arms plaques, a large map of Scotland, rugby cartoons, golf prints and a few pieces of horse tack. On the food side, evenings see a concentration on the restaurant and its à la carte menu. Typical of the choice are crayfish bisque (£2.50), Brie and apple pastries (£3.95), ragout of local game (£10.75), poached Tayside salmon with shellfish sauce (£12.50) and beef fillet with a choice of sauces. In the bar there is a blackboard 'lunch special' (3-courses, £6.25 eg. chilled melon, diced veal and broccoli in white wine sauce, Black Forest Gateau), a lunchtime bar menu including chicken en croute (£5.75) and ham and vegetable ragout (£4.60), plus a supper menu with similar fare. In addition, as we went to press new landlady Helen Doolan was also busy opening a chargrill steakhouse and tapas bar downstairs. Good overnight accommodation is provided in thirteen bedrooms, 11 of them housed in an extension, the upper floors of which connect with the main building via of a corridor. Ground-floor rooms are the largest, upper rooms very compact. All are furnished in unpretentious fashion with fitted units, matching curtains and duvets, with fully-tiled bathrooms (shower over the bath). The remaining two rooms are in the main house, neither of them en suite, but sharing a well-maintained bathroom. With 135 golf courses within a 35 mile radius, the Bein is popular with golfers. *Open 11-11 (Sun from 12).* **Bar Food** *12-2, 5-9.* **Restaurant Meals** *7-9. Children allowed in lounge or dining room to eat, children's menu. Free House.* **Beer** *Belhaven, Sandy Hunter's. Family Room.* **Accommodation** *13 bedrooms, 11 en suite, £56 (single £38). Children welcome overnight (under-5s stay free in parents' room, 3-10s £10), additional bed and cot available. Access, Visa.*

Glenfinnan   The Prince's House

Tel 01397 722246 Fax 01397 722307	**B&B**
on A830 Glenfinnan Highland PH37 4LT	Map 3 B4

Formerly called the Stage House (on the Road to the Isles), this prettily set late 17th-century pub alongside the main road near Loch Shiel has extensive fishing rights and several boats for hire (£20 per day including petrol). Accommodation is offered in nine rooms, all en suite (closed Dec-Mar, no children under 5). 'Chieftans' rooms are superior and recently upgraded. Mountain bike hire. *Open all day 11-11. Free House.* **Beer** *Burton Ale.* **Accommodation** *9 rooms, all en suite, £66/£76 (single £33/£38). Access, Visa.*

Greenlaw   Castle Inn

	FOOD
Tel 01361 810217 Fax 01361 810500	**B&B**
Greenlaw Borders TD10 6UR	Map 3 D6

Greenlaw is a small town on a major road, not far from Hume Castle and other attractions. The handsome Georgian Castle Inn is the sort of place you could take a variety of people for lunch and feel confident that they would find something to their taste. It is expensive for bar meals, by local standards, and falls into the middle ground of bar meal and restaurant. The Mirror Room, where drinking and dining take place, has a large mirror above a marble fireplace transforming what would otherwise be a hall into a splendid room, with a comfortable sitting area by the fireplace and elegant Georgian windows through which there's a view to well-kept gardens. The octagonal room or the small library make excellent rooms in which to take coffee, and the bar itself is popular with locals on Friday nights and weekend lunchtimes. The welcome is friendly but not intrusive. Family facilities are excellent: high-chairs, baby foods, a Freddy Fox children's menu, books in the library and cheerful, tolerant staff. The printed menu, supplemented by blackboard specials, is certainly very varied, with seafood-filled pancakes (£5.80), steak and mushroom pie (£4.50) or smoked haddock with cream sauce (£4.30) and a large vegetarian selection. Bread is crusty and fresh (mini-baguettes are used for sandwiches), butter comes in pots, tables are laid with mats rather than cloths, and puddings are displayed in a chill cabinet. A 2-course traditional Sunday lunch is served (£6.95) with a choice of ragout or roast. The cheese is good and always features Kelsey and Stitchill (cheese platter £2.50), and house wine very drinkable. **Bar Food** *12-2.30 (Sun from 2), 6.30-10 (Sun from 7). Children allowed in bar to eat, children's menu. Free House.* **Beer** *Caledonian 80/-, Broughton Greenmantle Ale. Garden. Family room.* **Accommodation** *6 bedrooms, 2 en suite £45 (single £22.50). Children welcome overnight (under-2s stay free in parents' room, family room £45/£48), additional beds and cots available. Access, Diners, Visa.*

Innerleithen   **Traquair Arms**

Traquair Road Innerleithen Borders EH44 6PD   Map 4 C1

Off the main road (well signposted) which runs through Innerleithen
and five minutes' walk from the River Tweed is the Traquair Arms
Hotel, a handsome stone building on the road leading to St Mary's
Loch, which is, incidentally, a delightful journey across country roads
to one of the most picturesque parts of the Borders. The bar leads off
the hotel reception area; dine here, or in the more comfortable dining
room, or, if weather permits, in the garden. A choice of dining areas
and a wide choice of freshly prepared meals is typical of the admirable
flexibility of the Traquair Arms, where children are positively
welcomed, even the most boisterous. For adults, a well-stocked bar
features the Traquair's own Bear Ale, with a teddy bear-clad pump.
Afternoon teas and high teas are also available. Service is genuine and
informal, the atmosphere convivial. A variety of omelettes (from
£3.10) and salads (from £4.20) is served in the bar and hot dishes
include Finnan Savoury (smoked haddock in cheese, onion and cream
sauce £4.95), Traquair steak pie (cooked in home-brewed ale –
£4.95), courgette gratin with almonds (£3.90). One benefit of dining
in the bar is that the glass doors lead off into the garden, which is
enclosed and safe for energetic children. The linen-laid dining room
proper, though pleasant in the evenings, is rather too formal for
lunchtime. Diners are offered 3- and 4-course table d'hote menus
(Wed-Sun £14.50, £18) with choices such as smoked pheasant with
lemon, crab crepes, and sautéed chicken with ginger and melon. The
cheeseboard features Scottish cheeses only (3 are local). Bed and
breakfast is recommended – particularly the handsome Scottish
morning meal, complete with superb kippers. Traquair House, next
door, is well worth a visit too, a romantic old house with pretty
grounds and its own ancient brewhouse; the front gates of Traquair
are firmly shut, and will never open again until a Stuart returns
to the throne of Scotland. *Open 11-11 (Sun to 12).* **Bar Food** *12-9.*
Restaurant Meals *Lunch for 12, 7-9. Children allowed in bar to eat. Free
House.* **Beer** *Traquair Bear Ale, Theakston's Best, Broughton Greenmantle
Ale, occasional guest beer. Garden, outdoor eating.* **Accommodation**
*10 bedrooms, all en suite, £58 (single £37). Children welcome overnight
(0-5yrs free in parents' room, 5-12 yrs 50% adult rate if sharing parents'
room), additional beds and cots available. Access, Visa.*

Kenmore   **Kenmore Hotel**

Kenmore by Aberfeldy Tayside PH15 2NU   Map 3 C5

The Kenmore claims to be Scotland's oldest inn, dating from 1572, in
a lovely Perthshire village overlooking the River Tay; at the east end
of Loch Tay on the A827. The Poet's Parlour bar, devoted to Burns, is
cosy, with green tartan seats; Archie's Bar is simpler, with glorious
views of the river. Bedrooms, 14 in a Victorian gatehouse opposite,
vary considerably in decor and furnishings with everything from
melamine to antiques. Guests have free use of the swimming pool
and leisure facilities at the nearby Kenmore Club. Kenmore attracts
both fishermen (they have 2 miles of private beats on the Tay) and
golfers. No real ales. *Riverside garden. Family room.* **Accommodation**
*39 bedrooms, all en suite, £117 (single £70). Children welcome overnight.
Dogs welcome in annexe only. Access, Visa.*

Zzzz...

Kilberry   Kilberry Inn   ★

FOOD

B&B

Tel 018803 223

Kilberry by Tarbert Strathclyde PA29 6YD

Map 3 A6

☺

This single-storey white cottage in an isolated, pretty little hamlet is located half a mile from a glorious coastline, and reached by an invigorating 16-mile drive down a winding, hilly, single-track road from the north, with superb views of Jura and other islands. John and Kath Leadbeater, English chef-proprietors, are vigorously interested in good food, and justifiably proud of their achievements here, in an out of the way spot where the vegetables come via van and taxi, and fresh fish is peculiarly hard to get. It's very much a dining pub, though locals and others are equally welcome to drop in for a drink. The building was originally a crofting house, and the snugly comfortable little bar, with a peat fire at one end, a wood-burning stove at the other, still has an unpretentious rural style. Leading off at the left, the brighter, plainer dining and family room has good-sized pine dining tables. The daily blackboard-listed short menu (perhaps only four or five main courses at lunchtime) is cheerfully annotated. John's role is circulating, chatting, advising and gossiping in between stints in the kitchen and bar, while Kath is very much behind the scenes, doing the hard work at the stove! Typical dishes might include fresh tomatoes stuffed with "locally-caught haggis" (£2.95), a hearty country sausage pie with fresh salad (£7.25) or local salmon fish pie (£8.25); at night a few fancier dishes are also added: perhaps chunks of rump steak cooked in Theakston Old Peculier Ale (£12.95) or prime pork fillet cooked in cider with apples (£10.95). Kath has a famously light hand and the pastry is superb. She also makes the bread as well as a selection of over 25 pickles, jams and chutneys on sale at the bar. Whatever you do, make sure you leave room for one of Kath's delicious fruit pies (from £3.25), which are laid out on the counter as soon as they come out of the oven. Equally scrumptious are the bread and butter pudding, fresh lemon cream, grapefruit cheesecake and chocolate fudge. Accommodation (not inspected) is offered in two "luxury" en-suite bedrooms (£50 double, £30 single, no smoking, children over 8 welcome overnight, breakfast served 8-9am, no food Sundays apart from breakfast): one double and one twin. Note that the pub is closed in winter and never opens on Sundays. *Bar Food 12.15-2, 6.30-9. Free House. Beer No real ale but large range of Scottish bottled beers: Greenmantle Ale, Scottish oat meal stout, Old Jock strong ale. Family room (no smoking). Inn closed Sun, also mid October-Easter (open at New Year for 10 days). Access, Visa.*

Killiecrankie   Killiecrankie Hotel

B&B

Tel 01796 473220   Fax 01796 472451

Killiecrankie by Pitlochry Tayside PH16 5LG

Map 3 C4

Zzzz...

A fine white-painted old property, a former dower house, in its own four acres of landscaped gardens overlooking the river Garry and the Pass of Killiecrankie (turn off the A9 north of Pitlochry) in glorious central Scotland scenery. The reception hall and mahogany-panelled bar (which has a sun-trap extension) of this smart, traditional country hotel have displays of stuffed animals and an upstairs lounge offers various board games plus a variety of books as distractions. Well-equipped pine-furnished bedrooms, all with smart modern bathrooms. No real ales. *Open 11-11 (Sun from 12). Garden. Accommodation 10 bedrooms, all en suite, £92 (single £48). Children welcome overnight (under-16s free if sharing parents room, half-price if in a separate twin room), additional beds and cots available. Pub & accommodation closed Jan and Feb. Access, Visa.*

Killin   Clachaig Hotel

FOOD

B&B

Tel 01567 820270

Falls of Dochart Killin Central FK21 8SL

Map 3 B5

18th-century ex-smithy and coaching inn, once closely linked with the McNab clan, and beautifully set overlooking the spectacular Falls of Dochart with the River Tay a five-minute walk down the road; very Richard Hannay-ish. Rather basic inside, though, its bar usurped by juke box and pool table, but bar food is plain and decently cooked – Scotch broth (£1.15), home-made steak pie (£4.50), haggis (£3.50), toasties from £1.50; and the dining room seats 48 in the evenings – Clachaig paté (£2.95), Highland venison (£8.95) and steaks, trout Rob Roy (£8.95), Loch Tay salmon (£9.25) and home-made puddings (£1.75). Restaurant meals are also available during the day in the bar. The clean and modest bedrooms are good value for the area, equipped with TVs, tea/coffee-making facilities and hairdryers on request. The best of them have dramatic views over the Falls. Choice of thirty-five malt whiskies at the bar. *Open 11-12 (Sat to 1am). Bar Food All day. Restaurant Meals 6.30-9.30. Children's menu (£1.50 per dish). Free House. Beer McEwan 80/-, Tartan. Garden, outdoor eating. Family room. Accommodation 9 bedrooms, 8 en suite, £40 (single £20). Children welcome overnight (under-3s stay free in parents' room). Pub closed 25 Dec. Access, Visa.*

Zzzz…

Kilmahog   Lade Inn

FOOD

Tel 01877 330152   Fax 01877 331078

Kilmahog by Callander Central FK17 8HD

Map 3 B5

Located 200 yards from the River Teith, this is a tremendously popular stone-built single-storey pub with a two-storey addition. One bar to the left of the entrance hall has panelling, pine tables and chairs; there's another bar to the right. The non-smoking dining area has large windows and leads out into the garden. The walls are mainly exposed stone and what looks like mock beams; bars are carpeted throughout, while prints and whisky boxes adorn the walls; the whole effect is clean, fresh and spacious. Tables are only set when food is ordered. Quiet and relaxing at 12.30, the lunch trade in summer is such that by 1 o'clock the Lade is usually packed with people. They come for the good, honest home cooking, like Cullen Skink (a traditional Shetland smoked haddock chowder £2.25), hearty steak pies (£4.95), vegetable Mexican in spicy tomato sauce (£4.95), venison sausages bordelaise (£4.85) – all main courses come with the inevitable chips (fairly inevitable in Scotland anyway), though you can opt for a jacket potato instead and a help-yourself salad. A separate menu caters for the evening meals and is more substantial – smoked salmon mousse (£2.50), Japanese prawns (£3.50), haggis écosse (£2.35), innkeeper special (3-courses £14.50), Laird's mixed grill (£10.95), venison pie (£8.95). Service is informal but good and friendly. The Lade Inn is worth knowing about as a genuine, good-value oasis in the often tourism-blighted Callander area. There are high-chairs for children. *Bar Food & Restaurant Meals 12-2.15 (Sun to 5.30), 6-9.30. Children's menu. Free House. Beer Ruddles County, Courage Directors, John Smith's, Webster's Yorkshire Bitter. Garden, outdoor eating. Family Room. Access, Visa.*

Kincardine O'Neil   **Gordon Arms Hotel**   **FOOD**

B&B

Tel 013398 84236

38 North Deeside Road Kincardine O'Neil Grampian AB34 5AA   Map 3 D4

An early 19th-century coaching inn of sombre grey stone, the Gordon Arms stands alongside the busy A93, almost opposite the derelict 13th-century village church. Behind a rather anonymous exterior is an inn of warm and informal atmosphere. The main bar area is spacious, sparsely furnished and utterly unpretentious, its high ceiling creating echoes on quiet days, plain-painted walls minimally dotted with pictures, and the part bare-floorboard, part modestly-carpeted floor topped with varying sizes of tables and a motley crew of cushioned chairs. A large rough-stone fireplace is decorated with old cider jars, and the wall above hung with a couple of fishing rods (this is a rich fishing area); there's a piano and splendid antique sideboard. A separate public bar has part panelled walls, old black and white photographs of the area, a television set and electronic games. There are two separate menus: a short bar choice with standard items like steak pie (£4.75), chicken curry (£4.25) and deep-fried haddock (£4.75), and a more interesting and enterprising dinner menu with an unusually wide choice of inventive vegetarian dishes (some suitable for vegans), like crispy pancakes with curry sauce (£5.25) and curried quorn and vegetables (£5.75). Carnivores aren't forgotten, though, with venison casserole, salmon and mushroom pie and a choice of steaks being typical: the house special, Scotty steak, is a sirloin steak on a crouton grilled with Banchory black cheese and bacon (£11.75). Bread is baked on the premises, and there's a fair selection of organic wines. Puddings are home-made (brandy oyster £1.95). They also do a very popular Scottish high tea, in which tea, toast, scones and cakes are included in the price of a main course. The seven bedrooms are comfortable and unfussy. Care has been taken to keep decor and furnishing in keeping with the building's age, and all are of useful size. Some fine pieces of antique furniture are partnered by a worn, but very comfortable armchair. Four of the en-suite rooms have compact shower rooms, the fifth a slightly larger bath/shower. *Open 11.30-11 (Sat & Sun to 12).* **Bar Food and Restaurant Meals** *12-2.00, 5-9.00 (Summer to 10). Children allowed in lounge bar to eat/children's menu. Free House.* **Beer** *Theakston Best, guest ales. Garden/terrace, outdoor eating.* **Accommodation** *7 bedrooms, 5 en suite, £45 (single £28). Children welcome overnight, (under-5s stay free in parents' room), additional beds (from £3), cots supplied. Access, Visa.*

Kippen   **Cross Keys**   **FOOD**

B&B

Tel 01786 870293

Main Street Kippen Central FK8 3DN   Map 3 C5

A simple, welcoming Scottish pub with rooms, rather than an inn proper, set in a pleasant rural village not far from Stirling. The locals' public bar is large and basic, with pool table, fruit machine and television; a smaller, long and narrow lounge is where most of the food is served, and a larger family room has high-chairs primed and ready for use. Most of the walls are of exposed stone, colour-washed white, and the furnishings a collection of old, polished tables and chairs. There's also a more modern small restaurant with seating for about 20. The restaurant is more modern. Bar food, which is well cooked rather than exciting, is chosen from a standard enough printed menu (bramble and port liver paté (£2.25), fresh salmon (£5.25) and steak pie (£5.50), enhanced by daily specials: breast of chicken with lemon and tarragon (£5.50) or trout in amaretto). Home-made beefburgers (£3.85), meaty and moreish, come with good crunchy buttered cabbage and chips. Soups are thick and warming. An apple pie is made daily (£1.95). The restaurant is open in the evenings and offers more elaborate dishes such as fresh smoked mackerel mousse served with Scottish bannocks (£4.25), roast haunch of venison with raspberry and red wine sauce (£9.50). Most of the produce is from local suppliers and Kippen's bakery supplies the bread. If staying the night, ask for one of the rooms under the eaves, which have sloping ceilings and fine views. Bedrooms are simple and homely, with the usual tea and coffee kits, and wash handbasins. Towels of good quality are provided, and there are extra blankets in the wardrobe. Housekeeping in the rooms is usually good. There is no residents' lounge, just the main bars downstairs, busy even midweek with diners and locals. Breakfasts, served on linen-laid tables in the restaurant, are hearty traditional fry-ups (but not too greasy) and service is pleasant and helpful. There's a beer garden at the rear with access from both the public and lounge bars. *Bar Food* 12-2 (*Sun from 12.30*), 5.30-9.30 (*Sat and Sun from 5.15*). *Restaurant Meals* 12-2 (*Sun from 12.30*), 7-8.45. *Free House* *Beer* Broughton Greenmantle, Younger's No.3. *Garden, outdoor eating. Family room.* *Accommodation* 3 bedrooms, sharing a bathroom, £42 (single £21). Children welcome overnight (under-5s stay free in parents' room). Check in by arrangement. Pub closed 1 Jan, accommodation closed 24, 25, 31 Dec and 1 Jan. Access, Visa.

Kirkcaldy   Hoffmans   ★

Tel 01592 204584	**FOOD**
435 High Street Kirkcaldy Fife KW1 2SG	Map 3 C5

Hoffmans is an extraordinary place. Situated to the east of the town centre (don't be confused by the High Street address), it's an unlikely looking venue for a pub serving imaginative food, but first impressions can deceive. Owned in partnership by Vince and Paul Hoffman, it opened in March 1990, after Vince returned to his home town and set up at a previous pub just down the road. The building they subsequently decided on to set up on their own was unpromisingly seedy; they smartened up the interior with subtly toned wall covering, brown upholstered bench seating, polished tables, a large central ceiling fan, angled mirrors, and fake greenery. The attractive seascape and still life oils are courtesy of Hoffman sisters, and rather fine colour photographs from a couple of regulars. But the food is the thing here, and so popular that booking is advised for lunch as well as dinner. And rightly so. Vince Hoffman is so confident in the quality of his raw ingredients that local suppliers are listed at the front of the menu, which is handwritten and changes daily. Often it's not even decided on until just before opening time, when suppliers and fishmongers have been visited and produce assessed. Fish is a particular interest of Vince's, from traditional deep-fried haddock (£3.95) to poached salmon with cucumber sauce (£3.95). The raw materials are first class (no dye in smoked fish), the handling first rate, and the prices remarkable: at lunchtime, main courses like Chicago pepperpot, poached haddock with Norwegian prawn sauce, pasta Toscana or roast stuffed lamb cost just over £3.50. A three-course lunch can be had for as little as £6.50! In the evening, the room is partitioned, half the space reserved for drinkers, the other run as an à la carte bistro, when tables are laid and candle-lit, and there's waitress service. Dishes are slightly more expensive, such as breast of duck (£8.25), wild rabbit (£6.85), and sirloin steak garni (£9.25). Vince's wife Jan makes all the puddings: Dundee Bonnet (£2.50), ice creams (£2.50). Capable service is also genuinely friendly, thanks to the Hoffman teamwork. There are high-chairs for children. *Open 11am-midnight. Bar Food 12-2, 7-10. Restaurant Meals 7-10. No food Sunday. Children allowed in bar to eat. Free House. Beer McEwan's No. 3, 80/- and Theakston XB, Castle Eden. Pub closed all Sun. No credit cards.*

Kirkcudbright　　Selkirk Arms Hotel

FOOD

Tel 01557 330402　Fax 01557 331639

B&B

Old High Street Kirkcudbright Dumfries & Galloway DG6 4JG

Map 4 B3

In 1974, Robert Burns was sufficiently impressed with the food here to compose the Selkirk Grace: "Some have meat and cannot eat; and some would eat that want it; but we have meat and we can eat; and sae the Lord be thanket." Today's visitor will be equally impressed with a bar supper menu that ranges from starters like deep-fried Brie with red wine and redcurrant sauce (£3.35), asparagus spears wrapped in smoked halibut (£3.75) and quennelles of three local patés (£3.50) to main courses such as local venison with honey and Madeira (£12.25), medallions of pork with baby apples (£9.45) and locally landed fish – perhaps Kirkcudbright Bay scallops with dry sherry and cream (£12.75). The lunchtime menu also features baked potatoes with various fillings (from £1.85), a range of open and toasted sandwiches, specials (poached plaice and prawn roulade – £5.50) and old favourites (steak and Guinness pie – £4.50), whilst a roast sirloin of beef, leg of lamb or loin of pork is available at £4.95 for Sunday lunch. The lounge bar is smart and comfortable with plush seating and light oak panelling which matches the light oak fitted furniture to be found in the majority of the well-kept bedrooms. All have TVs, direct-dial phones, hairdryers, beverage trays and modern bathrooms. There's also a particularly attractive, sheltered garden with tables for summer eating. No real ales. *Open 11-12 (Sun from 11). Bar Food & Restaurant Meals 12-2, 6.30-9.30 (restaurant from 7). Children allowed in bar to eat, children's menu. Garden, outdoor eating. Family Room. Accommodation 15 bedrooms, all en suite, £70 (single £45). Children welcome overnight (under-5s stay free in parents' room), additional beds available. Dogs by arrangement.* Access, Diners, Visa.

Kirkton of Glenisla　　Glenisla Hotel

FOOD

Tel 01575 582223

Glenisla nr Alyth Tayside PH11 8PH

Map 3 C4

This old coaching inn is set high up in Glenisla, one of the 'Angus Glens', and dates back over 300 years to the days before the Jacobite rebellion. A warm welcome avails today's travellers in the split level, beamed bar with its real fire (even in summer on chilly days) and posies of heather and wild flowers on the tables. Despite plans for a family room and bar extensions new landlords the Blakes have sensibly not changed the food formula here. At lunchtime the daily-changing menu still offers favourites like haddock and chips (£4), ploughman's (£3.95), Aberdeen Angus steaks (from £9), macaroni cheese and Cumberland sausage (around £4). At night, ever-popular main courses such as lamb cutlets grilled with rosemary (£6.75), fresh fillet of veal in lime and juniper berry sauce (£6.95) and breast of chicken in sesame seeds (£5.50), may be preceded by Orkney herring marinated in dill (£2.95), fresh Orkney mussels steamed in Guinness

(£1.95), salad of melon and prawns (£3.25) or home-made chicken liver paté (£2.50), and followed by homely afters such as rhubarb fool, plum crumble and hot toffee pudding (all £2.95). Afternoons bring cream teas with scones fresh from the oven and home-made jam. A pretty restaurant opens for both lunch and dinner. Children have their own games room with a pool table. *Open 11-11 Mon-Sun.* **Bar Food & Restaurant Meals** *12-2.30, 6-9 (In winter to 8.30). Children allowed in bar to eat.* **Beer** *Theakston's Best, McEwan's 80/-, Boddingtons. Garden, outdoor eating. Family room. Pub closed 25 & 26 Dec. Access, Visa.*

Kylesku	Kylesku Hotel	FOOD
Tel 01971 502231		B&B
Kylesku Highland IV27 4HW		Map 2 B2

By-passed by the new bridge over Loch Glencoul in the early 80s, the modest Kylesku Hotel enjoys a glorious location down by the old ferry slipway where today small boats land the local seafood that forms the backbone of the blackboard menu in a rather unprepossessing bar. Mussels baked in garlic (£3.45), scallops, grilled salmon (£6.75), fresh Lochinver haddock (£4.85), langoustines grilled in their shells and served with a spicy mayonnaise dip (£5.95) and locally smoked salmon (£6.25). Other items include omelettes (£3.75), roast chicken and fries (£6.55) and a few home-made puds (£1.95-£2.50). A pretty residents' lounge in blue and pink with frilly curtains has Trivial Pursuit and a stock of jigsaw puzzles for rainy days. Five of the bedrooms are en suite, two share a bathroom and shower. The bar has 25 malts plus two speciality 'whiskies of the fortnight'. Open all year but ring to check first if you want to stay between November and February. *Open 11-11, usual hours Sun.* **Bar Food** *11-2.30, 6-9.45. Free House.* **Beer** *Tennent's 80/-, McEwan's Export. Garden, outdoor eating, barbecues. Family room.* **Accommodation** *7 bedrooms, 5 en suite, £48 (single £25). Children welcome overnight (under-6s stay free in parents' room). Access, Visa.*

Loch Eck	Coylet Hotel	FOOD
Tel 0136 984322		B&B
Loch Eck nr Kilmun Strathclyde PA23 8SG		Map 3 B5

It's the setting that makes the Coylet really special: just the west coast road to Dunoon, shrouded in trees, separates the pretty white building from the glorious beauty of Loch Eck and the hills beyond. Not another house can be seen in any direction; be early for a window seat in the bar or dining room. Inside, it charms in an unaffected way. The public bar is handsome and cosy, and friendly local ghillies and others gather on bar stools to pass the time of day. Through the hall is an attractively simple little dining bar, where families (even tiny babies) are welcome. Through into the dining room proper are half a dozen tables (one, large group size, in the prize window spot), wheelback chairs and a piano. The food is a mix of standard bar menu stuff, from sandwiches (even in the evening) and ploughman's to vast, well-cooked platefuls of haddock and chips, or sizzling steaks; the quality draws both locals and tourists. But it's worth choosing off the specials board – a twice-daily changing short blackboard list. It might typically feature home-made liver paté (£2.30) and Scotch broth (£1.30), local game in season (from £6.50), steak and kidney pie (£4.75), salmon fishcakes (£4.20), grilled local salmon (from £5.75) or trout at lunchtime. In the evening, the board may feature mushrooms au gratin (£2.60), rack of lamb with honey and ginger (£8.50) and langoustine risotto (£8.50). If the risotto is on, you should order it and enjoy a generous pile of tender, fresh Loch Fyne langoustines in a delicious sauce with garlic, cream, wine and herbs: a true and memorable bargain. Vegetables are also exceptional: crisp mangetout, perfect new potatoes, tender carrots; all included in the main-course price. Puddings, all home-made, are also good, and come in hefty portions (all £2.50): chocolate roulade, pineapple cheesecake or a real apple pie are typical of the choice. Upstairs are three tiny little bedrooms which offer simple comfort. All have sash windows with views over the loch, and pretty cottage print paper and fabrics. The twin is a bit bigger than the two doubles. The shared bathroom, a very attractive, immaculately clean, carpeted and pine-panelled room, is bigger than any of them. Breakfasts are ungreasy and commendably accommodating of personal preferences. Finally, a word about the service, which is genuine and friendly from both the resident owners and their few, able staff. Lochside garden. *Bar Food & Restaurant Meals 12-2 (Sun from 12.30), 5.30-10 (Sun 7-9). Free House. Beer Younger's No. 3, McEwan's 80/-, Deuchars IPA. Garden, outdoor eating. Family room. Accommodation 3 bedrooms, sharing facilities, £35 (single £17.50). Children welcome overnight, cots available. Check-in by arrangement. No dogs. No credit cards.*

Markinch	Town House Hotel	FOOD
Tel 01592 758459 Fax 01592 741238		B&B
High Street Markinch Fife KY7 6DQ		Map 3 C5

Framed music hall song-sheets and old photographs of the locals and the locality grace the watered silk-effect walls of the plush bar/lounge at this town-centre inn which is now very much designed for eating rather than just drinking. Scottish favourites such as haggis platter (£2.95) and fillet of Tay salmon (£7.95) share the menu with such exotic fare as Cajun chicken (£7.95), beef Madeira (£7.95) plus seafood crepe (£2.95), prawn fritters (£2.95), steaks, and broccoli and leek bake. Puds are equally eclectic with peach schnapps delight (£2.25) and calypso sunrise (£1.85) alongside sticky toffee pudding. A special limited-choice lunch menu is available every day at £5.95 and a similar supper menu from Sunday to Thursday at £8.45. Spicing and flavours are less adventurous than the choice of dishes but cooking is careful and sound. Waitress service. Four, bright, well-kept bedrooms offer TV and tea/coffee-making facilities plus little extras like tissues and cotton wool balls but no telephones. Three have en-suite bathrooms, the other a private but not en-suite shower room with WC. *Open 12-11. Bar Food 12-2, 6.15-9. Free House. Beers Drybrough's Heavy 80/-. Accommodation 4 bedrooms, 3 en suite £50 (Single £40). Check-in by arrangement. Pub closed 25 & 26 Dec, 1 & 2 Jan. Access, Diners, Visa.*

Melrose	Burts Hotel	FOOD
Tel 0189 682 2285 Fax 0189 682 2870		B&B
Market Square Melrose Borders TD6 9PN		Map 4 C1

Located 200 yards from the River Tweed – "Scotland's favourite salmon river" – is the imposing 18th-century inn at the heart of still-fairly-sleepy, affluent Melrose. Bar food shows an appetising balance of the comfortingly traditional and modern aspirational – and this philosophy could be said to sum up the whole hotel. The choice may be lentil and bacon soup (£1.40), roulade of venison and rabbit

(£3.25), chicken curry, julienne of beef in mushroom and brandy sauce and braised lamb scented with honey and grapes (all £4.90). The bar is comfortable rather than quaint. Good Scottish produce is featured on two table d'hote menus in the rather smart restaurant – 'Menu de la Semaine' dinner £19.50 and lunch £13.75, in addition to à la carte dishes – cassoulet of scallops, salmon and prawns in Thermidor sauce, supreme of chicken filled with mango and dusted in coconut or medallions of venison rolled in oatmeal with drambuie cream. A choice of eight cheeses is always on offer including locals such as Bonchester, Teviotdale and Lanark Blue; Sunday lunch is always a roast at £5.60 for a main course. The bedrooms are light, contemporary and in pristine order; five have just shower/WC. Over 40 malts whiskies, eight wines by the glass. *Bar Food & Restaurant Meals 12-2, 6-9.30 (Sat to 10). Children allowed in bar to eat. Free House. Beer Belhaven 80/-, Courage Directors, guest beer. Garden, outdoor eating. Accommodation 21 bedrooms, all en suite, £72 (single £43). Children welcome overnight (under-2s stay free in parents' room, 3-12s £12), additional beds and cots (£2.50) available. Access, Diners, Visa.*

Moffat   **Black Bull**

Tel 01683 20206 Fax 01683 20483	**B&B**
Churchgate Moffat Dumfries & Galloway DG10 9EG	**Map 4 C2**

Modernised 16th-century street-side local with a beer garden outside and duckpond nearby in a curiously old-fashioned, isolated little spa town, whose life blood is coach party tourism. There is now a total of eight bedrooms – four look on to the courtyard and four on to the churchyard opposite. Each bedroom has a different colour scheme and is fully equipped with TV, telephone (in en-suite rooms), and tea/coffee-making facilities. Over 100 malt whiskies at the bar. *Open 11-11 (Sat to 1 am). Beer Theakston's Best, McEwans 80/-, two guest ales changing weekly. Garden, outdoor eating. Family Room. Accommodation 8 bedrooms, 6 en suite, from £40 (single £25). Children welcome overnight (under-14s stay free in parents' room), additional cots available. No dogs. Access.*

Monymusk   **Grant Arms Hotel**

	FOOD
Tel 01467 651226 Fax 01467 651494	**B&B**
The Square Monymusk Inverurie Grampian AB51 7HJ	**Map 3 D4**

With 6,000 acres of rough and driven shooting and 10 miles of salmon and trout fishing on the river Don this is very much a sporting inn as the decor of the panelled bar – antlers, stag's head, stuffed bird and old fishing rods – confirms. A typically solid, unspectacular 18th-century Scottish inn on the village green, the bedrooms are clean and bright if not luxurious. All have radio alarms, telephones and tea/coffee-making facilities but no televisions (there is one in the residents' lounge). The bar menu offers something for most tastes whether traditional – fresh oysters (£7.50 per 6), fish soup stocked with salmon, trout, sole, crab, garlic, tomato and spices (£2.50), farmhouse mixed grill (£5.95) and steaks, or slightly more exotic – supreme of chicken filled with ham and Gruyère, breaded and pan-fried (£6.95) and a collection of shellfish bound in rich lobster bouillabaisse (£14). *Pub open 11-3, 5-11 (Sat to 11.45), Sun Noon-11. Bar Food Noon-2.30, 6.30-9 (to 9.45 Sat & Sun). Free House. Beer Scottish & Newcastle 80/-, 2 guest beers. Garden, outdoor eating, children's play area. Family room. Accommodation 16 bedrooms, 7 en suite £62 (single £43). Children welcome overnight (under-4s stay free in parents' room, 4-12s £12). Access, Visa.*

Netherley   Lairhillock Inn

Tel 01569 730001   Fax 01569 731175

Netherley Stonehaven Grampian AB3 2QS

FOOD

Map 3 D4

Standing alone surrounded by fields, the Lairhillock is easily spotted
from the B979, thanks to the large white INN daubed on its roof.
The closest major village to the inn is Peterculter, some four miles to
the north; Netherley's a mile to the south. Formerly a farmhouse, the
original building is 17th-century, extensions are in sympathy, and the
interior is full of old rustic atmosphere. The large lounge is dominated
by a central log-burning fireplace; walls are half-panelled, and exposed
floorboards covered with numerous rugs. The public bar, in the oldest
part, is by far the most characterful room, with its exposed stone,
panelling, open fire, old settles and bench seating, every kind of horse
tack, polished brasses and numerous other bits and pieces. Bar food is
certainly taken seriously at the Lairhillock, where only fresh produce
is used, cooked to order. The menu carries a fair choice, changing
daily. Typically there might be wild boar terrine (£3.95), escalope of
venison with wild mushroom sauce (£7.95), locally-made Swiss-style
sausage with mushroom and onion sauce (£5.95). Puddings like sticky
toffee pudding and clootie dumpling (both £2.50) are changed daily.
It gets extremely busy, especially on Friday and Saturday evenings.
Across from the main building, in the old stables, is the evening
restaurant, with its high beamed ceiling, stone walls, red-tiled flooring
and solid polished tables. There's candle-light and a pianist plays
nightly. There's a wide and interesting choice of dishes here too –
smoked sturgeon with served (£7.50), lamb Wellington (£14.95).
A variety of Scottish cheeses is always available. Service is pleasantly
informal but always efficient. A recently built conservatory with
panoramic views furnished with Lloyd Loom tables and chairs
provides an ideal room for families to eat. *Bar Food* 12-2, 6-9.30
(6-10 Fri/Sat). *Restaurant Meals* 12-2 *(Sun only)*, 7-9.30. *Children's
portions. Free House.* **Beer** *Courage Directors, Thwaites Craftsman,
McEwan's 80/-, Boddingtons, Flowers, three guest ales. Patio/Terrace,
outdoor eating. Access, Diners, Visa.*

New Abbey   Criffel Inn

Tel 0138785 305

New Abbey nr Dumfries Dumfries & Galloway DG2 8BX

FOOD

B&B

Map 4 B2

Meeting Jenny McCulloch, it's difficult to believe that she has been
running the Criffel Inn for 38 years. A solid Victorian pub where
things don't change much from year to year, there's an unpretentious
'locals' bar, slightly smarter lounge bar and dining room with red
banquettes and blue and gold carpet. Upstairs, the residents' lounge has
a domestic feel and bedrooms, with wood-effect melamine fitted
furniture, go in for a medley of floral patterns. Two bedrooms are
now en suite, one has a 'tin' shower cubicle in the room and two
others share an immaculate bathroom. Foodwise, the highlights are the
local Solway salmon (£6.50) and first-rate home-cooked York ham
(£5.50) which share the menu with gammon steak (£6), sausages
with bacon and eggs and breaded fish (from £4.80). At lunchtime
there are also a couple of 'starters' and toasted sandwiches, while in the
evening the same dishes appear as bar suppers or 'high teas' (dishes
from £4.80 to £8.40) when they come with scones, home-made
cakes, bread and butter and a pot of tea. Choice of eighty malt

whiskies at the bar. **Bar Food** *12-2, 4.30-7. Free house.* **Beer** *Broughton Bitter, Belhaven Best. Patio, outdoor eating.* **Accommodation** *5 bedrooms, 2 en suite, £46 (single £20). Children welcome overnight (under-5s stay free in parents' room, 6-12s half-price), additional beds and cots available. Access, Visa.*

Newton Stewart   Creebridge House Hotel

	FOOD
Tel 01671 402121 Fax 01671 403258	B&B
Minnigaff Newton Stewart Dumfries & Galloway DG8 6NP	Map 4 A2

Formerly home to the Earls of Galloway, the 18th-century, stone-built Creebridge House, set in pretty gardens, is a hotel rather than an inn but the bar (which has recently undergone a full refurbishment including the reclamation of its old oak beams) offers a good range of bar meals. The more 'snacky' lunchtime menu includes sandwiches (from £2.50), Arbroath smokie ramekins with oatcakes (£2.95), chicken curry (£6.10), poached local salmon (£7.50), plus various blackboard specials like home-roast Galloway beef salad (£5.95) and pan-fried fillet of sea bream (£8.10). Evening meals are set at £17.50 for three courses and range from pan-fried fillet of pork with apple and apricot to oven roast brace of quail stuffed with chestnut. Start with the likes of home-cured gravad lax and a salad of smoked duck, finish with death by chocolate, fresh fruit pavlova or ecclefechan tart (sultanas, butter, eggs and sugar baked on a short pastry base). Eight of the twenty bedrooms, which include three family suites, have been newly refurbished in antique pine. All are well kept and equipped with TVs (some remote-controlled), telephones, hairdryers and tea/coffee-making kits – although room service is also available throughout the day and evening. Good, modern en-suite bathrooms, all with shower and tub plus the normal toiletries. Day rooms include an elegantly proportioned Georgian lounge. £1 charge on credit card payments. Visitors are invited to sample 'a taste of Scotland' from a choice of some 40 malt whiskies. **Bar Food** *12-2 (Sun from 12.30), 6-9 (Sat to 10, Sun from 7). Children allowed in the bar to eat. Free House.* **Beer** *Tetley's and Orkney Dark Islander, 2 guest beers. Garden, outdoor eating. Family room.* **Accommodation** *20 bedrooms, all en suite, £75 (single £40). Children welcome overnight (under-12s free if sharing in parents' room), additional beds and cots supplied. Access, Visa.*

Portpatrick   Crown Hotel

	FOOD
Tel 01776 810261 Fax 01776 810551	B&B
North Cresent Portpatrick Stranraer Dumfries & Galloway DG9 8SX	Map 4 A2

Right down by the harbour, the blue and white-painted Crown is a bustling, friendly place where the several unpretentious rooms that form the bar – with a real fire even in summer on chilly days, and a motley collection of prints above dado panelling – contrast with a stylishly informal restaurant and smart, appealing bedrooms. The latter have loose rugs over polished parquet floors, a variety of good freestanding furniture and attractive floral fabrics along with pristine bathrooms and the standard modern necessities of direct-dial phone and TV. Restaurant and bar share the same menu (except for the basket meals and sandwiches that are served in the bar only), which majors on seafood. Chef Robert Campbell knows that the lobster and crabs are fresh because he's out in his boat at 6 o'clock each morning to collect them. Much of the other fish is bought direct from the Fleetwood trawlers that call in at Portpatrick to unload their catches. Grilled scallops wrapped in bacon (£4.95), moules marinière (£4.05), prawns and sweet pickled herring (£4.40), whole plaice with almonds and chips (£6.60), vegetarian pancake (£6.15), beef hot-pot (£4.85) and chicken and chips (£4.60) are a few examples from a longish menu. Service is swift and efficient, no smoking in the 40-seated conservatory/restaurant area. *Open 11-11.30 (Sun 12-11).* **Bar Food & Restaurant Meals** *12-2.30, 6-10 (Sun from 6.30). Free House. Children allowed in bar to eat, high teas 5pm.* **Beer** *S&N 80/-, Tartan Export. Garden, outdoor eating. Family room.* **Accommodation** *12 bedrooms, all en suite, £70 (single £35). Children welcome overnight (under-4s stay free in parents' room, 4-10s £10), additional beds supplied. Access, Visa.*

Ratho   Bridge Inn

Tel 0131-333 1320	**FOOD**
27 Baird Road Ratho Lothian EH28 8RA	Map 3 C6

Starting life as a farmhouse and becoming a hostelry when the Union Canal was built alongside, the Bridge Inn fell into decline along with the canal and was almost derelict when taken over by the irrepressible Ronnie Rusack some 23 years ago. Not content with just reviving the Inn, Ronnie has been instrumental in making some seven miles of the canal navigable again and runs two restaurant barges, specially adapted barges to give the disabled trips along the canal (a charity he founded and which has now spread to other Scottish canals), a boat for short pleasure trips and other smaller craft for hourly hire (picnic hampers can be provided); he has even established a duck breeding programme! Inside, the original Inn features boarded walls and a collection of the many old bottles found when clearing the canal; a new family-orientated extension (the 'Pop Inn') features wheelback chairs and views over the water. One can choose form the Pop Inn's informal menu throughout the day – Bargees broth (£1.40), crunchy salmon fishcakes (£3.25), 'roast of the day' (£5.25), home-made burgers (£5), grilled trout (£5.25) and various locally made puds (all at £2.95) – or from the à la carte menu (main courses from £11 to £15) served lunch and evening in the bar, which becomes fairly restaurany in the evening with cloths on the tables. Steaks are a good bet here with good Scottish meat cooked on an open grill in full view. Children have their own special menu of favourites (two courses £2.90, three courses £3.40) with the likes of fish fingers, chicken drumsticks and fruit jelly and ice cream. There's an 'adult-powered' carousel on the patio, a 'pirate boat' play area in the grounds, proper baby changing and nursing facilities (that come complete with complimentary nappies and baby powder etc) and plenty of high-chairs and booster seats. There is hardly room to list everything that goes on here, the annual Scottish Open Canal Jump Competition is held each June and before Christmas there are special 'Santa Cruises' to a 'grotto' built each year on an island by the local art college. Five miles from Edinburgh airport. *Pub open noon-11 (Fri 11am-12pm, Sun 12.30-11).* **Bar Food** *Noon-9.30 (Sun 12.30-8).* **Restaurant Meals** *12-2 (Sun from 12.30),6.30-9 (except Sun eve). Children allowed in bar to eat, children's menu. Free House.* **Beer** *Belhaven 80/-, Best, guest beer. Garden, outdoor eating, children's play area. Family room. Access, Diners, Visa.*

St Andrews   Grange Inn

FOOD

Tel 01334 72670

Grange Road St Andrews Fife KY16 8LJ

Map 3 D5

Part of a group of pretty little old cottages about a mile out of town
(to the south-east) and with fine views over St Andrews and the Tay
Estuary. The Grange Inn is now almost exclusively a restaurant
although there is a tiny atmospheric bar with flagstone floor, ancient
fireplace and beams. Officially there's a minimum charge of £5 at
lunchtime and £11.50 at night for food served only in one of the
three (two for non-smokers) cottagey dining rooms, but if they're not
busy they will serve just a single dish from the menu: soup of the day
(£2.60), princess scallops (£4.75), wild Highland venison steak
(£10.95), salmon with prawns and herb butter (£8.55), baby guinea
fowl with tarragon cream sauce (£11), sticky toffee pudding (£2.65)
and chocolate mousse (£2.65). **Bar Food** 12.30-2.15, 6.30-9.15.
Beer McEwan's 80/-. Garden. Family room. Access, Diners, Visa.

St Boswells   Buccleuch Arms Hotel

FOOD

B&B

Tel 01835 822243   Fax 01835 823963

The Green St Boswells Borders TD6 0EW

Map 4 C1

Alongside the main A68, this substantial red stone inn/hotel dates back
to the 1700s when this was one of the main coaching routes between
Scotland and England. A spacious wood-panelled bar boasts pink
draylon upholstery and a nicely varied bar menu available throughout
the day: home-made chicken liver paté (£2), mushroom heads filled
with game terrine (£2.75), slices of goat's cheese coated with ground
walnuts with walnut salad, sautéed chicken with leeks and white wine
(£5.75), haggis wrapped in a savoury pancake with whisky and
mushroom sauce (£4.95), fillet of haddock (£4.50) and various
home-made puds (all around £2). For residents there is an elegantly
proportioned lounge spoilt only by rather tired soft furnishings.
Bedrooms are in good order, with traditional darkwood furniture
and colourfully matching duvet covers and curtain. All have TV,
telephone and tea/coffee-making facilities (although room service is
also offered) and all but two have decent en-suite bathrooms, though
towels are a bit small. Rooms to the rear are quieter but there is little
or no traffic noise at night. Friendly staff create a pleasant atmosphere.
From May to September a marquee in the garden handles functions
for up to 250 people. *Open 11-11 (Sun from 12)*. **Bar Food** 12-2, 6-9
(to 10 Sat). Free House. **Beer** Broughton Greenmantle Ale. Garden,
outdoor eating. Family room. **Accommodation** 19 bedrooms, 17 en-suite,
£68 (single £38). Children welcome overnight (under-14s stay free in
parents' room). Access, Visa.

St Mary's Loch   Tibbie Shiels Inn

FOOD

Tel 01750 42231

St Mary's Loch Borders TD7 5NE

Map 4 C1

The Tibbie Shiels Inn itself is a lovely whitewashed single storey
cottage with add-ons, on the shore of St Mary's Loch, in the glorious
Yarrow valley. Tibbie Shiels started the Inn in 1826 and it's now
famous throughout the Borders and elsewhere. It can be recommended
for three main things: first, the atmospheric bar, busy with friendly
locals and fishing and sailing types, second the quality of the meat
dishes (Scottish lamb and Aberdeen Angus beef), and third the
situation of the Inn itself: the large, and recently completely

refurbished, dining room overlooks the beautiful loch and surrounding hills in this utterly remote and enchanting place. Dishes include spicy chicken and rice (£3.75), holy mole chili (£4.50), Yarrow trout (£4.50), 8oz lamb chop (£7.25), supreme of chicken with apricot, Pernod and walnut sauce (£7.25), venison in red wine (£7.25), and home-made cloutie dumpling (£1.70). The Tibbie is an excellent place to stop after a sojourn on the Southern Upland Way. Five rooms are available for bed and breakfast (£46) – two have just been (and all will soon be) fitted with en-suite facilities. *Open 11-11 (Sun from 12.30, to midnight Fri & Sat). **Bar Food** 12.30-2.30, 4-8.30. **Restaurant Meals** 6.30-8.30. No food in bar or restaurant Mar-Nov. Free House. **Beer** Belhaven 80/-, Broughton Greenmantle. Children allowed in bar to eat until 8pm. Patio/terrace, outdoor eating. Family room. Pub closed on Monday in Nov-Mar. Access, Visa.*

Sheriffmuir   Sheriffmuir Inn

| Tel 01786 823285   Fax 01786 823969 | **FOOD** |
| Sheriffmuir nr Dunblane Central FK15 0LH | Map 3 C5 |

Built just 6 months before the battle of Sheriffmuir was fought almost literally on its doorstep between the Jacobites and the Hanoverians, the Inn has a wild and lovely location high up in the Ochil Hills, yet is easy to reach and well signposted from the main A9. Inside, all is neat and comfortable with pink plush upholstery and a warm welcome. Go for the home-made items from a menu that ranges from ploughman's, filled baked potatoes (lunchtime only), garlic mushrooms (£2.75) and good freshly-made soups to steak and Guinness pie (£4.85), chili (£4.85), chicken fajitas (£5.25) and steaks. A daily-changing blackboard menu adds a few more dishes like a hearty game casserole (£4.95) and creole prawns (£6.50). Since the change in ownership in January 1994 bed and breakfast is no longer available. *Open 11.30-11 Sat, 12-11 Sun, regular hours other days. **Bar Food** 11.30-2.30 (Sat & Sun to 9), 5.30-9. Free House. **Beer** Burton Ale, Alloa, guest beers. Garden, outdoor eating, children's play area. Family room. Access, Visa.*

Stonehaven   Marine Hotel

	FOOD
Tel 01569 62155 Fax 01569 66691	**B&B**
9 The Shorehead Stonehaven Grampian AB3 2JY	Map 3 D4

Down by the harbour, the ground-floor bar of the Marine Hotel is very pubby with boarded walls, copper-topped tables, games machine, juke box, pool table and a changing selection of real ales. The same menu (with the addition of a few bought-in items like steak pies) is served here as in the more family-oriented, first-floor dining room with its blue nautical decor and waitress service. Varied offerings range from Mexican nachos (£2.25) and onion bhaji and vegetable samosa (£1.95) to golden fried haddock (£4.65), chili with garlic bread (£4.45), steaks and salads. For children there are the usual fish finger/pizza offerings and a couple of high-chairs. Six modest but clean bedrooms (the two largest are family rooms with cots available) all have harbour views and are furnished with fitted white melamine units and matching duvets and curtains, have shower cabinets in the rooms but share two loos. All have phones, televisions and beverage kits. *Open 11-11.45 (Sun from 12). **Bar Food & Restaurant Meals** 12-2, 5-9.30 (to 9 in winter). Children welcome overnight (under-3s stay free in parents' room, 3-12s £5). Free House. **Beer** Bass, Taylor. Children's play area. Family room. **Accommodation** 6 bedrooms, £37.50 (single £27.50). Access.*

Strathblane   **Kirkhouse Inn**

| Tel 01360 770621   Fax 01360 770896 | **B&B** |

Glasgow Road Strathblane Central G63 9AA | Map 3 B5

Ten miles north of Glasgow on the A81 Stirling and Aberfoyle road, this roadside inn is at the foot of the Campsie Fells and thus popular with walkers. It's an ideal touring centre as Loch Lomond, the Trossachs, Glasgow and Stirling are all within 30 minutes by car. Sprucely kept public areas include a busy public bar and quieter lounge and restaurant. Pastel colours are used in the bedrooms, which include a honeymoon suite with a sunken bath. All rooms have TVs, radios, telephones and beverage trays. *Bar open 11-11 Mon-Thu, 11am-midnight Fri & Sat, 12.30-11 Sun. Free House. **Beer** Maclay's 80/-. Garden, beauty salon. **Accommodation** 15 rooms, all en suite, £72 (suite £82, single £55.25). Children welcome overnight (under-12s free if sharing parents' room), additional beds and cots available. Access, Diners, Visa.*

Swinton   **Wheatsheaf Hotel**

| Tel 01890 860257 | **FOOD** |
| | **B&B** |

Main Street Swinton Borders TD11 3JJ | Map 3 D6

☺

The village of Swinton is six miles north of Coldstream, on the way to nowhere, and is easy to miss. The Wheatsheaf, dominating this simple Scots farming hamlet, overlooks the plain little village green and has very limited parking; at busy periods, the main street is full up with cars. This is very much a dining pub (drinking – and smoking – go on in the pool-tabled, fruit-machined public bar at the back, so separate from the food operation that most visitors aren't even aware it exists) with a very well-regarded restaurant, the Four Seasons, and it's wise to book even for bar meals, such is the reputation of the pub in the Borders. The emphasis is on fresh food: a menu reproduced on one blackboard, daily specials listed on another – filo parcel of seafood on a rich prawn sauce (£4.90), braised oxtails with root vegetables (£5.45), roast loin of pork with apricots in a sage and cider sauce (£6.90), cold poached salmon (£6.95), contrefillet of beef borderlaise (£7.90) and a choice of home-made puddings (creme brulée £2.85). Tables are laid with cloths and place mats; freshly baked wheaten rolls are presented as a matter of course, and butter comes in a slab on a saucer, with no foil packets or sauce sachets in sight. Salads are imaginative and fresh. Service is assured from uniformed waitresses. Due to recent improvements, all bedrooms are now en suite and have modern facilities. ***Bar Food and Restaurant Meals*** *(except Mon) 12-2 (Sun from 12.30), 6-9.30 (Sun 6.30-9). Children allowed in bar to eat until 8pm. Free House. **Beer** Broughton Greenmantle Ale, Special Bitter, two guest beers. Garden, outdoor eating, children's play area. Family Room. **Accommodation** 4 bedrooms, 4 en suite, £58 (single £42). Children welcome overnight (under-5s stay free in parents' room, 5-10s £5), additional beds & cots available. Pub closed all Mon, last two weeks Feb & last week Oct. Access, Visa.*

Talladale   **Loch Maree Hotel**

| Tel 0144 584 288   Fax 0144 584 241 | **B&B** |

Talladale by Achnasheen Highland IV2 2HL | Map 2 B3

A purpose-built fishing hotel beautifully situated on the banks of the loch between Gairloch and Kinlochewe. The glorious outdoors is certainly a major attraction, and inside things have changed

Zzzz...

dramatically from the former time-warp Victorian cosiness. The hotel owns eight boats (complete with mandatory ghillies) for sea trout and salmon fishing on the loch. *Bar open 11-11. Garden, fishing, boating.* **Accommodation** *30 bedrooms, all en suite, from £60 to £90 (single from £30 to £40). Children welcome overnight (under-14s £12 if sharing parents' room), additional beds and cots available. Access, Visa.*

Tayvallich   **Tayvallich Inn**

`Tel 015467 282`   **FOOD**

Tayvallich by Lochgilphead Strathclyde PA31 8PR   **Map 3 A5**

This simple, white-painted dining pub – though it's fine to pop in for a drink, most people come for the food – is in a marvellously pretty location at the centre of a strung-along-the-road, scattered village stretching around the top of Loch Sween. Sit outside, on the front terrace, at one of the five parasolled picnic tables, and enjoy the view of a dozen little boats, and low wooded hills fringing the lochside; the word Tayvallich means "the house in the pass". Inside, the Tayvallich is surprisingly modern – smartly pine-clad, with a little bar and larger adjoining dining room proper. The bar is tile-floored, with raffia back chairs and little wood tables, the dining room similar, but spacious and relaxing, with a woodburning stove, attractive dresser, and bentwood chairs around scrubbed pine dining tables. The star of the handwritten menu is the freshest local seafood which is so local that oysters (half a dozen £6) come from just yards away in Loch Sween itself, and scallops from the Sound of Jura (£9.50) just round the coast. Langoustines are local and beautifully fresh (stir-fried £10), as is lobster (£15-17); plump mussels (£2.50/£5), imaginative and crisp salads. Finger bowls are provided, and clean napkins with each course. Portions are generous, and the whole atmosphere is very informal and relaxed. Holidaymakers turn up in shorts, and babies are commendably tolerantly treated, with clip-on chairs and specially rustled up toddler food – they'll even find chips for philistine youngsters. Puddings (all £2.50), made by the landlady, are of the chocolate nut slab and banoffi pie sort; few dedicated seafood lovers, having munched through two courses already, get that far though! Non-fish choices could include Cajun chicken (£4.90) or vegetable and cheese bake (£4.25). *Open 11-midnight Monday-Sunday July & August 11-2.30, 5-11 (to 1am Sat, midnight Sun).* **Bar Food** *12-2, 6-9.* **Restaurant Meals** *7-9. Children allowed in no-smoking area of the bar to eat. Free House.* **Beer** *Tetley. Patio/grassy foreshore, outdoor eating. Inn closed all Monday from 1 November to 31 March. Access, Visa.*

Turriff   **Towie Tavern**

`Tel 018885 11201`   **FOOD**

Auchterless nr Turriff Grampian AB53 8EP   **Map 2 D3**

A favourite for its satisfying, wholesome food, this is a roadside pebbledash pub on the A497, some four miles south of Turriff and a short distance from the National Trust's 13th-century Fyvie Castle. Seafood is featured at the Towie and the menu changes monthly, with daily blackboard specials. The 'Fisherman's choice' offers whatever is available that day: plaice, herring, mackerel or perhaps haddock (poached or deep-fried £5.50). The food is more elaborate in the restaurant with such dishes as supreme of chicken Cassandra (£9.75), rack of Scottish spring lamb (£11.25), roast beef (on Sundays – £6.75). Vegetarians are catered for (broccoli and cauliflower cheese bake £4.60) and puddings are home-made (butterscotch meringue

£2.50). Smartly rustic decor and a children's play area outside. Music in the non-smoking dining room. 50 whiskies. *Open 11-11 (Sat to 12, Sun from 12.30, Sun usual hours in winter). Bar Food 12-2 (Sun to 2.30), 6-9 (Sun from 5). Restaurant Meals 6-9 (Sat to 9.30, Sun from 5). Children's menu (£1.95-£2.50 per dish). Children allowed in bar to eat. Free House. Beer McEwan's Export, Theakston, guest beer. Patio/terrace, outdoor eating.* Access, Visa.

Tweedsmuir   Crook Inn

| Tel 0189 97 272   Fax 0189 97 294 | **B&B** |

Tweedsmuir nr Biggar Borders ML12 6QN | Map 4 C1

Famous old drovers' inn standing on the A701 Moffat to Edinburgh road, in glorious Tweed valley countryside. A strange but winning amalgam of old stone-flagged farmers' bar and 1930s' ocean liner-style lounges in the airy modern extension. Burns wrote *Willie Wastle's Wife* in what is now the bar, and locally-born John Buchan set many of his novels in the area. Neat bedrooms are simple in their appointments, with no TVs or telephones. There are a few Art Deco features in the lounge and some of the bathrooms. A craft centre (glass-making a speciality) has recently been created from the old stable block. Guests can also enjoy free fishing on 30 miles of the River Tweed. *Bar open 11-11.45. Free House. Beer Broughton Greenmantle Ale. Garden. Family room. Accommodation 7 bedrooms, 6 en suite, £52 (single £46). Children welcome overnight (under-10s stay free in parents' room, 10-16s £10), additional beds and cots available.* Access, Diners, Visa.

Ullapool   Argyll Hotel

| Tel 0185 461 2422 | **B&B** |

Argyll Street Ullapool Highland IV26 2UB | Map 2 B2

A white-painted inn close to the shore of Loch Broom. There's plenty of local character in its modest, neatly kept bars. Overnight accommodation is provided by twelve bedrooms, with TVs, tea-making facilities and quilts and electric heaters. Six bedrooms have full en-suite facilities while the others share two bathrooms; all overlook the loch. Children welcome inside. *Open all day 11am-11.30pm (Sun 12.30-11). Free House. Beer Bass. Accommodation 12 bedrooms, 6 en suite, £40 (single £25) – prices change seasonally. Children welcome overnight, additional beds and cots available. No dogs.* Access, Visa.

Ullapool   Ceilidh Place

| Tel 01854 612103   Fax 01854 612886 | **FOOD** |
| | **B&B** |

West Argyle Street Ullapool Highland IV26 2TY | Map 2 B2

Located 200 yards from Loch Broom, this is a celebrated northern community centre, which started as a coffee shop, and, like Topsy, just growed. Three cottages in this seaside village were knocked into one and Ceilidh Place was created. The pastry chef is kept busy all day providing scones, pancakes and cakes from 9.30am (to 9pm) in the coffee shop and home-made puddings (trifle, pavlova, crème brulée) for lunch or supper. Extremely informal and friendly; musicians perform live music during the summer (traditional Scottish, opera, chamber); regularly changing exhibitions take place throughout the year, and the restaurant, which opens at 8am for breakfast, also offers a fixed-price "ally carte" (£24 for three courses): grilled whole sole with parsley butter, scallops, turbot or halibut, vegetarian options and

home-made puddings. The bar has a wide range of salads, fresh
shellfish, hot tarts (£3.95), stovies (£2.95) and chili bean casserole
(£3.45). An evening coffee shop menu (served 6.30-9pm) encompasses
haggis (£3.25), bouillabaisse (£3.75), good vegetarian main courses
(£up to £6.95), crab, lobster and salads (around £6). The pretty
bedrooms are comfortable and spotless; the ten rooms that are en suite
also have phones. *Open all day 11-11, Sun usual hours.* **Bar Food** *12-6,
6.30-9.30.* **Restaurant Meals** *7-9 (restaurant open April-Oct only).
Children's portions. Children allowed in bar to eat. Free House. No real ale,
but good bottled beers and over 30 malt whiskies. Garden, patio, outdoor
eating, children's play area.* **Accommodation** *13 bedrooms, 10 en suite
(£96), (single £48, £35 without bath); Bunkhouse rooms £18.50 per
person (ring for details). Children welcome overnight, additional beds (from
£6), cots supplied. Check-in after midday. Pub and accommodation closed
two weeks mid January. Access, Diners, Visa.*

Ullapool	**Morefield Motel**	**FOOD**
Tel 01854 612161 Fax 01854 612840		**B&B**
North Road Ullapool Highland IV26 2TH		Map 2 B2

Most of the specials at the Morefield involve scallops, prawns or
langoustines in some form or another; it's the week's recurrent
leitmotif. They're very much dependent on what's in season and in
the catch at this remote north western location on the shore of Loch
Broom. There are personal reasons for the pre-eminence of shellfish
here too: the co-owners, including resident licensee David Smyrl,
were previously skippers of a pair of fishing and diving boats, who
diversified into activity holidays and ploughed all their profits into
buying the Morefield Motel. That was over 13 years ago, and their
expertise has built an international reputation for genuinely sea-fresh
fish and seafood. A sneaky glimpse of the visitors' book reveals fan
messages from all over the world, but particularly Germany, for some
reason – and it's especially revealing that so many of their remarks
declare (in a tone of some astonishment) that they were unable to
finish their meal. Portion control is a foreign language up here; when
something's in season, it's generally piled high, and the seafood
extravaganza is particularly unfinishable (£19.95 in the restaurant;
£13.95 in the bar). Aside from the Mariners restaurant (booking
essential in summer), you can eat in the lounge bar or beer garden,
and enjoy superb bar food at value-for-money prices. The printed
broadsheet menu offers meat and fish in about equal proportions –
this may be the king of seafood bars, but the Scottish meat is also
praiseworthy; try a T-bone Titanic (£12.50), tick-cut roast rump
(£8.95) or sirloin surf and turf with prawns and scallops (£11.95);
steaks in the bar are from £8.95. The strong fish list ranges from
beer-battered haddock (£5.95) to scampi imperial (£6.25), lobster and
whole sole on the bone (£5.95). Bedrooms are equipped with tea and
coffee-making facilities, colour TVs and hairdryers, and irons and
boards are available. **Bar Food** *12-2, 5.30-9.30.* **Restaurant Meals**
6-9.30. Children's menu (£2.50 per dish). Free House. **Beer** *Belhaven,
McClay's. Garden, outdoor eating, children's play area.* **Accommodation**
*11 bedrooms, all en suite, £40 (single £30). Children welcome overnight,
additional beds (£10), cots supplied. Access, Visa.*

Weem   Ailean Chraggan Hotel

FOOD

Tel 01887 820346

B&B

Weem by Aberfeldy Tayside PH15 2LD   Map 3 C4

Delightful little cottage inn, beautifully located against a steep
woodland backdrop, and with two acres of gardens overlooking the
Tay valley. The bright, sunny, well-kept bar has a central log-burning
stove, with a dining area beside the picture windows. Simple, well-
cooked food is highlighted by superb local seafood; try the Loch Etive
mussels (£6.50), served in huge steaming portions with garlic bread
or the Sound of Jura prawn platter (£12.50). Bedrooms are also
recommended: spacious and light with nice pieces of old furniture,
armchairs, and, in two rooms, small dressing areas. All are equipped
with TVs, hairdryers and tea/coffee making facilities. Ask for one of
the front bedrooms, which have inspiring views to wake up to. Patio
and lawned garden to front and side. *Open 11-11 (Sun from 12.30)
April-end October, regular hours in winter.* **Bar Food** *12-2, 6.30-9.15.
Children allowed in bar to eat. Free House.* **Beer** *Tartan Special. Garden,
outdoor eating, children's play area.* **Accommodation** *3 bedrooms, all en
suite, £52 (single £26). Children welcome overnight (half price),
additional beds and cots available. Closed two weeks in January.
Access, Visa.*

Wales

Aberdovey   Penhelig Arms Hotel

FOOD

B&B

Tel 01654 767215   Fax 01654 767690

Aberdovey Gwynedd LL35 OLT

Map 8 C3

Built in the early 1700s as Y Dafarn Fach (The little Inn) and for
generations an integral part of the village's history. The black-and-
white painted inn stands right on the main road (A493) with
unrivalled views across the Dyfi estuary to Ynyslas. In front, now the
tiny car park and sun terrace, was a shipbuilder's yard at the turn of
the century, while behind the Towyn to Macchyulleth train rumbles
out of a tunnel to the request stop at Penhelig Halt. For such a narrow
site the Penhelig Arms utilises every square inch of available space and
parks in a wealth of charm under the ever-present guidance of
Proprietors Robert and Sally Hughes (worthy winners of our 1995
Pub Hosts of the Year new award). Its popularity at lunchtime ensures
a regular overflow from bar to dining room. Menus are up-dated
daily supplementing bacon and cheese baguettes (£3.95), four seasons
pizza (£4.95) and Spanish omelettes (£4.95) with daily dishes from
carrot and orange soup (£1.95) and seafood pancakes (£4.75) to the
likes of tagliatelle with mushrooms, tomato and basil sauce (£5.25)
and grilled Conwy plaice with herb butter (£6.50). As quality and
price move up a gear at dinner (3 courses for a very reasonable
£17.50), there are regular treats of top-quality food to be enjoyed in
the bar, or on the terrace, at truly give-away prices: a splendid terrine
of duck livers, perhaps (£3.50), fresh crevettes in garlic butter (£9.50
per dozen!) and pork fillet in spicy tomato sauce (£5.75). In addition
to Tetley's, Burton Ale and regular guest ales, there's a range of house
wines from an enthusiast's cellar which are notable as much for quality
as for value. The same care and attention to detail has gone into
ensuring residents' every comfort in a relaxed atmosphere which
contrives to make one feel immediately at home. What the smaller
bedrooms lack in space they make up in appealing interior design,
careful addition of up-to-date comforts from TV and telephone to
hairdryers and quality toiletries, and immaculately-kept en-suite
bathrooms. All but one have a share of the view, one of the finest of
any hotel in Wales, and three superior rooms have a little extra space
with easy chairs and super little front-facing balconies. It goes almost
without saying that a splendid, comprehensive Welsh breakfast sets
everyone up for the day's touring, sightseeing or just lazing around
which lies ahead. *Bar & Restaurant Meals* 12-2, 7-9. No bar food Sun
lunch. Free House. *Beers* Tetley Bitter, Dark Mild, guest beers. Outdoor
eating. *Accommodation* 10 bedrooms, all en suite, from £66 (single £38).
Children welcome overnight, extra beds and cots supplied. Check-in all day.
Pub closed 25 & 26 Dec. Access, Visa.

Zzzz...

Abergavenny   Llanwenarth Arms Hotel

FOOD

B&B

Tel 01873 810550   Fax 01873 811880

Brecon Road Abergavenny Gwent NP8 1EP

Map 9 D5

A refined roadside inn (on the A40) some 3 miles west of
Abergavenny standing on an escarpment above the Usk valley.
Chef/landlord D'Arcy McGregor's creative cooking leaves little to
chance, his bar menus making full use of the best local produce
available. French onion soup (£2.95), home-made fresh salmon
fishcakes (£3.95) for a lunchtime bite, or breast of chicken with
cream cheese and ham filling (£10.95) and fresh vegetables make a
truly hearty meal. Seasonally revised menus are equally well balanced,

served throughout the two bars, family dining area and splendid summer terrace set some 70 feet above the river with views across to Sugar Loaf Mountain. Residents enjoy the use of their own lounge, and a Victorian-style conservatory furnished with comfortable cane furniture. Bedrooms, approached by way of a sheltered courtyard, are attractively furnished and immaculately kept, each one enjoying its fair share of the view. TVs, telephones, trouser presses, tea/coffee making facilities and hairdryers are all standard; bathrooms also have over-bath showers and ample supplies of toiletries. *Bar Food & Restaurant Meals 12-2 (Sun to 1.30), 6.30-9.45 (Sun 7-9.30). Children's menu, high tea 6pm. Free House. Beer Bass, Worthington, Wadworth 6X. Garden, outdoor eating. Family room. Accommodation 18 bedrooms, all en suite, £59 (single £49). Children welcome overnight (half price), additional beds and cots supplied. No dogs. Access, Diners, Visa.*

Abergorlech   **Black Lion**

Tel 01558 685271	**FOOD**

Abergorlech nr Carmarthen Dyfed SA32 7SN   Map 9 B5

At the heart of one of Wales's best-kept villages, the white-painted Black Lion stands between a tiny stone chapel and the Gothi River bridge; private fishing beats are nearby. The single bar with flagstone floors and high settles leads to a flat-roofed dining extension. On the main menu, pink trout, fillet steaks (£8.95) and generous salads (from £3.95) satisfy the heartiest appetites, while blackboard daily specials might feature lasagne, chicken Kiev and vegetable lasagne (all under £6). Opposite the pub, a scenic riverside garden with picnic tables features regular summer barbecues. Children welcome. *Bar Food & Restaurant Meals 12-2.30, 7-9.30, children allowed in bar to eat. Free House. Beer Worthington, Wadworth 6X. Riverside garden, outdoor eating. Family room. Access, Visa.*

Afon-wen   **Pwll Gwyn Hotel**

Tel 01352 720227	**FOOD**
	B&B

Afon-wen nr Mold Clwyd CH7 5UB   Map 8 C2

Formerly a 17th-century coaching inn of some renown with an unusual remodelled Victorian frontage (on the A541), Pwll Gwyn's fortunes are being revived today by enthusiastic and energetic young tenants Andrew and Karen Davies. Andrew provides the brains (and the brawn) behind an intelligently run kitchen whose output is much dictated by his shopping from Liverpool's markets. Best bets for the bar food, therefore, come from the daily blackboard: avocado, chicken and curry mayonnaise (£2.90), liver and smoked bacon with gravy and potato cake (£4.95) or fillets of brill with mushrooms, wine and cream (£6.40). Desserts, too, are impressive: cappuccino cake (£2.30) and toffee crunch cheesecake (£2.40) feature on a long list of home-made delights. More substantial cooking with a classical base comes in the form of weeekly changing specials available in the two separate dining rooms (one for non-smokers); special event evenings (Italian, Chinese, Indian) and summer barbecues are a regular feature. Four large double bedrooms are currently in use, one with a full bathroom; installation of WC and shower rooms by the owning brewery is currently in hand. *Bar Food & Restaurant Meals 12-2.30, 7-9.30. Beer Greenalls. Garden, outdoor eating. Family room. Accommodation 3 bedrooms, £30 (single £15). Children welcome overnight reductions available. No dogs. Access, Visa.*

Babell Black Lion Inn

Tel 01352 720239

FOOD

Babell nr Holywell Clwyd CH8 8PZ

Map 8 D1

Eating in the patio dining-room here offers not only impressive views of the Clywdian range without but also tempting value on the menu and blackboard within. For starters, black pudding in mustard sauce (£2.75) or grilled smoked mackerel (£2.75) and to follow, the likes of kidneys Turbigo (£6.25), beef casserole (£6.55) and grilled plaice with lemon butter sauce (£5.95). Nightly, except Sunday, in the Liszt Room, a three-course dinner is more formally silver-served and priced according to choice of main course. A classical French-biased wine list includes some carefully selected "Landlord's Delights", while listed separately are "Syd's wines of the month" – a Californian Kinderwood Ruby Cabernet, perhaps, or a Mexican Fumé Blanc; "Syd" is the hospitable Fosters' equally effervescent daughter. Sadly, after 28 years of undimming enthusiasm for good food and impeccable service, the Fosters have now put the Black Lion up for sale. *Bar Food 12-2 (except Sat & Sun), 7.15-10.30 (except Sun). Restaurant Meals 7.15-10 (except Sun). Garden. Family room. Free House. Beer Trophy bitter, Boddingtons. Pub closed lunch Sat & all day Sun (except Easter Sun & Mother's Day). Access, Visa.*

Beaumaris Liverpool Arms Hotel

Tel 01248 810362

FOOD

B&B

Castle Street Beaumaris Anglesey Gwynedd LL58 8BA

Map 8 B1

A handsome Georgian-fronted inn with a maritime history recalling the days when there was a busy shipping trade between Beaumaris and Liverpool. At its heart the Admiral's Tavern contains a wealth of memorabilia and relics which include timbers both from Nelson's "Victory" and the 1830's HMS "Conway" which was wrecked in the Menai Strait in 1953. A Quarterdeck and non-smoking Port Room are ideally set aside for sampling from Colleen Evans' daily changing fare with "traces of an Australian accent". Thus gammon, served traditionally today with egg and tomato, may appear tomorrow on a sizzling plateful of mango sauce. Among the popular lunchtime platters may be choices of Coronation chicken (£3.65), beef stir-fry (£4.50) and assorted smoked fish (£4.50), while evening specials can range from sausage and apple slice (£4.50) to a 20 oz rump steak served with Stilton sauce (£13.95). The White Star Line replicated signs to "First Class Accommodation", approached by a fine listed oak-panelled staircase, are no longer an exaggeration. Fallen ceilings have been replastered, plumbing effectively restored in the smartly retiled bathrooms and decor boldly revamped in all the bedrooms. With tea trays, TVs and dial-out telephones all are adequately equipped for both business and holiday requirements, with provision for honeymooners also in the four-poster suite and for youngsters in the two family rooms, one with bunk beds. *Pub open 11-3, 6-11 (Sat 11-11, Sun 12.3, 7-10.30). Bar Food 12-2, 6-9. Children's menu. Free House. Beer Tetley Best, Ind Coope's Burton Ale. Family room. Accommodation 10 bedrooms, all en-suite, from £50 (four-poster £76, family from £70, single £30). Access, Visa.*

Beaumaris   Ye Olde Bull's Head

Tel 01248 810329   Fax 01248 811294

Castle Street Beaumaris Anglesey Gwynedd LL58 8AP

FOOD

B&B

Map 8 B1

A stone's throw from Beaumaris Castle, the Grade II listed Bull dates
back to 1472, though it was largely rebuilt in 1617. The original
posting house of the borough, its courtyard arch houses the largest
single-hinged gate in Britain. Within its cavernous bars is a valuable
array of antique weaponry, an ancient brass water clock and the
town's old ducking stool. With its newly-extended family room to the
rear, this makes an ideal spot for lunch. Daily menus offer the best
local produce splendidly scaled down for pubby enjoyment: alongside
a smoked chicken and lentil broth (£1.85) and Welsh cheese
ploughman's (£3.10) may be baked fillet of codling with herb crust
or strips of roast sirloin of beef with marinaded peppers (both £4.95).
A grilled hamburger comes with rosemary and onion gravy (£4.95),
amply garnished sandwiches include roast beef, cottage cheese and tuna
(£1.60-£2.75): sweets may be warm almond tart or bread and butter
pudding with home-made custard (£1.75). Toby jugs and tun dishes
adorn the hammer beams and roof struts of a first-floor restaurant
which overlooks the courtyard. Keith Rothwell's dinners take over
from bar food in the evenings, but with mixed success and quite high
prices. The smartly refurbished bedrooms are named after characters
from the novels of Charles Dickens, a frequent visitor to the inn. Each
room is individually decorated and contains its own special features:
exposed rafters and beams, oddly-shaped doors and ingeniously fitted
bathrooms, all remain sympathetic to the Bull's unbroken history,
while the phones, TVs and bedside radios satisfy today's requirements.
Open 11-11, usual hours Sunday. **Bar Food** *12-2.30 (Sun 12-1.30).*
Children's portions. Free House. **Beer** *Bass, Tetley Best Bitter,*
Worthington, guest beer. Family room. **Accommodation** *11 bedrooms, all*
en suite, £72 (single £42). Children welcome overnight, additional beds
(£15), cots supplied (£7.50). No dogs. Pub closed 25 Dec evening.
Access, Visa.

Bettws Newydd   The Black Bear

Tel 01873 880701

Bettws Newydd Usk Gwent WP5 1JN

FOOD

Map 9 D5

Food by Stephen Molyneux is "of the moment" in an unfashionable-
looking old pub off the B4598 two miles from Usk. Down just three
steps from a single bar with its black and red quarry-tiled floor, the
half dozen neatly set tables with pink cloths and cane chairs seem
almost incongruous; yet there's a refreshing air of wayward
spontaneity here which looks set to challenge traditional concepts of
the British pub, and gently chides us for slow acceptance. Prominently
displayed, the "fish board" reflects astute daily shopping for sardines
(grilled £4.25), brill (with lobster and brandy sauce) and monkfish
(with spring onion, ginger and oyster sauce – both £10) – frills are
minimal and quirky. The flavours forceful and highly individual. The
Black Bear reopened from a period of closure in early 1994 following
a chequered history which left it run-down and in exceedingly poor
repair. As we went to press plans were well in hand to give it a much-
needed face-lift with light meals and snacks promised all day (crab
open sandwiches £2.50, warm salad of crisp duck £4.50). Thus far,
Molyneux's food speaks for itself confidently and with touches of class,
yet the Black Bear remains essentially a pub with just a hint of

restaurant. *Pub open 11-11 (Sun 12-3, 7-10.30)* **Bar Food** *12-10 (Sun 12-2.30, 7-10).* **Restaurant Meals** *as the bar. Free House.* **Beer** *Boddington, Flowers IPA, Crown Buckley Rev James. Garden, lawned and walled, outdoor eating, tables in garden. Access, Visa.*

Betws-Yn-Rhos   Ffarm Hotel

Tel 01492 680287	**FOOD**
Betws-Yn-Rhos nr Abergele Clwyd LL22 8AR	Map 8 C1

Eating is the main event at the Lomax family's discreet venue, hiding signless behind an impressive crenellated stone facade. The 18th-century granite manor house set in two acres of garden has been comfortably modernised and guests can choose to eat in either the bar, hall or library (suitable for families). The daily-changing blackboard menu offers specials such as rack of Welsh lamb in a redcurrant sauce (£8.25), salmon with crab sauce (£8.75), chicken creole and rice (£6.25), leek, cheese and herb risotto bake (£5.50) followed by locally made ice creams or apple, apricot and sultana steamed pudding (£2.25). Very young children are not encouraged. Smiling service. **Bar Food** *7-9.30, and occasionally for lunch – ring before travelling. Free House.* **Beer** *Tetley Traditional. Garden, outdoor eating. Access, Visa.*

Bodfari   Dinorben Arms

Tel 01745 710309 Fax 01745 710580	**FOOD**
Bodfari nr Denbigh Clwyd LL16 4DA	Map 8 C2

The 17th-century Dinorben Arms, which you'll find off the A541, taking the B5429 and sign to Tremeirchion, has changed hands this year but still enjoys a prodigious output. Lunchtimes concentrate on the self-served smörgåsbord (£7.50) and in the evenings both cold starters and sweets are mostly served buffet-style in the Well Bar. The "Chicken Rough" (£4.45), originally presented to be eaten with fingers, lives on since being introduced in 1961; the Farmhouse Buffet (Wed/Thu £8.95) and Carverboard (Fri/Sat £12.95) are more recent evening additions. Special dishes nightly may include rack of Welsh lamb (£6.75) or grilled trout (£6.50), however there are plenty more snacky items, children's and vegetarian choices (aubergine moussaka £4.75). Families are well catered for in their own room and on the smart, flower-decked, tiered patios and at the top of the extensive hillside gardens is a children's adventure play area. For dedicated drinkers, there's a good pint of Thwaites Best Bitter, eight wines by the glass, 25 cognacs, and over 120 whiskies! **Bar Food & Restaurant Meals** *12-3.30, 6-11 (Sun to 10.15). Free House.* **Beer** *Thwaites, Courage, John Smiths, Websters, Ruddles, two guest beers. Garden, outdoor eating, children's play area. Family room. Access, Visa.*

Burton Green   Golden Grove Inn

Tel 01244 570445	**A**
Llyndir Lane Burton Green nr Wrexham Clwyd LL12 0AS	Map 8 D2

Best found by turning off the B5445 at Rossett, by the signs to Llyndyr Hall; at the end of a lane seemingly leading nowhere stands a group of black and white timber-framed buildings which comprise the pub and its many outhouses. Within is a treasure trove of antiquity with some splendid 14th-century oak beams and magical old inglenooks and fireplaces. A modern extension housing a carvery dining-room leads to drinking patios and a large, safe garden replete with swings and play equipment, justifiably popular in the summer

months. Choice of 35 malt whiskies. Marston's Brewery.
Beer Marston's Best & Pedigree. Garden, outdoor eating, children's play area. Family room. Access, Visa.

Cardigan   Black Lion Hotel

Tel 01239 612532	B&B
High Street Cardigan Dyfed SA43 1HJ	Map 9 B4

The Black Lion claims to be the oldest coaching inn in Wales, having established itself in 1105 as a "one room grog shop". Much enlarged, but originally medieval town-centre inn, with a characterful beamed interior, complete with linenfold panelling in one of the bars. Pine-furnished bedrooms, and a comfortable upstairs television lounge, as well as a quaint little writing room. Bedrooms are equipped with tea/coffee-making facilities, TV and telephone. Hotel has been refurbished since last year. *Free House. Beer Bass, Hancock's. Accommodation 14 bedrooms, all en suite, £40 (single £30). Children welcome overnight. Additional beds (no charge under 10 years), cots supplied. No dogs. Access, Visa.*

Chepstow   Castle View Hotel

	FOOD
Tel 01291 620349 Fax 01291 627397	B&B
16 Bridge Street Chepstow Gwent NP6 5EZ	Map 9 D6

Four miles from the M4 Junction 22, this 300-year-old house was constructed mostly using stone from Chepstow Castle which commands the huge riverbank opposite. Ivy-covered today and genuinely welcoming, it's immaculately kept by Martin and Vicky Cardale. The original stone walls and timbers enhance the setting for a snack. Through both light and 'bigger bites', the bar menu encompasses omelettes and steak sandwiches, vegetables crepes (£3.95) and hazelnut and mushroom fettuccine (£4.95), with turkey, ham and sweetcorn (£4.95) or steak, kidney and Tetley pie (£5.95) as carnivorous alternatives. In the dining room, an evening table d'hote (2-courses for £12.95) is supplemented by a short à la carte on which the local Wye salmon is a regular feature. Sunday lunch also (main course £5.95). Up-to-date bedrooms with smart mahogany furniture and en-suite bathrooms (two with shower/WC only); radio and TV (with use of videos), mini-bars, direct-dial phones and beverage trays are standard throughout. The cottage suite (sleeping up to four) incorporates a quiet residents' lounge, and overlooking the garden, a restful spot, are two spacious family rooms. *Bar Food 12-2, 6.30-9.30. Restaurant Meals 12-2 (Sun only), 6.30-9.30. No food Sun eve. Children allowed in the bar to eat. Free House. Beer Tetley, Butcombe. Garden, outdoor eating. Accommodation 13 bedrooms, all en suite, £59.95 (single £39.95). Children welcome overnight (under-14s stay free in parents' room, 14-16s ½-price) additional beds and cots available. No dogs. Access, Diners, Visa.*

Clarbeston Road   Picton Inn

Tel 01437 731615	A
Clarbeston Road nr Haverfordwest Dyfed SA63 4UH	Map 9 A5

The village lies amid fertile farmland between the Presseli hills and Cardigan Bay. Abutting the railway halt, Clarbeston Road's rebuilt Victorian inn exudes a general air of mock antiquity, assisted by a genuinely smoky fire under its huge oak lintel. A red brick pine-shelved column divides the bar from an open-plan eating area.

Recommended for food in last year's Guide, but a new cook has
recently taken over. *Open 11-11, Sun 12-3, 7-10.30.* **Beer** *Bass.
Garden, outdoor eating. No credit cards.*

Clydach   **The Drum and Monkey**   ★

Tel 01873 831980	**FOOD**
Clydach Blackrock Abergavenny Gwent NP7 0LW	Map 9 D5

Perched at the side of the A465 in a spectacular position overlooking
Clydach Gorge, the pub was rescued from dereliction only last year.
Look carefully for the old road, signed to Clydach North, as the pub
is inaccessible from the main highway. 'A restaurant with lounge bar'
most aptly describes the interior: half-a-dozen bar tables set round the
open fire, its stone walls hung with horsebrasses, and the dining room
with widely-spaced tables a touch more formal. Chef-patron John
West's sensible policy, however, is that diners may eat in either
location. Moreover, the choice is impressive and his food is superb.
For a snack try platter of smoked salmon with lemon (£4.75), Scotch
black pudding with creamed potato (£3.50) or terrine of smoked
duck (£3.95). Fresh daily specials from the fish-board may be red
mullet in shellfish (£11.95) or king scallops in leeks and ginger
(£12.45, or as a starter £4.50), while some classy skills are exhibited
in the baked smoked mackerel and asparagus tartlet (£3.25) and loin
of pork steak with creamed spinach (£7.25). A three-course early
evening menu at £12.45 offers excellent value for money; leave
room for the superb light and dark chocolate cheesecake.
Bar Food & Restaurant Meals *12-2, 6-9.30 (Sun 7-9). Free House.*
Beer *Boddingtons. Garden, outdoor eating. Family room. No credit cards.*

Clytha   **Clytha Arms**

Tel 01873 840206	**FOOD**
Clytha nr Abergavenny Gwent	Map 9 D5

Clytha stands on the old main road (now the B4598) between
Abergavenny and Usk. Three years ago, it was closed and close to
dereliction; today it is decidedly a pub for eating in, and chef-patron
Andrew Canning certainly knows how to cook. For starters sample
the asparagus with parmesan or lemon butter (£4.70) or plump for
the grilled mixed shellfish Italian (£12.95 for 2). Main courses deliver
some fine fresh fish (Dover sole with tarragon and prawns £11.95)
and country-style cooking from supreme of chicken Basque-style
(£8.50) to wild mushroom lasagne (£7.25). Results may be variable,
though the intent is serious. In lighter mood, bar snacks are typified
by home-made fish soup (£2.80), laverbread with bacon and cockles
(£3.95), faggots with peas and beer gravy (£3.20) and treacle sponge
and custard (£3). The flagstoned public bar with its dartboard and
skittles table may present unforeseen hazards – to which the tree-lined
garden provides a serene summer alternative. *Open 11.30-11 Sat, usual
hours other days.* **Bar Food & Restaurant Meals** *12-2.15 (restaurant and
bar Sun from 12.30), 7.30-9.30 (no food Sun eve or Mon lunch). Children
allowed in bar to eat. Free House.* **Beer** *Hook Norton, Theakston's XB,
Hancock's HB, over 200 different guest beers a year. Garden, outdoor eating
area, children's play area. Family room. Pub closed Mon lunch.
Access, Visa.*

Creigiau   **Caesar's Arms**

Tel 01222 890486   Fax 01222 892176

FOOD

Cardiff Road Creigiau nr Cardiff Mid Glamorgan CF4 8NN

Map 9 C6

A mostly-dining country pub in a dip of the road just outside the village (8 miles from the centre of Cardiff and 3 miles from the M4) is the latest venture of Champers' restaurant owners, Benigno Martinez, Mark Sharples and Earl Smikle (also the chef). The well-tried formula of chargrilled steaks and fish, cooked in full view, with accompanying self-served salads, garlic bread and chip shop-style chips works equally well here. Examples off the menu include Bajan fishcakes (£3.25), marinated seafood salad (£3.55) or dressed crab (£5.95) as starters; sirloin steak (£10.95), monkfish (£8.95), sea bass cooked in rock salt (£10.95 per lb), Barbados chicken fillets (£6.95 or beef kebab (£8.25) as main courses and puddings may be apple and pistachio strudel or sticky toffee pudding (£2.95). In front of the pub, the patio has been converted into a summer dining area with the installation of free-standing (but fixed) gas turbine heaters. Excellent wine list, with several available by the glass. There's a garden and the neighbouring paddock is home to a horse. Children are "tolerated" but not encouraged. Open 12-11 (Sun 12-3). *Bar Food 12-2.30 (Sun to 3), 7-10.30 (except Sun eve). Children are allowed in bar to eat. Beer Hancocks HB. Garden. Closed Sunday evening. Access, Diners, Visa.*

Crickhowell   **Bear Hotel**

FOOD

B&B

Tel 01873 810408   Fax 01873 811696

Brecon Road (A40) Crickhowell Powys NP8 1BW

Map 9 D5

ZZz_z...

One of the original coaching inns on the London to Aberystwyth route, the Bear today bristles with personality and honest endeavour. Front bars, a hive of activity, are resplendent with oak panelling, ornamental sideboards and welcoming log fires. Recent refurbishment of three of the inn's oldest bedrooms has revealed open stone fireplaces which date it back to 1432. Further top-grade bedroom accommodation is housed in a modern Tudor-style courtyard extension, and in a garden cottage containing two bedrooms and a suite with its own spa bath. Four-poster beds and antique furniture abound. Meals in the bar are hearty and traditional by design. Winter favourites include faggots and mushy peas (£4.95) or perhaps bubble and squeak with bacon, replaced in summer by salmon béchamel pie (£6.50) and Welsh lamb cutlets (£7.50). House speciality bread-and-butter pudding and lemon crunch pie (£2.90) are available all year round. Plenty of standards (paté, filled pancakes and pork pie) for little people in small portions: filo parcels of Brie (£3.90) and aduki bean and peanut rissoles (£5.95) for vegetarians. A la carte restaurant in the evenings. 2-course Sunday lunch £7.95. *Bar Food 11-2, 6-10 (Sun 7-9.30). Restaurant Meals 11-2, 7-9.30 (except Sun). Free House. Beer Bass, Ruddles Best & County, Webster's Yorkshire Bitter. Garden, outdoor eating. Family room. Accommodation 28 bedrooms, all en suite, £52-£68 (single £42-£49). Children welcome overnight, additional beds and cots available. Access, Visa.*

Crickhowell   Nantyffin Cider Mill

Tel 01873 810775 Fax 01873 810775	**FOOD**
Brecon Road Crickhowell Powys NP8 1SG	Map 9 D5

A pink-painted former cider mill (the original cider press is preserved in the recently completed dining room) which stands on the Tretower estates bordering the north-west bank of the Usk. Bar snacks and light meals are served in an intimate, carpeted lounge bar and in summer, in the length of a riverside garden. Daily fresh fish and seafood features on the blackboard (salmon baked in filo with crab and chili filling £10.25, mixed hot seafood platter £14.50). Snacks vary from mixed Chinese platter (£3.95) to home-made chicken liver and brandy paté (£2.95). More substantial offerings might be steak and kidney pie with Stout (£5.95), chargrilled hickory sirloin steak (£11.95). There's also a good selection of desserts and Welsh cheeses. Also a comprehensive Sunday lunch menu, including a set price meal at £10.45. *Bar Food 12-2.30, 6.45-9.45 (Sat 6.30-10, Sun 7-9.45). Children allowed in bar to eat. Free House. Beer All guest beers (6X, Reverend James, Old Speckled Hen, Spitfire), guest beer & Old Rosy and Weston's West Country cider. Garden, outdoor eating. Pub closed 2 weeks Jan and Mondays Oct, Nov, Jan, Feb & Mar. Access, Visa.*

Dinas Mawddwy   The Dolbrodmaeth Inn

Tel 01650 531333	**B&B**
Dinas Mawddwy Machynlleth Powys SY20 9LP	Map 8 C3

A former farmhouse tucked off the A470 with gardens running down to the River Dovey, this is a little gem in the making. Engineer Graham Williams, once with the BBC, and wife Jean, a former cookery teacher, have been several years in the reconstruction of a building, virtually destroyed by fire in 1982, which now houses their two cosy bars and an airy dining lounge with picturesque views of grounds which include a paddock, river walk and private fishing. The eight bedrooms thus far completed are floored with carpet tiles and sport bright home-spun curtains and duvets, designed and made by an artistic daughter. Though small, the bathrooms are brightly tilted with over-bath showers and multifarious energy-conscious features – even the beer cooling system boasts hot water output. Children welcome overnight; cot provided free of charge. *Pub open 11-11 (Sun 12-3, 7-10.30). Free House. Beer Tetley Best, Burton Ale. Garden, lawn, outdoor eating, tables in garden. Family room. Accommodation 8 bedrooms, all en suite, from £45 (single £35). Children welcome over night, free in cots if sharing parents' room, £10 for additional bed. Pub closed two weeks Feb. Access, Visa.*

East Aberthaw   Blue Anchor

Tel 01446 750329	**FOOD**
East Aberthaw nr Barry South Glamorgan CF6 9DD	Map 9 C6

The old village of Aberthaw is hidden away between the Vale of Glamorgan and the sea. Long before a vast power station came along to spoil the view talk here was of smuggling, and the Blue Anchor played its full part in contraband. Its warren of tiny rooms had more than its share of hidey-holes and stone staircases now leading nowhere, giving the whole pub a wonderfully evocative feel. These days you'll not get robbed for the price of a pint (with fully half-a-dozen real ales to choose from) and in the bar meals scarcely cost a King's ransom. For starters or a snack are traditional Welsh rarebit (£3.50), lemon marinated sardines (£3.75) or spicy chicken provençale served in a taco shell (£3.95). Curry of the day, a local rabbit, mushroom and prune pie and tuna, pasta shell and nut bake are all around £4.20, and there's a Welsh farmhouse cheese ploughman's at £3.95. The usual glut of sandwiches and ploughman's fills out the menu, with fish fingers and chicken nuggets (£1.60) added as children's choices. The Blue Anchor has always taken pride in its food and its service. More recently, however, the success of its popular restaurant (in yet another hidden extension) appears rather to have spoiled the romance of it all with both food and service sometimes slipping. *Pub open 11-11 (except Sun). Bar Food 12-2 7-9.30. No bar food Sun eve. Free House. Beer Buckleys Best, Marston's Best & Pedigree, Wadworth 6X, Bass, guest beers. Outdoor eating. Access, Visa.*

Erbistock   Boat Inn

Tel 01978 780143	**FOOD**
Erbistock nr Ruabon Clwyd LL13 0DL	Map 8 D2

A dead end lane past the Victorian church leads to the Boat, in an unrivalled position on the banks of the Dee; there was once a ferry crossing here. Essentially pubby with its cosy flagstoned bar and open fires, it's a fine spot year round for a casual drink, but their is also a fairly serious attitude to food. At lunchtimes sandwiches (£1.95-£3) and Dee salmon (£4.10) are a big draw (plain sliced or crispbreads available on request). On a daily bar menu, carrot and chive soup (£2.10), Cumberland sausage with raspberry sauce (£4.95) and Barnsley lamb chop (£5.95) are typical choices. Table d'hote menus in the dining rooms start at £11.95 (lunch) with seasonal alternatives à la carte. Serious attention to raw materials and cooking is without question, though the service at times can be painfully slow. No under-14s in bar. *Bar Food 12-2. Restaurant Meals 12-2, 7-9.30. Beer Local brew Plassey, Cains Formidable Ale, Shepherd Neame. Riverside garden, outdoor eating. Family room. Access, Visa.*

Felindre Farchog   Salutation Inn

Tel 01239 820564	**B&B**
A487 Felindre Farchog nr Crymych Dyfed SA41 3UY	Map 9 B5

Felindre, a dot on the map where the A487 road bridge crosses the Nyfer, *is* the Salutation. Well-tended lawns slope down to the river, and there are gardens and terraces for a peaceful drink. The single-storey bedroom wing is neat and well-appointed. Bright duvets set the tone, with satellite TV, radio alarms, tea-makers and hairdryers providing up-to-date refinements. Three family rooms have bunk beds, and cots are also provided free of charge. Bar snacks and restaurant. *Free House. Beer Federation Bitter. Riverside garden, outdoor eating. Family room, High Tea 5.30pm. Accommodation 9 bedrooms, all en suite, £48 (single £30). Children welcome overnight, (under-2s stay free in parents' room, 2-14s £5) additional beds and cots available. Access, Visa.*

Glanwydden   Queen's Head

Tel 01492 546570 Fax 01492 546487	**FOOD**
Llandudno Junction Glanwydden Gwynedd LL31 9JP	Map 8 C1

One mile from Rhos-on-Sea and three miles from Llandudno, the Queen's Head is particularly popular for a lunch stop-off. Hidden down a maze of country lanes, Glanwydden is best found by following the Llanrhos road from Penrhyn Bay (B5115). Motivator of the Queen's Head's admirable food operation is chef/landlord Robert Cureton, who sets great store by careful shopping for his daily-updated menus. Fresh fish thus plays a major part: there are prawns in garlic butter (£7.75), the "house speciality" seafood platter (£8.95) and a prize-winning dish of Conwy mussels topped with smoked Caerphilly (£4.95). Meat-based signature dishes carry more weight, as in fillet of pork with apricot, orange zest and cider (£7.95), noisettes of Glanwydden lamb with redcurrant and port sauce (£7.50) and breast of chicken with white wine sauce (£6.75). Start, perhaps, with potted local seafood (£4.25) or a locally smoked breast of goose with kiwi (£4.35) and finish with a wide choice of nursery puddings – including fruit crumble, treacle tart or creamy chocolate brandy trifle (all £2.20). From a lighter snack menu there are 'tasty baps' (£3.75) and open rolls (£2.25). Hand-pulled beers are suitably well kept and house wines by the glass sensibly supplemented by special offer bin ends; an above-average wine list comes from Rodney Densen of Nantwich. Parties of six or more may only book for the early evenings or Sunday lunch. *Bar Food* 12-2, 6.30-9 (*Sun from 7*). *Beer* Tetley, Burton, guest ale. Terrace, outdoor eating. Pub closed 25 Dec. Access, Visa.

Hanmer   Hanmer Arms

Tel 01948 74532	**B&B**
Hanmer nr Whitchurch Clwyd SY13 3DE	**Map 6 A3**

Standing in the shadow of St Chad's church at the heart of a quiet hamlet now mercifully by-passed by the A539. The mellow brick Hanmer Arms is certainly of 16th-century origin with a history more firmly linked to the old communities of the Shropshire Lake District than the present-day county of Clwyd. In a newly hollowed-out interior are contained two bars, reception lounge and restaurant, with further dining and function rooms on the upper level. Bar floors are polished wood and on the walls is gleaming brassware retaining much of the feel of a traditional local but with little authenticity left beyond its brick facade. The strong point here lies in the apartment-style bedrooms laid out in the reconstructed barn and outhouses which stand around a central cobbled courtyard full of old farming artefacts. Decorated in country style with full en-suite bathrooms, they are well equipped with phones, radio alarms and satellite TV. The most spacious have plenty of room to accommodate families overnight, while for the businessman there's also plenty of work space. Children under 9 stay free in parents' room. Boardroom and conferences for up to 90 delegates. *Pub open* 11.30-11 (*Sun* 12-3, 7-10.30). Free House. *Beer* Tetley Best, Burton Ale. Garden, lawned and fenced-in. Family room. *Accommodation* 26 bedrooms, all en-suite, from £52 (£42 single). Children welcome overnight, (under-9s share parents' room free). Access, Diners, Visa.

Hay-on-Wye   Kilverts

Tel 01497 821042 Fax 01497 821580	**FOOD**
	B&B
Bull Ring Hay-on-Wye Powys HR3 5AG	**Map 9 D5**

Co-proprietor and food buff Colin Thomson has come a long way: much further, in fact, than the 150 yards from his previous Lion's Corner House venture. With him has come his inimitable hat collection, Victorian Spy cartoons and the nightly-played baby grand which imbue the bar with such character. Still a top seller in his new-

Zzzz...

☺

found location is the home-made 6oz beefburger, alongside daily specials ranging from laverbread, bacon and cockles on toast (£3.70) to stuffed vine leaves (3.75); fresh fish (shark steak – £4.50) is available Thursdays to Sundays. Home-made desserts like tiramisu, crème brulée and summer pudding. Residents' accommodation is both comfortable and stylish with brass bedsteads, smoked-glass tables and attractive floral bed linen. In addition to tea trays, direct-dial phones, TVs and radios (incorporating a baby-listening service), accoutrements include hairdryers and trouser presses. Bathrooms are a little utilitarian, nonetheless incorporating powerful showers and copious amounts of hot water. *Open 11-11 (bank holidays to 11-30). Bar Food 12-2, 7-9.30. Children allowed in the bar to eat, children's menu available on request. Free House. Beer Boddingtons, Castle Eden, Bass. Patio, garden, outdoor eating. Accommodation 11 bedrooms, all en suite (5 with shower only), £54 (single £27). Children welcome overnight, (under-7s stay free in parents' room, 7-12s £6) additional beds and cots available. Pub closed 24 & 25 Dec. Access, Visa.*

Our inspectors *never* book in the name of Egon Ronay's Guides. They disclose their identity only if they are considering an establishment for inclusion in the next edition of the Guide.

Landshipping   Stanley Arms

FOOD

Tel 01834 891227

Landshipping nr Narberth Dyfed SA67 8BE   Map 9 A5

One must cultivate a certain desire to come to the Stanley Arms: it's five miles by road from Canaston Bridge (on the A40), a lengthy walk through the Minwear Forest and 200 yards from the moorings at Landshipping Cove, high up the Cleddau estuary. It is therefore a true pub-lovers' pub with a good mix of locals, yachtsmen, walkers and caravanners. Those with a serious taste for real ale will enjoy a splendid pint of Buckley's "Reverend James" while any potential wastage is enthusiastically incorporated in Trish Fursse's "Rev. James Beef Casserole" (£4.95). Alongside pints of shell-on prawns (£2.95) and daily fresh fish in summer (around £5) are bites of broccoli with cheesy dip (£2.25), tuna and pasta bake (£4.85) and the ever-popular grilled one-pound Cumberland sausage (£3.85). There's live music weekly and authentic Indian curries are offered as late evening take-aways – it's a long way to the nearest alternative! *Bar Food 12-2, 7-9.30. Free House. Beer Bass, Worthington, Crown Buckley Reverend James, guest beers. Garden, outdoor eating. Family area. No credit cards.*

Llanarmon Dyffryn Ceiriog   West Arms Hotel

FOOD

B&B

Tel 0169176 665   Fax 0169176 622

Llanarmon Dyffryn Ceiriog nr Llangollen Clwyd LL20 7LD   Map 8 D2

In a picturesque hamlet at the head of the Ceiriog valley, this 16th-century former farmhouse stands to the front of well-manicured gardens which run down to the river bridge. Black and white painted outside and bedecked with creeper and summer flowers, it's a haven of cosy comfort within, the tone set by open log fires, flagstone floors, blackened beams and rustic furniture. Tucked round the back, the

Zzzz...

Wayfarers' Bar serves a modest selection of well-prepared snacks in chintzy surroundings with an adjacent family lounge and patio. Following soup (£2.75), chicken liver paté (£3.75) and herb mushrooms with garlic butter (£3.25), local Ceiriog trout (£6.95) heads a list of main meals which might include Cumberland sausages (£5.95), vegetable croissant with Shropshire Blue cheese (£4.75) or chicken and sweetcorn pancake (£5.95). Jam roly-poly and bread-and-butter pudding are typical of the traditional puddings. Bedrooms retain the period comfort afforded by handsome antique furnishings alongside modern fitted bathrooms: homely extras include pot pourri and quality toiletries. Five rooms are reserved for non-smokers and the two suites have plenty of space for family use. Table d'hote dinner is available to residents and others, priced around £22.50 per head. *Open 11-11 Mon-Sat, regular hours Sun. **Bar Food** 12-2, 7.30-9 (Sun from 7). **Restaurant Meals** 12-2.30 Sundays (Mon-Sat prior bookings only), 7-9.30. Children allowed in the bar to eat. Free House. **Beer** Boddingtons. Garden, outdoor eating. Family room. **Accommodation** 14 bedrooms, all en suite, from £80 (single £50). Children welcome overnight, additional beds (£25) and cots (£5) are available. Hotel closed last week Jan and first two weeks Feb. Access, Diners, Visa.*

Llanddarog   **Butchers Arms**

Tel 01267 275330

FOOD

Llanddarog nr Carmarthen Dyfed SE32 8NS

Map 9 B5

Well into a second decade at the Butcher's, self-taught butcher, proprietor and accomplished chef David James still runs his kitchen with unbridled enthusiasm. There have been changes aplenty over the years, of which the by-passing of Llanddarog by the A40 is not the least significant; hidden up a side road by the church, the Butchers Arms is now a serene spot. As fads have come and gone, however, the kitchen here has remained constant and the food consistent. Familiar lunch dishes include avocado and bacon salad (£3.60), cheese, ham and potato pie (£4.20) and seasonal tagliatelle with prawns and asparagus (£4.85). Home-made potato pies with spinach (£3.80) or ham and cheese (£4.20) are as popular today as a decade ago. In the evenings, generously-priced specials which supplement the menu are even more substantial. Fresh fish may be salmon en croute with lemon sauce (£8.50) or trout with orange and almonds (£7.80); a home-made lasagne may contain chicken and sweetcorn (£5.80). There may be Welsh lamb with mint and cider sauce (£5.85), chicken à la King (£6.85) and perhaps King Henry's feast, a single beef rib roast (£9.80). All this occurs in a pub which is by any standards tiny. Mavis James looks after the bookings (advised at weekends) and ordering with the same care that she applies to polishing the ubiquitous brass and miners' lamps, tending a roaring winter fire or arranging the floral displays which fill the fireplace in summer. The Butchers remains a village local, with a robust pint of Felinfoel a firm favourite among the loyal band of Welsh-speaking regulars. **Bar Food** 11-2.30 (except Sun), 6-9.30 (Sat 5.30-9.45, Sun 7-9.30). Children's menu. Free House. **Beer** Felinfoel, guest beers. Patio, outdoor eating. Family room. Access, Visa.

Llandovery   King's Head Inn

Tel 01550 20393	B&B
Market Square Llandovery Dyfed SA20 0AB	Map 9 C5

Medieval stonework and timbers are still in evidence throughout the bars of this black-painted town-centre building. Charles I's insignia, incorporated in the Inn's sign, commemorates the later construction of the upper storeys. Here the bedrooms have been sympathetically added and are kept reasonably up-to-date with neat bathrooms, tea-makers and radio-alarms. There is also a first-floor residents' TV lounge. A flagstoned rear entrance in Stone Street leads into the Old Bank (which once it was) where light meals and bar snacks are served. There are no reductions for children, except where they stay in parents' room in their own cot. *Open 11-11, seven days a week. Free House.* **Beer** *Hancock's, Worthington.* **Accommodation** *4 bedrooms, all en suite, £44 (single £26). Children by arrangement. No credit cards.*

Llanfair Waterdine   Red Lion Inn

Tel 01547 528214	B&B
Llanfair Waterdine nr Knighton Shropshire LD7 1TU	Map 9 D4

You cross the River Teme, just off the B4355, some four miles from Knighton (Powys) and in so doing enter England. The Red Lion is a low, stone, whitewashed pub in a tiny hamlet containing a Post Office and the parish church (opposite); to the side is an attractive walled garden with picnic tables from where the ground slopes away, sharply, down to the river Teme. Within, there's a stone-flagged village bar and a red-carpeted lounge-bar-with-dining with a huge inglenook fire flanked by piles of logs, plus much brass and tack. A small conservatory dining area is to the rear. Two of the three small but neatly kept bedrooms have washbasins and share bathroom facilities, the third has an en-suite bathroom. There's an air of total peace and quiet and there are fine views down the valley. Children are not allowed indoors. *Free House.* **Beer** *Marston Pedigree, Tetley, guest beer. Garden.* **Accommodation** *3 bedrooms, 1 en suite, £40 (single £25). No children overnight. No dogs. Check-in by arrangement. Pub closed lunchtime Tuesdays. Accommodation closed over Christmas period. No credit cards.*

Llanfihangel Crucorney   Skirrid Inn

Tel 01873 890258	A
Llanfihangel Crucorney Gwent NP7 8DH	Map 9 D5

With some justification, the bloody Skirrid claims to be the oldest pub in Wales. It is recorded that one John Crowther was hanged here for sheep stealing in 1116; that the legendary Owain Glyndwr marshalled his troops in this yard before his march upon Pontrilas; and that rope marks on the old oak beams are from sentences handed down by the hanging Judge Jeffries following the papist plot of 1679. Today's high-ceilinged bar retains original Welsh slate, some Tudor oak settles and a collection of beaten copper pans and salvers echoing the inn's long and colourful history. Children are welcomed in the dining room and garden only; hitching posts for horses in the yard. Three bedrooms include one en suite with a four-poster; there are rumours of hauntings! 4½ Miles north of Abergavenny, signposted left off the A465 Hereford road. **Beer** *Ushers. Garden. Family room. No dogs. No credit cards.*

Llanfihangel-nant-Melan — Red Lion Inn

FOOD
B&B

Tel 01544 21220

Llanfihangel-nant-Melan nr Radnor Powys LD8 2TN

Map 9 D4

A popular stopping point on the A44 between the Midlands and Aberystwyth, the Johns family's pub is enjoying a welcome revival. Not least among its virtues is chef Gareth's unstinting attention to fresh "real food" which sees his fried cod with mushy peas (£3.95) and traditional bangers with mash and gravy (£3.95) as popular at lunchtimes as are the more accomplished escalope of peppered pork (£5.95), grilled wild salmon steak (£6.95) and Oriental breast of duck (£7.95) on the evening menu. Family roast lunch on Sundays (main course £4.95), home-made nursery puddings (£1.95) and a commendable board of British cheeses (including Welsh Cheddar, Sage Derby, and several locally produced farmhouse cheeses) provides further proof that the kitchen here is in good hands. Three spacious chalet bedrooms without TV or telephones offer abundant peace and quiet, well back from the road, with lightweight candy-striped duvets in summer and "hotties" provided for winter nights. Bathrooms, with shower/WC only, are best described as practical, if a little spartan. *Bar Food 11.30-2.30, 6.30-9.30 (Sun from 12). Children's menu. Free House. Beer Hook Norton. Garden, outdoor eating. Family room. Accommodation 3 bedrooms, all en suite, £30 (single £17.50). Children welcome overnight (under-2s stay free in parents' room, over-2s £5). Check-in by arrangement. Access, Visa.*

Llanfrynach — White Swan

FOOD

Tel 01874 86276

Llanfrynach nr Brecon Powys LD3 7BZ

Map 9 C5

Polished flagstones, open log fire in a vast inglenook, exposed oak beams and cattle byres separating the tables lend the White Swan a general air of antiquity, to which piped classical music adds a surprising footnote. There's plenty of space inside and an attractive rear patio of stone-topped tables under a straggling trellis. Food scarcely ventures beyond the well-tried standards but quantities are generous – Welsh lamb chops (£7.75), cottage pie (£6), and home-made sweets such as crème caramel (£2), sherry trifle (£2.25). Llanfrynach is a sleepy village just off the A40 three miles from Brecon; quiet periods seem to impart a similar somnambulance to the service. *Bar Food 12-2 (Sun to 1.30), 7-10 (Sun to 9); no food Mondays and last three weeks in Jan. Children allowed in bar to eat. Children's menu. Free House. Beer Brains, Flowers, IPA. Garden, outdoor eating. Family room. Pub closed lunch Mon, 3 wks Jan. Access, Visa.*

Llangattock — Vine Tree

FOOD

Tel 01873 810514

The Legar Llangattock nr Crickhowell Powys NP8 1HG

Map 9 D5

A picturesque row of low, pink-painted cottages just across a meadow from the Usk, fronted by roadside picnic tables and a fine magnolia. Opposite, the stone packhorse bridge marks the old river crossing into Crickhowell. Exposed original stonework divides the pub into a succession of cosy alcoves, devoted almost entirely to eating. A blackboard menu runs the gamut of safe choices (prawn cocktail, melon balls, fresh fish and steaks) interspersed with more adventurous selections. Try, perhaps, baked eggs provençale (£2.45), ham and asparagus Ardenne (£3.80), pork in almond and cheese sauce (£7.95)

or the speciality "Chicken Cymru" with bacon, wine and tomato sauce
(£6.55). Vegetarian options include vegetable chasseur (£5.45) and
vegetable curry (£5.45). Families are decidedly welcome and small
portions readily available: booking though, is well advised. *Bar Food
12-2.30, 6.30-10 (Sun from 7). Children allowed in bar to eat. Free
House. Beer Boddingtons, Bass, Hook Norton. Family room.
No credit cards.*

Llangollen   **Britannia Inn**

Tel 01978 860144	**B&B**
Horseshoe Pass Llangollen Clwyd LL20 8DW	**Map 8 D2**

Cut back into the hillside by the A542 below the spectacular
Horseshoe Pass, the inn stands two miles above the town: directly   Zzzz...
below are the ruins of Crucis Abbey. Quite possibly this site started
out in the 11th century as a hostel for the abbey and the monks' ale
house, waters from the adjacent stream being used for the brew.
Today's ales are a little more sophisticated, as is the accommodation,
though some original and some later, 15th-century, features can still be
seen. Bedrooms now are cottage-style with lacy cotton bedspreads and
a predominance of brass four-posters. All are on the small side with
compact en-suite facilities (three with WC and showers only), colour
TVs and coffee making kits. Telephones are sensibly avoided: guests
simply wake to the dawn chorus to enjoy some memorable valley
views. *Free House. Beers Whitbread, Boddingtons, Flowers IPA &
Original. Family room. Accommodation 7 bedrooms, all en suite, from
£50 (single £25). Children welcome overnight, additional beds (£5) &
cots supplied. Check in by arrangement. No dogs. Access, Diners, Visa.*

Llangorse   **Red Lion**

Tel 01874 84238	**B&B**
Llangorse nr Brecon Powys LD3 7TY	**Map 9 D5**

Just a mile from Llangorse Lake, at the heart of the village by St.
Paulinus Church, stands the Rosiers' welcoming local. Picnic tables in
front by the village stream make it a picturesque spot. Riding, fishing
and water-skiing (mid-week only), all available locally, draw many
regulars to the Red Lion. Accommodation in neat pastel-shade
bedrooms with attractive duvets is practical rather than luxurious,
though TV, radio-alarms and tea-makers ensure an acceptable level of
comfort. Five have well-kept bathrooms en suite, the remainder (with
showers and washbasins only) share a couple of adjacent toilets. Built
into the hillside, all rooms have level access to a rear garden reserved
for residents. Good selection of twenty malt whiskies. *Free House.
Beer Flowers Original, Old Speckled Hen, Brains SA and Boddingtons.
Streamside terrace/patio, outdoor eating. High Tea 6pm. Family room.
Accommodation 10 bedrooms, 5 en suite, £48 (single £24). Children
welcome overnight. Additional beds (no charge under 12 yrs) and cots
supplied. No dogs. Pub closed lunchtime Mon-Fri, Nov-Mar.
No credit cards.*

Llangrannog   **The Ship Inn**

Tel 01239 654423	**FOOD**
Llangrannog Dyfed SA44 6SL	**Map 9 B4**

Just 50 yards from the beach, the white-painted Ship Inn is located
down a narrow winding road (watch out for a very steep hairpin
bend) in a delightful little seaside village. It's run by two couples, the

Boxes and the Browns: Lynne and De are responsible for the bar menu which, in addition to standard items like steak and kidney pie (£4.95), steaks (well hung by the local butcher – from £7.95), ploughman's (from £3.50), jacket potatoes and sandwiches, roams far and wide with pizza (£2.95-£5.95), and from the blackboard 'Specials' menu, Dijon kidneys (£4.75), broccoli and cheese pie (£3.95) and tandoori chicken masala (£4.95). Local seafood features strongly in summer with dressed crab, local baked herring (£2.85), skate, or, given 24hrs' notice, a special seafood platter that includes lobster, scallops, cockles, mussels, whelks, crab and prawns. Drinks are served from noon to 11 pm every day and guests can eat in one of the two bars or outside under colourful awnings that keep the showers at bay while you watch the world go by. *Open all day 12-11, Sun usual hours. **Bar Food** 12-3, 6-10 (Sun from 7). Children's menu. Free House. **Beer** Courage Directors & Best, Ruddles, Brains Dark. Outdoor eating. Family room. No credit cards.*

Llangynwyd   The Olde House Inn

Tel & Fax 01656 733310	**A**
Llangynwyd nr Maesteg Mid Glamorgan CF34 9SB	Map 9 C6

At the heart of Llangynwyd's original village off the A4063, the Olde House is notable for its antiquity (dating back to 1147), its massive thatched roof, metre-thick Welsh stone walls and ubiquitous memorabilia. Modern-day amenities include a spacious conservatory dining room, vast graded patios with a barbecue pit and a children's adventure playground complete with an old tractor. Selection of approximately 60 malt whiskies. *Open 11-11 (Sun usual hours). Free House. **Beer** Brains SA, Flowers IPA & Original, guest beer. Garden, children's play area. Access, Visa.*

Llannefydd   Hawk & Buckle

Tel 01745 540249 Fax 01745 540316	**B&B**
Llannefydd nr Denbigh Clwyd LL16 5ED	Map 8 C1

Stone-built in the 17th century, tiny Llannefydd stands high up in the Denbigh hills. At the Hawk & Buckle seven years of steady improvements have produced an inn of high quality, run and personally supervised by Bob and Barbara Pearson. Residents enjoy use of their own lounge bar and may mull over their morning papers without fear of noisy intrusion. En-suite bedrooms with TVs, direct-dial telephones and fully equipped bathrooms are decorated in co-ordinating fabrics and mostly pastel shades; guests may choose between duvets or traditional bedding. The best rooms, one of them with a pine four-poster, are on the upper floor from where guests enjoy the finest views down to Cefn Meiriadog and the North Wales coast. No real ales. *Free House. **Accommodation** 10 bedrooms, all en suite, £50 (single £38). No children under 8 years overnight. No dogs. Pub closed lunchtimes Mon, Tue, Thu & Fri in winter (Oct-end Apr). Closed 25 Dec. Access, Visa.*

Llantrisant   Greyhound Inn

Tel 01291 672505 Fax 01291 673255	**B&B**
LLantrisant nr Usk Gwent NP5 1LE	Map 9 D6

Just 2½ from Usk, the Greyhound occupies a hillside, with fine views of the Lowes River valley which flows to the sea at Newport some 9 miles downstream. The low stone 17th-century farm house is much extended now with split-level bar and succession of drinking and eating rooms stepped into the hill. Recent conversion of the farmer barn has produced a dozen en-suite bedrooms with blackened roof trusses and decorated in a cottage style becoming both the building's nature and its rural location. Up-to-the-minute equipment includes remote-control TV and direct-dial phones with baby listening facilities: two larger family rooms have an extra bed; all have both bath and showers. The best, ground floor, rooms' French windows open onto private patios in a garden setting with lily pond and ornamented fountain. From here traffic on the A449 dual carriageway can be seen, and heard, thundering by though from it there is no direct access. Be sure, therefore, to obtain exact directions on booking. No dogs. *Free House.* **Beer** *Wadworth 6X, Flowers, Marston's Pedigree, Boddingtons, guest beers. Garden, Patio. Family Room.* **Accommodation** *Rooms 10, all en suite £55 (single £45). Children welcome overnight (babies stay free in parents' room), additional beds (£5), and cots available. Accommodation closed 24 & 25 Dec. No credit cards.*

Llanyre   The Bell

Tel 01597 823959	**B&B**
Llanyre Llandrindod Wells Powys LD1 6DY	Map 9 C4

Standing in hills above Llandrindod Wells, just two miles away, Llanyre is handily placed for visitors to mid-Wales with the Elan and upper Wye valleys nearby and multifarious outdoor activity within handy reach. Built originally for drovers headed with their flocks to "foreign parts" (Gloucester and Hereford), the Bell provided clean straw and stabling throughout the 17th and 18th centuries. Today's version is well-prepared for the twenty-first, with high quality accommodation in recently completed extensions. Standard equipment includes satellite TV, radio alarms and telephones as well as beverage trays, trouser presses and hair dryers. Bedrooms are brightly decorated in pastel shades with generously-sized duvets and bathrooms sport smart white porcelain fitments with powerful over-bath showers. Two larger rooms are suitable for family use (under-11s stay free and a cot is available), one of these on the ground floor is quite suitable for disabled guests. *Pub open 11-3, 6-11 (Sun 12-3, 7-10.30) 11-11 in summer. Free house.* **Beer** *Theakstone XB. Small garden.* **Accommodation** *9 bedrooms, all en-suite, from £57.50 (single £32.50). Children welcome overnight, under-11s stay free in parents' room, additional bed supplied. Pub closed Christmas Day & Boxing Day.*

Llowes   Radnor Arms

Tel 01497 847460	**FOOD**
Llowes Powys HR3 5JA	Map 9 D5

Landlord of the Radnor Arms for nearly ten years, Brian Gorringe offers culinary refinement in this 1000-year-old drinking house. The old stone building with a stone roof is overlooked by the Black Mountains on one side, the Beacons on another and the Beggins on the third. With only a dozen tables and no more than 40-60 seats, it's surprising to encounter six blackboards announcing 99 starters, snacks, main dishes and puddings from which to choose! The Radnor Arms divides by means of heavy oak panels into the bar area proper, popular by day, and a more spacious, lofty-beamed garden side for more leisurely evening enjoyment, and for which you ought to book. Either way, there's good beer on handpump plus a few unusual bottled beers and a modest selection of house wines. The menu on the blackboards might include French onion soup (£2.20), cottage pie (£4.70), paella Valenciana (£7.75), venison in port wine and Guinness (£10.75), tiger prawns with garlic bread (£7.65), haddock mornay (£7.20), or monkfish with princess scallops in lemon and champagne sauce (£12.25). Puddings include gateau Véronique (£2.95) and omelette viennoise (£3.95). Some homely touches help to extend a warm Welsh welcome. Cruets and coffee sets are of hand-made Black Mountain pottery, and there are woolly dolls and framed three-dimensional paper cut-outs for sale. *Bar Food 11-2.30, 6.30-11 (except Sun eve and Mon). Free House. Beer Felinfoel Traditional. Garden, outdoor eating. Pub closed all Mon and Sun eve (except Bank Holidays). No credit cards.*

Llwyndafydd   Crown Inn

| Tel 01545 560396 | **FOOD** |
| Llwyndafydd nr New Quay Dyfed SA44 6FH | Map 9 B4 |

A handsome, white-painted 18th-century inn at the head of the hidden romantic valley of Cwmtudn below which German U-boats may have landed to obtain fresh water during the Great War. This highly popular spot with families in summer has a large patio and play area for the children, whose low-priced menu varies little beyond pizza, fish fingers and burgers (from £2.25). In addition to an equally predictable range of adult bar food (the evening restaurant menu is even more so – just pricier). There are well-made curries (£5.95), daily fish dishes – haddock with mushroom and tarragon sauce, perhaps (£5.35) and a few other specials – maybe braised pigeon breast with tomato and mushrooms (£6.95). *Pub open 11-3, 6-11 (Sun 12-3, 7-10.30). Bar Food 12-2, 6-9, (Sun 7-9). Restaurant Meals 7-9 Mon-Sat, 12-2 Sun. Children's menu. Free House. Beer Boddington, Flowers IPA, Original Bass. Garden, outdoor eating area, tiered patios. Pub closed Sun evenings Oct-Mar. Access, Visa.*

Llyswen   Griffin Inn   ★

Tel 01874 754241 Fax 01874 754592	**FOOD**
	B&B
Llyswen Brecon Powys LD3 0OU	Map 9 D5

Mythically speaking, the griffin is a creature of vast proportions, half lion, half dragon, its whole being considerably less awesome than its constituent parts. No such problems exist for Richard and Di Stockton, for their Griffin is nothing short of splendid in all departments and conspicuously well run. That locally-caught salmon and brook trout feature so regularly on the menu is scarcely surprising as the Griffin employs its own ghillie, and fishing stories abound in the bar, which is the centre of village life. It's hung with framed displays of fishing flies and maps of the upper and lower reaches of the Wye valley, and dominated by a splendid inglenook fire. Beer is also taken seriously and kept in tip-top condition, summer brews giving way to sturdier guest beers in winter. In the adjacent lounge, low tables, high-backed Windsor chairs and window seats make a comfortable setting for either a light snack or one of the daily-changing hot dishes, perhaps cream of mushroom soup (£2.90), deep-fried whitebait (£2.90), ratatouille pasta (£4.75), fisherman's crumble (£8.90) or braised oxtail in Irish Stout (£8.50). Evening meals provide a wider choice of more substantial fare, either in the no-smoking restaurant or the bars, as space allows. Here you might order pheasant terrine (£4.15), then roast Welsh lamb with mint sauce

Zzzz…

(£9.50) or ragout of game in port (£9.90), followed by Welsh cheeses (£3.75), a home-made ice cream or sorbet (£2), or treacle tart (£2.85). Sunday bar food is only a roast. The eight bedrooms, all but one with en-suite facilities, revert to the fishing theme. To say that they are cottagey is not to decry the pretty floral curtains and bed-covers; they are wonderfully tranquil, and though there are telephones, television is considered superfluous. The splendid residents' lounge on the upper floor of the inn's oldest part is dramatically set under original rafters dating, it is thought, back to its origins as a 15th-century sporting inn. Children stay in parents' room free and there's no charge for additional beds or cots. There is no garden but children may eat in the bar and small portions are served. Two high-chairs. *Bar Food 12-2, 7-9 (except Sun – cold supper for residents only).* *Restaurant Meals 1-3 (Sun only – £11.50), 7-9pm. Children allowed in bar to eat. Free House. Beer Boddingtons, Flowers IPA, Bass, Brains, Marston's Pedigree. Patio, outdoor eating. Accommodation 8 bedrooms, 7 en suite, £50 (single £28.50). Children welcome overnight. Additional beds and cots available. Access, Diners, Visa.*

Lydart   Gockett Inn

| Tel 01600 860486 | **FOOD** |

Lydart nr Monmouth Gwent NP5 4AD   Map 9 D5

This former staging post on the St David's to London route stands atop an escarpment (now the B4293) three miles outside Monmouth; "Gockett" was the local name for the black grouse which inhabited these heathlands until their extinction a century or so ago. Central to the Inn's modern attractions are Hazel Short's daily selected menus, wherein brevity is made a virtue by careful buying of top-quality foodstuffs, and by her innovative approach to traditional recipes, e.g. popular pies are peppered steak (£5.95) and steak and kidney (£5.25). Home-made soups (£2.50) are thick, flavourful, and popular, along with the likes of prawns with fresh raspberry vinaigrette (£3.95), paté maison with Cumberland sauce (£2.95), tagliatelle with smokey bacon (£3.75), leek and bacon pudding tart (£3.50). Though all are officially starters, a light lunch of two of them is equally acceptable, except on Sundays, when bookings should be made for the fixed-price lunch (3 courses £10.50). Alongside the hefty pies other main courses are equally substantial: poussin with mild fresh fruit curry sauce (£8.50), fillet of beef en croute filled with Stilton cheese with Madeira sauce (£11.50) and vegetarian lasagne (£6.95). A variety of cheeses is always available and the pudding list which follows is simple but commendable in scope (all £2.50). Leather banquettes, silk flowers and gathered drapes lend a bright, cottagey feel to the original dining room which is hung with horse brasses and copper bed-warmers. A more recent extension to the bar has increased the space and leads to an enclosed rear patio, and a neat garden for alfresco eating in fine weather. *Bar Food & Restaurant Meals 12-2, 7-10 (7-9 Sun). Children's portions. Children allowed in bar to eat. Free House. Beer Local brew; Free Miners, Bass, guest beers. Garden, outdoor eating, disabled WC. Family room. Access, Visa.*

Marford   Trevor Arms

Tel 01224 570436	B&B
Marford Wrexhall Clwyd	Map 8 D2

Quaint 17th-century architecture is a feature of Marford's original
buildings, which all incorporate a cross to ward off evil spirits. The
Trevor Arms, built later as a coaching inn, echoes these features and
also plays its full part in village life centred on a very busy locals' bar
which occupies the pub's oldest part. The original and somewhat
modest bedrooms are also housed here. Though not lacking in modern
appointments such as TV, radio and direct-dial phones they offer only
shower/WC en-suite bathrooms. In addition to its large garden and
children's play area, the latest attraction is a covered barbecue patio
complete with freestanding gas heaters for use on chillier evenings.
*Pub open 11-11 (Sun 12-3, 7-10.30). **Beer** Thomas Greenall's Original,
Greenalls Draught, Stones Draught. Garden, summer barbecue, lawn.
Family room. **Accommodation** 16 bedrooms, all en-suite, from £39.50
(single £29.50). Children welcome overnight, additional bed (from £5).
No dogs. Access, Visa.*

Mold   We Three Loggerheads

Tel 01352 85337	FOOD
Loggerheads nr Mold Clwyd CH7 5PG	Map 8 D2

Standing alongside the A494, some three miles from Mold, a squarish
16th-century stone pub with somewhat inelegant white-painted brick
additions. Public bars and games room are a touch charmless; the
extension, a pine-clad pillared room with closely set tables, captain's
chairs and banquette seating is devoted to eating. In addition to the
printed menu of rather straightforward pub grub is a daily blackboard
of refreshingly different fare which merits attention from a wider
pub-going public. Peking duck (£4.95) and 'Mexican feast' (Central
American chips and dips, £7.45 for 2) precede some well-spiced main
courses: Cajun chicken with egg-fried rice (£7.25), spicy chili burritos
with melted Cheddar (£7.25) and Louisiana blackened steak (£10.95).
There are roadside picnic tables on the patio, next to the Alun River
bridge. Bass Taverns. *Open 11-11 Fri & Sat. **Bar Food** 12-2.30, 6-10
(Sun 7-9.30). Children's menu. Riverside patio, outdoor eating. Family
room. **Beer** Bass, Worthington. Access, Visa.*

Nevern   Trewern Arms Hotel

Tel 01239 820295	B&B
Nevern nr Newport Dyfed SA42 0NB	Map 9 A5

This hidden hamlet in a valley on the B4582 is a world all on its own
with historic pilgrims' church and Celtic cross, nurseries, cheese dairy
and cake shop. Across the stone bridge over the Nyfer (or "Nevern"),
the Trewern Arms is creeper-clad with sparkling fairy lights, exuding
a magical air. Bedrooms, carefully added to the original 18th-century
stone building, are furnished in cane and pine with floral curtains and
matching duvets. The bathrooms are all en suite (7 with shower/WCs
only); TVs and tea-makers are standard. There are three spacious
family rooms. A foyer lounge upstairs has plenty of literature for
walkers and fishermen, and the lounge bar below sports comfortable
armchairs and sofas. Unambitious bar food and à la carte restaurant.
Children's room; garden and play area. *Free House. **Beer** Castle Eden,
Flowers Original, Boddingtons, guest beers. Garden, outdoor eating,
children's play area. Family room. **Accommodation** 9 bedrooms, all en*

Zzzz...

☺

suite, £45 double (single £28), £55 family room. Children welcome overnight, additional beds and cots supplied. No dogs. Access, Visa.

Nottage   **Rose & Crown**

| Tel 01656 784850   Fax 01656 772345 | **B&B** |

Nottage Heol-y-Capel nr Porthcawl Mid Glamorgan CF36 5ST   Map 9 C6

Just a mile from Royal Porthcawl Golf Club and the town's West Bay stands this white-painted row of stone-built former cottages at the heart of a tiny hamlet. In an area short of good pub accommodation, its friendly, refurbished village bar and neat cottage bedrooms are justly popular. Pastel shaded decor with fitted pine furniture, practical bathrooms and room comforts including phone, TV and trouser press promise a restful and comfortable stay. Scottish & Newcastle Hotel. *Pub open 11-11 Sat, usual hours Sun.* **Beer** *Courage, Ruddles County & Best, Webster's Yorkshire. Garden, children's play area.* **Accommodation** *8 bedrooms, all en suite, £39.95 (single £35.95). Children welcome overnight (under-2s stay free in parents' room, 2-11s £2.50), additional beds and cots available. Guide dogs only. Access, Diners, Visa.*

Old Radnor   **Harp Inn**   **FOOD**

| Tel 01544 21655 | **B&B** |

Old Radnor Presteigne Powys LO8 2RH   Map 9 D4

A special pub, with all the promise of becoming one of mid-Wales's most notable. It's worth the drive scarcely a mile uphill from the A44 just to soak in the views of the Radnor Forest and surrounding hills from the common ground which separates the Harp from Old Radnor's Norman church. Flagstone floors and abundant old beams epitomise the character of the three interlinked rooms which form the bar and dining areas. A wonderful mish-mash of antique settles, assorted tables and bric-a-brac imbue it with a comfortably lived-in feel. On a mantlepiece beside the bar the candle of welcome (an expedient accessory when the power fails) burns in perpetuity. The Copes' kitchen adopts a homely approach and Dee makes a virtue of simplicity. A steak and mushroom club sandwich (£3.95) heads a list of popular snacks: creamed mushrooms are served on toast (£2.95), a summer salad niçoise with French bread (£4.95). More fillingly, giant Yorkshires are piled with steak and kidney or chicken fricassée (£5.95). For dinner, fish comes weekly from Billingsgate for a praiseworthy salmon hollandaise (£7.95), game in season and the much-praised faggots in mushroom and red wine sauce are typical alternatives. Booking is advised for dinner. Four spotless bedrooms, cosy and quiet without phones or TVs, share a brace of bathrooms in a higgledy-piddledy upper floor whose creaking, uneven floors and wood-pegged roof trusses are further evidence of the Harp's antiquity (reputedly 15th-century). Ever-practical, they've even adapted the roof-space for passing walkers to bed down in. And then there's breakfast – cooked to order, or not, as the mood so takes. A tiny galley kitchen is fully stocked with a wide range of provisions to cook for yourself, though as one reader has commented "that may not amuse duchess types wanting waiter service". For those to whom all this strikes a chord, however, the Harp will be harmoniously in tune. *Pub open 11.30-11 (Sun 12-3, 7-10.30).* **Bar Food** *12-2.30, 7-9.30 (closed Mon).* **Restaurant Meals** *as in bar. Free house.* **Beer** *Woods Special, Wye Valley Bitter, Hereford Pale Ale, guest beer in summer. Garden, outdoor eating, summer barbecue at weekends.*   *See over*

Accommodation 4 bedrooms, share 2 bathrooms, from £35 (single £25). Children welcome, additional beds in parents' room £10. Pub closed some mid-week afternoons Oct-Easter. No credit cards.

Pant Mawr   Glansevern Arms

Tel 015515 240	**B&B**
Pant Mawr nr Llangurig Powys SY18 6SY	Map 9 C4

On the A44, four miles west of Llangurig, personally owned and managed for 27 years by Mr Edwards and family, the Glansevern Arms commands a magnificent position overlooking the upper reaches of the Wye. An intimate bar and lounge soak in the glorious hill scenery by day and glow with warmth from log fires at night. Residents equally enjoy the peace and quiet afforded by bedrooms with private sitting areas, uninterrupted by any phones, where the views should provide a greater attraction than television. *Beer Bass. Accommodation 7 rooms, all en suite, £55 (single £35). Children welcome overnight (under-12s half-price), additional bed available. Closed 1 week Christmas. No credit cards.*

Pembroke Ferry   Ferry Inn

Tel 01646 682947	**FOOD**
Pembroke Ferry nr Pembroke Dock Dyfed SA72 6UD	Map 9 A5

Fresh fish and seafoods rightly predominate at the Ferry, which stands by ripping tidal waters right under the Cleddau bridge – turn off the A477 by the tolls. Local oysters (£3.30 for 6) and sweet and sour prawns (£3.45) share prominence on the daily blackboard with the likes of hake florentine in cheese sauce (£5.25) and whole baby turbot (£5.75). For those of less fishy persuasion are the home-cured ox tongue (£3.55), sirloin steak (£7.95), bacon steak with parsley sauce (£4.25), sherried mushrooms on herb toast (£2.95) or hazelnut and rice burgers with gooseberry sauce (£3.95). Children are very much of secondary concern, being welcome inside at lunchtime, if well behaved, or free to roam the riverside patio and rocks when weather and tide permit. Sunday lunch carvery (£6.95). Choice of 20 malt whiskies. *Bar Food 12-2 (carvery lunch Sun to 1.30), 7-10 (Sun to 9.30). Free House. Beer Bass, Hancock's HB. Waterside patio/terrace, outdoor eating. Pub closed 25 & 26 Dec. Access, Visa.*

Penallt   Boat Inn

Tel 01600 712615	**A**
Long Lane Penallt nr Monmouth Gwent NP5 4AJ	Map 14 A2

Despite its Monmouthshire address, this Wye valley pub is commonly known as "The Boat at Redbrook"; a signpost will direct you to park by the football field on the A466 Monmouth to Chepstow road and cross by a footbridge adjoining the disused railway line. In the pub garden, log tables teeter on the hillside by-passed on two sides by streams which cascade into the Wye. Beer aficionados, attracted in part by Tuesday's folk and Thursday's jazz nights, select beers direct from the cask, in ascending order of strength from Thwaites Best through Fuller's London Pride and Theakston's XB to Spitfire and Old Peculier. Pot meals of country cidered pork and rice (£4.50), rogan josh (£4.25), Pan Haggerty (£3.70) and aubergine Parmesan (£3.70) mostly assume secondary importance. There are rolls most lunchtimes, occasional barbecues in the summer months, and a many and varied selection of country wines on offer. Open all day during the footballing season. *Free House.* **Beer** *8-10 regularly changing real ales available – Thwaites, Fuller's London Pride, Theakston's XB & Old Peculier, Spitfire. Riverside garden. Family room. Pub closed 25 Dec pm. Access, Visa.*

Penmaenpool   George III Hotel

| Tel 01341 422525   Fax 01341 423565 | **B&B** |

Penmaenpool nr Dolgellau Gwynedd LL40 1YD   Map 8 C3

Squeezed in between the A493, which is at roof level, and the head of the Mawddach Estuary, the 17th-century George III Hotel enjoys magnificent views – shared by all but two of the bedrooms – across the water to wooded hills beyond. The unpretentious Dresser bar – so named because the bar counter is made out of the bottom half of an old Welsh dresser – is a place where wooden tables are polished, brass ornaments gleam and a welcoming fire burns in the grate. The rustic cellar bar (actually at ground level) is open only in the summer when there are also tables outside, on what was a railway line, next to the water. Residents have there own cosy lounge with beamed ceiling and inglenook fireplace. Now run by five members of the Cartwright family the bedrooms, half of which are in the adjacent, former Victorian railway station, have all benefited from recent refurbishment and have traditional free-standing furniture and pretty floral fabrics – William Morris in the old station rooms – plus smart modern bathrooms. All have direct-dial phones, TV, trouser press and beverage kit. Free fishing permits for residents. *Open 11-11 (Sun usual hours). Free House.* **Beer** *Ruddles, John Smith's. Garden.* **Accommodation** *12 bedrooms, all en suite, £88 (single £45). Children welcome overnight (under-12s £12.50 & babies free if sharing parents' room), additional beds an cots available. Access, Visa.*

Penybont   Severn Arms Hotel

| Tel 01597 851224   Fax 01597 851693 | **B&B** |

Penybont nr Llandrindod Wells Powys LD1 5UA   Map 9 C4

A white-painted former coaching inn by the junction of the A488 and A44, at the heart of the Ithon Valley. Loved by JB Priestley for its creaky floors, old oak beams and sloping ceiling, it has some of the best family rooms around, tucked under the eaves of the pub's top storey, with pastoral views down the garden to a wooden bridge over the river. Caring management by Geoff and Tessa Lloyd has extended over eleven years and the bedrooms are both immaculately kept and well equipped; all en suite, most have trouser presses and all have TV, radio, direct-dial phones and tea-making facilities. From the flagstoned entrance there's access to the village bar festooned with local football trophies, a more sedate lounge bar and extensive dining room. Residents enjoy use of their own quiet TV lounge on the first floor. *Free house.* **Beer** *Tetley, Worthington, Bass, guest beer. Garden, outdoor eating. Family room.* **Accommodation** *10 bedrooms, all en suite, £50 (single £28). Children welcome overnight. Accommodation closed one week Christmas-New Year. Access, Diners, Visa.*

Pisgah   **Halfway Inn**

Tel 01970 884631	**A**
Devil's Bridge Road Pisgah Aberystwyth Dyfed SY23 4NE	Map 9 C4

650 feet up overlooking the Rheidol Valley below, this is a
marvellous country pub in a lovely setting with magnificent views.
Well known as a beer-lovers' favourite, with its choice of six beers.
Never modernised or extended, this 250-year-old Inn retains its
traditional feel – candle-lit in the evenings and log fire in winter.
Families use the Stone Room bar (walls made of stone). *Pub open 11-
11 Mon-Fri mid-July to end Aug, 11-11 Sat all year, usual hours Sun and
other times. Children allowed in bar to eat, children's menu. Free House.*
*Beer Felinfoel Double Dragon, Flowers Original, Castle Eden, Wadworth
6X, Bateman 3XB, guest beers. Garden, children's play area. Family room.
No credit cards.*

Pont-ar-Gothi   **Cresselly Arms**

Tel 01267 290221	**FOOD**
Pont-ar-Gothi nr Carmarthen Dyfed SA31 7NG	Map 9 B5

Tucked off the A40 by the Gothi River bridge, this friendly pub
makes full use of a riverside summer garden (no unaccompanied
children, please) and dining room with restful river views. In the two
spacious bars hung with fish nets and horse brasses, snacks encompass
sandwiches, hot platters (fish bake £4.75), pot meals (steak and kidney
£4.50) and standard vegetarian and children's fare. Daily specials
weigh in with lemon sole fillets (£5.95), breast of chicken stuffed
with apricots (£4.95) and vegetarian options such as mushroom
goulash (£4.75). Popular restaurant menu. *Free House.* **Bar Food**
*12-2.15, 6.30-9.30 (Sun 7-9). Restaurant Meals 12-1.30, 7-9.30 (Sun
7-9). Children's menu. Beer Flowers Original, Marston's Pedigree.
Riverside garden, children's play area. Family room. Access, Visa.*

Raglan   **Beaufort Arms Hotel**

Tel & Fax 01291 690412	**B&B**
High Street Raglan Gwent NP5 2DY	Map 9 D5

Recent alterations uncovered remains of the original Tudor
timberwork which are now preserved in the unusual and characterful
Country Bar. Rumour has it that there still remains a secret
underground passage from here to nearby Raglan Castle. Residents
have use of their own lounge and bedrooms are kitted out with white
wood furniture, floral fabrics, radios, telephones, TVs and beverage
trays. *Beer Courage Directors & Best, Boddingtons, Wadworth 6X.*
*Accommodation 15 bedrooms, all en suite, £45 (single £35). Children
welcome overnight (family room £55). Dogs by arrangement. Access,
Diners, Visa.*

Red Wharf Bay   **Ship Inn**

Tel 01248 852568	**FOOD**
Red Wharf Bay Anglesey Gwynedd LL75 4RJ	Map 8 B1

Fronted by hanging baskets, the low white-painted Ship stands right
on the shore of Menai Strait at Traeth Loch. The quarry tiled floors
and genuine exposed beams and stonework make for an interesting
interior where the ship's wheels and chiming clocks, Tom Browne
cartoons and Toby Jug collection give it great character. With food as
the main draw, there's a steady stream of early arrivals and local

regulars to sample from a selection of bar food which is sensibly varied daily between cold and hot choices and never overly long. Fresh seafoods are prominent depending on availability, with prawns and avocado (£5.95), smoked salmon with salad (£5.80) preceding perhaps a salmon and broccoli mornay (£6.50). For potential ploughmen, there's a two-cheese version (£4.20) with a miniature cottage loaf, and for true trenchermen cold chicken and ham pie with pickles (£4.30). Good vegetarian choices such as cheesy carrot roulade (£4.55) and hearty grills of gammon with fresh pineapple (£5.80) further expand the choice. There's a separate children's menu served in a smaller rear family room or out in the garden shore-side. A no-smoking restaurant opens upstairs for diners at weekends. Andrew Kenneally, landlord for over 20 years keeps a good pint of Tetley's with a guest ale such as Friary Meux also available. *Pub open 11-3, 7-11 (all day Sat, Sun 12-3, 9-10.30), 11-11 all week July–Sept. Bar Food 12-2.15, 7-9.15 (Sun 12-2, 7-9). Children's menu. Free House. Beer Tetley Best, Dark Mild, Burton Ale, regular guest beer. Garden, front patio, outdoor eating area, tables in garden. Family room. Access, Visa.*

Shirenewton   Carpenters Arms   FOOD

Tel 01291 641231

Shirenewton nr Chepstow Gwent NP6 6BU   Map 9 D6

On the B4235 Usk road, 4 miles from Chepstow (turn by the race course) the Carpenters is a row of roadside cottages which once housed the local smithy and carpenter's shop, now quite literally hollowed out into a succession of seven interconnecting rooms served from a single bar. Seven real ales, too, with regular guest options, are a perennial draw and a plethora of baguettes and baked potatoes the regular lunchtime accompaniments. Amid a blackboard menu relying in large part on convenience items there's still room to seek out a quality sirloin steak (£7.50), home-made steak and mushroom pie (£4.95) and a famously popular rhubarb crumble (£2.25). Cars park right up to the door on a bend in the road where some picnic tables front the building amid a blaze of summer flowers in tubs and hanging baskets. There is no garden here, and well-behaved children are just about tolerated within. *Bar Food 12-2, 7-9.30. Children's menu. Free House. Beer Wadworth 6X, Boddingtons, Marston's Pedigree, Owd Rodger and changing guest beers. Patio, outdoor eating. No credit cards.*

Shirenewton   Tredegar Arms   FOOD
                                                           B&B

Tel 011291 641274

Shirenewton nr Chepstow Gwent   Map 9 D6

Dominating the crossroads at the heart of this small hillside village of stone cottages (signed both from A48 and B4285 some five miles from Chepstow), the Tredegar Arms has long been at the centre of community life. Reopened recently following a spell of closure, it has quickly regained this prominence in the sure hands of experienced locals Rob and Val Edwards. Facing a servery ingeniously cut back under a central staircase, the lounge bar is the focal point for food which already shows a refreshing balance between conventional and empirical fare! Tandoori chicken pieces (£2.95) and sesame prawn toasts (£2.45) are among less usual curtain raisers to traditional main courses such as liver, bacon and onions (£4.50) and grilled trout with roasted almonds (£5.50). Decidedly different specials recently on offer included a honeyed lamb ragout with mint (£5.25), a 'cock-a-roosting

Zzzz...

fricassee' in parsley and lemon sauce (£4.95), 'Bully Hole Bottom Pepperpot' and a fiery 'Welsh Dragon pie', actually made with lamb (both £5.25). Freshly recarpeted and fitted out with Windsor and library chairs and cushioned banquettes, this has proven so popular a venue that plans were already afoot as we went to press to convert, or incorporate, the exisiting rear patio into additional eating space. No such expansion, however, is possible upstairs where just two letting bedrooms are available, each with its own WC and shower room en suite. Equipped with new colour TVs and tea- and coffee-making equipment, they are unfussily furnished and spotlessly kept and enjoy super views down the valley to the distant Severn estuary. A truly restful night is followed by gargantuan country breakfasts. *Open 11-3, 6-11, Sun 12-3, 7-10.30.* **Bar Food** *12-2, 7-9.30 (to 9 Sun). Free House.* **Beer** *Hook Norton Best, Flowers IPA, Wadworth 6X, two guest beers.* **Accommodation** *2 rooms, both en suite, £40 (single £25). Children welcome overnight, extra camp bed supplied. Check-in by arrangement. No dogs. No credit cards.*

Swansea   Langland Court Hotel

Tel 01792 361545 Fax 01792 362302	**B&B**
31 Langland Court Road Langland Swansea West Glamorgan SA3 4TD	**Map 9 C6**

Especially favoured by those less enamoured of Swansea's noisy nightlife, Langland Court has a fine hilltop location on Mumbles Head some four miles from the city. Take the A4067 along the seafront and follow signs to Caswell from Mumbles village. Striking first impressions are created by the grand oak staircase which dominates the foyer. To one side the former Polly Garter's bar, named in commemoration of local boy Dylan Thomas, is now more a wine bar and bistro, with residents finding relaxation in the lounge and bar whose patio doors open onto the garden. Tudor-style front bedrooms, some with antique four posters, and the stylish attic rooms with third-bed alcoves are the pick of the main house accommodation, enjoying fine views down to the Bristol Channel. Alternative accommodation is in more modestly-sized bedrooms across a quiet road in the Coach House. Bathrooms, bedroom facilities which include TV, radio and direct dial phones and housekeeping generally are of a high standard throughout. Children welcome overnight. Dogs allowed in the Coach House only. *Open 12-9.30pm, Sun to 9. Free House. No real ales. Garden.* **Accommodation** *21 bedrooms, all en suite, £78 (single £56). Children welcome overnight (under-16s £12), additional beds & cots (£3) supplied. Dogs by arrangement. Access, Visa.*

Zzzz...

Trecastle   The Castle Coaching Inn

	FOOD
Tel 01874 636354 Fax 01874 636457	**B&B**
Brecon Road Trecastle Brecon Powys LO3 84H	**Map 9 C5**

Whilst sensibly avoiding sweeping changes, new brooms have certainly been at work cleaning and sprucing up this famous inn on the old coaching route through the Brecons. The bar and dining areas have been agreeably opened out to make much better use of natural daylight, yet retaining sufficient of the pub's best features, such as the flagstone floors and vast open fireplace, to preserve the Castle's unique character. Menus so far have remained sensibly short while the new management team finds its feet. Fresh fish from Swansea market is much in evidence, with fresh cod in batter (£5.95), a large whole plaice grilled for two (£9) and an unusual surf'n'turf combining fillet steak with a salmon cutlet in lobster sauce. In addition to the ever-popular steak in ale pie (£5.75), meat-eaters meanwhile are enjoying the addition of chasseur sauce to their rump steaks (£9.95) and béarnaise with the sirloin (£10.25). Bedroom improvements have come on apace: all are now en suite with smartly tiled bathrooms and up-to-date amenities including direct-dial phones, TVs, radio alarm clocks and hairdryers. There are two good-sized family rooms, one with bunk beds (children stay free in their parents' room). To the pub's rear there's a safe, enclosed garden in which to enjoy panoramic views down the Gwyddor valley. *Bar Food 12-2, 6-9.30. Free House. Beer Courage Directors, John Smith's, Ruddles Best, guest beer. Garden. Accommodation 10 bedrooms, all en suite, £40 (single £35). Children welcome overnight, additional beds and cots available. No dogs. Access, Visa.*

Trellech	The Village Green	FOOD
Tel 01600 860119		B&B
Trellech nr Monmouth Gwent NP5 4PA		Map 9 D5

Bob and Jane Evans's once-derelict, 450-year-old village local is today in the vanguard of the fashionable trend towards combining bistro-style food with the more traditional concept of pub-with-restaurant. Thus we find here a combination of all three with an à la carte restaurant (recommended in our *1995 Hotels and Restaurants Guide*) and a brace of pubby bars offering a complete selection of ploughman's (from £3.50), sandwiches and baked potatoes. Between the two, a stone-walled bistro, festooned with dried flowers hanging from its rafters, offers comprehensive alternative choices. Deep-fried Brie and bacon (£3.75), caramelised onion tartlet (£3.50) and stuffed pear with Stilton and mint dressing (£3.75) are substantial snacks in themselves. Main dishes, might include salmon with grain mustard (£9), beef Kashmiri (£8.25) and occasionally even braised ostrich in a sage and onion gravy (£10.50). Ever-popular speciality sweets include crème brulée, sticky toffee pudding and iced coffee terrine (£3). Alongside the pub two small bedroom suites with kitchenettes are let on a bed-and-breakfast or self-catering basis. There is room for a small family (children accommodated free) and TV is provided, but no phones; the en-suite facilities have WC and showers only. *Bar Food 12-2, 7-9.45. No real ales. Accommodation 2 bedrooms, both en suite, from £45 (single £35). Children welcome overnight (accommodated free in parents' room), extra beds & cots supplied. Check-in by arrangement.* Pub closed Sun eve, all Mon (except Bank Holiday Mons), 10 days Jan. No dogs. Access, Visa.

Tremeirchion	Salusbury Arms	
Tel 01745 710262		FOOD
Tremeirchion St Asaph Clwyd LL17 0HN		Map 8 C1

A former estate coaching house with origins dating back to the 14th-century. The Grade II listed pub takes its name from Tremeirchion's ancestral owners. At the heart of village life once again following a period of closure, the Salusbury Arms is enjoying a fresh lease of life in its new ownership. Arriving on the first anniversary of the re-opening, we found the building carefully restored and spick-and-span within, with a cosy feel to its interlinked village bar, lounges and dining room, and the new proprietors exhibiting fierce pride in their product. Yorkshireman Jim O'Boyle operates a cellar whose range of regularly-changing real ales runs to four or five on any given day, while Heulwen, a bubbling landlady, enthuses over menus which, while not yet overly imaginative, rely in large part on quality and consistency. The Salusbury Grill and home made steak and kidney (both £5.95) are already established favourites, and there's an expanding range of specials such as the Korai chicken curry (£5.95), beef stroganoff (£7.50) and salmon Jeanette with hollandaise sauce (£8.75). There's a cheery welcome for children, (who'll find a lovely garden to play in) a burgeoning trade in family Sunday lunches (booking advised), and a Welsh songstress entertains on weekend evenings. *Pub open 11-11 (Sun 12-3, 7-10.30). Bar Food 12-2.30 7-9.30. No food Sun evening. Restaurant Meals as in bar. Children allowed in the bar to eat, children's menu. Free House Beer Marston's Best and Pedigree. Regularly changing guest beers. Garden, lawn, outdoor eating, tables in garden. Family room. Access, Visa.*

Tyn-y-Groes — The Groes Inn

Tel 01492 650545	**FOOD**
Tyn-y-Groes nr Conwy Gwynedd LL32 8TN	Map 8 C2

Claiming to be the first licensed house in Wales, "Taverne-y-Groes" (by the cross) boasts a history unbroken since 1573. The present building (from which are splendid views of the Conwy estuary) contains much 16th- and 17th-century interior timberwork in a succession of low-ceilinged rooms that have been extended these days to include a formal dining room and non-smoking conservatory that leads to the large rear garden. Daily blackboards proclaim the most promising bar food: Indian haddock (£5.25), crispy roast duck (£7.50), lamb with rosemary and apricot casserole (£5.95), with the likes of sticky toffee pudding (£2.50) to follow. Bookings may be made for a three-course lunch (Sunday £10.50), and there's à la carte dining nightly. This establishment is generally not suitable for children under 10: over-10s are confined to the conservatory and garden. *Bar Food & Restaurant Meals 12-2, 6.45-9 (Sun 12-2.15, 7-9), children allowed in bar to eat. Free House. Beer Tetley, Burton. Garden, outdoor eating. Family room. Pub closed Sun nights in winter. Access, Visa.*

Usk — Three Salmons

Tel 01291 672133 Fax 01291 673979	**B&B**
Usk Gwent NP5 1BQ	Map 9 D5

For long an inn of renown, the Three Salmons once hosted a civic luncheon to mark the opening of the nearby Chain bridge over the Usk, in 1812 (tickets 2S 6d). Much of the original listed building has recently undergone a massive restoration including total retiling of the roof in Welsh grey slate (tiles £2.50). The single bar and public areas at street level are once again immaculate following years of neglect and there's a friendly sense of purpose again amongst the staff. A separate bar and function room have also been revived on the first floor. In the main building, little expense has been spared in upgrading the bedrooms to modern-day requirements: nestling under high-pitched eaves and roof timbers they are individual in character and furnished to a high standard with smart new en-suite bathrooms in gleaming, gold-tapped, white porcelain. An annexe across the street was once the "Livery and Bait Stables"; outside the Ostlers's Bell still hangs. The dozen bedrooms within are now scheduled for further modernisation. *Pub open 11-11 (except Sun). Free House. Beer Whitbread Best, Flowers IPA & Original. Family Room. Accommodation 21 rooms, all en suite, from £60 (single £40). Children welcome overnight additional beds (£5) & cots supplied. Pub closed 25/26 Dec. No dogs. Access, Visa.*

Zzzz...

Whitebrook   **Crown at Whitebrook**

FOOD

Tel 01600 860254   Fax 01600 860607

B&B

Whitebrook nr Monmouth Gwent NP5 4TX

Map 14 A2

It is a *long* mile uphill from the A466 at the Bigswear bridge to this
hidden, woodland Wye valley inn. Roger and Sandra Bates's 'auberge'
(which perfectly describes the place), exudes homely comfort and
promises plenty in terms of culinary surprises. 'Bar snacks' is surely
a misnomer for light lunches of which smoked salmon and avocado
pancakes (£5.50), sautéed chicken livers with pine kernels (£4.95)
and cheese bacon and onion tartlet (£4.95) are typical: follow with
flambéed pancakes or one of the excellent home-made ice creams –
coffee bean and Tia Maria, perhaps. Three-course lunches, good value
at £14.95, and a rather more formal dinner reveal cooking of real
quality; sautéed lambs kidneys with black pudding, roasted half guinea
fowl with tarragon, and rhubarb mousse with orange sauce might be a
typically balanced and tasty feast. Lightly whispering trees are likely to
be the only intrusion to a thoroughly restful night. The bedrooms are
bright and comfortable, decorated in pastel colours with up-to-date
accoutrements including direct-dial phones, tea-makers, TVs and clock
radios: bathrooms are neatly carpeted and spotless. Hearty Welsh
breakfasts are served on request in the room. Don't come looking for
real ales, instead savour some of the 15 malt whiskies, 16 cognacs and
some 160 wines (seven of which are available by the glass) on offer.
*Bar Food 12-2 (except Mon). Restaurant Meals 7-9.30 (except Sun
eve). Free House. Beer No real ale. Garden, outdoor eating, children's play
area. Family room. Accommodation 12 bedrooms, all en suite, £80 (single
£50). Children welcome overnight, additional beds and cots available.
Pub closed Sun eve, lunchtime Mon & first two weeks January. Access,
Diners, Visa.*

Zzzz...

Channel Islands
& Isle of Man

Alderney

St Anne	The Georgian House ★	
Tel & Fax 01481 822471		**FOOD**
Victoria Street St Anne Alderney		Map 13 F4

Behind the Georgian facade of this old three-storey Alderney house is
a cosy little bar and dining room with a strong traditional feel. Recent
redecoration has included the addition of two open fireplaces. The
'Garden Beyond' has an open-air bar and grill and is a strong asset in
the summer. Food here is of the highest standard and a far cry from
standard pub grub. Locally caught fish and crustaceans feature
strongly. The lunch menu is kept simple with the likes of wonderful
moules à la crème (£4.25), whole fresh Alderney crab (price depends
on weight), beef stroganoff (£4.75), choice of omelette (£3.50) or
ploughman's lunches (£3.50). In addition, the chalkboard announces
daily specials like home-made chicken and leek soup (£2), Herm
oysters (£4.50 for 6), fresh plaice (£6.50) or half a lobster salad
(priced according to weight). The dinner menu is more elaborate with
a platter of *fruits de mer* (24hrs' notice recommended) or 12oz sirloin
from the bone flambéed in brandy (£11.50). Home-made desserts are
a must – summer pudding in the form of a layered terrine is made
with local berries and the raspberry flan with fruit from the garden
of the owners, Liz and Stephen Hope. Special 3-course Sunday lunch
menu (£8.75). A courtesy car to the harbour is available if booked at
the time of reservation. *Bar Food & Restaurant Meals 12-2.30, 7-10.
Children allowed in bar to eat, children's menu. Free House.*
*Beer Ringwood Bitter, Real Ale & Old Thumper. Garden, outdoor eating.
Pub closed Tue eves. Access, Diners, Visa.*

Guernsey

Le Bourg	Deerhound Inn Hotel & Poachers Restaurant	
		FOOD
Tel 01481 38585		**B&B**
Le Bourg Forest Road Forest Guernsey		Map 13 E4

Located off a main road, not far from the airport, this converted old
Guernsey farmhouse is situated above Petit Bot valley and beach and
offers a particularly warm welcome. New proprietors the Piriou and
Bonthelius families have completely redecorated the restaurant and all
of the rooms. Chef's specials include stir-fry beef (£4.50), vegetable
soup (£2.95), fish platter (£3.95) and chicken Kiev. A Sunday roast
lunch is £8.95 including two main courses. One of the bedrooms is a
family room with bunk beds; the TV lounge can act as a children's
playroom and there are swings in the garden. *Bar Food & Restaurant
Meals 12-1.45, 7-9.30. Children's menu. Beer Tetley, Theakston. Garden,
outdoor eating, children's play area. Family room. **Accommodation***
*10 bedrooms, 2 en suite, £37 (single £18.50). Children welcome overnight
(under-3s stay free in parents' room, 4-12s half-price), baby listening,
additional beds and cots available. Access, Diners, Visa.*

Castel   Hotel Hougue du Pommier

Tel 01481 56531 Fax 01481 56260	**B&B**
Castel Guernsey GY5 7FQ	Map 13 E4

'Hougue du Pommier' means 'apple-tree hill' and the apples from the ten acres of orchards surrounding this fine old Guernsey farmhouse were once used to make local cider. Now a lovely inn, the building dates back to 1712. The Tudor Bar features a traditional atmosphere, with beams and an inglenook fireplace. Quiet bedrooms (including six new de luxe rooms) overlooking the particularly well-kept gardens are comfortable, with remote-control TVs, telephones and beverage trays. The solar-heated swimming pool is in a secluded spot surrounded by trees. Nearby is a 10-hole pitch-and-putt golf course and an 18-hole putting green. The sandy beaches of Grandes Rocques and Cobo are ten minutes' walk away. *High Tea 5.30pm. Free House.* **Beer** *Captains, Champion. Garden, games room, sauna, solarium.* **Accommodation** *43 bedrooms, all en suite, £71 (de luxe £81, single £35.50). Children welcome overnight (0-5 yrs free, 5-11 yrs £17.75), additional beds and cots available. Guide dogs only. Sunday open to diners and residents only. Access, Diners, Visa.*

Kings Mills   Fleur du Jardin

	FOOD
Tel 01481 57996 Fax 01481 56834	**B&B**
Kings Mills Castel Guernsey GY5 7JT	Map 13 E4

This 16th-century inn in the centre of Kings Mill village and close to Vazon Bay has a tastefully traditional country feel. Several low-ceilinged dining rooms interconnect, creating a quiet atmosphere. The cooking is the highlight here. While the extensive menu offers the usual pub fare, the daily specials are strong on fish and game: oven-baked lemon sole lemon and butter (£7.75), local sea bass (£6.25), game pie with juniper berries (£6.25). Also a popular place for a Sunday roast lunch which is £9.45 for four courses in the bar or restaurant. The bedrooms are attractive and amenities include remote-control TVs, telephones and tea/coffee-making facilities; some rooms have trouser presses and small refrigerators. There's a beautiful view of the surrounding countryside from the heated outdoor swimming pool. Eight or nine wines available by the glass. Plenty of parking. *Bar Food & Restaurant Meals 12-2, 6.30-9.30 (Sun 7-9). Children allowed in bar to eat, children's menu. Free House.* **Beer** *Guernsey Brewery. Garden, outdoor eating, children's play area.* **Accommodation** *17 bedrooms, all en suite, £72. Children over 4 welcome overnight (4-12 50% adult rate if sharing parents' room, high-tea included), additional beds and cots available. No dogs. Access, Visa.*

Pleinmont   Imperial Hotel

Tel 01481 64044 Fax 01481 66139	**B&B**
Pleinmont Torteval Guernsey GY8 0PS	Map 13 E4

Attractive little hotel ideally located at the south end of Rocquaine Bay. Bar, restaurant and most of the bedrooms benefit from a beautiful view of the bay. Ongoing refurbishment is improving the clean and bright accommodation with tea and coffee-making facilities, TVs and direct-dial telephones. Four rooms have attractive balconies with patio furniture. Children are welcome if well behaved. Special rates include car hire. Safe garden and a short walk from the beach. Hotel leads onto twenty miles of cliff walks. *Open 10.30-11.45 (Mon-Wed to 11 in winter, Sun 11-3).* **Beer** *Randalls. Garden, outdoor eating.*

See over

Accommodation 17 bedrooms, all en suite, £49 (single £24.50). Children welcome overnight (0-2 years £5, 2-11 50% reduction). Pub closed Sun eve (but restaurant open as usual, 7-9). Access, Visa.

St Peter Port — Ship & Crown

Tel 01481 721368 | **A**

Pier Steps St Peter Port Guernsey | **Map 13 E4**

Usually-buzzing yachting pub opposite the marina. St Peter Port's most traditional pub with lots of maritime pictures and memorabilia in both the simply-furnished, busy main bar and quieter back drinking area. This was the Germans' naval HQ during the World War II island occupation. Thanks to the new Guernsey laws children are now welcome in the bar all day. *Open 10am-11.45pm, Sun usual hours.* **Beer** *Sunbeam, guest beer. No credit cards.*

Herm

Herm Island — The Ship Inn

Tel 01481 722159   Fax 01481 710066 | **FOOD**

Herm Island via Guernsey | **Map 13 E4**

The only hotel on the island, the White House offers comfortable accommodation (on half-board terms only) for those who want to escape the hurly-burly of mainland life. Under the same ownership as the hotel is the Ship Inn – a small bar area connected to the first-floor Captain's coffee shop, a carvery-style restaurant. 'To pipe you aboard' are the likes of crab cocktail (£3.50) or Herm oysters (6 for £3.50!); continue with 'the daily catch' (perhaps fresh plaice £6.85), one of an extensive selection of baguettes (from £2.50), 'midshipman's main courses' (steaks £6.75-£10.75 or vegetarian salad £5.75) or the lunchtime carvery (daily roast £4). Children are very welcome and offered their own young sea dogs' menu (king-size sausage, fish fingers, chicken nuggets, all £2.75). Afternoon teas. *Open from 10am-10.45pm (Sun 12-2.30).* **Bar Food** *10am-9.30pm. Children's menu. Patio, outdoor eating. Pub closed Oct to Mar.*

Jersey

Gorey — Dolphin Hotel

Tel 01534 853370   Fax 01534 857618 | **B&B**

Gorey Pier Gorey Jersey JE6 3EW | **Map 13 F4**

The Dolphin Hotel is right on Gorey Pier, beneath the medieval Mont Orgueil castle, on Jersey's east coast and not far from the wide Grouville Bay which offers safe bathing and beach sports. Fish nets and boating accessories adorn the Fisherman's Bar & Grill. Adequate bedrooms are equipped with remote-control TVs, telephones, radios, trouser presses, hairdryers and beverage trays. Best rooms are on the top floor overlooking the Pier. *Pub open 9.30am-11pm, Sun usual hours. Free House.* **Beer** *Theakston, Mary Anne Special & Best, Flowers, John Smith's. Family room.* **Accommodation** *17 bedrooms, all en suite,*

£58 (single £29). Children welcome overnight (under-4s stay free in parents' room, over-4s negotiable). Check-in by arrangement. No dogs. Access, Visa.

St Aubin   Old Court House Inn   **FOOD**

Tel 01534 46433   Fax 01534 45103   **B&B**

St Aubin The Bulwarks Jersey   **Map 13 F4**

Dating back to 1450, the original 'Courthouse' at the rear of the building was largely restored in 1611. The front portion of the property was a wealthy merchants' homestead with enormous cellars, which (from the 17th century) stored privateers' plunder alongside legitimate cargo. It's a family-run hotel/restaurant/inn with a young outlook and a popular alfresco eating trade – bar snacks on the front terrace overlooking the harbour and à la carte in the rear courtyard. Bar snacks include moules marinière (£4.70), grilled prawns (£6.60), Cumberland sausage (£4.50) and ploughman's lunches (from £2.95). Seafood is the real speciality with good fisherman's platters (£45 for two with a whole lobster), oysters (£3.90 for 6) and more involved dishes like lobster Thermidor and "crab to pick". Vegetarians are offered vegetable lasagne (£4.50) and children have their own short menu or smaller portions, charged accordingly. The beamed cellar bars and upstairs Mizzen Mast Bar (well-known to *Bergerac* fans as the *Royal Barge* pub) are favourite rendezvous. The Sunday lunch menu (£11.95) is served downstairs. Charming bedrooms, the best with harbour views, are furnished with old pine; the two-bedroomed suite offers a large bathroom, a pleasant lounge with a beautiful view of the harbour and a private patio with garden furniture. *Pub open 11-11 Sun usual hours.* **Bar Food & Restaurant Meals** *12.30-2.30, 7.30-9.30. Free House.* **Beer** *Marston's Pedigree, Theakston, Flowers, up to 5 guest beers. Family room.* **Accommodation** *9 rooms, all en suite, £80, single £40. Family room. Children welcome overnight (half-price if sharing parents' room), additional beds provided. No dogs. Access, Diners, Visa.*

St Brelade   Old Smugglers Inn   **FOOD**

Tel 01534 41510

Ouaisné Bay St Brelade Jersey   **Map 13 F4**

Two 13th-century fishermen's cottages were rebuilt from their ruins in 1721 by local fishermen and remained as such until the early 1900s when they were enlarged and developed into a small residential hotel retaining most of the original granitework, beams and fireplaces. After the German occupation the property underwent further changes and the Old Smugglers emerged. Today, it is one of the few 'genuine' free houses on the island. A succession of small dining rooms (including the newly opened 50-seater family room) serve food from 'The Treasure Chest' menu. Food is taken seriously and there's an extensive selection of tempting dishes – Yankee fried potato skins (£2.50), local seafood chowder (£1.95), king prawns won ton with sweet chili sauce (£3.95), chef's spicy barbecue-style baby back ribs (£4.95), Smugglers' ocean bake (£4.75), lasagne (£4) or Greek vegetable moussaka (£4.20). No smoking area. No children under 14 in the bar. Folk nights on Sunday. *Open 11-11, Sun usual hours.* **Bar Food & Restaurant Meals** *12-2, 6-8.45 (all day Sun, except no food Sunday eve in winter). Free House.* **Beer** *Bass, three guest beers. Terrace. Family room. No credit cards.*

St Lawrence   British Union Hotel

Tel 01534 861070

Main Road St Lawrence Jersey

FOOD

Map 13 F4

Across the road from St Lawrence Parish Church, this is a pleasant pub with a good atmosphere and warm welcome. A central bar divides two lounges with an additional family/games room to the rear. Well-prepared daily specials like steak and ale pie (£5), chicken and mushroom pancake (£5.50), or fresh Jersey plaice with garlic prawns (£6.50); ice cream with gateau or apple pie (£1) for dessert. Good for families with a small 'children only' patio at the rear. *Pub open 9am-11pm Mon-Sat, Sun usual hours.* **Bar Food** *12-2 (except Sun), 6-8.15 (Sun from 6.30). Children's menu/children allowed in bar to eat.* **Beer** *Sunbeam, Ann's Treat. Garden, outdoor eating, children's play area. Family room. No credit cards.*

St Peter's Village   Star & Tipsy Toad Brewery

Tel 01534 485556   Fax 01534 485559

St Peter's Village Jersey

FOOD

Map 13 F4

Right on the A12, in St Peter's Village, the only pub on the island with its own brewery. The attractive decor retains some character with the granite walls, old coat stoves and oak panelling. Young, enthusiastic staff prepare good basic pub food like surf and turf (£8.90), chicken Kiev (£4.50) or grilled tuna steak (£5.75). The brewery can be visited on arranged tours. Indoor and outdoor play areas in addition to the 'Little Toadies' menu (everything £1.50 plus free ice cream!) and baby-changing facilities make this a perfect pub for families. There is live music Friday to Sunday nights and the Tipsy Toad folk festival is held during the 3rd week of September. As we went to press the *Tipsy Toad Town House* had just opened at 57 New Street St. Helier (Tel 01534 615000). *Pub open 10am-11pm Sun usual hours.* **Bar Food** *12-2.15, 6-8.15, no food Sun. Children's menu. Free House.* **Beer** *Tipsy Toad Brewery: Jimmy's Bitter, Horny Toad. Beer garden, children's play area, disabled facilities. Family room, indoor play area. Access, Diners, Visa.*

Sark

Sark   Dixcart Bar

Tel 01481 832015   Fax 01481 832164

Sark via Guernsey GY9 0SD

FOOD

Map 13 E4

Surrounded by 50 acres of gardens, a charming public bar adjacent to the Dixcart Hotel and under the same ownership. Oak wall panelling, solid pine furniture and paintings by local artists on the walls give a warm atmosphere. Bar snacks come from the hotel kitchen and include home-made fish pie (£3.70), breaded plaice (£3.15) and sandwiches (from £1.30), as well as an extensive list of daily dishes like oxtail soup (£1.50) or prawns in garlic butter (£1.65). Children have their own 'Snug'. No real ales, but Guinness is on draught. *Open 11-11.30.* **Bar Food** *12-3, 6-9.30. Garden, outdoor eating. Family room. Access, Diners, Visa.*

Isle of Man

Peel   Creek Inn

Tel 01624 842216

FOOD

The Quayside Peel Isle of Man

Map 4 A4

Robert and Jean McAleer, industrious and friendly landlords of this bustling pub right by Peel harbour offer seafood specialities from the fish yard in their large, bright and unpretentious bar. Home-made Manx kipper paté (£3.45), fresh crab salad (£4.80), Manx scallops ('Queenies') served on the shell in a mornay sauce (£4.95), avocado sunrise (fresh crab, prawns and pineapple £4.95) might all feature on the menu or among the blackboard specials. Other offerings range from open sandwiches (£1.95-£3.95) to curries, and steak and kidney pie (£3.95). Several fruit tarts or home-made gateaux (£1.75) to follow. Junior diners pay £1.50 or £1.75 for their portions. Full selection of Irish spirits, and at least 12 wines that can be opened to order. Easy parking. *Pub open 11-10.45 Mon-Sat & 12-1.30, 8-10 Sun.* **Bar Food** *11-10.45 (Sun 12-1.45, 8-10). Children's menu.* **Beer** *Worthington, Okells Bitter & Mild. Outdoor eating on the quayside. Children welcome in bar 12-2.30 only if eating. Pub closed 25 Dec. No credit cards.*

Northern Ireland

Ballycastle   **House of McDonnell**

Tel 012657 62975	**A**
21 Castle Street Ballycastle Co Antrim BT64 6AS	Map 20 D1

Unusually, even for a characterful old pub, McDonnell's is a listed
building and as such no changes are allowed inside or out. Not that
change is much on the cards anyway, as it has been in the family for
250 years and is clearly much loved – as visitors soon discover from
the colourful chatelaine Eileen O'Neill, affectionately known as 'the
Tipperary Tinker'. She enjoys nothing better than sharing the history
of the long, narrow, mahogany-countered bar which was once
a traditional grocery-bar. Alas, no food is now offered, but The Open
Door, a good traditional Northern Ireland bakery across the road, has
hot snacks and a wide range of fresh sandwiches to order. *Open 11.30-
11 (Sun 12.30-2.30 & 7-10). No credit cards.*

Belfast   **Crown Liquor Salon**

Tel 01232 325368	**A**
44 Great Victoria Street Belfast Co Antrim	Map 20 D2

Belfast's most famous and best-preserved bar, High Victorian and
wonderful in its exuberant opulence. The building belongs to the
National Trust and is run by the donors, Bass Taverns, who acquired
it in 1979. Upstairs, The Britannic Lounge, with an Edwardian feel,
is fitted out with original timbers from the *SS Britannic*, sister ship
to the *Titanic*. *Open 11.30-11.30 Sun 12-2 & 7-10. No credit cards.*

Belfast   **Kelly's Cellars**

Tel 01232 324835	**A**
30/32 Bank Street Belfast Co Antrim	Map 20 D2

A protected building, this characterful bar boasts the oldest cellars in
Ireland, dating back to 1720. Food is served in the upstairs bar at
lunchtime. Friday and Saturday bring live traditional Irish music.
*Open 11.30-11 (till 1am Thur-Sat). Closed Sun & some Bank Holidays.
Access, Visa.*

Bushmills   **Bushmills Inn**

Tel 012657 32339 Fax 012657 32048	**B&B**
25 Main Street Bushmills Co Antrim BT57 8QA	Map 20 C1

After the Giant's Causeway, the world's oldest distillery at Bushmills is
the biggest attraction in the area (and well worth a visit; mid-week is
most interesting); the Bushmills Inn also attracts year-round local
support. The exterior, including a neat garden at the relocated (back)
main entrance, creates a welcoming impression that extends into the
hall, with its open fire and country antiques, and other public areas
that encompass several bars and a large dining room. Bedrooms are
quite modest, individually decorated and comfortably furnished; some
family rooms are remarkable for their ingenious use of space (one has
a 'balcony' beds, while another has two). A beamed loft provides a
splendid setting for private functions (up to 85 people) and the 'secret
library' a unique venue for special occasions. *Accommodation 11 rooms,
all en suite, £74 (single £48). Children welcome overnight (£18 if
sharing, cots £8). Garden, fishing. Access, Visa.*

Carnlough   **Londonderry Arms**

Tel 01574 885255	**FOOD**

20 Harbour Road Carnlough Glens of Antrim Co Antrim BT44 0EU   Map 20 D1

In the same family for nearly half a century, this hotel and bar makes a good stop at a most attractive little harbour on the famous scenic coastal route and it's well known for 'good, plain food'. The same snacks are available in both bars (hotel and public): soup with home-baked wheaten bread, scones, open prawn sandwich, paté, chef's lunchtime roast. *Open 11.30-11.30 (Sun 12-11).* **Bar Food** *10am-8pm (only sandwiches after 6). Garden. Access, Diners, Visa.*

Carnlough   **The Waterfall**

No Telephone	**A**

High Street Carnlough Co Antrim   Map 20 D1

Not as old as it may first appear to be, the little public bar is nevertheless full of charm, with red-tiled floor and low beamed ceiling. Both the fireplace and bar are made of reclaimed bricks from an old mill across the road and there's a clatter of memorabilia hanging from the ceiling; the walls are used to show off a collection of horse tackle and old posters. Behind, there's a cosy lounge bar with stained-glass window (from the owner's previous pub), decorative plates and another brick fireplace, where bar meals are served. A welcoming place with a lovely friendly atmosphere. *No credit cards.*

Crawfordsburn   **Old Inn**

Tel 01247 853255 Fax 01247 852775	**B&B**

15 Main Street Crawfordsburn Co Down BT19 1JH   Map 20 D2

Located off the main Belfast to Bangor road, this 16th-century inn is in a pretty village setting and is supposed to be the oldest in continuous use in all Ireland. Its location is conveniently close to Belfast and its City Airport. Oak beams, antiques and gas lighting emphasise the natural character of the building, an attractive venue for business people (conference facilities for 150, banqueting for 90) and private guests alike. Individually decorated bedrooms vary in size and style; most have antiques, some four-posters and a few have private sitting rooms; all are non-smoking. Romantics and newly-weds should head for the honeymoon cottage. Free private car parking for overnight guests. No dogs. *Accommodation 34 rooms, £85. Garden. Closed 24-26 Dec. Access, Diners, Visa.*

Cushendall   **P J McCollam**

No Telephone	**A**

23 Mill Street Cushendall Co Antrim BT4 0RR   Map 20 D1

In the family for 300 years and under the current ownership of Joe McCollam for the last 73 years, this magical place has a tiny front bar complete with a patchwork of photographs of local characters, many of them sheep farmers (and great fiddle players) who come down from the glens at weekends. The range in the old family kitchen behind the bar is lit on cold evenings and a converted 'cottage' barn across the yard makes a perfect setting for the famous traditional music sessions. Hospitable and full of character. *Open 11.30-11 (Sun 7-10pm only). Closed Sunday lunchtime. No credit cards.*

Dundrum   **Buck's Head Inn**

Tel 013967 51868   Fax 013967 51898   **FOOD**

77 Main Street Dundrum nr Newcastle Co Down BT33 0LU   Map 20 D2

Situated on the main Belfast-Newcastle road, this attractive, welcoming family-run pub offers fairly traditional bar food from a blackboard menu which changes daily. Although recently renovated, the decor within the pub is traditional in a comfortably understated way, creating a warm, relaxed atmosphere. The restaurant is in a new conservatory area added to the back of the pub, looking out on to a walled garden where tables are set up in summer. Light, bright and pleasantly furnished with cane chairs and well-appointed tables, the menu includes variations on old favourites like deep-fried Brie on a bed of crispy salad with hot garlic butter or roast duckling with orange and ginger sauce, but also less predictable offerings such as grilled sardines with fresh tomato sauce. Three-course Sunday lunch £10.90 includes tea/coffee. Local produce is put to good use in both bar and restaurant meals. *Open 11.30-11, Sun 12-2.30, 5.30-10.* **Bar Food** *all day.* **Restaurant Meals** *12-2.30, 5.30-9.30 (not Sun eve). High tea 5.30-8.30. Children allowed in bar to eat. Garden, outdoor eating. Closed 25 Dec. Access, Visa.*

Enniskillen   **Blakes of the Hollow**

Tel 01365 322143   **A**

6 Church Street Enniskillen Co Fermanagh BT74 3EJ   Map 20 C2

Named after the natural dip at the centre of the town where it is located, Blakes has been in the same family since 1929. Although its age and agelessness (it was restored in 1882) are the main attractions, body and soul can be kept together on the premises by the consumption of sandwiches and soup (the latter at lunchtime only). *Open 11.30-11 (Sun 7-10). Closed lunch Sun. No credit cards.*

Republic of Ireland

Irish pubs are definitely different – this and the fascination of their diversity are things everyone agrees on. Gaming machines in pubs are forbidden by law, for a start; however, the same cannot be said of television. The great old Dublin pub is in a league of its own – books have been written about it, and no wonder; but the rest of the country has plenty to say too. An element of eccentricity, although not essential, is a common denominator, linking many exceptional pubs of all types throughout the country. The rural tradition is generally spartan, with the once-common shop-pub a classic example of the Irish talent for mixing business with pleasure.

Atmosphere and a generally relaxing ambience are the most important features of a pub in Irish eyes – drinking, socialising and, in some cases, music are the main attractions and, although much more family-oriented than comparable establishments in Britain, food is very much an afterthought. But times are changing and where food is on the agenda at all it is improving very rapidly – in Dublin pubs, where the turnover is huge, a practical approach often prevails, with predictable food at reasonable prices; many country pubs, especially those with a thriving passing trade, fall into the same category.

But the best thing of all about Irish pubs is their great variety – and there is no sign of this diminishing. In all the 10,000 or so pubs in Ireland there is however, a common theme – the quality of the pint is discussed at length and more often than not (even though lager continues to attract the younger market) the contents of the glass is Ireland's most famous export: stout, which must surely also rank as one of Ireland's most famous attractions!

Opening times: Unless there are exceptional circumstances – service of food affects the rules, or there may be a special licence – official opening times in Ireland are: Monday-Saturday 10.30am-11.30pm in summer, 10.30am-11pm in winter (ie from the first Monday in October). Sunday 12.30-2 and 4-11 (all year). Half an hour's 'drinking up time' is allowed. Nevertheless, idiosynrasy rules and when they're open they're open . . . similarly, when the food runs out that's when they stop serving food!

When calling from outside the Republic of Ireland omit the initial zero and prefix the number with 010-53.
For example, The Lord Bagenal Inn, Leighlinbridge 010-353 503 21688.

Prices quoted are in Irish Punts.

Abbeyfeale   The Cellar

Tel 068 31085   **A**

Abbeyfeale Co Limerick   **Map 21 B5**

Easily spotted as you drive through Abbeyfeale by the rows of bottles
of every shape and size displayed in the end window, this very
pleasant old-fashioned pub will not disappoint – the locals are friendly
and the open fire and piano are not just for show, so sessions can get
going at the drop of a hat. Nice walled garden at the back for
sheltered summer drinking. The back part of the bar has recently been
opened up to give more space. *Open 10.30am-11.30pm (11 in winter),*
Sun 12.30-2, 4-11. No credit cards.

Abbeyleix   Morrissey's

Tel 0502 31233   Fax 0502 31357   **A**

Main Street Abbeyleix Co Laois   **Map 21 C4**

A discreet black and gold sign singles out Morrissey's from its
neighbours in this handsome village; inside the lofty shelf-lined
grocery-bar, old-fashioned shades of black and brown predominate,
relieved here and there by a little cream. Mundane groceries change
hands along with their special blend of tea (packed on the premises)
and an unusually wide selection of loose sweets like aniseed balls,
pineapple chunks and bull's eyes, kept in rows of big glass jars and sold
by the 1/4lb in paper pokes. On cold days customers reflect on their
pints around an ancient pot-bellied stove while reading the paper or
exchanging the news of the day – but card-playing and singing are not
allowed. A good place to take a break on the Dublin-Cork road but,
although a cup of tea or coffee will be served with charm, don't
expect any food, other than a sandwich. The landlord, Paddy Mulhall,
is also undertaker, travel agent and newsagent – typically Irish!
Open 10.30am-11.30pm, Sun 4-11. No credit cards.

Ahakista   Ahakista Bar

No Telephone   **A**

Ahakista nr Bantry Co Cork   **Map 21 A6**

Unchanged for as long as anyone can remember, this little bar is just
opposite the entrance to the *Shiro Japanese Dinner House* and its
corrugated iron roof conceals as pleasant an old-fashioned dart-playing
pub as is to be found. Beyond the unspoilt bar lies another treasure –
a delightfully ungroomed garden reaching right down to the beach,
with a big lawn where, as landlord Tom Whitty puts it, 'kids can
scream and run around'; not much room inside, though, for children.
Open 3.30-11 (winter), 1-11.30 (summer) Mon-Sat, 12.30-2 & 4-11 Sun
(all year). Garden. No credit cards.

Annascaul   Dan Foley's

Tel 066 57252   **A**

Annascaul Co Kerry   **Map 21 A5**

Dan Foley's pub owes its colourful, much-photographed exterior to
the theatrical personality of the man himself – farmer, expert on local
history and magician. Inside, it's a great, unspoilt bar in the rural
tradition, made special by Dan's particular interest in people and chat –
and an unexpected collection of about fifty liqueurs. Food is not the
thing here although 'emergency rations' of sandwiches, sausage rolls
and the like will be served (11am-8pm) to those who resist directions

to the proper restaurant next door. Children during daylight hours only. One of Ireland's most famous pubs. *Open 11-11 (to 11.30 Mon-Sat in Summer), Sun 12.30-2.30, 4-11. No credit cards.*

Athleague   Fitzmaurice's Tavern

Tel 0903 63383	**A**
Athleague Co Roscommon	Map 20 B3

This award-winning, seriously olde-worlde pub could take prizes as an agricultural museum, but it's a very real place when it comes to efficient, cheerful service and a good local, judging by the gathering likely to be found around the open fire on a winter evening. "Whether or not everybody likes the clutter, it's always a great conversation piece" – which is fair enough and, anyway, it is interesting rather than twee. There's been a new landlord, Hugh Mitchell, recently. Food here is basically generous sandwiches of home-cooked meats, although you might get soup in winter (but don't bank on it!). *Open 12-11.30, Sun 12.30-2, 4-11. Garden. No credit cards.*

Athlone   Higgins's

Tel 0902 92519	**B&B**
2 Pearce Street Athlone Co Westmeath	Map 20 C3

West of the river, in the interesting old part of the town near the Norman castle (which has a particularly good visitor's centre for history – siege of Athlone 1691 – and information on the area, including flora and fauna of the Shannon), the Higginses run a nice hospitable pub with accommodation in four recently-refurbished rooms upstairs. Rooms vary from a single to a family room with three single beds (also an extra child's bed available), but all have secondary glazing, neat shower rooms, television and hairdryer and there are communal tea/coffee-making facilities in the dining room where breakfast is served. There's also a cosy residents' lounge, with television and comfortable armchairs. No evening meals (soup and sandwiches only in the bar), but there's a good evening restaurant nearby and also a middle-market restaurant recommended by the Higginses for family meals. *Pub open 10.30am-11pm (Sun 12.30-2, 4-11).* **Accommodation** *4 bedrooms, all en suite, from £28 (single £15). Children welcome overnight (under-10s stay free in parents' room), additional beds & cots supplied. Pub closed 25 Dec, Good Fri, 2 weeks January. No dogs. No credit cards.*

Athlone   Sean's Bar

Tel 0902 92358	**A**
13 Main Street Athlone Co Westmeath	Map 20 C3

Sean Fitzsimons' seriously historic west bank bar in the oldest, most characteful part of Athlone lays claim to being the pub with the longest continuing use in Ireland – quite reasonably, it seems, as all of the owners since 1630 are on record. On entering from the street, the sloping floor is the first of many interesting features to strike the first-time visitor; now strikingly covered in bold black and white tiles, the floor is cleverly constructed to ensure that flood water drained back down to the river again as the waters subsided. A handy watering hole for visitors cruising the Shannon – there's still direct access to the river through the back bar and beer garden – the bar has some nice old pieces, including a mahogany counter and mirrored mahogany shelving as well as a very large settle bed, which seems particularly appropriate to the soothing, dimly-lit ambience. A glass case containing a section of old wattle wall original to the building and a letter about it from the National Museum highlights the age of the bar, but it's far from being a museum piece. Food is restricted to sandwiches and coffee, but the proper priorities are observed and they serve a good pint. *Pub open 10.30am-11.30pm Mon-Sat (to 11 in winter), Sun 12.30-2, 4-11. Garden. Closed 25 Dec, Good Fri. No credit cards.*

Ballisodare   The Thatch

Tel 071 67288	A
Ballisodare Co Sligo	Map 20 B2

This attractive, low-ceilinged thatched pub just south of Sligo town is very much a local and its open fire is as welcoming on a winter evening as the tables outdoors on a fine summer day. Whatever the weather the welcome from Brian and Denise Fitzpatrick (long-standing owners for 22 years of this family business) is warm and the pint is good. Traditional music is played 3 or 4 nights a week. No children under 15 inside. *Open 11am-11.30pm, Sun 12.30-2, 4-11. Garden. No credit cards.*

Ballydehob   Levis Bar

Tel 028 37118	A
Corner House Main Street Ballydehob Co Cork	Map 21 A6

A friendly welcome awaits visitors to this 150-year-old grocery store and bar, which sisters Julia and Nell Levis have run for "years and years". The bar is not only host to 'resident' drinkers but also serves as a reception and aperitif area for the tiny *Annie's* restaurant over the road. *Open 10.30am-11.30pm (Sun 12.30-2 & 4-11). No credit cards.*

Ballyferriter   Long's Pub

Tel 066 56344	A
Ballyferriter Village Ballyferriter Co Kerry	Map 21 A5

Right next door to the Well House in Ballyferriter village, this colourful little Irish-speaking pub has probably changed little since it first opened in 1854. A good spot for a quiet pint during the day, or traditional music sessions, held nightly in summer. Just open sandwiches available from 11-6. En-suite accommodation promised from October. *Open 10.30am-11.30pm, Sun 12.30-2, 4-11. Garden. No credit cards.*

Ballyvaughan   Monks Pub

Tel 065 77059	FOOD
The Quay Ballyvaughan Co Clare	Map 21 B4

In 1983 Bernadette and Michael Monks took over this away-from-it-all quayside pub, modernised it sensitively so that it has retained its cottagey character, then set about acquiring a reputation for good, simple bar food, especially local seafood. There are several smallish, low-ceilinged, white-walled interconnecting rooms with wooden country-kitchen furniture. Open fires give a cosy atmosphere. Interest in food is emphasised by a cluster of sturdy family-sized tables at the far end of the main bar and in summer the pier provides a sunny overspill. Everything is home-made by Bernadette, or under her supervision – and she has the wisdom to keep it simple. Regulars include a big bowl of seafood chowder, served with home-made brown bread, or a seafood platter which varies with the catch but might typically include salmon, crab, Dublin Bay prawns, mussels and oysters; home-made apple pie is always popular and there may be daily specials added to the short bar menu. *Bar Food 12-9.30 (Oct-May to 6.30). Children's portions. No credit cards.*

Baltimore   Bushe's Bar

Tel 028 20125	**B&B**
Baltimore Co Cork	Map 21 B6

Richard and Eileen Bushe have run their famous old bar overlooking the harbour for over 20 years; it has a remarkable collection of maritime artefacts in the public bar, including admiralty charts, tide tables, ships' clocks, compasses, lanterns, pennants – all of real interest and guaranteed to make those arriving in Baltimore under sail feel at home. Eileen's homely bar food includes a choice of soups – always a fish one and something vegetable-based, changed daily in summer – and open or closed sandwiches with fresh or smoked salmon, smoked mackerel and a choice of meats such as turkey, ham, roast beef and corned beef, all home-cooked. Three large en-suite rooms have television, comfortable armchairs and kitchenette facilities (with food provided) for making Continental breakfast. Children welcome "if controlled"; each room has both a double and single bed. Showers in the bar for sailors and fishermen – could this be anywhere else but Ireland? No dogs. *Open 9.30am-11pm (11.30 in summer) & 12.30-2, 4-11 Sun. Garden. **Accommodation** 3 bedrooms, all en suite, £25 (single £20). Outdoor eating. Visa.*

Baltimore   McCarthy's Bar

Tel 028 20159	**FOOD**
The Square Baltimore Co Cork	Map 21 B6

A lively bar, next door to the restaurant *Chez Youen*, overlooking the harbour. Decor takes two main themes, one nautical (including a map of sea disasters in the area), the other musical, with a wall of photographs relating to the music business back in the '60s. The bar food is recommended and covers a good range of dishes, from garlic mussels and crab claws via spaghetti bolognese and lasagne (beef or vegetarian £5.45) to Irish stew (£5), seafood casserole and garlic mussels (£6.95). These dishes are available only in the summer – at other times the choice is limited to soup and sandwiches. *Open 10.30am-11.30pm (12-11 in winter), Sun 12.30-2 & 4-11. **Bar Food** (Summer) 12-11, Sun 12-2 & 4-11). Oct. Outdoor eating in the square. Access, Diners, Visa.*

Banagher   JJ Hough's

No Telephone	**A**
Main Street Banagher Co Offaly	Map 21 C4

Vines abound in Banagher – in summer the colourful red and white frontage of this atmospheric 250-year-old pub almost disappears behind the luxuriant vine that grows around the door, making it instantly recognisable from anywhere along the main street. Inside, all is dim, especially in the small side and back rooms off the front bar – well-suited to the cheerful eccentricity of the current owner, Michael Hough, and equally well-liked by the locals and groups on cruising holidays, both Irish and visitors, who come up from the harbour for the 'crack' and the music. *Pub open 10.30-11.30 Mon-Sat (to 11 in winter), Sun 12.30-2, 4-11. Pub closed 25 Dec, Good Fri. No credit cards.*

Banagher   The Vine House

Tel & Fax 0509 51463	**FOOD**
Westend Banagher Co Offaly	Map 21 C4

At the bottom of the village in an almost-waterside location, this is a bar with a history; the original restaurant area at Vine House was once Cromwell's refectory – the barracks and a house providing accommodation for his generals are next door – and the bar itself is in the stables. More recently (and in considerable contrast), there is a literary connection – with the Brontë sisters, who also lived here. The interior is very attractive, with indoor vines a major feature, and the current owner (who, despite going by the anglicised name, Julian Barry, is actually Italian) continues the Continental feeling through to the menu in authentic renditions of popular pasta dishes like lasagne, tagliatelle napolitana or bolognese, which take their place quite comfortably alongside local favourites such as Irish stew and steaks. *Open 10.30-11 (Sun 12.30-2, 4-11). **Bar Food** 12-8pm. No bar food Sun. Garden, outdoor eating. Pub Closed 25 Dec, Good Fri. Access, Visa.*

Bantry   Anchor Tavern

Tel 027 50012	**A**
New Street Bantry Co Cork	Map 21 A6

A town-centre pub with a history going back 140 years, run for 33 years by William E O'Donnell (the third generation of his family to hold the reins) with his son. Pubs are for conversation and the exchange of ideas, says William, who sees the family's vast collection of mainly nautical memorabilia displayed around the two bars as a talking point most of all – although he does admit to a special fondness for one item, an original 'croppy pike' from the rising of 1798 which will go with him if he ever leaves. There's also a morning crossword club for regulars and soup and sandwiches are offered as sustenance throughout opening hours. Well-behaved children are welcome at reasonable hours (not after 9pm). *Open 10.30am-11/11.30pm in season, 12.30-2, 4-11 Sun (rest of year). No credit cards.*

Barna   Donnelly's of Barna

Tel 091 92487 Fax 091 64379	**FOOD**
Barna Co Galway	Map 21 B4

Seafood is the thing at Donnelly's (it's only 100yds from the sea), built as a thatched cottage, extended at the turn of the century and run by the same family ever since. In the cosy, cottagey bar-rooms the menu choices run from smoked fish and potato cakes, seafood pancakes and crab claws for starters ('bait') to grilled trout, salmon and mushrooms with white wine sauce and a festival of seafood and pasta as main courses ('the catch'). Also a few meat dishes and an evening menu in the restaurant at the back: Donnelly trio of monkfish, scallops and salmon (£12.95), deep-fried plaice stuffed with salmon mousse (£8.95), salmon stuffed with prawns, cod and spinach (£11.50). Traditional roast Sunday lunch (£6.95). *Open 12-11.30 (to 11 in winter), Sun 12.30-2, 4-11. **Bar Food** 12-10. Patio, outdoor eating. Access, Diners, Visa.*

Birdhill   Matt the Thresher

Tel 061 379227   **FOOD**

Birdhill Co Tipperary   Map 21 B4

On the main Dublin road a few miles outside Limerick, this pub has
succeeded in becoming one of Ireland's best-known inns since Ted and
Kay Moynihan took over in 1987. It's as reliable for its food as for its
foolproof location overlooking the Shannon estuary and makes a
perfect meeting place. Characterful in the modern mode – red-tiled
floors, country-kitchen furniture (including some settles, thankfully
cushioned) and bar stools made from old tractor seats – chintzy
curtains and gas coal-effect fires introduce a slightly suburban note.
But the agricultural theme is developed to its logical conclusion in an
unexpected way – home-grown, stone-ground flour is used in all the
bread, which is baked on the premises and served with a wide variety
of home-made soups and bar snacks on the 'Snug Menu'. Seafood is a
speciality, with West Cork mussels and crab claws, or salmon from
local rivers served hot, or cold in salads (smoked salmon £9.50) and
open sandwiches, while carnivores may prefer home-baked ham, a
good steak, cheese and bacon burger (£6) or steak and kidney pie
(£4.50). 10% service charge is added to 'After Six' dishes (served 6-
10pm, to 9pm Sun) such as avocado with crab and grilled fresh
salmon. Ample parking in the yard, which backs on to a quality craft
shop. "Children must remain seated and under parental control at all
times." *Open 10am-11.30, Sun 12.30-11.* **Bar Food** *11am-10pm (Fri &
Sat to 10.30, Sun 12-9). Garden. Access, Visa.*

Blackrock   The Brake Tavern

Tel 042 21393   **FOOD**

Main Street Blackrock nr Dundalk Co Louth   Map 20 D3

A warm, bustling seafront pub with a characterful wooden interior
and mountains of fascinating local memorabilia. The bar is broken up
into several room-sized areas, with unpretentious but comfortable
arrangements of country furniture in welcoming groups and –
increasingly unusual these days – a real open fire to settle round. The
Brake is especially well known for the quality and variety of food,
served only in the evenings. Seafood is a speciality – Dublin Bay
prawns (£8.95), lobster (when available, as a starter course £5.50),
fish platters, fresh sea trout (£8.95), salmon mayonnaise, crab claws in
garlic butter – but there's also a good choice for carnivores, including
a range of steaks, casseroles and the like. Everything is home-made and
very wholesome. No children under 10 allowed. *Open 2-11.30, Sat
12.30-11.30, Sun 12.30-2, 6-11.* **Bar Food** *6.30-10.30 (Sun to 9.30).
Access, Visa*

Butlersbridge   Derragarra Inn

Tel 049 31003   Fax 043 83327   **FOOD**

Butlersbridge Co Cavan   Map 20 C3

A few miles north of Cavan, on the N3, the Derragarra Inn is well
situated to break a journey and is easily recognised by its thatched roof
and the old agricultural implements and rural artefacts at the door.
The agricultural theme is developed inside with items of local interest
as well as curiosities from further afield such as a wall covered with
currencies from different countries. The inn's riverside location means
freshwater fish will be on the menu, as well as ever-popular seafood

like smoked salmon (£4.35), garlic mussels (£3.95) and fish pie (£3.95), but carnivores are also well catered for with the likes of burgers (£3.75), dressed pork chop in sweet and sour sauce (£3.95), steaks, mixed grill (£5.95) and beef and Guinness casserole (£3.95). The restaurant menu is also available in the bar, extending to stuffed whiting, chicken curry and surf and turf. Music is also an attraction, with traditional Irish music on Friday nights from June to September. *Open 10.30-11.30, Sun 12.30-11. Breakfast 10.30-12 (6 days).* **Bar Food** *12-3 (from 12.30 Sun), 3-11.30.* **Restaurant Meals** *12.30-3 (Sun only), 7-10. Riverside terrace, outdoor eating. Closed Good Friday, 25 Dec. Access, Visa.*

Butlerstown   O'Neills

Tel 023 40228	A
Butlerstown Bancon Co Cork	Map 21 B6

A nice old-fashioned pub in a pretty terrace with views over farmland that slopes away down towards the sea at Dunworley; its gleaming mahogany bar counter and fresh paintwork in pinks and lilacs (somewhat unexpectedly echoing the 'West Cork pastels' exterior theme so familiar throughout the area) create a pleasingly cared-for setting for friendly locals and visitors alike. *Pub open 10.30am-11.30pm Mon-Fri (to 11pm Sat & in winter), Sun 12.30-2.30, 4-11. Garden. Closed 25 Dec, Good Fri. No credit cards.*

Cahirciveen   The Point Bar

Tel 066 72165	FOOD
Renard Point Cahirciveen Co Kerry	Map 21 A6

In the same family for ten generations (at least 150 years), this magical little place, at what was until 1960 the final stop on the Great Southern & Western Railway line, overlooks Valentia Island and harbour and has been sympathetically modernised to retain its charm without gimmicks. During the summer Michael and Bridie O'Neill serve ultra-fresh fish and seafood in simple, wholesome dishes ranging from plain and toasted sandwiches (£1.25-£1.75) to fresh lobster salad (£11.95 per pound). Other dishes might include monkfish (Point Special £7.95) or Roman-style hake pan-fried with garlic and olive oil (£6.95). For fine weather there's a very pleasant patio with tubs and tables looking past the old terminal to the sea. Children must be supervised – the bar can get very busy. *Open 10.30-11.30, Sun 5-11.* **Bar Food** *10.30-9.30 (from 5 Sun). Garden, outdoor eating area. No credit cards.*

Carlingford   PJ O'Hare's Anchor Bar

Tel 042 73106	FOOD
Carlingford Co Louth	Map 20 D3

Grocer's shop and bar share the same room at PJs, which stands right in the heart of a picturesque medieval village. Carlingford oysters are the speciality on the bar menu (£3 for 6), with smoked salmon and the day's soup (65p) among the rival attractions. It's a favourite spot with the local sailing community, and the walls are covered with items of nautical interest. The enclosed yard by the bar is a popular summer rendezvous. *Open 10.30am-11.30pm (Sun 12.30-2, 4-11).* **Bar Food** *10.30am-10.30pm (Sun 12.30-2, 4-10.30). No credit cards.*

Carne   **Lobster Pot**   ★

| Tel 053 31110   Fax 053 31401 | **FOOD** |
| Carne Co Wexford | Map 21 D5 |

Pub, seafood bar and restaurant – Ciaran and Anne Hearne's Lobster
Pot has it all and attracts a loyal clientele. In a prime roadside location,   ☺
the long, low building is typical of traditional houses in the area;
inside several small, cosy interconnecting bar areas are furnished in
simple, practical style with sturdy furniture designed for comfortable
eating – augmented, in fine weather, by an ample supply of picnic
tables out at the front. One smallish room is given over to a slightly
more formal restaurant area, but the atmosphere throughout is very
relaxed and the emphasis is on providing good value and efficient
service. The bar menu offers seafood chowder (£2.50), daily home-
made soup (£1.20), Wexford mussels in garlic (£3.50), oven-baked
crab mornay (£4.95), crab claws in garlic (£6.95) and a pasta dish
(£5.50) as its hot dishes plus a plethora of cold plates (from £2.25 for
egg mayonnaise to £10.50 for generous seafood platters; also
sandwiches and a handful of homely puddings (hot apple sponge and
cream £1.50, Harvey's sherry trifle £1.50). More substantial evening-
only à la carte offerings in the restaurant (recommended in our *1995
Hotels & Restaurants Guide*) might inlude prawn cocktail (£5.95),
Barrow Bay or Rossmore oysters (£5.95 for half a dozen), wild
salmon either smoked (£5.95), grilled or poached (£9.95), scallops
(£11.50), grilled Dover sole (£12.95), seafood mornay (£10.95) and
lobster from the tank (from £13 per pound). Also a 'landlubber's
choice' of chicken Kiev (£8.95), crispy duckling (£9.90) and various
steaks (from £11). 4-course Sunday lunch in winter only £8.95
(children £5) – but usual bar menu in summer; winter Wednesday
evening table d'hote £12.95. Smoking is discouraged. Tables outside
in the summer. No children under 10 after 8.30pm. Parents are
requested to keep an eye on their children and children are requested
to keep an eye on their parents – best behaviour all round! *Open
10.30-11.30 (to 11 in winter), Sun 12.30-2, 4-11; January bar only open
(no food): Mon-Thur 6-11 only, Fri 3-11 only, Sat 10.30-11 & Sun
12.30-2, 4-11.* **Bar Meals** *12-10, Sun 12.30-2, 4-10 (to 9 in winter).*
Restaurant Meals *6.30-9 (not Mon or Sun in winter Sep-May, except
Bank Holiday weekends) & Sun Lunch (Sep-May). Paved fourcourt with
ten tables. Closed Good Friday, 25 Dec. Access, Visa.*

Cashel   **Dowling's**

| Tel 062 62130 | **A** |
| Cashel Co Tipperary | Map 21 C5 |

Pat and Helen Dowling have changed the name of their pub from
Meaney's, but that's about the only change. It stands handily on the
main street and its attractions include traditional decor, a cosy open
fire and good simple snacks. But above all this is a place for music:
there are traditional Irish sessions organised on Friday and Sunday
nights (also Wednesday in summer), but anyone with an instrument is
always welcome and impromptu sessions can get going at any time.
No credit cards.

Castleconnell   Bradshaw's Bar

Tel 061 377724	A
Castleconnell Co Limerick	Map 21 B4

The Bradshaw family bought this atmospheric 19th-century village pub in the 1920s and since the current owner, Ger Bradshaw, took over in 1992 he has worked hard to make improvements while remaining true to the old traditions – so, although an extra room has been opened up to increase space, it has retained the authentic feeling, with bare floor, fairly spartan furniture and an open fire. *Open from 5pm weekdays, usual pub hours at weekends. Closed 25 Dec & Good Friday. No credit cards.*

Castletownbere   MacCarthy's

Tel 027 70014	A
Town Square Castletownbere Co Cork	Map 21 A6

One of the first drinking places to be granted a licence in Ireland, MacCarthy's has been in the same family for 150 years (Adrienne MacCarthy is the fourth generation). It's not only a pub, but also a grocery which provisions the trawlers that are based in the harbour. In the front – the grocery section – one of the last remaining match-making booths (traditionally used by the match-maker and the bride's and groom's parents to arrange marriage terms) is now used as a snug, while in the back bar darts and live music make for a very sociable ambience. *No credit cards.*

Castletownshend   Mary Ann's Bar & Restaurant   ★

Tel 028 36146 Fax 028 36377	FOOD
Castletownshend nr Skibbereen Co Cork	Map 21 B6

This famous, low-ceilinged haven from the 'soft' West Cork weather has been in the capable hands of Fergus and Patricia O'Mahony since 1983 and celebrated its 150th birthday last year. Most famous for its star-worthy bar food: home-made soup £1.45, seafood chowder £2.80, chicken liver and herb paté £3.40, crab cocktail £4.50 or prawn cocktail £3.50; sandwiches £1.20-£3, a few hot dishes (scallops Mary Ann £9.50, steaks from £8.50, chicken Kiev £6.50, daily special £5), and salads (smoked salmon or crab £5.50, seafood platter £11.95) served with home-made bread also feature. However, Patricia's good home-cooking is now making a name for The Contented Sole restaurant (seaparately recommended in our *1995 Hotels & Restaurants Guide*) upstairs, where you'll find excellent super-fresh local seafood and also local lamb and good steaks. On the 4-course dinner menu (£19.95) you might commence with tagliatelle of seafood, baked avocado and crab, home-made seafood soup and bread, grilled black sole on the bone, roast duckling on a sauce of grapes and oranges, herb-crusted rack of West Cork lamb with a red wine jus, coquilles St Jacques au gratin, and pan-fried medallions of monkfish in a light prawn and white wine sauce. Desserts (£2 in the bar) lean towards homely favourites like lemon meringue pie or strawberry shortcake and the farmhouse cheese plate is as generous as it is good. No children under 4 after 7.30pm. Plenty of room in the garden for open-air eating and a back bar area with TV that is popular with visitors in holiday homes locally. *Open 12.30-11.30 (to 11 in winter), Sun 12-2, 4-11. **Bar Food** 12.30-2.30, 6-8.30. **Restaurant Meals** Tue-Sat 6.30-9.30 & Sun lunch in winter (12-2). Children allowed in bar to eat. Outdoor eating for bar food. Access, Visa.*

Castlewarren   Langton's

`Tel 0503 26123`   **A**

Castlewarren Co Kilkenny   Map 21 C4

A bit of a curiosity – not a real pub at all but a relic of what used to
be so common in rural Ireland – the kitchen-cum-grocery-cum-bar.
A visit here will take the traveller away from main roads through the
pleasant countryside of a little-known corner of Ireland and back in
time. A row of high stools beside the bacon slicer at the counter and
a good shelf of bottles over it are the only real clues to the nature of
the premises but, once you're ensconced, Josie Langton, here for 25
years, will put the world to rights with you and rustle up a bit of a
sandwich in the kitchen on demand. *Pub closed Sun eve. No credit cards.*

Ceanannas Mor (Kells)   O'Shaughnessy's

`Tel 046 41110`   **FOOD**

Market Street Ceanannas Mor (Kells) Co Meath   Map 20 C3

A reasonably new pub, comfortably and pleasantly decorated on an
old-style theme. Unpretentious, fairly-priced bar food is the main
attraction – food like Irish stew, chicken or beef curry, lasagne,
quiches and pizzas, but better and cheaper than most. You'll find
O'Shaughnessy's just behind St Columba's Church (where a copy of
the *Book of Kells* is kept). Now under new ownership. *Bar Food
10.30-11.30 (Summer to 11, no food Sun). Closed 25 Dec & Good Friday.
Access, Visa.*

Cheekpoint   McAlpin's Suir Inn

`Tel 051 82220`   **FOOD**

Cheekpoint Co Waterford   Map 21 C5

When this tiny black-and-white pub was built in 1750 Cheekpoint
was the main port for the boats from England. Today it's a quiet little
backwater, although much of the seafood which forms the bulk of the
bar menu here is still landed at the quay opposite the inn. Inside, the
single bar is as neat as a new pin with old photos and plates decorating
the red walls, around which are thinly upholstered banquettes and
varnished rustic tables. The menu offers about eight starters – shrimp
cocktail (£3.95), grilled smoked mackerel (£2.95), crab claws in
garlic butter (£3.95) – and eight main dishes – wild salmon
mayonnaise (£8.95), king scallops in cheese and white wine sauce
(£8.95), curried chicken breasts (£7.50). There's always a fruit pie
made with Mrs McAlpin's excellent pastry. *Open evening only 5.30-
11.30 (6-11 in winter). Closed Mon (except July & Aug). Bar Food
6-9.30 Tues-Sat (& Mon in July & Aug). No food Tues Oct-Easter.
Access, Visa.*

Clarenbridge   Paddy Burke's

`Tel 091 96226   Fax 091 96016`   **FOOD·**

Clarenbridge Co Galway   Map 21 B4

Synonymous with Clarenbridge, a steady stream of the great and
famous have made their way to Paddy Burke's – and there's been
plenty of time to do it in, as the history of the pub goes right back to
1650. Especially famous for their oysters (£4.50 for 6, £9 for 12) –
"The world is your oyster at Paddy Burke's" – they also offer a wide
range of bar food including an excellent Galway Bay chowder
(£2.20), served with home-made brown bread, or delicious seafood

crumble (£4.25). "Just Desserts" include Peggy Kelly's deep-crust apple pie (£1.60). Seafood is the main attraction, but there's plenty of choice besides and more formal restaurant meals (£15.50/£17.50 2/4-course) are served in the evening. *Pub open 10.30am-11.30pm Mon-Sat (to 11 in winter) Sun 12-2, 4-11.* **Bar Food** *10.30am-10.30pm (Sun 12-2, 4-9.30). Garden. Pub closed Good Friday, 25 Dec. Access, Diners, Visa.*

Clifden   E J King's

Tel 095 21330	FOOD
The Square Clifden Co Galway	Map 20 A3

On the square in the centre of town, a lively old bar on two floors, retaining an essentially traditional character despite modern touches in its atrium and striking primary colour schemes on the upper floors. Menus lean towards local seafood, especially oysters, crab and smoked salmon but typical blackboard specials might include bacon and cabbage or roast beef or rack of lamb, plus there's a choice of farmhouse cheeses. Trenchermen should head for the fisherman's platter, complete with smoked salmon, prawns, crab, mussels, salmon, cod, smoked trout and mackerel and salad! Live music, mainly folk and ballads, features nightly in season, 2 or 3 times a week in winter. **Bar Food** *10.30-9 (Sun from 12.30). Terrace. Access, Diners, Visa.*

☺

Clonakilty   An Sugan

Tel 023 33498	FOOD
41 Strand Road Clonakilty Co Cork	Map 21 B6

On a corner site, An Sugan is reassuringly easy to find on the way into town after leaving the N71 and this colourful, characterful pub sums up everything that now makes Clonakilty such a delightful place to visit; it's spick-and-span, there's a genuinely friendly welcome and a well-deserved reputation for excellent bar food. Seafood is the main attraction in everything from chowder with home-made brown bread, through light dishes like garlic-stuffed Bantry Bay mussels (£4.50), to hearty seafood platters or seafood crepe topped with cheese. But the daily blackboard menu also includes traditional dishes like bacon and cabbage, pie of the day, steaks – flamed with Irish whiskey, perhaps – and hot chicken dishes such as a stir-fry, or goujons served with a garlic dip and vegetarians are well catered for too. All three stouts are available on tap (predictably, perhaps, Murphy's is the most popular) and whisky connoisseurs should enquire about the extensive range of Scotch malts. *Pub open 10.30am-11.30pm Mon-Sat (to 11 in winter), Sun 12.30-2, 4-11.* **Bar Food** *12-9.30pm (Sun to 9). Pub closed 25 Dec, Good Fri. Access, Visa.*

Cobh   Mansworths

Tel 021 811965	A
Midleton Street Cobh Co Cork	Map 21 B6

Well up the hill, a hundred yards from St Colman's Cathedral, Mansworths is Cobh's oldest-established pub and has been run by the same family for as long as anyone can remember. A warm, welcoming place by any standards, this unspoilt, traditional bar is especially worth visiting for its fascinating collection of memorabilia connected with the naval history of the port, both past and present – many of the more recent photographs feature the present owner, John Mansworth, an enthusiastic promoter of Cobh in general and its maritime characteristics in particular. Not really a food place, although light snacks (soup, sandwiches, pizzas) are available, but there's an unusually good choice of non-alcoholic drinks, including wines. *Pub open 10.30am-11.30pm Mon-Sat (to 11pm in winter), Sun 12.30-2, 4-11. Closed 25 Dec, Good Friday. No credit cards.*

Cork   An Spailpín Fánac

Tel 021 277949   **FOOD**

28/29 South Main Street Cork Co Cork   **Map 21 B6**

Food at this pleasant, low-ceilinged pub is of the simple, wholesome variety: freshly cut sandwiches, toasted Kiev and doorstep special with fries, lasagne, shepherd's pie, bacon and cabbage, Irish stew, minced beef and onion pie, a fish special. The name of the pub translates roughly as 'the jobbing traveller', recalling a once-familiar Irish character who used to keep on the move around the country in search of work. No children after 6.30pm, but they are welcome during the day. *Open 12-11 (summer to 11.30).* **Bar Food** *12-3.*

Cork   Dan Lowrey's Seafood Tavern

Tel 021 505071   **FOOD**

13 MacCurtain Street Cork Co Cork   **Map 21 B6**

A delightfully old-fashioned pub, a perfect place to meet or eat. It's small, with two interconnecting rooms (the one in the back with an open fire) and is now named after a much-lamented local theatre. The pub's history goes back to 1875 and many of the original tavern features have been retained, including the wooden floor and a remarkable mahogany bar unit with unusual shelving and antique bevelled mirrors. The stained-glass windows on the street are also of special interest, as they came from Kilkenny Cathedral. The food is the source of justifiable pride: the bar menu offers an above-average choice of simple soups served with home-made bread (£1.20), salads, seafood or meat platters (£4.20 for ham to £7.50 for wild Irish smoked salmon) and a wide selection of sandwiches – fresh, toasted or open (£1.35-£1.50) – but it is the emphasis on the home-made and attention to detail (such as the freshest prawns, served only when available) which make this place special. **Bar Food** *12-3. No credit cards.*

Cork   Reidy's Wine Vaults   ★

Tel 021 275751   **FOOD**

Lancaster Quay Western Road Cork Co Cork   **Map 21 B6**

Imaginatively converted from a wine warehouse (and conveniently situated just opposite the entrance to *Jurys Hotel*), Reidy's is quite large and stylish, with vaulted ceilings, a minstrel's gallery housing country antiques, dark green and terracotta paintwork, traditional black-and-white tiles and a pleasing mixture of old and new furnishings. The focal point is the main bar fixture – a massive mahogany piece, complete with a London clock, bevelled mirrors, stained glass and all the original Victorian details. Bar food is prepared to a high standard by Noelle Reidy, starting with bread and quiches baked on the premises in the early morning and with choices noted on the blackboard as the day progresses. The menu dishes might typically include steak and kidney pie, Irish stew (£4.95), chicken curry (£4.95), steak and kidney pie or lasagne (both £4.95), savoury pancakes (chicken and mushroom £3.95) and seafood platter (£8).

Sandwiches and home-made soup (£1.50) also available. Children are welcome "as long as they are well behaved" (but not after 7pm). *Open 10.30am-11.30pm (winter to 11), Sun 12.30-2, 4-11. Closed 25 Dec, Good Friday. Access, Diners, Visa.*

Crookhaven   O'Sullivan's

Tel 028 35200	**A**
Crookhaven Co Cork	Map 21 A6

One of the most popular traditional pubs in Ireland, sited beside the delightful little sandy-beached harbour at 'Crook'. O'Sullivan's has been family-run for 20 years and nowadays it's run by Billie and Angela O'Sullivan, who somehow successfully combines the function of providing a proper local for the lobster fishermen and the kind of pub dreams are made of for families on holiday. The stone-flagged bar is practical for sandy feet and parents can easily keep an eye on castle-builders when the tide is right. Angela looks after the food herself, making soups and chowders, bread and good, simple dishes based on local seafood – fresh and smoked salmon, smoked mackerel, crab or shrimp – and more-ish home-made ices or apple crumble. Six tables are almost on the water's edge. Live solo music every night in summer. Next door, the Welcome Inn is under the same ownership, has a restaurant in summer (July & August) and two self-contained apartments to let (not inspected). *Open 10.30-11.30, Sun 12-2, 4-11.* **Bar Food** *10.30-9 (Sun 12-2 & 4-9). Closed Monday afternoons in winter (Nov-May). No credit cards.*

Crosshaven   Cronin's Bar

Tel 021 831207 Fax 021 832243	**FOOD**
Crosshaven Co Cork	Map 21 B6

Lots of wood, soft furnishings in country prints and selected bric-a-brac create a homely atmosphere at this welcoming bar overlooking the marina, but the real point of interest is a great collection of pictures, prints and photographs of local interest, notably maritime history. Excellent food is made on the premises by owner Sean Cronin's Dutch wife, Thecla, from snacky sandwiches (£1.30-£3.50, open brown sandwiches made with sodabread are a speciality – try the rare roast beef or 'rasher special') and salads (ploughman's £2.95, wild smoked salmon £6.25) to evening seafood specials (large 'Dublin Bay' prawns are very popular – they're actually caught off the west and south Cork coast!) and steaks (£9/£12). Children are welcome and there's a dining area at the back especially suitable for family meals. A self-catering cottage is available (not inspected). *Open 10.30am-11.30pm, Sun 12.30-2, 4-11.* **Bar Food** *11-3, 6-8 (3-6 soup and sandwiches only, summer bar food to 6). Sunday coffee and scones only. Access, Visa.*

Culdaff   McGuinness's

Tel 077 79116	**A**
Culdaff Inish Owen Co Donegal	Map 20 C1

Just the kind of place the traveller might hope to happen upon, this traditional country pub has been in the McGuinness family for generations (albeit some under different names) and always has a welcoming turf fire burning in the public bar. This is simply furnished in a pleasant way with plain furniture, old prints, plates and notices of local interest. Next door, a comfortable lounge bar has great appeal, with homely chintzy sofas, cushioned chairs and a nice old-fashioned conservatory on the back of the pub with a few more tables leading on to the small back garden. Food requirements other than very simple snacks are dealt with in a practical way – by telephoning orders to the village restaurant, which is under the same ownership. The bar also acts as an off-licence, so a variety of wines can be served by the glass. Well-behaved children are welcome during the day, but they "must be kept under control". *Open 10.30-11.30, Sun 12.30-2, 4-11. Garden. Visa.*

Dalkey   The Queens

| Tel 01 285 4569   Fax 01 285 8345 | **FOOD** |
| Castle Street Dalkey Co Dublin | Map 21 D4 |

One of South Dublin's most famous pubs, The Queens is a characterful and extremely professionally-run operation, with open fires, old pine and whiskey jars creating atmosphere and friendly, efficient staff dispensing the good food and drink which has earned it so many awards. The bar menu features sandwiches (closed or open), ploughman's salads, paté and a very popular seafood chowder and garlicky mussels. Sunday brunch fry-up is £4.95. There's also an Italian restaurant, La Romana. *Open 10.30-1.30, Sun 12-11. **Bar Food** 12-6 (Sun brunch menu 12-3). **Restaurant Meals** 5.30-11. Children allowed in bar to eat until 6.30pm only. Front and back patios. Closed Good Friday, 25 Dec. Access, Visa.*

Delgany   The Wicklow Arms

| Tel 01 287 4611   Fax 01 287 3878 | **FOOD** |
| Delgany Co Wicklow | Map 21 D4 |

A friendly, well-maintained pub that's a popular weekend spot with Dubliners and visitors alike. Practicalities are well thought out, with a sensibly designed car park backing on to an attractively planted seating area which leads down to the back bar. Inside, the atmosphere is comfortable no-nonsense, with plenty of space to relax and enjoy generous, unpretentious food from the lounge menu such as open sandwiches served with salad (from £5), paté, seafood chowder, garlicky mussels or breaded mushrooms (£2.98), and hot main courses served with chips (boiled potatoes or side salad for calorie-counters): baked chicken and scallop mornay (£8.98), veal stuffed with smoked salmon and cream cheese (£8.45). Finish with an Irish coffee soufflé (£1.98). A long wine list includes 20 half bottles. *Pub hours 6-11.30 (Sat from 2, Sun 12-11). **Bar Food** 7-10.15 (Sat from 6), (Sun & Bank Hols 12.30?). **Restaurant Meals** 12.30-3 (Sun only) 7-9.30 (except Sun & Mon). Children allowed in bar to eat but not in restaurant for Sunday lunch (4 courses £11.50). Garden. Access, Diners, Visa.*

Dingle   Dick Mack's

| No Telephone | **A** |
| Green Lane Dingle Co Kerry | Map 21 A5 |

Amazingly unspoilt shop-bar, once a cobbler's, now selling modern leather items and wellington boots. Basic bar, no pretensions. The cashier's booth remains as a snug and all is as it should be. *No credit cards.*

Dingle　　James Flahive

Tel 066 51634	**A**
The Quay Dingle Co Kerry	**Map 21 A5**

Down by the harbour near the marina, this comfortable, welcoming
and most friendly of pubs has been run by James and Peggy Flahive
(Gregory Peck is her cousin, but don't tell anyone, now will you?)
for 30 years. It's a great favourite of sailing people. Photographs of
distinguished visitors adorn the walls but none is more proudly
displayed than that of Dingle's best-loved resident, Fungie the dolphin.
No food, but you're assured of a good pint of Guinness. *Open 10.30am-
11.30pm, Sun 12-2 & 4-11. No credit cards.*

Dingle　　Lord Baker's Bar & Restaurant

Tel 066 51277	**FOOD**
Main Street Dingle Co Kerry	**Map 21 A5**

Tom Baker – businessman, councillor, auctioneer and poet, and
affectionately known as Lord Baker – acquired these premises in 1890
and they've gradually developed from general supplier and function
caterer to a popular and thriving restaurant and bar. Locally-made
tapestries are an eye-catching display in the main eating area, beyond
which is a conservatory extension leading into the garden. Choose
between the full restaurant menu (recommended in our *Hotels &
Restaurants Guide*) and the less formal bar menu, which offer similar
choices from seafood soup, Dingle Bay smoked salmon and capers
(£6.50), marinated herring and Waldorf salad (£3.90), seafood
mornay (£10.50), open crab sandwich (£4.20). Particularly favoured
for Sunday lunch (£10.50). *Bar Food 12.30-2.30, 6-10. Closed 25 Dec.
Access, Diners, Visa.*

Dingle　　O'Flaherty's

Tel 066 51461	**A**
Bridge Street Dingle Co Kerry	**Map 21 A5**

Large square room, high-ceilinged, with flagstones, a stove, barrel
tables, an old piano and masses of old shelving for a collection of
antique signs and local bric-a-brac. Traditional Irish music is the main
attraction, with regular sessions in summer (nightly May-Sep), other
impromptu sessions and occasional bursts on any instrument you can
imagine by landlord Fergus O'Flaherty. Access to the harbour from
the back of the bar. No food. *Open 10.30am-11.30pm, Sun 12-2, 4-11.
Closed Good Friday, 25 Dec. No credit cards.*

Dromahair　　Stanford's Village Inn

Tel 071 64140	**FOOD**
Dromahair Co Leitrim	**Map 20 B2**

Situated just south of Lough Gill on the ever beautiful Yeats country
route, Stanford's has been in the McGowan family for five generations
and the front bar remains, as a testament to the Irish country pub of
yesteryear – not a sentimental reconstruction, but the real thing.
Elsewhere in this fisherman's hideaway, there are comfortable bars
with fires and good, simple fare (home-made soup £1, Irish stew
£3.50, salads from £6.50, sandwiches from 80p) and a 32-seat
restaurant (3-course lunch £6, 4-course dinner £12) for those who
prefer to sit at a table. Sunday lunch £4. Live music on summer
Saturday or Monday nights. Straightforward accommodation is also

offered in five rooms (£28, one family room, but not inspected). *Open 10.30-11.30, Sun 12.30-4-11.* **Bar Food** *11am-10pm, Sun 11-2, 4-10.* **Restaurant Meals** *1-2.30 (Sun to 3.30), 7-9. Children allowed in bar to eat, children's menu. Garden, outdoor eating. Closed 25 Dec, bar closed Good Friday. Access, Visa.*

Drumcliffe   Yeats Tavern & Davis's Pub

Tel 071 63117	**FOOD**
Drumcliffe Co Sligo	**Map 20 B2**

Efficiently run, sympathetically modernised Yeats country pub beside Drumcliffe river, whose restaurant has recently been doubled in size. The bar menu holds few surprises, but there's plenty of variety, from vegetable soup, garlic mushrooms and barbecue ribs to home-made burgers, omelettes, chicken (breaded, Kiev, Maryland, curry), cod, plaice, salads and omelettes; poached salmon hollandaise (£4.95), bacon and cabbage (£4) and braised steak (£4.50) might also be on offer. Also snacks of sandwiches and filled baked potatoes. Sunday lunch £4.50. Children's menu. Fancier restaurant menu (lemon sole with crab meat £8.50, chicken stuffed with salmon £8.50, steaks £10.50). Country and Western music every weekend. *Open (& **Bar Food** served) 12-10. Children allowed in bar to eat, children's menu. Access, Diners, Visa.*

Dublin   Ashtons

Tel 01 283 0045	**FOOD**
Clonskeagh Dublin 6	**Map 21 D4**

Behind a frontage which can only be described as a cross between those old country garages with facades disguising Nissen huts and a glossy Chinese restaurant, all shiny marble, black and gold, lies a large pub on a number of levels – one of Dublin's most surprising pubs. It descends down to the River Dodder and as many tables as possible are positioned to take advantage of the river view with its ducks and waterfowl, the occasional swan foraging among the reeds and locals pottering along the banks. Inexpensive bar snacks include excellent home-made soups and brown bread with walnuts and hazelnuts, but it is the lunchtime buffet for which they are famous. There's always a roast joint (£5.95) and a selection of hot dishes (stuffed trout with scallop and monkfish £6.25, stuffed aubergine £5.75) plus an imaginative cold buffet and salad bar, where a whole dressed salmon takes pride of place surrounded by dressed crab, crab claws, prawns and other freshly cooked seafood is available. Sunday lunch is £5.95. From a varied choice of desserts try, perhaps, their banoffi cheesecake (£1.90). After the lunchtime buffet is cleared a separate bar snack menu operates until 8pm: burgers (£4.75), minute steaks (£4.75), crab claws (£4.75) and open sandwiches (£2.50). A full à la carte dinner menu is served downstairs in the restaurant. *Open 10.30-11.30, Sun 12.30-2.30, 4-11.* **Bar Meals** *lunch 12.30-2.30, snacks 3.30-8.* **Restaurant Meals** *6-10. Children allowed to eat in the bar. Outdoor eating. Closed Good Fri, 25 Dec. Access, Diners, Visa.*

Dublin   The Bleeding Horse

Tel 01 475 2705	**FOOD**
24 Upper Camden Street Dublin 2	Map 21 D4

Family-owned and partly family-run on sound, traditional principles
of service and efficiency, the Bleeding Horse is lofty and impressive,
with vast dark timbers and a huge fireplace in the smaller bar. A
balcony runs right around the centre, giving an almost medieval feel.
Trendy young staff serve a simple selection of food, basically soup
(chicken and sweetcorn), home-made bread sandwiches, salads and
desserts such as banoffi pie, meringues, apple tart and gateaux. Sunday
brunch £3. Open 12-11.30, Sun 12-2, 4-11. *Bar Food from 12.30.
Children allowed in bar to eat. Beer garden. No credit cards.*

Dublin   The Brazen Head

Tel 01 677 9549	**FOOD**
20 Lower Bridge Street Dublin 8	Map 21 D4

Dublin's oldest pub is worth a visit out of curiosity alone (and was a
real curiosity until a few years ago when they finally got electricity)
but, although it is undoubtedly ancient, with a series of thick-walled,
low-ceilinged, rather dark rooms, it isn't caught in a time-warp and
does a thriving trade with locals as well as visitors. Handy for the law
courts just across the bridge and a lot of offices around Christchurch,
so the lunchtime carvery is especially popular (latecomers must expect
to queue). But it's a pleasant place for a quiet drink at other times,
either beside the fire in the back bar in winter, or in the yard on a fine
summer day. *Bar Food Carvery to 2pm, bar menu to 6.30/7, (sandwiches
only at weekends). Pub closed 25 & 26 Dec, Good Friday. Visa.*

Dublin   Davy Byrnes

Tel 01 677 5217 Fax 01 677 5849	**FOOD**
21 Duke Street Dublin 2	Map 21 D4

At the heart of Dublin life (and immortalised in James Joyce's *Ulysses*),
Davy Byrnes is not only a mecca for literary-minded tourists, but also
a pleasant, well-run and conveniently central place well used by
Dubliners in town on business, shopping in nearby Grafton Street or
simply having a day out. Decor-wise, it is in a 1920s' time-warp and is
likely to remain so through future redecorations as it has done in the
past; however, for such a famous pub, it is remarkably unselfconscious.
It has always had a good reputation for food. At its simplest,
sandwiches (£1.60-£3.75) are invariably fresh and there's a good
choice of six or so moderately-priced hot dishes (£3.95-£5.95) on a
blackboard every day. They take pride in seafood, particularly, with
fresh crab or king prawn salads (around £6.95) featuring among the
lunchtime dishes, and grilled salmon steak with hollandaise (£6.95),
Irish stew (£5.95), grilled sirloin steak with black pepper sauce
(£5.95) appearing among additional hot dishes in the evening. Oysters
(£4.50 in season), salads and open sandwiches complete the picture.
Sunday brunch £5.50. No children under 7. *Open 10.30-11.30,
Sun 12.30-2, 4-11. **Bar Food** 12-10 (Sun 12-2, 4-10). Access, Visa.*

Dublin   Doheny & Nesbitt

Tel 01 676 2945   Fax 01 676 0655

A

5 Lower Baggot Street Dublin 2

Map 21 D4

Only a stone's throw across the road from *Toners*, Doheny & Nesbitt is another great Dublin institution, but there the similarity ends. Just around the corner from the Irish parliament, this solid Victorian pub has traditionally attracted a wide spectrum of Dublin society – politicians, economists, lawyers, business names, political and financial journalists – all with a view to get across, or some scandal to divulge, so a visit here can often be unexpectedly rewarding. Like the *Shelbourne Hotel* down the road, which has a similar reputation and shares the clientele, half the fun of drinking at Nesbitt's is anticipation of 'someone' arriving or 'something' happening, both more likely than not. Apart from that it is an unspoilt, very professionally run bar with a traditional emphasis on drinking. Traditional Irish music on Sunday nights. *Open 10.30-11.30 (winter to 11), Sun 12.30-2, 4-11. Access, Visa.*

Dublin   The Goat

Tel 01 298 4145   Fax 01 298 4687

FOOD

Goatstown Dublin 14

Map 21 D4

"Dublin's Sporting Pub" is a real city landmark. Big, with an even bigger car park (complete with house mini-bus to ferry customers home safely), it has its own clock tower and would be unmissable even without its current coat of pink paint. Inside, despite its size, it is a friendly sort of place where families are made especially welcome. The lounge menu offers sandwiches, omelettes, steaks and salads, and there's a more formal Anvil restaurant. ***Bar Food** 12-3, 3.30-9. Children allowed in bar to eat, children's menu. Patio & garden. Access, Diners, Visa.*

Dublin   Kavanagh's

No Telephone

A

Prospect Square Glasnevin Dublin 9

Map 21 D4

An entertaining, unselfconscious pub that's been in the Kavanagh family since 1833. It's known locally as the 'Gravediggers Arms' because of its location at the back of Dublin's largest cemetery. It's a small place, with a stone floor, rather rickety woodwork breaking up the bar, and fittings and decorations which are simple, original and authentic. Pints of Guinness are the main liquid sustenance. *No credit cards.*

Dublin   Kielys

Tel 01 283 0209

FOOD

22/24 Donnybrook Road Donnybrook Dublin 4

Map 21 D4

Kielys is a Donnybrook landmark with its long, impressive frontage. Inside, it's rather sober – a masculine image that does nothing to prepare the first-time visitor for the contrast inside, where art nouveau decorations writhe around the mirrors, especially at the impressive mahogany bar area, creating a feminine feeling. This unexpectedly fin de siècle atmosphere is reinforced by the use of traditional mahogany tables on curvaceous wrought-iron bases, stained-glass windows at the back (although clear glass at the front lets in the midday sunshine and allows a refreshing view of the little green across the road) and a semi-snug, the size of a domestic sitting room, which creates the feeling of a club within the pub. Typical lunchtime meals from the blackboard might include a roast joint (£5.50), cod mornay, beef stroganoff or lasagne verdi (£4.95), which, like lighter food (basket meals) later in the day, is ordered from the bar and served to your table. Sunday brunch £3.25. Another surprise awaits the curious – at the back there is another pub, *Ciss Madden's,* a very traditional old Dublin spit'n'sawdust kind of a place; it has a separate entrance but can also be reached through Kielys bar. The locals clearly think all this quite normal. Furthermore, there's an Italian restaurant, *La Finezza,* upstairs (Tel 01 283 7166, open from 5.30pm, bar and restaurant menus). *Open 10.30-11.30, Sun 12.30-2, 4-11. **Bar Food** 12.30-3 (Sun 12.30-2), 3-8 (Sun from 4). Children allowed in the bar to eat. Closed Good Friday, 25 Dec. Access, Visa.*

Dublin   Kitty O'Shea's Bar

Tel 01 660 8050 Fax 01 668 3979	**FOOD**
23/25 Upper Grand Canal Street Dublin 4	**Map 21 D4**

One of Dublin's best-known and best-loved pubs, a favourite meeting place before or after a rugby match at Lansdowne Road and a popular spot for a snack or a meal. Typical dishes on the luncheon menu include chicken liver paté (£1.75), prawn cocktail, lasagne, roast pork and devils on horseback (£4.75, lamb's liver stuffed and wrapped in bacon). Similar evening choice, with apple pie a dessert always in demand. Live traditional Irish music each night. No small children after 5. Saturday and Sunday brunch (£3.95) a speciality. *Open 10.30-11.30 (winter to 11), Sun 12.30-2, 4-11. **Bar Food** 10.30-10, Sun 12.30-2, 4-11 (plus snacks at other times). Beer garden, outdoor eating. Access, Visa.*

Dublin   The Lord Edward

Tel 01 454 2420	**FOOD**
23 Christchurch Place Dublin 8	**Map 21 D4**

This very traditional bar has become something of an institution and, although always well supported by a loyal clientele, recent rapid growth in the area has brought an influx of new customers (including many from the Jury's Christchurch Inn, next door) who seem to like it exactly as it is – an anti-fashion statement, perhaps. Seafood has always been the thing here and lunch time bar food always includes specialities like smoked salmon salad and fish of the day – typically sole or cod bonne femme – as well as popular dishes like curried beef or chicken fricassee. Desserts are sent down from the restaurant upstairs, but usually include ever-popular home-made apple pie. *Pub open 10.30am-11.30pm Mon-Sat (to 11pm in winter), Sun 12.30-2, 4-11. **Bar Food** 12.30-2.30 (sandwiches only at other times). No bar food Bank Holidays. Pub closed 25 Dec, Good Fri. Access, Diners, Visa.*

Dublin   McCormack's Merrion Inn

Tel 01 269 3816	**FOOD**
188 Merrion Road Dublin 4	**Map 21 D4**

They take their lunch and its comfortable consumption seriously at this well-established pub. Despite its considerable age – and more than a passing nod to tradition where serious matters such as service, friendliness and efficiency are concerned – a modern hand has been at work with the decor, but the unexpectedly bright colours work surprisingly well to create a cheerful atmosphere, with various styles of seating and a generous distribution of tables and bar space to enjoy food and drink in comfort. Soup and sandwiches are available at the bar and there is a hot and cold buffet at the back. Choices on the blackboard change daily, but there is always a roast, typically roast beef with roast potatoes and a selection of five other vegetables (£5.95), a traditional casserole such as beef and Guinness (£4.95), plus perhaps pork Madras (£4.95), vegetable lasagne (£4.95) or chicken Kiev (£5.45); there's also usually a range of salads and good desserts (all £1.50) like pear and chocolate tart or banoffi pie. Sunday brunch is the works (including black pudding) for £4.95. Children "under control" are welcome at lunchtimes and until 6pm on Sunday. No parking, use the hospital's car park over the road. *Bar Food 12-2.30 (Sun to 2) only. Garden, outdoor eating. Closed 25 Dec, Good Friday. Access, Diners, Visa.*

Dublin   O'Dwyer's

| Tel 01 676 3574   Fax 01 676 2281 | **A** |

Mount Street Dublin 2   **Map 21 D4**

This large, bustling pub in pseudo-Victorian style always has a good buzz – well supported at lunchtime and early evening by a thriving local business and professional community. Later, a night club attracts a younger crowd especially appreciative of the famous O'Dwyer's pizzas. Professionally run, cheerful, central. Major refurbishment (perhaps even a complete change of theme) was imminenet as we went to press. *Open 10.30-11.30, Sun 12.30-2, 4-11. Access, Diners, Visa.*

Dublin   The Old Stand

| Tel 01 677 7220   Fax 01 677 5849 | **FOOD** |

37 Exchequer Street Dublin 2   **Map 21 D4**

A sister pub to *Davy Byrnes* (see entry), The Old Stand is a comfortable, old-fashioned place, attractive in a strong, sensible way with black paint outside and dark mahogany inside, good detail behind the bar and a loyal local following. The food is simple but good – they are famous for their sirloin steaks, both 6oz (£5.30) and 12oz (£9.50); there is a daily special (keenly priced at only £3.95 and always the most popular dish, whatever it is – perhaps corned beef with cabbage and potatoes), plus grills, omelettes (£4.50), salads (£2.95-£6.75) and open sandwiches (smoked salmon or prawn £3.95). Snacks and sandwiches only between 3.30 and 5 in the afternoon. A well-run, gimmick-free pub. *Open 10.30-11.30, Sun 12.30-2, 4-11. Bar Food 12.30-3, 5-9.30, Sun 12.30-2, 4-8. Access, Visa.*

Dublin   P Hedigan: The Brian Boru

| Tel 01 830 8514 | **FOOD** |

5 Prospect Road Glasnevin Dublin 9   **Map 21 D4**

Named after an 11th-century High King of Ireland, this smartly maintained pub is also known as *Hedigan's* after owner Peter Hedigan. Original Victorian themes – mahogany, stained glass and, especially, very fine tiling – have been carried through faithfully as alterations have been made through the years, everything is neat and clean and the eye is drawn past an abundance of strong tables and seating, to a patio/beer garden at the back, also furnished with comfortable eating in mind. It comes as no surprise that the Brian Boru has been in the same family since 1904. Bar food is best described as traditional: lunchtime carvery £3.95-£5.25; evenings – chicken Kiev (£5.25), sirloin steak with pepper sauce (£5.95), apple pie (£1.50). Sunday lunch £3.95-£5.25. *Open 10.30-11.30, Sun 12.30-2, 4-11. Bar Food 12-3 (to 2.30 Sun), 3-8 (not Sun). Garden, outdoor eating. Access, Visa.*

Dublin   The Pembroke

Tel 01 676 2980   Fax 01 676 6579   **A**

31 Lower Pembroke Street Dublin 2   Map 21 D4

A warm, welcoming city-centre pub with a cosy, real coal fire and exceptionally fine etched mirrors behind the bar, highlighting the mainly 1920s' decor. Dark mahogany woodwork and small, snug-like seating areas confirm this impression of intimacy and it comes as a pleasant surprise to find that you do not have to leave the premises to find good bar food at a fair price, and even outside normal meal times they will run up a simple snack. The cellar Buffet Bar serves salads and a hot food buffet at lunchtimes; fancier evening fare. Traditional Irish music Thursday evenings. *Open 10.30-11.30. Bar Food 12.30-2.30, 5-8.30. Pub closed Sun. Access, Diners, Visa.*

Dublin   Ryans of Parkgate Street

Tel 01 677 6097   **FOOD**

28 Parkgate Street Dublin 8   Map 21 D4

One of Dublin's finest Victorian pubs, Ryans of Parkgate Street has been in the same family for three generations – the present building is a reconstruction dating from 1896 and retains many original features, including two snugs at the back, a magnificent carved oak and mahogany central bar (its centrepiece a double-faced mechanical clock), brass gas lamps and an outstanding collection of antique mirrors. Bar fare runs from a choice of soups (seafood chowder £1.50) and simple light snacks to traditional hot dishes (stek and kidney pie £4.75, quiches, pastas), with slightly more variety in the evening. There are also different menus at lunchtime and in the evening (lunch £13, dinner à la carte). *Open 10.30-11.30, Sun 12.30-2, 4-11. Bar Food 12.30-2.30 (Sat & Sun 10.30-11.30, L soup and sandwiches only), 5.30-7.30. Restaurant Meals Mon-Fri 12.30-4, Tue-Sat 7-10. Access, Visa.*

Dublin   The Stag's Head

Tel 01 679 3701   **A**

1 Dame Court Dublin 2   Map 21 D4

Although small by comparison with the vast drinking emporiums being built today, The Stag's Head remains one of Dublin's most impressive old pubs – a lofty, spacious bar and one of the few with its original late-Victorian decor more or less untouched. Sit at the long granite bar and regret the absence of hand pumps which used to grace it, but enjoy the acres of original mahogany and admire its hand-worked detail. Some of it frames the marvellous bevelled mirrors that soar up to finish in curvaceous arches over the panelling and original fittings behind the bar. *Open usual pub hours (10.30am-11.30pm) but only 7-11pm on Sunday and Bank Holidays. Closed Good Friday, 25 Dec. No credit cards.*

Dublin   The Station House

Tel 01 831 3772

FOOD

3-5 Station Road Raheny Dublin 5

Map 21 D4

Outside may be deceptively like any other fairly traditional Dublin pub, but inside, the Station House has surprising Spanish-style decor – heavy, rustic furniture upholstered in warm, 'aged' tapestry and carpet-bagging fabrics sit comfortably around tile-topped tables on hard wooden floors enlivened by the occasional trompe l'oeil 'rug' strategically placed to trip the unwary. Traditional bar food from the carvery is freshly cooked and wholesome: roast rib of beef (£5.10), soup (£1.30), plaice and chips (£3.95), vegetable stir-fry (£4.25), steaks (£4.50/£8.95); also sandwiches and salads. A la carte menu (with a few children's favourites) during the afternoons and evenings. Staff are friendly and helpful and there's a walled garden at the back. Barbecues most weekends (weather permitting). Open 10.30-11.30, Sun 12.30-2, 4-11. *Bar Food & Meals carvery 12-2.30 (Sun to 2), à la carte 2.30-9 (Sun 4-8). Children allowed to eat in the lounge until 7.30, children's menu. Garden, outdoor eating. Closed Good Friday, 25 & 26 Dec. Access, Visa.*

Dublin   Toners Pub

Tel 01 676 3090

A

139 Lower Baggot Street Dublin 2

Map 21 D4

Situated only a few hundred yards from the *Shelbourne Hotel* and St Stephen's Green, this rare survivor of a style of pub which has all but disappeared in Dublin is now fiercely resistant to change. Owners, regulars and visitors alike blossom in its dimly-lit interior, where pints are drunk in the hard-benched little snug, or on high wooden stools at the bar with its rackety old combed-wood divisions. Journalists from offices across the road discuss the issues of the day, actors on location in the city come to share the buzz and everyone enjoys the genuine charm of Toners. Totally Irish, great crack… "you couldn't change this place". *No credit cards.*

Dublin   The Yacht

Tel 01 336364   Fax 01 333009

FOOD

73 Clontarf Road Dublin 3

Map 21 D4

This old-established local is known variously as 'The Yacht' and 'Tobin's,' and is like a great white steamer looking over to the port. Within, decorative buff 'sails' soften the height of the light, airy bar and a mixed collection of maritime bric-a-brac – some of it genuinely old and including artefacts from the much-loved old back bar 'the Tiller Room' – combine old and new to create a lively atmosphere which goes far beyond the usual 'theme decor'. Bar food at this friendly, well-run pub is unpretentious, wholesome, good value – and predictably popular, and luckily there is plenty of counter and table space for a fair crowd to eat in comfort. Everything is home-made, roast beef from the carvery is good value (£4.95) and comes with two styles of potato and four other fresh vegetables; Pavlova (£1.30) is the favourite dessert. The wide pavement is popular for alfresco relaxation in summer, despite the traffic. *Food carvery 12.30-3. Bar Food 3-8.30 (Sun 12.30-2 only). Children allowed in bar to eat, children's menu. Patio, outdoor eating. Access, Visa.*

Dublin   Yellow House

Tel 01 932994	FOOD
Willbrook Road Rathfarnham Dublin 14	**Map 21 D4**

The Yellow House is named after the unusual shade of the bricks with which it was built, and is the landmark pub of Rathfarnham. It makes a perfect rendezvous point, with no chance of confusion. Tall and rather forbidding from the outside, the warmth of the interior comes as a pleasant surprise and repays closer examination of pictures and old decorative items of local historical interest. Daily lunchtime carvery in the lounge bar; basket snacks and straightforward dishes like steak sandwich (£4.95), fresh pasta with smoked salmon and cream (£3.95) in the evening. Evening à la carte (and Sunday lunch) in the restaurant (no children after 7.30pm). *Bar Food Mon-Fri 5-8 (Sat 12-8). Carvery Mon-Fri 12.30-2.30. Children allowed in bar to eat, children's menu. Access, Diners, Visa.*

Dunmore East   The Ship

Tel 051 83144	A
Dunmore East Co Waterford	**Map 21 C5**

This well-located roadside bar/restaurant is situated high up over the bay, but is more remarkable for its atmosphere and seafood than a sea view. The solidly-built house dates back to Victorian times and, since the mid-80s, has enjoyed a national reputation under the present ownership for local seafood served in pleasantly informal surroundings. The bar area near the entrance develops gradually into a dining area, with unusual, sturdy furniture made from old barrels, darkwood walls and a strongly nautical theme – the interior is dimly atmospheric in contrast to the bright roadside patio area used for casual summer meals. They no longer serve bar food, but the à la carte menu is available lunch and dinner in summer (lunch Sun only in May & Oct, dinner in winter except Sun & Mon). *Access, Visa.*

East Ferry   The Marlogue Inn

Tel 021 813390	A
East Ferry Marina Cobh Co Cork	**Map 21 B6**

Despite the name, which somehow conveys the impression of an old-established hostelry, this beautifully located little waterside pub was only opened in 1992 and improvements are still ongoing, especially in the patio/barbecue area on the river side. As we went to press the pub was closed for redecoration and the style of bar food was likely to change. *Bar Food 12-3, 6-10. Access, Visa.*

Ennis   The Cloister

Tel 065 29521	FOOD
Abbey Street Ennis Co Clare	**Map 21 B4**

Built right in the walls and garden of a 13th-century Franciscan abbey, this famous pub is steeped in history and the back windows of its cosy low-ceilinged rooms overlook the friary and its brilliant emerald-green grass surrounds. The main restaurant incorporates rooms from the original abbey kitchen. In winter, fires create a sense of cheer and, in the event of fine summer weather, an attractive patio garden provides an escape from the unseasonable dimness of the bar.
Although well supported by locals, the reputation for good food here extends far beyond the immediate area with a compact, well-balanced

à la carte restaurant menu and an £18, three-course table d'hote offering a good choice – from game and foie gras roulade to Fergus salmon with gazpacho sauce and winter's fruit pudding with brandy butter. Lunchtime sees the likes of fish pie, scrambled eggs with smoked salmon, lasagne, Irish stew, chicken pot pie along with daily fish and meat specials. After 6pm the bar menu incorporates both snacks (soup of the evening with brown bread, goat's cheese salad with port sauce) and more substantial dishes (Dijon chicken en croute, steamed Ballyvaughan mussels with garlic bread, herby rack of lamb). *Bar Food 12-4, 6-9.30 Nov-mid Mar, 12-9.30 mid Mar-end Oct. Children's menu and portions available. Patio, outdoor eating. Access, Visa.*

Glandore Hayes' Bar ★

Tel 028 33214

Glandore Co Cork

FOOD

Map 21 B6

The beautifully situated village of Glandore boasts a surprising number of excellent hostelries, each with its own particular character and most with pavement tables and lovely harbour views, but when choices have to be made Hayes' Bar has a powerful attraction in Ada Hayes' famous bar food. Sensible tables and chairs, the right height for comfortable consumption, provide the first promising hint of priorities, then there's an unusual emphasis on wine, both decorative and actual: clearly this is not your average Irish bar. The menu is short and inscrutable – chicken & vegetable soup, sandwiches, a few 'specials' like paté on toast or prawn salad – but the soup reminds you of the kind your granny used to make and the sandwiches are nothing short of a new culinary art form. A prawn sandwich, for example, is made with lovely fresh brown bread stuffed with masses of freshly cooked prawns in home-made mayonnaise, quartered and prettily served with thinly-sliced fruit – apple, plum, orange – and a cocktail stick kebab of cherry tomatoes, olives and cucumber, then garnished with a mixed-leaf salad. Everything is served on different plates (Ada is a collector and never returns from her frequent travels without a new batch of ware) and attention to detail is outstanding, even for something as simple as a cup of coffee: a little tray is laid with an individual cafetière, a large French cup and saucer with matching tiny jug of cream and bowl of sugar, a café noir biscuit and a neapolitan chocolate – and all for 80p! Spiced beef, too often restricted to the role of Christmas fare, is a speciality here and makes excellent sandwiches and the (farmhouse) cheese and (home-made) chutney is an unusually good vegetarian alternative. *Pub open 12-11.30pm Mon-Sat (to 11pm in winter), Sun 12.30-2, 4-11pm: June-Sept, Christmas, Easter & all weekends. Bar Food all day. Pub closed weekdays Sept-June except Christmas & Easter. No credit cards.*

Glandore Marine Hotel

Tel 028 33366 Fax 028 33600

Glandore Co Cork

FOOD

Map 21 B6

Right down beside the harbour, this comfortable family hotel offers a good range of bar food and is especially strong on seafood which is landed daily from their own boat within yards of the kitchen. Specialities include their version of many popular dishes – chowder, garlic mussels, dressed crab, salmon mayonnaise, deep-fried plaice – but carnivores also get a fair choice; vegetarian dishes include several

starters and a main-course quiche or salad and there's a separate
children's menu. *Pub open 10.30am-11.30pm Mon-Sat (to 11pm in
winter), Sun 12.30-2, 4-11.* **Bar Food** *12-2.30, 6.30-9.30. Pub closed
25 Dec, Good Fri, 1-16 Mar. Access, Diners, Visa.*

Glasson   Grogan's

Tel 0902 85158	**FOOD**
Glasson nr Athlone Co Westmeath	Map 20 C3

Grogan's is a delightfully quaint, family-run pub in the pretty and
accessible village of Glasson, near Athlone. The cosy, low-ceilinged
front bar is divided in the traditional manner, with an open fire at one
end and a fair choice of chilled or 'soft' Guinness at both. Simon
Grogan presides over the kitchen and supplies as wholesome a range of
simple bar meals as anyone could wish for, with home-made soup and
bread (£1), smoked salmon (£2.55), fresh Dublin Bay prawn cocktail
(£3.25) and oysters, fresh or grilled with garlic butter (£3.50/£3.75),
as well as salads and snacks including speciality toasted sandwiches such
as black pudding (£1.45). There's also a larger back bar and a beer
garden where summer barbecues are held. **Bar Food** *12.30-3, 7-9
(Sun in summer only 12-2, 4-8). Children allowed in bar to eat. Garden.
No credit cards.*

Glencullen   Fox's Pub

Tel 01 295 5647 Fax 01 295 8911	**FOOD**
Glencullen Co Dublin	Map 21 D4

"Eat fish – live longer; eat oysters – love longer; eat mussels – last
longer; eat from the sea to see your way back to Fox's Famous
Seafood Pub!" One of the best-known pubs in the south Dublin area,
Anthony and Geraldine McMahon's pub is situated in a hamlet in the
Dublin mountains and claims (albeit along with numerous other pubs
around the country) to be the highest licensed premises in Ireland.
Purists may wince a little at the inevitable sawdust strewn on the stone
floor and the somewhat contrived collection of bric-à-brac and old
country furniture, but it's a friendly, entertaining place and the open
fires have real warmth. Famous for traditional Irish music since the
1950s when RTE broadcast regular Sunday night sessions from here
on the wireless, and, more recently, for 'Fox's Seafood Kitchen', an
extensive choice of home-cooked seafood in the bar. Lobster bisque
(£1.75), steamed mussels (£4.50), wild Irish oak-smoked salmon
(£5.95, with prawns and salad £9.75), hot vegetable and pasta bake
(£5.95), hot crab claws tossed in garlic butter (£5.50), 1lb lobster
£19.95, and even Beluga caviar with blinis £95; open sandwiches
(£2.60-£4.95) for the smaller pockets and appetites! A wooden
inscription on the wall reads: "There are no strangers here, only
friends who have never met". *Pub open 10.30-11.30 Mon-Sat (to 11
winter) Sun 12-2, 4-11.* **Bar Food** *12-10 (Sat to 9, Sun 4-10). Access,
Diners, Visa.*

Glengarriff   The Blue Loo

Tel 027 63167	**A**
Main Street Glengarriff Co Cork	Map 21 A6

Philip Harrington's unusually named pub may well inspire a first visit
out of curiosity alone, but its friendliness will ensure a return. Spick
and span, with a choice of sitting indoors in a pleasant traditional
country atmosphere or at roadside tables and benches out in the sun,
it is a pleasingly simple place, with food (May-Oct) to match – fresh

crab and fresh or smoked wild salmon are the specialities, served in open or closed sandwiches. *Open 10.30am-11.30pm (Sun 12.30-2, 4-11). No credit cards.*

Greencastle   Kealy's Seafood Bar

Tel 077 81010

FOOD

Greencastle Co Donegal

Map 20 C1

Unexpected sophistication awaits the visitor to this rugged commercial fishing port – James and Tricia Kealy's bar is more cocktail than fisherman's and, although tables are simply laid with paper napkins and inexpensive cutlery and glasses, it is immediately obvious that the food is taken seriously. Wholesome all-day snacks give way to a good value four-course dinner menu, often including popular dishes lifted out of the ordinary by giving them a new twist – avocado may come with pesto and sun-dried tomatoes, for instance, poached salmon with a wild mushroom sauce, even the ubiquitous seafood cocktail, though simply described as 'a mixture of white fish', has been known to conceal large chunks of lobster. Sirloin steak is offered as a concession to non-fish eaters, vegetables are served simply and generously on a platter and desserts range from homely and hot (apple pie, crepes suzette) to sophisticated cold (passion fruit delight); black plates are used to good effect for fish and desserts. No smoking. *Restaurant Meals 12.30-5, 7-9.30. Closed Mon, 1 week Mar, 1 week Oct, Good Friday, 25 Dec. Access, Diners, Visa.*

Howth   Abbey Tavern

Tel 01 390307   Fax 01 390284

A

Howth Co Dublin

Map 21 D4

Halfway up a hill above the picturesque harbour, the Abbey has all the hallmarks of a cosy, convivial pub. Blazing fires warm the two rooms, which are characterised by thick stone walls, flagstone floors with converted church pews and polished darkwood furniture adding flavours to a venue that is popular with locals as well as visitors from the Dublin area. A major attraction is the Irish evenings of music and song held here most nights and for which booking is required. *Open 3pm-11pm Mon-Fri, 1pm-11pm Sat (1pm-11.30pm in summer), 12.30pm-11pm Sun. Closed Good Friday, 25 & 26 Dec. No credit cards.*

Inishbofin Island   Day's Bar

Tel 095 45829

FOOD

Inishbofin Island Co Galway

Map 20 A3

Conveniently situated close to the ferry, a very pleasant family-friendly bar run by John and Olive Day, with Olive's good home cooking on offer seven days a week from the beginning of June to mid-September. After that it's a matter of pot luck but winter visitors only have to ask: 'Nobody need go hungry', says John. Given the location, seafood is unsurprisingly popular, typically in scallops mornay, garlic prawns or scampi, but steaks are also in great demand and Olive often does roasts of lamb, pork or beef. Vegetarians can choose from a selection of omelettes or a special salad and there's a short children's menu as well as half portions. No special facilities for children but they're happy playing on the beach in front of the bar. *Pub open 10.30am-11.30pm Mon-Sat (to 11 in winter), Sun 12.30-2, 4-11. **Bar Food** 12-5, 7-10. Pub closed 25 Dec, Good Fri. Access, Visa.*

Kanturk   Alley Bar

Tel 029 50171	**A**
Strand Street Kanturk Co Cork	Map 21 B5

A little gem of a drinking pub, run by the same family for several decades (daughter Alice has recently taken over from mother Mary). It's opposite the creamery and tucked away behind a modest grocery which is stocked with some items not held by many more glamorous shops. Look out for 'The Ballad of Ned Jones's Toyota', a true story in verse. *Open 9.30am-midnight (Sun 12.30-2.30 & 4-11.30).*

Kanturk   The Vintage

Tel 029 50549	**FOOD**
O'Brien Street Kanturk Co Cork	Map 21 B5

Stephen Bowles has owned this pleasant, well-run riverside pub since 1985 and it is well worth a visit, whether for a quiet pint or a bite to eat. The interior is pleasingly traditional and comfortably furnished. Suitable for just a quick snack or a complete meal; choose from traditional dishes like bacon and cabbage or Irish stew, T-bone steak or a traditional roast on Sundays. Daily-changing blackboard specials always include a vegetarian main dish. *Open 10.30am-11.30pm Mon-Sat, 12.30-2 & 4-11 Sun. **Bar Food** 12.30-9.30 Mon-Sat, 12.30-2 & 6-9.30 Sun. Access, Visa.*

Kenmare   The Horseshoe

Tel 0164 41553	**FOOD**
3 Main Street Kenmare Co Kerry	Map 21 A6

Behind its unassuming exterior The Horseshoe hides a pleasantly rustic old-fashioned bar, and behind this again, a cosy, informal 35-seat restaurant with open fire, oil-clothed tables with (real) cattle stall divisions and an unpretentious menu backed up by owner-chef Irma Weland's simple, wholesome food. Old favourites like deep-fried mushrooms with garlic mayonnaise take on a new lease of life in Irma's hands (crisp, light, very hot and full of contrasts), and, while steaks and fish are reliable, a vegetarian main course such as tagliatelle with creamy leek, mushroom and garlic sauce can be memorable. Similarly, a daily specials board can provide superior dishes and good desserts may include a more-ish caramelised apple and pear flan. Tables outside in summer. *Open 11am-10pm. **Meals** 12-4, 6-9.30. Closed February, Good Friday, Tues in winter, 25 Dec. No credit cards.*

Kenmare   The Purple Heather

Tel 064 41016	**FOOD**
Henry Street Kenmare Co Kerry	Map 21 A6

One of those delightful Kerry establishments which begins as a bar near the door and goes on to declare its real interest in food with tables and chairs properly set up for comfortable eating towards the back, the Purple Heather began serving good, simple food long before it was fashionable in these parts, in 1975. Gutsy home-made soups served with home-made, crusty brown bread (£1.60), wild smoked salmon with salad (£6.75), home-made chicken liver terrine with Cumberland sauce (£3.75), omelettes (from £4) and a wide range of sandwiches (from £1.30) – regular, open and toasted – are typical savoury offerings, followed by irresistible desserts like wholemeal apple crumble or hazelnut meringue. *Bar Food noon-6pm. Closed Sun. No credit cards.*

Kilcolgan   Moran's Oyster Cottage   ★

Tel 091 96113   Fax 091 96503

FOOD

The Weir Kilcolgan Co Galway

Map 21 B4

Willie Moran, champion oyster-opener, is the sixth generation of Morans to run this immaculate thatched cottage pub, whose bar looks out on to the pier. Gigas oysters (£7.50 a dozen) are available all year round, others from September to April. Alternatives include crab and smoked salmon (platters or sandwiches), mussels, seafood chowder, seafood cocktail and egg mayonnaise. All dishes are served with home-made brown bread. *Open 10am-midnight (Sun 12-2 & 4-11). Bar Food served all day. Garden, outdoor eating. Access, Visa.*

Kilkenny   An Caisléan Uí Cuain

Tel 056 65406

FOOD

2 High Street Kilkenny Co Kilkenny

Map 21 C5

Eccentric, perhaps, but popular nonetheless, this tall, narrow pub on three floors is situated on a prominent corner in the city centre and is striking, both inside and out. The interior is a mix of simple modern and traditional, with lots of aged wood and a good scattering of original posters. It has a relaxed, friendly and comfortable atmosphere and attracts a youngish, cosmopolitan crowd; writers, artists and musicians tend to congregate here due to the bar's reputation for lively discussion in Irish and for their live music. Officially, all year round, Monday night is traditional Irish music night but, in practice, an impromptu session can take off without warning at any time, to the great delight of all. Food varies according to seasonal demand and, in addition to conventional bar fare (soup £1.20, starters £2.75, main courses £3.95, desserts £1.50) there's now an à la carte restaurant at the top of the pub. *Bar Meals 10-8 (Sun 12.30-2 in summer only). Children allowed in bar to eat. No credit cards.*

Kilkenny   Langton's

Tel 056 65133   Fax 056 63693

FOOD

69 John Street Kilkenny Co Kilkenny

Map 21 C5

One of the best-known (and most praised) pubs in the country, run by Edward Langton since 1978 when he took over from his father. Edward has made a point of adding an extension or opening up a new area every year, so the huge premises are now a series of bars, each with its own individual style but all furnished to the highest standards in durable materials. Open fires with attractive basket grates are generously distributed through the various seating areas, all equally comfortable but with different attractions – one low-ceilinged area has a clubby atmosphere with buttoned leather wing chairs and banquette seating, while the next features an atrium, with walls of hanging plants and a genteel 'afternoon hotel tea' sort of atmosphere. Well-trained staff in black-and-white uniforms are helpful and efficient and bar menus offer food appropriate to the time of day – lunchtime sees a long list of sensibly-priced dishes (from chicken, honey and almond salad or fresh soup to smoked cod with egg and caper sauce, oyster-cut bacon and cabbage), through to a greater choice of dishes (like egg and Kilkenny ham mayonnaise, brunch, mussels farci, chicken curry and a

daily special) in the afternoon and evening. Leave room for the likes
of hot banana sponge pudding served with a brandy and coconut sauce
(£1.25). Both fixed-price (£13.50 & £17.50) and à la carte menus are
offered in the restaurant. Dancing Tue & Sat eves. **Bar Food &
Restaurant Meals** L 12-3, bar snacks 3-7, D 6 till late. Children allowed
in bar to eat, children's menu. Garden. Access, Diners, Visa.

Kilkenny   Shem's

Tel 056 21543	**FOOD**
61 John Street Kilkenny Co Kilkenny	Map 21 C5

Pleasantly unfussy, clean-lined premises run along the lines of the
simple old country pubs by Shem and Julie Lawlor. Lots of wood and,
in winter, generosity with the heating, make this a warm and
welcoming place and its relative simplicity and small size will please
those who find larger premises somewhat overpowering. Julie looks
after the cooking herself and takes pride in preparing simple food well
– home-made daily soups (seafood chowder, Chinese chicken, Irish
potato, all 95p), main courses (all £3.95) such as poached smoked
haddock with parsley sauce, daily pasta dishes, Hungarian beef goulash,
plus the likes of bread-and-butter pudding, grape pavlova and gateau
Diane to finish (all puddings £1.25). Sandwiches (open, closed,
toasted) also on an all-day bar snack menu. Children's menu of
favourites (3 courses £3.50). **Bar Food** L 12-3, bar snacks 3-6.
Children allowed in bar to eat, children's menu. Access, Visa.

Kilkenny   Tynan's Bridge House Bar

Tel 056 61828	**A**
Bridge House 2 Johns Bridge Kilkenny Co Kilkenny	Map 21 C5

One of the most genuine and interesting of Kilkenny's old pubs,
Tynan's has had the same landlord for over 50 years – Michael Tynan,
and his father was here before him. The spotless little bar features a
marble counter, lots of mahogany and a charming tapestry on a wall.
No children after 7pm. No credit cards.

Killaloe   Goosers   ★

Tel 061 376792	**FOOD**
Killaloe Ballina Co Tipperary	Map 21 B4

This delightful pub, in a quiet situation just across the road from the
lake, has built up a formidable reputation for its double act of good
food and characterful ambience. Settle into your choice of several
intimate bar areas, each with its own fireplace and simply but
comfortably furnished with country furniture and a finely-judged
selection of decorative rustic bric-a-brac, and enjoy anything from a
quick snack to a 3-course meal from the blackboard menu. Seafood is
the star among the bar food, including oysters, mussels (£4.50) and
scallops. Sandwiches and salads provide satisfying snacks, and larger
appetites will be allayed by bacon and cabbage (£5), Irish stew or
a steak. Open (& **Bar Food** served) 10.30-10, Sun 12.30-2, 4-10.
Children's menu and portions available. Closed 25 Dec. Access, Visa.

Killarney   Yer Man's Pub

Tel & Fax 064 32688	**FOOD**

24 Plunkett Street Killarney Co Kerry   Map 21 A5

Underneath *The Strawberry Tree* restaurant and in common
ownership, a characterful, old-fashioned pub is to be found. The
modern accoutrements nowadays essential to a well-run bar have been
skilfully disguised, while the comforts of yesteryear are much in
evidence – the long narrow bar has two open turf fires, each with its
own collection of mismatched but comfortable seating, including an
old leather-upholstered car seat and the top half of an Edwardian
armchair, easily set on a box. Plenty of shelf-height hooks for
outerwear and a small back bar with original black range add to the
appeal. Wholesome soups (perhaps chowder £2.45 or vegetable
£1.95), sandwiches, five or so salads (£5.95-£9.95), venison terrine
(£5.95) and seafood (oysters, smoked salmon, garlic mussels) from *The
Strawberry Tree* kitchen are offered on a short bar menu. Also home-
made ice cream (£2.45). Live music most nights in high season. *Open
12.30-1am, Sun 12.30-2, 4-12.* **Bar Food** *12-3 (no food Sun). Closed
Good Friday, 25 Dec. Access, Diners, Visa.*

Kilmoon   The Snail Box

Tel 01 835 4277	**A**

Kilmoon Ashbourne Co Meath   Map 20 D3

Four miles north of Ashbourne on the N2, this pleasant local has a
pool table bang in the middle of the friendly public bar and a
comfortable lounge in rustic style, both with open fireplaces. But its
curious name and the story of its origins are unique, going back to the
early 1800s when the site was common land and a hedge schoolmaster
settled there for a while. Taking exception to this intrusion, the local
landlord took him to court to get him evicted – but the justice of the
day ruled that 'the snail and his box can settle where he chooses'. No
food. *Open 4-11.30 (Fri & Sat from 12.30, Sun 12.30-2, 4-11). Garden,
outdoor tables. Closed Good Friday, 25 Dec. No credit cards.*

Kinsale   Blue Haven Hotel

Tel 021 772209 Fax 021 774268	**FOOD**
	B&B

3 Pearse Street Kinsale Co Cork   Map 21 B6

Serious fishermen and trenchermen alike should head for the small,
cosy, blue-and-white Blue Haven hotel near the quay, where not only
is there a 36' ocean-going angling boat for hire, but also good food
and comfortable accommodation after a hard day's sport. Bedrooms
vary from quite small to reasonably large (three have three beds), but
all are neat with smart white furniture and pictures by local artists.
Only one has a bath; the rest have showers or share a bathroom. The
diner is left with no doubt as to the specialities of the characterful
restaurant (recommended in our *1995 Hotels & Restaurants Guide*),
which has a strong maritime theme and overlooks an attractive
courtyard garden. Chef Stanley Matthews revels in fresh seafood and
there's a well-rounded wine list which offers very fair prices with little
over £20. The bar serves a good choice of imaginative food – from a
choice of soups (seafood chowder £3.25) to good seafood (home-
smoked salmon, half a dozen Rossmore oysters £7.25, daily line fish
specials £7.75) – and is very attractive, with wood panelling, natural
stone and a log fire, and has many snug corners opening on to a cane-
furnished conservatory which, in turn, leads on to a patio. The hotel

entrance has been upgraded recently and a new wine shop/delicatessen opened just off the lobby. *Bar open 10.30-11.30, Sun 12.30-2, 4-11.* ***Bar & Conservatory Food*** *12.30-3, Sun 12.30-2 & 5.30-9.30 (teas & light snacks 3-5pm). Restaurant Meals 7-10.30. Garden, outdoor eating.* ***Accommodation*** *18 rooms, all en suite, £90. Children welcome overnight (charged according to age), extra bed provided. Check-in by arrangement. No dogs. Closed 25 Dec. Access, Diners, Visa.*

Kinsale   The Bulman Bar

Tel 021 772131	A
Summer Cove Kinsale Co Cork	Map 21 B6

About a mile along the harbour in the Charles Fort direction, this traditional little waterside bar enjoys a tremendous setting looking over the harbour towards Kinsale. The bar is sometimes quiet and cosy, at other times very busy, and the large car park is liable to turn into "the biggest lounge bar in Ireland". *Open 10.30am-11.30pm, Sun 11-2, 4-11. outdoor tables. Closed Good Friday, 25 Dec. No credit cards.*

Kinsale   The Dock Bar

Tel 021 772522	A
Castle Park Kinsale Co Cork	Map 21 B6

Well situated between the small marina at Castle Park and one of the few south-facing sandy beaches in the area (a few hundred yards across the peninsula), this traditional black and white pub looks over towards Kinsale and, although the town is very near, it feels like a world apart. The patio, where tables have a choice of sun or leafy shade, has a slightly Continental atmosphere and the interior is comfortable in the modern Irish idiom – quarry tiles, varnished tables, upholstered benches and photographs of some of landlord Michael Vance's winning horses to remind him of his years as a trainer. *Open 10.30-11.30, Sun 12.30-2 & 4-11. Garden, outdoor eating area. No credit cards.*

Kinsale   1601

Tel 021 772529	FOOD
Pearse Street Kinsale Co Cork	Map 21 B6

Named after the year of the battle of Kinsale, details of which form an interesting and decorative presentation in the front lounge, this centrally located pub has earned a reputation for good bar food and is popular with locals and visitors alike. Their well-priced, freshly home-made food is worth waiting for; the menu changes daily. There's always a choice of chowder (£2.75) and another soup of the day (£1.60) and a short, well-balanced menu offers starters/light main courses such as a warm salad of goat's cheese (£4.25), crabmeat cocktail (£4.25), several local seafood dishes, traditional Irish fare like boiled bacon and cabbage with parsley sauce (£5) and Irish stew (£4.95) and the house special, '1601 Battle Burger' (£4.95), a home-made burger served with chips, salad and a choice of piquant dipping sauces such as chili, ketchup and chutney. The rear of the Lounge Bar is the Art Gallery restaurant, where food is served all day when it's busy. Food also served all day in summer. Live traditional Irish music on Monday nights. *Open 10.30-11.30, Sun 12.30-11.* ***Bar Food*** *12.30-3, 6.30-10 (to 7 Sun). Children allowed in the bar to eat. Closed Good Friday, 25 Dec. Access, Visa.*

Kinsale The Spaniard Inn

Tel 021 772436 **FOOD**

Scilly Kinsale Co Cork Map 21 B6

High above the harbour near the *Man Friday* restaurant, the Spaniard dispenses good cheer, good food and good music. Mary O'Toole's bar food is plain and simple, running from salads, soups and open sandwiches (try one with smoked Kinsale wild salmon £3.75) to old favourites like Irish stew or bacon and cabbage (£4.75); also cheese platter with home-made relish and soda bread (£3.75), home-made apple pie (£1.75) and ice cream (£1.75). Lunch can be taken on the terrace when the sun shines. Music sessions include light jazz, rock and blues (winter) and Irish traditional. The inn comprises several low-beamed rooms with stone floors, country furniture and assorted items of local interest – notably a 35lb salmon caught in 1912 at Little Island, Ardfinnan. *Open 10.30am-11.30pm Mon-Sat (to 11 in winter, Sun 12-2.30 & 4-11).* **Bar Food** *12.30-3 May-Sept, snacks only in evenings and all day Sun. Patio, outdoor eating. Closed Good Friday, 25 Dec. No credit cards.*

Kinvara Tully's

Tel 091 37146 **A**

Kinvara Co Galway Map 21 B4

A real local pub in the old tradition, with a little grocery shop at the front and stone-floored bar at the back, Tully's has a small enclosed garden with a few parasoled tables for fine weather but, better still, a fine old stove in the bar for cosy winter sessions. Not a food place – although sandwiches and tea or coffee are always available – but, as the old photographs and newspaper cuttings around the walls proclaim, definitely a spot for traditional music. *Pub open 10.30am-11.30pm Mon-Sat (till 11 in winter), Sun 12.30-2, 4-11. Pub closed 25 Dec, Good Fri. No credit cards.*

Lecanvey Staunton's

Tel 098 64850 **A**

Lecanvey Westport Co Mayo Map 20 A3

In the same family ownership for about two hundred years, the current landlord of this roadside pub (it is on a shallow bed and hard to miss when driving from Louisburgh to Westport) is a charming young lady, Therese Staunton, who inherited it recently from an aunt. It's a 'real' pub, traditional but not hide-bound by age and custom, with a good, comfortable atmosphere and is popular with locals and visitors alike. Don't go for food, but Therese does admit to making soup and sandwiches. *Pub open 10.30am-11.30pm, Sun 12.30-2, 4-11 (to 10 in winter). Closed Good Friday, 25 Dec. No credit cards.*

Leighlinbridge The Lord Bagenal Inn ★

Tel 0503 21668 **FOOD**

Leighlinbridge Co Carlow Map 21 C4

Food, wine and hospitality are all dispensed in good measure at this renowned old inn just off the main M9 Waterford-Carlow road. The style of cooking is always evolving, and more modern dishes are joining old favourites like oysters and mussels, crabs and scallops, home-made patés, steaks (£7.50-£12) and fine fresh fish (monkfish £9.50); vegetarian options. The whole family is made very welcome

and there's a special children's menu. Also a new tourist menu
(£11.50) and plenty of vegetarian dishes. Farmhouse cheeses. There
are surprisingly few half bottles on the superb, fairly-priced wine list
that provides helpful notes; obviously a labour of love, the veritable
tome covers a wonderful range of wines. *Set L £9.50 Set D
£11.50/£14.95. Open 10.30-11.30, Sun 10.30-2, 4-11. **Bar Food**
12.15-10, Sun 12.15-2, 4-9. Restaurant Meals 12.30-2.30 (Sun only),
6-10.30 (Sun 5-9.30. Closed 25 Dec, Good Friday. Garden, outdoor
eating, children's play area. Access, Diners, Visa.*

Monkstown   Purty Kitchen

Tel 01 284 3576	**FOOD**
Old Dunleavy Road Monkstown Co Dublin	Map 21 D4

Passers-by might be forgiven for thinking that this is the kind of pub
that looks too good to be true. It was established in 1728, which
makes it the second oldest pub in Dublin (after *The Brazen Head*) and
the oldest in Dun Laoghaire. However, changes have been made under
the current ownership: amazingly, the whole ground floor has been
lowered, and it is well worth a visit just to work out how it was done.
The result is generally deemed to be honourable – meaning that the
new arrangement (which looks old to a first-time visitor) is not a
travesty of the original pub. Soothingly cool and dark, it has plenty of
tables dotted around for the comfortable consumption of food from a
tempting bar menu that ranges from the usual soups and nibbles –
chowder (£2.95, half bowl £1.95), 'crab toes' in garlic butter (£4.50)
– to deep-fried goat's cheese with plum sauce (£4.50), open seafood
sandwiches served on home-made brown bread (£3.95,£5.50), steak
and even duck sandwiches (on home-made white bread £5.95) to full
main courses such as fillet steak with pebble mustard and Jameson
sauce (£12.95), or even hot buttered lobster (£22). Also seafood
specialities like baked cocotte – a combination of fresh and smoked
cod in a mushroom cream sauce topped with breadcrumbs. Desserts
range from perennial favourites like apple crumble or tangy, light
lemon tart to seasonal specialities such as a very moreish chocolate
roulade with fresh strawberries and cream. *Pub open 10.30am-11.30pm
Mon-Sat (Sun 12-2, 4-11). **Bar Food** 12-7. Pub closed Good Friday,
25 Dec. Access, Visa.*

Moone   Moone High Cross Inn   ★

Tel 0507 24112	**FOOD**
Bolton Hill Moone Co Kildare	Map 21 C4

The Clynch family are the most welcoming of hosts, and their
rambling 18th-century pub is up among the front-runners in the
hospitality and home cooking stakes. Morning coffee, lunch, afternoon
tea and evening meals are all available, and the menus are based on the
best of ingredients, simply cooked and generously served. The lounge
service menu (lunch every day) announces that Jacob sheep roam
freely around the inn – at their peril, perhaps, because they also appear
inside as roasts; other favourites on the various menus include brown
bread sandwiches with home-cooked meats or local Cheddar,
vegetable soup, traditional bacon and cabbage, Irish stew and the
grandmother of apple pies. Steaks feature on the evening à la carte;
Sunday lunch is a particularly popular occasion. There is a proper
dining room (not recommended here – it is the bar food that is

particularly good), but many visitors opt for a seat by the fire in the back bar, or a spot in the new beer garden. *Bar Meals 12-3, 7-9. Children allowed in bar to eat. Garden, outdoor eating. Access, Visa.*

Moydow   The Vintage

Tel 043 22122	**FOOD**
Moydow Co Longford	Map 20 C3

Former cookery teacher Regina Houlihan has developed her bar into quite a catering enterprise, looking after both local functions and running what is primarily a restaurant with a public bar. Officially they don't serve bar food but, as there's always something going on in the kitchen, their natural hospitality gets the better of them. Your request for a bite to eat is likely to be met with a typcially Irish response: "We don't do bar food, but I'll go and see what there is. What sort of thing do you feel like?" – it's that kind of a place (and there's an open fire while you wait). The Sunday lunch menu (£8.95, children £4) may be a seafood platter followed by home-made soup, then roast rib of beef, and a pudding to follow. The evening dinner menu (£14.95) offers a reasonable choice; typical restaurant dishes might be quail stuffed with chicken mousseline, cream of carrot and ginger soup, melon sorbet, fillet of beef medallions with brandy and cream sauce, and crème brulée. LArge beer garden off the 25-seater conservatory. No children under 12 after 8.30pm, but they're welcome at other times (particularly for Sunday lunch); high-chairs provided. Ring before travelling to confirm opening times. *Open 6.30-12. Closed Lunch Mon-Wed, 25 Dec, Good Friday. Restaurant Meals 1-7 (not Mon-Wed), 7-11. Garden, outdoor eating. Access, Diners, Visa.*

Naas   Fletcher's

Tel 045 97328	**A**
Commercial House Naas Co Kildare	Map 21 C4

A characterful pub that's well worth a visit just for the interest of being there. It's a very old-fashioned place, a long, narrow hall, broken up into sections in the traditional way with a mahogany divider complete with stained-glass panels. Having escaped the scourge of modernisation, Fletcher's remains somewhat austere and masculine: the plain wooden floor and very long mahogany bar with its full complement of built-in drawers and shelves behind is softened by the occasional aspidistra in an old cachepot and a collection of magnificent meat plates displayed high on the end wall. Masculine – and adult, too: they prefer no children in the bar. *No credit cards.*

Naas   The Manor Inn

Tel 045 97471	**FOOD**
Main Street Naas Co Kildare	Map 21 C4

The Manor Inn offers warmth, hospitality and good food in refreshingly 'undesigned' surroundings. Local interest is reflected in pictures and mementos connected with horses and the army base at the nearby Curragh, car racing at Mondello (note the clock in a racing helmet) and a clutter of notices giving due warning of upcoming local events. The menu offers a wide variety of familiar pub fare, from sandwiches, salads and omelettes to pasta, burgers, pies, grills, steaks and four choices 'from the smoke house'. *Bar Food 12-11 (Sun 12.30-2.30 & 5-10.30). Children allowed in bar to eat, children's menu. Access, Diners, Visa.*

New Quay   Linnane's Bar

Tel 065 78120	**FOOD**
New Quay Burrin Co Clare	Map 21 B4

This unassuming country pub has sliding doors at the back, which open virtually on to the rocks in summer and bring the magnificent seascape beyond right inside. In winter, it is inward-looking, as visitors (who may have had difficulty finding it if, as sometimes happens, gales have blown down local road signs) cluster round the peat fire. It has rightly attracted attention for the quality of its seafood: in addition to luxury lobster there's plenty of good but less expensive fare at Linnane's, with the best choice in summer: a steaming bowl of chowder, perhaps, served with brown bread; scallops New Quay, cooked in a wine sauce and served in a gratin dish, layered with rice to mop up the aromatic juices; or a huge crab salad, the plate burgeoning with the white meat of at least a pair of crabs. Simply delicious. *Bar Food 12-9 Apr-Oct (daily in summer, weekends only in low season), 5-9 Nov-Mar. Children's portions. No credit cards.*

Oughterard   Powers

Tel 091 82712	**A**
The Square Oughterard Co Galway	Map 20 B3

Despite its picturesque exterior, unchanged for 180 years, this little thatched pub in the middle of Oughterard is a genuine local and all the better for that. The previous owners had it in the family for a century and a half and, when the current owner Frank O'Meara took over in 1990 after it had been disused for a decade, he was determined that the oldest pub in the town should retain its character. There's a big open fire in the original front bar in winter and, although no food is currently available, there are plans to provide bar meals for the summer season in 1995. *Pub open 10.30-11.30 (to 11 in winter, Sun 12.30-2, 4-11 all year). Closed 25 Dec, Good Fri. No credit cards.*

Portsalon   Rita's

Tel 074 59107	**A**
The Pier Portsalon Letterkenny Co Donegal	Map 20 C1

"Nothing's changed here in 100 years" says Rita Smyth, landlady of this multi-purpose establishment by the beach. The grocery bar serves as a general store for locals and holiday-makers, and there are two other bars – harbourside at the front and a cosy back bar with an open fire. Self-contained flats are let in summer, with meals and baby-sitting available. *Open 10.30am-11pm, Sun 12.30-2 & 4-11. No credit cards.*

Rathpeacon   Country Squire Inn

Tel 021 301812	**FOOD**
Mallow Road Rathpeacon Co Cork	Map 21 B6

A couple of miles out of Cork on the N20 towards Mallow, Pat McSweeney's immaculate roadside pub is very much geared up to eating. The small bar has not only old 'sewing machine' tables but also some of the original cast-iron 'Singer' stools, now comfortably upholstered to match the banquette seating. Bar lunches are a blackboard affair with the likes of vegetable soup (£1.20), grilled garlic-stuffed mussels (£2.30), cheese-topped shepherd's pie (£3.50) and cold ham with salad (£3.95); the evening offerings on a written menus are a bit more extensive – sirloin steak with garlic butter or pepper sauce (£11.75), lemon sole stuffed with crab in a fresh prawn sauce (£10), half a roast chicken with ham and stuffing (£6.75). The home-cooked food is generously portioned, so bring a healthy appetite. In the evenings (only), a cosy, 28-seat candle-lit restaurant offers similar fare with meals from around £19 (priced according to one's choice of main course). No children under 12. *Open 12-2.30 (not Sun) & 4.30-11. **Bar Food** 12.30-2.30 (not Sun) & 6.30-9.30 (to 10 Sun). No bar food Bank Holidays. **Restaurant** 6.30-10 Tues-Sat. Closed L Sun & 1 week Jan. Access, Visa.*

Rosses Point	**Austie's**	
Tel 071 77111		**FOOD**
Rosses Point Co Sligo		Map 20 B2

Named after the previous owner, Austie Gillen, and close to the house where Yeats and his brother used to stay on summer holidays (now neglected and in disrepair), this 200-year-old pub overlooking Sligo Bay is a nautical place – not a 'theme' pub but one that has always been associated with a seafaring family and is crammed full of nautical paraphernalia which is both decorative and fascinating to anyone with an interest in maritime history. The simple bar menu is strong on local seafood – chowder, garlic mussels, open sandwiches or salads with crab, prawns and salmon. ***Bar Food** 12-5.30 summer only. A la carte menu 6-9.30 all year. Pub closed until 4pm in winter. Waterside terrace. Access, Visa.*

Rossnowlagh	**Smugglers Creek Inn**	★	**FOOD**
Tel 072 52366			**B&B**
Rossnowlagh Co Donegal			Map 20 B2

Conor Britton's imaginatively restored pub and restaurant is perched high on the cliffs overlooking the wonderful golden strand at Rossnowlagh. Visitors have the endless fascination of watching the powerful Atlantic rollers come in from afar to spend themselves on the beach far below – and all this while sitting in considerable comfort, with open fires and chef Maire Morrow's delicious bar food from which to choose. Across the corridor from the bar (and sharing the same dramatic view), the stone-floored restaurant is furnished in country style and, although the menu works the smugglers theme to death, the same excellent kitchen is common to bar and restaurant. So start, perhaps, with Donegal Bay oysters or a warm salad that includes smoked bacon, blue cheese and croutons, followed by a main course from a wide choice of seafood or, perhaps, vegetarian tagliatelle or a stir-fry. Children are well catered for and there's a selection of special coffees for their parents. Accommodation is offered in five interestingly decorated rooms, all of which have sea views. Rooms vary considerably and most are on the small side – one corner room, with windows in two walls, is slightly larger than average and has even better views. Winner of our Ireland Pub of the Year award last year. ***Bar Food** 1-9.30pm. Set Sun L (12.30-3) £8.75. **Accommodation** 5 rooms, all en suite, £39. Garden. Pub closed 24 & 25 Dec, Mon & Tue in winter. Access, Visa.*

Roundstone   O'Dowd's Seafood Bar and Restaurant

Tel 095 35809	**FOOD**
Roundstone Co Galway	**Map 21 A4**

A reassuringly unchanging traditional pub and seafood bar
overlooking the harbour. It's an oasis of calm where regular summer
visitors – notably Dublin lawyers and doctors, plus the odd politician
– return to recharge their batteries. The simple, old-fashioned bar is a
relaxing place to renew old friendships over a pint and a bite from the
reasonably-priced bar menu, which includes a good range of seafood
choices – chowder (a speciality), Mannin Bay oysters, crab claws in
garlic, stuffed mussels, crab salad, smoked salmon pasta and an
unusually named salmon burger with spicy tomato sauce – plus old
favourites like shepherd's pie and sirloin steak for carnivores and
vegetarian specialities such as bean burgers. Salmon is smoked or cured
for gravlax locally; herbs and lettuce come from their own garden.
Lobster, grilled oysters, game (mallard, quail, venison and pheasant)
and blackberry and apple pie are always popular in the restaurant;
a roast goose is a traditional offering on New Year's Eve. *Bar Food
11-10 (Sun 12.30-2, 4-10). **Restaurant Meals** 12.30-3, 6-9.30 (Sun
12.30-2, 4-10). Restaurant closed mid Oct-Christmas & 2nd week Jan-
Easter. Access, Visa.*

Roundwood   **Roundwood Inn**   ★

Tel 01 281 8107	**FOOD**
Roundwood Co Wicklow	**Map 21 D4**

Set amidst spectacular scenery in the highest village in the Wicklow
Hills, Jürgen and Áine Schwalm's 17th-century inn is furnished in
traditional style with wooden floors, darkwood furniture and huge log
fires throughout. Excellent bar food can be enjoyed in comfort and is
available every day. Typically, it might include, typically, soup
(£1.60), sandwiches, fresh, smoked or cured salmon (gravadlax
£7.50), Galway Bay oysters, smoked trout salad (£4.80), half a roast
chicken (£4.70) in the basket, goulash with red cabbage (£6.95) and
generously served Irish stew (£5.90) made with lean local lamb.
Blackboard specials might include crab bisque with Madeira or a
particularly good venison ragout (£6.95) and are where you're likely
to find the real winners. Leave room for a pud! Chef Paul Taube's
restaurant menu (separately recommended in our *1995 Hotels &
Restaurants Guide*) leans towards bigger dishes like rack of Wicklow
lamb, roast wild Wicklow venison (a speciality for a long time) and
other game in season. German influences are evident in long-
established specialities like wiener schnitzel, triple liqueur parfait and
a feather-light fresh cream gateau which is not to be missed. 3-course
Sunday lunch £13.95. A mainly European wine list, strongest in
France and Germany, starts at under £10 for the house selection and
ascends to 40 times that for a 1967 Pauillac. No children after 7.30pm.
*Open 10.30-11.30, Sun 12-2, 4-11. **Bar Food** 12-10, Sun 12-2, 4-10.
Restaurant Meals (not Mon all day or Sun eve – ring for Bank Holiday
weekend opening times) 1-2.15, 7.30-9.30. Closed 25 Dec, Good Friday.
Access, Visa.*

Schull   Bunratty Inn

Tel 028 28341	**FOOD**
Schull Co Cork	Map 21 A6

Since taking over in 1986, Val and Vera Duffy have built up a well-deserved reputation for the bar food in this comfortably appointed pub – and apart from providing an interesting menu overall, they are justifiably proud of several specialities. When roast pork is offered, for example, it is no ordinary meat – kitchen waste from Bunratty Inn goes to feed pigs on a farm in Gubbeen, which eventually supplies the bar with free-range pork: hence their unique 'recycled pork'. Such curiosities aside, their brown bread is renowned and ingredients are locally sourced wherever possible. There's a good choice of local seafood – Union Hall smoked salmon, Rossmore oysters and smoked mackerel, crab claws – farmyard duck from Ballydehob and of course all those lovely West Cork cheeses in, for example, a ploughman's selection plate of several including Milleens and Durrus or in speciality open toasted sandwiches made with smoked salmon and Gubbeen or Cashel Blue. Don't forget to leave room for desserts like home-made ice creams, fresh strawberry cheesecake or individual pavlovas with chocolate sauce. *Pub open 10.30am-11.30pm Mon-Sat (to 11pm in winter), Sun 12.30-2, 4-11.* **Bar Food** *12-4. Pub closed 25 Dec, Good Fri. Access, Visa.*

Schull   T J Newman's

Tel 028 28223	**A**
Main Street Schull Co Cork	Map 21 A6

On the corner of the main street and the road that leads down to the quay, this characterful little bar makes up in charm and warmth what it lacks in cubic capacity. That capacity is supplemented on summer evenings by the pavement. *Open 10.30am-11pm (to 11.30 in summer), Sun 12.30-2, 4-11. No credit cards.*

Skryne   O'Connell's

Tel 046 25122	**A**
Skryne nr Tara Co Meath	Map 20 C3

The old castle on top of the hill is your marker for this delightfully unspoilt old country pub, whose main attraction is a good pint pulled by charming landlady Mary O'Connell (she has held the reins for 10 years, but the pub has been in her husband's family for three generations). The two simple bars contain friendly locals, records of sporting endeavours and a history of the nearby monastery. The pub was up for sale as we went to press. *Open usual pub hours. No credit cards.*

Sligo   Hargadon's

Tel 071 70933	**A**
O'Connell Street Sligo Co Sligo	Map 20 B2

Hargadon's is one of the great legendary pubs of Ireland: bought by a British MP in 1868, it passed into the hands of the Hargadon family in 1908 and has been maintained by them, unspoilt, ever since. When they decided to venture into providing food (served from 10.30-6, to 7 in summer) it was soup and sandwiches bought in from talented local (Ballymaloe-trained) caterers; now they offer a full bar food service. Dinner is served in a room at the back where it will not interfere with the real business of running a bar. Otherwise it is as it was – the snugs, the pot-belly stove, the wooden benches and the shelves which used to hold groceries. Children allowed in the bar during the daytime only. Go and enjoy. Beer garden. *No credit cards.*

Sligo　McGettigan's (An Cruiscín Lán/Cruskeen Lawn)

Tel 071 62857	**FOOD**
Connolly Street Sligo Co Sligo	Map 20 B2

The McGettigan family's comfortable, unselfconscious pub is well supported by locals and visitors alike. It reputation is based on serving good, plain food at a very fair price; the emphasis throughout is on old-fashioned courtesy and service rather than on quaintness of decor or tradition. Expect simply presented, middle-of-the-road food in generous portions, with value for money firmly in mind. Good-value lunches offer the likes of Irish stew and roast stuffed chicken and bacon; bar snacks, including children's favourites, are served all day every day. Leave room for sherry trifle and custard or home-made apple tart and cream (both £1.20). Accommodation is also offered in 11 modest rooms (B&B £27 for two). *Bar Meals 12.30-2.30 (except Sat & Sun). Children allowed in bar to eat, children's menu, cot & highchair provided. Pub closed in winter months 3-5pm. No credit cards.*

Spiddal　Bridge House Hotel

Tel 091 83118	**B&B**
Spiddal Connemara Co Galway	Map 21 B4

All the bedrooms at Esther Feeney's spruce little hotel on Galway Bay are now en suite, and all have colour TVs. The neat pine-clad bar has French windows opening on to the garden and the Stirrup Room is open all day for food. No children under 2. No dogs. *Accommodation 14 rooms, all en suite, £65. Garden. Closed Christmas-mid Feb. Access, Visa.*

Stillorgan　The Mill House

Tel 01 288 8672　Fax 01 283 6353	**FOOD**
Lower Kilmacud Road Stillorgan Co Dublin	Map 21 D4

The Mill House is hard to miss with its coat of bright pink and shiny gold paintwork. Inside, once past the rather off-putting porch/hall area, the interior is surprisingly calm and peaceful, broken up into a number of small semi-snug areas with plenty of gas coal-effect fires. The large, irregular mahogany bar is pleasingly solid and there's a lot of dark wood in the traditional style, successfully offset by plenty of mirrors, pictures and plants in old china cachepots. Traditional lunchtime pub grub includes basket snacks (£2.95) and the likes of lasagne (£3.95), burger, curry, chicken Kiev (£4.95) and fried fillet of plaice. *Bar Food 12-2.30, 5-8. Patio. Access, Diners, Visa.*

Stillorgan　The Stillorgan Orchard

Tel 01 288 8470	**FOOD**
Stillorgan Co Dublin	Map 21 D4

Despite its slightly incongruous situation close to a large suburban shopping centre, the Orchard's main claim to fame is 'the largest thatched roof in Ireland'. Inside, there's a surprisingly genuine country cottage atmosphere with low ceilings, small windows, lots of tapestry style and chintzy seating in snugs and alcoves and all the traditional clutter of brass, copper and old plates on the walls. Bar food is not adventurous, but everything is fresh and wholesome. Standard, short printed menus for lunch and evening bar food are augmnted by daily specials including a roast, a traditional dish such as baked Limerick ham with parsley sauce (£5.25), steak (£7.15), some kind of chicken (braised breast £5.15) and a fish of the day, plaice perhaps, or sometimes something more unusual such as grilled sea trout with caper butter (£5.05). *Bar Food 12.30-3, 5-8. Children allowed to eat in bar until 4pm (Sun to 7pm). Garden. Access, Diners, Visa.*

Timoleague   Dillon's

Tel 023 46390	**FOOD**
Mill Street Timoleague Co Cork	Map 21 B6

That one can see in through the plant-filled clear shop window immediately distinguishes Dillon's from the usual Irish town bar; their description of themselves as a café-styled bar is very apt. There's a conventional bar counter down one side of the single room, a mixture of furniture that includes a few Lloyd Loom chairs around eating-height tables and arty black-and-white photos of the likes of James Dean and Billie Holliday on the walls. It's run by two French sisters, Isabelle (Dillon) and Anne (Boulineau), who originally procured all the food from nearby Lettercollum House restaurant (which is no disadvantage) but are increasingly substituting dishes of their own. Thus one gets beef bourguignon (£5.50), free-range chicken cooked in white wine (£6.50) and tarte tartin (£1.95) along with shepherd's pie (£2.90), lasagne (£3.95) and cheesecake (£2.20). The same menu is available throughout the opening hours. Good cafetière coffee and pots of tea are served alongside the pints of stout. *Open (& Bar Food served) noon-11 (to 11.30 in summer). Closed Tues (except June-Aug), Nov-mid March (except 3 weeks Christmas). No credit cards.*

Tubbercurry   Killoran's Traditional Restaurant & Lounge

Tel 071 85679 Fax 071 85111	**FOOD**
Main Street Tubbercurry Co Sligo	Map 20 B2

"The welcome doesn't die on the doormat" is the motto at Tommy and Anne Killoran's whale of a place; no-nonsense, reliably priced food and authentic entertainment are the draws. On Thursday nights from Jun-Sept its 60-seater bar/restaurant/lounge (call it what you will) is crammed to the gunwales, with all and sundry tucking into boxty, potato cakes, crubeens and cali – a local name for hot potato, spring onion and melted butter, better known as champ – to help along the traditional music and Irish dancing. Visitors can even try their hand at butter-churning in the middle of it all. Organic vegetables, local goat's cheese (cheese plate £3) and home-made brown bread are regulars on the menu, alongside more everyday fare. In season, the salmon comes from the river right on the doorstep. There's nowhere else quite like it in Ireland – Killoran's is an original. Not elegant, not folksy, but definitely different. "Children are welcome at any time." *Open 9am-12pm, Sun 10am-10pm. Bar Food 12.30-3, 7-9 (bar snacks only winter eves). Garden. Access, Diners, Visa.*

Waterford   Jack Meade's Bar

| Tel 051 73187 | A |

Ballycanvan Little Halfway House Waterford Co Waterford   Map 21 C5

This delightful early 18th-century pub has been in the same family for
150 years and has managed to retain its essential character and charm
remarkably well. The building, which is well kept and cottagey, has
not been altered or extended and they make the most of its sun-trap
position, with flower tubs at the door and climbing plants up the
walls contrasting with the cool, dark, low-ceilinged interior with its
two small traditional bars complete with pictures and photographs of
local interest and open fires for cold weather; in summer there's
traditional music in the open and a barbecue. A museum of farm
machinery and (across the bridge) an old limekiln (for making
fertiliser) and ice house (for preserving fish) are among the things
to look at. *No credit cards.*

Waterville   The Huntsman

| Tel 066 74124 | FOOD |

Waterville Co Kerry   Map 21 A6

Owner-chef Raymond Hunt has been serving up specialities like
lobster (from the tank), Dublin Bay prawns and local salmon in this
well-established bar and restaurant since 1978 – and red is the
predominant colour in the decor too, so the cool blues and greys of
the sea and sky make a welcome contrast. The snack menu offers a
wide choice of sensibly priced dishes ranging from a choice of soups,
including fresh crab bisque with home-made bread, through grilled or
natural oysters, mussels marinière, smoked Waterville salmon salad
and deep-fried sole with French fries to a popular selection including
hamburgers, spaghetti bolognese, omelettes and curries ... and Irish
stew. There's also a full restaurant menu. The wine list is serious, with
France particularly well represented, though the New World gets a
look in as well. Accommodation is available – B&B or half-board (not
inspected). **Bar Food** *12-10. Access, Diners, Visa.*

Waterville   The Smugglers Inn

| Tel 066 74330   Fax 066 74422 | FOOD |

Waterville Co Kerry   Map 21 A6

In a beachside location by Waterville championship golf course, Harry
Hunt and his wife Lucille took a 100-year-old farmhouse and turned it
into a warm and welcoming bar and restaurant with accommodation.
There's a strong emphasis on seafood, from oysters and mussels
marinière to smoked salmon mousse, cod provençal, sautéed
monkfish, poached scallops au gratin and black sole grilled and served
with garlic butter. A snack menu, including sandwiches, is available all
day. The bay was once notorious for smuggling – wine, brandy, gold
and silk inwards, wool and poteen out! *L 12-3 D 6.30-9.30. Bar snacks
12-9.30. Set L £12.95 Set D £20. Access, Diners, Visa.*

Westport   The Asgard

Tel 098 25319

FOOD

The Quay Westport Co Mayo

Map 20 A3

Named after the sail training ship *Coiste Asgard* (a well-loved visitor
to the port), Michael and Mary Cadden's famous quayside bar is
appriately decorated with nautical artefacts. The bar menu, served
daily from noon until 9pm, also underlines links with the sea in a
varied fish selection including favourites such as seafood chowder
(£1.50), Clew Bay oysters (£4.50 half dozen) and main dishes like
fisherman's platter (£9) and prawn salad (£7); carnivores are well
catered for, too: traditional Irish lamb stew (£5) or curried chicken
(£5.50). The Asgard restaurant upstairs offers more formal meals in
the evening. *Pub open 10.30-11.30 Mon-Sat (to 11 in winter), Sun
12.30-2, 4-11.* **Bar Food** *12-9. Garden. Pub closed Good Friday, 25 Dec.
Access, Diners, Visa.*

Westport   The Olde Railway Hotel

Tel 0198 25166

B&B

The Mall Westport Co Mayo

Map 20 A3

Beautifully situated along the tree-lined Carrowbeg River on the Mall
in the centre of Westport, the Olde Railway Hotel is the real McCoy.
Once described by William Thackeray as 'one of the prettiest,
comfortablist hotels in Ireland', it was built in 1780 as a coaching inn
for guests of Lord Sligo. Now, in the hands of the Rosenkranz family,
who have owned it since 1983, it retains considerable character and is
well known for its antique furniture and a pleasing atmosphere of
slight eccentricity, although concessions to the present generation of
traveller have been made in the form of en-suite bathrooms, satellite
television and private car parking, also a secretarial service including
use of fax machine and computer. Public areas include a conservatory
dining room quietly situated at the back of the hotel and a rather
splendid recently restored function room with original stone walls.
The large bar is the public face of an essentially private hotel and the
main entrance is from the mall. Children up to 12 stay free in parents'
room. *Accommodation 24 rooms, all en suite, £75 including 10% service
charge. Children welcome overnight, extra bed (£10) and cot provided.
Closed 25 Dec. Access, Visa.*

Westport   Towers Bar

Tel 098 26534

FOOD

The Harbour The Quay Westport Co Mayo

Map 20 A3

A pair of ancient towers (now preserved buildings) inspired the name
of this characterful, family-friendly pub. Bar food is offered daily from
12 noon. In addition to a range of seafood – typically smoked
mackerel paté (£2.40), fish pie (£4.25), baked stuffed mussels (£4.25),
seafood salad (£7.25) – there's simple fare like ploughman's lunch
(£3), home-made burger (£1.30) or cheese burger and a vegetarian
salad (£2.95) option. Although on the harbour side of the road, there
is a walled garden with a safe play area that includes a tree house and a
sand pit. *Pub open 10.30am-11.30pm Mon-Sat (till 11 in winter), Sun
12.30-2, 4-11.* **Bar Food** *12-9 (except 2-4 Sun). Garden, outdoor eating.
Pub closed Good Friday, 25 Dec. Access, Visa.*

Recommended by

EGON RONAY'S GUIDES

1995

YOUR GUARANTEE
OF
QUALITY AND INDEPENDENCE

- Establishment inspections are anonymous

- Inspections are undertaken by qualified
Egon Ronay's Guides inspectors

- The Guides are completely independent
in their editorial selection

- The Guides do not accept advertising,
hospitality or payment from listed
establishments

Hotels & Restaurants	Pubs & Inns
Europe	Just a Bite
Family Hotels & Restaurants	Paris
Oriental Restaurants	Ireland
New Zealand & South Pacific	Australia

Egon Ronay's Guides are available from all good bookshops or can be
ordered from Leading Guides, 35 Tadema Road, London SW10 0PZ
Tel: 071-352 2485 / 352 0019   Fax: 071-376 5071

County
Round-Up

PUBS & INNS COUNTY ROUND-UP 1995

LONDON listed by postal district

Please refer to the **How to use this Guide** section at the beginning of this Guide for explanations of Categories (FOOD, B&B, A) & Symbols (Family, Star).
Please note: some pubs may be closed on certain days — refer to entries in gazetteer for complete opening times.

Location	Establishment	Star	Food	Atmos	Family	Waterside	Tel	Open all day?
E14	Grapes			Atmos		Water	0171-987 4396	
EC1	Cock Tavern		Food				0171-248 2918	
EC1	The Eagle	*	Food				0171-837 1353	
EC1	Fox & Anchor		Food				0171-253 4838	
EC1	The Hope & Sir Loin	*	Food				0171-253 8525	
EC1	The Peasant		Food				0171-336 7726	
EC1	Thomas Wethered		Food				0171-278 9983	
EC1	Ye Olde Mitre Tavern			Atmos			0171-405 4751	All Mon-Fri only
EC2	Old Dr Butler's Head			Atmos			0171-606 3504	All Mon-Fri only
EC3	Lamb Tavern		Food				0171-626 2454	
EC4	Black Friar			Atmos			0171-236 5650	All exc Sat & Sun
EC4	Old Bell Tavern			Atmos			0171-583 0070	
EC4	Witness Box		Food				0171-353 6427	
EC4	Ye Olde Cheshire Cheese			Atmos			0171-353 6170	All exc Sun
N1	Albion		Food				0171-607 7450	
N1	Eagle Tavern			Atmos			0171-253 4715	All Mon-Fri
N1	Marquess Tavern		Food				0171-354 2975	All exc Sun
N1	Slug & Lettuce		Food				0171-226 3864	All exc Sun
NW1	The Lansdowne		Food				0171-483 0409	All exc Sun & Mon
NW3	Flask			Atmos			0171-435 4580	All Sat only
NW3	Jack Straw's Castle			Atmos			0171-435 8885	All

NW3	Spaniards Inn			Atmos		0181-455 3276	All exc Sun
NW8	Crockers Folly		Food			0171-286 6608	All exc Sun
SE1	Anchor			Atmos	Water	0171-407 1577	All exc Sun
SE1	Founders Arms			Atmos	Water	0171-928 1899	All exc Sun
SE1	George Inn			Atmos		0171-407 2056	All exc Sun
SE1	Horniman's		Food		Water	0171-407 3611	
SE5	Phoenix & Firkin		Food			0171-701 8282	All exc Sun
SW1	Buckingham Arms		Food			0171-222 3386	All Mon-Fri
SW1	The Grenadier		Food			0171-235 3074	
SW1	Morpeth Arms		Food			0171-834 6442	All exc Sun
SW1	Nag's Head		Food			0171-235 1135	All exc Sun
SW1	Orange Brewery			Atmos		0171-730 5984	
SW3	The Australian		Food			0171-589 3114	All exc Sun
SW3	Coopers Arms		Food			0171-376 3120	
SW3	Front Page		Food			0171-352 2908	All exc Sun
SW3	Phene Arms		Food			0171-352 3294	All exc Sun
SW6	Imperial Arms		Food			0171-736 9179	
SW6	White Horse		Food			0171-736 2115	
SW10	Sporting Page		Food			0171-352 6465	
SW11	The Castle		Food			0171-228 8181	All exc Sun
SW18	Alma		Food			0181-870 2537	All exc Sun
SW18	The Ship		Food		Water	0181-870 9667	All exc Sun
SW19	Fox & Grapes		Food	Atmos		0181-946 5599	
W1	The Guinea		Food			0171-499 1210	All Mon-Fri
W1	Mulligans of Mayfair		Food			0171-409 1370	
W1	Newman Arms		Food			0171-636 1127	
W2	Monkey Puzzle		Food			0171-723 0143	All
W4	Bell & Crown		Food		Water	0181-994 4164	
W4	City Barge			Atmos	Water	0181-994 2148	All exc Sun
W6	Dove		Food	Atmos		0181-748 5405	All exc Sun
W8	Britannia					0171-937 1864	All exc Sun
W8	Churchill Arms		Food			0171-727 4242	All exc Sun

Location	Establishment	Star	Food	Atmos	Family	Waterside	Tel	Open all day?
W8	Windsor Castle			Atmos			0171-727 8491	All exc Sun
W11	Ladbroke Arms			Atmos			0171-727 6648	All
WC1	Cittie of York			Atmos			0171-242 7670	All exc Sun
WC1	Lamb		Food				0171-405 0713	All exc Sun
WC1	Princess Louise			Atmos			0171-405 8816	All Mon-Fri only
WC2	Lamb & Flag		Food				0171-237 4088	All exc Sun
WC2	Opera Tavern		Food				0171-836 7321	All exc Sun
WC2	Salisbury			Atmos			0171-836 5863	All exc Sun

ENGLAND

Please refer to the **How to use this Guide** section at the beginning of this Guide for explanations of Categories (FOOD, B&B, A) & Symbols (Family, Star).

Avon

Location	Establishment	Star	Food	B&B	Atmos	ZZzz	Family	Waterside	Tel	Open all day?
Abbots Leigh	George Inn		Food						01275 372467	All Sat only in summer
Almondsbury	Bowl Inn			B&B		ZZzz			01454 612757	
Aust	Boar's Head				Atmos				01454 632278	
Bathampton	George Inn		Food				Family	Water	01225 425079	
Bathford	Crown		Food				Family		01225 852297	
Bristol	Highbury Vaults				Atmos				0117 973 3203	All exc Sun
Combe Hay	Wheatsheaf		Food						01225 833504	
Congresbury	White Hart		Food				Family		01934 833303	
Kelston	Old Crown Inn				Atmos				01225 423032	
Oldbury-on-Severn	Anchor Inn		Food					Water	01454 413331	
Tormarton	Compass Inn			B&B					01454 218242	All exc Sun

Bedfordshire

Location	Establishment	Star	Food	B&B	Atmos	ZZzz	Family	Waterside	Tel	Open all day?
Bedford	Embankment Hotel			B&B				Water	01234 261332	All exc Sun
Broom	Cock Inn				Atmos				01767 314411	
Houghton Conquest	Knife & Cleaver			B&B					01234 740387	All
Keysoe	Chequers Inn				Atmos		Family		01234 708678	
Little Odell	Mad Dog				Atmos				01234 720221	
Odell	Bell		Food					Water	01234 720254	
Radwell	Swan Inn		Food						01234 781351	
Turvey	Three Cranes			B&B					0123 064 305	
Woburn	Black Horse		Food						01525 290210	

Berkshire

Location	Establishment	Star	Food	B&B	Atmos	ZZzz	Family	Waterside	Tel	Open all day?
Aldworth	Bell Inn								01635 578272	
Benham Village	Six Bells		Food	B&B	Atmos				01734 713368	
Chaddleworth	Ibex		Food				Family		01488 638311	
Cookham Dean	Inn on the Green		Food				Family		01628 482638	
Cookham Dean	Jolly Farmer		Food				Family		01628 482905	
Crazies Hill	Horns		Food						01734 401416	
East Garston	Queens Arms			B&B					01488 648757	All exc Sun
East Ilsley	Swan			B&B			Family		01635 281238	All
Eton	Christopher Hotel			B&B					01753 852359	
Frilsham	Pot Kiln				Atmos				01635 201366	
Hampstead Marshall	White Hart Inn		Food	B&B					01488 658201	
Hare Hatch	Queen Victoria		Food						01734 402477	All exc Sun
Hurley	Dew Drop Inn				Atmos				01628 824327	
Inkpen	Swan Inn		Food						01488 668326	
Kintbury	Dundas Arms		Food	B&B					01488 658263	All exc Sun
Knowl Hill	The Bird in Hand			B&B		ZZzz		Water	01628 826622	
Marsh Benham	Water Rat		Food						01635 582017	
Shefford Woodlands	Pheasant Inn		Food						01488 648284	
Sonning	Bull				Atmos				01734 693901	
Stanford Dingley	Bull Country Inn		Food				Family		01734 744409	All Sat in summer only
West Ilsley	Harrow Inn		Food				Family		01635 281260	All
Yattendon	Royal Oak	★	Food	B&B		ZZzz			01635 201325	

Buckinghamshire

Location	Establishment	Star	Food	B&B	Atmos	ZZzz	Family	Waterside	Tel	Open all day?
Amersham	King's Arms				Atmos				01494 726333	All exc Sun
Aston Clinton	The Oak		Food						01296 630466	
Beaconsfield	Greyhound		Food						01494 673823	

Bellingdon	Bull		Food				Family	01494 758163	All exc Sun
Bledlow	The Lions of Bledlow		Food		Atmos			0184 44 3345	
Bolter End	Peacock		Food					01494 881417	All exc Sun
Easington	Mole & Chicken		Food		Atmos			01844 208387	
Fingest	Chequers Inn				Atmos			01491 638335	
Ford	Dinton Hermit		Food					01296 748379	
Forty Green	Royal Standard of England		Food	B&B	Atmos			01494 673382	All exc Sun
Great Kimble	The Bernard Arms							0184 44 6172	
Great Missenden	George		Food	B&B	Atmos			01494 862084	
Ibstone	The Fox			B&B		ZZzz		01491 638289	
Ley Hill	Swan		Food				Family	01494 783075	
Little Hampden	Rising Sun		Food				Family	01494 488393	
Long Crendon	The Angel	*	Food	B&B		ZZzz		01844 208268	
Penn Street	Hit or Miss		Food	B&B			Family	01494 713109	All Sat only
Saunderton	Rose & Crown Inn			B&B				0184 44 5299	
Skirmett	Old Crown		Food					0149 163 435	
Stony Stratford	Cock Hotel			B&B				01908 567733	
Turville	Bull & Butcher		Food					01491 638283	
Waddesdon	Five Arrows Hotel	*	Food	B&B		ZZzz	Family	01296 651727	All exc Sun
West Wycombe	George & Dragon		Food					01494 464414	All Sat only
Whitchurch	White Swan				Atmos			01296 641228	
Whiteleaf	Red Lion			B&B				0184 44 4476	
Winslow	Bell Hotel			B&B				01296 712741	
Wooburn Common	Chequers Inn		Food	B&B			Family	01628 529575	All exc Sun

Cambridgeshire

Location	Name	Food	Atmos	Phone	Notes
Barrington	Royal Oak	Food		01223 870791	
Bartlow	Three Hills	Food		01223 891259	
Bythorn	White Hart	Food		01832 710226	
Cambridge	Eagle		Atmos	01223 301286	All exc Sun
Cambridge	Free Press	Food		01223 68337	
Cambridge	Tram Depot		Atmos	01223 324553	

Location	Establishment	Star	Food	B&B	Atmos	ZZzz	Family	Waterside	Tel	Open all day?
Duxford	John Barleycorn		Food						01223 832699	
Fen Drayton	Three Tuns				Atmos				01954 30242	
Fenstanton	King William IV		Food						01480 462467	
Fowlmere	Chequers Inn		Food						01763 208369	
Grantchester	The Rupert Brooke		Food		Atmos				01223 840295	All exc Sun
Holywell	Old Ferry Boat Inn			B&B			Family	Water	01480 63227	
Horningsea	Plough & Fleece		Food						01223 860795	
Keyston	Pheasant Inn	*	Food						01832 710241	
Madingley	Three Horseshoes	*	Food		Atmos				01954 210221	
Milton	Jolly Brewers								01223 860585	
Molesworth	Cross Keys			B&B					01832 710283	
Needingworth	Pike & Eel			B&B					01480 63336	All
Newton	Queen's Head		Food						01223 870436	
St Neots	Chequers Inn		Food				Family		01480 472116	
St Neots	Eaton Oak			B&B			Family		01480 219555	
Stilton	Bell Inn		Food	B&B					01733 241066	
Sutton Gault	Anchor Inn		Food					Water	01353 778537	
Swavesey	Trinity Foot		Food						01954 230315	
Wansford-in-England	The Haycock Hotel	*	Food	B&B		ZZzz		Water	01780 782223	All

Cheshire

Location	Establishment	Star	Food	B&B	Atmos	ZZzz	Family	Waterside	Tel	Open all day?
Bickley Moss	Cholmondeley Arms		Food	B&B			Family		01829 720300	
Bollington	Church House Inn		Food						01625 574014	
Brereton Green	Bears Head		Food	B&B					01477 535251	
Chester	Ye Olde Kings Head			B&B					01244 324855	All exc Sun
Cotebrook	Alvanley Arms		Food						01829 760200	
Fullers Moor	Copper Mine		Food				Family		01829 782293	
Higher Burwardsley	The Pheasant	*	Food	B&B		ZZzz	Family		01829 70434	
Lower Peover	Bells of Peover				Atmos				0156 572 2269	

Location	Name	Food	B&B	Atmos	ZZzz	Family	Water	Phone	Open
Macclesfield	Sutton Hall	Food	B&B		ZZzz			01260 253211	All exc Sun
Ollerton	Dun Cow	Food	B&B					01565 633093	All exc Sun
Over Peover	The Dog	Food	B&B					01625 861421	
Stockport	Red Bull	Food						0161-480 2087	All exc Sun
Tarporley	Rising Sun	Food						01829 732423	All
Tarporley	Swan Hotel	Food	B&B					01829 733838	All
Tushingham	Blue Bell Inn			Atmos		Family		01948 662172	
Wybunbury	Swan	Food				Family		01270 841280	All

Cleveland

Location	Name	Food	B&B	Atmos	ZZzz	Family	Water	Phone	Open
Ellerby	Ellerby Hotel	Food	B&B		ZZzz	Family		01947 840342	All
Guisborough	Fox Inn		B&B					01287 632958	All
Sedgefield	Dun Cow Inn		B&B		ZZzz			01740 20894	All exc Sun, exc winter

Cornwall

Location	Name	Food	B&B	Atmos	ZZzz	Family	Water	Phone	Open
Charlestown	Pier House Hotel		B&B				Water	01726 67955	All exc Sun
Charlestown	Rashleigh Arms		B&B					01726 73635	All exc Sun
Constantine	Trengilly Wartha Inn	Food	B&B		ZZzz	Family		01326 40332	
Egloshayle	Earl of St Vincent			Atmos				01208 814807	
Fowey	King of Prussia		B&B		ZZzz	Family	Water	01726 832450	All exc Sun
Fowey	Ship Inn		B&B		ZZzz		Water	0172 683 3751	All exc Sun, summer only
Gunwalloe	Halzephron Inn *	Food	B&B	Atmos			Water	01326 240406	
Helford	Shipwrights Arms	Food	B&B			Family	Water	01326 231235	
Kingsand	Halfway House Inn	Food	B&B				Water	01752 822279	
Lostwithiel	Royal Oak			Atmos				01208 872552	All exc Sun
Ludgvan	White Hart	Food		Atmos		Family		01736 740574	
Mithian	Miners Arms							01872 552375	
Morwenstow	Bush			Atmos				01288 83242	
Mousehole	Ship Inn		B&B				Water	01736 731234	
Mylor Bridge	Pandora Inn	Food					Water	01326 372678	All

Location	Establishment	Star	Food	B&B	Atmos	ZZzz	Family	Waterside	Tel	Open all day?
Padstow	Old Custom House Inn			B&B			Family	Water	01841 532359	All exc Sun
Pelynt	Jubilee Inn			B&B			Family		01503 220312	
Penelewey	Punch Bowl & Ladle				Atmos				01872 862237	
Perranuthnoe	Victoria Inn			B&B					01736 710309	
Philleigh	Roseland Inn		Food				Family		01872 580254	All
Polkerris	Rashleigh Inn				Atmos			Water	0172 681 3991	
Port Gaverne	Port Gaverne Hotel			B&B		ZZzz		Water	01208 880244	All exc Sun
Porthleven	Harbour Inn			B&B				Water	01326 573876	All exc Sun
Porthleven	Ship Inn				Atmos			Water	01326 572841	All exc Sun
Sennen Cove	Old Success Inn			B&B		ZZzz		Water	01736 870232	All exc Sun
St Agnes	Driftwood Spars Hotel			B&B			Family	Water	01872 552428	All exc Sun
St Austell	White Hart			B&B			Family		01726 72100	
St Kew	St Kew Inn				Atmos			Water	0120 884 259	
St Mawes	Rising Sun		Food	B&B			Family	Water	01326 270233	All exc Sun
St Mawgan	Falcon Inn				Atmos				01637 860225	
Tregadillett	Eliot Arms				Atmos				01566 772051	

Cumbria

Location	Establishment	Star	Food	B&B	Atmos	ZZzz	Family	Waterside	Tel	Open all day?
Ainstable	New Crown Inn			B&B					01768 896273	
Appleby-in-Westmorland	Royal Oak Inn			B&B					017 6 83 51463	
Armathwaite	Duke's Head Hotel			B&B		ZZzz		Water	0169 74 72226	
Askham	Punch Bowl		Food						01931 712443	
Bassenthwaite Lake	Pheasant Inn			B&B					017 6 87 76234	
Beetham	Wheatsheaf			B&B					0153 95 62123	
Boot	Burnmoor Inn			B&B					0194 67 23224	
Bowland Bridge	Hare & Hounds			B&B		ZZzz	Family		0153 95 68333	All
Buttermere	Bridge Hotel			B&B				Water	017 6 87 70252	All
Cartmel Fell	Masons Arms	★	Food				Family		0153 95 68486	
Casterton	Pheasant Inn			B&B					0152 42 71230	All

Dent	Sun Inn			Atmos				0158 75 208	All Sat only
Elterwater	Britannia Inn		B&B		ZZzz			0153 94 37210	All exc Sun
Eskdale Green	Bower House Inn	Food	B&B		ZZzz	Family	Water	0194 67 23244	All exc Sun
Faugh	String of Horses Inn	Food	B&B		ZZzz			01228 70297	
Gretna	Gretna Chase Hotel		B&B					01461 337517	All exc Sun
Hawkshead	Drunken Duck Inn	Food	B&B		ZZzz			0153 94 36347	
Hawkshead	Queen's Head Hotel	Food	B&B			Family		0153 94 36271	All exc Sun
Hesket Newmarket	Old Crown			Atmos				0169 74 78288	
Kirkby Lonsdale	Snooty Fox Tavern		B&B			Family		015242 71308	All exc Sun
Langdale	Three Shires Inn		B&B		ZZzz		Water	0153 94 37215	All exc Sun
Loweswater	Kirkstile Inn		B&B			Family		01900 85219	All exc Sun
Melmerby	Shepherds Inn	Food				Family	Water	01768 881217	
Metal Bridge	Metal Bridge Inn		B&B			Family	Water	01228 74206	
Ravenstonedale	Black Swan Hotel		B&B				Water	0153 96 23204	All
Ravenstonedale	The Fat Lamb		B&B					0153 96 23242	
Scales	White Horse	Food						0176 87 79241	
Talkin Village	Blacksmiths Arms	Food	B&B					0169 77 3452	
Troutbeck	Mortal Man Inn	Food	B&B		ZZzz			0153 94 33193	
Ulverston	Bay Horse Inn & Bistro	Food	B&B				Water	01229 583972	All
Wasdale Head	Wasdale Head Inn	Food	B&B		ZZzz		Water	0194 67 26229	All summer only
Winster	Brown Horse	Food						0153 94 43443	

Derbyshire

Ashford-in-the-Water	Ashford Hotel		B&B					01629 812725	All
Bamford	Yorkshire Bridge Inn	Food	B&B		ZZzz	Family		01433 651361	All
Birch Vale	Sycamore Inn	Food	B&B			Family		01663 742715	All exc Sun
Birchover	Druid Inn	Food				Family		01629 650302	
Brassington	Ye Olde Gate			Atmos				0162 985 448	
Calver	Chequers Inn	Food	B&B		ZZzz			01433 630231	
Castleton	Castle Hotel		B&B			Family		01433 620578	All exc Sun
Castleton	Ye Olde Nag's Head	Food	B&B					01433 620248	All exc Sun
Derby	Abbey Inn			Atmos				01332 558297	

Location	Establishment	Star	Food	B&B	Atmos	ZZzz	Family	Waterside	Tel	Open all day?
Derby	Ye Olde Dolphin Inn				Atmos				01332 49115	All exc Sun
Dronfield	Old Sidings		Food					Water	01246 410023	All exc Sun
Eyam	Miners Arms		Food	B&B					01433 630853	All
Grindleford	Maynard Arms		Food	B&B		ZZzz	Family		01433 630321	
Hathersage	Hathersage Inn			B&B					01433 650259	
Hope	Poachers Arms			B&B					01433 620380	
Little Longstone	Packhorse				Atmos				01629 640471	
Litton	Red Lion				Atmos				01298 871458	
Over Haddon	Lathkil Hotel		Food	B&B		ZZzz			01629 812501	
Tideswell	George			B&B					01298 871382	
Wardlow	Bull's Head		Food						01298 871431	
Woolley Moor	White Horse		Food				Family		01246 590319	
Devon										
Alphington	Double Locks		Food				Family	Water	01392 56947	All exc Sun
Ashprington	Durant Arms		Food						01803 732240	
Ashprington	Waterman's Arms		Food	B&B		ZZzz	Family	Water	01803 732214	
Bantham	Sloop Inn			B&B				Water	01548 560215	
Beer	Anchor Inn		Food	B&B		ZZzz		Water	01297 20386	All
Blackawton	Normandy Arms		Food	B&B					0180 421 316	
Branscombe	Masons Arms		Food	B&B					01297 80300	
Brendon	Stag Hunters Hotel		Food	B&B				Water	0159 87 222	All exc Sun
Broadhembury	Drewe Arms		Food		Atmos				01404 841267	
Butterleigh	Butterleigh Inn								01884 855407	
Cheriton Bishop	Old Thatch Inn		Food	B&B					01647 24204	
Chillington	Chillington Inn		Food	B&B			Family		01548 580244	All
Cockwood	Anchor Inn		Food					Water	01626 890203	
Cockwood	Ship Inn		Food					Water	01626 890373	All
Coleford	New Inn		Food	B&B		ZZzz		Water	01363 84242	All

Town	Name	Food	B&B	Atmos	ZZzz	Family	Water	Phone	Open
Cornworthy	Hunters Lodge	Food						01803 732204	
Cullompton	Manor House Hotel		B&B			Family		01884 32281	All exc Sun
Dalwood	Tuckers Arms	Food	B&B					0140 488 342	
Dartington	Cott Inn	Food	B&B		ZZzz			01803 863777	All
Dartmouth	Cherub	Food						01803 832571	All exc Sun
Dartmouth	Royal Castle Hotel	Food	B&B		ZZzz	Family	Water	01803 833033	
Doddiscombleigh	Nobody Inn				ZZzz			01647 52394	
Drewsteignton	Drewe Arms			Atmos				01647 21224	
Frithelstock	Clinton Arms	Food	B&B					01805 23279	
Harberton	Church House Inn			Atmos				01803 863707	
Hatherleigh	George Hotel		B&B			Family		01837 810454	All
Hatherleigh	Tally Ho	Food	B&B		ZZzz			01837 810306	
Haytor Vale	Rock Inn	Food	B&B		ZZzz			01364 661305	All
Holne	Church House Inn	Food	B&B					0136 43 208	
Horndon	Elephant's Nest	Food						01822 810273	
Horsebridge	Royal	Food					Water	0182 287 214	
Kingskerswell	Barn Owl Inn	Food	B&B		ZZzz			01803 872130	
Kingsteignton	Old Rydon Inn	Food				Family		01626 54626	
Knowstone	Masons Arms	Food						0139 84 231	
Lifton	Arundell Arms	Food	B&B					01566 784666	All
Lower Ashton	Manor Inn	Food						01647 52304	
Lydford	Castle Inn	Food	B&B		ZZzz	Family	Water	0182 282 242	
Lynmouth	Rising Sun Hotel		B&B					01598 53223	
Moretonhampstead	White Hart Hotel		B&B					01647 440406	All
Newton St Cyres	Crown & Sceptre	Food				Family	Water	01392 851278	
Plymouth	China House	Food					Water	01752 260930	
Rockbeare	Jack in the Green	Food						01404 822240	
Shaldon	Ness House Hotel		B&B			Family	Water	01626 873480	All exc Sun
Silverton	Silverton Inn	Food						01392 860196	
Slapton	Tower Inn	Food				Family		01548 580216	All
South Pool	Millbrook Inn	Food						01548 531581	
South Zeal	Oxenham Arms		B&B					01837 840244	
Spreyton	Tom Cobley Tavern		B&B					0164 723 1314	
Staverton	Sea Trout Inn		B&B				Water	01803 762274	

Location	Establishment	Star	Food	B&B	Atmos	ZZzz	Family	Waterside	Tel	Open all day?
Stockland	King's Arms Inn		Food	B&B					01404 881361	
Stokenham	Tradesman's Arms		Food						01548 580313	
Thelbridge	Thelbridge Cross Inn			B&B			Family		01884 860316	
Torcross	Start Bay Inn		Food				Family	Water	01548 580553	
Totnes	Kingsbridge Inn		Food						01803 863324	
Trusham	Cridford Inn	★	Food	B&B					01626 853694	
Tuckenhay	Floyd's Inn (Sometimes)		Food	B&B		ZZzz		Water	01803 732350	
Weston	The Otter		Food				Family	Water	01404 42594	
Widecombe-in-the-Moor	Rugglestone Inn		Food					Water	0136 42 327	

Dorset

Location	Establishment	Star	Food	B&B	Atmos	ZZzz	Family	Waterside	Tel	Open all day?
Abbotsbury	Ilchester Arms			B&B		ZZzz			01305 871243	All exc Sun
Askerswell	Spyway Inn				Atmos				01308 85250	
Blandford Forum	Crown Hotel			B&B				Water	01258 456626	All
Bridport	Bull Hotel			B&B					01308 22878	All exc Sun
Bridport	George Hotel		Food			ZZzz	Family		01308 23187	
Buckland Newton	Gaggle of Geese				Atmos				01300 345249	
Cerne Abbas	New Inn		Food	B&B				Water	01300 341274	
Cerne Abbas	Red Lion		Food						01300 341441	
Church Knowle	New Inn				Atmos		Family		01929 480357	
Corfe Castle	Fox				Atmos				01929 480449	
Corscombe	Fox Inn	★	Food					Water	01935 891330	All Sat only
Cranborne	Fleur de Lys			B&B					01725 517282	
East Chaldon	Sailors Return		Food						01305 853847	
Farnham	Museum Hotel		Food	B&B					01725 516261	
Horton	Horton Inn		Food	B&B					01258 840252	All
Loders	Loders Arms		Food						01308 422431	
Milton Abbas	Hambro Arms		Food	B&B					01258 880233	
Motcombe	Coppleridge Inn		Food	B&B		ZZzz	Family		01747 51980	
Nettlecombe	Marquis of Lorne		Food	B&B			Family		01308 485236	All exc Sun

Location	Name	Food	B&B	Atmos	ZZzz	Family	Water	Phone	Opening
North Wootton	Three Elms		B&B			Family		01935 812881	
Piddlehinton	Thimble Inn			Atmos				01300 348270	
Pimperne	Anvil Hotel		B&B				Water	01258 453431	All
Plush	Brace of Pheasants	Food				Family		0130 04 357	All
Powerstock	Three Horseshoes Inn	Food	B&B		ZZzz	Family		01308 485328	
Semley	Benett Arms	Food						01747 830221	
Shave Cross	Shave Cross Inn			Atmos				01308 868358	
Shroton	Cricketers	Food	B&B					01258 860421	
Sturminster Newton	The Swan Inn		B&B					01258 472208	All exc Sun
Sutton Poyntz	Springhead	Food				Family		01305 832117	
Trent	Rose & Crown	Food				Family		01935 850776	
West Bexington	Manor Hotel	Food	B&B				Water	01308 897616	All exc Sun
West Stafford	Wise Man Inn	Food						01305 263694	
Winkton	Fisherman's Haunt Hotel		B&B				Water	01202 484071	

Durham

Location	Name	Food	B&B	Atmos	ZZzz	Family	Water	Phone	Opening
Blanchland	Lord Crewe Arms Hotel	Food	B&B		ZZzz	Family		01434 675251	
Cotherstone	Fox and Hounds	Food	B&B		ZZzz			01833 50241	
Fir Tree	Duke of York	Food	B&B					01388 762848	All
Greta Bridge	Morritt Arms	Food	B&B					01833 627232	
Middleton-in-Teesdale	Teesdale Hotel	Food	B&B					01833 40264	
Romaldkirk	Rose and Crown	Food	B&B		ZZzz			01833 650213	
Running Waters	Three Horse Shoes Inn *	Food	B&B					0191-372 0286	

Essex

Location	Name	Food	B&B	Atmos	ZZzz	Family	Water	Phone	Opening
Burnham-on-Crouch	Ye Olde White Harte Hotel		B&B				Water	01621 782106	
Clavering	Cricketers	Food						01799 550442	
Colchester	Foresters Arms	Food						01206 42646	All Fri & Sat only
Colchester	Rose & Crown		B&B			Family		01206 866677	All exc Sun
Dedham	Marlborough Head Hotel	Food	B&B					01206 323124	All

Location	Establishment	Star	Food	B&B	Atmos	ZZzz	Family	Waterside	Tel	Open all day?
Elsenham	Crown		Food				Family		01279 812827	
Gosfield	Green Man		Food				Family		01787 472746	
Great Chesterford	Plough				Atmos				01799 530283	
Hastingwood Common	Rainbow & Dove				Atmos		Family		01279 415419	
High Roding	Black Lion				Atmos				01371 872847	
Horndon-on-the-Hill	Bell Inn	★	Food	B&B		ZZzz			01375 673154	
Little Braxted	Green Man		Food						01621 891659	
Little Canfield	Lion & Lamb		Food	B&B	Atmos		Family		01279 870257	
Littlebury	Queen's Head						Family		01799 22251	All exc Sun
Mill Green	Viper				Atmos				01277 352010	
Rickling Green	Cricketers' Arms			B&B	Atmos		Family		01799 543210	All summer only
Saffron Walden	Eight Bells		Food						01799 522790	
Saffron Walden	Saffron Hotel		Food	B&B					01799 522676	All exc Sun
Thaxted	Farmhouse Inn			B&B					01371 830864	
Tillingham	Cap & Feathers				Atmos				01621 779212	
Toot Hill	Green Man		Food						0137 882 2255	

Gloucestershire

Location	Establishment	Star	Food	B&B	Atmos	ZZzz	Family	Waterside	Tel	Open all day?
Amberley	Black Horse				Atmos		Family		01453 872556	
Ampney Crucis	Crown of Crucis			B&B		ZZzz		Water	01285 851806	All
Barnsley	The Village Pub			B&B					01285 740421	
Bibury	Catherine Wheel		Food	B&B				Water	01285 740250	All exc Sun
Birdlip	The Air Balloon				Atmos				01452 862541	All exc Sun
Blockley	Crown Inn & Hotel		Food	B&B		ZZzz			01386 700245	All exc Sun, summer only
Broad Campden	Bakers Arms		Food						01386 840515	
Brockhampton	Craven Arms		Food						01242 820410	
Chipping Campden	Eight Bells Inn		Food	B&B					01386 840371	
Chipping Campden	Noel Arms			B&B		ZZzz			01386 840317	All
Clearwell	Wyndham Arms		Food	B&B		ZZzz	Family		01594 833666	All exc Sun

Location	Name		Food	B&B	Atmos	ZZzz	Family/Water	Phone	When open
Colesbourne	Colesbourne Inn		Food	B&B			Family	0124 870376	All exc Sun
Coln St Aldwyns	The New Inn	*	Food	B&B		ZZzz		01285 750651	All Sat only
Ewen	Wild Duck Inn			B&B		ZZzz		01285 770310	All exc Sun
Ford	Plough		Food	B&B			Family	01386 73215	All
Frampton Mansell	Crown Inn	*	Food	B&B		ZZzz		01285 760601	All Sat only
Great Rissington	The Lamb		Food	B&B		ZZzz		01451 820388	
Gretton	Royal Oak		Food				Family	01242 602477	
Guiting Power	Ye Olde Inne		Food					01451 850392	
Kingscote	Hunters Hall		Food	B&B			Family	01453 860393	
Little Compton	Red Lion		Food	B&B				0160 874 397	
Lower Oddington	The Fox	*	Food					01451 870888	
Moreton-in-Marsh	Redesdale Arms		Food	B&B		ZZzz		01608 650308	All
Northleach	Wheatsheaf Hotel		Food	B&B		ZZzz	Family	01451 860244	
Oddington	Horse & Groom			B&B			Water	01451 30584	
St Briavels	George			B&B				01594 530228	
Stroud	Old Nelson			B&B				01453 765821	All
Waterley Bottom	New Inn			B&B		ZZzz		01453 543659	
Winchcombe	Old White Lion			B&B				01242 603300	
Woodchester	Ram Inn				Atmos			01453 873329	

Greater Manchester

Location	Name	Food	B&B	Atmos	ZZzz	Family/Water	Phone	When open
Didsbury	Royal Oak Hotel		B&B				0161-445 3152	All exc Sun
Diggle	Diggle Hotel			Atmos			01457 872741	All exc Sun
Manchester	Lass O'Gowrie	Food					0161-273 6932	All exc Sun
Manchester	Mark Addy		B&B			Water	0161-832 4080	All exc Sun
Manchester	New Ellesmere	Food				Family	0161-728 2791	All
Mellor	Devonshire Arms	Food		Atmos			0161-427 2563	
Middleton	Olde Boars Head		B&B				0161-643 3520	
Saddleworth	Green Ash Hotel				ZZzz		01457 871035	All
Strinesdale	Roebuck Inn	Food				Family	0161-624 7819	

Hampshire

Location	Establishment	Star	Food	B&B	Atmos	ZZzz	Family	Waterside	Tel	Open all day?
Alresford	Globe on the Lake		Food				Family	Water	01962 732294	
Beauworth	Milbury's				Atmos		Family		01962 771248	
Bentworth	Sun		Food		Atmos				01420 562338	
Boldre	Red Lion								01590 673177	
Bramdean	Fox Inn		Food						01962 771363	All exc Sun Sum, Sat only W'in
Buckler's Hard	Master Builder's House Hotel			B&B				Water	01590 616253	
Buriton	Five Bells		Food						01730 263584	
Bursledon	Jolly Sailor				Atmos			Water	01703 405557	
Cadnam	White Hart		Food				Family		01703 812277	
Cheriton	Flower Pots		Food	B&B					01962 771318	
Crawley	Fox & Hounds		Food	B&B		ZZzz			01962 772285	
Damerham	Compasses Inn		Food	B&B		ZZzz	Family		0172 53 231	
Dummer	The Queen		Food						01256 397367	
Dunbridge	Mill Arms Inn		Food						01794 340401	
East Meon	Ye Olde George Inn		Food	B&B				Water	01730 823481	All summer only
Ellisfield	Fox		Food						01256 381210	
Emery Down	New Forest Inn		Food	B&B			Family		01703 282329	All exc Sun
Faccombe	Jack Russell Inn			B&B		ZZzz	Family	Water	0126 487 315	
Highclere	The Yew Tree		Food	B&B					01635 253360	
Langstone	Royal Oak				Atmos			Water	01705 483125	All
Linwood	High Corner Inn			B&B			Family		01425 473973	
Longstock	Peat Spade Inn		Food				Family		01264 810612	
Lower Froyle	Prince of Wales		Food						01420 23102	
Lower Wield	Yew Tree Inn		Food						01256 389224	All
Micheldever	Dever Arms		Food						01962 774339	
Odiham	George Hotel			B&B					01256 702081	All exc Sun
Ovington	Bush Inn		Food					Water	01962 732764	All
Pilley	Fleur de Lys		Food						01590 672158	All exc Sun

Location	Name	Food	B&B	★	Atmos	ZZzz	Family	Water	Phone	Open
Priors Dean	White Horse	Food					Family		01420 58387	
Rockbourne	Rose & Thistle	Food							0172 53 236	
Sherfield English	Hatchet Inn	Food							01794 22487	
Sparsholt	Plough	Food					Family		01962 776353	
Steep	Harrow Inn	Food							01730 62685	
Stratfield Turgis	Wellington Arms	Food	B&B			ZZzz			01256 882214	All exc Sun
Tangley	Fox Inn	Food	B&B			ZZzz			01264 70276	
Testcombe	Mayfly	Food						Water	01264 860283	All exc Sun
Tichborne	Tichborne Arms	Food							01962 733760	
Titchfield	Fisherman's Rest				Atmos			Water	01329 842848	All
Upton Grey	Hoddington Arms	Food					Family		01256 862371	
Well	Chequers	Food							01256 862605	
Winchester	Wykeham Arms	Food	B&B	★					01962 853834	All exc Sun

Hereford & Worcester

Location	Name	Food	B&B	★	Atmos	ZZzz	Family	Water	Phone	Open
Bretforton	Fleece Inn	Food			Atmos		Family		01386 831173	
Brimfield	The Roebuck	Food	B&B	★		ZZzz			01584 711230	
Carey	Cottage of Content		B&B			ZZzz		Water	01432 840242	
Dorstone	Pandy Inn	Food							01981 550273	All Sat only
Fownhope	Green Man		B&B			ZZzz	Family		01432 860243	
Kempsey	Walter de Cantelupe Inn	Food	B&B				Family	Water	01905 820572	
Knightwick	Talbot Hotel	Food	B&B						01886 21235	
Ledbury	The Feathers	Food	B&B						01531 635266	All exc Sun
Ledbury	Ye Olde Talbot Hotel		B&B				Family		01531 2963	All exc Sun
Leominster	Royal Oak		B&B				Family		01568 612610	All exc Sun
Little Cowarne	The Three Horseshoes	Food	B&B			ZZzz	Family		01885 400276	
Ombersley	King's Arms	Food							01905 620315	
Pembridge	New Inn	Food							01544 788427	
Ruckhall	Ancient Camp Inn	Food	B&B			ZZzz		Water	01981 250449	
Sellack	Loughpool Inn	Food							01989 730236	
Shobdon	Bateman Arms	Food							01568 708374	
Upton Bishop	The Moody Cow	Food							01989 780470	
Weobley	Ye Olde Salutation Inn	Food	B&B			ZZzz			01544 318443	

Location	Establishment	Star	Food	B&B	Atmos	ZZzz	Family	Waterside	Tel	Open all day?
Whitney-on-Wye	Rhydspence Inn	*	Food	B&B		ZZzz			01497 831262	
Winforton	Sun Inn		Food	B&B		ZZzz			01544 327677	
Woolhope	Butchers Arms		Food	B&B		ZZzz		Water	01432 860281	
Wyre Piddle	Anchor Inn		Food				Family	Water	01386 552799	

Hertfordshire

Location	Establishment	Star	Food	B&B	Atmos	ZZzz	Family	Waterside	Tel	Open all day?
Ashwell	Bushel & Strike Inn		Food						0146 274 2394	All
Ayot St Lawrence	Brocket Arms			B&B		ZZzz	Family		01438 820250	
Barley	Fox & Hounds		Food				Family		01763 848459	
Chenies	Red Lion		Food						01923 282722	
Chorleywood	Sportsman Hotel			B&B					0192 78 5155	
St Albans	Garibaldi		Food						01727 855046	All exc Sun
St Albans	Rose & Crown				Atmos				01727 851903	
Watton at Stone	George & Dragon		Food						01920 830285	All Sat only

Humberside

Location	Establishment	Star	Food	B&B	Atmos	ZZzz	Family	Waterside	Tel	Open all day?
Barnoldby-le-Beck	Ship Inn				Atmos				01472 822308	
Bishop Wilton	Fleece Inn			B&B			Family		01759 368251	All
Driffield	Bell Hotel			B&B					01377 256661	All exc Sun
Low Catton	Gold Cup Inn				Atmos		Family	Water	01759 71354	
Market Weighton	Londesborough Arms		Food						01430 872219	
North Dalton	Star Inn			B&B					01377 217688	
Pocklington	Feathers Hotel			B&B			Family		01759 303155	All exc Sun
Skidby	Half Moon Inn		Food				Family		01482 843403	All exc Sun

Isle of Wight

Location	Name	Food	B&B	Atmos	Family	Water	Phone	Open
Bonchurch	Bonchurch Inn	Food	B&B	Atmos	Family		01983 852611	
Chale	Clarendon Hotel & Wight Mouse	Food	B&B		Family	Water	01983 730431	All
Seaview	Seaview Hotel	Food	B&B		Family	Water	01983 612711	
Ventnor	Spyglass Inn	Food	B&B			Water	01983 855338	
Yarmouth	Bugle	Food	B&B	Atmos			01983 760272	All

Kent

Barming	The Bull		Food		Atmos				01622 726468	All exc Sun
Benenden	King William IV		Food						01580 240636	All Sat only
Biddenden	Three Chimneys		Food	B&B		ZZzz	Family		01580 291472	All Sat only
Boughton Aluph	Flying Horse Inn		Food	B&B					01233 620914	
Burham	Golden Eagle		Food						01634 668975	
Canterbury	Falstaff Hotel			B&B					01227 462138	All exc Sun
Charing	Royal Oak Hotel			B&B					01233 712307	All
Chiddingstone	Castle Inn				Atmos				01892 870247	All Sat only
Chilham	White Horse				Atmos				01227 730355	All exc Sun
Chilham	Woolpack			B&B			Family		01227 730208	
Cliffe	Black Bull		Food						01634 220893	
Eastling	Carpenters Arms		Food	B&B					01795 890234	
Fordcombe	Chafford Arms		Food						01892 740267	
Goudhurst	Star & Eagle Inn			B&B					01580 211512	All
Ightham Common	Harrow Inn	*	Food						01732 885912	
Ivy Hatch	The Plough	*	Food						01732 810268	
Lenham	Dog & Bear			B&B			Family		01622 858219	
Linton	Bull Inn	*	Food						01622 743612	
Marshside	Gate Inn		Food						01227 860498	
Newnham	George Inn		Food				Family	Water	01795 890237	
Pluckley	Dering Arms		Food				Family		01233 840371	
Ringlestone	Ringlestone Inn		Food				Family		01622 859900	
Selling	White Lion		Food				Family		01227 752211	

Location	Establishment	Star	Food	B&B	Atmos	ZZzz	Family	Waterside	Tel	Open all day?
Sevenoaks	Royal Oak		Food	B&B					01732 451109	
Smarden	Chequers Inn		Food	B&B					01233 770217	
Smarts Hill	Bottle House Inn		Food						01892 870306	All
Speldhurst Hill	George & Dragon		Food						01892 863125	
Stalisfield Green	Plough Inn		Food				Family		01795 890256	
Tunbridge Wells	Sankeys Cellar Wine Bar & Bist		Food						01892 511422	All
Ulcombe	Pepper Box		Food						01622 842558	
Warren Street	Harrow Inn		Food	B&B		ZZzz			01622 858727	
Worth	St Crispin Inn			B&B		ZZzz			01304 612081	
Wye	New Flying Horse Inn			B&B		ZZzz			01233 812297	

Lancashire

Location	Establishment	Star	Food	B&B	Atmos	ZZzz	Family	Waterside	Tel	Open all day?
Blacko	Moorcock Inn		Food				Family		01282 614186	
Downham	Assheton Arms		Food						01200 441227	
Goosnargh	Bushells Arms		Food						01772 865235	
Mellor	Millstone Hotel		Food	B&B		ZZzz	Family		01254 813333	All exc Sun
Rochdale	Egerton Arms				Atmos		Family		01706 46183	All
Slaidburn	Hark to Bounty Inn			B&B		ZZzz	Family	Water	01200 446246	All
Whitewell	Inn at Whitewell		Food	B&B				Water	01200 448222	
Yealand Conyers	New Inn		Food						01524 46732	All

Leicestershire

Location	Establishment	Star	Food	B&B	Atmos	ZZzz	Family	Waterside	Tel	Open all day?
Braunston	Blue Ball Inn		Food						01572 722135	
Braunston	Old Plough		Food				Family		01572 722714	
Empingham	White Horse		Food	B&B		ZZzz	Family		01780 460221	All exc Sun
Glooston	Old Barn		Food	B&B					01858 545215	
Hallaton	Bewicke Arms		Food				Family	Water	0185 889 217	

Location	Name	Food	B&B	Other	Phone	Opening
Kegworth	Cap & Stocking	Food			01509 674814	
Leicester	Welford Place	Food			0116 947 0758	All
Lyddington	Old White hart	Food			01572 821703	
Market Overton	Black Bull	Food			01572 767677	
Old Dalby	Crown Inn	Food		Family	01664 823134	
Shardlow	The Old Crown	Food		Water	01332 792392	
Somerby	Old Brewery Inn		B&B	Atmos	0166 477 866	
Waltham-on-the-Wolds	Royal Horseshoes		B&B		0166 478 289	
Whitwell	Noel Arms		B&B		01780 460334	All

Lincolnshire

Alford	White Horse Hotel	Food	B&B		01507 462218	
Aswarby	Tally Ho	Food	B&B		0152 95 205	
Collyweston	Cavalier Inn		B&B		0178 083 288	
Donington-on-Bain	Black Horse		B&B	ZZzz	01507 343640	
Duddington	Royal Oak Hotel		B&B	Family	0178 083 267	
Gedney Dyke	The Chequers	Food			01406 362666	
Lincoln	Wig & Mitre	Food			01522 523705	All
Louth	Masons Arms		B&B		01507 609525	All exc Sun
Newton	Red Lion	Food		Family	0152 97 256	
Springthorpe	New Inn	Food			0142 783 254	
Stamford	Bull and Swan		B&B		01780 63558	
Stamford	The George of Stamford	Food	B&B	ZZzz	01780 55171	All

Merseyside

Barnston	Fox & Hounds	Food			0151-648 1323	All Sat & Sun only
Liverpool	Philharmonic Dining Rooms			Atmos	0151-709 1163	All Mon-Fri
Raby	Wheatsheaf Inn			Atmos	0151-336 3416	

Location	Establishment	Star	Food	B&B	Atmos	ZZzz	Family	Waterside	Tel	Open all day?
Middlesex										
Shepperton	Anchor Hotel			B&B					01932 221618	
Shepperton	King's Head				Atmos				01932 221910	All Wed-Sat only
Shepperton	Warren Lodge			B&B		ZZzz		Water	01932 242972	
Norfolk										
Blicking	Buckinghamshire Arms			B&B		ZZzz	Family	Water	01263 732133	
Brisley	Bell		Food						01362 668686	
Burnham Market	Hoste Arms		Food	B&B		ZZzz	Family		01328 738257	
Burnham Thorpe	Lord Nelson				Atmos		Family		01328 738241	
Cley-next-the-Sea	George & Dragon Hotel			B&B			Family		01263 740652	
East Dereham	King's Head			B&B			Family		01362 693842	
Eastgate	Ratcatchers Inn		Food						01603 871430	
Great Ryburgh	Boar Inn			B&B					0132 878 212	All
Holkham	Victoria Hotel			B&B					01328 710469	
Kings Lynn	Tudor Rose			B&B					01553 762824	All exc Sun
Norwich	Adam & Eve				Atmos				01603 667423	All exc Sun
Scole	Scole Inn			B&B					01379 740481	All exc Sun
Smallburgh	Crown		Food	B&B					01692 536314	
Snettisham	Rose & Crown		Food	B&B			Family		01485 541382	
Stiffkey	Red Lion		Food				Family		01328 830552	
Stow Bardolph	Hare Arms		Food				Family		01366 382229	
Swanton Morley	Darby's		Food	B&B		ZZzz	Family		01362 637647	All Sat only
Thompson	Chequers Inn				Atmos		Family		01953 483360	
Thornham	Lifeboat Inn		Food	B&B		ZZzz	Family		01485 512236	All exc Sun
Tiverstshall St Mary	Old Ram			B&B		ZZzz	Family		01379 676794	
Upper Sheringham	Red Lion		Food						01263 825408	All
Warham All Saints	Three Horseshoes		Food	B&B					01328 710547	

Location	Pub Name	Food	B&B	Atmos	ZZzz	Family	Water	Phone	Days
Wells-Next-The-Sea	Crown Hotel	Food	B&B					01328 710209	All
Winterton-on-Sea	Fisherman's Return	Food	B&B					01493 393305	
Wolterton	Saracens Head	Food	B&B		ZZzz	Family		01263 768909	
Woodbastwick	Fur & Feather			Atmos				01603 720003	

Northamptonshire

Location	Pub Name	Food	B&B	Atmos	ZZzz	Family	Water	Phone	Days
Blakesley	Bartholomew Arms		B&B					01327 860292	
Castle Ashby	Falcon Inn	Food	B&B		ZZzz			01604 696200	
East Haddon	Red Lion Hotel		B&B			Family		01604 770223	
Easton-on-the-Hill	Exeter Arms	Food						01780 57503	
Fotheringhay	Falcon Inn	Food						0183 26 254	All
Nassington	Black Horse Inn	Food						01780 782324	
Upper Benefield	Wheatsheaf Hotel	Food	B&B			Family		0183 25 254	
Woodnewton	White Swan	Food						01780 750010	All exc Sun

Northumberland

Location	Pub Name	Food	B&B	Atmos	ZZzz	Family	Water	Phone	Days
Bamburgh	Lord Crewe Arms		B&B					01668 214243	
Belford	Blue Bell Hotel		B&B		ZZzz	Family		01668 213543	
Carterway Heads	Manor House Inn	Food	B&B					01207 55268	
Chatton	Percy Arms Hotel		B&B			Family		0166 85 244	
Corbridge	Angel Inn	Food	B&B		ZZzz			01434 632119	
Craster	Jolly Fisherman			Atmos			Water	01665 576461	
Dunstan	Cottage Inn		B&B					01665 576658	
Haltwhistle	Milecastle Inn	Food						01434 320682	
Haydon Bridge	General Havelock Inn	Food				Family		01434 684376	
Hexham	Dipton Mill Inn	Food						01484 606577	
Longframlington	Granby Inn	Food	B&B					01665 570228	
Low Newton by the Sea	The Ship			Atmos			Water	01665 576262	All exc Sun
Newton-on-the-Moor	Cook & Barker Inn	Food	B&B		ZZzz			01665 575234	
Remington	Mason's Arms		B&B					01665 577275	

Location	Establishment	Star	Food	B&B	Atmos	ZZzz	Family	Waterside	Tel	Open all day?
Seahouses	Olde Ship Hotel		Food	B&B		ZZzz		Water	01665 720200	
Stannersburn	Pheasant Inn		Food	B&B		ZZzz			01434 240382	
Wall	Hadrian Hotel			B&B					01434 681232	
Warenford	Warenford Lodge	*	Food						01668 213453	

Nottinghamshire

Location	Establishment	Star	Food	B&B	Atmos	ZZzz	Family	Waterside	Tel	Open all day?
Arnold	Burnt Stump				Atmos		Family		0115 963 1508	All exc Sun
Colston Bassett	Martins Arms		Food						01949 81361	
Drakeholes	Griff Inn		Food	B&B				Water	01777 817206	
Elkesley	Robin Hood Inn		Food				Family		01777 838259	All Sat only
Nottingham	Lincolnshire Poacher				Atmos				0115 941 1584	All exc Sun
Nottingham	Ye Olde Trip to Jerusalem				Atmos				0115 947 3171	
Redmile	Peacock Inn		Food					Water	01949 42554	
Upton	French Horn		Food						01636 812394	All

Oxfordshire

Location	Establishment	Star	Food	B&B	Atmos	ZZzz	Family	Waterside	Tel	Open all day?
Aston	Flower Pot		Food	B&B		ZZzz			01491 574721	
Banbury	Ye Olde Reine Deer Inn		Food						01295 264031	
Barnard's Gate	The Boot Inn		Food						01865 881231	All
Beckley	Abingdon Arms		Food						01865 351311	
Bledington	King's Head Inn	*	Food	B&B		ZZzz	Family		01608 658365	
Blewbury	Blewbury Inn		Food	B&B					01235 850496	
Brightwell Baldwin	Lord Nelson		Food						01491 612497	
Burcot	Chequers		Food						01865 407771	
Burford	The Angel		Food	B&B					01993 822438	All
Burford	Inn For All Seasons		Food	B&B		ZZzz			01451 844324	
Burford	Lamb Inn		Food	B&B					01993 823155	

Location	Name	Food	B&B	Atmos	ZZzz	Family	Water	Phone	Open
Chadlington	Tite Inn	Food						01608 676475	
Charlbury	Bell Hotel		B&B		ZZzz	Family		01608 810278	
Charlbury	The Bull at Charlbury	Food	B&B					01608 810689	
Chipping Norton	Crown & Cushion		B&B		ZZzz			01608 642533	
Chislehampton	Coach & Horses		B&B					01865 890255	
Church Enstone	Crown Inn		B&B					01608 677262	All
Clanfield	The Plough at Clanfield	Food	B&B		ZZzz			0136 781 222	All exc Sun
Clifton	Duke of Cumberland's Head	Food	B&B					01869 338534	All
Clifton Hampden	The Plough	Food	B&B		ZZzz	Family	Water	0186 730 7811	All exc Sun
Cumnor	Bear & Ragged Staff			Atmos				01865 862329	
Dorchester-on-Thames	George Hotel		B&B					01865 340404	
Drayton	Roebuck	Food	B&B					01295 730542	
Duns Tew	White Horse Inn	Food	B&B					01869 40272	All exc Sun
Eynsham	Newlands Inn	Food				Family		01865 881486	
Finstock	The Plough	Food	B&B		ZZzz			01993 868333	
Freeland	Shepherd Hall Inn		B&B			Family		01993 881256	
Frilford Heath	Dog House Hotel		B&B			Family		01865 390830	All
Fyfield	White Hart			Atmos				01865 390585	
Godstow	Trout			Atmos			Water	01865 54485	All
Great Tew	Falkland Arms	Food	B&B					01608 683653	
Hailey	The Bird In Hand	Food	B&B		ZZzz	Family		01993 868321	All exc Sun
Henley-on-Thames	Argyll	Food			ZZzz			01491 573400	
Henton	Peacock Hotel		B&B					01844 53519	
Kidmore End	New Inn	Food				Family		01734 723115	
Longworth	Blue Boar	Food						01865 820494	
Lower Brailes	George Hotel	Food	B&B			Family		01608 685223	
Lower Shiplake	Baskerville Arms	Food	B&B			Family		01734 403332	
Maidensgrove	Five Horseshoes	Food						01491 641282	
Middleton Stoney	Jersey Arms		B&B		ZZzz			01869 343234	
Nettlebed	White Hart	Food	B&B					01491 641245	All exc Sun
Nuffield	Crown	Food						01491 641335	
Oxford	The Bear			Atmos				01865 721783	All exc Sun
Oxford	Queen's Arms	Food						01865 204060	
Remenham	The Little Angel	Food					Water	01491 574165	

Location	Establishment	Star	Food	B&B	Atmos	ZZzz	Family	Waterside	Tel	Open all day?
Roke	Home Sweet Home Inn		Food						01491 838249	
Satwell	Lamb Inn				Atmos		Family		01491 628482	
Shenington	Bell		Food						01295 670274	
Shipton-under-Wychwood	Lamb Inn		Food	B&B					01993 830465	All exc Mon
Shipton-under-Wychwood	Shaven Crown Hotel		Food	B&B					01993 830330	
Sibford Gower	Wykham Arms		Food						01295 78351	
South Leigh	Mason Arms				Atmos		Family		01993 702485	
Stanton St John	Star Inn		Food				Family		01865 351277	
Steeple Aston	Red Lion		Food				Family		01869 340225	
Sulgrave	Star Inn		Food	B&B		ZZzz			01295 760389	
Sutton Courtenay	Fish at Sutton Courtenay	★	Food						01235 848242	
Thame	Abingdon Arms		Food				Family		0184 421 2969	All exc Sun
Watlington	Chequers				Atmos				0149 161 2874	
Woodstock	Feathers Hotel		Food	B&B		ZZzz			01993 812291	
Wytham	White Hart				Atmos				01865 244372	

Shropshire

Location	Establishment	Star	Food	B&B	Atmos	ZZzz	Family	Waterside	Tel	Open all day?
Bridgnorth	Down Inn		Food				Family		0174 635 624	
Bridgnorth	Falcon Hotel			B&B					01746 763134	
Brockton	Feathers		Food					Water	0174 636 202	
Hanmer	Hanmer Arms			B&B					01948 74532	All exc Sun
Heathton	Old Gate Inn				Atmos				01746 710431	
Hopesgate	Stables Inn		Food						01743 891344	
Hopton Wafers	Crown Inn		Food	B&B		ZZzz	Family	Water	01299 270372	
Little Stretton	Ragleth Inn				Atmos				01694 722711	
Llanymynech	Bradford Arms		Food						01691 830582	
Ludlow	Church Inn		Food	B&B					01584 872174	All exc Sun
Ludlow	Unicorn Inn		Food	B&B		ZZzz		Water	01584 873555	
Much Wenlock	Talbot Inn		Food	B&B					01952 727077	

Location	Name	Rating	Food	B&B	Atmos	ZZzz	Family	Water	Phone
Much Wenlock	Wenlock Edge Inn		Food	B&B		ZZzz	Family		0174 636 403
Norton	Hundred House Hotel		Food	B&B		ZZzz	Family		0195 271 353
Picklescott	Bottle & Glass		Food	B&B		ZZzz	Family	Water	0169 45 345
Shifnal	Oddfellows		Food	B&B					01952 461517

Somerset

Location	Name	Rating	Food	B&B	Atmos	ZZzz	Family	Water	Phone
Axbridge	Lamb Inn			B&B					01934 732253
Axbridge	Oak House			B&B					01934 732444
Batcombe	The Batcombe Inn	*	Food				Family		01749 850359
Beckington	Woolpack Inn	*	Food	B&B			Family		01373 831244
Bradley Green	Malt Shovel			B&B					01278 653432
Castle Cary	George Hotel			B&B			Family		01963 350761
Cranmore	Strode Arms				Atmos				01749 880450
Croscombe	Bull Terrier			B&B					01749 343658
Exford	The Crown		Food	B&B		ZZzz			0164 383 554
Haselbury Plucknett	Haselbury Inn		Food			ZZzz	Family		01460 72488
Hinton St George	Poulett Arms		Food						01460 73149
Kilve	Hood Arms		Food	B&B		ZZzz			01278 741210
Knapp	Rising Sun		Food						01823 490436
Langley Marsh	Three Horseshoes		Food						01984 23763
Luxborough	Royal Oak		Food	B&B					01984 40319
Lympsham	Batch Farm Country Hotel			B&B					01934 750371
Monksilver	Notley Arms	*	Food				Family	Water	01984 56217
Montacute	King's Arms Inn		Food	B&B		ZZzz			01935 822513
North Perrott	Manor Amrs			B&B			Family		01460 72901
North Wootton	Crossways Inn			B&B			Family		01749 890237
Norton St Philip	George Inn		Food						01373 834224
Nunney	George Inn			B&B				Water	01373 836458
Over Stratton	Royal Oak		Food				Family		01460 240906
Rudge	The Full Moon			B&B					01373 830936
Shepton Mallet	Kings Arms			B&B					01749 343781
Stanton Wick	Carpenters Arms		Food	B&B				All	01761 490202

Location	Establishment	Star	Food	B&B	Atmos	ZZzz	Family	Waterside	Tel	Open all day?
Staple Fitzpaine	Greyhound Inn				Atmos				01823 480277	
Stoke St Gregory	Rose & Crown		Food	B&B				Water	01823 490296	
West Camel	Walnut Tree		Food	B&B					01935 851292	
West Huntspill	Crossways Inn			B&B					01278 783756	
West Pennard	Lion at Pennard		Food	B&B			Family		01458 832941	
Winsford	Royal Oak Inn		Food	B&B		ZZzz		Water	0164 385 455	
Withypool	Royal Oak Inn		Food	B&B		ZZzz			0164 383 506	
Woolverton	Red Lion		Food						01373 830350	All

Staffordshire

Location	Establishment	Star	Food	B&B	Atmos	ZZzz	Family	Waterside	Tel	Open all day?
Alstonefield	George Inn				Atmos				0133 527 205	
Baldwin's Gate	Slater's			B&B		ZZzz	Family		01782 680052	All
Cauldon	Yew Tree				Atmos				01538 308348	
Cresswell	Izaak Walton Inn		Food						01782 392265	All
Eccleshall	St George Hotel			B&B					01785 850300	All exc Sun
Onecote	Jervis Arms		Food				Family	Water	01538 304206	
Tatenhill	Horseshoe Inn				Atmos		Family		01283 64913	All BH & prec Sat
Tutbury	Ye Olde Dog & Partridge Inn			B&B		ZZzz			01283 813030	All exc Sun
Waterhouses	George Inn		Food				Family		01578 308228	All Sat only
Whitmore	Mainwaring Arms		Food		Atmos				01782 680851	

Suffolk

Location	Establishment	Star	Food	B&B	Atmos	ZZzz	Family	Waterside	Tel	Open all day?
Bardwell	Six Bells		Food	B&B			Family		01359 50820	
Bury St Edmunds	The Nutshell				Atmos				01284 764867	All exc Sun
Chelsworth	Peacock Inn		Food	B&B					01449 740758	
Cockfield	Three Horseshoes		Food						01284 828177	
Dunwich	Ship Inn		Food	B&B			Family		0172 873 219	

Glemsford	Black Lion		Food						01787 280684	
Horringer	Beehive		Food				Family		01284 735260	
Hoxne	Swan		Food						01379 668275	
Icklingham	Red Lion		Food						01638 717802	
Ixworth	The Pykkerell Inn		Food						01359 230398	
Lamarsh	Red Lion		Food		Atmos				01787 227918	All exc Sun
Lavenham	Angel Inn		Food	B&B			Family		01787 247388	
Laxfield	King's Head		Food			ZZzz	Family		01787 247388	
Long Melford	Bull Hotel			B&B					01787 378494	
Pin Mill	Butt & Oyster				Atmos			Water	01473 780764	All exc Sun
Snape	Golden Key		Food						01728 688510	
Southwold	The Crown	★	Food	B&B		ZZzz			01502 722275	
Sproughton	Beagle		Food						01473 730455	
Stoke-by-Nayland	Angel Inn	★	Food	B&B		ZZzz	Family		01206 263245	
Thornham Magna	Four Horseshoes			B&B			Family		01379 71777	
Westleton	Crown			B&B					0172 873 777	

Surrey

Albury Heath	King William IV		Food						01483 202685	
Bentley	The Star		Food						01420 23184	
Blackbrook	Plough		Food						01306 886603	
Caterham	Royal Oak		Food		Atmos				0188 33 43510	All exc Sun
Chiddingfold	Crown Inn		Food	B&B		ZZzz			01428 682255	All exc Sun
Elstead	Woolpack		Food						01252 703106	
Grayswood	Wheatsheaf Inn	★	Food	B&B			Family		01428 644440	
Hascombe	White Horse		Food				Family		01486 208258	All Sat in summer only
Mickleham	King William IV		Food		Atmos				01372 372590	
Reigate Heath	Skimmington Castle				Atmos				01737 243100	
Richmond	Orange Tree				Atmos			Water	0181-940 0944	All exc Sun
Richmond	White Swan		Food	B&B					0181-940 0959	All exc Sun
Shamley Green	Red Lion		Food						01483 892202	All Sat only
Surbiton	Fox and Hounds		Food				Family		0181-390 3408	

Location	Establishment	Star	Food	B&B	Atmos	ZZzz	Family	Waterside	Tel	Open all day?
Thursley	Three Horseshoes				Atmos				01252 703268	
Walliswood	Scarlett Arms				Atmos				01306 627243	

East Sussex

Location	Establishment	Star	Food	B&B	Atmos	ZZzz	Family	Waterside	Tel	Open all day?
Alciston	Rose Cottage								01323 870377	
Berwick	Cricketers				Atmos				01323 870469	
Blackboys	Blackboys Inn				Atmos			Water	01825 890283	
Brighton	Greys		Food						01273 680734	All Sat only
Cousley Wood	Old Vine		Food						01892 782271	
Firle	Ram Inn		Food	B&B					01273 858222	
Fletching	Griffin Inn		Food	B&B		ZZzz	Family		01825 722890	
Forest Row	Brambletye Hotel			B&B					01342 824144	
Horam	Gun Inn		Food				Family		01825 872361	
Kingston	The Juggs		Food				Family		01273 472523	
Mayfield	Rose & Crown		Food	B&B		ZZzz			01435 872200	
Old Heathfield	Star Inn		Food				Family		01435 863570	All summer only

West Sussex

Location	Establishment	Star	Food	B&B	Atmos	ZZzz	Family	Waterside	Tel	Open all day?
Burpham	George & Dragon Inn		Food					Water	01903 883131	
Byworth	Black Horse		Food						01798 42424	
Chilgrove	White Horse Inn		Food						01243 535219	
Compton	Coach & Horses		Food						01705 631228	
Edburton	Tottington Manor		Food	B&B		ZZzz			01903 815757	
Elsted	Three Horseshoes				Atmos				01730 825746	
Elsted Marsh	Elsted Inn		Food				Family		01730 813662	
Fittleworth	Swan Inn			B&B			Family		0179 882 429	All exc Sun
Fulking	Shepherd & Dog		Food						01273 857382	

Hermitage	Sussex Brewery			Atmos				01243 371533	All exc Sun
Lodsworth	Halfway Bridge Inn	Food					★	0179 85 281	
Lower Beeding	Jeremy's at The Crabtree	Food					★	01403 891257	
Lurgashall	Noah's Ark			Atmos				01428 707346	
Midhurst	Angel Hotel	Food	B&B		ZZzz	Water		01730 812421	
Nuthurst	Black Horse			Atmos				01403 891272	
Oving	Gribble Inn			Atmos				01243 786893	
Petworth	Angel		B&B					01798 42153	
Petworth	Welldiggers Arms	Food						01798 42287	
Rusper	Star Inn			Atmos				01293 871264	All
South Harting	Ship Inn	Food						01730 825302	All exc Sun
South Harting	White Hart	Food				Family		01730 825355	
Sutton	White Horse		B&B					0179 87 221	
The Haven	The Blue Ship			Atmos				01403 822709	
Tillington	Horseguards Inn	Food	B&B		ZZzz			01798 42332	
Warnham	Greets Inn			Atmos				01403 265047	
West Hoathly	Cat Inn	Food						01342 810369	
Wineham	Royal Oak			Atmos				01444 881252	

Tyne & Wear

New York	Shiremoor House Farm	Food				Family	0191-257 6302	All exc Sun
Newcastle-upon-Tyne	Cooperage			Atmos		Water	091-232 8286	All exc Sun

Warwickshire

Alderminster	Bell	Food					01789 450414	
Alveston	Ferry Inn	Food					01789 269883	
Ashby St Ledgers	Olde Coach House Inn	Food	B&B	ZZzz	Family		01788 890349	All Sat only
Broom	Broom Tavern	Food			Family		01789 773656	
Ettington	Houndshill		B&B				01789 740267	
Ilmington	Howard Arms	Food	B&B	ZZzz			01608 682226	

Location	Establishment	Star	Food	B&B	Atmos	ZZzz	Family	Waterside	Tel	Open all day?
Lowsonford	Fleur de Lys				Atmos		Family	Water	01564 782431	All
Stratford-upon-Avon	Dirty Duck				Atmos				01789 297312	All exc Sun
Stratford-upon-Avon	Slug & Lettuce		Food						01789 299700	All Sat only
Temple Grafton	Blue Boar		Food						01789 750010	
Wilmcote	Mason's Arms		Food						01789 297416	
Wootton Wawen	The Bull's Head		Food						01564 792511	All

West Midlands

Location	Establishment	Star	Food	B&B	Atmos	ZZzz	Family	Waterside	Tel	Open all day?
Ansty	Ansty Arms			B&B			Family		01203 611817	All
Baginton	Old Mill Inn			B&B				Water	01203 303588	
Coventry	William IV		Food						01203 686394	
Himley	Crooked House				Atmos		Family		01384 238583	
Langley	Brewery Inn				Atmos			Water	0121-544 6467	
West Bromwich	Manor House				Atmos				0121-588 2035	All Mon-Sat in summer

Wiltshire

Location	Establishment	Star	Food	B&B	Atmos	ZZzz	Family	Waterside	Tel	Open all day?
Axford	Red Lion Inn		Food	B&B					01672 20271	
Bottlesford	Seven Stars		Food				Family		01672 851325	
Bowden Hill	Rising Sun				Atmos				01249 730363	
Box	Bayly's		Food	B&B					01225 743622	
Bradford-on-Avon	Bunch of Grapes		Food						01225 863877	All
Brinkworth	Three Crowns		Food						01666 510366	
Broad Chalke	Queens Head			B&B					01722 780344	All
Bromham	Greyhound Inn		Food						01380 850241	
Burton	Old House at Home		Food						01454 218227	
Burton	Plume of Feathers		Food	B&B					01454 218251	
Castle Combe	Castle Inn		Food	B&B		ZZzz			01249 782461	All exc Sun

Castle Combe	White Hart				Atmos				01294 782295	
Charlton	Horse & Groom		Food	B&B		ZZzz	Family		01666 823904	
Chicksgrove	Compasses		Food	B&B		ZZzz	Family		01722 714318	
Corsham	Methuen Arms			B&B					01249 714867	All
Devizes	Bear		Food	B&B					01380 722444	
Ebbesbourne Wake	Horseshoes Inn		Food	B&B		ZZzz	Family		01722 780474	
Fonthill Gifford	Beckford Arms			B&B					01747 870385	
Ford	White Hart at Ford		Food	B&B				Water	01249 782213	
Hindon	Lamb at Hindon		Food	B&B					01747 820573	All exc Sun
Holt	Old Ham Tree		Food	B&B					01225 782581	All exc Sun
Lacock	George Inn		Food						01249 730263	All
Little Bedwyn	Harrow Inn		Food	B&B		ZZzz			01672 870871	All exc Sun
Longleat	Bath Arms		Food	B&B			Family		01985 844308	
Melksham	King's Arms Hotel			B&B					01225 707272	
Nettleton	Nettleton Arms			B&B			Family		01249 782783	
North Newnton	Woodbridge Inn	*	Food	B&B			Family	Water	01980 630266	All exc Sun
Nunton	Radnor Arms		Food				Family		01722 329722	All
Pitton	Silver Plough		Food						01722 72266	
Ramsbury	Bell		Food						01672 20230	
Rowde	George & Dragon	*	Food						01380 723053	
Salisbury	Haunch of Venison				Atmos				01722 322024	All exc Sun
Salisbury	King's Arms			B&B					01722 327629	All
Semington	Lamb on the Strand		Food						01380 870263	
Sherston	Rattlebone Inn				Atmos				01666 840871	All Sat only
Stourton	Spread Eagle		Food	B&B		ZZzz	Family		01747 840587	
Wootton Rivers	Royal Oak		Food	B&B					01672 810322	

North Yorkshire

Asenby	Crab & Lobster	Food				01845 577286	
Askrigg	King's Arms Hotel	Food	B&B	ZZzz	Family	01969 650258	All Sat only
Bainbridge	Rose & Crown Hotel		B&B	ZZzz		01969 650225	
Brearton	Malt Shovel	Food				01423 862929	

Location	Establishment	Star	Food	B&B	Atmos	ZZzz	Family	Waterside	Tel	Open all day?
Buckden	Buck Inn		Food	B&B		ZZzz		Water	01756 760228	All exc Sun
Carlton-in-Coverdale	Foresters Arms		Food	B&B					01969 40272	
Carthorpe	Fox & Hounds		Food						01845 567433	
Coxwold	Fauconberg Arms		Food	B&B			Family		01347 868214	
Cray	White Lion						Family	Water	01756 760262	
Danby	Duke of Wellington			B&B	Atmos				01287 660351	
East Witton	Blue Lion		Food	B&B		ZZzz			01969 24273	All exc Sun
Elslack	Tempest Arms		Food	B&B		ZZzz	Family	Water	01282 842450	All Sat only
Goathland	Mallyan Spout		Food	B&B		ZZzz	Family		01947 86206	All exc Sun
Harome	Star Inn		Food				Family		01439 70397	
Helmsley	Feathers Hotel			B&B			Family		01439 70275	All
Hetton	Angel Inn	*	Food						01756 730263	
Horton-in-Ribblesdale	Crown Hotel		Food	B&B			Family	Water	01729 860209	
Hovingham	Worsley Arms Hotel			B&B		ZZzz			01653 628234	
Kirkbymoorside	George & Dragon Hotel		Food	B&B		ZZzz			01751 31637	
Linton-in-Craven	Fountaine Inn		Food				Family		01756 752210	
Middleham	Black Swan			B&B					01969 22221	
Moulton	Black Bull		Food						01325 377289	
Newton-on-Ouse	Dawnay Arms				Atmos		Family	Water	01347 848345	
Nosterfield	Freemason's Arms		Food						01677 470548	
Nunnington	Royal Oak		Food						01439 748271	
Osmotherley	Three Tuns		Food	B&B					01609 883301	
Pickering	White Swan		Food	B&B		ZZzz			01751 472288	
Pickhill	Nag's Head		Food	B&B		ZZzz			01845 567391	
Reeth	Buck Hotel			B&B			Family		01748 884210	
Ripley	Boar's Head Hotel		Food	B&B					01423 771888	
Rosedale Abbey	Milburn Arms		Food	B&B		ZZzz			01751 417312	All exc Sun
Rosedale Abbey	White Horse Farm Hotel		Food	B&B		ZZzz			01751 417239	
Sawley	Sawley Arms		Food						01765 620642	
Starbotton	Fox & Hounds	*	Food	B&B					01756 760269	
Threshfield	Old Hall Inn		Food				Family		01756 752441	

Topcliffe	Angel Inn			B&B		ZZzz	Family		01845 577237	All exc Sun
Wass	Wombwell Arms	*	Food	B&B		ZZzz			01347 868280	
Wath-in-Nidderdale	Sportsman's Arms		Food	B&B		ZZzz			01423 711306	All exc Sun
West Witton	Wensleydale Heifer		Food	B&B		ZZzz			01969 22322	
Wigglesworth	Plough Inn		Food	B&B			Family		01729 840243	
Wykeham	Downe Arms			B&B		ZZzz			01723 862471	All exc Sun

South Yorkshire

Cawthorne	Spencer Arms		Food		Atmos				01226 790228	
Penistone	Cubley Hall						Family		01226 766086	All

West Yorkshire

Grange Moor	Kaye Arms		Food						01942 848385	All exc Sun
Harewood	Harewood Arms			B&B		ZZzz			0113 288 6566	
Haworth	Old White Lion Hotel			B&B					01535 642313	All
Heath	King's Arms				Atmos				01924 377527	All
Holywell Green	Rock Inn Hotel			B&B					01422 79721	All exc Sun
Ledsham	Chequers Inn				Atmos				01977 683135	
Leeds	Whitelocks				Atmos				0113 245 3950	
Meltham	Will's O'Nat's		Food						01484 850078	
Pontefract	Parkside Inn			B&B			Family		01977 709911	All
Ripponden	Old Bridge Inn				Atmos				01422 822595	All Sat only
Shelf	Duke of York			B&B				Water	01422 202056	All exc Sun
Shelley	Three Acres	*	Food	B&B		ZZzz			01484 602606	All Mon-Fri
Sowerby Bridge	The Hobbit		Food	B&B			Family		01422 832202	
Thornton	Ring O'Bells		Food						01274 832296	

SCOTLAND

Please refer to the **How to use this Guide** section at the beginning of this Guide for explanations of Categories (FOOD, B&B, A) & Symbols (Family, Star).

Borders

Location	Establishment	Star	Food	B&B	Atmos	ZZzz	Family	Waterside	Tel	Open all day?
Greenlaw	Castle Inn		Food	B&B			Family		0136 16 217	
Innerleithen	Traquair Arms		Food	B&B			Family		01896 830229	All
Melrose	Burts Hotel		Food	B&B		ZZzz			0189 682 2285	
St Boswells	Buccleuch Arms Hotel		Food	B&B					01835 822243	All
St Mary's Loch	Tibbie Shiels Inn		Food					Water	01750 42231	
Swinton	Wheatsheaf Hotel		Food	B&B			Family		01890 860257	
Tweedsmuir	Crook Inn			B&B					0189 97 272	All

Central

Location	Establishment	Star	Food	B&B	Atmos	ZZzz	Family	Waterside	Tel	Open all day?
Brig o'Turk	Byre Inn		Food						0187 376 292	
Killin	Clachaig Hotel		Food	B&B		ZZzz		Water	01567 820270	All
Kilmahog	Lade Inn		Food						01877 330152	
Kippen	Cross Keys		Food	B&B			Family		01786 870293	
Sheriffmuir	Sheriffmuir Inn		Food				Family		01786 823285	
Strathblane	Kirkhouse Inn			B&B		ZZzz			01360 770621	All

Dumfries & Galloway

Location	Establishment	Star	Food	B&B	Atmos	ZZzz	Family	Waterside	Tel	Open all day?
Canonbie	Riverside Inn		Food	B&B		ZZzz		Water	0138 73 71512	
Kirkcudbright	Selkirk Arms Hotel		Food	B&B		ZZzz	Family		01557 330402	All
Moffat	Black Bull			B&B			Family		01683 20206	All

Location	Pub/Inn	Food	B&B	Atmos	ZZzz	Family	Water	Phone	Opening
New Abbey	Crifel Inn	Food	B&B			Family		0138 785 305	
Newton Stewart	Creebridge House Hotel	Food	B&B		ZZzz	Family		01671 402121	
Portpatrick	Crown Hotel	Food	B&B		ZZzz	Family	Water	01776 810261	All

Fife

Location	Pub/Inn	Food	B&B	Atmos	ZZzz	Family	Water	Phone	Opening
Anstruther	Dreel Tavern			Atmos				01333 310727	All
Crail	Golf Hotel		B&B					01333 450206	All
Dysart	Old Rectory Inn	Food					Water	01592 651211	All
Elie	Ship Inn	Food				Family	Water	01333 330246	All
Kirkcaldy	Hoffmans	Food	B&B	*		Family		01592 204584	All exc Sun
Markinch	Town House Hotel	Food	B&B					01592 758459	All
St Andrews	Grange Inn	Food						01334 472670	All

Grampian

Location	Pub/Inn	Food	B&B	Atmos	ZZzz	Family	Water	Phone	Opening
Aberdeen	Prince of Wales	Food						01224 640597	All
Fochabers	Gordon Arms	Food	B&B					01343 820508	All
Kincardine O'Neill	Gordon Arms Hotel	Food	B&B					0133 98 84236	All
Monymusk	Grant Arms Hotel	Food	B&B					01467 651226	All
Netherley	Lairhillock Inn & Restaurant	Food				Family		01569 30001	
Stonehaven	Marine Hotel	Food	B&B			Family	Water	01569 62155	All
Turriff	Towie Tavern	Food						0188 84 201	All

Highland

Location	Pub/Inn	Food	B&B	Atmos	ZZzz	Family	Water	Phone	Opening
Applecross	Applecross Inn	Food	B&B				Water	0152 04 262	All
Ardvasar	Ardvasar Hotel		B&B					0147 14 223	All
Busta, Shetland	Busta House Hotel	Food	B&B		ZZzz		Water	0180 622 506	All summer only
Carbost	Old Inn		B&B				Water	0147 842 205	All
Cromarty	Royal Hotel		B&B		ZZzz		Water	01381 600217	All
Garve	Inchbae Lodge	Food	B&B				Water	0199 75 269	All

Location	Establishment	Star	Food	B&B	Atmos	ZZzz	Family	Waterside	Tel	Open all day?
Glenelg	Glenelg Inn		Food	B&B		ZZzz	Family		0159 982 273	
Glenfinnan	The Prince's House		Food	B&B					01397 83246	All
Kylesku	Kylesku Hotel		Food	B&B				Water	01971 502231	All exc Sun
Talladale	Loch Maree Hotel			B&B		ZZzz			0144 584 288	All
Ullapool	Argyll Hotel			B&B				Water	01854 2422	All
Ullapool	Ceilidh Place		Food	B&B					01854 612103	All exc Sun
Ullapool	Morefield Motel & Steakplace		Food	B&B				Water	01854 612161	All exc Sun

Lothian

Location	Establishment	Star	Food	B&B	Atmos	ZZzz	Family	Waterside	Tel	Open all day?
Edinburgh	Doric Tavern Wine Bar & Bistro		Food						01311-225 1084	All
Edinburgh	Fishers		Food					Water	01311-554 5666	All
Edinburgh	Stockbridge Bar		Food						01311-220 3774	All
Edinburgh	Tattler		Food						0131-554 9999	All
Edinburgh	Waterfront Wine Bar		Food					Water	0131-554 7427	All
Gifford	Tweeddale Arms		Food	B&B			Family		01620 810240	All
Ratho	Bridge Inn		Food				Family	Water	0131-333 1320	All

Strathclyde

Location	Establishment	Star	Food	B&B	Atmos	ZZzz	Family	Waterside	Tel	Open all day?
Ardentinny	Ardentinny Hotel		Food	B&B		ZZzz	Family	Water	01369 810209	All Sun only
Castlecary	Castlecary House Hotel			B&B					01324 840233	
Clachan Seil	Tigh-an-Truish Inn		Food	B&B				Water	01852 300242	All summer only
Clachan Seil	Willowburn Hotel		Food	B&B		ZZzz		Water	0185 23 276	
Glasgow	Babbity Bowster		Food						0141-552 5055	All
Glasgow	Ubiquitous Chip		Food						0141-334 5007	All
Kilberry	Kilberry Inn	★	Food	B&B			Family		0188 03 223	
Loch Eck	Coylet Hotel		Food	B&B			Family		0136 984 322	
Tayvallich	Tayvallich Inn		Food				Family	Water	0154 67 282	

Tayside

Location	Name	Food	B&B	Atmos	ZZzz	Family	Water		Phone	
Almondbank	Almondbank Inn	Food							01738 83242	
Burrelton	Burrelton Park Inn	Food	B&B			Family	Water		0182 87 207	
Dundee	Mercantile Bar			Atmos					01382 225500	All
Glendevon	Tormaukin Hotel	Food	B&B						01259 781252	All
Glenfarg	Bein Inn	Food	B&B				Water		01577 830216	
Kenmore	Kenmore Hotel		B&B		ZZzz		Water		01887 830205	
Killiecrankie	Killiecrankie Hotel		B&B		ZZzz				01796 473220	All
Kirkton of Glenisla	Glenisla Hotel	Food				Family			0157 582 223	All
Weem	Ailean Chraggan Hotel	Food	B&B						01887 820346	

WALES

Please refer to the **How to use this Guide** section at the beginning of this Guide for explanations of Categories (FOOD, B&B, A) & Symbols (Family, Star).

Clwyd

Location	Establishment	Star	Food	B&B	Atmos	ZZzz	Family	Waterside	Tel	Open all day?
Afonwen	Pwll Gwyn Hotel		Food	B&B			Family		01352 720227	
Babell	Black Lion Inn		Food						01352 720239	
Betws-yn-Rhos	Ffarm Hotel		Food						0149 260 287	
Bodfari	Dinorben Arms		Food				Family		01745 710309	
Burton Green	Golden Grove Inn				Atmos		Family		01244 570445	
Erbistock	Boat Inn		Food					Water	01978 780143	
Llanarmon Dyffryn Ceiriog	West Arms Hotel		Food	B&B		ZZzz	Family	Water	0169 176 665	All exc Sun
Llangollen	Britannia Inn			B&B		ZZzz			01978 860144	
Llannefydd	Hawk & Buckle Inn			B&B		ZZzz			01745 540249	
Marford	Trevor Arms			B&B			Family		01244 570436	All exc Sun
Mold	We Three Loggerheads		Food					Water	0135 285 337	All Fri & Sat
Tremeirchion	Salusbury Arms		Food				Family		0174 575 262	All exc Sun

Dyfed

Location	Establishment	Star	Food	B&B	Atmos	ZZzz	Family	Waterside	Tel	Open all day?
Abergorlech	Black Lion		Food						01558 685271	
Cardigan	Black Lion							Water	01239 612532	All exc Sun
Clarbeston Road	Picton Inn			B&B	Atmos				01437 731615	All exc Sun
Felindre Farchog	Salutation Inn			B&B			Family	Water	01239 820564	
Landshipping	Stanley Arms		Food					Water	01834 891227	
Llanddarog	Butchers Arms		Food				Family		01267 275330	
Llandovery	King's Head Inn			B&B					01550 20393	All

Location	Name	Food	B&B	Atmos	ZZzz	Family	Water	Phone	Days
Llangrannog	Ship Inn	Food					Water	01239 654423	All exc Sun
Llwyndafydd	Crown Inn	Food				Family		01545 560396	
Nevern	Trewern Arms Hotel		B&B		ZZzz	Family	Water	01239 820395	
Pembroke Ferry	Ferry Inn	Food					Water	01646 682947	
Pisgah	Halfway Inn			Atmos		Family		0197 084 631	
Pont-ar-gothi	Cresselly Arms	Food				Family	Water	01267 290221	All Sat/Mon-Fri midSummer

South Glamorgan

Location	Name	Food	B&B	Atmos	ZZzz	Family	Water	Phone	Days
East Aberthaw	Blue Anchor Inn	Food						01446 750329	

Mid Glamorgan

Location	Name	Food	B&B	Atmos	ZZzz	Family	Water	Phone	Days
Creigiau	Caesar's Arms	Food						01222 890486	All exc Sun
Llangynwyd	Olde House Inn			Atmos		Family		01656 733310	All exc Sun
Nottage	Rose & Crown		B&B					01656 784850	All Sat only

West Glamorgan

Location	Name	Food	B&B	Atmos	ZZzz	Family	Water	Phone	Days
Swansea	Langland Court Hotel		B&B		ZZzz			01792 361545	All exc Sun

Gwent

Location	Name	Food	B&B	Atmos	ZZzz	Family	Water	Phone	Days
Abergavenny	Llanwenarth Arms Hotel	Food	B&B			Family	Water	01873 810550	All exc Sun
Bettws Newydd	Black Bear	Food						01873 880701	
Chepstow	Castle View Hotel	Food	B&B					01291 620349	All exc Sun
Clydach	Drum & Monkey	Food						01873 831980	
Clytha	Clytha Arms ★	Food				Family		01873 840206	
Llanfihangel Crucorney	Skirrid Inn			Atmos				01873 890258	
Llantrissant	Greyhound Inn		B&B			Family		01291 672505	All exc Sun
Lydart	Gockett Inn	Food						01600 860486	

Location	Establishment	Star	Food	B&B	Atmos	ZZzz	Family	Waterside	Tel	Open all day?
Penallt	Boat Inn							Water	01600 712615	
Raglan	Beaufort Arms Hotel			B&B	Atmos				01291 690412	
Shirenewton	Carpenters Arms		Food	B&B					01291 641231	
Shirenewton	Tredegar Arms		Food	B&B		ZZzz			01291 641274	
Trellech	Village Green		Food	B&B		ZZzz	Family		01600 860119	
Usk	Three Salmons			B&B		ZZzz			01291 672133	All exc Sun
Whitebrook	Crown at Whitebrook		Food	B&B		ZZzz		Water	01600 860254	

Gwynedd

Location	Establishment	Star	Food	B&B	Atmos	ZZzz	Family	Waterside	Tel	Open all day?
Aberdovey	Penhelig Arms Hotel & Restaura		Food	B&B		ZZzz		Water	01654 767215	
Beaumaris	Liverpool Arms Hotel		Food	B&B		ZZzz			01248 810362	All Sat only
Beaumaris	Ye Olde Bulls Head Inn		Food	B&B		ZZzz			01248 810329	
Glanwydden	Queen's Head		Food						01492 546570	
Penmaenpool	George III Hotel			B&B		ZZzz		Water	01341 422525	All exc Sun
Red Wharf Bay	Ship Inn		Food				Family	Water	01248 852568	All Sat only
Tyn-y-Groes	Groes Inn		Food						01492 650545	All

Powys

Location	Establishment	Star	Food	B&B	Atmos	ZZzz	Family	Waterside	Tel	Open all day?
Crickhowell	Bear Hotel		Food	B&B		ZZzz			01873 810408	
Crickhowell	Nantyffin Cider Mill		Food					Water	01873 810775	
Dinas Mawddwy	Dolbrodmaeth Inn			B&B					01650 531333	
Hay-on-Wye	Kilverts		Food	B&B		ZZzz	Family		01497 821042	
Hay-on-Wye	Old Black Lion		Food	B&B					01497 820841	All exc Sun
Llanfair Waterdine	Red Lion Inn			B&B					01547 528214	All exc Sun
Llanfihangel-Nant-Melan	Red Lion Inn		Food	B&B		ZZzz			01544 21220	
Llanfrynach	White Swan		Food						01874 86276	

			Food	B&B	ZZzz	Family	Water	Phone
Llangattock	Vine Tree		Food					01873 810514
Llangorse	Red Lion			B&B		Family	Water	01874 84238
Llanyre	Bell Country Inn			B&B				01597 823959
Llowes	Radnor Arms		Food					01497 847460
Llyswen	Griffin Inn	*	Food	B&B	ZZzz	Family		01874 754241
Old Radnor	Harp Inn		Food	B&B	ZZzz			01544 21655
Pant Mawr	Glansevern Arms			B&B				0155 15 240
Penybont	Severn Arms Hotel			B&B				01597 851224
Trecastle	Castle Coaching Inn		Food	B&B		Family		01874 636354

CHANNEL ISLANDS & ISLE OF MAN

Please refer to the **How to use this Guide** section at the beginning of this Guide for explanations of Categories (FOOD, B&B, A) & Symbols (Family, Star).

Location	Establishment	Star	Food	B&B	Atmos	ZZzz	Family	Waterside	Tel	Open all day?
Alderney										
St Anne	Georgian House	★	Food						01481 822471	
Guernsey										
Castel	Hougue du Pommier			B&B		ZZzz	Family		01481 56531	
Kings Mills	Fleur du Jardin		Food	B&B		ZZzz	Family		01481 57996	
Le Bourg	Deerhound Inn		Food	B&B			Family		01481 38885	All
Pleinmont	Imperial Hotel			B&B			Family		01481 64044	All exc Sun
St Peter Port	Ship & Crown				Atmos				01481 721368	All exc Sun
Herm										
Herm	The Ship Inn		Food						01481 722159	All exc Sun
Jersey										
Gorey	Dolphin Hotel			B&B					01534 853370	All exc Sun
St Aubin	Old Court House Inn		Food	B&B				Water	01534 46433	All
St Brelade	Old Smugglers Inn		Food						01534 41510	All exc Sun
St Lawrence	British Union Hotel		Food				Family		01534 861070	
St Peter's Village	Star & Tipsy Toad Brewery		Food				Family		01534 485556	All exc Sun

Sark

Sark	Dixcart Hotel	Food	Family		01481 832015	All

Isle of Man

Peel	Creek Inn	Food		Water	01624 842216	All exc Sun

NORTHERN IRELAND

Please refer to the **How to use this Guide** section at the beginning of this Guide for explanations of Categories (FOOD, B&B, A) & Symbols (Family, Star).

Location	Establishment	Star	Food	B&B	Atmos	ZZzz	Family	Waterside	Tel	Open all day?
Co Antrim										
Ballycastle	House of McDonnell				Atmos				0126 57 62975	All exc Sun
Belfast	Crown Liquor Saloon				Atmos				01232 249476	All exc Sun
Belfast	Kelly's Cellars				Atmos				01232 324835	All exc Sun & BH
Bushmills	Bushmills Inn			B&B					0126 57 32339	All
Carnlough	Londonderry Arms		Food						01574 885255	
Carnlough	The Waterfall				Atmos				No telephone	
Cushendall	PJ McCollam				Atmos				No telephone	All exc Sun
Co Down										
Crawfordsburn	Old Inn			B&B					01247 853255	
Dundrum	Buck's Head Inn		Food						0139 67 51868	
Co Fermanagh										
Enniskillen	Blakes of the Hollow				Atmos				01365 322143	All exc Sun

REPUBLIC OF IRELAND

Please refer to the **How to use this Guide** section at the beginning of this Guide for explanations of Categories (FOOD, B&B, A) & Symbols (Family, Star).

Location	Establishment	Star	Food	B&B	Atmos	ZZzz	Family	Waterside	Tel	Open all day?
Co Carlow										
Leighlinbridge	Lord Bagenal Inn	★	Food				Family		0503 21668	All exc Sun
Co Cavan										
Butlersbridge	Derragarra Inn		Food					Water	049 31003	All
Co Clare										
Ballyvaughan	Monks Pub		Food				Family		065 77059	
Ennis	The Cloister		Food				Family		065 29521	
New Quay	Linnane's Bar		Food					Water	065 78120	All
Co Cork										
Ahakista	Ahakista Bar				Atmos			Water	No telephone	All exc Sun
Ballydehob	Levis Bar				Atmos				028 37118	All exc Sun
Baltimore	Bushe's Bar			B&B			Family	Water	028 20125	All exc Sun
Baltimore	McCarthy's Bar		Food					Water	028 20159	All exc Sun
Bantry	Anchor Tavern				Atmos		Family		027 50012	All exc Sun & winter
Butlerstown	O'Neill's				Atmos				023 40228	All exc Sun

Location	Establishment	Star	Food	B&B	Atmos	ZZzz	Family	Waterside	Tel	Open all day?
Castletownbere	MacCarthy's	*			Atmos				027 70014	All exc Sun
Castletownshend	Mary Ann's Bar & Restaurant		Food						028 36146	All exc Sun
Clonakilty	An Sugan		Food						023 33498	All exc Sun
Cobh	Mansworths				Atmos				021 811965	All exc Sun
Cork	An Spailpin Fanac		Food				Family		021 277949	All exc Sun
Cork	Dan Lowrey's Seafood Tavern		Food						021 505071	All exc Sun
Cork	Reidy's Wine Vaults	*	Food					Water	021 275751	All exc Sun
Crookhaven	O'Sullivan's				Atmos			Water	028 35200	All exc Sun
Crosshaven	Cronin's Bar		Food				Family	Water	021 831207	All exc Sun
East Ferry	Marlogue Inn		Food				Family	Water	021 813390	All
Glandore	Hayes Bar	*	Food						028 33214	All exc Sun
Glandore	Marine Hotel		Food					Water	028 33366	All exc Sun
Glengarriff	The Blue Loo				Atmos				027 63167	All exc Sun
Kanturk	Alley Bar				Atmos				029 50171	All exc Sun
Kanturk	The Vintage		Food						029 50549	All exc Sun
Kinsale	Blue Haven Hotel		Food	B&B					021 772209	All exc Sun
Kinsale	The Bulman Bar				Atmos			Water	021 772131	All exc Sun
Kinsale	The Dock Bar				Atmos		Family	Water	021 772522	All exc Sun
Kinsale	1601		Food				Family		021 772529	All
Kinsale	The Spaniard Inn		Food					Water	021 772436	All exc Sun
Rathpeacon	Country Squire Inn		Food						021 301812	All exc Sun
Schull	TJ Newman's				Atmos				028 28223	All exc Sun
Timoleague	Dillon's		Food				Family		023 46390	All exc Sun

Co Donegal

Location	Establishment	Star	Food	B&B	Atmos	ZZzz	Family	Waterside	Tel	Open all day?
Culdaff	McGuinness's				Atmos				077 79116	All exc Sun
Greencastle	Kealy's Seafood Bar		Food					Water	077 81010	All exc Mon
Portsalon	Rita's				Atmos			Water	074 59107	
Rossnowlagh	Smugglers Creek Inn	*	Food	B&B			Family		072 52366	

Co Dublin

Dalkey	The Queens	Food			01 285 4569	All exc Sun
Dublin	Ashtons	Food		Water	01 283 0045	All exc Sun
Dublin	Bleeding Horse	Food			01 475 2705	All exc Sun
Dublin	Brazen Head	Food			01 677 9549	
Dublin	Café en Seine	Food			01 677 4369	All exc Sun
Dublin	Davy Byrnes	Food			01 677 5217	All exc Sun
Dublin	Doheny & Nesbitt		Atmos		01 676 2945	All exc Sun
Dublin	The Goat	Food		Family	01 298 4145	All exc Sun
Dublin	Hedigan's: The Brian Boru	Food			01 830 8514	All exc Sun
Dublin	Kavanagh's		Atmos		No telephone	
Dublin	Kielys	Food			01 283 0209	All exc Sun
Dublin	Kitty O'Shea's Bar	Food			01 660 8050	All exc Sun
Dublin	The Lord Edward	Food			01 454 2420	All exc Sun
Dublin	McCormack's Merrion Inn	Food			01 269 3816	All exc Sun
Dublin	O'Dwyer's		Atmos		01 676 3574	All exc Sun
Dublin	The Old Stand	Food			01 677 7220	All exc Sun
Dublin	The Pembroke		Atmos		01 676 2980	All exc Sun
Dublin	Ryans of Parkgate Street	Food			01 671 9352	All exc Sun
Dublin	Stag's Head		Atmos		01 679 3701	All exc Sun
Dublin	The Station House	Food		Family	01 831 3772	All exc Sun
Dublin	Toners Pub		Atmos		01 676 3090	All exc Sun
Dublin	The Yacht	Food		Water	01 833 6364	All exc Sun
Dublin	Yellow House	Food			01 493 2994	All exc Sun
Dublin	Fox's Pub & Seafood Kitchen	Food			01 295 5647	All exc Sun
Glencullen	Abbey Tavern		Atmos		390307	All exc Sun
Howth	Snail Box		Atmos		01 835 4277	All exc Sun
Kilmoon	Purty Kitchen	Food			01 284 3576	All exc Sun
Monkstown	The Mill House	Food			01 288 8672	All exc Sun
Stillorgan	Stillorgan Orchard	Food			01 288 8470	All exc Sun

Co Galway

Location	Establishment	Star	Food	B&B	Atmos	ZZzz	Family	Waterside	Tel	Open all day?
Barna	Donnelly's of Barna		Food					Water	091 92487	All exc Sun
Clarenbridge	Paddy Burke'e		Food					Water	091 96226	All exc Sun
Clifden	E J King's		Food				Family		095 21330	All exc Sun
Ihishbofin Island	Day's Bar		Food						095 45829	All exc Sun
Kilcolgan	Moran's Oyster Cottage	★	Food					Water	091 96113	All exc Sun
Kinvara	Tully's				Atmos				091 37146	All exc Sun
Oughterard	Powers				Atmos				091 82712	All exc Sun
Roundstone	O'Dowd's Seafood Bar & Restaur		Food					Water	095 35809	All exc Sun
Schull	Bunratty Inn		Food						028 28341	All exc Sun
Spiddal	Bridge House Inn			B&B					091 83118	All exc Sun

Co Kerry

Location	Establishment	Star	Food	B&B	Atmos	ZZzz	Family	Waterside	Tel	Open all day?
Annascaul	Dan Foley's				Atmos				066 57252	All exc Sun
Ballyferriter	Long's Pub				Atmos				066 56344	All exc Sun
Cahirciveen	The Point Bar		Food				Family	Water	066 72165	All exc Sun
Dingle	Dick Mack's				Atmos				No telephone	
Dingle	James Flahive				Atmos			Water	066 51634	All exc Sun
Dingle	Lord Baker's Bar & Restaurant		Food						066 51277	
Dingle	O'Flaherty's				Atmos			Water	066 51461	All exc Sun
Kenmare	The Horseshoe		Food						064 41553	All
Kenmare	Purple Heather		Food						064 41016	All exc Sun
Killarney	Yer Man's Pub		Food						064 32688	All exc Sun
Waterville	The Huntsman		Food					Water	066 74124	All
Waterville	Smugglers Inn		Food					Water	066 74330	All

Co Kildare

Moone	Moone High Cross Inn	*	Food			0507 24112	All exc Sun
Naas	Fletcher's			Atmos		045 97328	All exc Sun
Naas	Manor Inn		Food		Family	045 97471	All exc Sun

Co Kilkenny

Location	Name	Food	Atmos	Phone	Opening
Castlewarren	Langton's	Food	Atmos	0503 26123	All exc Sun
Kilkenny	Caislean Ui Cuain	Food		056 65406	All
Kilkenny	Langton's	Food		056 65133	All
Kilkenny	Shem's			056 21543	All exc Sun
Kilkenny	Tynan's Bridge House Bar		Atmos	056 61828	All exc Sun

Co Laois

Abbeyleix	Morrisseys	Atmos	0502 31233	All exc Sun

Co Leitrim

Location	Name	Food	Family	Phone	Opening
Dromahair	Stanford's Village Inn	Food	Family Water	071 64140	All exc Sun

Co Limerick

Abbeyfeale	The Cellar	Atmos	068 31085	All exc Sun
Castleconnell	Bradshaw's Bar	Atmos	061 377724	All Sat only

Co Longford

Moydow	The Vintage	Food	Family	043 22122

Co Louth

Blackrock	Brake Tavern	Food	042 21393	
Carlingford	P J O'Hare's Anchor Bar	Food	042 73106	All exc Sun

Location	Establishment	Star	Food	B&B	Atmos	ZZzz	Family	Waterside	Tel	Open all day?
Co Mayo										
Lecanvey	Staunton's								098 64850	All exc Sun
Westport	The Asgard		Food		Atmos			Water	098 25319	All exc Sun
Westport	The Olde Railway Hotel			B&B					098 25166	
Westport	The Towers Bar		Food				Family		098 26534	All exc Sun
Co Meath										
Ceanannas Mor (Kells)	O'Shaughnessy's		Food						046 41110	All
Skryne	O'Connell's Pub				Atmos				046 25122	All exc Sun
Co Offaly										
Banagher	JJ Hough's				Atmos				No telephone	All exc Sun
Banagher	The Vine House		Food					Water	0509 51463	All exc Sun
Co Roscommon										
Athleague	Fitzmaurice's Tavern				Atmos				0903 63383	All exc Sun
Co Sligo										
Ballisodare	The Thatch		Food		Atmos				071 67288	All exc Sun
Drumcliffe	Yeats Tavern & Davis' Pub		Food					Water	071 63117	All
Rosses Point	Austie's							Water	071 77111	All exc Sun
Sligo	Hargadon's				Atmos				071 70933	All exc Sun

Sligo	McGettigan's		Food		Family	071 62857	
Tubbercurry	Killoran's Traditional Restaur		Food		Family	071 85679	All

Co Tipperary

Birdhill	Matt the Thresher		Food		Water	061 379227	All
Cashel	Dowling's			Atmos		062 62130	All exc Sun
Killaloe	Goosers	*	Food		Water	061 376792	All exc Sun

Co Waterford

Cheekpoint	McAlpin's Suir Inn		Food			051 82220	
Dunmore East	The Ship		Food			051 383141	
Waterford	Jack Meade's Bar			Atmos	Family	051 73187	All exc Sun

Co Westmeath

Athlone	Higgin's			B&B		0902 92519	All exc Sun
Athlone	Sean's Bar			Atmos	Water	0902 92358	All exc Sun
Glasson	Grogan's		Food			0902 85158	All exc Sun

Co Wexford

Carne	Lobster Pot	*	Food			053 31110	All

Co Wicklow

Delgany	Wicklow Arms		Food			01 287 4611	All Sun only
Roundwood	Roundwood Inn	*	Food			01 281 8107	All exc Sun

Recommended by

EGON RONAY'S GUIDES

1995

---

*YOUR GUARANTEE
OF
QUALITY AND INDEPENDENCE*

- Establishment inspections are anonymous

- Inspections are undertaken by qualified
  Egon Ronay's Guides inspectors

- The Guides are completely independent
  in their editorial selection

- The Guides do not accept advertising,
  hospitality or payment from listed
  establishments

Hotels & Restaurants   Pubs & Inns

Europe   Just a Bite

Family Hotels & Restaurants   Paris

Oriental Restaurants   Ireland

New Zealand & South Pacific   Australia

Maps

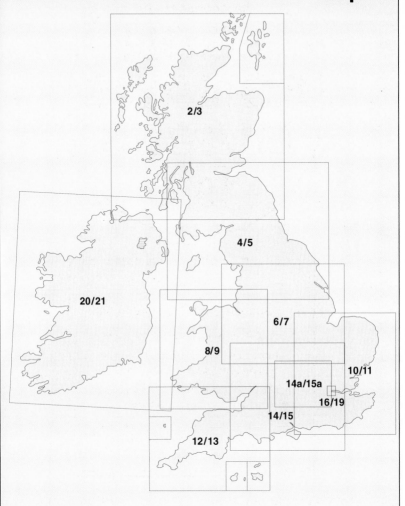

2/3

4/5

20/21

6/7

8/9

10/11

14a/15a

16/19

14/15

12/13

	Motorways	●	Food
	Primary Routes	□	B & B
	Other Roads	⊡	Food and B & B
	County Boundaries	△	Atmosphere

Designed and produced by
European Map Graphics Ltd. Finchampstead, Berks

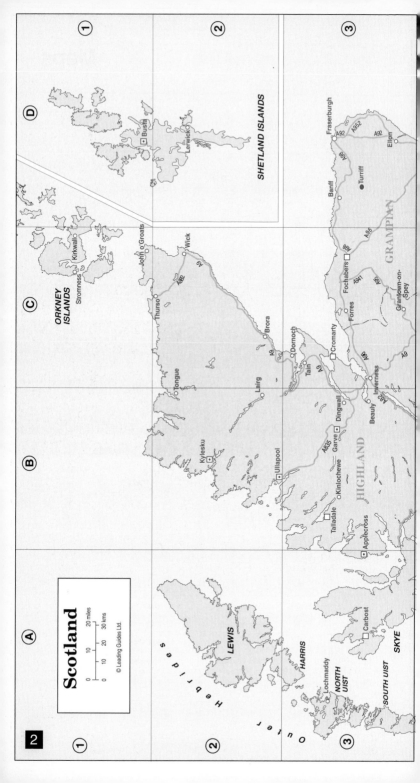

Scotland

20 miles
30 kms

© Leading Guides Ltd.

ORKNEY ISLANDS

SHETLAND ISLANDS

Stromness
Kirkwall

John o'Groats
Wick

Thurso

Tongue

Brora

Lairg

Kylesku

Ullapool

Dornoch
Tain

Dingwall
Garve
Kinlochewe

Talladale

Applecross

Cromarty

Inverness
Beauly

HIGHLAND

A835

A9

A96

A82

A9

A9

Fraserburgh
A92
A952
A92
Elgin

Banff
Turriff

GRAMPIAN

A96

Fochabers

A941
Forres

Grantown-on-Spey

A96

A98

A98

A9

Busta
Lerwick

LEWIS

HARRIS

NORTH UIST

SOUTH UIST

Outer Hebrides

Lochmaddy

Carbost

SKYE

2

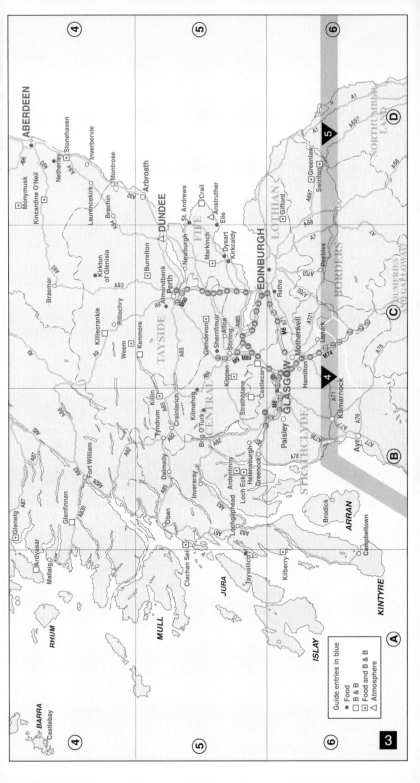

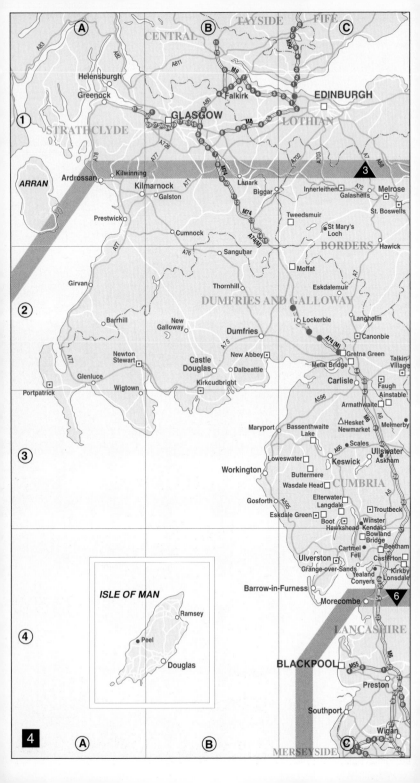

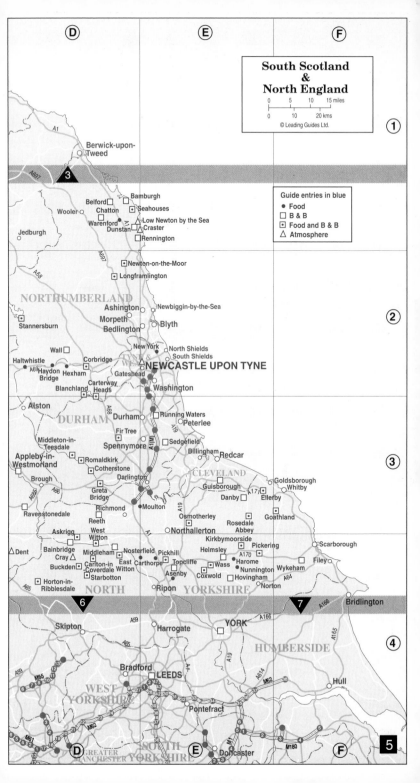

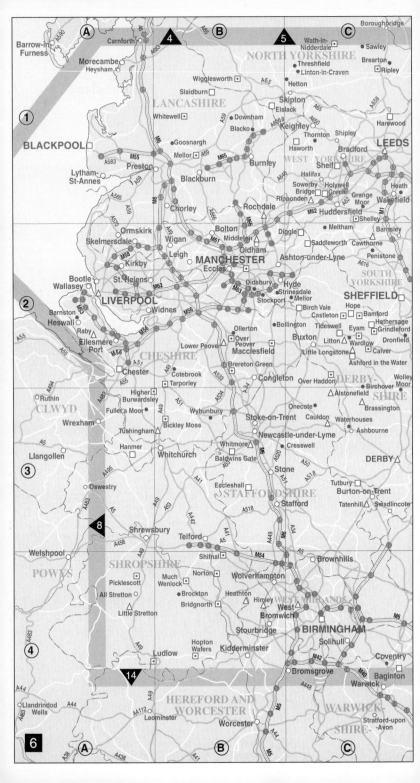

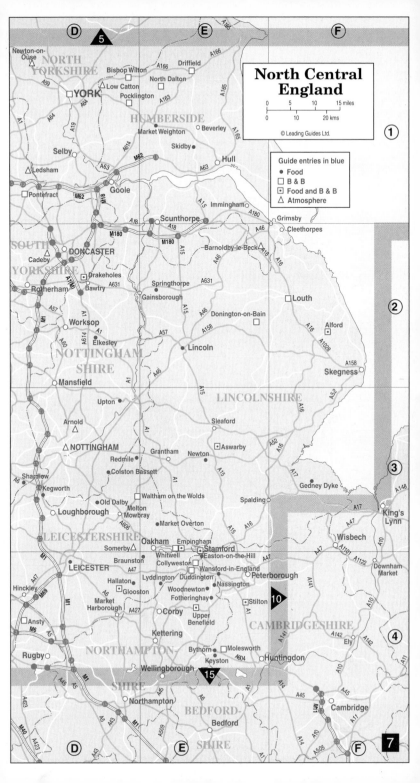

North Central England

0	5	10	15 miles
0	10	20 kms	

© Leading Guides Ltd.

Guide entries in blue
- ● Food
- □ B & B
- ⊡ Food and B & B
- △ Atmosphere

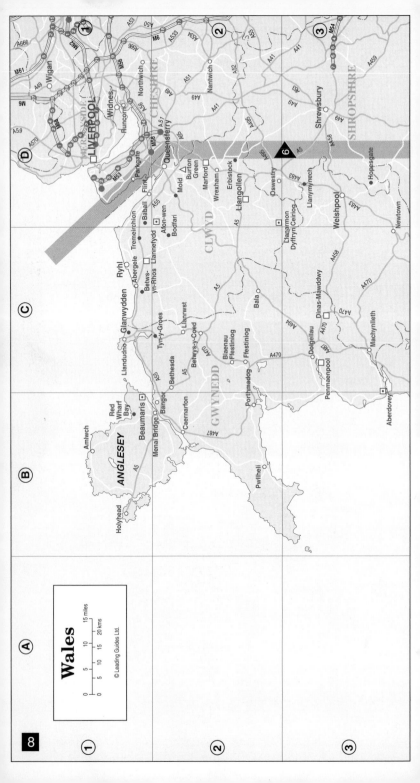

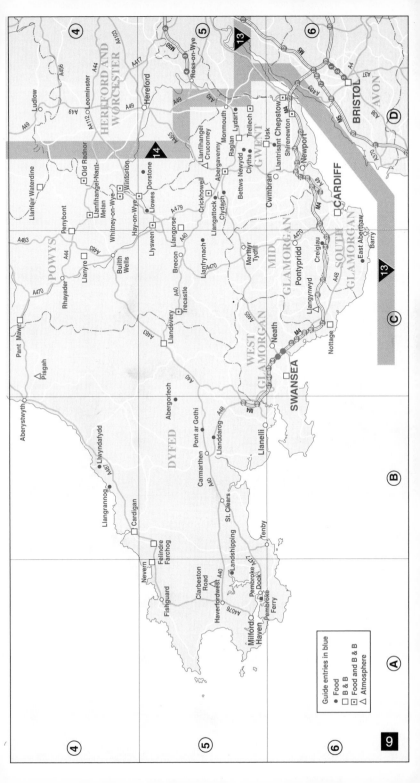

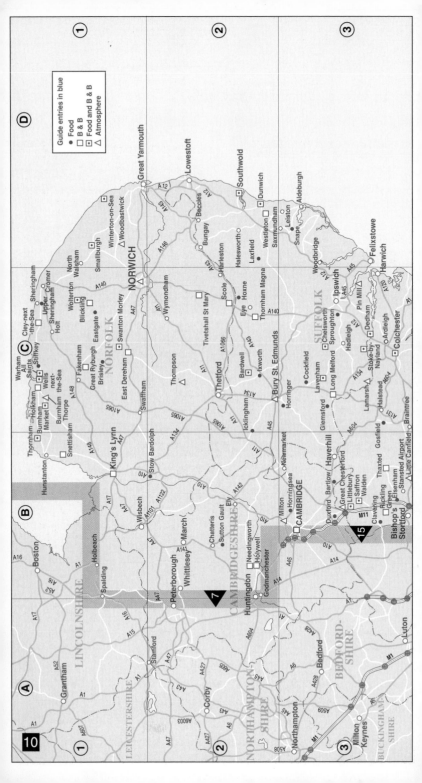

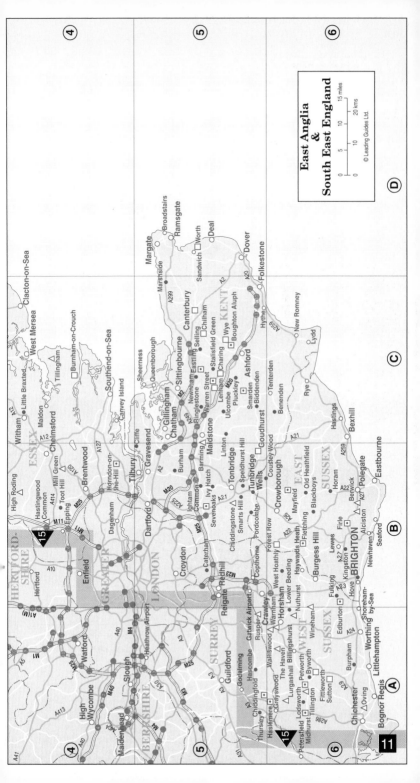

**East Anglia
&
South East England**

© Leading Guides Ltd.

| 0 | | 5 | | 10 | | 15 miles |
| 0 | 10 | | 20 kms | | | |

Guide entries in blue
- Food
- □ B & B
- ⊡ Food and B & B
- △ Atmosphere

A **B** **C**

○Tenby

Llanelli

▲9

①

Ilfracombe

ISLES OF SCILLY

TRESCO

ST. MARTIN'S

ST. MARY'S

② Bideford○
Great
Torrington
Frithelstock⊡

0 ___ 2 miles
0 ___ 2 kms

Morwenstow△

Bude○

Holsworthy○

Lifton⊡
Launceston○
Lydford⊡
Tregadillet

Horndon
Horsebridge
Tavistock

Port Gaverne□
Padstow□ △St Kew
Wadebridge⊡
△Egloshayle
Bodmin○
Liskeard○

Newquay○ △St Mawgam
A38

CORNWALL
Lostwithiel⊡
Pelynt
Torpoint⊡
St Agnes○●Mithian
St. Austell□ △
Charlestown⊡
Polkerris△
Looe□
Fowey⊡
PLYMOUTH
Kingsand●

St. Ives○
Truro○
Penelewey△
Camborne●
Mylor Bridge●
Philleigh●
□St Mawes
Ludgvan△
Perranuthnoe□
Falmouth□
Penzance○
Helston○
Constantine⊡
Sennen Cove□
Porthleven⊡ △
Land's End○ Mousehole□
Gunwalloe Helford△

③

④

**South West
England**

0 ___ 5 ___ 10 miles
0 ___ 5 ___ 10 ___ 15 kms

© Leading Guides Ltd.

12

A **B** **C**

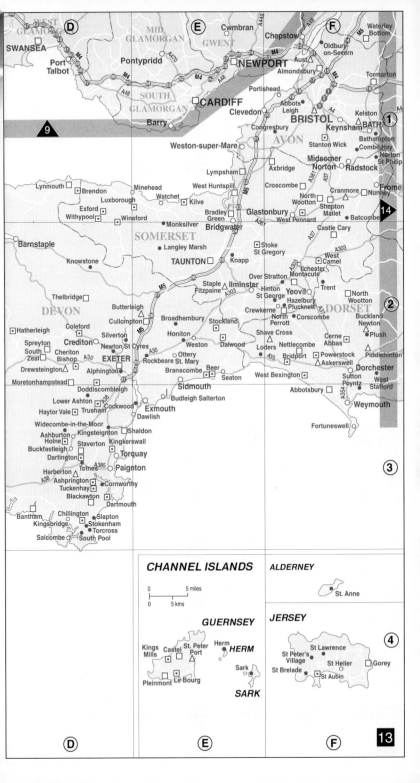

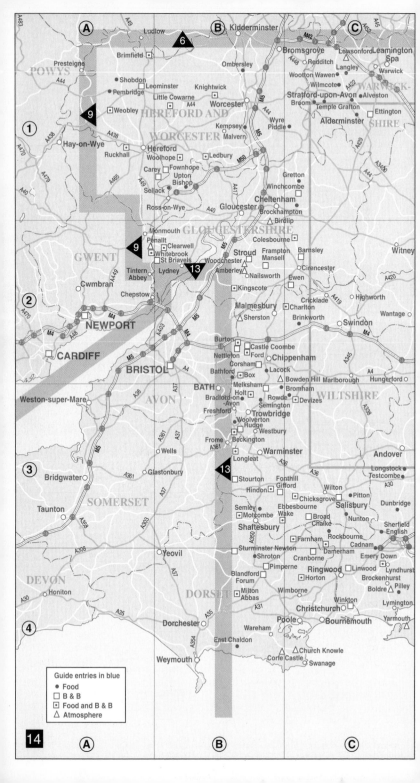

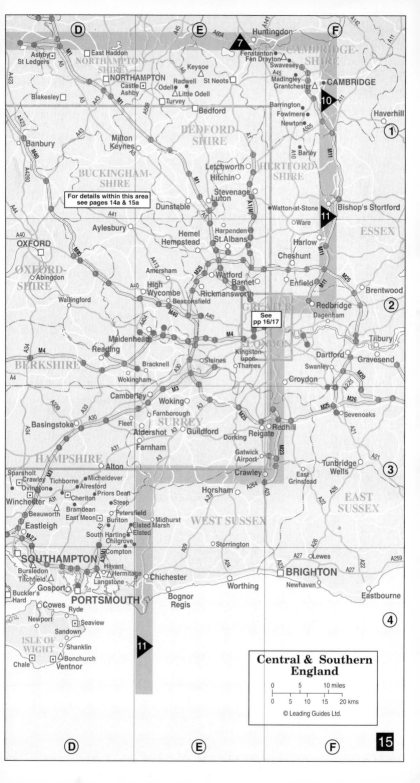

Central & Southern England

```
0          5          10 miles
0    5    10    15    20 kms
```

© Leading Guides Ltd.

15

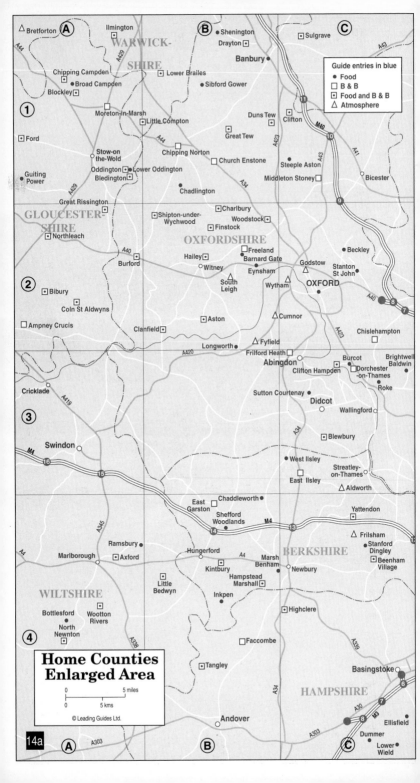

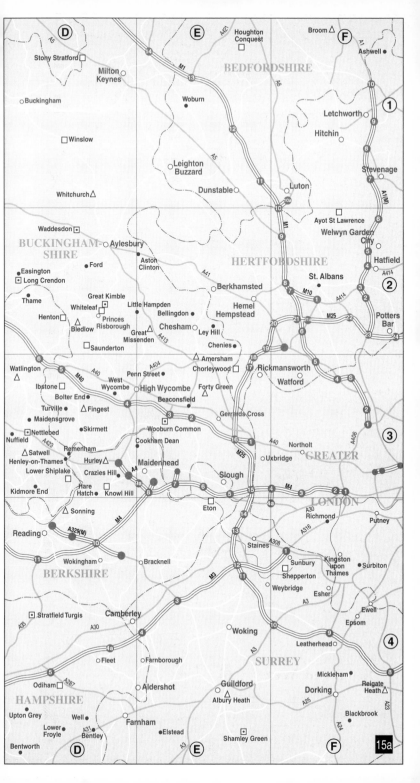

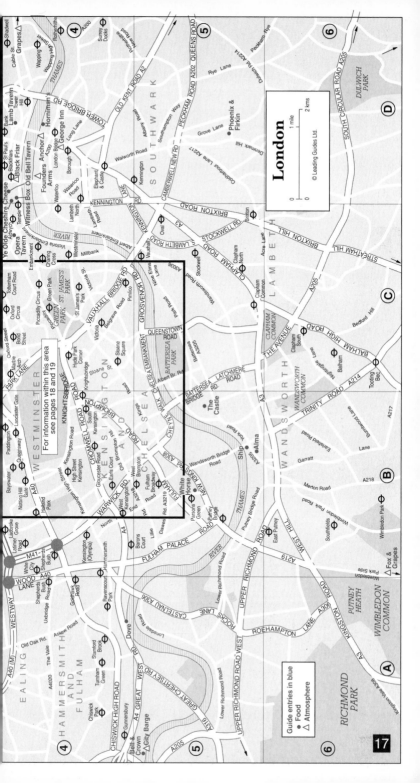

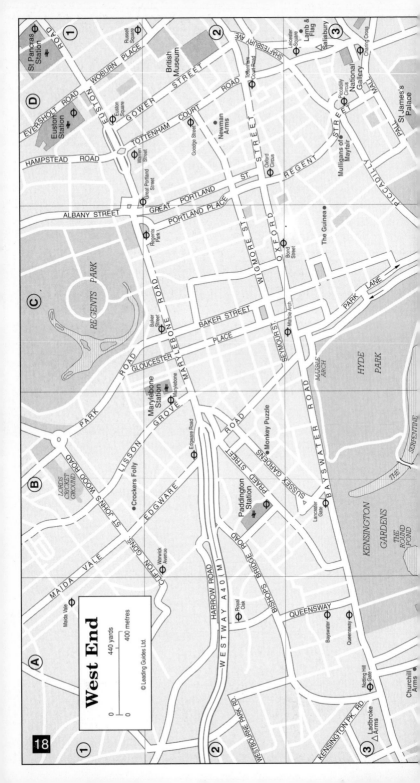

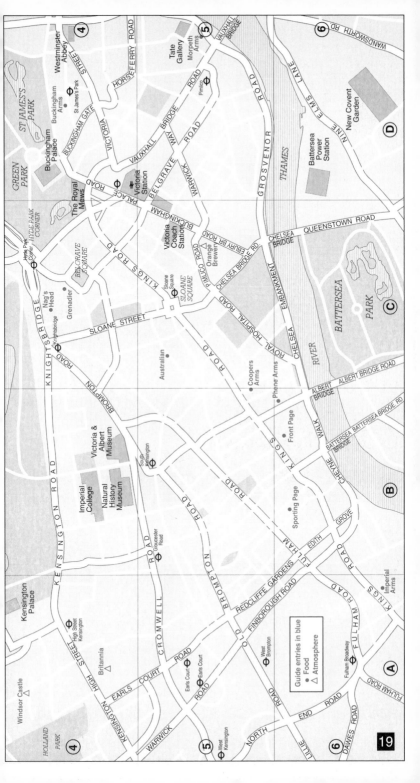

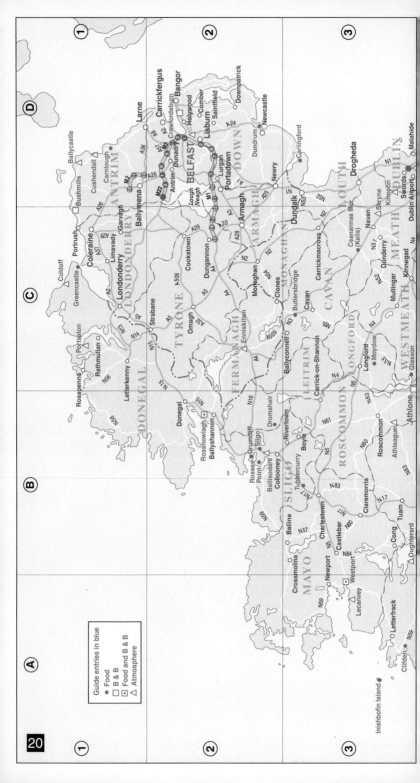

20

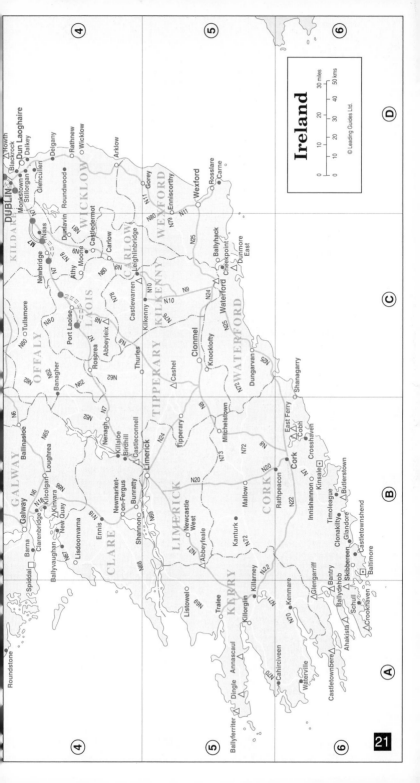

Ireland

© Leading Guides Ltd.

21

Index

Recommended by

EGON RONAY'S GUIDES

1995

YOUR GUARANTEE
OF
QUALITY AND INDEPENDENCE

- Establishment inspections are anonymous
- Inspections are undertaken by qualified Egon Ronay's Guides inspectors
- The Guides are completely independent in their editorial selection
- The Guides do not accept advertising, hospitality or payment from listed establishments

---

Hotels & Restaurants	Pubs & Inns
Europe	Just a Bite
Family Hotels & Restaurants	Paris
Oriental Restaurants	Ireland
New Zealand & South Pacific	Australia

Egon Ronay's Guides are available from all good bookshops or can be ordered from Leading Guides, 35 Tadema Road, London SW10 0PZ
Tel: 071-352 2485 / 352 0019   Fax: 071-376 5071

Special Purchase Offer: Reserve Your 1996 Guide Now!

Reserve your **free** copy of *Egon Ronay's Heineken Guide 1996 Pubs & Inns* by buying *Egon Ronay's Britvic Guide 1995 Just a Bite* NOW.
Just a Bite 1995 is published in December 1994 at £9.99.
The 1996 edition of *Pubs & Inns* will be published in November 1995 at an estimated price of £12.99!

To take advantage of this special purchase offer please fill in the form below and return with payment of £9.99 per offer (inc free p&p) to:

**Egon Ronay's Guides, Special Purchase Offer,
35 Tadema Road, London SW10 0PZ**

▶ Please find enclosed cheque to the value of £......... made payable to **Leading Guides Ltd** or
▶ Please charge to my Access Mastercard / Visa / American Express account (delete as appropriate) the sum of £.........

Card Number: .... Expiry Date: ..../........

Name ....

Address ....

....

....

Post Code .... Daytime Tel No: ....

Delivery address (if different): ....

....

....

....

Offer Valid until 31st August 1995. Maximum order: two per household.

Orders will be despatched within 28 days of receipt or, if received in advance of publication, within 28 days of publication.

Recommended by

EGON RONAY'S GUIDES

1995

YOUR GUARANTEE
OF
QUALITY AND INDEPENDENCE

- Establishment inspections are anonymous

- Inspections are undertaken by qualified
  Egon Ronay's Guides inspectors

- The Guides are completely independent
  in their editorial selection

- The Guides do not accept advertising,
  hospitality or payment from listed
  establishments

Hotels & Restaurants	Pubs & Inns
Europe	Just a Bite
Family Hotels & Restaurants	Paris
Oriental Restaurants	Ireland
New Zealand & South Pacific	Australia

Egon Ronay's Guides are available from all good bookshops or can be
ordered from Leading Guides, 35 Tadema Road, London SW10 0PZ
Tel: 071-352 2485 / 352 0019   Fax: 071-376 5071

READERS' COMMENTS

Please use this sheet, and the continuation overleaf, to recommend pubs and inns of **really outstanding quality and to comment on existing entries.**

Complaints about any of the Guide's entries will be treated seriously and passed on to our inspectorate, but we would like to remind you always to take up your complaint with the management at the time.

We regret that owing to the volume of readers' communications received each year, we will be unable to acknowledge all these forms, but they will certainly be seriously considered.

Please post to: **Egon Ronay's Guides, 35 Tadema Road, London SW10 0PZ**

Please use an up-to-date Guide. We publish annually. (Pubs & Inns 1995)

Name and address of establishment	Your recommendation or complaint

Readers' Comments continued

Name and address of establishment	Your recommendation or complaint

Your Name (BLOCK LETTERS PLEASE)

Address

READERS' COMMENTS

Please use this sheet, and the continuation overleaf, to recommend pubs and inns of **really outstanding quality and to comment on existing entries.**

Complaints about any of the Guide's entries will be treated seriously and passed on to our inspectorate, but we would like to remind you always to take up your complaint with the management at the time.

We regret that owing to the volume of readers' communications received each year, we will be unable to acknowledge all these forms, but they will certainly be seriously considered.

Please post to: **Egon Ronay's Guides, 35 Tadema Road, London SW10 0PZ**

Please use an up-to-date Guide. We publish annually. (Pubs & Inns 1995)

Name and address of establishment	Your recommendation or complaint

Readers' Comments continued

Name and address of establishment   **Your recommendation or complaint**

_____   _____

_____   _____

_____   _____

_____   _____

_____   _____

_____   _____

_____   _____

_____   _____

_____   _____

_____   _____

_____   _____

_____   _____

_____   _____

_____   _____

Your Name (BLOCK LETTERS PLEASE)

_____

Address

_____

_____

_____

_____

READERS' COMMENTS

Please use this sheet, and the continuation overleaf, to recommend pubs and inns of **really outstanding quality and to comment on existing entries.**

Complaints about any of the Guide's entries will be treated seriously and passed on to our inspectorate, but we would like to remind you always to take up your complaint with the management at the time.

We regret that owing to the volume of readers' communications received each year, we will be unable to acknowledge all these forms, but they will certainly be seriously considered.

Please post to: **Egon Ronay's Guides, 35 Tadema Road, London SW10 0PZ**

Please use an up-to-date Guide. We publish annually. (Pubs & Inns 1995)

Name and address of establishment	Your recommendation or complaint

Readers' Comments continued

Name and address of establishment   **Your recommendation or complaint**

_____   _____

_____   _____

_____   _____

_____   _____

_____   _____

_____   _____

_____   _____

_____   _____

_____   _____

_____   _____

_____   _____

_____   _____

_____   _____

Your Name (BLOCK LETTERS PLEASE)

_____

Address

_____

_____

_____

_____

READERS' COMMENTS

Please use this sheet, and the continuation overleaf, to recommend pubs and inns of **really outstanding quality and to comment on existing entries.**

Complaints about any of the Guide's entries will be treated seriously and passed on to our inspectorate, but we would like to remind you always to take up your complaint with the management at the time.

We regret that owing to the volume of readers' communications received each year, we will be unable to acknowledge all these forms, but they will certainly be seriously considered.

Please post to: **Egon Ronay's Guides, 35 Tadema Road, London SW10 0PZ**

Please use an up-to-date Guide. We publish annually. (Pubs & Inns 1995)

Name and address of establishment	Your recommendation or complaint

Readers' Comments continued

Name and address of establishment	Your recommendation or complaint

Your Name (BLOCK LETTERS PLEASE)

Address